Index of Applications

Social and Behavioral Sciences Applications

CALCULUS CONCEPTS

An Applied Approach
to the Mathematics
of Change

Donald R. LaTorre
Clemson University

John W. Kenelly
Clemson University

Iris B. Reed
Clemson University

Laurel R. Carpenter
Charlotte, Michigan

Cynthia R. Harris
Reno, Nevada

Sherry Biggers
Clemson University

Houghton Mifflin Compay
Boston · New York

Publisher: Richard Stratton
Senior Sponsoring Editor: Molly Taylor
Marketing Manager: Jennifer Jones
Senior Development Editor: Maria Morelli
Associate Project Editor: Susan Miscio
Art and Design Manager: Gary Crespo
Photo Editor: Jennifer Meyer Dare
Composition Buyer: Chuck Dutton
New Title Project Manager: Susan Brooks-Peltier
Editorial Assistant: Andrew Lipsett
Marketing Associate: Mary Legere
Editorial Assistant: Joanna Carter

TI-83, TI-84 PLUS are registered trademarks of Texas Instruments Incorporated.

Excel, Microsoft and Windows are either registered trademarks or trademarks of Microsoft Corporation in the United States and/or other countries.

Custom Publishing Editor: Glen Garrett
Custom Publishing Production Manager: Christina Battista
Project Coordinator: Jennifer Feltri

Cover Design: Majel Peters
Cover Art: Stock.xchng

This book contains select works from existing Houghton Mifflin Company resources and was produced by Houghton Mifflin Custom Publishing for collegiate use. As such, those adopting and/or contributing to this work are responsible for editorial content, accuracy, continuity and completeness.

Printed in the United States of America.

ISBN-13: 978-0-618-99686-5
ISBN-10: 0-618-99686-9

1027184

2 3 4 5 6 7 8 9 – AB – 09 08 07

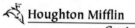 **Houghton Mifflin**
Custom Publishing

222 Berkeley Street • Boston, MA 02116

Address all correspondence and order information to the above address.

Contents

2 Describing Change: Rates   94

5 Accumulating Change: Limits of Sums and the Definite Integral   283

6 Analyzing Accumulated Change: Integrals in Action

379

10 Analyzing Multivariable Change: Optimization   614

Preface

Bridging Concepts

Philosophy

This book presents a fresh, intuitive approach to the concepts of calculus for students in fields such as business, economics, liberal arts, management, and the social and life sciences. It is appropriate for courses generally known as "brief calculus" or "applied calculus."

Our overall goal is to improve learning of basic calculus concepts by involving students with new material in a way that is different from traditional practice. The development of conceptual understanding coupled with a commitment to make calculus meaningful to the student are guiding forces. The material in this book involves many applications of real situations through its data-driven, technology-based modeling approach. It considers the ability to correctly interpret the mathematics of real-life situations of equal importance to the understanding of the concepts of calculus in the context of change.

Fourfold Viewpoint   Complete understanding of the concepts is enhanced and emphasized by the continual use of the fourfold viewpoint: numeric, algebraic, verbal, and graphical.

Data-Driven   Many everyday, real-life situations involving change are discrete in nature and manifest themselves through data. Such situations often can be represented by continuous or piecewise continuous mathematical models so that the concepts, methods, and techniques of calculus can be utilized to solve problems. Thus we seek, when appropriate, to make real-life data a starting point for our investigations.

The use of real data and the search for appropriate models also expose students to the reality of uncertainty. We emphasize that sometimes there can be more than one appropriate model and that answers derived from models are only approximations. We believe that exposure to the possibility of more than one correct approach or answer is valuable.

Modeling Approach   We consider modeling to be an important tool and introduce it at the outset. Both linear and nonlinear models of discrete data are used to obtain functional relationships between variables of interest. The functions given by the models are the ones used by students to conduct their investigations of calculus concepts. It is the connection to real-life data that most students feel shows the relevance of the mathematics in this course to their lives and adds reality to the topics studied.

Interpretation Emphasis   This book differs from traditional texts not only in its philosophy but also in its overall focus, level of activities, development of topics, and attention to detail. Interpretation of results is a key feature of this text that allows students to make sense of the mathematical concepts and appreciate the usefulness of those concepts in their future careers and in their lives.

Informal Style   Although we appreciate the formality and precision of mathematics, we also recognize that this alone can deter some students from access to mathematics. Thus we have sought to make our presentations as informal as possible by using nontechnical terminology where appropriate and a conversational style of presentation.

Pedagogical Features

- *Chapter Opener* Each chapter opens with a real-life situation and several questions about the situation that relate to the key concepts in the chapter. These applications correspond to and reference an activity in the chapter.

- *Chapter Outline* An outline of section titles appears on the first page of each chapter.

- *Concepts You Will Be Learning* The Concepts You Will Be Learning feature appears at the beginning of each chapter and lists the objectives of the chapter.

- *Concept Inventory* A Concept Inventory listed at the end of each section gives students a brief summary of the major ideas developed in that section.

- *Section Activities* The Activities at the end of each section cement concepts and allow students to explore topics using, for the most part, actual data in a variety of real-world settings. Questions and interpretations pertinent to the data and the concepts are always included in these activities. The activities do not mimic the examples in the chapter discussion and thus require more independent thinking on the part of the students. Possible answers to odd activities are given at the end of the book.

- *Chapter Summary* A Chapter Summary connects the results of the chapter topics and further emphasizes the importance of knowing these results.

- *Concept Check* A checklist is included at the end of each chapter summarizing the main concepts and skills taught in the chapter along with sample odd activities corresponding to each item in the list. The sample activities are to help students assess their understanding of the chapter content and identify on which areas to focus their study.

- *Concept Review* A Concept Review activity section at the end of each chapter provides practice with techniques and concepts. Complete answers to the Concept Review activitities are included in the answer key located at the back of the text.

- *Projects* Projects included after each chapter are intended to be group projects with oral or written presentations. We recognize the importance of helping students develop the ability to work in groups, as well as hone presentation skills. The projects also give students the opportunity to practice the kind of writing that they will likely have to do in their future careers.

Content Changes in the Fourth Edition

This new edition contains pedagogical changes intended to improve the presentation and flow of the concepts discussed. It contains many new examples and activities. In addition, many data sets have been updated to include more recent data. Three important pedagogical and context changes include the streamlining of the presentation of models, restructuring of activity sets, and the addition of certain topics.

Streamlining The first two chapters of previous editions have been condensed into one chapter on functions and modeling in the fourth edition. Thus, the instructor can spend less time on preliminaries and start teaching calculus sooner. The important concept of limits has been moved into later sections so it can be taught at the time it is first needed during the development of derivatives.

Activity Sets Activity sections have been divided into subsections by type of activity. *Getting Started* activities give students a chance to practice basic skills. *Applying Concepts* activities are the main activities of each section and are designed to apply the concepts taught in the section to real-world situations. *Discussing Concepts* activities are designed to encourage students to communicate in written form. The authors consider *Writing Across the Curriculum* to be important.

Additional Topics Discussions of L'Hôpital's Rule, Integration by Substitution, and Elasticity of Demand are new topics in the fourth edition. Also a chapter on proportionality, slope fields, and differential equations that in previous editions was available only on the website is now presented in the printed fourth edition as Chapter 7.

Bridging Technology

Technology as a Tool

Graphing Calculators and Spreadsheets Calculus has traditionally relied upon a high level of algebraic manipulation. However, many nontechnical students are not strong in algebraic skills, and an algebra-based approach tends to overwhelm them and stifle their progress. Today's easy access to technology in the forms of graphing calculators and computers breaks down barriers to learning imposed by the traditional reliance on algebraic methods. It creates new opportunities for learning through graphical and numerical representations. We welcome these opportunities in this book by assuming continual and immediate access to technology.

This text requires that students use graphical representations freely, make numerical calculations routinely, and find functions to fit data. Thus continual and immediate access to technology is essential. Because of their low cost, portability, and ability to personalize the mathematics, the use of graphing calculators or laptop computers with software such as Excel or Maple is appropriate.

Technology Guides Because it is not the authors' intent that class time be used to teach technology, we provide two Technology Guides for students: a ***Graphing Calculator Instruction Guide*** containing keystroke information adapted to materials in the text for the TI-83/84 Plus models, and an ***Excel Instruction Guide*** providing the same instruction for Excel spreadsheets. In the student text, open book icons refer readers to applicable sections within the appropriate technology guide.

It is worth noting that different technologies may give different model coefficients than those given in this book. We used a TI-83 graphing calculator to generate the models in the text and the answer key. Other technologies may use different fit criteria for some models than that used by the TI-83.

Eye on Computers and the Internet   The *Calculus Concepts* **Website** (accessible through **college.hmco.com/pic/latorre4e**) provides an exceptional variety of valuable resources for instructors and students alike. The instructors' website includes worksheets, presentation slides, additional projects, data sets categorized by type for use on tests and quizzes, and other resource materials.

The student website provides a glossary of terms, skill and drill problems, and Excel and TI-84 Plus data for all tables presented in the text.

Building Bridges to Better Learning

Resources for Instructors   In addition to the resources found at the website, the online *Instructor's Resource Guide with Complete Solutions* gives practical suggestions for using the text in the manner intended by the authors. It gives suggestions for various ways to adapt the text to your particular class situation. It contains sample syllabi, sample tests, ideas for in-class group work, suggestions for implementing and grading projects, and complete activity solutions.

The *Instructor's Annotated Edition* is the text with margin notes from the authors to instructors. The notes contain explanations of content or approach, teaching ideas, indications of where a topic appears in later chapters, indications of topics that can be easily omitted or streamlined, suggestions for alternate paths through the book, warnings of areas of likely difficulty for students based on the authors' years of experience teaching with *Calculus Concepts*, and references to topics in the *Instructor's Resource Guide* that may be helpful.

NEW! Eduspace® (powered by Blackboard™)   Eduspace is a web-based learning system that provides instructors with powerful course management tools and students with text-specific content to support all of their online teaching and learning needs. Eduspace makes it easy to deliver all or part of a course online. Resources such as algorithmic automatically-graded homework exercises, tutorials, instructional video clips, an online multimedia eBook, live online tutoring with SMARTHINKING™, and additional study materials all come ready-to-use. Instructors can choose to use the content as is, modify it, or even add their own.

NEW! Also available are Powerpoint presentations for **Digital Lessons** created by one of the authors and a long-time user of *Calculus Concepts*.

Learning Resources for Students

1. The *Student Solutions Manual* contains complete solutions to the odd activities.
2. The *Graphing Calculator Guide* contains keystroke information adapted to material in the text for the TI-83 and TI-86 models. Instruction on using the TI-89 graphing calculator can be found on the companion website.

3. An ***Excel Guide*** provides basic instruction on this spreadsheet program. These two Technology Guides contain step-by-step solutions to examples in the text and are referenced in this book by a supplements icon.

4. The ***Calculus Concepts Website*** (accessible through **college.hmco.com/pic/latorre4e**) contains extra practice problems, help with algebra, links to updated data needed for certain activities, a glossary of terms, practice quizzes, and other assistance.

5. The ***Calculus Concepts DVD Series*** contains chapter-by-chapter lectures by a master teacher. The DVD series can be used by students who miss a class or by students who think they would benefit from seeing another teacher explain a particular topic. These DVDs can also be used as training tools for graduate teaching assistants.

6. A series of **Lecture and Notetaking Guides** written by one of the authors and a long-time user of *Calculus Concepts* is available through Houghton Mifflin Custom Publishing. Students follow along with the lecture. These notes are especially designed to help new and/or adjunct instructors cut down on preparation time. The *Notetaking Guide* assists students by integrating the discussion of concepts with a visual or graphical emphasis, providing guided solutions of examples illustrating concepts in a real-world situation, and offering specific calculator instruction and a practical interpretation of the results of the calculations.

Acknowledgments   We gratefully acknowledge the many teachers and students who have used this book in its previous editions and who have given us feedback and suggestions for improvement. In particular, we thank the following reviewers whose many thoughtful comments and valuable suggestions guided the preparation of the revision of the fourth edition.

Marsha Austin—Oklahoma City Community College
William L. Blusbaugh—University of Northern Colorado
Marcia Frobish—Northern Illinois University
Donald R. Griffin—Greenville Technical College
Karla Karstens—University of Vermont
Doreen Kelly—Mesa Community College
Robert Lewis—Linn-Benton Community College
Mehdi Razzaghi—Bloomsburg University
David Ruch—Metropolitan State College of Denver
Debra Swedburg—Casper College

We especially acknowledge the help of

Jennifer LaVare—Clemson University

Special thanks to Carrie Green for her careful work in checking the text and answer key for accuracy. The authors express their sincere appreciation to Charlie Hartford, who first believed in this book, and to Molly Taylor, Maria Morelli, Susan Miscio, Andrew Lipsett, and Joanna Carter at Houghton Mifflin Company for all their work in bringing this fourth edition into print.

Heartfelt thanks to our husbands, Sherrill Biggers and Dean Carpenter, without whose encouragement and support this edition would not have been possible. Thanks also to Jessica, Travis, Lydia, and Carl, whose cooperation was much appreciated.

Fourfold Viewpoint

Complete understanding of the concepts is enhanced and emphasized by the continual use of the fourfold viewpoint: numeric, algebraic, verbal, and graphical.

The first inset page:

With words:

The team starts with 80 customers, and 5 new customers are added each week.

With data (see Table 1.10):

TABLE 1.10

Weeks	0	1	2	3	4	5	6	7
Number of customers	80	85	90	95	100	105	110	115

With graphs (see Figure 1.21):

FIGURE 1.21

With a model:

$$C(w) = 5w + 80 \text{ customers}$$

where w stands for the number of weeks since the team began the subscription drive $0 \le w \le 7$.

Each of these four representations is indicative of a linear model.

Two graphical representations of the linear model are shown in Figure 1.21. The graph in Figure 1.21a is a **scatter plot**—a discrete representation of the data from the table. The graph in Figure 1.21b is the graph associated with the continuous function modeling the data. Because calculus is the study of continuous functions and their behavior, once we have a continuous function modeling data, we will use the function instead of the data and, likewise, will use the continuous graph instead of the scatter plot.

Slope and Intercept

A linear equation is determined by two constants: a starting value and the amount of the incremental change. All linear functions appear algebraically as

$$f(x) = ax + b$$

where a is the incremental change per unit input and b is the

Linear functions are graphed as lines, where a is the slope steepness) and b is the *vertical axis intercept* (that is, the output crosses the $x = 0$ vertical axis). The slope of a graph is of pri

---

John Henley/CORBIS

Determining Change: Derivatives

3

Concepts Outline

3.1 Drawing Rate-of-Change Graphs

3.2 Simple Rate-of-Change Formulas

3.3 Exponential and Logarithmic Rate-of-Change Formulas

3.4 The Chain Rule

3.5 The Product Rule

3.6 Limiting Behavior Revisited: L'Hôpital's Rule

Concept Application

The aging of the American population may be one of the demographic changes that has the greatest impact on our society over the next several decades. Given a model for the projected number of senior Americans (65 years of age or older), the function and its derivative can be used to answer questions such as the following:

• What is the projected number of senior Americans in 2030?

• How rapidly will that number be changing in 2030?

• What is the estimated percentage rate of change in the number of senior Americans in 2030?

You will be able to answer these questions by using the model given in Activity 30 of Section 3.2 and the derivative rules presented in this chapter.

163

Real-World Motivated

Many everyday, real-life situations involving change are discrete in nature and manifest themselves through data. Thus we seek, when appropriate, to make real-life data a starting point for our investigations. Real-world data has been completely updated for this edition. Spreadsheets containing data sets that relate to exercises are also available on the companion websites.

Modeling Approach

Modeling is an important tool and is introduced at the outset. Students use real data and graphing technology to build their own models and interpret results. Real-world data has been completely updated for this edition. Spreadsheets containing data sets that relate to exercises are also available on the companion websites.

30. Costs Suppose the managers of a dairy company have found that it costs them approximately $c(u) = 3250 + 75 \ln u$ dollars to produce u units of dairy products each week. They also know that it costs them approximately $s(u) = 50u + 1500$ dollars to ship u units. Assume that the company ships its products once each week.

  a. Write the formula for the total weekly cost of producing and shipping u units.

  b. Write the formula for the rate of change of the total weekly cost of producing and shipping u units.

  c. How much does it cost the company to produce and ship 5000 units in 1 week?

  d. What is the rate of change of total production and shipping costs at 5000 units? Interpret your answer.

31. Tuition CPI The consumer price index (CPI) for college tuition between 1990 and 2000 is shown in the table.

Year	CPI	Year	CPI	Year	CPI
1990	175.0	1994	249.8	1998	306.5
1991	192.8	1995	264.8	1999	318.7
1992	213.5	1996	279.8	2000	331.9
1993	233.5	1997	294.1		

(Source: *Statistical Abstract*, 2001.)

  a. Align the data as the number of years since 1980, and find a log model for the CPI.

  b. Use the model to find the rate of change of the CPI in 1998.

32. Income The Bureau of the Census reports the median family income since 1947 as shown in the table. (Median income means that half of American families make more than this value and half make less.)

Year	Median family income (constant 1997 dollars)
1947	20,102
	26,133
	35,076
	40,656
	43,756
	44,568

  a. Find a model for the data.

  b. Find a formula for the rate of change of the median family income.

  c. Find the rates of change and percentage rates of change of the median family income in 1972, 1980, 1984, 1992, and 1996.

  d. Do you think the above rates of change and percentage rates of change affected the reelection campaigns of Presidents Nixon (1972), Carter (1980), Reagan (1984), Bush (1992), and Clinton (1996)?

33. iPods The cumulative revenue realized by Apple on the sales of iPods is shown in the table.

Fiscal year (ending September)	iPod revenue (millions of dollars)
2002	53
2003	174
2004	711
2005	1923
2006*	9423

*projected
(Source: Based on data from "Apple Reports Fourth Quarter Results," 2003–2005, Apple Computer, Inc.)

  a. Find an exponential model for the data.

  b. Write the derivative formula for the model.

  c. Determine the revenue, rate of change in revenue, and percentage rate of change in revenue in 2005. Interpret these values.

34. VCR Homes The percentage of households with TVs that also have VCRs from 1990 through 2001 is shown in the table.

Year	Households (percent)	Year	Households (percent)
1990	68.6	1996	82.2
1992	75.0	1998	84.6
1994	79.0	2001	86.2

(Sources: *Statistical Abstract*, 1998, and Television Bureau of Advertising.)

  a. Align the input data as the number of years since 1987, and find a log model for the data.

  b. Write the rate-of-change formula for the model in part a.

As in the heart rate example, the estimate improves as the number of intervals increases. Thus we obtain the exact average value by finding the limit of the estimate as n approaches infinity:

$$\text{Average value} = \lim_{n \to \infty} \frac{[f(x_1) + f(x_2) + \cdots + f(x_{n-1}) + f(x_n)]\Delta x}{b - a}$$

which can be written as

$$\text{Average value} = \frac{\int_a^b f(x)\,dx}{b - a}$$

Thus we have

Average Value

If $y = f(x)$ is a smooth, continuous function from a to b, then the average value of $f(x)$ from a to b is

$$\text{Average value of } f(x) \text{ from } a \text{ to } b = \frac{\int_a^b f(x)\,dx}{b - a}$$

EXAMPLE 1 *Finding Average Value and Average Rate of Change*

5.5.1

Temperature Suppose that the hourly temperatures shown in Table 5.18 were recorded from 7 A.M. to 7 P.M. one day in September.

TABLE 5.18

Time	Temperature (°F)	Time	Temperature (°F)
7 A.M.	49	2 P.M.	80
8 A.M.	54	3 P.M.	80
9 A.M.	58	4 P.M.	78
10 A.M.	66	5 P.M.	74
11 A.M.	72	6 P.M.	69
noon	76	7 P.M.	62
1 P.M.	79		

  a. Find a cubic model for this set of data.

  b. Calculate the average temperature between 9 A.M. and 6 P.M.

  c. Graph the equation together with the rectangle whose upper edge is determined by the average value.

  d. Calculate the average rate of change of temperature from 9 A.M. to 6 P.M.

Technology as a Tool

Spreadsheet and graphing calculator usage is integrated throughout the text.

The open-book icon highlights examples discussed in the *Excel Guide* and in the *Graphing Calculator Guide*, two online supplements.

from the building at a rate of 3 feet per second, how quickly is the ladder sliding down the wall when the top of the ladder is 6 feet from the ground? At what speed is the top of the ladder moving when it hits the ground?

23. Height   A hot-air balloon is taking off from the end zone of a football field. An observer is sitting at the other end of the field 100 yards away from the balloon. If the balloon is rising vertically at a rate of 2 feet per second, at what rate is the distance between the balloon and the observer changing when the balloon is 500 yards off the ground? How far is the balloon from the observer at this time?

24. Kite   A girl flying a kite holds the string 4 feet above ground level and lets out string at a rate of 2 feet per second as the kite moves horizontally at an altitude of 84 feet. Find the rate at which the kite is moving horizontally when 100 feet of string has been let out.

25. Softball   A softball diamond is a square with each side measuring 60 feet. Suppose a player is running from second base to third base at a rate of 22 feet per second. At what rate is the distance between the runner and home plate changing when the runner is halfway to third base? How far is the runner from home plate at this time?

26. Volume   Helium gas is being pumped into a spherical balloon at a rate of 5 cubic feet per minute. The pressure in the balloon remains constant.
   a. What is the volume of the balloon when its diameter is 20 inches?
   b. At what rate is the radius of the balloon changing when the diameter is 20 inches?

27. Snowball   A spherical snowball is melting, and its radius is decreasing at a constant rate. Its diameter decreased from 24 centimeters to 16 centimeters in 30 minutes.
   a. What is the volume of the snowball when its radius is 10 centimeters?
   b. How quickly is the volume of the snowball changing when its radius is 10 centimeters?

28. Salt   A leaking container of salt is sitting on a shelf in a kitchen cupboard. As salt leaks out of a hole in the side of the container, it forms a conical pile on the counter below. As the salt falls onto the pile, it slides down the sides of the pile so that the pile's radius is always equal to its height. If the height of the pile is increasing at a rate of 0.2 inch per day, how quickly is the salt leaking out of the container when the pile is 2 inches tall? How much salt has leaked out of the container by this time?

29. Yogurt   Soft-serve frozen yogurt is being dispensed into a waffle cone at a rate of 1 tablespoon per second. If the waffle cone has height $h = 15$ centimeters and radius $r = 2.5$ centimeters at the top, how quickly is the height of the yogurt in the cone rising when the height of the yogurt is 6 centimeters? (*Hint:*
1 cubic centimeter = 0.06 tablespoon and $r = \frac{h}{6}$.)

30. Volume   Boyle's Law for gases states that when the mass of a gas remains constant, the pressure p and the volume v of the gas are related by the equation $pv = c$, where c is a constant whose value depends on the gas. Assume that at a certain instant, the volume of a gas is 75 cubic inches and its pressure is 30 pounds per square inch. Because of compression of volume, the pressure of the gas is increasing by 2 pounds per square inch every minute. At what rate is the volume changing at this instant?

Discussing Concepts

31. Demonstrate that the two solution methods referred to in part d of Example 1 yield equivalent related-rates equations for the equation given in that part of the example.

32. In what fundamental aspect does the method of related rates differ from the other rate-of-change applications seen so far in this text? Explain.

33. Which step of the method of related rates do you consider to be most imp... answer.

Section Activities

Activity sections have been divided into subsections by type of activity. *Getting Started* activities give students a chance to practice basic skills. *Applying Concepts* activities are the main activities of each section and are designed to apply the concepts taught in the section to real-world situations. *Discussing Concepts* activities are designed to encourage students to communicate in written form. The authors consider *Writing Across the Curriculum* to be important.

Project 6.1 Arch Art

Setting

A popular historical site in Missouri is the Gateway Arch. Designed by Eero Saarinen, it is located on the original riverfront town site of St. Louis and symbolizes the city's role as gateway to the West. The stainless steel Gateway Arch (also called the St. Louis Arch) is 630 feet (192 meters) high and has an equal span.

In honor of the 200th anniversary of the Louisiana Purchase, which made St. Louis a part of the United States, the city has commissioned an artist to design a work of art at the Jefferson Expansion Memorial which is a National Historic Site The artist plans to construct a hill beneath the Gateway Arch, located at the Historic Site, and hang strips of Mylar from the arch to the hill so as to completely fill the space. (See Figure 6.45.) The artist has asked for your help in determining the amount of Mylar needed.

Tasks

1. If the hill is to be 30 feet tall at its highest point, find an equation for the height of the cross section of the hill at its peak. Refer to the figure.

2. Estimate the height of the arch in at least ten different places. Use the estimated heights to construct a model for the height of the arch. (You need not consider only the models presented in this text.)

3. Estimate the area between the arch and the hill.

4. The artist plans to use strips of Mylar 60 inches wide. What is the minimum number of yards of Mylar that the artist will need to purchase?

5. Repeat Task 4 for strips 30 inches wide.

6. If the 30-inch strips cost half as much as the 60-inch strips, is there any cost benefit to using one width instead of the other? If so, which width? Explain.

Reporting

Write a memo telling the artist the minimum amount of Mylar necessary. Explain how you came to your conclusions. Include your mathematical work as an attachment.

The Gateway Arch in St. Louis
Figure 6.45

450

Projects

End-of-chapter projects help students develop the ability to work in groups, as well as hone presentation skills. The projects also give students the opportunity to practice the kind of writing that they will likely have to do in their future careers.

Supplements for the Instructor

Online Instructor's Resource Guide with Complete Solutions This manual offers step-by-step solutions for all text exercises, as well as section-by-section hints for teaching reform calculus. The guide is useful for instructors who are new to the *Calculus Concepts* approach or who want a fresh approach to a concept.

Digital Lessons Presentation slides for lectures corresponding to each of the sections in the text can be custom published in a variety of formats including PowerPoint and transparencies. These visuals allow instructors to minimize lecture preparation time.

HM Testing™ (Powered by Diploma®) "Testing the way you want it" *HM Testing* offers all the tools needed to create, author, deliver, and customize multiple types of tests—including authoring and editing algorithmic questions.

 Online Teaching Center

Supplements for the Students

Student Solutions Manual This manual offers step-by-step solutions for all odd-numbered text exercises.

Student Lecture and Notetaking Guide This notebook includes prepared class notes with blanks to be filled in by the students during class and correlates with the *Lecture Visuals*. The *Lecture Visuals* and *Student Lecture and Notetaking Guide* are authored by a *Calculus Concepts* author and available through Houghton Mifflin custom publishing.

 Online Study Center

Includes *Online Graphing Calculator Guide*, *Excel Guide,* graphing calculator programs, data sets, and more.

Supplements for the Students and the Instructor

 Instructional DVDs   These DVDs cover selected sections of the text and provide explanations of key concepts, applications in a lecture-based format.

Eduspace® (powered by Blackboard™)

Eduspace is a web-based learning system that provides instructors with powerful course management tools and students with text-specific content to support all of their online teaching and learning needs. Eduspace makes it easy to deliver all or part of a course online. Resources such as algorithmic automatically-graded homework exercises, tutorials, instructional video clips, an online multimedia eBook, live online tutoring with SMARTHINKING™, and additional study materials all come ready-to-use. Instructors can choose to use the content as is, modify it, or even add their own. *Visit **www.eduspace.com** for more information.*

SMARTHINKING™ Live, online tutoring

SMARTHINKING provides an easy-to-use and effective on-line, text-specific tutoring service. A dynamic **Whiteboard** and **Graphing Calculator function** enables students and e-structors to collaborate easily. *Visit **smarthinking.college.hmco.com** for more information.*

Online Course Content for Blackboard®, WebCT®, and eCollege®

Deliver program or text-specific Houghton Mifflin content online using your institution's local course management system. Houghton Mifflin offers homework, tutorials, videos, and other resources formatted for Blackboard®, WebCT®, eCollege®, and other course management systems. Add to an existing online course or create a new one by selecting from a wide range of powerful learning and instructional materials.

For more information, visit **college.hmco.com/pic/latorre4e** or contact your Houghton Mifflin sales representative.

Ingredients of Change: Functions and Models

Larry Dale Gordon/TIPS IMAGES

Concept Application

On February 16, 2005, the Kyoto Protocol, a multinational attempt to slow global warming by curbing air pollution, finally came into force seven years after the initial accord was signed. The Kyoto Protocol is a legally binding treaty requiring that ratifying, developed nations decrease their overall emissions of the six greenhouse gases: carbon dioxide, methane, nitrous oxide, sulfur hexafluoride, hydrofluorocarbons, and perfluorocarbons. Here are some questions about greenhouse-gas emissions that can be answered mathematically by using functions and/or calculus:

- What was the collective amount of the six greenhouse-gases released into the atmosphere in 1990? in 1997? in 2002?

- At what rate was the amount of greenhouse-gas emissions increasing between 1990 and 2002?

- Based on data accumulated since 1990, what amount of greenhouse gases will be released into the atmosphere in 2012?

This chapter will provide you with some of the tools that make it possible to answer such questions. The information needed to answer these questions is found in Activity 29 of Section 1.2.

Chapter Introduction

The primary goal of this book is to help you understand the two fundamental concepts of calculus—the derivative and the integral—in the context of the mathematics of change. This first chapter is therefore devoted to a study of the key ingredients of change: functions and mathematical models. Functions provide the basis for analyzing the mathematics of change because they enable us to describe relationships between variable quantities.

This chapter introduces the process of building mathematical models. Many of the models we use are formed from data gathered in applied situations. Although linear functions and models are among the most frequently occurring ones in non-science settings, nonlinear functions apply in a variety of situations. We begin with linear, exponential, and logarithmic functions and then consider situations in which exponential growth is constrained in some manner. Such a situation can often be modeled by a logistic function. The final functions we consider are quadratic and cubic polynomials.

Concepts You Will Be Learning

- Evaluating and interpreting functions at specified inputs or outputs (1.1)
- Using operations and function composition to construct new functions (1.1)
- Interpreting models for profit, revenue, and other business concepts (1.1)
- Finding and interpreting the rate of change (slope) of a linear model (1.2)
- Fitting a linear model to a data set (1.2)
- Using limits to interpret end behavior of a function (1.3)
- Recognizing an inverse relationship between two functions (1.3)
- Finding and interpreting doubling time and half-life of exponential functions (1.3)
- Finding equations of the horizontal asymptotes for logistic equations (1.4)
- Visually locating and verbally interpreting inflection points on a graph (1.4)
- Using quadratic and cubic models (1.5)
- Fitting one of six models to a data set (1.2 – 1.5)

1.1   Models and Functions

Calculus is the study of change—how things change and how quickly they change. We begin our study of calculus by considering how we describe change. Let us start with a situation that affects nearly all of us—the price of a gallon of gas and the quantity that we purchase. According to the American Petroleum Institute, on September 5, 2005, the national average retail price (including taxes) of regular-grade gasoline reached what was at that time the record price of $3.069 per gallon. Using this price, we can represent the cost of a varying number of gallons of gas in four ways:

With numerical data, such as Table 1.1.

With a graph, such as Figure 1.1.

TABLE 1.1

Amount of gas (gallons)	Cost of gas (dollars)
0	0
1	3.069
5	15.345
10	30.69
15	46.035
20	61.38

FIGURE 1.1

With words:

> $C(g)$ is the cost (in dollars) for pumping g gallons of gasoline when the price is $3.069 per gallon.

With a mathematical model:

> $C(g) = 3.069\, g$ dollars

> where $C(g)$ is the cost of pumping g gallons of gasoline, $g \geq 0$.

Most of the mathematical formulas considered in this text can be viewed from each of four perspectives: numerical, algebraic, verbal, and graphical. Each of these representations adds a different facet to our understanding of the formula and what it represents.

Mathematical Models

Even though all four representations enhance our understanding of the situation they describe, only the equation and the graph enable us to apply calculus concepts to that situation in order to study change. The process of translating a real-world problem into a usable mathematical equation is called **mathematical modeling,** and the equation (with the variables described in the context) is referred to as a **model.**

EXAMPLE 1   *Model Construction*

Pressure Under Water   The pressure exerted on a person who is open-water diving can cause a painful and dangerous condition known as decompression sickness or, in scuba diving jargon, "the bends." In order for divers to avoid this condition, it is important for them to understand how much pressure they can expect at different depths. Pressure is measured in atmospheres, a unit that is abbreviated atm. At sea level, the pressure exerted by the air is 1 atm. As a diver descends, the water exerts an additional 1 atm for every 33 feet of added depth. Table 1.2 shows the pressure for several different depths, and Figure 1.2 depicts the pressure for depths up to 132 feet below sea level.

TABLE 1.2

Depth (feet)	Pressure (atm)
surface	1
33	2
66	3
99	4
132	5

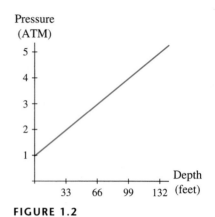

FIGURE 1.2

Use the verbal description to write a model for pressure in terms of depth.

Solution

At sea level (that is, at a depth of 0 feet), the pressure is 1 atm, and the pressure increases by 1 atm for each additional 33 feet of depth. In other words, the pressure increases by $\frac{1}{33}$ atm for each additional 1 foot of depth. We can write this information as follows:

Pressure in atm is equal to 1 atm plus $\frac{1}{33}$ atm for every foot below the surface of the water.

Using y as the amount of pressure in atm and x as the number of feet below sea level, we can convert that statement into the equation

$$y = 1 + \frac{1}{33}x \text{ atm (of pressure)}$$

where x is the number of feet below the surface, $0 \le x \le 132$. ●

Example 1 serves as a preview to our use of mathematical models in calculus. It uses the available data to produce a mathematical equation (model) that describes the relationship between the variable quantities of interest (depth below sea level and pressure). The remaining sections of this chapter deal with modeling in more detail. However, before we do more modeling, we need to understand some of the special properties of the models that are useful in calculus.

Functions

In this chapter, we have considered the cost of gas given the amount of gas pumped, as well as the pressure on an object given the depth of that object under water. Each of these is an example of the relationship between one variable, called an **input,** and a second variable, called an **output.** In both cases, four representations (numerical data, a

graph, words, and an equation) were used to describe the relationship, a[
cases, a rule was defined that assigned exactly one output to each input. 1
tionships are examples of *functions* because a rule is a function if each input produces
exactly one output. If any particular input produces more than one output, then the
rule is not a function. In order to state the input/output relationship mathematically,
when f is a rule relating an input x to a specific output, we write the output as $f(x)$.

A **function** is a rule that assigns exactly one output to each input.

Function notation: $f(x)$ is the output of function f when x is the input.

To verify that the rule for the cost of gas is a function, we must ask, "Can a certain
amount of gas have different costs if the price per gallon is fixed at $3.069?" Of course
not. If the price per gallon is fixed, then the cost for a given amount of gas is also fixed.
In this case, g is the number of gallons of gasoline purchased at $3.069 per gallon (the
input). The notation for the output is $C(g)$. The g is enclosed in parentheses to remind
us that g is the input, and the C remains outside the parentheses to remind us that C
is the rule that gives the output. Thus $C(10) = 30.69$ means that when 10 gallons of
gasoline are purchased (the input is 10), the amount of the purchase is $30.69 (the
output is 30.69).

When a rule is a function, we can visualize the relationship using an **input/out-put diagram.** Figure 1.3 shows an input/output diagram for the rule relating cost for
a purchase of gas and the amount of gas pumped.

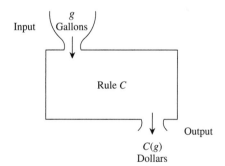

FIGURE 1.3

You probably recall from previous math courses that the standard terms for the
set of inputs and the set of outputs of a function are *domain* and *range*, respectively.
Other terms for input and output include *independent variable* and *dependent variable* and *controlled variable* and *observed variable*. In this book, however, we use the
terms *input* and *output*.

In the table representation of the cost-of-gas function, the set of inputs is {0, 1, 5,
10, 15, 20}, and the set of outputs is {0, 3.069, 15.345, 30.69, 46.035, 61.38}. In the graph
representing the cost of gas, the set of inputs is all real numbers (not just integers) between 0 and 20 ($0 \leq$ gallons ≤ 20), and the set of outputs is all real numbers between 0

and 61.38 ($0 \leq$ dollars ≤ 61.38). In the verbal description and equation, the set of inputs is all nonnegative real numbers, and the set of outputs is all nonnegative real numbers. We call the graph of this function (see Figure 1.1) **continuous** because it can be drawn without lifting the writing instrument from the page. We will give a more precise definition of *continuous* in Chapter 2.

EXAMPLE 2   *Identifying Functions, Inputs, and Outputs*

Pressure Under Water   Consider again the amount of pressure encountered by a scuba diver at certain depths under water. In Example 1, the following model was developed:

$$y = 1 + \frac{1}{33}x \text{ atm (of pressure)}$$

where x is the number of feet below the surface, $0 \leq x \leq 132$.

a. Rewrite the equation as $P(x)$ using function notation, and draw an input/output diagram.

b. Identify the set of inputs and the set of outputs.

c. Is P a function of x?

Solution

a. Using the letter P to represent the rule giving pressure as output when depth x is the input, we can rewrite the model as

$$P(x) = 1 + \frac{1}{33}x \text{ atm (of pressure)}$$

where x is the number of feet below the surface, $0 \leq x \leq 132$. The input/output diagram for P is shown in Figure 1.4.

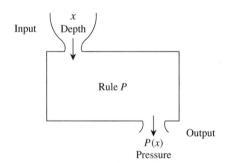

FIGURE 1.4

b. The input variable represents the depth of the diver in feet. In this case, the set of inputs is all real numbers between 0 and 132. The output variable represents the amount of pressure. The set of outputs is all real numbers between 1 and 5.

c. P is a function of x because there is only one pressure (output) corresponding to each given depth (input). ●

Determining Function Output

The way to find the output that corresponds to a known input depends on how the function is represented. In a table, simply locate the desired input in the input row or column. The output is the corresponding entry in the adjacent row or column. For example, the output corresponding to the input 10 in Table 1.1 is 30.69, and we write $C(10) = 30.69$.

If a function is represented by a formula, simply substitute the value of the input everywhere that the variable appears in the formula and calculate the result. To use the formula $C(g) = 3.069g$ to find the cost of purchasing 4 gallons of gas at \$3.069 per gallon, substitute 4 for g in the formula: $C(4) = 3.069 \cdot 4 = 12.276 \approx 12.28$ dollars.

In a function represented by a graph, our convention is to place the input on the horizontal axis. Locate the desired value of the input on the horizontal axis, move directly up (or down) along an imaginary vertical line until you reach the graph, and then move left (or right) until you encounter the vertical axis. (You will find a see-through ruler helpful for improved accuracy.) The value at that point on the vertical axis is the output. For example, Figure 1.5 shows the graph of average faculty salaries at a private liberal arts college. When the input is 2003, the output is approximately \$56,000.

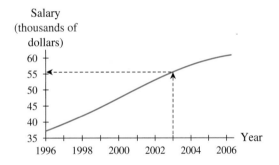

FIGURE 1.5

If at any input you can draw a vertical line that crosses the graph in two or more places, then the graph does not represent a function. The graph in Figure 1.6 shows P as a function of t because every input produces only one output. The graph in Figure 1.7 does not describe y as a function of x because each positive x-value produces two different y-values. This method of visual assessment is known as the **Vertical Line Test.**

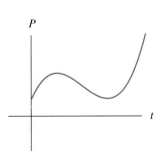

This graph is a function.
FIGURE 1.6

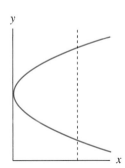

This graph is not a function.
FIGURE 1.7

> ### Vertical Line Test
>
> Suppose that a graph has inputs located along the horizontal axis and outputs located along the vertical axis. If at any input you can draw a vertical line that crosses the graph in two or more places, then the graph does not represent a function.

One way to determine whether a formula represents a function is to graph the equation and then apply the Vertical Line Test.

Interpreting Model Output

In learning how functions and graphs model the real world, it is important that you understand the **units of measure** of the input and output of functions. In the cost-of-gasoline example, the unit of measure of the input is *gallons,* and the unit of measure of the output is *dollars.* The units of measure in Figure 1.5 can be read from the graph. The unit of measure of the output is *thousands of dollars,* and the unit of measure of the input is *year.* Note that the unit of measure is always a word or short phrase telling *how* the variable is measured, not an entire description telling what the variable represents. For example, it would be incorrect to say that the unit of measure of the output in Figure 1.5 is "average faculty salary in thousands of dollars." This is a description of the output variable, not the unit of output.

EXAMPLE 3   *Interpreting Output*

This symbol indicates that instructions specific to this example for using your calculator or computer are given in a technology supplement.

1.1.1

Land Value   The value of a certain piece of property between the years 1985 and 2005 is given by the model

$$v(t) = 3.5(1.095^t) \text{ thousand dollars}$$

where t is the number of years since the end of 1985.

A graph and some output values of this function are given in Figure 1.8 and Table 1.3, respectively.

TABLE 1.3

Year	Value (thousand dollars)
1985	3.5
1990	5.5
1995	8.7
2000	13.7
2005	21.5

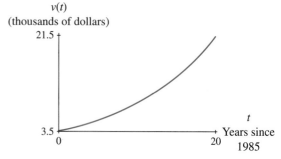

FIGURE 1.8

The situation modeled by v can be described as follows: The value of a piece of property worth \$3.5 thousand at the end of 1985 increased by 9.5% each year since 1985.

a. Describe the input variable and the output variable. What is the unit of measure for each variable?

b. What was the land value in 2000?

c. When did the land value reach \$20,000?

Solution

a. The input variable t is the number of years since the end of 1985. Its unit of measure is years. The output variable $v(t)$ is the value of a piece of property. Its unit of measure is thousands of dollars.

b. The input $t = 15$ corresponds to 2000, so the value of the land in 2000 was

$$v(15) = 3.5(1.095^{15}) \approx \$13,655$$

c. In this question you know the output, and you need to find the corresponding input. You must solve for t in the equation $20 = 3.5(1.095^t)$. You can either solve the equation algebraically (using logarithms) or use technology. In either case, you should find that $t \approx 19.2$. Note that because t is defined as the number of years since the *end* of 1985, $t = 19$ corresponds to the end of 2004, so $t = 19.2$ corresponds to early in the year 2005. Thus the land reached a value of \$20,000 in 2005.   ●

Many real-world applications require us to construct more complicated functions from simpler functions. The basic techniques we will discuss are *combining functions* using addition, multiplication, subtraction, or division, and *composing functions*.

Combining Functions

We explore the processes of combining functions via function addition, multiplication, subtraction, and division by using some basic concepts from business. These familiar concepts are fixed costs (or overhead), variable costs, total cost, revenue, profit, average cost, and break-even point. The formulas we give here will be used throughout the text.

Total cost = fixed costs + variable costs

$$\textbf{Average cost } = \frac{\text{total cost}}{\text{number of units produced}}$$

Profit = revenue − total cost

The **break-even point** occurs when revenue equals total cost and thus profit equals 0.

Concept Development: Function Addition [$h(x) = f(x) + g(x)$]   Consider the total cost to a dairy company for producing milk on the xth day of last month. The company incurred *fixed costs* (costs that do not change with, or depend on, the level of production) that amounted to $20,100 for last month. The fixed cost can be represented by the function $F(x) = 20,100$ dollars each month. The company also had variable cost that changed according to how many gallons of milk were produced on a given day. The model for *variable cost* is $V(x) = -0.32x^2 + 6x + 360$ dollars each day, where x is the xth day of last month. Input/output diagrams for F and V are shown in Figure 1.9.

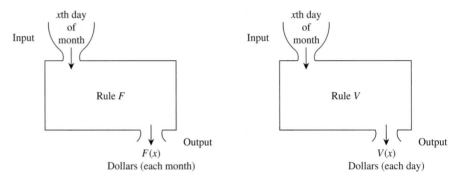

FIGURE 1.9

Total cost is defined as the sum of the fixed cost and the variable cost. By adding the output of the function for *fixed costs* for a specific input value to the output of the function for *variable costs* for that same input value, we can find the *total cost* at that input value. Before doing so, however, we need to ask ourselves two questions: "Is the set of input values the same for each function?" and "Are the output values given in the same unit of measure?" The answer to the first question is yes; the xth day of the last month is the input for both function F and function V. The answer to the second question is no. The unit of measure for the output of V is dollars each day, whereas the unit of measure for the output of F is dollars each month. Tables 1.4 and 1.5 show the outputs of $F(x)$ and $V(x)$ for selected input values as well as the outputs of $F(x)$ adjusted to dollars each day. Considering the month to have 30 days, we divide the fixed costs per month by 30 to obtain the output in dollars each day instead of dollars per month: $\frac{20,100}{30} = 670$ dollars each day.

TABLE 1.4

Day	Fixed cost (dollars each month)	Adjusted fixed cost (dollars each day)
7	20,100	670
14	20,100	670
21	20,100	670
28	20,100	670

TABLE 1.5

Day	Variable cost (dollars each day)
7	386.32
14	381.28
21	344.88
28	277.12

When the units of the outputs are identical, the outputs can be added, as shown in Table 1.6.

TABLE 1.6

Day	Adjusted fixed cost (dollars per day)		Variable cost (dollars per day)		Total cost (dollars per day)
7	670	+	386.32	=	1056.32
14	670	+	381.28	=	1051.28
21	670	+	344.88	=	1014.88
28	670	+	277.12	=	947.12

FIGURE 1.10

1.1.2

Instead of performing this addition for only the outputs displayed in a table, we can construct a function C that will give the total cost per day for any given day x. We first convert the function F into a function that will give fixed costs in terms of dollars each day. An input/output diagram for this adjusted fixed-cost function is given in Figure 1.10.

The total-cost function can now be found by adding the adjusted fixed-cost function to the variable-cost function:

$$C(x) = \frac{F(x)}{30} + V(x)$$
$$= 670 + (-0.32x^2 + 6x + 360)$$
$$= 670 - 0.32x^2 + 6x + 360$$
$$= -0.32x^2 + 6x + 1030$$

Thus $C(x) = -0.32x^2 + 6x + 1030$ dollars is the total cost for milk production on the xth day of last month. Figure 1.11 shows an input/output diagram for the total-cost function.

Combining functions in this manner is known as **function addition**.

Concept Development: Function Multiplication $[h(x) = f(x) \cdot g(x)]$
A meaningful new function can be constructed by multiplying the outputs of two existing functions as long as their inputs are the same and the product of the outputs makes sense in context. The calculation of *revenue* is an example of function multiplication. In business, *revenue* is defined as the price per unit at which a commodity is sold times the number of units sold.

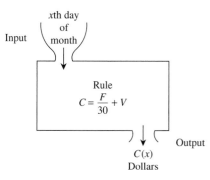

FIGURE 1.11

EXAMPLE 4   *Function Multiplication*

Revenue   Suppose that the price of milk was $M(x) = 0.02x + 1.90$ dollars per gallon on the xth day of last month, $0 \le x \le 30$, and that $S(x) = 1.5 + 0.5(0.8^x)$ thousand gallons of milk were sold on the same day x, $0 \le x \le 30$.

a. Draw separate input/output diagrams for M and S.

b. Determine whether M and S are compatible for function multiplication and, if so, what the resulting output unit of measure for $(M \cdot S)(x)$ will be.

c. Draw an input/output diagram for the multiplication function.

d. Write a function for daily revenue from milk sales.

Solution

a. Input/output diagrams for M and S are shown in Figure 1.12.

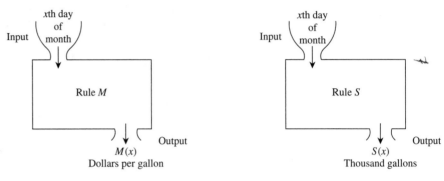

FIGURE 1.12

b. The input values and their unit of measure for both functions are the same. When the output values are multiplied, with unit of measure (dollars per gallon)(thousand gallons), the result is the revenue in thousand dollars on the xth day of last month.

c. An input/output diagram for $R(x) = M(x) \cdot S(x)$ is given in Figure 1.13.

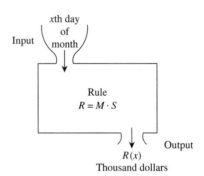

FIGURE 1.13

d. A function for revenue is

$$R(x) = M(x) \cdot S(x)$$
$$= [0.02x + 1.90] \cdot [1.5 + 0.5(0.8^x)] \text{ thousand dollars}$$

on the xth day of last month, $0 \le x \le 30$ ●

Concept Development: Function Subtraction $[h(x) = f(x) - g(x)]$ Function subtraction is similar to function addition. As in function addition, it is important that both the set of input values and the output unit of measure for each of the functions to be subtracted are the same. The dairy company introduced earlier in this section would be interested in profit, not just in revenue. *Profit* is the difference between revenue and total cost—that is, profit is equal to revenue minus cost.

The functions R for revenue and C for total cost can be combined using function subtraction to create a function for profit. However, we must be careful, because even though the sets of inputs agree, the output unit of measure for revenue is thousands of dollars and the output unit of measure for cost is dollars. In order to combine the two functions, we convert the units of one function so that the units of R and C are in agreement. We can multiply the revenue function by 1000 so that the output unit of measure will be dollars. The function for profit can thus be written

$$P(x) = 1000R(x) - C(x)$$
$$= 1000 \cdot \{[0.02x + 1.90] \cdot [1.5 + 0.5(0.8^x)]\} - [-0.32x^2 + 6x + 1030]$$
$$= 1000 \cdot \{[0.02x + 1.90] \cdot [1.5 + 0.5(0.8^x)]\} + 0.32x^2 - 6x - 1030 \text{ dollars}$$

on the xth day of last month, $0 \le x \le 30$.

Note: An alternative solution would be to divide the cost function by 1000 so that the output unit of measure will be a thousand dollars. We find the profit as follows:

$$P(x) = R(x) - \frac{C(x)}{1000}$$
$$= \{[0.02x + 1.90] \cdot [1.5 + 0.5\,(0.8^x)]\} - \frac{[-0.32x^2 + 6x + 1030]}{1000}$$

thousand dollars on the xth day of last month, $0 \le x \le 30$.

Concept Development: Function Division $[h(x) = \frac{g(x)}{f(x)}$, where $f(x) \ne 0]$
Function division is useful when we are finding averages, percentages, and other ratios, but in order to use function division to construct a new function, we must confirm that the original functions have the same set of inputs and the same unit of measure for those inputs. For instance, if we know that $Q(x) = -1.6x^2 + 30x + 1800$ gallons of milk were produced on the xth day of last month and that the total cost of production is $C(x) = -0.32x^2 + 6x + 1030$ dollars, where x represents the same input in both functions, we can construct a function for the average cost for producing one gallon of milk on the xth day of last month. *Average cost* is defined as the total cost of production divided by the number of units produced, so

Average cost =

$$A(x) = \frac{C(x)}{Q(x)}$$
$$= \frac{-0.32x^2 + 6x + 1030 \text{ dollars}}{-1.6x^2 + 30x + 1800 \text{ gallons}}$$
$$= \frac{-0.32x^2 + 6x + 1030}{-1.6x^2 + 30x + 1800} \text{ dollars per gallon}$$

on the xth day of last month, $0 \le x \le 30$.

We summarize the four function combinations as follows:

If the inputs of functions f and g are identical (corresponding values and unit of measure), then the following new functions can be constructed and are valid models under the given conditions:

- **Function addition:** $h = f + g$ if the output units are identical (corresponding values and unit of measure)
- **Function subtraction:** $j = f - g$ if the output units are identical (corresponding values and unit of measure)
- **Function multiplication:** $k = f \cdot g$ if the output units are compatible
- **Function division:** $l = \dfrac{f}{g}$, where $g(x) \neq 0$, as long as the output units are compatible

---

An important point in business applications is the **break-even point**. The break-even point is defined as the point at which revenue equals total cost and thus profit is zero. Example 5 uses constructed functions and graphs to determine the break-even point for a dairy company.

EXAMPLE 5   *Combining Functions*

Break-even Point   Suppose that a month's total cost for the production of g gallons of milk can be modeled as $K(g) = 20{,}100 + 0.2g$ dollars, $0 \leq g \leq 30$. During the same month, the average price for a gallon of milk is \$2.20, so revenue can be modeled as $T(g) = 2.2g$ dollars for g gallons of milk, $g > 0$.

a. Graph $K(g) = 20{,}100 + 0.2g$ and $T(g) = 2.2g$ on the same set of coordinate axes.

b. Write a function giving the profit from the production and sale of g gallons of milk. Graph the profit function.

c. How much milk needs to be produced/sold in order for the dairy company to break even? Show this point on the graphs from parts *a* and *b*.

Solution

1.1.3

a. Figure 1.14 shows total cost and revenue graphed together.

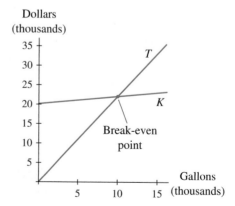

FIGURE 1.14

b. Because profit is defined as revenue minus total cost, a model for profit can be written as

$$P(g) = 2.2g - (20{,}100 + 0.2g)$$
$$= 2.0g - 20{,}100 \text{ dollars}$$

where g is the number of gallons produced and sold, $g > 0$. See Figure 1.15.

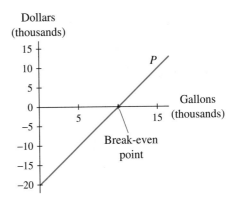

FIGURE 1.15

c. The dairy company will break even when the output of profit is zero—that is, when $P(g) = 2.0g - 20{,}100 = 0$. Solving for g yields $g = 10{,}050$ gallons. The dairy company must produce/sell 10,050 gallons of milk during the month in order for revenue to equal total cost. See the break-even point depicted in Figures 1.14 and 1.15. ●

Composing Functions $[h(x) = (g \circ f)(x) = g(f(x))]$

Another way in which we construct functions is called **function composition.** This method of constructing functions uses the output of one function as the input of another. Consider Tables 1.7 and 1.8. Table 1.7 gives the altitude of an airplane as a function of time, and Table 1.8 gives air temperature as a function of altitude.

TABLE 1.7

t = time into flight (minutes)	$F(t)$ = thousand feet above sea level
0	4.4
1	7.7
2	13.4
3	20.3
4	27.2
5	32.9
6	36.2

TABLE 1.8

F = thousand feet above sea level	$A(F)$ = air temperature (degrees Fahrenheit)
4.4	71.0
7.7	14.0
13.4	−34.4
20.3	−55.7
27.2	−62.6
32.9	−64.7
36.2	−65.2

It is possible to combine these two data tables into one table that shows air temperature as a function of time. This process requires using each of the output values from Table 1.7 as the corresponding input value for Table 1.8. The only restriction is that both the numerical values and the unit of measure in the output of one function must match those in the input of the other function. Figure 1.16 illustrates the output of one function being used as the input of the next function. The resulting new function is shown in Table 1.9.

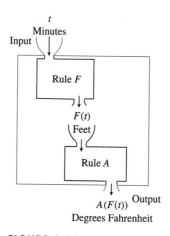

FIGURE 1.16

TABLE 1.9

t = time into flight (minutes)	$A(F)$ = air temperature (degrees Fahrenheit)
0	71.0
1	14.0
2	−34.4
3	−55.7
4	−62.6
5	−64.7
6	−65.2

Because we used the output values of Table 1.7, $F(t)$, as the input values for Table 1.8, the representation for the output of the new function is commonly written as $A(F(t))$. The A is placed outside the parentheses to remind us that the output is air temperature. The $F(t)$ inside the parentheses reminds us that altitude from Table 1.7 is the connecting link and that time t is the input of the new function. It is customary to refer to A as the *outside function* and to F as the *inside function*. The mathematical symbol for the composition of an inside function F and an outside function A is $A \circ F$, so

$$(A \circ F)(t) = A(F(t))$$

The altitude data can be modeled as $F(t) = -0.2t^3 + 1.8t^2 + 1.7t + 4.4$ thousand feet above sea level, where t is the time into the flight in minutes. The air temperature can be modeled as $A(F) = 279 \cdot (0.85^F) - 66$ degrees Fahrenheit, where F is the number of feet above sea level. The composition of these two functions is

$$A(F) = A(F(t))$$
$$= 279 \cdot (0.85^{-0.2t^3 + 1.8t^2 + 1.7t + 4.4}) - 66 \text{ degrees Fahrenheit}$$

where t is the time in minutes into the flight.

We formalize the process of function composition as follows:

> Given two functions *f* and *g*, we can form their **composition** if the outputs from one of them, say *f*, can be used as inputs to the other function, *g*. In this case, the unit of measure for the output of function *f* must be identical to the unit of measure for the input of function *g*.
>
> Notation: $h(x) = g(f(x)) = (g \circ f)(x)$

In terms of inputs and outputs, we have those shown in Figure 1.17. In this case, we can replace the portion of the diagram within the teal box by forming the composite function $g \circ f$, whose input/output diagram is shown in Figure 1.18.

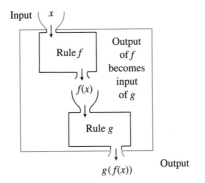

FIGURE 1.17   **FIGURE 1.18**

EXAMPLE 6   *Finding a Composite Function*

Lake Contamination   Consider the word descriptions of the following two functions and their input/output diagrams, which are shown in Figure 1.19.

$C(p)$ = parts per million of contamination in a lake when the population of the surrounding community is *p* people

$p(t)$ = the population in thousands of people of the lakeside community in year *t*

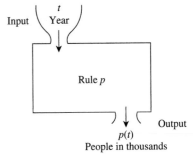

FIGURE 1.19

a. Draw an input/output diagram for the composition function that gives the contamination in a lake as a function of time.

b. The contamination in the lake can be modeled as $C(p) = \sqrt{p}$ parts per million when the community's population is p people, $p > 0$. The population of the community can be modeled by $p(t) = 0.4t^2 + 2.5$ thousand people t years after 1980, $t \geq 0$. Write the function that gives the lake contamination as a function of time.

Solution

a. Note that the unit of measure of the output of the second function may be converted to the unit of measure of the input of the first function. If we multiply $p(t)$ by 1000 to convert the unit of measure of the output from thousands of people to people, we have the function $P(t) = 1000p(t)$ people in year t, $t \geq 0$. Now we can compose the two functions C and P to create the new function $C \circ P$, whose input/output diagram is shown in Figure 1.20.

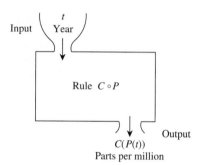

FIGURE 1.20

Input — t Year

Rule $C \circ P$

Output

$C(P(t))$
Parts per million

b. Use the population of the community given by $P(t) = 1000p(t)$ as input in the function $C(p)$. $P(t) = 1000(0.4t^2 + 2.5)$ people t years after 1980, $t \geq 0$. Thus the contamination in the lake can be modeled as

$$C \circ P(t) = C(P(t)) = \sqrt{1000(0.4t^2 + 2.5)} \text{ parts per million}$$

t years after 1980, $t \geq 0$. ●

Calculus is the mathematics of change that occurs over continuous portions of functions. As we embark on our study of calculus, we will consider modeling primarily as a tool for developing continuous functions. Once we can model data with a function, we can use the tools of calculus to analyze that model—especially to determine rates of change and identify maxima, minima, and inflection points.

1.1 Concept Inventory

- Mathematical models
- Function
- Function notation
- Inputs and outputs
- Input/output diagram
- Units of measure
- Graphs of functions
- Vertical Line Test
- Function addition and subtraction
- Function multiplication and division
- Cost, revenue, profit, break-even point
- Function composition

1.1 Activities

Getting Started

For each of the rules in Activities 1 through 4, a. specify the input and output descriptions, the input and output variables, and the input and output units of measure, b. determine whether each rule is a function, and c. draw an input/output diagram.

1. $R(w)$ = the first-class domestic postal rate (in cents) of a letter weighing w ounces

2. $H(a)$ = your height (in inches) at age a years

3. $A(m)$ = the amount (in dollars) you pay for lunch on the mth day of any week

4. $C(m)$ = the amount of credit (in dollars) that Citibank Visa will allow a 20-year-old with a yearly income of m dollars

Determine whether the tables in Activities 5 through 8 represent functions. Assume that the input is in the left column.

5.

Year	iPod sales (millions of units)
2002	0.14
2003	0.336
2004	2.016
2005	6.451

(Source: Compiled from "Apple Reports Fourth Quarter Results," 2003–2005, Apple Computer, Inc.)

6.

Military rank (4 years of service)	Basic monthly pay in 2005 (dollars)
Second Lieutenant	2948
First Lieutenant	3541
Captain	3823
Major	4388
Lt. Colonel	4961
Colonel	5784
Brigadier General	7119
Major General	8459

(Source: Defense Finance and Accounting Service.)

7. The table gives the maximum "no-compression" dive times for open-water scuba diving with air-filled tanks.

Depth of dive (feet)	Maximum dive time (minutes)
50	80
60	55
70	45
80	35
90	25
100	22
110	15
120	12

(Source: Burks Oakley II, *Nitrox Scuba Diving*, April 30, 2000.)

8.

Run of advertisement (weeks)	Total new customers (people)
1	1
3	3
5	8
7	18
10	20

9. Which of the following graphs represent functions? (The input axis is horizontal.)

a.

b.

c.

10. Which of the following graphs represent functions? (The input axis is horizontal.)

a.

b.

c.
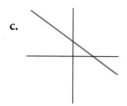

11. Prices $P(m)$ is the median sale price (in thousands of dollars) of existing one-family homes in metropolitan area m in 2000. Write the following statements in function notation.
(Source: *Statistical Abstract*, 2001.)

a. The median sale price in Honolulu, Hawaii, was $295,000.

b. In Providence, Rhode Island, the median sale price was $137,800.

c. $170,100 was the median sale price in Portland, Oregon.

12. Darkness Hours $H(d)$ is the number of hours of darkness in Anchorage, Alaska, on the dth day of the year. Write the following statements in function notation.

a. On the 121st day of the year, Anchorage has 7.5 hours of darkness.

b. The duration of darkness in Anchorage on the 361st day of the year is 18.5 hours.

c. In Anchorage there are only 4.5 hours of darkness on the 181st day of the year.

13. Exports $E(t)$ is the value of cotton exports (in millions of dollars) in year t. Write sentences interpreting the following mathematical statements.
(Source: *Statistical Abstract*, 1994.)

a. $E(1988) = 1975$

b. $E = 1999$ when $t = 1992$

14. Population $P(r)$ is the percentage of U.S. residents in the year 2000 who were of origin r. Write

sentences interpreting the following mathematical statements. (Source: *Statistical Abstract*, 2001.)

a. $P(\text{Hispanic}) = 11.8$

b. $P = 4.1$ when $r =$ Asian and Pacific Islander

15. Sales   A music store offers one free CD with the purchase of four CDs priced at $18 each (tax included).

a. Construct a graph showing the cost of buying x CDs. Show input values from 0 to 10.

b. What is the cost of 6 CDs?

c. How many CDs could you buy if you had $36?

d. How many CDs could you buy if you had $100?

16. Sales   A fraternity is selling T-shirts on the day of a football game. The shirts sell for $8 each.

a. Complete the table. Revenue is defined as the number of units sold times the selling price.

Number of shirts sold	Revenue (dollars)
1	
2	
3	
4	
5	
6	

b. Construct a revenue graph by plotting the points in the table.

c. How many T-shirts can be purchased with $25?

d. If an 8% sales tax were added, how many T-shirts could be purchased with $25?

17. Weight   A baby weighing 7 pounds at birth loses 7% of her weight in the 3 days after birth and then, over the next 4 days, returns to her birth weight. During the next month, she steadily gains 0.5 pound per week. Sketch a graph of the baby's weight from birth to 4 weeks. Accurately label both axes.

18. Medicine   A patient is instructed by her doctor to take one pill containing 500 milligrams of a drug. Assume that each day the patient's body uses 20% of the remaining amount of the drug. The amount of the drug remaining at the beginning of day x can be modeled as

$$f(x) = 500(0.8^x) \text{ milligrams}$$

a. Graph the model.

b. Use the model to determine how much of the drug is left in the patient's body after 3.5 days.

c. Use a graph of the model to estimate when the concentration of the drug will be 60 milligrams. Use the model to find the exact value.

19. Payment You are interested in buying a used car and in financing it for 60 months at 10% interest. As a special promotion, the dealer is offering to finance with no down payment. The accompanying graph shows the value of the car as a function of the amount of the monthly payment.

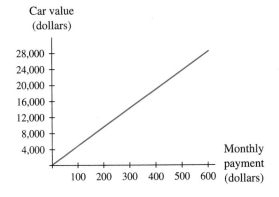

Car value (dollars)

a. Estimate the value of the car you can buy if your monthly payment is $200.

b. Estimate the monthly payment for a car that costs $16,000.

c. Estimate the amount by which your monthly payment will increase if you buy a $20,000 car rather than a $15,000 car.

d. How would the graph change if the interest rate were 12.5% instead of 10%?

20. Payment You have decided to purchase a car for $18,750. You have 20% of the purchase price to use as a down payment, and the purchase will be financed at 10% interest. The accompanying graph shows the monthly loan payment in terms of the number of months over which the loan is financed.

a. What is the actual amount being financed?

b. Estimate your monthly payment if you finance the purchase over 36 months.

c. Estimate the number of months you will have to pay on the loan if you can afford to pay only $300 a month.

d. If you decrease the time financed from 48 to 36 months, by how much will your payment increase?

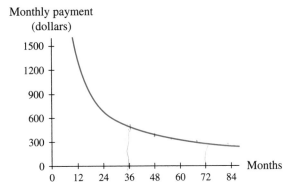

Monthly payment (dollars)

21. Social Security The accompanying graph shows the percentage by which Social Security checks increased as a result of cost-of-living adjustments every year from 1999 through 2005.

a. What was the cost-of-living increase in 2002?

b. When was the cost-of-living increase the greatest? Estimate the cost-of-living increase in that year.

c. When was the cost-of-living increase 2.1%?

d. Did Social Security benefits increase or decrease between 2002 and 2003? Explain.

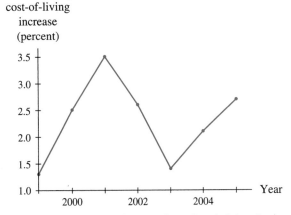

Social Security cost-of-living increase (percent)

(Source: Based on data from Social Security Administration.)

22. Wages The accompanying graph compares the minimum wage with its value in constant 1996 dollars. Because the minimum wage is not indexed to the price level, it has been legislatively increased from time to time to make up for the loss in its value due to inflation. The last general Fair Labor Standards Act amendments were adopted in 1996, at which time the current federal minimum wage was set at $5.15 per hour. This wage became effective in 1997.

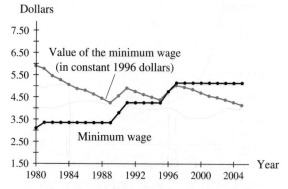

Dollars

(Source: Based on data from Bureau of Labor Statistics.)

a. Estimate the minimum wage in 2005 and the value of the minimum wage in constant 1996 dollars in that same year.

b. Over what intervals did the minimum wage remain constant? What happened to the buying power of the minimum wage during these intervals?

c. In what years was the 1996 value of the minimum wage above $5?

d. Estimate the year in which the graphs intersect. Discuss the meaning of this point of intersection.

For Activities 23 through 26, find the output of the function corresponding to each input value given.

23. $t(s) = 3s + 6$; $s = 5$, $s = 10$

24. $f(x) = 7.2x + 3$; $x = 20$, $x = -2$

25. $R(w) = 9.4(1.8^w)$; $w = 3$, $w = 0$

26. $S(t) = \dfrac{120}{1+3e^{-2t}}$; $t = 10$, $t = 2$

For Activities 27 through 30, find the input of the function corresponding to each output value given.

27. $t(s) = 3s + 6$; $t(s) = 18$, $t(s) = 0$

28. $f(x) = 7.2x + 3$; $f(x) = 6.6$, $f(x) = 3$

29. $R(w) = 9.4(1.8^w)$; $R(w) = 9.4$, $R(w) = 30$

30. $S(t) = \dfrac{120}{1+3e^{-2t}}$; $S(t) = 60$, $S(t) = 30$

For each of the functions in Activities 31 through 34, determine whether an input or an output value is given, and find its corresponding output or input.

31. $A(t) = 32e^{0.5t}$; $t = 15$

32. $g(x) = 4x^2 + 32x - 13$; $g(x) = 247$

33. $f(x) = 3(1.04^x)$; $f(x) = 3.65$

34. $p(m) = \dfrac{100}{1+2e^{-0.3m}}$; $m = 2.3$

35. The total cost for producing x units of a commodity is $4.2 million, and the revenue generated by the sale of x units is $5.3 million.

a. What is the profit on x units of the commodity?

b. Assuming $T(x)$ is the total cost and $R(x)$ is the revenue for the production/sale of x units of a commodity, write an expression for profit.

36. The total cost for producing x units of a commodity is $400, and the revenue generated by the sale of x units is $300.

a. What is the "profit" on x units of the commodity?

b. What does negative profit indicate?

37. A company posted revenue of $35 million and a profit of $19 million during the same quarter.

a. What was the company's cost during that quarter?

b. Assuming $P(x)$ is the profit and $R(x)$ is the revenue posted by the company in the xth quarter, write an expression for total cost.

38. A company posted a net loss of $3 billion last quarter.

a. What was its profit?

b. If last quarter's revenue was $5 billion, what was its cost?

39. It cost a company $19.50 to produce 150 glass bottles.

a. What was the average cost of production of a glass bottle?

b. Assuming $C(x)$ is the total cost for producing x units, write an expression for average cost per unit.

40. **Natural Gas Trade** The following two functions have a common input, year t. I is the projected amount of natural gas imports in quadrillion Btu, and E is the projected natural gas exports in trillion Btu.

a. Using function notation, show how you could combine the two functions to create a third function, N, giving net trade of natural gas in year t.

b. What does it mean when net trade is negative?

41. **Debit Cards** The following two functions have a common input, year y. D is the total number of debit card transactions, and P is the number of point-of-sale transactions.

    a. Using function notation, show how you could combine the two functions to create a third function, r, showing the percentage of debit card transactions that were conducted at the point of sale in year y.

    b. What are the output units of the new function?

42. **Gas Prices** The following two functions have a common input, year t. R is the average price (in dollars) of a gallon of regular unleaded gasoline, and P is the purchasing power of the dollar as measured by consumer prices based on 2001 dollars.

    a. Using function notation, indicate how to combine the two functions to create a third function showing the price of gasoline in constant 2001 dollars.

    b. What are the output units of the new function?

43. **Earnings** The salary of one of Compaq Computer Corporation's senior vice presidents from 1996 through 1998 can be modeled by

    $$S(t) = 69{,}375t + 380{,}208 \text{ dollars}$$

    t years after 1996. His other, nonsalary compensation during the same period can be modeled by

    $$C(t) = -31.67t^2 + 137.15t + 233.5 \text{ thousand dollars}$$

    t years after 1996. In addition, each year he received an average bonus of $650,000.
    (Source: Based on data from Compaq's 1999 Notice of Annual Meeting.)

    a. Construct a model for this VP's total yearly salary package, including nonsalary compensation and bonuses.

    b. Estimate the VP's 1997 total salary package.

44. **Milk Consumption** Per capita milk consumption in the United States between 1980 and 1999 can be modeled by

    $$M(t) = -0.219t + 45.23 \text{ gallons per person per year}$$

and consumption of whole milk for the same period can be modeled by

$$W(t) = 0.01685t^2 - 3.49t + 188$$

gallons per person per year

In both models, t is the number of years since 1900. Use the models to construct a model giving the per capita consumption of milk other than whole milk, and estimate this per capita consumption for the year 2000.
(Source: *Statistical Abstract*, 2001.)

45. **Credit Cards** The total amount of credit card debt from 1998 and projected through 2005 can be expressed by the function

    $$D(y) = 42.4y + 219.5 \text{ billion dollars}$$

    y years after 1990. The number of cardholders during that same time interval can be expressed by the function

    $$H(y) = 1.7y + 140.3 \text{ million cardholders}$$

    (Source: *Statistical Abstract*, 2000 and 2001.)

    a. Construct a function that expresses the average credit card debt per cardholder.

    b. Estimate the average debt of a cardholder in 2005.

46. **Transplants** The number of kidney and liver transplants performed in the United States between 1992 and 1996 can be modeled by

    $$K(x) = 9.09 + 1.7 \ln x \text{ kidney transplants}$$
    $$L(x) = 2.42 + 9.2 \ln x \text{ liver transplants}$$

    where x is the number of years since 1990.
    (Source: *Statistical Abstract*, 1998.)

    a. Construct a model for the number of kidney and liver transplants between 1992 and 1996.

    b. Use the model to estimate the number of kidney and liver transplants in 1995.

47. **Births** The number of births during the 1980s to women who were 35 years of age or older can be modeled as
    $$n(x) = -0.034x^3 + 1.331x^2 + 9.913x + 164.447$$
    thousand births

    x years after 1980.
    The following model gives the number of cesarean-section deliveries for each 1000 live births among

women in the same age bracket during the same time period:

$$p(x) = -0.183x^2 + 2.891x + 20.215 \text{ deliveries}$$
$$\text{per 1000 live births}$$

x years after 1980.

Write an expression for the number of cesarean-section deliveries performed on women 35 years of age or older during the 1980s.

(Source: *Statistical Abstract*, 1992.)

Determine whether the pairs of functions in Activities 48 through 51 can be combined by function composition. If so, give function notation for the new function, and draw and label its input/output diagram.

48. $P(c)$ is the profit in dollars generated by the sale of c computer chips.

$C(t)$ is the number of computer chips a manufacturer has produced after t hours of production.

49. $C(t)$ is the number of cats in the United States at the end of year t.

$D(c)$ is the number of dogs in the United States at the end of year c.

50. $C(t)$ is the average number of customers in a restaurant on a Saturday night t hours after 4 P.M.

$P(c)$ is the average amount in dollars of tips generated by c customers.

51. $R(x)$ is the revenue in deutsche marks from the sale of x soccer uniforms.

$D(r)$ is the dollar value of r deutsche marks.

In Activities 52 through 55, rewrite each pair of functions as one composite function.

52. $f(t) = 3e^t; t(p) = 4p^2$

53. $h(p) = \dfrac{4}{p}; p(t) = 1 + 3e^{-0.5t}$

54. $g(x) = \sqrt{7x^2}; x(w) = 4e^w$

55. $c(x) = 3x^2 - 2x + 5; x(t) = 4 - 6t$

Discussing Concepts

56. Why is it important to understand the units of measure of input and output for a given function? How can labeling units help in function construction?

57. Describe the types of compatibility necessary between input units and output units for each of the following types of function construction: addition, multiplication, division, and composition.

58. Discuss the advantages of each of the four perspectives from which a mathematical model can be viewed: numerical, algebraic, verbal, and graphical.

1.2 Linear Functions and Models

Having explored the concept of a function in the last section, we turn our attention in the remainder of the chapter to several specific types of functions that will be helpful as we seek to describe real-life situations with mathematical models. Our goal is to give you an understanding of the behavior underlying certain functions in order to help you determine which one of those functions is most appropriate in a particular modeling situation.

Representations of a Linear Model

We begin with the simplest of all functions: the linear function. A **linear function** is one that repeatedly and at even intervals adds the same value to the output. The output values form the pattern of a line when graphed; thus we use the term *linear* to describe the data. For example, consider a newspaper delivery team that makes weekly deliveries of newspapers and devotes their Saturday mornings to selling new subscriptions. The function describing the number of customers can be represented in four ways.

With words:

The team starts with 80 customers, and 5 new customers are added each week.

With data (see Table 1.10):

TABLE 1.10

Weeks	0	1	2	3	4	5	6	7
Number of customers	80	85	90	95	100	105	110	115

With graphs (see Figure 1.21):

FIGURE 1.21

With a model:

$$C(w) = 5w + 80 \text{ customers}$$

where w stands for the number of weeks since the team began the subscription drive $0 \leq w \leq 7$.

Each of these four representations is indicative of a linear model.

Two graphical representations of the linear model are shown in Figure 1.21. The graph in Figure 1.21a is a **scatter plot**—a discrete representation of the data from the table. The graph in Figure 1.21b is the graph associated with the continuous function modeling the data. Because calculus is the study of continuous functions and their behavior, once we have a continuous function modeling data, we will use the function instead of the data and, likewise, will use the continuous graph instead of the scatter plot.

Slope and Intercept

A linear equation is determined by two constants: a starting value and the amount of the incremental change. All linear functions appear algebraically as

$$f(x) = ax + b$$

where a is the incremental change per unit input and b is the starting value.

Linear functions are graphed as lines, where a is the slope (a measure of the line's steepness) and b is the *vertical axis intercept* (that is, the output value at which the line crosses the $x = 0$ vertical axis). The slope of a graph is of primary importance in our study of calculus. As we shall see in Chapter 3, the slope of most functions is determined using calculus; however, the slope of a line can be calculated more simply.

The directed horizontal distance from one point on a graph to another is called the *run,* and the corresponding directed vertical distance is called the *rise.* The quotient of the rise divided by the run is the **slope** of the line connecting the two points. Consider again the newspaper subscription graph in Figure 1.21. We have chosen the points on the graph that correspond to 0 and 7 weeks. The rise and run corresponding to those two points are shown in Figure 1.22.

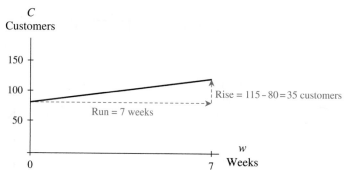

FIGURE 1.22

The slope is calculated as $\frac{\text{rise}}{\text{run}} = \frac{35 \text{ customers}}{7 \text{ weeks}} = 5$ customers per week. (The slope value will be the same regardless of which two points are chosen for the calculation.) The steeper a line, the greater the magnitude of the value of the slope. Lines that fall rather than rise have negative slope. Unlike the slope, the steepness of a line does not depend on whether it rises or falls.

Although the slope of a particular linear model never changes, the graph of the model may look different when the horizontal or vertical scale is changed. By using a different vertical scale for the graph of customers (see Figure 1.23), we obtain what appears to be a steeper line. However, a calculation of slope reveals that the difference is only visual. Appearances can deceive, so be careful when comparing graphs with differing scales.

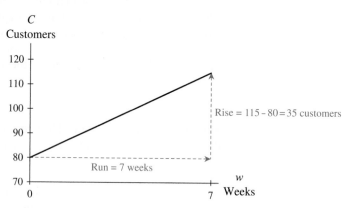

FIGURE 1.23

The slope of a graph of a function at a particular point is a measure of how quickly the output is changing as the input changes at that point. This measure is called the **rate of change** of the function at that point, and we discuss it more thoroughly in Chapters 2 and 3. Because linear functions are characterized by constant incremental change, their slope (rate of change) is constant at all points. Other types of functions have a different slope at every point; that is, their rate of change is not constant.

EXAMPLE 1   *Calculating Slopes*

Sales   The resale value of a used car is represented graphically in Figure 1.24.

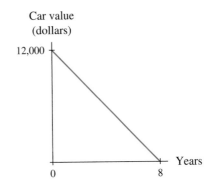

FIGURE 1.24

a. Locate and interpret the point at which the input is 0 and the point at which the output is 0.

b. Calculate the slope of the graph.

c. Does the slope depend on the direction in which it was calculated?

d. Interpret the slope.

e. Write a linear model for the graph.

Solution

a. The point at which the input is 0 is where the line intercepts the vertical axis—that is, at point (0, 12,000). The vertical axis intercept is $12,000 and corresponds to the value of the car when it was purchased.

   The point at which the output is 0 is where the line intercepts the horizontal axis—that is, at point (8, 0). The horizontal axis intercept is 8 years and indicates the first year in which the car had essentially no value.

b. To travel from the horizontal axis intercept 8 to the vertical axis intercept 12,000 on the graph requires that you move 12,000 units up (+ $12,000 = rise) and 8 units to the left (−8 years = run). See Figure 1.25. The quotient of the rise divided by the run is $\frac{\$12,000}{-8 \text{ years}} = -\$1500$ per year.

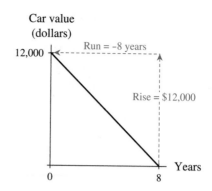

FIGURE 1.25

c. If you traveled from the vertical axis intercept 12,000 to the horizontal axis intercept 8, the run would be positive and the rise negative. The quotient of the rise divided by the run would be $\frac{-\$12,000}{8 \text{ years}} = -\$1500$ per year. Note that the quotient $\frac{\text{rise}}{\text{run}}$ is the same either way you compute it.

d. The quotient $\frac{\text{rise}}{\text{run}}$ is equal to the slope of the linear model and is the rate of change of the value of the car. We say that the car depreciated at a rate of $1500 per year.

e. The equation of the line that represents the value of the car has slope -1500 and starting value 12,000. If we let the variable t represent the number of years since the car was purchased, $0 \le t \le 8$, the model for the value of the car is

$$\text{Value} = -1500t + 12,000 \text{ dollars} \quad \bullet$$

It is important to be able to describe the behavior of a function or graph. We use the words *increasing, decreasing,* and *constant* to describe the output behavior of a graph or function. If a graph is rising as you move from left to right along the horizontal axis, then it is said to be **increasing.** A graph is said to be **decreasing** if it is falling as you move from left to right along the horizontal axis. The portion of a graph that neither rises nor falls is called **constant.** The function shown in Figure 1.21 is increasing. The function shown in Figure 1.24 is decreasing. In the case of the increasing linear function the slope a is positive, and in the case of the decreasing linear function the slope is negative.

We summarize our discussion of linear equations as follows:

Linear Model

Verbally: A linear model is one that has a constant rate of change.
Algebraically: A linear model has an equation of the form

$$f(x) = ax + b$$

where a and b are constants.

Graphically: The graph of a linear function is a line (see Figure 1.26). The value a in the equation is the constant rate of change of the output and is the slope of the line. The value b is the output at which the input is zero.

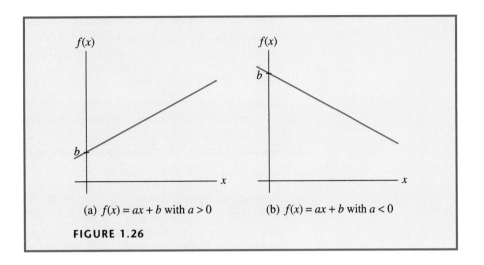

(a) $f(x) = ax + b$ with $a > 0$ (b) $f(x) = ax + b$ with $a < 0$

FIGURE 1.26

Finding a Linear Model from Data

Suppose you are the sole proprietor of a small business that has seen no growth in sales for the last several years. You have noticed, however, that your federal taxes have increased as shown in Table 1.11.

TABLE 1.11

Year	1999	2000	2001	2002	2003	2004
Tax	$2532	$3073	$3614	$4155	$4696	$5237

Upon close examination of the data, you note that taxes increased by the same amount every year.

1.2.1

The changes in successive output, which are called **first differences,** are constant. This constant increase is the incremental change where the increment is one year. Because the incremental change is constant, we know that the data represent a linear increase in taxes. Because the data show the tax amount each year, this incremental change is the rate of change of the tax amount and the slope of the underlying linear model. If the data had shown taxes every other year, the first differences would still be constant, indicating a linear pattern, but the value of the first differences would be twice the slope. Slope values are always expressed per unit increase in input.

On the basis of the calculation of first differences, we make the following equivalent statements:

Taxes increased by $541 per year.
The slope of the linear function described by the data is $541 per year.
The rate of change of the tax amount is $541 per year.

If we consider 1999 to be our starting point, then the starting tax value is $2532. We express the tax function verbally as follows: The tax amount began in 1999 at $2532 and increased each year by $541. We express the function algebraically as

Tax $= 541t + 2532$ dollars

where t represents the number of years since 1999. Such models are important because they often enable us to analyze the results of change. With certain assumptions, they may even allow us to make cautious predictions about the short-term future. For example, to predict the tax amount owed in 2007, we substitute $t = 8$ into the tax model.

Tax $= 541(8) + 2532 = \$6860$

Admittedly, in this instance, an equation is not necessary to make such a prediction, but there are many situations in which it is difficult to proceed without a model.

It is important to understand that when we use mathematical models to make predictions about the short-term future, *we are assuming that future events will follow the same pattern as past events.* This assumption may or may not be true. That does not mean that such predictions are useless, only that *they must be viewed with extreme caution.*

A Word of Caution

When you use a model to predict output values for input values that are *within* the interval of input data used to obtain the model, you are using a process called **interpolation.** Predicting output values for input values that are *outside* the interval of the input data is called **extrapolation.** Because you do not know what happens outside the range of given data, *estimates obtained by extrapolation must be viewed with caution and may result in misleading predictions.*

We have already noted that the rate of change of the tax amount is $541 per year, which is how much taxes increase during a 1-year period. Thinking about rate of change in this way helps us answer questions such as

- If you pay taxes twice a year, how much will taxes increase each time?

  $(\$541 \text{ per year})\left(\frac{1}{2} \text{ year}\right) = \$270.50$

- How much will taxes increase each time if you pay taxes quarterly?

  $(\$541 \text{ per year})\left(\frac{1}{4} \text{ year}\right) = \$135.25$

- How much will taxes increase during a 3-year period?

  $(\$541 \text{ per year})(3 \text{ years}) = \$1623$

EXAMPLE 2   *Writing a Linear Model*

Business Survival   Table 1.12 shows the percent of U.S. companies that are still in business after a given number of years in operation.

a. Find the constant rate of change in the percent of businesses surviving.

b. Find a model for the percent of companies still in business as a function of years of operation. Graph the model and give a verbal description of that graph.

Solution

a. Calculating the first differences of the data in Table 1.12 indicates that the percent of businesses surviving decreased by 3 percentage points per year. We could also say that the rate of change of the survival percentage is -3 percentage points per year.

   Caution: Note that this result is not the same as a rate of change of -3 percent per year. When the output of a function is a percent, units on the rate of change must be expressed in terms of percentage points per input unit.

b. The data reveal that the percent begins with 50% and that each year after the first table value, the percent declines by 3 percentage points. We write this mathematically as

   $P(t) = -3t + 50$ percent of businesses that are still in business

   t years after the fifth year in operation. Figure 1.27 depicts the graph of P.

TABLE 1.12

Years	Companies (percent)
5	50
6	47
7	44
8	41
9	38
10	35

(Source: Cognetics, Cambridge, Massachusetts, 1998.)

FIGURE 1.27

The function $P(t) = -3t + 50$, its graph, and the data in Table 1.12 all show that the percent of U.S. companies that are still in business declines by 3 percentage points for each year after 5 years of operation and that at the end of 5 years, 50% of those companies are still in business. ●

The preceding examples illustrate methods of finding a linear model of the form $f(x) = ax + b$ for data points that fall on a line. However, real-life data values are seldom perfectly linear. For instance, the tax data we considered earlier are not likely to occur in real-life situations, because tax rates and the revenues of most businesses change from year to year. Consider the following modification to the tax data:

Year	1999	2000	2001	2002	2003	2004
Tax	$2541	$3081	$3615	$4157	$4703	$5242

$540 $534 $542 $546 $539

The first differences are not constant but "nearly constant." A linear model may be used if first differences are close to constant. Be sure to calculate first differences only for data that are evenly spaced.

An examination of the scatter plot in Figure 1.28 reinforces our earlier observation from an examination of the first differences, that the data are close to being linear. How do we get a linear model in this situation? Use the linear regression routine

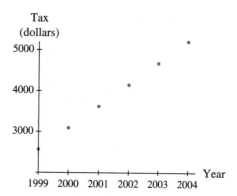

FIGURE 1.28

that is built into your calculator or computer to find a linear equation that fits the data. You should find the model to be

$$\text{Tax1} = 540.371t - 1{,}077{,}663.581 \text{ dollars}$$

where t is the year. Overdrawing the line of best fit on the scatter plot confirms our observation that a linear model is appropriate.

Aligning Data

1.2.2

When the input data are years, it is often desirable to modify how the years are numbered to reduce the number of digits you have to enter, as well as to reduce the magnitude of some of the coefficients in the model equation. We refer to the process of renumbering data as **aligning** the data. For example, if we renumber the years in the tax data so that 1999 is year 0, 2000 is year 1, and so on, we obtain the data shown in Table 1.13.

TABLE 1.13

Aligned year	0	1	2	3	4	5
Tax	$2541	$3081	$3615	$4157	$4703	$5242

The aligned years are described as "the number of years since 1999." Using a calculator or computer to obtain a linear model for this aligned data, we have

$$\text{Tax2} = 540.371t + 2538.905 \text{ dollars}$$

where t is the number of years since 1999. Note that this equation and the equation for the unaligned data have the same slope (rate of change) but differ in the vertical axis intercept. That is, the parameter a in the equation $f(x) = ax + b$ is unchanged, but the b-value differs. Aligning the data has the effect of shifting the data (usually to the left). This does not change the slope of the line, but it does change where the line crosses the vertical axis.

When using a model obtained from aligned data, it is important that you keep the description of the input variable in mind at all times. If we are willing to assume that the rate of change remains constant at about $540.37 per year, then we can estimate the tax in 2006 by using a value of $t = 2006$ in the Tax1 model or a value of $t = 7$ in the Tax2 model (the number of years that 2006 is counted from 1999).

$$\text{Tax1} = 540.371(2006) - 1{,}077{,}663.58 \text{ dollars} \approx \$6322$$
$$\text{Tax2} = 540.371(7) + 2538.905 \text{ dollars} \approx \$6322$$

These models give the same output values. They are equivalent. Note that the model with the lower-numbered input (Tax2) has the smaller intercept value. It also has the advantage that the constant term (\$2538.905) is the approximate beginning amount shown in the table.

To summarize, when the input is years, it is desirable to align data to make the data entry faster and to reduce the magnitude of some of the coefficients. In general, the smaller the magnitude of the input data, the smaller the magnitude of the coefficients in the function that models the data.

Numerical Considerations: Reporting Answers

When dealing with numerical results, it is important to understand the accuracy of the data and how precise the results need to be. For instance, imagine that you have a bank account with a balance of \$18,532.71 paying interest at a rate of $5\frac{1}{4}\%$ compounded annually. At the end of the year, the bank calculates your interest to be $(18{,}532.71)(0.0525) = \$972.967275$. Would you expect your next bank statement to record the new balance as \$19,505.67728? Obviously, when reporting numerical results dealing with monetary amounts, we do not consider partial pennies. The bank reports the balance as \$19,505.67. The precision required is only two decimal places.

> You should always round numerical results in a way that *makes sense* in the context of the problem.

TABLE 1.14

Year	Net sales (millions of dollars)
1998	115.6
1999	80.6
2000	45.7

Generally, results that represent people or objects should be rounded to the nearest whole number. Results that represent money usually should be rounded to the nearest cent or, in some cases, to the nearest dollar. Consider, however, an international company that reports net sales as shown in Table 1.14.

A linear model for these data is $y = -34.95x + 69{,}945.683$ million dollars, where x is the year. If we wished to estimate net sales in 2001, we would substitute $x = 2001$ in the model to obtain $y = \$10.73333333$ million. Should we report the answer as \$10,733,333.33 or \$10,733,333? Neither! When we are dealing with numerical results, our answer can be only as accurate as the least accurate output data. In this case, the answer would have to be reported as \$10.7 million or \$10,700,000.

> You should round numerical results to the same accuracy as the least accurate of the output data given.

Keep in mind that a number by itself is likely to be absolutely worthless. For example, it would not make sense for an international company to publish, in its annual report, that net sales were 10.7. This could mean 10.7 dollars, 10.7 thousand euros,

10.7 million yen, and so on. The label makes a big difference in our understanding of the number.

> A number is useless without a label that clearly indicates the units involved.

Numerical Considerations: Calculating Answers

Although the correct rounding and reporting of numerical results are important, it is even more important to calculate the results correctly. Because you must sometimes round your answers, it is tempting to think that you can round *during* the calculation process. Don't! Never round a number unless it is the final answer that you are reporting. Rounding during the calculation process may lead to serious errors. Your calculator or computer is capable of working with many digits. Keep them all while you are still working toward a final result.

When you use your calculator or computer to fit a function to data, it finds the parameters in the equation to many digits. Although the text shows rounded coefficients and it may be acceptable to your instructor for you to round the coefficients when reporting a model, make sure that you use all of the digits while working with the model. This helps reduce the possibility of round-off error.

For example, suppose that your calculator or computer generates the following equation for a set of data showing an airline's weekly profit for a certain route as a function of the ticket price.

$$\text{Weekly profit} = -0.00374285714285x^2 + 2.5528571428572x$$
$$- 52.71428571429 \text{ thousand dollars}$$

where x is the ticket price in dollars. In the answer key, you would see the model reported to three decimal places:

$$\text{Weekly profit} = -0.004x^2 + 2.553x - 52.714 \text{ thousand dollars}$$

However, if you used the rounded model to calculate weekly profit, your answers would be incorrect because of round-off error. Table 1.15 shows the inconsistencies between the rounded and unrounded models.

TABLE 1.15

Ticket price	Profit from rounded model	Profit from unrounded model
$200	$298 thousand	$308 thousand
$400	$328 thousand	$370 thousand
$600	$39 thousand	$132 thousand

> Never use a rounded model to calculate, and never round intermediate answers during the calculation process.

The number of decimal places shown in models in the text will vary. However, whenever we calculate with a model, we use all the digits available at that point in the text. If the data are given, the unrounded model will be used in calculations. When a model found earlier is used in a later section and the data are not repeated, all calculations will be done with the rounded model given in that later section. For convenience and consistency, the answer key will report all models with three decimal places in coefficients and six decimal places in exponents.

The Four Elements of a Model

It is important to print the fewest digits possible under the conditions that (a) the rounded model visually fits the data, and (b) the rounded model gives values fairly close to answers obtained with the full model. In particular, if there is a difference between the results from the full model and those from the rounded model, that difference should appear only in the last digit for which we can claim accuracy.

A model is an equation describing the relationship between an output variable and an input variable, together with their defining statements. The first element of a model is the equation itself. As previously noted, equations obtained from data using technology generally have coefficients with many digits. When using the model, do not round the coefficients, but when you are reporting the model, it may be acceptable to your instructor if you round the parameters to three or four decimal places as we have done throughout the text.

The second element of a model is a description of what the output variable represents. Look back to the models we obtained for the small business's tax. Tax is *what* is measured, and dollars is a label telling *how* it is measured. Always label a model equation with output units to indicate how the output is measured.

The third element of a model is the description of the input variable. If all that was written for the tax model had been Tax2 $= 540.371t + 2538.905$ dollars, you might have erroneously predicted that your federal taxes in 2006 would be $540.371(2006) + 2538.905 = \$1,086,524$. However, there is a statement with the equation that reads "where t is the number of years since 1999." Because 2006 is the 7th year since 1999, you should correctly predict your federal taxes in 2006 to be $540.371(7) + 2538.905 = \$6322$.

When both the data and a model are present, the interval information is not always restated. The answer key usually restates the interval.

The final element of a model is a description of the valid input interval. The tax model was obtained from data between 1999 and 2004. It is important, when giving a model that will be used without the data from which it was obtained, that you indicate the interval of input values over which the model is valid. This is the only way that other people who use the model will know whether they are interpolating or extrapolating. Here is the convention we will adopt: When a model is presented without the data from which it was obtained, we will indicate the range of input data used. For example, we would report the tax model by saying, "The tax between 1999 and 2004 can be modeled as Tax $= 540.371t + 2538.905$ dollars t years after 1999." This statement incorporates the four elements of a model.

There are four important elements of every model:
1. An equation.
2. A label denoting the units on the output.
3. A description (including units) of what the input variable represents.
4. An indication of the interval of input values over which the model is valid. This information should be given whenever the model is presented or used apart from the data from which it was obtained.

As you proceed through this course, take the time to record your models completely and to report your answers accurately. If you practice proper reporting while you work through the activities on linear models, you will begin to develop a habit that will help you throughout your study of calculus in this text. In the next section we will consider models other than the linear model. These reporting guidelines hold true for them as well.

1.2 Concept Inventory

- Algebraic form of a linear function: $f(x) = ax + b$
- Rate of change (slope) of a linear model is constant
- Slope as $\frac{\text{rise}}{\text{run}}$
- First differences
- Interpolation and extrapolation
- Calculation guidelines and rounding rules
- Units of measure on answers
- Four elements of a model

1.2 Activities

Getting Started

For the linear functions given in Activities 1 through 4, a. find the rate of change of the function, and b. find the output of the function when the input is 0. Affix the proper units to your answers.

1. $f(x) = 3x + 5$ dollars where x is the year

2. $k(t) = -0.5t + 3.2$ million people of age t (in years)

3. $r(p) = 2p - 4.5$ thousand dollars when p hundred units are sold

4. $p(r) = 5r + 12$ hundred pounds for r inches of rainfall

For the linear functions given in Activities 5 through 8, a. determine whether the slope is positive or negative, b. tell whether the function is increasing or decreasing, and c. determine the vertical axis intercept.

5. $f(x) = -2x - 4$

6. $g(t) = 2t + 5$

7. $k(r) = -3r + 7$

8. $s(p) = 3p - 2$

In Activities 9 through 12, write an appropriate linear model for the given rate of change and initial output value. Label the linear model.

9. Cost increases by 30 cents per unit produced and the fixed cost is 150 dollars.

10. Population, which was 49.5 thousand in 2000, has been increasing at a constant rate of 2.5 thousand people per year.

11. Snow fell at a rate of 0.25 inch per hour. Three inches had fallen by noon.

12. The speed increased at a constant rate of 2 mph per second from an initial speed of 30 mph.

Applying Concepts

13. **Profit**   The accompanying graph shows a corporation's profit, in millions of dollars, over a period of time.

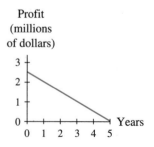

a. Is the profit function increasing or decreasing? Is the slope of the graph positive or negative?

b. Estimate the slope of the graph, and write a sentence explaining the meaning of the slope in this context.

c. What is the rate of change of the corporation's profit during this time period?

d. Identify the points where input is zero and where output is zero, and explain their significance to this corporation.

14. Temperature   The air temperature in a certain location from 8 A.M. to 3 P.M. is shown in the accompanying graph.

a. Is the temperature function increasing or decreasing? Is the slope of the graph positive or negative?

b. Estimate the slope of the graph, and explain its meaning in the context of temperature.

c. How fast is the temperature rising between 8 A.M. and 3 P.M.?

15. Organ Donors   The number of organ donors in the United States between 1988 and 1996 can be modeled by

$$D(t) = 382.5t + 5909 \text{ donors}$$

t years after 1988.

(Source: Based on data from United Network for Organ Sharing.)

a. Is the rate of change positive or negative? Is the function increasing or decreasing?

b. According to the model, what is the rate of change of the number of organ donors?

c. Sketch a graph of the model. What is the slope of the graph?

d. Find the point at which input is zero, and explain its significance in context.

16. Bankruptcy   Total Chapter 12 bankruptcy filings between 1996 and 2000 can be modeled by

$$B(t) = -83.9t + 1063 \text{ filings}$$

t years after 1996.

(Source: Based on data from Administrative Office of U.S. Courts.)

a. Is the rate of change positive or negative? Is the function increasing or decreasing?

b. What is the rate of change of the number of Chapter 12 bankruptcy filings?

c. Sketch a graph of the model. What is the slope of the graph?

d. Find the point at which input is zero, and explain its significance in context.

17. Revenue   The revenue for International Game Technology was $2128.1 million in 2003 and $2484.8 million in 2004. Assume that revenue was increasing at a constant rate.

(Source: Hoover's, Inc.)

a. Find the rate of change of revenue.

b. By how much did revenue increase each quarter of 2004?

c. Assuming that the rate of increase remains constant, complete the following table.

Year	Revenue (millions of dollars)
2003	
2004	
2005	
2006	

d. Find an equation for revenue in terms of the year.

18. Car Value   Suppose you bought a Honda Civic Hybrid in 2005 for $24,000. In 2007 it was worth $18,200. Assume that the rate at which the car depreciates is constant.

a. Find the rate of change of the value of the car.

b. Complete the following table:

Year	Value
2005	
2007	
2008	
2009	
2010	

c. Find an equation for the value in terms of the year.

d. How much will the value of the car change during a 1-month period? Round your answer to the nearest dollar.

19. **Sales**   A house sells for $97,500 at the end of 2000 and for $112,000 at the end of 2007.

   a. If the market value increased linearly from 2000 through 2007, what was the rate of change of the market value?

   b. If the linear increase continues, what will the market value be in 2010?

   c. In what year might you expect the market value to be $100,000? $150,000?

   d. Find a model for the market value. What does your model estimate for the market value in 2005? What assumption did you make when you created the model?

20. **Births**   Thirty-two percent of U.S. births that occurred in 1995 were to unmarried women. The percentage of U.S. births to unmarried women in 2002 was 34.
   (Source: *National Vital Statistics Reports*, vol. 53, no. 9.)

   a. Find the rate of change of the percentage of births, assuming that the percentage of births to unmarried women increased at a constant rate.

   b. Estimate the percentage of births to unmarried women in 2003.

21. **Credit**   Consumer credit in the United States was $1719 billion in 2000 and $2040 billion in 2003. Assume that consumer credit increases at a constant rate.
   (Source: *Statistical Abstract*, 2004–2005.)

   a. Find the rate of increase.

   b. On the basis of the rate of increase, estimate consumer credit in 2006.

   c. Is the assumption that consumer credit increases at a constant rate valid? Explain.

   d. Assuming a constant rate of change, when will consumer credit reach $3 trillion?

22. **Break-even Point**   You and several of your friends decide to mass-produce "I love calculus and you should too!" T-shirts. Each shirt will cost you $2.50 to produce. Additional expenses include the rental of a downtown building for a flat fee of $675 per month, utilities estimated at $100 each month, and leased equipment costing $150 per month. You will be able to sell the T-shirts at the premium price of $14.50 because they will be in such great demand.

   a. Give the equations for monthly revenue and monthly cost as functions of the number of T-shirts sold.

   b. How many shirts do you have to sell each month to break even? Explain how you obtained your answer.

23. **Population**   In 1999, the U.S. Bureau of the Census estimated that the world's population had reached 6 billion people. A newspaper article about the population stated that "Despite a gradual slowing of the overall rate of growth, the world population is still increasing by 78 million people a year. . . . [T]he number of humans on the planet could double again to 12 billion by 2050 if the current growth rate continues."
   (Source: "Population of World Ready to Hit 6 Billion," *Chicago Tribune*, October 21, 1999, p. A1.)

   a. According to the article, what is the rate of change of the world's population?

   b. Find a linear model for the population of the world, assuming that the population was 6 billion at the beginning of 2000.

   c. According to the model in part *b*, when will the world's population be 12 billion? Does this agree with the estimate given in the article?

   d. What assumption did you make when you made the prediction in part *c*?

24. **Heating Oil**   The following table gives the number of gallons of oil in a tank used for heating an apartment complex *t* days after January 1 when the tank was filled.

t	Oil (gallons)
0	30,000
1	29,600
2	29,200
3	28,800
4	28,400

   a. What is the rate of change of the amount of oil?

   b. How much oil can be expected to be used during any particular week in January?

c. Predict the amount of oil in the tank on January 30. What assumptions are you making when you make predictions about the amount of oil?

d. Find and graph an equation for the amount of oil in the tank in terms of the number of days since January 1.

25. Postal Rates   The following table shows first-class U.S. domestic postage for mail up to 9 ounces in the year 2006.

Weight not exceeding	Postage
1 oz	$0.39
2 oz	0.63
3 oz	0.87
4 oz	1.11
5 oz	1.39
6 oz	1.59
7 oz	1.83
8 oz	2.07
9 oz	2.31

(Source: U.S. Postal Service.)

a. Observe a scatter plot of these data. Determine visually whether a linear model is appropriate.

b. Verify your observations in part *a* by calculating first differences in the postal rates.

c. Find a formula for the postage in terms of weight. Be specific about what the variables represent.

26. Union Pressure   In order to put pressure on a company to negotiate a contract that is more favorable to employees, a workers' union may order a slowdown on labor. Consider, for instance, a slowdown of laborers at ports along the U.S. Pacific seaboard. The accompanying table shows the volume (in cartons) of cargo that is unloaded each day by one team of cargo handlers during a work slowdown when cargo handlers reduce their efficiency by $x\%$.

Percent slowdown	10	25	50	65	80
Cartons	108	90	60	42	24

a. Find a linear model for the volume of cargo handled by a team during an $x\%$ slowdown.

b. Use the model to estimate the volume handled if no slowdown occurs.

c. For your model, what are the points at which input is zero and output is zero? Discuss in context the information given by these points.

d. What is the slope for your model? Interpret the slope in context.

27. Enrollment   The accompanying table shows the enrollment for a particular university from 1965 through 1969.

Year	1965	1966	1967	1968	1969
Students	5024	5540	6057	6525	7028

a. Find a linear model for these data.

b. Use the model to estimate the enrollment in 1970.

c. The actual enrollment in 1970 was 8038 students. How far off was your estimate? Do you consider the error to be significant or insignificant? Explain your reasoning.

d. Would it be wise to use the model to predict the enrollment in the year 2000? Explain.

28. Cost   You are an employee in the summer at a souvenir shop. The souvenir shop owner wants to purchase 650 printed sweatshirts from a company. The catalog contains a table of costs and includes directions to call the company for costs on orders greater than 350. The catalog costs are shown in the table. The shop owner, who has tried unsuccessfully for a week to contact the company, asks you to estimate the cost for 650 shirts.

Number purchased	Total cost (dollars)	Number purchased	Total cost (dollars)
50	250	250	700
100	375	300	825
150	500	350	950
200	600		

a. Find a linear model to fit the data.

b. Use the model to predict the cost for 650 shirts. Note that all costs in the table are integer multiples of $25.

c. Determine the average cost per shirt for 650 shirts.

d. The shop owner is preparing a newspaper advertisement to be published in a week. If the standard markup is 700%, what should the advertised price be?

e. How many of the 650 shirts will need to be sold at the price determined in part *d* in order to pay for the cost of all 650 shirts (the break-even point)?

29. Kyoto Emissions   The aggregate emissions by the United States of the six greenhouse gases as defined in the Kyoto Protocol can be modeled as $e(t) = 0.107t + 5.11$ million gigagrams (CO_2 equivalent), where t is the number of years since 1990. The model is based on information for 1990 through 2002. (Source: FCCC/CP/2004/5 and FCCC/WEB/2004/3 available at http://unfccc.int)

a. What were the aggregate emissions of the six greenhouse gases released into the atmosphere in 1990? in 1997? in 2002?

b. At what rate was the amount of greenhouse-gas emissions increasing between 1990 and 2002?

c. Assuming that the constant rate of change of the model will continue to apply, what aggregate amount of greenhouse gases will be released into the atmosphere in 2012?

Discussing Concepts

30. Explain the difference between using a model for interpolation and using it for extrapolation. Does interpolation always give an accurate picture of what is happening in the real world? Does extrapolation? Why or why not?

31. Discuss the necessity for each of the four elements of a model.

32. Compare and contrast the terms *slope, steepness,* and *rate of change* as they are used to describe linear models.

1.3   Exponential and Logarithmic Functions and Models

In Section 1.2 we studied linear functions whose output resulted from the repeated *addition* of a constant at regular intervals. We now turn to a function whose output is the result of repeated *multiplication* by a constant at regular intervals.

Concavity and Exponential Growth and Decay

For example, in the case of a bacterial culture that starts with 10,000 cells and doubles every hour, the current size of the culture is determined by repeated multiplication. The size of the culture at the end of each of the first 4 hours is shown in Table 1.16.

TABLE 1.16

Hour	0	1	2	3	4
Cells	10,000	20,000	40,000	80,000	160,000

$P(t)$
Cells

Concave up and increasing
FIGURE 1.29

When we examine a scatter plot of the culture size over the first 10 hours, we see that the points certainly do not fall on a line. (See Figure 1.29.) In fact, these points seem to lie along a specific curve. We describe curvature in terms of **concavity.** In this case, the graph is **concave up,** not because it is increasing from left to right, but because it appears to be a portion of an arc opening upward.

The culture grows more rapidly in the later hours. We note that the starting culture size is 10,000 cells and that the size each hour is twice the prior size. The repeated multiplication by 2 makes the hour variable t appear as an exponent on 2; that is, the hour value counts the number of times that 2 has been used as a multiplier. A model for the bacterial culture size is

$$P(t) = 10{,}000(2^t) \text{ cells}$$

t hours after the culture was first counted. The curve underlying the scatter plot in Figure 1.29 is the graph of the function P.

Because the variable t appears in the exponent, we call the equation an **exponential equation**. If the multiplier is greater than 1, the change is referred to as **exponential growth.**

Exponential equations also arise when we see a *decreasing* amount of the original substance, such as in the study of radioactive material. For example, if 400 grams of a radioactive substance decays by 2% per day, then the amount of the substance remaining each day is 98% of the previous day's amount. The amount of the radioactive substance after x days of decay is given by the model

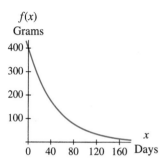

$f(x)$
Grams

Concave up and decreasing
FIGURE 1.30

$$f(x) = 400(0.98^x) \text{ grams}$$

In this case, the multiplier is between 0 and 1. Such a situation, wherein an amount diminishes by a constant multiplier, is referred to as **exponential decay.** Looking at a graph of f in Figure 1.30, we see that the graph again appears to be a portion of an arc opening upward, even though the outputs are decreasing. We say that the graph of f is concave up and decreasing.

Any change in a quantity that results from repeated multiplication by a constant generates an exponential function. In general, if we start with an amount a and multiply by a constant positive factor b each year, then the quantity that we have at the end of x years is given by the exponential equation

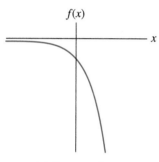

$f(x)$

(a) Concave down
and decreasing

$$f(x) = ab^x$$

defining f as a function of x. In the cases where a is positive, the function outputs are positive and the graphs of the function f will be similar to those in Figures 1.29 and 1.30. However, when a is negative, the function outputs are negative and the graphs of the function f will be similar to one of the two graphs in Figure 1.31.

The graph in Figure 1.31a is concave down and decreasing. The graph in Figure 1.31b is concave down and increasing. We do not often use negative exponential functions as models, but they do exist.

Percentage Change and Exponential Models

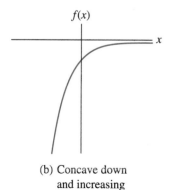

$f(x)$

(b) Concave down
and increasing

FIGURE 1.31

Linear functions exhibit a constant rate of change, but exponential functions exhibit a constant **percentage change.** Percentage change occurs when the amount of growth or decay is determined by the current size. For the exponential equation $f(x) = ab^x$, we determine the constant percentage change by calculating $(b - 1)100\%$. For the bacterial growth model $P(t) = 10{,}000(2^t)$ cells, the constant percentage change is $(2 - 1)100\% = 100\%$; that is, the bacterial population increases by 100% each hour. For the remaining amount of radioactive substance given by $f(x) = 400(0.98^x)$ grams after x days of decay, the constant percentage change is $(0.98 - 1)100\% = (-0.02)100\% = -2\%$. Thus the amount decreases by 2% each day.

An alternative form of the exponential model $f(x) = ab^x$ is $f(x) = ae^{kx}$.
It is easy to convert from one form to the other using $k = \ln b$ and $b = e^k$.

$ab^x = ae^{kx} \rightarrow b^x = e^{kx} \rightarrow$
$b = e^k \rightarrow k = \ln b$

Exponential Model

Verbally: An exponential model has a constant percentage change.
Algebraically: An exponential model has an equation of the form

$$f(x) = ab^x$$

where $a \neq 0$ and $b > 0$. The percentage change is $(b - 1)100\%$, and the parameter a is the output corresponding to an input of zero.

Graphically: An exponential model graph with positive a has the form of one of the two graphs in Figure 1.32.

(a) Exponential growth
$f(x) = ab^x$ with $b > 1$

(b) Exponential decay
$f(x) = ab^x$ with $0 < b < 1$

FIGURE 1.32

Note that the equation in the box defines a function f with input x. From now on, when we refer to an exponential equation or function, we will consider the equation to be of the form $f(x) = ab^x$. In the case of either exponential growth or exponential decay (as long as $a \geq 0$), a graph of the exponential function $f(x) = ab^x$ is concave up ⌣ or ⌐. Its output values approach zero in one direction and increase without bound in the opposite direction.

EXAMPLE 1   *Using Percentage Change to Write an Exponential Model*

iPods   Apple introduced the iPod™, an MP3 digital music player, on October 23, 2001. iPod sales were 0.14 million units the first year and until 2005 increased approximately 260% each year. *Note*: Apple's fiscal year ends in September. (Source: Based on data from "Apple Reports Fourth Quarter Results," 2003–2005, Apple Computer, Inc.)

a. Why is an exponential model appropriate for iPod sales?

b. Find a model for iPod sales.

c. According to the model, what were 2006 iPod sales expected to be?

d. In November of 2005, Needham & Co. analyst Charles Wolf forecasted 2006 iPod sales to be 23.5 million units. (Source: **http://www.macworld.co.uk/news/** posted on November 26, 2004.) How close is your estimate of 2006 sales to Wolf's forecast?

Solution

a. An exponential model is appropriate because the percentage change is constant.

b. Because the percentage change is 260% per year, the constant multiplier is $1 + 2.6 = 3.6$. The sales of iPods can be modeled by the equation

$$s(x) = 0.14(3.6^x) \text{ million units}$$

where $x = 0$ is the fiscal year ending in September 2002, $0 \le x \le 3$.

c. The input for the fiscal year ending in 2006 is $x = 4$. According to the model, the sales of iPods in 2006 were expected to be $s(4) = 0.14(3.6^4) \approx 23.5$ million units

d. The model gave essentially the same estimate for 2006 sales as that given by Wolf. ●

Percentage Differences and Modeling from Data

Often we do not know what repeated multiplier we should use to write an exponential model. However, if we are given data, sometimes we can look at percentage differences to determine the repeated multiplier. **Percentage differences** are calculated from data with increasing input values by dividing each first difference by the output value of the lesser input value and multiplying by 100.

We look at how to calculate percentage differences by considering a small town's dwindling population. After closing a state-subsidized steel mill near a small town, the state has funded a six-year mandate for the town council to study the impact of the closing. The population data (measured at the end of each year) are shown in Table 1.17, and a scatter plot of the data is shown in Figure 1.33.

TABLE 1.17

Year of mandate	Population
0	7290
1	5978
2	4902
3	4020
4	3296
5	2703
6	2216

$f(x)$

FIGURE 1.33

Because the inputs are evenly spaced, we examine the output data in greater detail by calculating first differences:

7290	5978	4902	4020	3296	2703	2216
	-1312	-1076	-882	-724	-593	-487

As indicated by the shape of the scatter plot in Figure 1.33, the first differences show us that the change in population from year to year is not constant. However, if we calculate the percentages that these yearly changes represent, we notice a pattern. During the first year, the population decreased by 1312 people. This represents an 18% (approximate) decrease in one year from the initial population of 7290 people.

$$\frac{-1312 \text{ people}}{7290 \text{ people}} \approx -0.17997 \approx -18\%$$

During the second year, the population decreased by 1076 people. This also represents about an 18% decrease in one year from the previous year's population.

$$\frac{-1076 \text{ people}}{5978 \text{ people}} \approx -0.17999 \approx -18\%$$

The percent symbol (%) means to divide by 100. For example, $8\% = \frac{8}{100} = 0.08$. When changing a decimal number into a percent, rewrite the number using "divide by 100." For example, $4.39 = \frac{439}{100}$. When you remove "divide by 100," insert "%." That is, $\frac{439}{100} = 439\%$.

In fact, every year the population decreased by approximately 18%.

Third year: $\dfrac{-882 \text{ people}}{4902 \text{ people}} \approx -0.17993 \approx -18\%$

Fourth year: $\dfrac{-724 \text{ people}}{4020 \text{ people}} \approx -0.18010 \approx -18\%$

Fifth year: $\dfrac{-593 \text{ people}}{3296 \text{ people}} \approx -0.17992 \approx -18\%$

Sixth year: $\dfrac{-487 \text{ people}}{2703 \text{ people}} \approx -0.18017 \approx -18\%$

1.3.1

We can use technology to determine an equation for the data. Enter the data points and use your calculator or computer to fit an exponential equation. You should obtain the model

$$P(x) = 7290.366(0.819995^x) \text{ people}$$

where x is the number of years since the beginning of the mandate, $0 \leq x \leq 6$.

If we assume that the population continues to decline by the same percentage (approximately 18%), we can estimate that at the end of the seventh year after the mill closing, the town's population was 82% of the population at the end of the study:

$$2216(0.82) \approx 1817 \text{ people}$$

This estimation can also be computed using the unrounded equation for population with input $x = 7$:

$$T(7) = 7290.366(0.819995^7) \approx 1817 \text{ people}$$

This estimate from the model agrees with the one calculated using only the data.

Although both of these predictions are valid, for consistency we adopt the following rule of thumb:

> Once an equation has been fitted to data, we will use the equation to answer questions rather than using data points or rounded estimates.

The technology-generated equation indicates that the starting value of the population was 7290.366 and that the population declined by 18.0005%. However, rounding these values to report reasonably, we would say that the starting value of the population was 7290 and the percentage change was 18%. Note that these values agree with the data and with the percentage differences calculated. That is because, in this case, the data have input values that are 1 unit apart and the percentage differences are approximately constant. When these two conditions are true, the constant percentage differences equal the percentage change, $(b - 1)100\%$, and we can use the terms interchangeably.

Doubling Time and Half-Life

One property of exponential models is that when the quantity being modeled either doubles (during exponential growth) or halves (during exponential decay), it does so over a constant interval. For instance, the value of an initial investment of $1000 that increases by 8% each year can be modeled by the exponential function

$$I(t) = 1000(1.08^t) \text{ dollars}$$

t years after the initial investment. How long will it take for the investment to be worth $2000? We find this out by solving the equation $2000 = 1000(1.08^t)$ for t by using either technology or algebra. We find that $t \approx 9.00646$. The investment will be worth $2000 by $t \approx 9$ years. In order to find out when it will double again, we solve $4000 = 1000(1.08^t)$. The investment will double again by $t \approx 18$ years. We say that 9 years is the *doubling time* of the investment. In general, the **doubling time** in exponential growth is the amount of time it takes for the output to double (or the time it takes for the output to increase by 100%).

Similarly, the **half-life** in exponential decay is the amount of time it takes for the output to decrease by half (or the time it takes for the output to decrease by 50%).

Doubling time is the amount of time it takes for the output of an increasing exponential function to double.
Half-life is the amount of time it takes for the output of a decreasing exponential function to decrease by half.

Example 2 illustrates the process of building an exponential decay model given information about half-life.

EXAMPLE 2   *Writing an Exponential Decay Model*

Medicine   Dilantin* is a drug used to control epileptic seizures. On Monday a patient takes a 300-mg Dilantin tablet at 4 P.M. Eight hours later the Dilantin reaches its peak plasma concentration of 15 μg/mL. The average plasma half-life of Dilantin is 22 hours. (*Plasma half-life* is the amount of time it takes for the concentration of the drug in the plasma to reach half of its peak concentration.)

a. Write a model for the concentration of Dilantin in the patient's plasma as a function of the time after peak concentration is reached.

* Based on information obtained from **www.parke-davis.com** (accessed 6/11/00).

b. What is the concentration of Dilantin in this person's plasma at 8 A.M. on Tuesday?

c. The minimum desired concentration of Dilantin is 10 μg/mL. Will the concentration dip below that level before the patient takes a second tablet on Tuesday at 4 P.M.?

Solution

a. The input of the model is the time after the peak concentration that occurs at midnight on Monday, and the initial amount we consider is the peak concentration of 15 μg/mL. After 22 hours, the concentration will be half its peak, or 7.5 μg/mL. Using the two data points (0, 15) and (22, 7.5), we obtain the model

$$C(h) = 15(0.96898^h) \text{ μg/mL}$$

is the concentration of Dilantin in a person's plasma, h hours after midnight, $h > 0$.

b. Eight hours after midnight, the plasma concentration is

$$C(8) = 15(0.96898^8) \approx 11.7 \text{ μg/mL}$$

c. To determine when the plasma concentration reaches 10 μg/mL, solve the equation $10 = 15(0.96898^h)$ using technology or algebra. You should obtain $h \approx 12.9$ hours. It takes approximately 12.9 hours after the peak concentration at midnight for the concentration to reach 10 μg/mL. This corresponds to approximately 1 P.M. on Tuesday. Thus the concentration will be below 10 μg/mL when the patient takes another tablet at 4 P.M. on Tuesday.   ●

Aligning Exponential Data

As you work with exponential models, keep in mind the following principle:

When using technology to find the equation for an exponential model, align the input data using reasonably small values to avoid numerical computation errors such as overflow or round-off errors.

Graphically, this aligning of input values does not change the nature of the exponential function. Aligning input values simply shifts the graph of the function to the left, as illustrated in Figure 1.34.

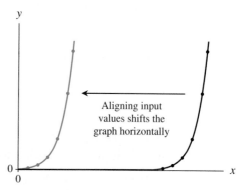

Original data and function in black. Aligned data and function in teal.

FIGURE 1.34

An exponential function is characterized by increasingly rapid growth (or increasingly slow decay), so its graph in one direction approaches and stays close to the horizontal axis (namely $y = 0$) and, in the other direction, tends to increase more and more quickly. (See Figures 1.35a and 1.35b.) There is another class of functions that exhibit the opposite behavior; that is, they are defined for only positive numbers and start by hugging the vertical axis (namely $x = 0$), and as x increases, the outputs $f(x)$ increase (or decrease) but more and more slowly. (See Figures 1.35c and 1.35d.) This class of functions is known as the logarithmic functions. In the following discussion, we turn our attention to situations that lead to logarithmic models.

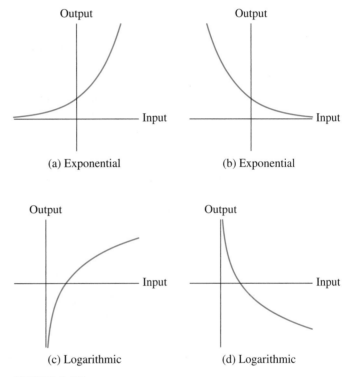

FIGURE 1.35

Logarithmic Models

Altitude and air pressure are intrinsically related. Altimeters are instruments that determine altitude by measuring air pressure. For an altimeter, the input is air pressure and the output is altitude. Table 1.18 shows altimeter data, and Figure 1.36 shows a scatter plot of the data.

Although the scatter plot has the basic declining, concave-up appearance of an exponential function, an exponential function does not fit these data well. However, there is another function, called a **logarithmic function** or **log function,** that exhibits similar behavior. The log equation used by most technologies is

$$f(x) = a + b \ln x$$

This equation defines a function f with input x. The b-term in this equation determines whether the function increases or decreases and how rapidly the increase or decrease occurs. The a-term determines the vertical shift of the function. From now

TABLE 1.18

Air pressure (inches of mercury)	Altitude (thousands of feet)
13.76	20
5.56	40
2.14	60
0.82	80
0.33	100

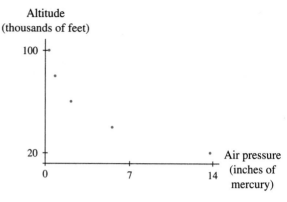

FIGURE 1.36

on, when we refer to a log equation or function, we will consider the equation to be of the form $f(x) = a + b \ln x$.

The end behavior of log functions is particularly important in determining when they are appropriate to use to fit data. An increasing log function increases without bound as the input increases, and a decreasing log function decreases without bound as the input increases. Log functions are not defined for negative or zero input, and as the input approaches zero from the right, the function either increases or decreases without bound.

Logarithmic Model

Verbally: A logarithmic (log) function has a vertical asymptote (the line $x = 0$) and continues to grow or decline as x becomes large.

Algebraically: A log model has an equation of the form

$$f(x) = a + b \ln x$$

where $b \neq 0$.

Graphically: The graph of a log model has the form of one of the two graphs shown in Figure 1.37.

(a) $f(x) = a + b \ln x$ with $b > 0$ (b) $f(x) = a + b \ln x$ with $b < 0$

FIGURE 1.37

Again consider the graphs in Figure 1.37. Note that log functions exhibit increasingly smaller changes in output for constant changes in input. This slow growth or decline characterizes log functions. The characteristic that makes log functions different from any other functions that we will study is that their growth or decline becomes increasingly slower but their output never approaches a horizontal limiting value, as do the outputs of declining exponential functions and, as we will see later, logistic functions.

Returning to the altitude example, we use technology to find the log model that fits the data in Table 1.18.

$$A(p) = 76.174 - 21.331 \ln p \text{ thousands of feet above sea level}$$

where p is the air pressure in inches of mercury. Figure 1.38 shows a graph of the function A overdrawn on a scatter plot of the data.

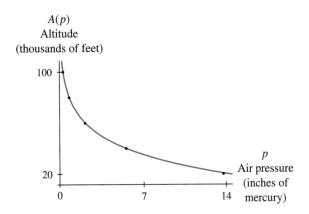

FIGURE 1.38

EXAMPLE 3 *Finding a Log Model*

Investment An international investment fund manager models bond rates of countries as a tool when making investment decisions. The manager uses the data in Table 1.19 to create a yield curve for Germany, where long-term bond rates are higher than short-term rates.

TABLE 1.19

Time to maturity (years)	German bond rate (percent)	Time to maturity (years)	German bond rate (percent)
1	3.60	6	4.65
2	4.10	7	4.75
3	4.25	8	4.80
4	4.40	9	4.90
5	4.50	10	4.95

(Source: *Investment Digest*, VALIC, vol. 12, no. 1, 1998.)

a. Sketch a scatter plot of the data.

b. Find a log model for the data.

c. This investment manager estimates a 5.25% rate for 20-year bonds and a 5.50% rate for 30-year bonds. How closely does the log model match these estimates?

Solution

a. The scatter plot in Figure 1.39 suggests the slow growth modeled by a log function.

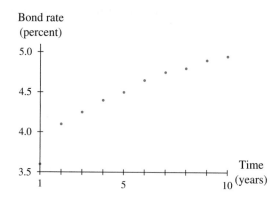

FIGURE 1.39

b. A log model for the data is

$$R(t) = 3.6296 + 0.5696 \ln t \text{ percent}$$

is the yield of a German bond with a maturity time of t years, $1 \leq t \leq 10$.

c. The model in part b predicts the following rates for 20- and 30-year bonds:

$$R(20) \approx 5.34, \text{ and } R(30) \approx 5.57$$

These predictions are slightly higher than the estimates made by the fund manager. ●

Aligning Log Data

Recall that aligning yearly data to small input values is convenient when finding a linear model and essential when finding an exponential model so that the coefficients in the equation will not be unnecessarily large values and to avoid round-off error. In both the linear and exponential cases, aligning input does not affect how well the model fits the data. It simply causes a graph of the model to be shifted horizontally closer to or farther from the origin.

However, because log models have the property that the output approaches negative or positive infinity as the inputs approach 0 from the right, differently aligned data result in better- or worse-fitting models. For this reason, we will give a recommended input alignment when we ask you to model using log functions for data that need to be shifted. When aligning the input data for a log model, it is important to remember that the log function is not defined for negative or 0 input. If you align the data so that the first input value is 0, your calculator or computer will return an error message when you attempt to find a log equation.

Creating Inverse Functions

Given a function, we can sometimes create a new function by reversing the input and output of the original function. We can use this new function as an inverse function. To illustrate, we again consider the German bond rates in Table 1.19. Figure 1.40 shows an input/output diagram for this function.

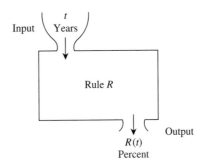

FIGURE 1.40

If we exchange the input values with the output values for this function, we have Table 1.20.

TABLE 1.20

German bond rate (percent)	Time to maturity (years)
3.60	1
4.10	2
4.25	3
4.40	4
4.50	5
4.65	6
4.75	7
4.80	8
4.90	9
4.95	10

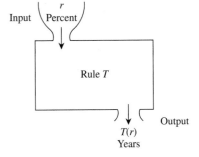

FIGURE 1.41

Each bond rate (input) corresponds to only one maturity value (output), so Table 1.20 represents a function, the inverse of the original function. Figure 1.41 shows an input/output diagram for the inverse function.

When an equation represents a function, finding an algebraic expression for an inverse function requires that you solve for the input variable of a function in terms of the output variable. Sometimes this is simple, sometimes it is difficult, and sometimes it is impossible. Because most of the models we use in this text are built from data, if we need a model to approximate the inverse relationship, we simply invert the data and model the inverted data. In most cases, this technique will not yield the exact inverse function but will yield a good approximation of the inverse function.

In this case, modeling the inverted data with an exponential function yields the time to maturity as

$$T(r) = 0.0018(5.723^r) \text{ years}$$

where r is the bond rate (as a percentage), $3.60 \leq r \leq 4.95$.

You may recall from previous math courses that when a function f is used as the input for its inverse function g, the result is simply the input variable. That is, when a function and its inverse are combined to create a composite function, the composition has the result of "undoing" the effects of the two functions.

Composition Property of Inverse Functions

If f and g are inverse functions, then

$$f(g(x)) = (f \circ g)(x) = x \quad \text{and} \quad g(f(x)) = (g \circ f)(x) = x$$

In the German bond rate example, the functions $R(t) = 3.6296 + 0.5696 \ln t$ and $T(r) = 0.0018(5.723^r)$ are approximate inverses of each other.

As we noted earlier, the log functions and exponential functions have opposite characteristics. If we have data whose input/output relationship can be modeled by an exponential function, then the inverse (output/input) relationship can be modeled by a log function, and vice versa.

Exponential functions, with their constant percentage change, and log functions, with their slowing but not leveling end behavior, are common in health and life sciences and in social sciences. Their importance leads us to include them in our discussion. As we continue our exploration of calculus concepts, you will become familiar with both log and exponential functions.

The relationship between exponential and logarithmic functions in its simplest form can be stated as follows:

If $f(x) = \ln x$ and $g(x) = e^x$, then $f(g(x)) = \ln(e^x) = x$ and $g(f(x)) = e^{\ln x} = x$ as long as x is positive.

The inverse relationships for the model equations are more involved but still exist:

If $f(x) = a + b \ln x$ with $b \neq 0$, then $f^{-1}(x) = AB^x$, where $A = e^{-\frac{a}{b}}$ and $B = e^{\frac{1}{b}}$.

If $f(x) = ab^x$, then for $x > 0$, $b > 0$, and $b \neq 1$, $f^{-1}(x) = A + B \ln x$, where

$$A = \frac{-\ln a}{\ln b} \text{ and } B = \frac{1}{\ln b}$$

- Exponential function: $f(x) = ab^x$
- Exponential growth and decay
- Percentage change
- Doubling time and half-life
- Log function: $f(x) = a + b \ln x$
- End behavior of log and exponential functions
- Log and exponential functions as inverses

1.3   Activities

Getting Started

For Activities 1 through 8, match each graph with its equation.

1. $f(x) = 2(1.3^x)$
$f(x) = 2(0.7^x)$

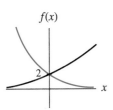

2. $f(x) = 2(1.3^x)$
$f(x) = -2(1.3^x)$

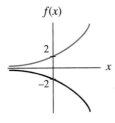

3. $f(x) = 3(1.2^x)$
$f(x) = 3(1.4^x)$

4. $f(x) = 2(0.8^x)$
$f(x) = 2(0.6^x)$

5. $f(x) = 2 \ln x$
$f(x) = -2 \ln x$

6. $f(x) = 3 + \ln x$
$f(x) = \ln x$

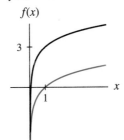

7. $f(x) = 2 \ln x$
$f(x) = 4 \ln x$

8. $f(x) = -4 \ln x$
$f(x) = -2 \ln x$

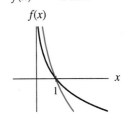

For Activities 9 through 12, indicate whether the function describes exponential growth or decay, and give the constant percentage change.

9. $f(x) = 72(1.05^x)$

10. $K(r) = 33(0.92^r)$

11. $y(x) = 16.2(0.87^x)$

12. $A(t) = 0.57(1.035^t)$

For Activities 13 and 14, find the constant percentage change, and interpret it in context.

13. **Bacteria**   After h hours, the number of bacteria in a petri dish during a certain experiment can be modeled as $B(h) = 100(0.61^h)$ thousand bacteria.

14. **Membership**   The membership of a popular club can be modeled by $M(x) = 12(2.5^x)$ members by the end of the xth year after its organization.

Applying Concepts

15. **Imports**   The U.S. Energy Information Administration projected that imports of petroleum products in 2005 would be 4.81 quadrillion Btu and would increase by 5.47% each year through 2020. (Source: Annual Energy Outlook, 2001.)

   a. Find a model for projected petroleum product imports between 2005 and 2020.

   b. According to the model, when will imports exceed 10 quadrillion Btu?

   c. Describe the end behavior of the model as time increases.

16. **Assets**   In 1994, Charles Schwab & Co. had approximately $135 billion of assets in customer accounts, and throughout the late 1990s that value grew by approximately 39% each year.

   a. Find a model for Schwab's customer account assets in the late 1990s.

   b. Use the model to estimate Schwab's customer account assets in 2000.

17. Social Security According to the Social Security Advisory Board, the number of workers per beneficiary of the Social Security program was 3.3 in 1996 and is projected to decline by 1.46% each year through 2030.

   a. Find a model for the number of workers per beneficiary from 1996 through 2030. Note that the unit of measure is workers per beneficiary. Keep one decimal place accuracy in your answer.

   b. What does the model predict the number of workers per beneficiary will be in 2030? How will this number affect your life?

18. Emissions In 1975 the EPA emissions standard for cars was 3.1 grams of nitrogen oxide per mile of driving. Assume that the EPA standard decreased by 9.3% each year between 1975 and 2000.

   a. Find a model for the emission standard between 1975 and 2000.

   b. Estimate the EPA standard in 2000.

19. Sales When a company stops advertising and promoting one of its products, sales often decrease exponentially, provided that other market conditions remain constant. At the time that publicity was discontinued for a newly released popular animated film, sales were 520,000 videotapes per month. One month later, videotape sales had fallen to 210,000 tapes per month.

   a. What was the monthly percentage decline in sales?

   b. Assuming that sales decreased exponentially, give the equation for sales as a function of the number of months since promotion ended.

   c. What will sales be 3 months after the promotion ends? 12 months after?

20. Waste The Environmental Protection Agency reports the total amount of municipal solid waste (MSW) recycled between 1960 and 2000 as shown in the accompanying table.

Year	Total MSW recycling (million tons)
1960	5.6
1970	8.0
1980	14.5
1990	33.2
2000	68.9

(Source: "Municipal Solid Waste in the United States: 2000 Facts and Figures," Executive Summary.)

   a. Find an exponential model for the data.

   b. According to the model in part *a*, what was the yearly percentage growth in recycled MSW from 1960 through 2000?

21. Computing Power During the last three decades, computing power has grown enormously. The accompanying table gives the number of transistors (in millions) in Intel processor chips.

Processor	Year	Transistors (millions)
4004	1971	0.0023
80286	1982	0.134
386DX	1986	0.275
486DX	1989	1.2
Pentium®	1993	3.1
Pentium® Pro	1995	5.5
Pentium® II	1997	7.5
Celeron	1999	19.0
Pentium IV	2000	42.0
Pentium IV	2002	55.0
Pentium M	2003	77
Pentium M	2004	140
Itanium 2	2005	600

(Source: www.Intel.com)

   a. Find an exponential model for the data.

   b. According to the model found in part *a*, what is the annual percentage increase in the number of transistors used in an Intel computer processor chip?

   c. On April 19, 1965, Intel co-founder Gordon Moore predicted that the number of transistors on a computer chip would double approximately every 2 years. This prediction is known as Moore's Law. Do the data (and does the model) support Moore's Law?

22. Farms The number of U.S. farms with milk cows has been declining since 1980. See the accompanying table.

Year	Farms (thousands)
1980	334
1985	269
1990	193
1995	140
2000	105

(Source: *Statistical Abstract,* 1998 and 2001.)

a. Find an exponential model for these data. What is the percentage change indicated by the model?

b. Express the end behavior of the model as time increases. Does this end behavior reflect what you believe will happen in the future to the number of farms with milk cows?

23. **Bottled Water Consumption** The per capita consumption of bottled water in the United States has increased dramatically in the past 20 years. The accompanying table shows selected years and the per capita bottled water consumption in those years.

Year	Bottled water consumption (gallons per person per year)
1980	2.4
1985	4.5
1990	8.0
1995	12.1
2000	17.4
2003	22.0

(Source: USDA/Economic Research Service. Last updated December 21, 2004.)

a. Find linear and exponential models for the data. Graph the equations for these models on a scatter plot of the data. Which model do you think better describes the per capita bottled water consumption?

b. Give the rate of change of the linear model and the percentage change of the exponential model.

c. Use the two models to estimate bottled water consumption in 2005.

d. According to each model, when will per capita bottled water consumption exceed 25 gallons per person per year?

24. **Decay** Carbon-14, ^{14}C, has a half-life of approximately 5580 years. If a sample of an artifact contains 0.027 gram of ^{14}C, how long ago did it contain 0.05 gram of ^{14}C?

25. **Decay** An abandoned building is found to contain radioactive radon gas. Thirty hours later, 80% of the initial amount of gas is still present.

a. Find the half-life of this radon gas.

b. Give a model for the amount of radon gas present after t hours.

c. What is the limit of the function in part b as time approaches infinity? Interpret this answer in the context of the radon gas.

26. **Half-Life** The elimination half-life of a certain type of penicillin is 30 minutes.

a. Write a model for the amount of this penicillin left in a person's body if the initial dose is 250 mg.

b. If it is safe to take another dose of this penicillin once the amount in the body is less than 1 mg, when should another dose be taken?

27. **Medicine** If a person takes Digoxin, a heart stimulant, the concentration in the person's blood stream t hours after the Digoxin reaches its peak concentration is

$$D(t) = D_0 e^{-0.0198t} \ \mu g/mL$$

where D_0 is the peak concentration in micrograms per milliliter. Find the half-life of Digoxin.

28. **Doubling Time** The amount of an investment of P dollars with 8% interest compounded continuously is modeled by the equation

$$A(t) = Pe^{0.08t} \text{ dollars}$$

t years after the initial investment. How long would it take this investment to double?

29. **Milk Storage** According to the back of a milk carton sold by Model Dairy, the number of days that milk will keep when stored at various temperatures is as shown in the table.

Temperature (degrees Fahrenheit)	Days
30	24
38	10
45	5
50	2
60	1
70	0.5

a. Find an exponential model for the data.

b. If a refrigerator is adjusted to 40°F from 37°F, how much sooner will milk spoil when stored in this refrigerator?

c. Invert the data, and fit a log model to the inverted data.

d. At what temperature should the refrigerator be set in order to keep the milk for one week?

30. **Weight**   The body weight of mice used in a drug experiment is recorded by the researcher. The data are given in the accompanying table.

Age beyond 2 weeks (weeks)	Weight (grams)
1	11
3	20
5	23
7	26
9	27

(Source: Estimated from information given in "Letters to Nature," *Nature*, vol. 381 (May 30, 1996), p. 417.)

   a. Find a log model for a mouse's weight, G, in terms of its age, w weeks.

   b. Estimate the weight of the mice when they are 4 weeks old.

   c. Invert the data and find an exponential model for a mouse's age, A, in terms of its weight, g grams.

   d. Calculate $A \circ G$ for $w = 1$, 5, and 7 and $G \circ A$ for $g = 11$, 23, and 27. How do the calculations support A and G being approximate inverse functions?

31. **Bond Rates**   In New Zealand, the long-term bond rates are lower than short-term rates. Consider the data given in the New Zealand bond rate table.

Time to maturity (years)	New Zealand bond rate (%)
0.25	9.40
2	7.90
3	7.65
4	7.50
6	7.30
10	7.10

   a. Find a log model for the bond rate, R, in terms of years to maturity, y.

   b. The fund manager estimates 15-year rates at 7.00%. How close does your model come to this estimate?

   c. Invert the data and find an exponential model for the time to maturity, T, in terms of the bond rate, p.

   d. Calculate $R \circ T$ for $p = 9.4$, 7.5, and 7.1 and $T \circ R$ for $y = 2$, 4, and 10. How do the calculations support R and T being approximate inverse functions?

32. **Contaminant**   The American Association of Pediatrics has stated that lead poisoning is the greatest health risk to children in the United States. Because of past use of leaded gasoline, the concentration of lead in soil can be described in terms of how close the soil is to a heavily traveled road. The accompanying table shows some distances and the corresponding lead concentrations in parts per million.

Distance from road (meters)	Lead concentration (ppm)
5	90
10	60
15	40
20	32

(Source: Estimated from information in "Lead in the Inner City," *American Scientist*, January–February 1999, pp. 62–73.)

   a. Find a log model for these data.

   b. An apartment complex has a dirt play area located 12 meters from a road. Estimate the lead concentration in the soil of the play area.

   c. Find an exponential model for the data. Compare this model to the log model found in part *a*. Which of the two models better displays the end behavior suggested by the context?

33. **Medicine**   The concentration of a drug in the blood stream increases the longer the drug is taken on a daily basis. The accompanying table gives estimated concentrations (in micrograms per milliliter) of the drug piroxicam taken in 20 mg doses once a day.

Days	Concentration (μg/mL)	Days	Concentration (μg/mL)
1	1.5	11	6.5
3	3.2	13	6.9
5	4.5	15	7.3
7	5.5	17	7.5
9	6.2		

a. Find a log model for the data.

b. Express the end behavior of the equation using limits.

c. Does the end behavior of the equation fit the end behavior suggested by the context?

d. Estimate the concentration of the drug after 2 days of piroxicam doses.

34. **Peaches** The following table gives the average yearly consumption of peaches per person based on that person's yearly family income when the price of peaches is $1.50 per pound.

Yearly income (tens of thousands of dollars)	Consumption of peaches (pounds per person per year)
1	5.0
2	6.4
3	7.2
4	7.8
5	8.2
6	8.6

a. Explain why the data are neither linear nor exponential.

b. Find a log function to fit the data.

c. Use the log model to estimate consumption for a person in a family with a yearly income of $35,000.

35. **Solution pH** The pH of a solution, measured on a scale from 0 to 14, is a measure of how acidic or how alkaline that solution is. The pH is a function of the concentration of the hydronium ion, H_3O^+. The accompanying table shows the H_3O^+ concentration and associated pH for several solutions.

Solution	H_3O^+ concentration (moles per liter)	pH
Cow's milk	$3.981 \cdot 10^{-7}$	6.4
Distilled water	$1.000 \cdot 10^{-7}$	7.0
Human blood	$3.981 \cdot 10^{-8}$	7.4
Lake Ontario water	$1.259 \cdot 10^{-8}$	7.9
Seawater	$5.012 \cdot 10^{-9}$	8.3

a. Find a log model for pH as a function of the H_3O^+ concentration.

b. What is the pH of orange juice with an H_3O^+ concentration $1.585 \cdot 10^{-3}$?

c. Black coffee has a pH of 5.0. What is its concentration of an H_3O^+?

d. A pH of 7 is neutral, a pH less than 7 indicates an acidic solution, and a pH greater than 7 shows an alkaline solution. Beer has an H_3O^+ concentration of $3.162 \cdot 10^{-5}$. Is beer acidic or alkaline?

36. **Cable Subscribers** On the basis of data recorded between 1995 and 2005, the number of cable subscribers in the United States as a function of the average monthly basic cable rate can be modeled as

$$S(r) = -1.7 + 20.8 \ln r \text{ million subscribers}$$

when the average basic rate is r dollars per month. (Source: Based on data from Kagan Research LLC, *Broadband Cable Financial Databook*, 2004.)

a. Use the model to estimate the number of subscribers (in millions) for the following monthly basic rates: $15, $30, $45.

b. Switch the input/output values for the three points found in part *a*. Use the three inverted points to find an inverse function R with input s.

Discussing Concepts

37. Why does it make sense to speak of *doubling time* and *half-life* for exponential models but not for linear models?

38. Discuss the impact of scale in the appearance of the graphs of exponential and log models and the conditions under which the graphs of exponential and log functions appear to be linear.

39. Describe the end behavior of the exponential and log models. Explain how this end behavior can help us determine which of these two functions to fit to a data set.

1.4   Logistic Functions and Models

Exponential Growth with Constraints

Although exponential models are common and useful, it is sometimes unrealistic to believe that exponential growth can continue forever. In many situations, there are forces that ultimately limit the growth. Here is a situation that may seem familiar to you.

You and a friend are shopping in a music store and find a new compact disc that you are certain will become a hit. You each buy the CD and rush back to campus to begin spreading the news. As word spreads, the total number of CDs sold begins to grow exponentially, as shown in Figure 1.42.

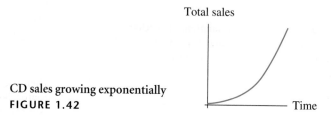

CD sales growing exponentially
FIGURE 1.42

However, this trend cannot continue forever. Eventually, the word will spread to people who have already bought the CD or to people who have no interest in it, and the rate of increase in total sales will begin to decline (Figure 1.43). In fact, because there is only a limited number of people who will ever be interested in buying the CD, total sales ultimately must level off. The graph representing the total sales of the CD as a function of time is a combination of rapid exponential growth followed by a slower increase and ultimate leveling off. See Figure 1.44.

CD sales leveling off
FIGURE 1.43

Total sales of a CD
FIGURE 1.44

S-shaped behavior such as this is common in marketing situations, the spread of disease, the spread of information, the adoption of new technology, and the growth of certain populations. A mathematical function that exhibits such an S-shaped curve is called a **logistic function.** Its equation is of the form

$$f(x) = \frac{L}{1 + Ae^{-Bx}}$$

From now on, when referring to a logistic equation or function, we will consider an equation of this form. The number L appearing in the numerator of a logistic equation determines a horizontal asymptote $y = L$ for a graph of the function f.

Logistic Model

Algebraically: A logistic model has an equation of the form

$$f(x) = \frac{L}{1 + Ae^{-Bx}}$$

We refer to L as the limiting value of the function.

Graphically: The logistic function f increases if B is positive and decreases if B is negative. The graph of a logistic function is bounded by the horizontal axis and the line $y = L$. (See Figure 1.45.)

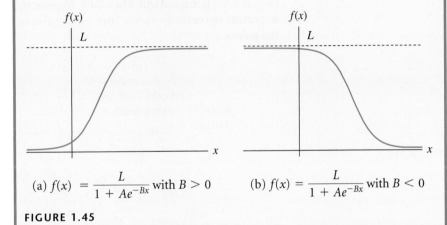

(a) $f(x) = \dfrac{L}{1 + Ae^{-Bx}}$ with $B > 0$ (b) $f(x) = \dfrac{L}{1 + Ae^{-Bx}}$ with $B < 0$

FIGURE 1.45

1.4.1

Be aware that some technologies do not have a built-in logistic regression routine. See the *Excel Instruction Guide* to obtain the logistic curve-fitting procedure we use in this text.

The graph of a positive, increasing logistic function (such as that shown in Figure 1.45a) is trapped between the horizontal axis ($y = 0$) and the **limiting value** $y = L$.

Finding Logistic Models

Consider a worm that has attacked the computers of an international corporation. The worm is first detected on 100 computers. The corporation has 10,000 computers, so as time increases, the number of infected computers can approach, but never exceed, 10,000. Consider the following representations (Table 1.21 and Figure 1.46) of the function describing the spread of the worm.

TABLE 1.21

Time (in hours)	Total number of infected computers (in thousands)
0	0.1
0.5	0.597
1	2.851
1.5	7.148
2	9.403
2.5	9.900

FIGURE 1.46

A logistic model to fit the data in Table 1.21 is

$$I(t) = \frac{10}{1 + 99e^{-3.676t}} \text{ thousand computers infected}$$

t hours after the initial attack, $t > 0$. Note that the limiting value here is $L = 10$ thousand computers.

A graph of the function I is shown in Figure 1.47. The dotted, horizontal line portrays the limiting value, $L = 10$. Note that the curvature on the left side of this graph is **concave up** ⌣, whereas the curvature on the right side is **concave down** ⌢. The point on the graph at which the concavity changes is called the **inflection point.** The inflection point on the logistic graph modeling the spread of the computer worm (Figure 1.47) is marked with a black dot. In some situations, inflection points have very important interpretations. We later use calculus to find and help interpret these special points.

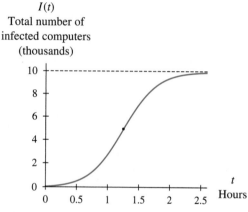

$I(t)$
Total number of
infected computers
(thousands)

FIGURE 1.47

In social science and life science applications, the limiting value is often called the carrying capacity or the saturation level. In other applications it is sometimes referred to as the leveling-off value.

When you use a calculator or a computer program to find an equation and construct the graph of a logistic model for a set of data, be sure to align the input data. The same numerical computation problems that we discussed for exponential models can occur with logistic models because of the exponential term in the denominator.

EXAMPLE 1   *Finding a Logistic Model*

Bacteria   Table 1.22 shows the number of bacteria counted in a biology experiment.

TABLE 1.22

Day	Bacteria	Day	Bacteria
1	4	6	619
2	15	7	733
3	52	8	771
4	165	9	782
5	391		

Find a logistic model that fits the data. What is the end behavior of the model as time increases?

Solution
A scatter plot of the data (Figure 1.48) suggests that a logistic model is appropriate.

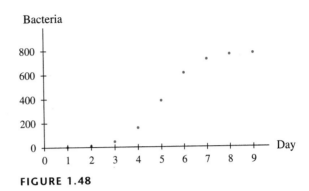

FIGURE 1.48

A possible logistic model is

$$B(x) = \frac{786}{1 + 732.9e^{-1.318x}} \text{ bacteria}$$

on day x, $1 \leq x \leq 9$.

The limiting value of this model is $L \approx 786$, or, in context, approximately 786 bacteria. The graph of B on a scatter plot appears to fit fairly well (see Figure 1.49). The dotted line in Figure 1.49 denotes the upper limiting value. As time increases, the number of bacteria approaches 786.

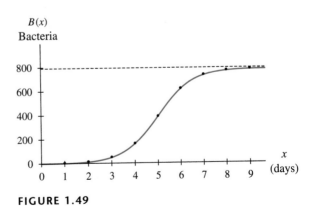

FIGURE 1.49

The preceding logistic curves begin near zero and then increase toward a limiting value L. As we have previously noted, there are also situations where the curve begins near its limiting value and then decreases toward zero. ●

EXAMPLE 2   *Aligning Input and Determining End Behavior*

Height   Of a group of 200 college men surveyed, the number who were taller than a given number of inches is recorded in Table 1.23.

TABLE 1.23

Inches	Number of men	Inches	Number of men	Inches	Number of men
64	200	68	139	72	23
65	194	69	105	73	12
66	184	70	70	74	6
67	166	71	42	75	3

Find an appropriate model for the data. What is the end behavior of the model as height increases?

Solution

A scatter plot of the data is shown in Figure 1.50.

FIGURE 1.50

We choose to align the input data by subtracting 65 from each value. A logistic model for the aligned data is

$$M(x) = \frac{205.51171}{1 + 0.05822e^{0.70106x}} \text{ men out of 200 men surveyed}$$

who are taller than $x + 65$ inches. The two horizontal asymptotes of a graph of this function are $y = 0$ and $y \approx 205.5$. Because the function decreases, the end behavior as height increases is given by the lower asymptote; that is, as the heights increase, the number of men taller than a particular height approaches zero.   ●

Recall that a logistic function is of the form $f(x) = \dfrac{L}{1 + Ae^{-Bx}}$. What happened to the negative sign before the B in Example 2? In that case, $B = -0.70106$. When the formula was written, the negatives canceled.

$$\text{Number of men} = \frac{205.51171}{1 + 0.05822e^{-1(-0.70106x)}} = \frac{205.51171}{1 + 0.05822e^{0.70106x}}$$

This will always be the case for a logistic function that decreases.

It is likely that a logistic model will have a limiting value that is lower or higher than the one indicated by the context. For instance, in Example 2 only 200 men were surveyed, but the limiting value is $L \approx 206$ men. This does not mean that the model is invalid, but it does indicate that care should be taken when extrapolating from logistic models.

In Example 2 we chose to shift the logistic model horizontally by realigning input data in order to avoid an extremely small value for A. It is possible to shift exponential and logistic models vertically by realigning output data. Such an alignment would change the lower limiting values from 0 to some other number. We do this *only* when there is reason to believe that the data approach a different limiting position than the input axis or, for the case of the logistic model, when it is obvious that there is an upper limiting value and the shift will significantly improve end-behavior fit. In this case, we will recommend a specific alignment.

Limits and the Infinitely Large

As we study functions in calculus, we pay attention to how the output of a function behaves as the input becomes larger and larger in the positive direction (increases without bound) or the magnitude of the input becomes larger and larger in the negative direction (decreases without bound). This behavior is called the **end behavior** of the function. We have already discussed end behavior for a few functions and will continue to use end-behavior analysis to choose models as well as to develop the calculus topics of limits of sums and integration in later chapters.

For an example of end behavior, consider the graph of the function shown in Figure 1.51. As x becomes arbitrarily large in the positive direction (moving from $x = 0$ to the right without bound along the graph of the function), the function outputs $u(x)$ increase while becoming closer and closer to 0.3. As the magnitude of x becomes larger and larger in the negative direction (moving from $x = 0$ to the left without bound on the function graph), again the function outputs become closer and closer to 0.3. We express these two facts mathematically by writing

$$\lim_{x \to \infty} u(x) = 0.3 \qquad \text{and} \qquad \lim_{x \to -\infty} u(x) = 0.3$$

or with the combined statement

$$\lim_{x \to \pm\infty} u(x) = 0.3$$

When a function approaches a number k as the input increases or decreases without bound, we call the horizontal line that has equation $y = k$ a **horizontal asymptote**. The function depicted in Figure 1.51 has a horizontal asymptote, $y = 0.3$. We say that the output of the function has a *limiting value* of $y = 0.3$.

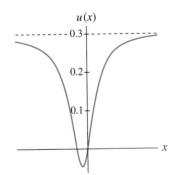

FIGURE 1.51

For an increasing logistic function f, where $f(x) = \dfrac{L}{1 + Ae^{-Bx}}$ with $B > 0$,

$$\lim_{x \to -\infty} f(x) = 0 \quad \text{and} \quad \lim_{x \to \infty} f(x) = L$$

Similarly, for a decreasing logistic function f, where $f(x) = \dfrac{L}{1 + Ae^{-Bx}}$ with $B < 0$ (as shown in Figure 1.45b), the end behavior can be described by the limit statements

$$\lim_{x \to -\infty} f(x) = L \quad \text{and} \quad \lim_{x \to \infty} f(x) = 0$$

Thus any logistic function has two horizontal asymptotes. We refer to $y = 0$ as the *lower asymptote* and to $y = L$ as the *upper asymptote* or the *limiting value* of the function.

Some functions appear to have no limiting value (horizontal asymptote) in at least one direction. We say that the output of a function is **increasing without bound** if the output continues to increase infinitely. If the output of a function continues to decrease infinitely, we say that the output is **decreasing without bound.** This end behavior is seen in the linear, exponential, and log functions, as well as in polynomial functions that we will discuss in Section 1.5. (See Figures 1.52 and 1.53.)

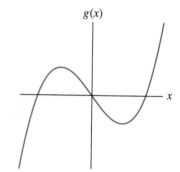

$f(x)$ decreases without bound as x becomes arbitrarily large in the positive direction. $f(x)$ increases without bound as x becomes arbitrarily large in the negative direction.

FIGURE 1.52

$g(x)$ increases without bound as x approaches positive infinity. $g(x)$ decreases without bound as x approaches negative infinity.

FIGURE 1.53

Just as we can often estimate end behavior from a graph, it is also possible to estimate the end behavior of a function numerically by evaluating the function at increasingly large values of the input variable. This process is illustrated in Example 3.

EXAMPLE 3   *Numerically Estimating End Behavior*

1.4.2

An equation for the function depicted in Figure 1.54 is $u(x) = \dfrac{3x^2 + x}{10x^2 + 3x + 2}$.
Numerically estimate $\lim_{x \to \infty} u(x)$ and $\lim_{x \to -\infty} u(x)$.

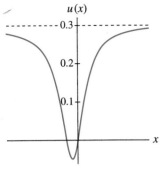

u(x)

FIGURE 1.54

Solution

To estimate the positive end behavior of u numerically, choose increasingly large positive values of x, as shown in Table 1.24.

TABLE 1.24

$x \to \infty$	10	100	1000	10,000
$u(x)$	0.300388	0.300094	0.3000099	0.3000009

It appears that as x approaches positive infinity, the function outputs approach 0.3. Next, consider the negative end behavior of u by choosing negative values of x with increasingly large magnitudes, as shown in Table 1.25.

TABLE 1.25

$x \to -\infty$	-10	-100	-1000	$-10,000$
$u(x)$	0.298354	0.299894	0.299990	0.299999

Here also, it appears that the limiting value of the outputs is 0.3. ●

As in the example, numerical evaluation of end behavior is especially useful for functions constructed by function division or composition. We will use a similar technique when we look at limits at a point during our discussion of the calculus topic of derivatives in Chapter 2.

Keep in mind that a function may oscillate and not approach any specific output value as x approaches infinity. Such is the case with the function j in Figure 1.55. In this case, we say that the limit of j as x approaches infinity *does not exist*. The sine and cosine functions are good examples of such functions.

j(x)

$\lim_{x \to \infty} j(x)$ does not exist.

FIGURE 1.55

1.4 Concept Inventory

- Logistic function: $f(x) = \dfrac{L}{1 + Ae^{-Bx}}$
- Equations of horizontal asymptotes
- Concave up and concave down
- Inflection point
- Limiting value and end behavior

1.4 Activities

Getting Started

Identify the scatter plots in Activities 1 through 6 as linear, exponential, logarithmic, logistic, or none of

these. If you identify the scatter plot as none of these, give reasons.

5. **6.**

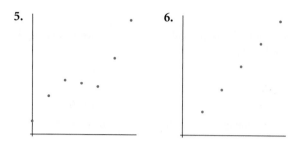

For Activities 7 through 10, indicate whether the function is an increasing or a decreasing logistic function. Also identify the upper limiting value of the function.

7. $f(x) = \dfrac{100}{1 + 9e^{-0.78x}}$

8. $A(t) = \dfrac{1925}{1 + 32e^{1.86t}}$

9. $h(g) = \dfrac{39.2}{1 + 0.8e^{3g}}$

10. $k(x) = \dfrac{16.5}{1 + 1.86e^{-0.43x}}$

Applying Concepts

11. Postage The following table gives the number of European, North American, and South American countries that issued postage stamps from 1840 through 1880.

Year	Total number of countries
1840	1
1845	3
1850	9
1855	16
1860	24
1865	30
1870	34
1875	36
1880	37

(Source: "The Curve of Cultural Diffusion," *American Sociological Review*, August 1936, pp. 547–556.)

a. Find a logistic model for the data, and discuss how well the equation fits.

b. Sketch the graph of the equation in part *a*, and mark where the curve is concave up and where it

is concave down. Label the approximate location of the inflection point.

12. P.T.A. The accompanying table gives the total number of states associated with the national P.T.A. organization from 1895 through 1931.

Year	Total number of states	Year	Total number of states
1895	1	1915	30
1899	3	1919	38
1903	7	1923	43
1907	15	1927	47
1911	23	1931	48

(Source: R. Hamblin, R. Jacobsen, and J. Miller, *A Mathematical Theory of Social Change*, New York: John Wiley & Sons, 1973.)

a. Find a logistic model for the data.

b. What is the maximum number of states that could have joined the P.T.A. by 1931? How does this number compare to the limiting value given by the model in part *a*?

13. Flu In the fall of 1918, an influenza epidemic hit the U.S. Navy. It spread to the Army, to American civilians, and ultimately to the world. It is estimated that 20 million people had died from the epidemic by 1920. Of these, 550,000 were Americans—over 10 times the number of World War I battle deaths. The accompanying table gives the total numbers of Navy, Army, and civilian deaths that resulted from the epidemic in 1918.

Week ending	Total deaths Navy	Total deaths Army	Total civilian deaths in 45 major cities
August 31	2		
September 7	13	40	
September 14	56	76	68
September 21	292	174	517
September 28	1172	1146	1970
October 5	1823	3590	6528
October 12	2338	9760	17,914
October 19	2670	15,319	37,853

Week ending	Total deaths		Total civilian deaths in 45 major cities
	Navy	Army	
October 26	2820	17,943	58,659
November 2	2919	19,126	73,477
November 9	2990	20,034	81,919
November 16	3047	20,553	86,957
November 23	3104	20,865	90,449
November 30	3137	21,184	93,641

(Source: A. W. Crosby, Jr., *Epidemic and Peace 1918*, Westport, Conn.: Greenwood Press, 1976.)

a. Find logistic equations to fit each set of data. In each case, graph the equation on a scatter plot of the data.

b. Write models for each of the data sets.

c. Compare the limiting values of the models in part *b* with the highest data values in the table. Do you believe that the limiting values indicated by the models accurately reflect the ultimate number of deaths? Explain.

14. **Visitors**   The total numbers of visitors to an amusement park that stays open all year are given in the accompanying table.

Month	Cumulative number of visitors by the end of the month (thousands)
January	25
February	54
March	118
April	250
May	500
June	898
July	1440
August	1921
September	2169
October	2339
November	2395
December	2423

a. Find a logistic model for the data.

b. The park owners have been considering closing the park from October 15 through March 15 each year. How many visitors will they potentially miss by this closure?

15. **Chemical Reaction**   A chemical reaction begins when a certain mixture of chemicals reaches 95°C. The reaction activity is measured in units (U) per 100 microliters (100 μL) of the mixture. Measurements during the first 18 minutes after the mixture reaches 95°C are listed in the accompanying table.

Time (minutes)	Activity (U/100 μL)	Time (minutes)	Activity (U/100 μL)
0	0.10	10	1.40
2	0.10	12	1.55
4	0.25	14	1.75
6	0.60	16	1.90
8	1.00	18	1.95

(Source: David E. Birch et al., "Simplified Hot Start PCR," *Nature*, vol. 381 (May 30, 1996), p. 445.)

a. Examine a scatter plot of the data. Estimate the limiting value. Estimate at what time the inflection point occurs.

b. Find a logistic model for the data. What is the limiting value for this logistic function?

c. Use the model to estimate by how much the reaction activity increased between 7 minutes and 11 minutes.

16. **Stolen Bases**   San Francisco Giants legend Willie Mays's cumulative numbers of stolen bases between 1951 and 1963 are as shown in the table on page 68.

a. Find a logistic model for the data. Comment on how well the logistic equation fits the data.

b. What is the interpretation of first differences in this context?

c. Use the model in part *a* to estimate the number of bases that Mays stole in 1964. Compare this estimate with 19, his actual number of stolen bases in 1964.

Year	Cumulative stolen bases
1951	7
1952	11
1953	11
1954	19
1955	43
1956	83
1957	121
1958	152
1959	179
1960	204
1961	222
1962	240
1963	248

17. **Population**   A 1998 United Nations population study reported the world population between 1804 and 1987 and projected the population through 2071. These populations are as shown in the accompanying table.

Year	Population (billions)	Year	Population (billions)
1804	1	1999	6
1927	2	2011	7
1960	3	2025	8
1974	4	2041	9
1987	5	2071	10

a. Find a logistic model for world population. Discuss how well the equation fits the data.

b. According to the model, what will ultimately happen to world population? Do you consider

the model appropriate to use in predicting long-term world population behavior?

c. Use the model to estimate the world population in 1850. In 1990. Are the estimates reliable? Explain.

For each function given in Activities 18 through 27, a. consider a graph of the function and describe its concavity, b. use limit notation to describe the end behavior of the function (for both the positive and negative directions), and c. verbally describe the end behavior.

18. $f(x) = -5x + 2$

19. $g(t) = 5(7^t)$

20. $h(s) = 5(0.7^s)$

21. $y(x) = 3 + 6 \ln x$

22. $j(u) = 3 - 6 \ln u$

23. $l(t) = \dfrac{52}{1 + 0.5e^{-0.9t}}$

24. $m(t) = \dfrac{14.3}{1 + 5e^{0.9t}}$

25. $n(k) = 4k^2 - 2k + 12$

26. $A(p) = -3p^2 + 4p + 8$

27. $C(q) = -2q^3 + 5q^2 - 3q + 7$

Discussing Concepts

28. Describe the graph of a logistic function using the words *concavity, inflection,* and *increasing/decreasing.*

29. Using the idea of limits, describe the end behavior of the logistic model, and explain how this end behavior differs from that of the exponential and log models.

1.5   Polynomial Functions and Models

Polynomial functions and models have been used extensively throughout the history of mathematics. Their successful use stems from both their presence in certain natural phenomena and their relatively simple application.

   Even though higher-degree polynomials are useful in some situations, we limit our discussion of polynomial functions and models to the linear, quadratic, and cubic cases.

Quadratic Modeling

A roofing company in Miami keeps track of the number of roofing jobs it completes each month. The data from January through June are given in Table 1.26.

TABLE 1.26

Month	January	February	March	April	May	June
Number of jobs	90	91	101	120	148	185

The first differences and percentage differences are not close to being constant, so we conclude that some model other than a linear model or an exponential model is appropriate in this case. Note, however, that the differences between the first differences are nearly constant. We call these **second differences.**

When first differences are constant, the data can be modeled by a linear equation. When second differences are constant, the data can be modeled by the **quadratic function** $f(x) = ax^2 + bx + c$ as long as $a \neq 0$. A quadratic equation of this form defines a function f with input x. From now on, when we refer to a quadratic equation or function, we will consider an equation of the form $f(x) = ax^2 + bx + c$.

The graph of a quadratic function is a **parabola.**

Quadratic Model

Algebraically: A quadratic model has an equation of the form

$$f(x) = ax^2 + bx + c$$

where $a \neq 0$.
Graphically: The graph of a quadratic function is a concave-up parabola if $a > 0$ and is a concave-down parabola if $a < 0$. (See Figures 1.56a and 1.56b.)

(a) $f(x) = ax^2 + bx + c$ with $a > 0$ (b) $f(x) = ax^2 + bx + c$ with $a < 0$

$\lim_{x \to \pm\infty} f(x) \to \infty$ $\lim_{x \to \pm\infty} f(x) \to -\infty$

FIGURE 1.56

Using technology to obtain a quadratic equation that fits the roofing job data, you should find the quadratic model to be

$$J(x) = 4.5x^2 - 12.5x + 98 \text{ jobs}$$

is the number of roofing jobs completed between January and June where $x = 1$ in January, $x = 2$ in February, and so on. Note in Figure 1.57 that the function J provides an excellent fit to the data.

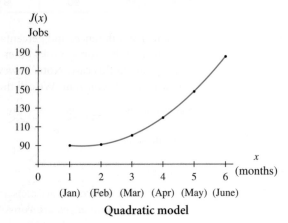

Quadratic model

FIGURE 1.57

If we are willing to assume that this quadratic function continues to model the number of roofing jobs for the next 3 months, how many jobs would we predict the company will have in August? Substituting $x = 8$ into the quadratic equation yields

$$J(8) = 4.5(8)^2 - 12.5(8) + 98 = 286 \text{ jobs}$$

EXAMPLE 1   *Finding a Quadratic Model*

Birthweight   The percentage of low-birthweight babies born before 37 weeks gestation as a function of the amount of weight gained by the mother is given in Table 1.27.

TABLE 1.27

Weight gain of mother (pounds)	18	23	28	33	38	43
Percentage of babies born before 37 weeks weighing less than 5 pounds 8 ounces	48.2	42.5	38.6	36.5	35.4	35.7

(Source: *National Vital Statistics Report*, vol. 50, no. 5, February 12, 2002.)

a. Find a quadratic model for the data.

b. Compare the minimum of the parabola with the minimum of the data.

Solution

a. A scatter plot of the data suggests a concave-up shape with a minimum around 38 pounds. See Figure 1.58.

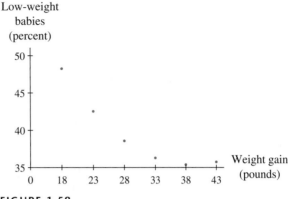

FIGURE 1.58

A quadratic model for the data is

$$P(g) = 0.0294g^2 - 2.286g + 79.685 \text{ percent}$$
of babies born before 37 weeks that weigh less than 5.5 pounds

when the mother's weight gain is g pounds, $18 \leq g \leq 43$.

b. Looking at the quadratic function graphed on the scatter plot (see Figure 1.59), we observe that the minimum of the parabola is slightly to the right and below the minimum data point. This means that the model slightly underestimates the minimum percentage and estimates that the minimum occurs slightly after it occurs in the data table.

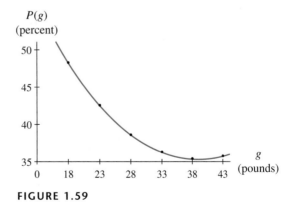

FIGURE 1.59

In the foregoing discussion and example, you have seen data sets that appear to be quadratic. That is, they may be reasonably modeled by a quadratic equation. In each case, the equation had a positive coefficient before the squared term. This value is called the **leading coefficient** because it is usually the first one that you write down in the equation $f(x) = ax^2 + bx + c$. Also, in each case, the graph of the equation appeared to be part of a parabola opening upward. Remember that we call such curvature *concave up*.

Table 1.28 gives the population (in thousands) of Cleveland, Ohio, from 1900 through 1980.

TABLE 1.28

Year	1900	1910	1920	1930	1940
Population	382	561	797	900	878
Year	1950	1960	1970	1980	
Population	915	876	751	574	

(Source: *Statistical Abstract*, 1998.)

A scatter plot of the data suggests a parabola opening downward (or *concave down*). The scatter plot and the graph of a quadratic equation fitted to the data are shown in Figure 1.60.

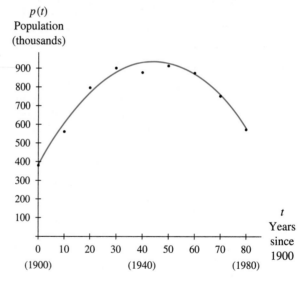

FIGURE 1.60

Would you expect the leading coefficient of the equation to be positive or negative? The population of Cleveland is given by

$$p(t) = -0.280t^2 + 24.9t + 375.3 \text{ thousand people}$$

where t is the number of years since 1900, $0 \leq t \leq 80$. When the graph of a quadratic function is concave up, its leading coefficient is positive; when the graph of a quadratic function is concave down, its leading coefficient is negative. Curvature will be important in later discussions that involve concepts of calculus.

Quadratic or Exponential?

Data sets that exhibit an obvious maximum or minimum are more easily identified as quadratic than data sets without a maximum or minimum. Sometimes, as shown in Example 2, all that is indicated by a scatter plot is the left side or right side of a parabola.

EXAMPLE 2   *Distinguishing Between Quadratic and Exponential Models*

Population   Table 1.29 shows the population of the contiguous states of the United States for selected years between 1790 and 1930.

TABLE 1.29

Year	Population (millions)	Year	Population (millions)
1790	3.929	1870	39.818
1810	7.240	1890	62.948
1830	12.866	1910	91.972
1850	23.192	1930	122.775

(Source: *Statistical Abstract,* 1998.)

Find an appropriate model for the data.

Solution   An examination of the scatter plot shows an increasing, concave-up shape (see Figure 1.61).

FIGURE 1.61

At first, it seems logical to try an exponential model for the data. An exponential model for the population of the contiguous United States is

$$E(t) = 4.558(1.285^t) \text{ million people}$$

where t is the number of decades since 1790, $0 \le t \le 14$. However, this equation does not seem to fit the data very well, as Figure 1.62 shows.

Exponential model

FIGURE 1.62

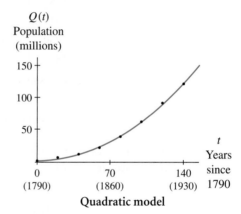

Quadratic model

FIGURE 1.63

Another possibility is a quadratic model. The right half of a parabola that opens upward could fit the scatter plot. A quadratic model for the population of the contiguous United States is

$$Q(t) = 0.66t^2 - 0.77t + 4.81 \text{ million people}$$

where t is the number of decades since 1790, $0 \le t \le 14$. When graphed on the scatter plot, this equation appears to be a very good fit (see Figure 1.63). It is the more appropriate model for the population of the contiguous United States on the basis of the given data. ●

Cubic Modeling

We saw that when the first differences of a set of evenly spaced data are constant, the data can be modeled perfectly by the linear equation $y = ax + b$. Likewise, when the second differences of evenly spaced input data are constant, the data can be modeled perfectly by the quadratic equation $y = ax^2 + bx + c$. It is also possible for the third differences to be constant. In this case, the data can be modeled perfectly by a cubic equation. A cubic equation of the form $f(x) = ax^3 + bx^2 + cx + d$ is a function with input x. From now on, when we refer to a cubic equation or function, we will consider the equation to be of this form.

Because in the real world we are extremely unlikely to encounter data that are perfectly cubic, we will not look at third differences. Instead, we will examine a scatter plot of the data to see whether a cubic model may be appropriate. Figure 1.64 shows the graphs of some cubic equations.

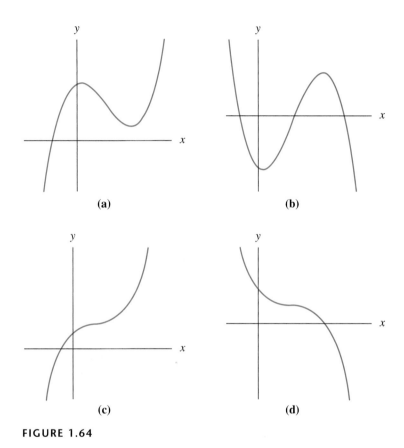

FIGURE 1.64

Every cubic function $f(x) = ax^3 + bx^2 + cx + d$ with $a \neq 0$ has a graph that resembles one of the four graphs in Figure 1.64. Figures 1.64a and 1.64c correspond to equations in which $a > 0$, and Figures 1.64b and 1.64d are graphs of equations in which $a < 0$. For a cubic equation $f(x) = ax^3 + bx^2 + cx + d$ with $a \neq 0$, the end behavior shows that $f(x)$ increases without bound in one direction and decreases without bound in the opposite direction.

Figure 1.65 (on page 76) shows scatter plots of data sets that could be modeled by cubic equations.

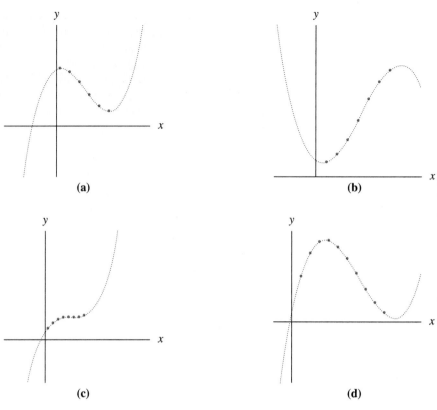

FIGURE 1.65

You may already have noticed that in every cubic function, the curvature of the graph changes once from concave down to concave up, or vice versa. As we noted with the graph of a logistic curve, the point on the graph at which concavity changes is called the *inflection point*. All cubic functions have one inflection point. The approximate location of the inflection point in each of the graphs in Figure 1.66 is marked with a dot. In Chapter 4, we will see how calculus can be used to determine the exact location of the inflection point of a cubic function.

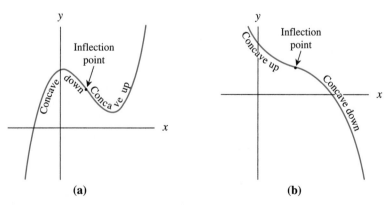

FIGURE 1.66

It is often the case that a portion of a cubic function appears to fit extremely well a set of data that can be adequately modeled with a quadratic function. In an effort to keep things as simple as possible, we adopt the following convention:

> If the scatter plot of a set of data fails to exhibit an inflection point, then it is not appropriate to fit a cubic equation to the data.

We must be extremely cautious when using cubic models to extrapolate. For the data sets whose scatter plots are shown in Figures 1.65a and 1.65c, the functions indicated by the dotted curves appear to follow the trend of the data. However, in Figure 1.65b, it would be possible for additional data to level off (as in a logistic model), whereas the cubic function takes a downward turn. Also, additional data in Figure 1.65d might continue to get closer to the x-axis, whereas the cubic function that is fitted to the available data begins to rise.

Cubic Model

Algebraically: A cubic model has an equation of the form

$$f(x) = ax^3 + bx^2 + cx + d$$

where $a \neq 0$.

Graphically: The graph of a cubic function has one inflection point and no limiting values. (See Figure 1.64.)

EXAMPLE 3   *Finding a Cubic Model*

Gas Price   The average price in dollars per 1000 cubic feet of natural gas for residential use in the United States for selected years from 1980 through 2005 is given in Table 1.30.

TABLE 1.30

Year	Price (dollars)	Year	Price (dollars)
1980	3.68	1998	6.82
1982	5.17	2000	7.76
1985	6.12	2003	9.52
1990	5.80	2004	10.74
1995	6.06	2005	13.84

(Source: *Statistical Abstract,* 1992 and 2001, and Energy Information Administration.)

a. Find an appropriate model for the data. Would it be wise to use this model to predict future natural gas prices?

b. Use the model in part *a* to estimate the price in 1993.

c. According to the model, when did the average price of 1000 cubic feet of natural gas first exceed $6.00?

Solution

a. An examination of a scatter plot shows that a cubic model is appropriate. Note that the scatter plot shown in Figure 1.67 appears to be mostly concave down between 1980 and 1990 but then is concave up between 1990 and 2005. That is, there appears to be an inflection point (a change of concavity) near 1990.

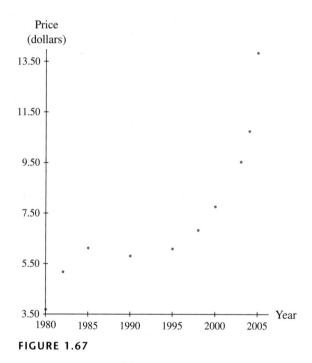

FIGURE 1.67

A cubic model for the price of natural gas is

$$P(x) = 0.00275x^3 - 0.0876x^2 + 0.842x + 3.72 \text{ dollars}$$

where x is the number of years since the end of 1980, $0 \leq x \leq 25$. A graph of the equation over the scatter plot is shown in Figure 1.68.

Note that the graph is increasing to the right of about 1993. Natural gas prices will probably not continue to rise indefinitely as the cubic function does, so it is unwise to use the model to predict future prices of natural gas. Additional data should be obtained to see the pattern past 2005.

b. In 1993 the average price of 1000 cubic feet of natural gas was $P(13) \approx \$5.89$.

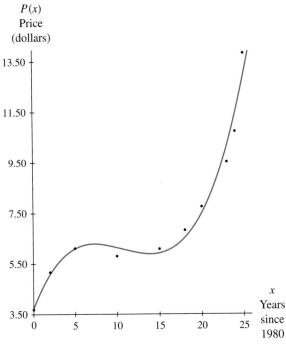

P(x)
Price
(dollars)

FIGURE 1.68

P(x)
Price
(dollars)

FIGURE 1.69

c. To determine when the average price first exceeded $6.00, solve the equation $P(x) = 6$. In Figure 1.69, a dotted line is drawn at $P(x) = \$6.00$. This line intersects the graph at three places, so there are three solutions to the equation $P(x) = 6$. The solutions are $x \approx 4.57, 11.40,$ and 15.90.

We seek the smallest solution ($x \approx 4.57$), which corresponds to the first time the output is 6.00. However, the data represent yearly averages. In 1984 the average price was less than $6.00, and in 1985 the average price was slightly more than $6.00. Therefore, the average price first exceeded $6.00 in 1985.   ●

We can also model the average price of natural gas in Example 3 with a cubic equation by renumbering the years so that x is the number of years since 1900. This new model for the average price of natural gas will be

Price $= 0.00275x^3 - 0.748x^2 + 67.69x - 2033.29$ dollars

where x is the number of years since 1900, $80 \le x \le 105$.

Although the two models have different inputs, they yield the same results. Note that the coefficient on x^3 is the same in both models. This will be the case for any alignment.

In real life, data do not come with instructions attached to tell what function to use as a possible model. It is important to consider first what underlying processes may be influencing the relationship between input and output and what end behavior may be exhibited. However, the following simple guidelines may help.

Steps in Choosing a Model

1. **Look at the curvature of a scatter plot of the data.**
   - If the points appear to lie in a straight line, try a linear model.
   - If the scatter plot is curved but has no inflection point, try a quadratic, an exponential, or a log model.
   - If the scatter plot appears to have an inflection point, try a cubic and/or a logistic model.

   Note: If the input values are equally spaced, it might be helpful to look at first differences versus percentage differences to decide whether a linear or an exponential model would be more appropriate, or to compare second differences with percentage differences to decide whether a quadratic or an exponential model would be better.

2. **Look at the fit of the possible equations.** In Step 1, you should have narrowed the possible models to at most two choices. Compute these equations, and graph them on a scatter plot of the data. The one that comes closest to the most points (but does not necessarily go through the most points) is normally the better model to choose.

3. **Look at the end behavior of the scatter plot.** If Step 2 does not reveal that one model is obviously better than another, consider the end behavior of the data, and choose the appropriate model.

4. **Consider that there may be two equally good models** for a particular set of data. If that is the case, then you may choose either.

1.5   Concept Inventory

- Second differences
- Quadratic function: $f(x) = ax^2 + bx + c$ (constant second differences, no change in concavity)
- Parabola
- Cubic function: $f(x) = ax^3 + bx^2 + cx + d$ (one change in concavity)
- Inflection point

1.5   Activities

Getting Started

Identify the curves in Activities 1 through 6 as concave up or concave down. In each case, indicate the portion of the horizontal axis over which the part of the curve that is shown is increasing or decreasing.

5.
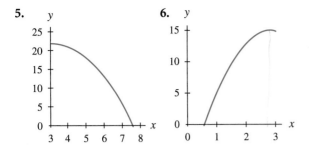

6.

For the graphs in Activities 7 through 12, describe the curvature by indicating the portions of the displayed horizontal axis over which each curve is concave down or concave up. Mark the approximate location of the inflection point on each curve.

7.

8.

9.

10.

11.
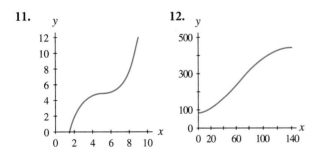

12.

Applying Concepts

13. Missile Height   During a training mission in the South Pacific, a Tomahawk cruise missile misfires. It goes over the side of the ship and hits the water. Suppose the data shown in the accompanying table,

giving the height of the missile, are collected via telemetry.

Seconds after launch	Feet above water
0	128
0.5	140
1	144
1.5	140
2	128
2.5	108
3	80
3.5	
4	

a. Without graphing, show that the data in the table are quadratic.

b. Without finding an equation, complete the accompanying table by filling in the missing values.

c. Find a quadratic model for the complete data.

d. Use the model to determine when the missile hits the water.

14. Profit   The accompanying table gives the price, in dollars, of a round-trip ticket from Denver to Chicago on a certain airline and the corresponding monthly profit, in millions of dollars, for that airline.

Ticket price (dollars)	Profit (millions of dollars)
200	3.08
250	3.52
300	3.76
350	3.82
400	3.70
450	3.38

a. Is a quadratic model appropriate for the data? Explain.

b. Find a quadratic model for the data.

c. As the ticket price increases, the airline should collect more money. How can it be that when the ticket price reaches a certain amount, profit decreases?

d. At what ticket price will the airline begin to post a negative profit (that is, a net loss)?

15. **Marriage Age**   As listed in *The 1999 World Almanac,* the median age (in years) at first marriage of females in the United States is shown in the accompanying table.

Year	1960	1970	1980	1990
Age	20.3	20.8	22.0	23.9

a. Refute or defend the following statement: "The data are perfectly quadratic."

b. Without finding an equation, estimate the age that corresponds to the year 2000.

c. Find a quadratic model for the data.

d. Use the model to estimate the median age in the year 2000. Is it the same as your answer to part *b*?

16. **Veggies**   The per capita consumption of commercially produced fresh vegetables in the United States from 1980 through 2000 was as shown in the accompanying table.

Year	Vegetable consumption (pounds per person)
1980	149.1
1985	156.0
1990	167.1
1995	179.1
2000	201.7

(Sources: *Statistical Abstract,* 2001, and www.ers.usda.gov, accessed 9/25/02.)

a. Find a quadratic model for the data, and examine the equation graphed on a scatter plot of the data.

b. Do you believe that the equation in part *a* is a good fit? Explain.

c. The per capita consumption in 2001 had not yet been tabulated when the data in the table were published. What does the quadratic model give as the per capita consumption in 2001? Do you believe that this estimate is reliable?

d. According to your model, in what year will consumption exceed 225 pounds per person?

17. **Mortality**   The accompanying table lists the death rates (number of deaths per thousand people whose age is *x*) in 1998 for the United States.

Age x	Death rate (deaths per thousand people)
40	2.0
45	3.0
50	4.4
55	6.7
60	10.7
65	16.5

(Source: *Statistical Abstract,* 2001.)

a. Find a quadratic model for the data in the table. Discuss how well the equation fits the data.

b. Use the model to complete the following table:

Age	Model prediction	Actual rate
51		4.7
52		5.1
53		5.6
57		8.1
59		9.7
63		14.1
70		25.5
75		38.0
80		59.2

c. What can you conclude about using a model to make predictions?

18. **Lead Paint**   Lead was banned as an ingredient in most paints in 1978, although it is still used in some specialty paints. Lead usage in paints from 1940 through 1980 is reported in the accompanying table.

Year	Lead usage (thousands of tons)
1940	70
1950	35
1960	10
1970	5
1980	0.01

(Source: Estimated from information in "Lead in the Inner Cities," *American Scientist,* January–February 1999, pp. 62–73.)

a. Examine a scatter plot of the data. Find quadratic and exponential models for lead usage. Comment on how well each equation fits the data.

b. What is the end behavior suggested by the data? Which function in part *a* has the end behavior suggested by the context?

c. Which model would be more appropriate to use to estimate the lead usage in 1955? Use that model to estimate the usage in 1955.

19. **Education**   The following table shows the amounts spent on reducing sizes of first-grade through third-grade public school classes in Nevada.

Year	Amount (millions)
1990	$3
1992	$31
1994	$37
1996	$42
1998	$66

(Source: Nevada Department of Education.)

a. Examine a scatter plot of the data. How does a scatter plot indicate that a cubic model might be appropriate?

b. Find a cubic model for the amount spent on class size reduction.

c. Use the model to estimate the amounts in 1993 and 1999. In which of these estimates can you have more confidence?

d. Compare the estimates from part *c* with the actual amounts of $34 million spent in 1993 and $99 million spent in 1999. Does this comparison support the statements you made in part *c* concerning the reliability of the estimates?

20. **Births**   The numbers of live births in the United States for selected years between 1950 and 2000 to women 45 years of age and older are as given in the accompanying table.

Year	Births	Year	Births
1950	5322	1980	1200
1960	5182	1990	1638
1970	3146	2000	4604

(Source: www.infoplease.com, accessed 9/24/02.)

a. Examine a scatter plot of the data in the table. Find a cubic model for the data, and graph the equation on the scatter plot. Discuss how well the equation fits the data.

b. What trend does the model indicate beyond 2000? Do you believe that the trend is valid? Explain.

c. Use the model to estimate the number of live births in 1940. The actual number was 7558. How close is the model estimate?

d. Do you believe your model would be an accurate predictor of the number of live births to women 45 years of age and older for the current year? Why or why not?

21. **Gender Ratio**   The accompanying table shows the number of males per 100 females in the United States calculated using census data. This number is referred to as the *gender ratio.*

Year	Males per 100 females
1900	104.6
1910	106.2
1920	104.1
1930	102.6
1940	100.8
1950	98.7
1960	97.1
1970	94.8
1980	94.5
1990	95.1
2000	96.3

(Source: U.S. Bureau of the Census.)

a. Examine a scatter plot of the data. What behavior of the data suggests that a cubic model is appropriate?

b. Find a cubic model for the gender ratio. What trend does the model indicate for the years beyond 2000? Do you believe that this is a good predictor of future gender ratios? Why or why not?

22.   The following table shows a manufacturer's total cost (in hundreds of dollars) to produce from 1 to 33 forklifts per week.

Weekly production	Total cost (hundreds of dollars)
1	18.5
5	80
9	125
13	160
17	185
21	210
25	225
29	245
33	280

a. Examine a scatter plot of the data in the table. What characteristics of the scatter plot indicate that a cubic model would be appropriate?

b. Find a cubic model for total manufacturing cost.

c. What does the model predict as the cost to produce 23 forklifts per week? 35 forklifts per week?

d. Convert the cubic equation in part b for total cost to one for average cost. Then find the average cost of producing 23 forklifts per week and that of producing 35 forklifts per week.

23. **Gender Ratio** The gender ratio in the United States is different for different age groups. The following table shows gender ratios corresponding to age that were calculated from the 2000 census data.

Age	Males per 100 females
under 1	105.0
10	105.2
20	104.7
30	102.8
40	99.7
50	96.6
60	92.0
70	81.9
80	63.1
90	37.6
100 and over	24.9

(Source: U.S. Bureau of the Census.)

a. According to the data, for what age are the numbers of males and females equal?

b. Find cubic and logistic models for the gender ratio as a function of age. Compare the fit of the two equations. Which equation do you believe is better for modeling these data?

c. Use the model you chose in part b to find the age for which there are twice as many women as men. What does this information tell you about death rates of men and women?

24. **Births** The accompanying table gives the cesarean delivery rate per 100 live births in the United States from 1990 through 2000.

Year	Cesarean delivery rate (per 100 live births)
1990	22.7
1992	22.3
1994	21.2
1996	20.7
1998	21.2
2000	22.9

(Source: *National Vital Statistics Report,* vol. 50, no. 5, February 12, 2000.)

a. Examine a scatter plot of the data in the table, and discuss its curvature. Should the data be modeled by a quadratic or a cubic equation? What is the model?

b. What does the model estimate as the Cesarean delivery rate in the United States in 1989 and 1999? Compare the model estimates to the actual rates of 22.8 births per 100 in 1989 and 22.0 births per 100 in 1999.

Discussing Concepts

25. Using the terms *increasing, decreasing,* and *concave,* describe the shape of the graphs of functions of the forms $y = ax^2 + bx + c$ and $y = ax^3 + bx^2 + cx + d$.

26. Discuss how to use end-behavior analysis in determining the differences among linear and polynomial functions and among exponential, log, and logistic functions.

SUMMARY

Mathematical Modeling and Functions

Mathematical modeling is the process by which we construct a mathematical framework to represent a real-life situation. In this book we often use mathematical modeling to mean fitting a line or curve to data. The resulting equation, together with output label, input description, and interval description, which we refer to as the mathematical model, provides a representation of the underlying relationship between the variable quantities of interest. A function is a description of how one thing (output) changes as something else (input) changes. We encounter functions represented in four ways: tables of data, graphs, word descriptions, and equations.

The Role of Technology

In order to construct mathematical models from data, we must use appropriate tools. Normally, these tools are graphing calculators or personal computers. You should clearly understand that we use technology simply as a tool in the service of mathematics and that no tool is a substitute for clear, effective thinking. Technology carries only the graphical and numerical computational burden. You yourself must perform the mathematical analyses, interpret the results, make the appropriate decisions, and then communicate your conclusions in a clear and understandable manner.

Function Combinations and Composition

There are several ways to create new functions by combining two or more other functions whose input and output units are compatible. The basic construction techniques are function addition, subtraction, multiplication, division, and composition. In each of these constructions, knowing the input and output units of the functions is the key to understanding how to combine the functions. Table 1.31 shows the necessary input and output compatibility.

TABLE 1.31

Function operation	Input compatibility	Output compatibility	New input units	New output units
Addition	Identical	Same unit of measure or units of measure capable of being combined into a larger group (sons + daughters = children)	Same as input unit of measure of original functions	Same as output unit of measure of original functions
Subtraction	Identical	Same unit of measure or units of measure capable of being subtracted (children − sons = daughters)	Same as input unit of measure of original functions	Same as output unit of measure of original functions
Multiplication	Identical	Unit of measure of one function should contain "per " unit of measure of the other function	Same as input unit of measure of original functions	The multiplication (reduced if possible) of the output unit of measure of the original functions
Division	Identical	Same unit of measure (or) unit of measure of the two functions should make sense in a phrase containing ". . . per . . ."	Same as input unit of measure of original functions	The numerator output unit of measure "per" the denominator output unit of measure
Composition	Output of one function (inside function) is identical to the input of the second function (outside function)		Same as input unit of measure of inside function	Same as output unit of measure of outside function

Linear Functions and Models

A linear function models a constant rate of change. Its underlying equation is that of a line: $y = ax + b$, where the constant a is called the slope of the line and is calculated as $\frac{\text{rise}}{\text{run}}$. Because the slope of a line is a measure of its rate of increase or decrease, the slope is also known as the rate of change for the linear model. The constant b appearing in the linear model $y = ax + b$ is simply the output of the model when the input is zero.

Exponential Functions and Models

Second in importance to linear functions and models are exponential functions and models. Based on the familiar idea of repeated multiplication by a fixed positive multiplier b (the base), the basic exponential function is of the form

$$f(x) = ab^x$$

The value a appearing in the equation is the output when the input is zero.

Exponential functions model constant percentage change. In terms of the function $f(x) = ab^x$, exponential growth occurs when b is greater than 1, and exponential decline (decay) takes place when b is between 0 and 1. The constant percentage growth or decline is given by $(b - 1)100\%$.

Logarithmic Functions and Models

The basic form of the log function that we use is

$$f(x) = a + b \ln x$$

The input of this function must be a value greater than zero. The log function is useful for situations in which the output grows or declines at an increasingly slow rate. When fitting a log equation to data, you must sometimes align the input data to ensure that the input values are greater than zero or to obtain a better fit. Aligning input data has the effect of shifting the data horizontally.

Logistic Functions and Models

Initial exponential growth followed by a leveling-off approach toward a limiting value L is characteristic of logistic growth, which is modeled by the logistic equation

$$f(x) = \frac{L}{1 + Ae^{-Bx}}$$

If the constant B is positive, the model indicates growth. If the constant B is negative, the model indicates decline in output toward the horizontal axis as the input values increase.

When fitting exponential and logistic equations to data, it is sometimes helpful to shift the output data. This vertical shift is particularly useful when the data appear to approach a value other than zero. The goal in shifting is to move the data closer to the horizontal axis.

Limits and End Behavior

The idea of a limiting value of a function is a fundamental theme of calculus that can be intuitively understood to be the behavior of the outputs of a function as the inputs of the function become infinitesimally close to a specific value. Limits can also be used to describe the end behavior of a function as the magnitude of the inputs becomes infinitely large.

Polynomial Functions and Models

Polynomial functions and models have a well-established role in calculus. In this text, we consider linear functions, quadratic functions, and cubic functions. Quadratic equations have graphs known as parabolas. The parabola with equation $f(x) = ax^2 + bx + c$ opens upward (is concave up) if a is a positive and opens downward (is concave down) if a is negative.

Cubic equations have graphs that show a change of concavity at an inflection point, but unlike logistic models, they do not have horizontal asymptotes limiting their end behavior. In using cubic models, we must be especially careful when extrapolating beyond the range of data values from which the models are constructed.

Choosing a Model

Although it is not always clear which (if any) of the functions we have discussed apply to a particular real-life situation, it helps to keep in mind a few general, common-sense guidelines: (1) Given a set of discrete data, begin with a scatter plot. The plot will often reveal general characteristics that point the way to an appropriate model. (2) If the scatter plot does not appear to be linear, consider the suggested concavity. One-way concavity (up or down) suggests a quadratic, exponential, or log model. (3) When a single change in concavity seems apparent, think in terms of cubic or logistic models. But remember that the graphs of logistic models tend to become flat on each end, whereas the graphs of cubic models do not. Never consider using a cubic or a logistic model if you cannot identify an inflection point.

CONCEPT CHECK

Can you	To practice, try	
• Identify functions, inputs, and outputs?	Section 1.1	Activities 1, 5, 9
• Interpret models?	Section 1.1	Activities 11, 13
• Work with functions?	Section 1.1	Activities 19, 21, 23, 29, 31
• Combine or compose two functions?	Section 1.1	Activities 35, 41, 43, 51, 53
• Construct a linear model given a constant rate of change?	Section 1.2	Activities 9, 11, 17, 19
• Find a linear model and determine its rate of change?	Section 1.2	Activities 17, 23, 26
• Construct an exponential model given a constant percentage change?	Section 1.3	Activities 17, 19
• Find an exponential model and determine its percentage change?	Section 1.3	Activities 21, 23
• Solve exponential growth and decay problems?	Section 1.3	Activities 15, 27
• Find and use a log model?	Section 1.3	Activities 31, 33
• Find and use a logistic model?	Section 1.4	Activities 15, 17
• Determine end behavior?	Section 1.4	Activities 19, 21, 23
• Find and use a quadratic model?	Section 1.5	Activities 17, 19
• Find and use a cubic model?	Section 1.5	Activities 23, 25
• Identify concavity and inflection points?	Section 1.5	Activities 11, 13, 15

CONCEPT REVIEW

For the figures in Activities 1 through 6:

a. Describe the direction and curvature of the scatter plot, noting concavity.

b. Describe the apparent end behavior of the scatter plot in both the negative direction and the positive direction.

c. Determine what type of model would best describe the data.

d. Assuming the function $f(x)$ from part c has been fit to the data, use limit notation to describe the end behavior of $f(x)$.

1.

2.

3.

4.

5.
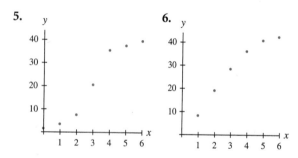

6.

7. At a large university, there is no student parking available on the main campus. A transit bus is available to transport students from satellite parking to main campus. Suppose $S(x)$ is the number of students who rode the bus, where x is the number of hours after 7 A.M., and $C(s)$ is the number of student cars on the main campus that have parking tickets, where s is the number of students who rode the bus?

   a. Draw input/output diagrams for $S(x)$ and $C(s)$.

   b. What function operation must be applied to $S(x)$ and $C(s)$ to construct function T, which gives the number of cars with parking tickets on them x hours after 7 A.M.

   c. Write the new function T using appropriate function notation.

   d. Write the input and output units for the new function.

8. Suppose $S(t)$ is the total number of applicants to your college or university in year t, and $M(t)$ is the number of male applicants to your college or university in year t.

   a. Draw input/output diagrams for $S(t)$ and $M(t)$.

   b. What function operation must be applied to $S(t)$ and $M(t)$ to construct function F, which gives the number of female applicants to your college or university in year t?

   c. Write the new function F using appropriate function notation.

   d. Write the input and output units for the new function.

9. Suppose $R(x)$ is the revenue, in millions of dollars, of a company x years after it has been in business, and $C(x)$ is the cost, in thousands of dollars, of a company x years after it has been in business.

   a. Draw input/output diagrams for $R(x)$ and $C(x)$.

   b. What function can be constructed from $R(x)$ and $C(x)$?

   c. Write the new function P using appropriate function notation.

   d. Write a statement of the model constructed in part c.

10. **Demand**   Suppose the daily demand for beef can be modeled by $D(p) = \dfrac{40}{1 + 0.03e^{0.4p}}$ million pounds, where p is the price of beef in dollars per pound.

    a. What function operation can be used with the given model to construct a function for revenue?

    b. Write the new function P using appropriate function notation.

    c. Write a statement of the model constructed in part b.

11. **Rearing Children**   According to the U.S. Census Bureau, the number of children living with their grandparents was 2.2 million in 1970 and 3.9 million in 1997. Assume that the number grew exponentially between 1970 and 1997.

    a. Find an exponential model for the number of children living with their grandparents as a function of the number of years since 1970.

    b. What is the percentage change indicated by the model?

c. According to the model, when will the number of children living with their grandparents reach 5 million?

d. What is the doubling time for the model found in part *a*? Interpret the doubling time in context.

12. **Demand**   When a certain variety of fish is marketed for human consumption, the demand for that fish can be modeled as $D(p) = 6.25(0.88^p)$ trillion pounds when the fish is marketed for *p* dollars per pound.

a. Is the function *D* an increasing or a decreasing exponential function? Looking only at the parameters of the function, what indicates this increase or decrease?

b. Find the demand for fish when the market price is 7 dollars; 14 dollars; 21 dollars.

c. What type of model is an inverse to an exponential model?

d. Using the information found in part *b*, find a model for market price given the amount of fish in demand.

13. **Jeep Value**   The following table shows the 2002 private-party resale value of a 2000 Jeep Grand Cherokee Laredo in excellent condition as a function of the mileage.

Mileage (thousands)	Resale value (dollars)
20	18,520
40	17,120
60	14,670
80	13,295
100	12,745
120	12,270

(Source: www.kbb.com, accessed 9/30/01.)

a. Examine a scatter plot of the data, and discuss its curvature. Why is a quadratic equation a good fit for these data? What is the model?

b. Use your model from part *a* to estimate the resale value for this jeep at 52 thousand miles.

c. Suppose the owner of a 2000 Jeep Grand Cherokee Laredo drives the jeep 4 thousand miles each month during 2002. At the beginning of 2002, the jeep already had 68 thousand miles on it. Write a model for the mileage on the jeep at the end of the *x*th month of 2002. What is the slope of this model? What is its rate of change?

d. Use the models developed in parts *a* and *c* to construct a model giving the resale value of the jeep at the end of the *x*th month of 2002.

14. **Epidemic**   In 1949 the United States experienced the second-worst polio epidemic in its history. (The worst was in 1952.) The accompanying table gives the cumulative number of polio cases diagnosed on a monthly basis.

Month	Total number of polio cases
January	494
February	759
March	1016
April	1215
May	1619
June	2964
July	8489
August	22,377
September	32,618
October	38,153
November	41,462
December	42,375

(Source: *Twelfth Annual Report*, National Foundation for Infantile Paralysis, 1949.)

a. Examine a scatter plot of the data. Describe the concavity, and estimate the location of the inflection point indicated by the scatter plot. What type of model would best describe these data?

b. Describe the end behavior suggested by the context.

c. What type of model would be most appropriate to describe these data and this context?

d. Write a model (of the type you chose in part *c*) for these data.

Project 1.1 Compulsory School Laws

Setting

In 1852, Massachusetts became the first state to enact a compulsory school attendance law. Sixty-six years later, in 1918, Mississippi became the last state to enact a compulsory school attendance law. The following table lists the first 48 states to enact such laws and the year in which each of these states enacted its first compulsory school attendance law.

State	Year	State	Year	State	Year
MA	1852	SD	1883	IA	1902
NY	1853	RI	1883	MD	1902
VT	1867	ND	1883	MO	1905
MI	1871	MT	1883	TN	1905
WA	1871	IL	1883	DE	1907
NH	1871	MN	1885	NC	1907
CT	1872	ID	1887	OK	1907
NM	1872	NE	1887	VA	1908
NV	1873	OR	1889	AR	1909
KS	1874	CO	1889	TX	1915
CA	1874	UT	1890	FL	1915
ME	1875	KY	1893	AL	1915
NJ	1875	PA	1895	SC	1915
WY	1876	IN	1897	LA	1916
OH	1877	WV	1897	GA	1916
WI	1879	AZ	1899	MS	1918

(Source: J. Richardson, "Variation in Date of Enactment of Compulsory School Attendance Laws," *Sociology of Education*, vol. 53 (July 1980), pp. 153–163.)

Tasks

1. Tabulate the cumulative number of states with compulsory school attendance laws for the 5-year periods shown in the following table.

1852–1856	1887–1891
1857–1861	1892–1896
1862–1866	1897–1901
1867–1871	1902–1906
1872–1876	1907–1911
1877–1881	1912–1916
1882–1886	1917–1921

2. Examine a scatter plot of the data in Task 1. Do you believe a logistic model is appropriate? Explain.

3. Find a logistic model for the data in Task 1.

4. What do most states in the third column of the original data have in common? Why would these states be the last to enact laws related to compulsory education?

5. The 17 states considered to be southern states (below the Mason-Dixon Line) are AL, AR, DE, FL, GA, KY, LA, MD, MO, MS, NC, OK, SC, TN, TX, VA, and WV. Tabulate cumulative totals for the southern states and the northern/western states for the dates shown in the following table.

Project 1.1 Compulsory School Laws, *continued*

Northern/western states	Southern states
1852–1856	1891–1895
1857–1861	1896–1900
1862–1866	1901–1905
1867–1871	1906–1910
1872–1876	1911–1915
1877–1881	1916–1920
1882–1886	
1887–1891	
1892–1896	
1897–1901	
1902–1906	

6. Examine scatter plots for the two data sets in Task 5. Do you believe that logistic models are appropriate for these data sets? Explain.

7. Find logistic models for each set of data in Task 5. Comment on how well each equation fits the data.

8. It appears that the northern and western states were slow to follow the lead established by Massachusetts and New York. What historical event may have been responsible for the time lag?

9. One way to reduce the impact of unusual behavior in a data set (such as that discussed in Task 8) is to group the data in a different way. Tabulate the cumulative northern state and western state totals for the following 10-year periods:

1852–1861
1862–1871
1872–1881
1882–1891
1892–1901
1902–1911

10. Find a logistic model for the data in Task 9. Comment on how well the function fits the data. Compare models for the data grouped in 10-year intervals and the data grouped in 5-year intervals (Task 6). Does how the data are grouped significantly affect how well the equation fits? Explain.

11. Find an equation that fits the data for the southern states better than the logistic equation. Write the model using the better-fitting equation. Explain your reasoning.

Reporting

1. Prepare a written report of your work. Include scatter plots, models, and graphs. Include discussions of each of the tasks in this project.

2. (Optional) Prepare a brief (15-minute) presentation of your work.

Project 1.2 Fundraising Campaign

Setting

In order to raise funds, the mathematics department in your college or university is planning to sell T-shirts before next year's football game against the school's biggest rival. Your team has volunteered to conduct the fundraiser. Because several other student groups have also volunteered to head this project, your team is to present its proposal for the fund drive, as well as predictions about its outcome, to a panel of mathematics faculty.

Tasks

1. Develop a slogan and a design for the T-shirt. Keep in mind that good taste is a concern. Decide on a target market, and determine a strategy to survey (at random) at least 100 students who represent a cross section of the target market to determine the demand for T-shirts (as a function of price) within that market. It is important that your sample survey group properly represent your target market. If, for example, you polled only near campus dining facilities at lunch time, your sample would be biased toward students who eat lunch at such facilities.

   The question you should ask is "How much would you be willing to spend on a T-shirt promoting the big football rivalry: $20, $18, $16, $14, $12, $10, $8, or not interested?" Keep an accurate tally of the number of students who answer in each category. In your report on the results of your poll, you should include information such as your target market; where, when, and how you polled within that market; and why you believe that your polled sample is likely to be a representative cross section of the market.

2. a. From the data you have gathered, determine how many students from your sample survey group would buy a T-shirt at $20, $18, $16, and so on.

Note: This project is also used as a portion of Project 4.2 on page 282.

Project 1.2 Fundraising Campaign, *continued*

b. Devise a marketing strategy, and determine how many students within your target market you can reasonably expect to reach. Assuming that your poll is an accurate indicator of your target population, determine the number of students from your target market who will buy a T-shirt at each of the given prices.

c. Taking into account the results of your poll and your projected target market, develop a model for demand as a function of price. Keep in mind that your model must make sense for all possible input values.

3. Use the partial price list (located on the website) to model a function for the cost to you when ordering T-shirts. Use the demand function from Task 2c to create equations for revenue, total cost, and profit as functions of price. (Revenue, total cost, and profit may not be among the basic models that were discussed in class. They are sums and/or products of the demand function with other functions.)

Reporting

1. Prepare a written report summarizing your survey and modeling. The report should include your slogan and design, your target market, your marketing strategy, the results from your poll (as well as the specifics of how you conducted your poll), a discussion of how and why you chose the model of the demand function, a discussion of the accuracy of your demand model, and graphs and equations for all of your models. Attach your questionnaire and data to the report as an appendix.

2. Prepare a 15-minute oral presentation of your survey, modeling, and marketing strategy to be delivered before a panel of mathematics faculty. You will be expected to have overhead transparencies of all graphs and equations, as well as any other information that you consider appropriate as a visual aid. Remember that you are trying to sell the mathematics department on your campaign idea.

2

Describing Change: Rates

Ted Horowitz/Corbis

Concept Application

The passenger airline industry has spent the first several years of the twenty-first century undergoing extensive changes in the way that it operates. Many of the airlines that operated during the latter part of the 1900s are no longer operating, and those that *are* still operating have had to adapt quickly in order to stay financially solvent. The changes that airline companies have had to react to include fluctuations in industry-wide demand for seats, fluctuations in market share, newly instituted security procedures, and increases in fuel prices. Airlines can use calculus to help answer questions such as the following:

- How quickly was the number of enplaned passengers changing at the end of 2005?

- At what point during the last decade was the price of Northwest Airline's common stock decreasing most rapidly?

- What was the percentage rate of change of airline fuel prices at the beginning of 2006?

This chapter will provide you with some of the tools that make it possible to answer questions like these. To estimate answers to such questions, see Activity 23 of Section 2.3, Activity 17 of Section 2.4, and Activity 7 of the Concept Review.

Chapter Introduction

Change is everywhere around us and affects our lives on a daily basis. In this chapter we consider several ways to describe change. Starting from the actual change in a quantity over an interval, it is a simple step to describe the change as a percentage change or as an average rate of change over that interval. The notion of average rate of change, when examined carefully in light of the underlying geometry of graphs, leads to the more subtle and challenging concept of instantaneous change. Indeed, the precise description of instantaneous change is a principal goal of calculus.

We therefore turn our attention to determining instantaneous rates of change. Because instantaneous rates of change are slopes of tangent lines, we consider the numerical estimation of these slopes. Then we generalize the numerical method to an algebraic method that gives us an analytic description—a formula of sorts—for the derivative of an arbitrary function.

Concepts You Will Be Learning

- Determining and interpreting change, percentage change, and average rate of change (2.1)
- Finding and interpreting the APY and APR in compound interest formulas (2.1)
- Estimating and interpreting slopes of secant and tangent lines on a graph (2.1, 2.2, 2.3)
- Relating the location of a tangent line to the concavity of a graph (2.2)
- Recognizing points on a graph where a derivative does not exist (2.2)
- Using derivative notation and interpreting given derivative values in context (2.3)
- Estimating and interpreting percentage rate of change (2.3)
- Numerically estimating rates of change (2.3)
- Using limits to find rate-of-change formulas algebraically (2.4)

2.1   Change, Percentage Change, and Average Rates of Change

Calculus gives a description of change. In preparation for learning how calculus describes change, we introduce three numerical ways of reporting change. We begin with a simple business example.

The yearly revenue for a large department store declined from $1.4 billion in 2000 to $1.1 billion in 2003. There are three common ways to express this change in revenue. We could use a negative sign to indicate the decrease in revenue and say that the **change** in revenue was $-$$0.3 billion over 3 years. We could also express this change by saying that the revenue declined by $0.3 billion (or $300 million) over 3 years.

It is often helpful to express the change as a percent of the 2000 revenue. This **percentage change** (or percent change) is found by dividing the change by the revenue in 2000 and multiplying by 100:

$$\text{Percentage change} = \frac{-\$0.3 \text{ billion}}{\$1.4 \text{ billion}} \cdot 100$$

$$\approx -21.4\%$$

The company saw a 21.4% decline in revenue between 2000 and 2003. You should already be familiar with percentage change from the discussion of exponential models. This method of calculating percentage change is the same as the way we calculated percentage differences using data in Section 1.3. However, you should note that even though constant percentage difference over equally spaced intervals is unique to exponential models, the percentage change in a quantity over a specific interval may be calculated and interpreted in almost any context.

The third way to express change involves evenly spreading the change over the input interval to obtain the **average rate of change.** This is done by dividing the change by the length of the interval. In the case of the department store revenue, the length of the interval is 3 years:

$$\text{Average rate of change} = \frac{-\$0.3 \text{ billion}}{3 \text{ years}}$$

$$= -\$0.1 \text{ billion per year}$$

On average, the revenue declined at a rate of $0.1 billion per year (or $100 million per year) between 2000 and 2003.

We summarize these three ways to describe change in the following box.

Change, Percentage Change, and Average Rate of Change

If a quantity changes from a value of m to a value of n over a certain interval from a to b, then

- The change in the quantity is found by subtracting the first value from the second.

$$\text{Change} = n - m$$

- The percentage change is the change divided by the first value and then multiplied by 100.

$$\text{Percentage change} = \frac{\text{change}}{\text{first value}} \cdot 100\% = \frac{n - m}{m} \cdot 100\%$$

- The average rate of change is the change divided by the length of the interval.

$$\text{Average rate of change} = \frac{\text{change}}{\text{length of interval}} = \frac{n - m}{b - a}$$

Interpreting Descriptions of Change

Correctly calculating these descriptions of change is important, but being able to state your result in a meaningful sentence in the context of the situation is equally important. When interpreting a description of change, you should answer the questions *when, what, how,* and *by how much.*

Interpreting Descriptions of Change

When describing change over an interval, be sure to answer the following questions:

- When? Specify the interval.
- What? Specify the quantity that is changing.
- How? Indicate whether the change is an increase or a decrease.
- By how much? Give the numerical answer labeled with proper units:

Description	Units
change	output unit of measure
percentage change	percent
average rate of change	output unit of measure per single input unit of measure

When stating an average rate of change, use the word *average* or the phrase *on average*.

EXAMPLE 1   *Describing Change Using a Table*

Temperature   Consider Table 2.1, which shows temperature values on a typical May day in a certain midwestern city. Find the following descriptions of change, and write a sentence giving the real-life meaning of (that is, interpret) each result.

TABLE 2.1

Time	Temperature (°F)	Time	Temperature (°F)
7 A.M.	49	1 P.M.	80
8 A.M.	58	2 P.M.	80
9 A.M.	66	3 P.M.	78
10 A.M.	72	4 P.M.	74
11 A.M.	76	5 P.M.	69
noon	79	6 P.M.	62

a. The change in temperature from 7 A.M. to 1 P.M.

b. The percentage change in temperature between 3 P.M. and 6 P.M.

c. The average rate of change in temperature between 8 A.M. and 5 P.M.

Solution

a. To find the change in temperature, subtract the temperature at 7 A.M. from the temperature at 1 P.M.

$$\text{Change} = 80°F - 49°F = 31°F$$

The interpretation statement answers the questions *when* (1 P.M. and 7 A.M.), *what* (the temperature), *how* (was greater than), and *by how much* (31°F): The temperature at 1 P.M. was 31°F greater than the temperature at 7 A.M.

b. To find percentage change, first find the change in temperature between 3 P.M. and 6 P.M.

$$\text{Change} = 62°F - 78°F = -16°F$$

Next, divide the change by the temperature at 3 P.M. (the beginning of the time interval under consideration), and multiply by 100.

$$\text{Percentage change} = \frac{-16°F}{78°F} \cdot 100\% \approx -20.5\%$$

The temperature declined by about 20.5% between 3 P.M. and 6 P.M. In this statement, "between 3 P.M. and 6 P.M." answers the question *when*, "the temperature" again identifies *what*, and "declined by about 20.5%" tells *how* and *by how much.*

c. Begin the calculation of the average rate of change by finding the change in the temperature from 8 A.M. to 5 P.M.

$$\text{Change} = 69°F - 58°F = 11°F$$

Next, divide the change by the length of the time interval (9 hours).

$$\text{Average rate of change} = \frac{11°F}{9 \text{ hours}} \approx 1.2°F \text{ per hour}$$

In interpreting this average rate of change, we must use the word *average* in our sentence in addition to answering the four questions. We state the interpretation as follows: Between 8 A.M. and 5 P.M., the temperature rose at an average rate of 1.2°F per hour. ●

Although these descriptions of change are useful, they have limitations. It appears from the answer to part *c* of Example 1 that the temperature rose slowly throughout the day. However, the average rate of change does not describe the 22°F rise in temperature followed by the 11°F drop in temperature that occurred between 8 A.M. and 5 P.M.

Finding Percentage Change and Average Rate of Change Using Graphs

You may have noticed that calculating the average rate of change is the same as calculating slope. This observation allows for the easy calculation of average rates of change if you are given a graph. For instance, when plotted, the May daytime temperatures in Example 1 fall in the shape of a parabola (see Figure 2.1).

FIGURE 2.1

To find the average rate of change between 9 A.M. and 4 P.M., first use a straightedge to draw carefully a line connecting the points at 9 A.M. and 4 P.M. (see Figure 2.2). We call this line connecting two points on a scatter plot or graph a **secant line** (from the Latin *secare,* "to cut"). Next, approximate the slope of this secant line by estimating the rise and the run for a portion of the line (see Figure 2.3).

FIGURE 2.2

FIGURE 2.3

$$\text{Average rate of change} = \frac{\text{rise}}{\text{run}} = \frac{\text{change in temperature}}{\text{change in time}}$$

$$= \frac{8°\text{F}}{7 \text{ hours}} \approx 1.1°\text{F per hour}$$

Between 9 A.M. and 4 P.M., the temperature rose at an average rate of 1.1°F per hour. Note that the rise is the change in temperature. To calculate percentage change from the graph, divide the rise by the estimated output of the first point.

$$\text{Percentage change} = \frac{\text{change in temperature}}{\text{temperature at 9 A.M.}} \approx \frac{8°\text{F}}{66°\text{F}} \cdot 100\% \approx 12.1\%$$

It is important to note that this graphical method of calculating descriptions of change is imprecise if you are given only a scatter plot or a graph. It gives only approximations of change, percentage change, and average rate of change. The method depends on drawing the secant line accurately and then correctly identifying two points on the line. Slight variations in sketching are likely to result in slightly different answers. This does not mean that the answers you obtain are incorrect. It simply means that descriptions of change obtained from graphs are approximations.

Example 1 and the subsequent discussion of air temperature use the term *between* two time values. There are other ways to describe intervals on the input axis, and we take a moment now to discuss one of them.

When we use data that someone else has collected, we often do not know when the data were reported or recorded. It seems logical to assume that yearly (or monthly or hourly and so forth) totals are reported at the *end* of the intervals representing those periods. For instance, a 2002 total covers the period of time from the end of 2001 through the end of 2002 (see Figure 2.4).

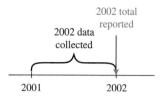

FIGURE 2.4

Therefore, we adopt the convention that "from *a* through *b*" on the input axis refers to the interval beginning at *a* and ending at *b*. If *a* and *b* are years and the output represents a quantity that can be considered to have been measured at the end of the year, then "from *a* to *b*" means the same thing as "from the end of year *a* through the end of year *b*." For our purposes, the phrases "between *a* and *b*" and "from *a* to *b*" have the same meaning as "from *a* through *b*." We use this terminology in the remainder of the text.

EXAMPLE 2   *Describing Change Using a Graph*

Social Security   The Social Security assets of the federal government between 2002 and 2030, as estimated by the Social Security Advisory Board, are shown in Figure 2.5. A smooth curve connecting the points is also shown.

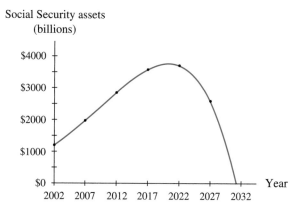

FIGURE 2.5
(Source: **www.ssab.gov** accessed on 10/1/02.)

a. Estimate the change, percentage change, and average rate of change in Social Security assets between 2002 and 2017. Write a sentence interpreting each answer in context.

b. Estimate the change, percentage change, and average rate of change in Social Security assets between 2022 and 2027. Write a sentence interpreting each answer in context.

Solution

a. Begin by estimating from the graph the Social Security assets in 2002 and 2017. One possible estimate is $1200 billion in 2002 and $3600 billion in 2017. To calculate change, subtract the 2002 value from the 2017 value.

$$\text{Change} = 3600 - 1200 = \$2400 \text{ billion}$$

Social Security assets are expected to rise about $2400 billion between 2002 and 2017.

Convert this change to percentage change by dividing by the estimated assets in 2002.

$$\text{Percentage change} = \frac{\$2400 \text{ billion}}{\$1200 \text{ billion}} \cdot 100\% = 200\%$$

Social Security assets are expected to increase about 200% between 2002 and 2017.

Convert the change to an average rate of change by dividing the change by the length of the interval between 2002 and 2017.

$$\text{Average rate of change} = \frac{\$2400 \text{ billion}}{15 \text{ years}}$$
$$= \$160 \text{ billion per year}$$

Social Security assets are expected to increase by an average of about $160 billion per year between 2002 and 2017. The average rate of change is the slope of the secant line through the point corresponding to 2002 and the point corresponding to 2017 shown in Figure 2.6.

b. Begin by estimating the output values in 2022 and 2027. We estimate $3700 billion in 2022 and $2600 billion in 2027. Following the same procedure as in part *a*, we have

$$\text{Change} \approx 2600 - 3700 = -\$1100 \text{ billion}$$

$$\text{Percentage change} \approx \frac{-\$1100 \text{ billion}}{\$3700 \text{ billion}} \cdot 100\% \approx -29.7\%$$

$$\text{Average rate of change} \approx \frac{-\$1100 \text{ billion}}{5 \text{ years}} = -\$220 \text{ billion per year}$$

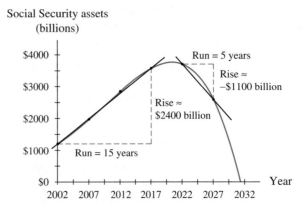

Social Security assets
(billions)

FIGURE 2.6

Between 2022 and 2027, Social Security assets are expected to decrease by about $1100 billion. This represents a percentage decrease of about 29.7%. On average, Social Security assets are expected to decrease by about $220 billion per year during this time. Again, the average rate of change is the slope of the secant line connecting the points on the graph that correspond to 2022 and 2027. (See Figure 2.6.) ●

Determining Percentage Change and Average Rate of Change Using an Equation

It is also possible to determine descriptions of change when we are given only an equation. We use the equation to determine numerical points with which to work and then calculate the change, percentage change, and average rate of change just as we would if we had been given data. Example 3 illustrates using an equation to determine descriptions of change.

EXAMPLE 3 *Descriptions of Change from an Equation*

A model for the temperature data on a typical May day in a certain midwestern city is

Temperature $= -0.8t^2 + 2t + 79°$F

where t is the number of hours after noon.

Calculate the percentage change and average rate of change between 11:30 A.M. and 6 P.M.

Solution
Note that at 11:30 A.M., $t = -0.5$ and that at 6 P.M., $t = 6$.

Substitute $t = -0.5$ and $t = 6$ into the equation to obtain the corresponding temperatures.

At 11:30 A.M.: Temperature $= -0.8(-0.5)^2 + 2(-0.5) + 79 = 77.8°$F

At 6 P.M.: Temperature $= -0.8(6)^2 + 2(6) + 79 = 62.2°$F

We find the change in temperature from 11:30 A.M. to 6 P.M. to be $62.2°F - 77.8°F = -15.6°F$.

To calculate percentage change, divide the change in temperature by the temperature at 11:30 A.M. and multiply by 100.

$$\frac{62.2°F - 77.8°F}{77.8°F} \cdot 100\% \approx -20\%$$

To find the average rate of change, divide the change in temperature by the change in time.

$$\frac{62.2°F - 77.8°F}{6 - (-0.5)} = \frac{-15.6°F}{6.5 \text{ hours}} = -2.4°F \text{ per hour}$$

Thus, between 11:30 A.M. and 6 P.M., the temperature fell by 15.6°F. This represents a 20% decline and an average rate of decline of 2.4°F per hour.   ●

Note that in Example 3, the temperature fell 15.6°F in 6.5 hours; however, when finding an average rate of change, we state the answer (in this case) as the number of degrees per *one* hour.

APR and APY

The world of finance yields a classic example of an important use of percentage change. On an investment of P dollars invested at an interest rate of $100r\%$ compounded *annually*, the dollar amount accumulated after t years is given by the interest formula

$$A = P(1 + r)^t \text{ dollars}$$

On an investment of P dollars invested at an interest rate of $100r\%$ compounded n times each year, the dollar amount accumulated after t years is given by the interest formula

$$A = P\left(1 + \frac{r}{n}\right)^{nt} \text{ dollars}$$

Suppose that $1000 is invested for one year in each of two accounts, one paying 6% compounded annually and the other paying 6% compounded monthly. The nominal rate or annual percentage rate (APR) for each investment is 6%.

When we write the formula for the amount in the account with interest paid annually, the exponential form is $A = 1000(1 + 0.06)^t = 1000(1.06)^t$. In one year, the amount accumulated in this account will increase by 6%. The percentage change is 6%. This percentage change of the accumulated amount is called the effective rate or annual percentage yield (APY).

For the investment with interest paid monthly, the annual percentage yield (APY) is slightly more than 6%; when we write the formula for the amount accumulated, we see the exponential form

$$A = 1000\left(1 + \frac{0.06}{12}\right)^{12t} = 1000(1.005)^{12t} \approx 1000(1.06168)^t$$

In one year, the amount accumulated in this account will increase by approximately 6.168%. The percentage change is 6.168%. For the investment with interest paid monthly, the annual percentage yield (APY) is slightly more than 6%.

When an investment has a nominal rate of $100r\%$ compounded n times during the year, the constant percentage change over the compounding period is $100\frac{r}{n}\%$. In the case of the investment with 6% APR compounded monthly, $\frac{0.06}{12} = 0.005 = 0.5\%$ is the constant percentage change over each 1-month period.

The following box summarizes our discussion of the general **compound interest formula**.

Compound Interest Formula

The amount accumulated in an account after t years when P dollars are invested at an annual interest rate of $100r\%$ compounded n times a year is

$$A = P\left(1 + \frac{r}{n}\right)^{nt} \text{ dollars}$$

The **nominal rate** or **annual percentage rate** (**APR**) is the percentage $100r\%$, and the percentage change of the amount accumulated over one compounding period is $100\frac{r}{n}\%$.

The **effective rate** or **annual percentage yield** (**APY**) is the percentage change of the amount accumulated over one year.

We illustrate the use of the general compound interest formula in Example 4.

EXAMPLE 4   *Using the Compound Interest Formula*

Suppose you are 25 years old and have $10,000 to invest for retirement.

a. What APR compounded monthly is needed for your money to grow to one million in 40 years?

b. What is the APY for this investment?

c. What are the annual and monthly percentage changes for this investment?

Solution

a. To answer the question posed, substitute 40 for t and 1,000,000 for $A(t)$ in the formula $A(t) = 10{,}000\left(1 + \frac{r}{12}\right)^{12t}$, and solve for r.

$$1{,}000{,}000 = 10{,}000\left(1 + \frac{r}{12}\right)^{12(40)}$$

Solving for r yields $r \approx 0.11568$.

An APR of approximately 11.57% compounded monthly is needed for $10,000 to grow to a million dollars in 40 years.

b. The APY that corresponds to the APR in part *a* is found by substituting the APR into the formula for $A(t)$ and rewriting in the form $A(t) = ab^t$.

$$A(t) = 10{,}000\left(1 + \frac{0.11568}{12}\right)^{12t} \approx 10{,}000(1.1220^t)$$

The APY is $(b - 1)100\% \approx 12.20\%$.

c. The annual percentage change in the amount of the investment is given by the APY, 12.20%. Because the interest is compounded monthly, the monthly percentage change in the amount of the investment is given by the APR divided by 12, or approximately 0.964%. ●

Even though the compound interest formula is a continuous function, it has a discrete interpretation because the amount changes only at the actual times of compounding. For instance, we can use the monthly compounding function $A(t) = 1000(1.06168^t)$ dollars after t years to find the amount of the investment at the end of the 3rd month of the 6th year by calculating $A(6.25) \approx \$1453.63$. (This value was calculated using the unrounded value of the base.) However, it would be incorrect to use $t = 6.2$ to calculate the amount in the account on the 14th day of the 3rd month of the 6th year, because interest is compounded monthly, not daily.

There is one well-known interest formula that has a continuous interpretation: the **continuously compounded interest** formula.

Continuously Compounded Interest Formula

The amount accumulated in an account after t years when P dollars are invested at a nominal rate (APR) of $100r\%$ compounded continuously is

$$A = Pe^{rt} \text{ dollars}$$

This formula is used to model situations where interest is considered to be compounded continuously. It arises as a direct result of considering what happens to the compound interest formula as compoundings occur more and more frequently. Given a 1-year period, the more often compounding occurs, the larger the number of compoundings n becomes. In order to consider compoundings to occur continuously, we must consider what happens as n becomes infinitely large. Numerically, it can be shown that $\lim_{n \to \infty} \left(1 + \frac{1}{n}\right)^n = e \approx 2.71828182846$. By using algebra, it can be shown that $\lim_{n \to \infty} P\left(1 + \frac{1}{n}\right)^{nt} = Pe^{rt}$. We will explore these limits numerically in the activities.

EXAMPLE 5   *Determining APR from APY for Continuous Compounding*

An investment that has interest compounded continuously has an APY of 9.2%. What is its APR?

Solution

For an investment of P dollars, we consider that we have a constant yearly percentage increase of 9.2%. We will use an exponential growth model with $a = P$ and $b = 1.092$. We model the amount in the investment with an initial deposit of P dollars as

$$A(t) = P(1.092^t) \text{ dollars after } t \text{ years, } t \geq 0$$

The APR for continuously compounded interest is represented by r in the formula $A = Pe^{rt}$. We set this expression equal to the formula for $A(t)$ and solve for r.

$$P(1.092^t) = Pe^{rt}$$

Solving for r yields $r \approx 0.0880$. The APR is approximately 8.8%. ●

When comparing compound interest investment opportunities, you should always consider annual percentage yields, because the nominal rates do not reflect the effect of the compounding periods.

EXAMPLE 6   *Comparing Annual Percentage Yields*

Consider three investment offers: an APR of 6.9% compounded annually, an APR of 6.8% compounded monthly, and an APR of 6.7% compounded continuously. Determine which investment offers the best annual percentage yield.

Solution

In order to compare the three investments, we must consider the percentage change of each over the same time interval. The easiest time interval to compare for all three investments will be a 1-year interval. We begin by writing a formula for each of the investments and converting those three formulas into the form $f(t) = ab^t$.

Investment Offer A: APR 6.9% compounded annually

$$A(t) = P(1 + 0.069)^t = P(1.069^t)$$

APY is 6.9%

Investment Offer B: APR 6.8% compounded monthly

$$B(t) = P\left(1 + \frac{0.068}{12}\right)^{12t} \approx P(1.07015^t)$$

APY is approximately 7.02%

Investment Offer C: APR 6.7% compounded continuously

$$C(t) = Pe^{0.067t} \approx P(1.06930^t)$$

APY is approximately 6.93%

The investment offer with the best annual percentage yield is Offer B, with an APR of 6.8% compounded monthly. ●

All three descriptions of change (change, percentage change, and average rate of change) discussed in this section are valuable, but the concept of average rate of change will be the bridge between the algebraic descriptions of change examined in this section and the calculus description of change that we begin exploring in the next section. The graphical interpretation of the average rate of change as a slope of a secant line will be particularly useful.

2.1   Concept Inventory

- Change
- Percentage change
- Average rate of change
- Secant line
- Slope of a secant line = average rate of change
- Descriptions of change
- Compound interest, APR, and APY

2.1   Activities

Getting Started

Rewrite the sentences in Activities 1 through 4 to express how rapidly, on average, the quantity changed over the given interval.

1. In five trading days, the stock price rose $2.30.

2. The nurse counted 32 heartbeats in 15 seconds.

3. The company lost $25,000 during the past 3 months.

4. The unemployment rate has risen 4 percentage points in the past 3 years.

For Activities 5 through 8, calculate the change, percentage change, and average rate of change over the interval specified. Write a sentence interpreting each description of change.

5. **Insurance**   In 2005 Northwest Airlines was the fourth-largest airline in the world. Northwest flew 55.4 million enplaned passengers during 2004 and 56.5 million enplaned passengers during 2005.
   (Source: Northwest Airlines, December 2005 Financial/Traffic Release.)

6. **Act Scores**   The national ACT college test composite average for females was 20.7 in 2002 and 20.9 in 2005.
   (Source: ACT, Inc.)

7. **Population**   The American Indian, Eskimo, and Aleut population in the United States was 362 thousand in 1930 and 2434 thousand in 2000.
   (Source: U.S. Bureau of the Census.)

8. **Internet**   The number of Internet users in China grew from 12 million in 2000 to 103 million in 2005.
   (Source: BDA (China), The Strategis Group and China Daily, July 22, 2005.)

Applying Concepts

9. **October Madness**

   a. On October 1, 1987, 193.2 million shares were traded on the stock market. On October 30, 1987, 303.4 million shares were traded. Find the percentage change and average rate of change in the number of shares traded per trading day between October 1 and October 30, 1987.

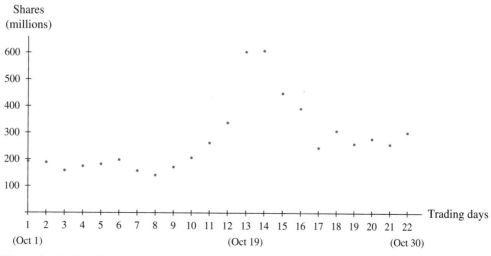

Figure for Activity 9

(Source: Phyllis S. Pierce, ed., *The Dow Jones Averages 1885–1990*, Homewood, IL: Business One Irwin, 1991.)

b. The scatter plot in the figure on page 107 shows the number of shares traded each day during October of 1987. On the scatter plot, sketch a line whose slope is the average rate of change between October 1 and October 30, 1987.

c. The behavior of the graph on October 19 and 20 has been referred to as "October Madness." Write a sentence describing how the number of shares traded changed throughout the month. How well does the average rate of change you found in part *a* reflect what occurred throughout the month?

10. Lake Level   The graph in the accompanying figure shows the highest elevations above sea level attained by Lake Tahoe (located on the California–Nevada border) from 1982 through 1996.

a. Sketch a secant line connecting the beginning and ending points of the graph. Find the slope of this line.

b. Write a sentence interpreting the slope in the context of Lake Tahoe levels.

c. Write a sentence summarizing how the level of the lake changed from 1982 through 1996. How well does your answer to part *b* describe the change in the lake level as shown in the graph?

11. Kelly Services   A graph of the equation for a model for the sales of services between 1991 and 2001 by Kelly Services, Inc., a leading global provider of staffing services, is shown below.

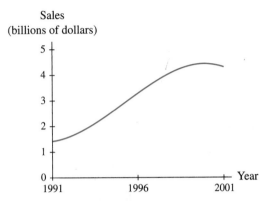

Sales
(billions of dollars)

(Source: Based on data from Kelly Services, Inc., Annual Reports, 1996–2001.)

a. Use the graph to estimate the average rate of change in Kelly's sales of services between 1996 and 2001. Interpret your answer.

b. Estimate the percentage change in the service sales between 1996 and 2001.

12. Marriage Age   The graph on page 109 shows the median age at first marriage for men in the United States.

a. Estimate by how much and how rapidly the median marriage age increased from 1980 through 1990.

Figure for Activity 10
(Source: Data from Federal Watermaster, U.S. Department of the Interior.)

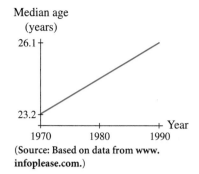

Median age (years)

(Source: Based on data from www. infoplease.com.)

b. What is true about the average rate of change between any two points on a linear graph?

c. The median age at first marriage for men in 2000 was 26.8 and in 2003 was 27.1. Did the median age of first marriage for men continue to grow at the same rate during the beginning of the twenty-first century as it did during the 1980s?

13. Profit   The table below gives the price, in dollars, of a round-trip flight from Denver to Chicago on a certain airline and the corresponding monthly profit, in millions of dollars, for that airline on that route.

Ticket price (dollars)	Profit (thousands of dollars)
200	3080
250	3520
300	3760
350	3820
400	3700
450	3380

a. Find a model for the data.

b. Use the model to estimate the average rate of change of profit when the ticket price rises from $200 to $350.

c. Use the model to estimate the average rate of change of profit when the ticket price rises from $350 to $450.

14. Cruise Tickets   A travel agent vigorously promotes cruises to Alaska for several months. The number of cruise tickets sold during the first week and the total (cumulative) sales every 3 weeks thereafter are given in the table.

Week	Total tickets sold
1	71
4	197
7	524
10	1253
13	2443
16	3660
19	4432
22	4785
25	4923

a. Find the first differences in the numbers of tickets sold, and convert them into average rates of change.

b. When were ticket sales growing most rapidly? How rapidly (on average) were they growing at that time?

c. If the travel agent made a $25 commission on every ticket sold, how rapidly on average did the agent's commission revenue increase between weeks 7 and 10?

15. Life Expectancy   The life expectancies of black males in the United States at various ages for 1998 are as shown in the following table.

Age (years)	Life expectancy (years)	Age (years)	Life expectancy (years)
At birth	68.3	40	32.3
10	59.6	50	24.3
20	50.0	60	17.5
30	41.1	70	11.8

(Source: *National Vital Statistics Reports*, vol. 49, no. 12, October 9, 2001.)

a. How rapidly (on average) does the life expectancy change between birth and the 70th year of life for black males in the United States?

b. Compare the average rates of change of life expectancy for the 10-year periods between ages 10 and 20 and ages 20 and 30.

16. Loan   The table shows the loan amount (the amount of money that a certain bank will lend) on the basis of a monthly payment of $600 per month with a 30-year term.

Monthly APR	Loan amount (thousand dollars)
6%	100
8%	81.7
10%	68.3
12%	58.3
14%	50.6

a. What are the units for the change, the average rate of change, and the percentage change in the loan amount when the interest rate changes?

b. Determine the change, the average rate of change, and the percentage change in the loan amount when interest rates increase from 8% to 12%.

c. Consider the inverse relationship represented by reversing the columns in the table. What are the input units and the output units of the inverse relationship? What are the units for the change, the average rate of change, and the percentage change of the inverse relationship?

d. Determine the change, the average rate of change, and the percentage change in the monthly APR when the loan amount increases from $58.3 thousand to $81.7 thousand.

17. Population   The population of Mexico between 1921 and 2000 is given by the model

Population $= 7.6(1.026^t)$ million persons

where t is the number of years since 1900.

(Source: Based on data from www.inegi.gob.mx, accessed 9/20/02.)

a. How much did the population change from 1940 through 1955? Convert the change to percentage change.

b. How rapidly was the population changing on average from 1983 through 1985?

18. AIDS   The number of persons living with AIDS from 1993 through 2001 can be modeled by

Cases diagnosed $= -1.51 + 2.15 \ln x$

hundred thousand cases

where x is the number of years since 1990.

a. How many more cases were diagnosed in 1997 than in 1995?

b. Find the percentage change and the average rate of change in cases diagnosed between 1995 and 1997.

(Source: Based on data from *HIV/AIDS Surveillance Report*, vol. 13, no. 2.)

19. Surcharges   The percentage of all banks that, between 1996 and 2001, levied surcharges on the use of automated teller machines can be modeled by the equation

$$s(t) = \frac{95.98}{1 + 24{,}612e^{-1.42t}} \text{ percent}$$

t years after 1990. Find the percentage change in the percent of banks assessing surcharges on ATMs between 1996 and 2001.

(Source: Based on data from U.S. Public Interest Research Group National Survey.)

20. Refuse CPI   The consumer price index (CPI) values $(1982 - 1984 = 100)$ for refuse collection between 1990 and 2000 can be modeled by the equation

$$R(t) = 133 + 54.5 \ln t$$

t years after 1988. Find the average rate of change in the CPI values for refuse collection between 1992 and 2000.

(Source: Based on data from *Statistical Abstract*, 1998.)

21. Consider the linear function $y = 3x + 4$.

a. Find the average rate of change of y over each of the following intervals:

   i. From $x = 1$ to $x = 3$

   ii. From $x = 3$ to $x = 6$

   iii. From $x = 6$ to $x = 10$

b. Find the percentage change in y for each of the following intervals:

   i. From $x = 1$ to $x = 3$

   ii. From $x = 3$ to $x = 5$

   iii. From $x = 5$ to $x = 7$

c. On the basis of the results in part *a* and your knowledge of linear functions from Chapter 1, what generalizations can you make about percentage change and average rate of change for a linear function?

22. Consider the exponential function $y = 3(0.4^x)$.

    a. Find the percentage change and average rate of change of y for each of the following intervals:

        i. From $x = 1$ to $x = 3$

        ii. From $x = 3$ to $x = 5$

        iii. From $x = 5$ to $x = 7$

    b. On the basis of the results in part *a* and your knowledge of exponential functions from Chapter 1, what generalizations can you make about percentage change and average rate of change for an exponential function?

23. Bank Account   Imagine that 6 years ago you invested $1400 in an account with a fixed interest rate and with interest compounded continuously.

You do not remember the interest rate, but your end-of-the-year statements for the first 5 years yield the data shown in the table.

End of year	Amount at end of year
1	$1489.55
2	$1584.82
3	$1686.19
4	$1794.04
5	$1908.80

    a. Use the data to find the change and percentage change in the balance from the end of year 1 through the end of year 5.

    b. Use the data to find the average rate of change of the balance from the end of year 1 through the end of year 5. Interpret your answer.

    c. Using the data, is it possible to find the average rate of change in the balance from the middle of the fourth year through the end of the fourth year? Explain how this could be done or why it cannot be done.

    d. Find a model for the data, and use the equation to find the average rate of change in the balance over the last half of the fourth year.

24. Births   The multiple-birth rate for births involving more than twins jumped 19.7% between 1995 and 1996 and 312.4% between 1980 and 1996.

    a. If the birth rate for births involving three or more babies was 152.6 per 100,000 births in 1996, find the multiple-birth rates in 1995 and 1980.

    b. Use the information presented in the table to find a model for the multiple-birth rate between 1971 and 2000.

Year	Multiple-birth rate (births per 100,000)
1971	29.1
1976	31.7
1981	39.4
1986	49.9
1991	80.2
1996	152.6
2000	180.5

(Sources: *Greenville News,* July 1, 1998, p. A1; *National Vital Statistics Reports,* vol. 50, no. 5, February 12, 2002.)

    c. Use the equation to estimate the multiple-birth rates in 1995 and 1980. How close are those values to the results of part *a*? Are these estimates found with interpolation or extrapolation?

    d. Suggest reasons why the multiple-birth rate has been rising rapidly.

25. Finance Charge   Your credit card statement indicates a finance charge of 1.5% per month on the outstanding balance.

    a. What is the nominal rate (APR), assuming that interest is compounded monthly?

    b. What is the effective rate of interest (APY)?

26. Payments   In order to offset college expenses, at the beginning of your freshman year you obtained a nonsubsidized student loan for $15,000. Interest on this loan accrues at a rate of 0.739% each month. However, you do not have to make any payments against either the principal or the interest until after you graduate.

    a. Write a function giving the total amount you will owe after t years in college.

    b. What is the nominal rate?

    c. What is the effective rate?

27. Doubling Time   How long would it take an investment to double under each of the following conditions?

    a. Interest is 6.3% compounded monthly.

    b. Interest is 8% compounded continuously.

    c. Interest is 6.85% compounded quarterly.

28. Investment   You have $1000 to invest, and you have two options: 4.725% compounded semiannually or 4.675% compounded continuously.

  a. Determine the better option by calculating the annual percentage yield for each.

  b. Verify your choice of option by comparing the amount the first option would yield with the amount the second option would yield after 2, 5, 10, 15, 25, and 50 years. Does your choice of option depend on the number of years you leave the money invested?

  c. By how much would the two options differ after 10 years?

29. Interest   Suppose that you invest $1 for 1 year at a rate of 100% compounded n times during the year.

  a. Use the compound interest formula to develop a function for the amount at the end of 1 year given n, the number of compoundings.

  b. Fill in the values of n on the following table.

Compounding	n	Amount
Yearly		
Semiannually		
Quarterly		
Monthly		
Weekly		
Daily		
Every hour		
Every minute		
Every second		

  c. Use the formula from part a to fill in the Amount column of the table. (Round values to two decimal places.)

  d. According to the table, what is the limit of the amount as n grows larger and larger?

  e. Write the limit found in part d in mathematical notation.

30. Interest   Suppose that you invest $1 for 1 year at a rate of $100r$% compounded n times during the year.

  a. Use the compound interest formula to develop a function for the amount at the end of 1 year. (*Hint*: n and r will both appear as variables in the formula.)

  b. Suppose $r = 0.1$ and create a table that shows n and the amount at the end of 1 year for the following compounding options: yearly, semiannually, quarterly, monthly, weekly, daily, every hour, every minute, and every second. (Round the amount to four decimal places.)

  c. According to your table, what is the limit of the amount as the number of compoundings becomes larger and larger?

  d. Use the information for this account and the continuous compounding interest formula to calculate the amount at the end of 1 year. How does your answer here compare to your estimate in part c?

  e. Repeat parts b through d for $r = 0.5$.

Discussing Concepts

31. Explain how average rate of change, percentage change, and change are related and how they differ.

32. Give a graphical interpretation of change and average rate of change.

2.2   Instantaneous Rates of Change

In Section 2.1 we considered the average rate of change over an interval. Now we consider the concept of the rate of change at a point. The most common example of an instantaneous rate of change is as close as the nearest steering wheel. Suppose that you begin driving north on highway I-81 at the Pennsylvania–New York border at 1:00 P.M. As you drive, you note the time at which you pass each of the indicated mile markers (see Table 2.2).

TABLE 2.2

Time	Mile marker
1:00 P.M.	0
1:17 P.M.	19
1:39 P.M.	42
1:54 P.M.	56
2:03 P.M.	66
2:25 P.M.	80
2:45 P.M.	105

These data can be used to determine average rates of change. For example, between mile 0 and mile 19, the average rate of change of distance is 67.1 mph. In this context, the average rate of change is simply the average speed of the car. Average speed between any of the mile markers in the table can be determined in a similar manner. Average speed will not, however, answer the following question:

> If the speed limit is 65 mph and a highway patrol officer with a radar gun clocks your speed at mile post 17, were you exceeding the speed limit by more than 10 mph?

The only way to answer this question is to know your speed at the instant that the radar locked onto your car. This speed is the **instantaneous rate of change** of distance with respect to time, and your car's speedometer measures that speed in miles per hour.

Just as an average rate of change measures the slope between two points, an instantaneous rate of change measures the slope at a single point. Figure 2.7 shows a continuous graph of air temperature as a function of time.

FIGURE 2.7

The graph reaches its peak value at approximately 1:15 P.M. Reading from left to right, the graph is rising until it reaches its peak at 1:15 P.M. and then is falling after

1:15 P.M. When we read the graph from left to right, it appears that the graph is slanted upward until we reach the peak and then slanted downward. We say that the slope of the graph is positive at each point on the left side of the peak and is negative at each point on the right side. The slope of the graph is zero at the top of the parabola. Note that the graph levels off as you move from 7 A.M. to 1:15 P.M. It is not as steep at 1 P.M. as it is at 7 A.M., so the slope at 1 P.M. is smaller than the slope at 7 A.M. In fact, at each point on the graph there is a different slope, and we need to be able to measure that slope in order to find the instantaneous rate of change at each point.

Instantaneous Rate of Change

The **instantaneous rate of change** at a point on a curve is the slope of the curve at that point.

In precalculus mathematics, the concept of slope is intrinsically linked with lines. In terms of lines, slope is a measure of the tilt of a line. Now we wish to measure how tilted any graph is at a point. We can consider the slope of a graph at a point as long as the graph is continuous and not sharp at that point. Intuitively, a continuous curve contains a *sharp point* when the pattern of the curve suddenly changes at that point. We call a continuous function **smooth** over an interval if it has no sharp points in the interval.

Local Linearity and Tangent Lines

For any smooth, continuous graph, we will eventually see a line as we look closer and closer. For example, consider the temperature graph in Figure 2.7. With the number of hours after 6 A.M. as input, close-ups of the graph 1/100 unit away from each labeled point in both horizontal and vertical directions are as shown in Figure 2.8.

FIGURE 2.8

The graphs in Figure 2.8 illustrate the principle of **local linearity.** As we zoom in on a point P on a smooth (no sharp points), continuous curve, the curve will look more and more like a line. We call this line the **tangent line,** and its slope is the instantaneous rate of change of the curve at the point P, the **point of tangency.** A tangent line (from the Latin word *tangere*, "to touch") at a point on a graph touches that point and is tilted exactly the way the graph is tilted at the point of tangency. The slope of the tangent line at a point is a measure of the slope of the graph at that point.

> ## Local Linearity
>
> If we look closely enough near any point on a smooth curve, the curve will look like a line. The line is the tangent line at that point.

The tangent lines at points *A*, *B*, and *C* are shown in Figure 2.9. Do you see that these are the same as the lines in Figure 2.8?

> The slope of a graph at a point is the slope of the tangent line at that point.

In Figure 2.10, tangent lines are drawn on the temperature graph at 7 A.M., noon, and 4 P.M. The tangent lines are tilted to match the tilt of the graph at each point. The tangent lines at points *D* and *E* are tilted up, so the slope at these points is positive. The slope at point *F* is negative, because the tangent line at point *F* is tilted down. Even though the tangent line at point *F* has the least slope of these three tangents, it is *steeper* than the tangent line at point *E* because the magnitude (absolute value) of its slope is larger than that of the line tangent to the curve at point *E*. That is, the temperature is falling more rapidly at 4 P.M. than it is rising at noon.

FIGURE 2.9

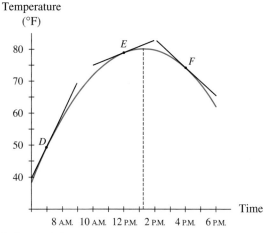

FIGURE 2.10

Examine Figure 2.10 carefully. The slope of the tangent line at point *D* is 10°F per hour. (A method for calculating this slope will be discussed later.) Therefore, the slope of the graph at 7 A.M. is also 10°F per hour. This is the same as saying that the instantaneous rate of change of the temperature at 7 A.M. is 10°F per hour. In other words, at 7 A.M., the temperature is rising 10°F per hour.

Similarly, the following statements can be made:

- The slope of the tangent line at point E is 2°F per hour.
- The slope of the graph at noon is 2°F per hour.
- The instantaneous rate of change of the temperature at noon is 2°F per hour.
- At noon, the temperature is rising 2°F per hour.

And

- The slope of the tangent line at point F is $-4.4°$F per hour.
- The slope of the graph at 4 P.M. is $-4.4°$F per hour.
- The instantaneous rate of change of the temperature at 4 P.M. is $-4.4°$F per hour.
- At 4 P.M., the temperature is falling 4.4°F per hour.

We summarize the results of this discussion in the following way:

> Given a function f and a point P on the graph of f, the instantaneous rate of change at point P is the slope of the graph at P and is the slope of the line tangent to the graph at P (provided the slope exists).

EXAMPLE 1   *Comparing Slopes*

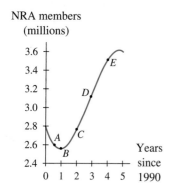

NRA members (millions)

Years since 1990

FIGURE 2.11

NRA Membership   Figure 2.11 shows the National Rifle Association membership between 1990 and 1995. Consider the following statements:

- The slope of the line tangent to the graph at A is -0.24 million members per year.
- The slope of the graph is zero at point B.
- The instantaneous rate of change of the NRA membership at point C is 340,000 members per year.
- NRA membership is increasing the most rapidly at point D. The greatest rate of increase is 0.42 million members per year.
- The slope of the line tangent to the graph at point E is 260,000 members per year.

Using this information, answer the following questions:

a. At which of the indicated points is the slope of the graph (i) the greatest? (ii) the least?

b. At which of the indicated points is the steepness of the graph (i) the greatest? (ii) the least?

c. What is the instantaneous rate of change of the NRA membership at point A? at point E?

d. What is the slope of the tangent line at point C? at point D?

Solution

a. The numerical values of the slopes, in million members per year, at the indicated points are

$$A:-0.24 \quad B:0 \quad C:0.34 \quad D:0.42 \quad E:0.26$$

The greatest value occurs at point D (the inflection point), and the least value occurs where the only negative slope occurs, at point A.

b. The steepness of the graph is a measure of how much the graph is tilted at a particular point. The direction of tilt is considered in the slope but is not considered when we are describing steepness. Thus the steepness at each of the indicated points is

$$A:0.24 \quad B:0 \quad C:0.34 \quad D:0.42 \quad E:0.26$$

The graph is steepest at point D. The steepness is least at point B.

c. The instantaneous rate of change at A is -0.24 million, or $-240{,}000$, members per year. At E the rate of change is 0.26 million, or $260{,}000$, members per year.

d. The slope of the tangent line at C is 0.34 million members per year. The slope at D is 0.42 million members per year. ●

Secant and Tangent Lines

In addition to understanding tangent lines in terms of local linearity, it is helpful to understand the relationship between secant lines and tangent lines.

Recall that a tangent line at a point on a graph touches that point and is tilted exactly the way the graph is tilted at that point. A secant line, on the other hand, is a line that passes through two points on a graph. We illustrate the relationship between secant lines and tangent lines with an example using points on a simple curve.

EXAMPLE 2   *Drawing Secant and Tangent Lines*

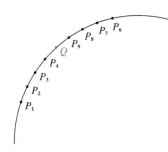

FIGURE 2.12

a. On the curve shown in Figure 2.12, draw secant lines through P_1 and Q, P_2 and Q, P_3 and Q, and P_4 and Q.

b. Which of the four secant lines drawn in part *a* appears to be tilted most like the curve at Q?

c. Again, on the curve shown in Figure 2.12, draw secant lines through P_6 and Q, P_7 and Q, P_8 and Q, and P_9 and Q. Which of these four secant lines appears to match most closely the tilt of the curve at Q?

d. Where could you place a point P_5 so that the secant line through P_5 and Q would be even closer than the secant lines in parts *a* and *c* to tilting the same way the curve does at Q?

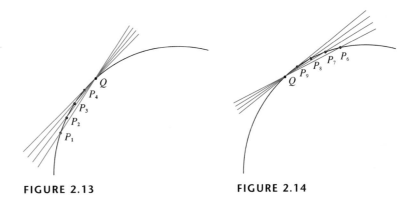

FIGURE 2.13   **FIGURE 2.14**

Solution

a. The four secant lines are shown in Figure 2.13.

b. The secant line through P_4 and Q appears almost to hide the curve near Q. That is, it appears to match the tilt of the curve at Q better than any of the other three secant lines.

c. The four secant lines are shown in Figure 2.14. Again, we see that the secant line through Q and the point closest to Q (P_9 in this case) appears to match the tilt of the curve at Q most closely.

d. The point P_5 should be placed even closer to Q than P_4 and P_9 in order for the tilt of the secant line to match the tilt of the curve at Q more closely.   ●

We generalize the results of Example 2 by saying that the tilt of the secant line through P and Q becomes closer and closer to the tilt of the curve at Q as P becomes closer and closer to Q. Indeed, if you draw a secant line through the point Q and a point P on the curve near Q, then the closer P is to Q, the more closely the secant line approximates the tangent line at Q. You can think of the tangent line at Q as the limiting position of the secant lines between P and Q as P gets closer and closer to Q.

Line Tangent to a Curve

The tangent line at a point Q on a smooth, continuous graph is the limiting position of the secant lines between point Q and a point P as P approaches Q along the graph (if the limiting position exists).

Sketching Tangent Lines

Although thinking of a tangent line as a limiting position of secant lines is vital to your understanding of calculus (and is a subject to which we will return), it is important for you to have an intuitive feel for tangent lines and to be able to sketch them without first drawing secant lines. In drawing a line with the same tilt as a curve at a point, you will find that in general, the line lies very close to the curve near the point but does not cut through the curve.

(a) If the curve is *concave up* at the point of tangency, then the tangent line will lie *below* the curve near the point of tangency.

General Rule for Tangent Lines

Lines tangent to a smooth nonlinear curve do not "cut through" the graph of the curve at the point of tangency and lie completely on *one side* of the graph near the point of tangency except at an inflection point.

(b) If the curve is *concave down* at the point of tangency, then the tangent line will lie *above* the curve near the point of tangency.

FIGURE 2.15

It is important to note that for the graph of a linear function, the only way to draw a line tangent to the graph at any point is to draw again the graph of the linear function.

Drawing a line tangent to a curve at an inflection point is dealt with after Example 3. For cases in which this exception does not apply, we can determine on which side of the curve the tangent line should lie by noting the concavity. If the curve is concave up at the point of tangency, then the tangent line will lie below the curve near the point of tangency. If the curve is concave down at the point of tangency, then the tangent line will lie above the curve near the point of tangency. See Figure 2.15.

EXAMPLE 3 *Using a Tangent Line to Estimate Slope*

Weight Loss A woman joins a national weight-loss program and begins to chart her weight on a weekly basis. Figure 2.16 shows the graph of a continuous function of her weight from the time when she began the program through 7 weeks into the program.

FIGURE 2.16

a. Carefully sketch a line tangent to the curve at 5 weeks.

b. Estimate the slope of the tangent line at 5 weeks.

c. How quickly was the woman's weight declining 5 weeks after the beginning of the program?

d. What is the slope of the curve at 5 weeks?

Solution

a.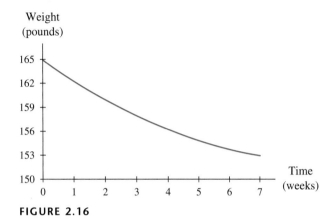

FIGURE 2.17

b. Slope $= \dfrac{\text{rise}}{\text{run}} \approx \dfrac{-5 \text{ pounds}}{4 \text{ weeks}} = -1.25$ pounds per week (See Figure 2.17.)

c. The woman's weight was declining by approximately 1.25 pounds per week after 5 weeks in the program.

d. The slope of the curve at 5 weeks is approximately -1.25 pounds per week. ●

As we mentioned in the general rule for tangent lines, there are exceptions to the principle that tangent lines do not cut through the graph and lie on only one side of the graph. At a point of inflection, the graph is concave up on one side and concave down on the other. As you might expect, the tangent line lies above the concave-down portion of the graph and below the concave-up part. To do this, the tangent line must cut through the graph. It does so at the point of inflection. When drawing tangent lines at inflection points, be careful to make sure that the tangent line is tilted to match the tilt of the graph at the point of tangency. See Figure 2.18.

FIGURE 2.18   **(a) Although this line lies above the concave-down portion and below the concave-up part of the graph, it is not a tangent line because it is not tilted in the same way that the graph is tilted at the point.**   **(b) This tangent line is correctly drawn at an inflection point.**

Where Does the Instantaneous Rate of Change Exist?

Our discussion of tangent lines would not be complete without mention of piecewise continuous functions. A **piecewise continuous function** is a function that is continuous over different intervals but has a break point. It is often defined by different equations over the different intervals. Consider Figure 2.19, which shows the population of Indiana by official census from 1950 through 2000.

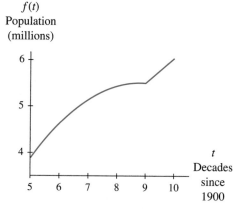

FIGURE 2.19

(Source: Based on data from *World Almanac and Book of Facts,* ed. William A. McGeveran, Jr., New York: World Almanac Education Group, Inc., 2003.)

The equation of the graph in Figure 2.19 is

$$f(t) = \begin{cases} -0.129t^2 + 2.2t - 3.88 \text{ million people} & \text{when } 5 \leq t < 9 \\ 0.536t + 0.72 \text{ million people} & \text{when } 9 \leq t \leq 10 \end{cases}$$

where t is the number of decades after 1900.

Consider the tangent line at the point where the function f is not continuous (1990). If we use the idea of a limiting position of secant lines, then we must conclude that we cannot draw a line tangent to the graph at $t = 9$ because the graph jumps at this input.

In fact, if we zoom in close to the point at $t = 9$, then we see something similar to Figure 2.20. In this case, we do not have a smooth curve, and we see two lines. Again we conclude that there is no tangent line at $t = 9$. Does this mean that there is no instantaneous rate of change in the population of Indiana in 1990? No, it simply means that we cannot use our piecewise continuous model to calculate the rate of change in 1990. If it is necessary to determine the instantaneous rate of change at 1990 (the break point), it would be advisable either to use a secant line estimate (an average rate of change) or, if possible, to re-model the data with a function that would be continuous and smooth at this point.

To help clarify the relationship between continuous and noncontinuous functions and rates of change, consider the graphs shown in Figure 2.21. The graph in Figure 2.21a is continuous everywhere and has a rate of change at every point. You may think that the same is true of the graph in Figure 2.21b; however, because a tangent line drawn at P is vertical, the slope of the tangent line is undefined. The graph in Figure 2.21c is also continuous; however, the graph is not smooth at P because of the sharp point there. We call a point P on the graph of a continuous function a **sharp point** when secant lines joining P to close points on either side of it have different limiting positions. That is, we cannot draw a tangent line at P, because secant lines drawn with points on the right and left do not approach the same slope.

FIGURE 2.20

  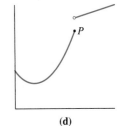

(a)   (b)   (c)   (d)

FIGURE 2.21

The graph in Figure 2.21d has a break at P and, therefore, is not continuous at P. This graph is similar to that of the Indiana population graph, and the slope does not exist at the break in the function. The slope does exist at all other points on the graph.

The graph in Figure 2.21d illustrates a general rule relating continuity and rates of change.

> Unless a function is continuous and smooth at a point, the instantaneous rate of change does not exist at that point.

If you keep in mind the relationships among instantaneous rates of change, slopes of tangent lines, slopes of secant lines, and local linearity, then you should have little difficulty determining the times when the instantaneous rate of change does not exist.

Recall from our discussion in Chapter 1 that calculus is applied to continuous portions of functions. As we have just seen, instantaneous rates of change do not exist where a function is not continuous. Modeling is a tool by which we transform data into a continuous function. Discrete data are useful for finding change, percentage change, and average rates of change, but a continuous or piecewise continuous function is necessary in order to find instantaneous rates of change.

2.2   Concept Inventory

- Instantaneous rate of change
- Local linearity
- Tangent line
- Slope of tangent line = instantaneous rate of change
- Slope and steepness of a tangent line
- The tangent line is the limiting position of secant lines
- Tangent lines lie beneath a concave-up graph
- Tangent lines lie above a concave-down graph
- Situations in which the instantaneous rate of change does not exist

2.2   Activities

Getting Started

1. In your own words, describe the difference between
   a. discrete and continuous.
   b. average rate of change and instantaneous rate of change.
   c. secant lines and tangent lines.

2. What are some advantages of using a continuous model instead of discrete data? What are some disadvantages?

3. How are average rates of change and instantaneous rates of change measured graphically?

4. Explain in your own words how to tell visually whether a line is tangent to a smooth graph.

5. Using Table 2.2, the time/mileage table given in this section, verify that the average speed of the car from mile marker 0 to mile marker 19 is 67.1 mph.

6. Use Table 2.2 to answer the following questions.
   a. What is the average speed (in mph) from:
      i. milepost 66 to milepost 80?
      ii. milepost 80 to milepost 105?
   b. What might account for the difference in speed?

7. Use the accompanying graph to answer the following questions.

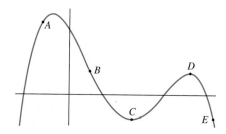

   a. At each labeled point on the graph, determine whether the instantaneous rate of change is positive, negative, or zero.
   b. Is the graph steeper at point *A* or at point *B*?

8. At each labeled point on the graph, determine whether the slope is positive, negative, or zero.

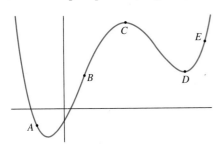

9. Consider the accompanying graph.

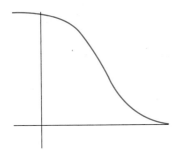

Estimate where the output is falling most rapidly. Mark that point on the graph.

10. Consider the accompanying graph.

Estimate where the slope is greatest. Mark that point on the graph.

For the figures in Activities 11 through 14, discuss the slopes of the graphs.

11.

12.

13.

14.

15. Which of the lines drawn on the graph are *not* tangent lines?

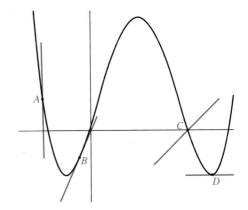

16. Which of the lines drawn on the graph are *not* tangent lines?

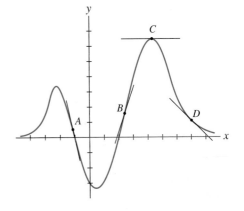

17. On the graph, draw secant lines through P_1 and Q, P_2 and Q, and P_3 and Q. Repeat for the points P_4 and Q, P_5 and Q, and P_6 and Q. Then draw the tangent line at Q.

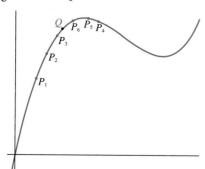

18. Draw secant lines through P_1 and Q, P_2 and Q, and P_3 and Q on the graph. Repeat for the points P_4 and Q, P_5 and Q, and P_6 and Q. Then draw the tangent line at Q.

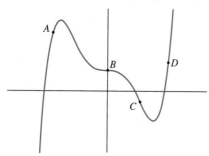

19. a. Is the graph shown concave up, concave down, or neither (an inflection point) at A, B, C, and D?

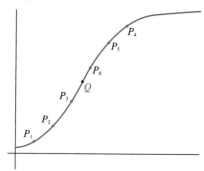

b. Should the tangent lines lie above or below the curve at each of the indicated points?

c. Carefully draw tangent lines at the labeled points on the figure.

d. At which of the labeled points is the slope of the tangent line positive? At which of the labeled points is the slope of the tangent line negative?

20. a. Is the accompanying graph concave up, concave down, or neither at A, B, C, and D?

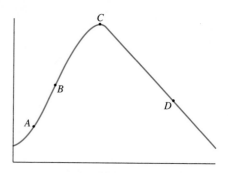

b. Should the tangent lines lie above or below the curve at each of the indicated points?

c. Carefully draw tangent lines at the labeled points.

d. At which of the labeled points is the slope of the curve positive? At which of the labeled points is the slope of the curve negative? Do any of the labeled points appear to be inflection points?

Use carefully drawn tangent lines to estimate the slopes at the labeled points in Activities 21 through 24.

21.

22.

23.

24.

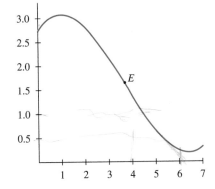

Applying Concepts

25. Subscribers The graph shows the total number of cellular phone subscribers from 1996 to 2001. The slope of the graph at point A is 23.1.

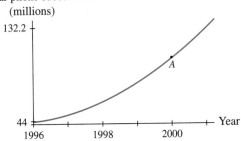

(Source: Based on data from the Cellular Telecommunications and Internet Association.)

a. What are the units on the slope at point A?

b. How rapidly was the number of subscribers growing in 2000?

c. What is the slope of the tangent line at A?

d. What was the instantaneous rate of change of the number of cell phone subscribers in 2000?

26. Phone Bill The graph shows the average monthly cellular phone bill since 1987. The slope of the curve at point A is −0.23.

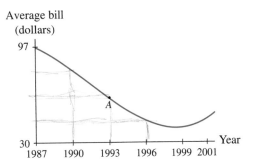

(Source: Based on data from the Cellular Telecommunications and Internet Association.)

a. What should be the units on the slope at point A?

b. How rapidly was the dollar amount growing in 1993?

c. What is the slope of the tangent line at point A?

d. What is the instantaneous rate of change of the amount at point A?

27. Growth Rate The growth of a pea seedling as a function of time can be modeled by two quadratic functions as shown. The slopes at the labeled points are (in ascending order) −4.2, 1.3, and 5.9.

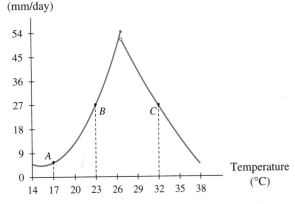

(Source: Based on data in George L. Clarke, *Elements of Ecology*, New York: Wiley, 1954.)

a. Match the slopes with the points, A, B, and C.

b. What are the units on the slopes for each of these points?

c. How quickly is the growth rate changing with respect to temperature at 23°C?

d. What is the slope of the tangent line at 32°C?

e. What is the instantaneous rate of change of the growth rate of pea seedlings at 17°C?

28. Beetles The graph shows the survival rate (percentage surviving) of three stages in the development of a flour beetle (egg, pupa, and larva) as a function of the relative humidity.

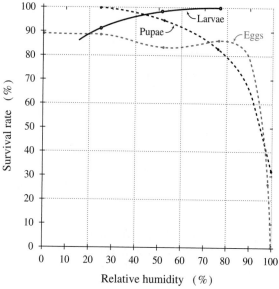

(Source: R.N. Chapman, *Animal Ecology*, New York: McGraw-Hill, 1931.)

In parts *a* through *g*, fill in each of the following blanks with the appropriate stage (eggs, pupae, or larvae).

a. At 60% relative humidity, the instantaneous rate of change of the survival rate of _____ is approximately zero.

b. An increase in relative humidity improves the survival rate of _____ and reduces the survival rate of _____.

c. At 97% relative humidity, the survival rate of _____ is declining faster than that of _____.

d. Any tangent lines drawn on the survival curve for _____ will have negative slope.

e. Any tangent lines drawn on the survival curve for _____ will have positive slope.

f. At 30% relative humidity, the survival rates for _____ and _____ are changing at approximately the same rate.

g. At 65% relative humidity, the survival curves for _____ and _____ have approximately the same slope.

29. Sun Declination The figure shows a graph of the declination of the sun (the angle of the sun from the equator) throughout the year.

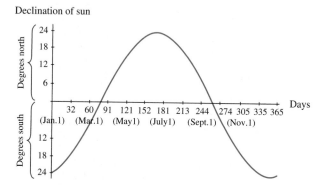

(Source: *The Mathematics Teacher*, March 1997, p. 238.)

a. A *solstice* is a time when the angle of the sun from the equator is greatest. Locate the summer and winter solstices on the graph. What is the slope of the graph at these points?

b. Locate the two steepest points on the graph. Estimate the slopes of the tangent lines at these two points. What is the significance of a negative slope in this context?

30. Grasshoppers The effects of temperature on the percentage of grasshoppers' eggs from West Australia that hatch are shown in the graph.

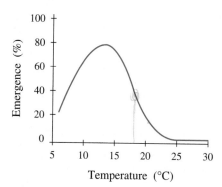

(Source: Figure adapted from George L. Clarke, *Elements of Ecology*, New York: Wiley, 1954.)

a. What is the optimum hatching temperature?

b. What is the slope of the tangent line at the optimum temperature?

c. Sketch tangent lines at 10°C, 17°C, and 22°C, and estimate the slopes at these points.

d. Where does the inflection point appear to be on this graph?

31. Population Predictions for the U.S. resident population from 1997 through 2050, as reported by *Statistical Abstract* for 1994, can be approximated by the model

$$p(t) = 2.37t + 39.79 \text{ million people}$$

where t is the number of years since 1900. A graph of p is shown.

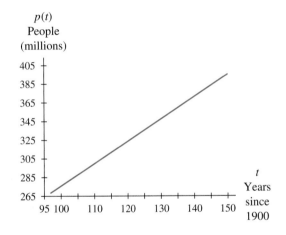

a. Sketch a tangent line at $t = 120$, and find its slope.

b. What is true about any line tangent to the graph of the function p?

c. What is the slope of any line tangent to this graph?

d. What is the slope at every point on the graph of this model?

e. According to the model, what is the instantaneous rate of change of the predicted population in any year from 1997 through 2050?

32. Population Predictions for the U.S. resident population from 2001 through 2050, as reported by

Statistical Abstract for 2001, can be approximated by the model

$$P(x) = 2.56x + 274.72 \text{ million people}$$

where x is the number of years since 2000.

a. Compare the model in this activity with the one in Activity 31. With the additional information about population available in *Statistical Abstract* for 2001, were the population projections adjusted up or down?

b. Was the growth rate adjusted up or down?

c. Find the slope of the graph of P at $t = 20$.

d. Describe the tangent line at $t = 20$.

e. How rapidly does the model predict the population will be changing in 2020?

33. Employees The number of Houghton Mifflin Company employees from 1993 through 2000 can be modeled by the accompanying graph.

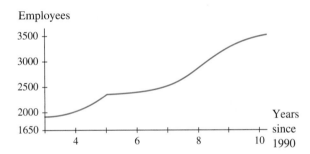

(**Source:** *Hoover's Online Company Capsules.*)

Draw tangent lines, if possible, to estimate how quickly the number of employees was changing in the indicated years. If it is impossible to do so, explain why.

a. 1994

b. 1995

c. 1998

34. Employment The graph on page 128 shows employment in Slovakia from 1948 through 1988.

a. Estimate how rapidly employment in agriculture and forestry was declining in 1958.

b. Estimate the instantaneous rate of change in industry employment in 1962.

c. Why is it not possible to sketch a tangent line to the industry graph at 1974?

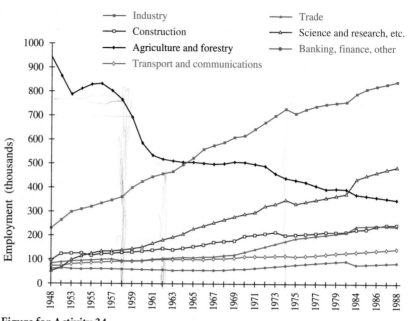

Figure for Activity 34

(Source: Figure from A. Smith, "From Convergence to Fragmentation," *Environment and Planning,* vol. 28, 1996. Pion Limited, London. Reprinted by permission. Data elaborated from *Statisticka rŏ centa* SUSR, various dates.)

Discussing Concepts

35. Explain, using your own words, the relationship between secant lines and tangent lines.

36. Most piecewise continuous models have discontinuities at their break points. Consider, however, piecewise continuous functions that are continuous at their break points. Is it possible to draw a tangent line at a break point for such a function? Discuss how and why this might or might not happen. You may find it helpful to use these two functions as examples:

$$f(x) = \begin{cases} -x^2 + 8 & \text{when } x \le 2 \\ x^3 - 9x + 14 & \text{when } x > 2 \end{cases}$$

$$g(x) = \begin{cases} x^3 + 9 & \text{when } x \le 3 \\ 5x^2 - 3x & \text{when } x > 3 \end{cases}$$

2.3   Derivative Notation and Numerical Estimates

Derivative Terminology and Notation

By now, you should be comfortable with the concepts of average rate of change and instantaneous rate of change. Let's summarize the differences between these two rates of change.

Average Rates of Change

- measure how rapidly (on average) a quantity changes over an interval
- can be obtained by calculating the slope of the secant line between two points
- require data points or a continuous curve to calculate

Instantaneous Rates of Change

- measure how rapidly a quantity is changing at a point
- can be obtained by calculating the slope of the tangent line at a single point
- require a continuous, smooth curve to calculate

Because instantaneous rates of change are so important in calculus, we commonly refer to them simply as **rates of change.** The calculus term for instantaneous rate of change is **derivative.** It is important to understand that the following phrases are equivalent.

Equivalent Terminology

All of the following phrases have the same meaning:

- instantaneous rate of change
- rate of change
- slope of the curve
- slope of the tangent line
- derivative

Even though we consider all these phrases synonymous, we must keep in mind that the last three phrases have specific mathematical definitions and so may not exist at a point on a function. However, the rate of change of the underlying situation does have an interpretation at that point in context. In such cases, we have to estimate the rate of change by using some other estimation technique.

There are also several symbolic notations that are commonly used to represent the rate of change of a continuous function f with input t. In this book, we use three different, but equivalent, symbolic notations:

Equivalent Notation

$\dfrac{df}{dt}$ This is read, "*d-f-d-t*," "*the rate of change of f with respect to t,*" or "*the derivative of f with respect to t.*"

(or)

$f'(t)$ This is read, "*f prime of t,*" or "*the rate of change of f with respect to t,*" or "*the derivative of f with respect to t.*"

(or)

$\dfrac{d}{dt}[f(t)]$ This is read, "*d-d-t of f of t,*" "*the rate of change of f with respect to t,*" or "*the derivative of f with respect to t.*"

Suppose that $G(t)$ is your grade out of 100 points on the next calculus test when you study t hours during the week before the test. The graph of G may look like that shown in Figure 2.22.

Note how the grade changes as your studying time increases. The grade slowly improves during the first 2 hours. The longer you study, the more rapidly the grade improves until you have studied for approximately 7 hours. After 7 hours, the grade improves at a slower rate. Your grade peaks after 14 hours of studying and then actually declines. What might explain the decline?

Let us compare the rates at which your grade is increasing when $t = 1$ hour and when $t = 4$ hours of study. Tangent lines at $t = 1$ and $t = 4$ are shown in Figure 2.23. After 1 hour of studying, your grade is increasing at a rate of approximately 1.7 points per hour. (We will show you how to calculate, not estimate, this rate in a later section.) This value is the slope of the curve when $t = 1$ hour. After 4 hours of studying, your grade is increasing at a rate of approximately 5.2 points per hour. Can you see that the graph is steeper when $t = 4$ than when $t = 1$? The grade is improving more rapidly after 4 hours of studying than it is after 1 hour. In other words, a small amount of additional study is more beneficial when you have already studied for 4 hours than it is when you have studied for only 1 hour.

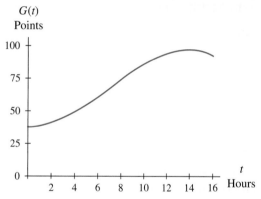

FIGURE 2.22

FIGURE 2.23   Tangent lines at $t = 1$ and $t = 4$

These rates can be summarized with the following notation:

$$\frac{dG}{dt} = 1.7 \text{ points per hour when } t = 1 \text{ hour, or}$$

$$G'(1) = 1.7 \text{ points per hour, and}$$

$$\frac{dG}{dt} = 5.2 \text{ points per hour when } t = 4 \text{ hours, or}$$

$$G'(4) = 5.2 \text{ points per hour.}$$

Interpreting Derivatives

As we have already mentioned, mathematical results are not very useful in real-world settings unless they are stated in a form that anyone can understand. For this reason, an **interpretation** of a result should be stated using a simple, nontechnical sentence. As in the case of interpreting descriptions of change in Section 2.1, you should answer the questions *when, what, how,* and *by how much* when interpreting a rate of change.

Again, consider your score $G(t)$ out of 100 points on the next calculus exam as a function of the number of hours t that you have studied for the exam. Which of the following is a valid interpretation of $\frac{dG}{dt} = 5.2$ points per hour when $t = 4$ hours?

a. The rate of change of my grade after 4 hours is 5.2 points per hour.

b. The slope of the line tangent to the grade curve at $t = 4$ is 5.2.

c. My grade increased 5.2 points after I studied 4 more hours.

d. When I have studied for 4 hours, my grade is improving by 5.2 points per hour.

Choice *a* only restates the mathematical symbols in words. It does not give the meaning of the derivative in the real-life context. Choice *b* is also a correct statement, but it uses technical words that a person who has not studied calculus probably would not understand. Also, the symbol *t* is used with no meaning attached to it, and units are not included with the value 5.2. The use of the word *increased* in choice *c* refers to an interval of time, not to change at a point in time. It is an incorrect statement. Choice *d* is the only valid interpretation.

You should note that because a rate of change is measured at a point, it describes something that is in the process of changing. Therefore, we must use the progressive tense (verbs ending with *-ing*) to refer to rates of change. For example, we say that "after 1 hour of studying, your grade *is increasing* by approximately 1.7 points per hour." It is incorrect to say that your grade *increased* or *increases* at a specific point. These verbs refer to change over an interval rather than at a point.

EXAMPLE 1   *Interpreting Derivatives*

Study Time   Interpret the following four mathematical statements in the context of studying time and grades according to the function G whose graph is shown in Figure 2.22.

a. $\frac{dG}{dt} = 6.4$ points per hour when $t = 7$ hours

b. $G'(12) = 3.0$ points per hour

c. The derivative of G with respect to t is 0 points per hour when $t = 14$ hours.

d. The slope of the tangent line when $t = 15$ hours is approximately -2 points per hour.

Solution

a. The first statement says that when you have studied for 7 hours, your grade is improving by 6.4 points per hour. As we later learn, this is the point of greatest slope—that is, the time when a small amount of additional study will benefit you the most.

b. The second statement says that after 12 hours of studying, your grade is improving by 3.0 points per hour. Does this mean that at 12 hours of studying, your grade is less than at 7 hours of studying? No! It simply means that a small amount of additional study time beyond 12 hours may not result in as many extra points on your test as the same amount of time produces after you have studied for only 7 hours.

c. The third statement says that after you have studied for 14 hours, your grade will no longer be improving. A glance back at Figure 2.23 shows that you have reached your best possible score; more study will not improve your grade.

d. The fourth statement tells you that after 15 hours of studying, your grade is actually declining by 2 points per hour. Additional study will only hurt your grade.

Make sure that you understand that these statements tell you nothing about what your grade is—they tell you only how quickly your grade is changing. ●

EXAMPLE 2   *Sketching Function Graphs Using Derivative Information*

Medicine $C(h)$ is the average concentration (in nanograms per milliliter, ng/mL) of a drug in the blood stream h hours after the administration of a dose of 360 mg. On the basis of the following information, sketch a graph of C.

$C(0) = 124$ ng/mL $C'(0) = 0$ ng/mL per hour
$C(4) = 252$ ng/mL $C'(4) = 48$ ng/mL per hour

The concentration of the drug is increasing most rapidly after 4 hours. The maximum concentration, 380 ng/mL, occurs after 8 hours. Between $h = 8$ and $h = 24$, the concentration declines at a constant rate of 14 ng/mL per hour. The concentration after 24 hours is 35.9 ng/mL higher than it was when the dose was administered.

Solution
The information about $C(h)$ at various values of h simply locates points on the graph of C. Plot the points $(0, 124)$, $(4, 252)$, $(8, 380)$, and $(24, 159.9)$.

Because $C'(0) = 0$, the curve has a horizontal tangent at $(0, 124)$. The point of most rapid increase, $(4, 252)$, is an inflection point. The graph is concave up to the left of that point and concave down to the right. The maximum concentration occurs after 8 hours, so the highest point on the graph of C is $(8, 380)$. Concentration declining at a constant rate between $h = 8$ and $h = 24$ means that over that interval, C is a line with slope $= -14$.

One possible graph is shown in Figure 2.24. Compare each statement about $C(h)$ to the graph.

$C(h)$
Drug concentration
(ng/mL)

FIGURE 2.24

Note in Figure 2.24 that we cannot assign a value to $C'(8)$. However, the maximum concentration occurs at 8 hours, and on the basis of that, we can estimate that the rate of change of the concentration at that time is zero. ●

Does *Instantaneous* Refer to Time?

We saw that the instantaneous rate of change at a point P on the graph of a continuous function is the slope of the tangent line to the graph at P. If the function inputs are measured in units of time, then it is certainly natural to use the word *instantaneous* when describing rates of change, because each point P on the graph of the function corresponds to a particular instant in time. In fact, the use of the word *instantaneous* in this context arose precisely from the historical need to understand how rapidly distance traveled changes as a function of time. Today, we are accustomed to referring to the rate of change of distance traveled as a function of time as *speed*.

You should be aware, however, that the use of the word *instantaneous* in connection with rates of change does not necessarily mean that time units are involved. For example, suppose that a graph depicts profit (in dollars) resulting from the sale of a certain number of used cars. In this case, the slope of the tangent line at any particular point (the instantaneous rate of change) expresses how rapidly profit is changing per car. The unit of change is dollars per car; no time units are involved.

You should also remember that units for instantaneous rates of change, like average rates of change, are always expressed in output units per input unit. Without proper units, a number that purports to describe a rate of change is meaningless.

EXAMPLE 3   *Writing Derivative Notation and Slope Units*

Temperature   The graph in Figure 2.25* shows the temperature, $T(k)$, of the polar night region (in °C) as a function of k, the number of kilometers above sea level.

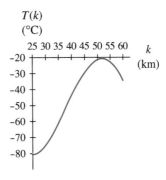

FIGURE 2.25

a.   Sketch the tangent line at 45 km and estimate its slope.

b.   What is the derivative notation for the slope of a line tangent to the graph of T?

c.   Write a sentence interpreting in context the meaning of the slope found in part *a*.

---

*"Atmospheric Exchange Processes and the Ozone Problem," in *The Ozone Layer*, ed. Asit K. Biswas, Institute for Environmental Studies, Toronto. Published for the United Nations Environment Program by Pergamon Press, Oxford, 1979.

FIGURE 2.26

Solution

a. From Figure 2.26 we calculate

$$\text{Slope} = \frac{\text{rise}}{\text{run}} \approx \frac{23°C}{10 \text{ km}} = 2.3°C \text{ per kilometer}$$

b. Correct derivative notations include $\frac{dT}{dk}$, $\frac{d}{dk}[T(k)]$, and $T'(k)$.

c. At 45 km above sea level, the temperature of the atmosphere is increasing 2.3°C per kilometer. In other words, the temperature rises by approximately 2.3°C between 45 and 46 km above sea level. ●

Percentage Rate of Change

Recall from Section 2.1 that percentage change is found by dividing change over an interval by the output at the beginning of the interval and multiplying by 100. Similarly, **percentage rate of change** can be found by dividing the rate of change at a point by the function value at the same point and multiplying by 100. The units of a percentage rate of change are percent per input unit.

Percentage Rate of Change

$$\text{Percentage rate of change} = \frac{\text{rate of change at a point}}{\text{value of the function at that point}} \cdot 100\%$$

Percentage rates of change are useful in describing the relative magnitude of a rate of change. For example, suppose you are a city planner and estimate that the city's population is increasing at a rate of 50,000 people per year. Any growth in population will affect your planning activities, but just how significant is a growth rate of 50,000 people per year? If the current population is 200,000 people, then the percentage rate of change of the population is $\frac{50,000 \text{ people per year}}{200,000 \text{ people}} \cdot 100\% = 25\%$ per year. Growth of 25% per year in population is fast growth. However, if the current population is 2 million, then the percentage rate of change of the population is $\frac{50,000 \text{ people per year}}{2,000,000 \text{ people}} \cdot 100\% = 2.5\%$ per year. The steps that you, as a city planner, must take to accommodate growth if the city is growing by 25% per year are different from the steps you must take if the city is growing by 2.5% per year. Expressing a rate of change as a percentage puts the rate in the context of the current size and adds more meaning to the interpretation of the rate of change.

EXAMPLE 4　　*Graphically Estimating Percentage Rate of Change*

Sales　The graph in Figure 2.27 shows sales (in thousands of dollars) for a small business from 1995 through 2003.

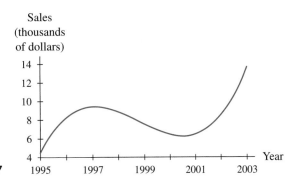

FIGURE 2.27

a.   Estimate the rate of change of sales in 1999 and interpret the result.

b.   Estimate and interpret the percentage rate of change of sales in 1999.

Solution

a.   A tangent line is drawn at 1999, as shown in Figure 2.28.

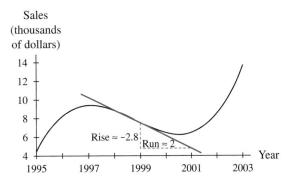

FIGURE 2.28

The slope is estimated to be

$$\frac{-\$2.8 \text{ thousand}}{2 \text{ years}} = -\$1.4 \text{ thousand per year} = -\$1400 \text{ per year}$$

In 1999, sales were falling at a rate of approximately $1400 per year.

b.   We can express this rate of change as a percentage rate of change if we divide it by the sales in 1999. It appears from the graph that the sales in 1999 were approximately $7.5 thousand dollars, or $7500. Therefore, the percentage rate of change in 1999 was approximately

$$\frac{-\$1400 \text{ per year}}{\$7500} \cdot 100\% \approx -0.187 \cdot 100\% \text{ per year} = -18.7\% \text{ per year}$$

In 1999, sales were falling by approximately 18.7% per year. Expressing the rate of change of sales as a percentage of sales gives a much clearer picture of the impact of the decline in sales. The business was experiencing a reduction in sales of nearly 20% per year in 1999.   ●

Finding Slopes by the Numerical Method

By now you should have a firm graphical understanding of rates of change. Although graphical approximations are often sufficient, there are times when we need to find a more precise answer.

Consider the relatively simple problem of finding the slope of the graph of $f(x) = 2\sqrt{x}$ at $x = 1$. Part of the graph of $f(x) = 2\sqrt{x}$ is shown in Figure 2.29a. Take a few moments to sketch carefully a line tangent to the graph at $x = 1$ and estimate its slope. You should find that the tangent line at $x = 1$ has a slope of approximately 1. See Figure 2.29b.

(a)

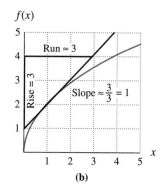
(b)

FIGURE 2.29

Another, more precise method of estimating the slope of the graph of $f(x) = 2\sqrt{x}$ at $x = 1$ uses a technique illustrated in Section 2.2. Recall that the tangent line at a point is the limiting position of secant lines through the point of tangency and other increasingly close points. In other words, *the slope of the tangent line is the limiting value of the slopes of secant lines* drawn through the point of tangency.

To illustrate, we begin by finding the slope of the secant line on the graph of $f(x) = 2\sqrt{x}$ through $x = 1$ and $x = 1.5$. (Note that $x = 1.5$ is an arbitrarily chosen value that is close to $x = 1$.) A graph of the secant line is shown in Figure 2.30. Its slope is calculated as follows:

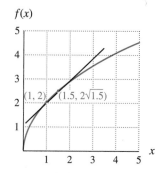

A secant line through $x = 1$ and $x = 1.5$

FIGURE 2.30

Point at $x = 1$: $(1, 2\sqrt{1}) = (1, 2)$

Point at $x = 1.5$: $(1.5, 2\sqrt{1.5}) \approx (1.5, 2.449489743)$

$$\text{Slope} \approx \frac{2.449489743 - 2}{1.5 - 1} = 0.8989794856$$

This value is an approximation to the slope of the tangent line at $x = 1$. To obtain a better approximation, we must choose a point closer to $x = 1$ than $x = 1.5$, say $x = 1.1$. (This is also an arbitrary choice.) See Figure 2.31.

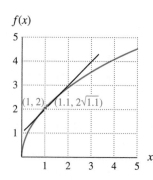

A secant line between $x = 1$ and $x = 1.1$

FIGURE 2.31

Point at $x = 1$: $(1, 2\sqrt{1}) = (1, 2)$

Point at $x = 1.1$: $(1.1, 2\sqrt{1.1}) \approx (1.1, 2.097617696)$

$$\text{Slope} \approx \frac{2.097617696 - 2}{1.1 - 1} = 0.9761769634$$

This is a better approximation to the slope of the tangent line at $x = 1$ than the value from the previous calculation. To get an even better approximation, we need only choose a closer point, such as $x = 1.01$.

Point at $x = 1$: $(1, 2\sqrt{1}) = (1, 2)$

Point at $x = 1.01$: $(1.01, 2\sqrt{1.01}) \approx (1.01, 2.009975124)$

Slope $\approx \dfrac{2.009975124 - 2}{1.01 - 1} = 0.9975124224$

We also use $x = 1.001$.

Point at $x = 1$: $(1, 2\sqrt{1}) = (1, 2)$

Point at $x = 1.001$: $(1.001, 2\sqrt{1.001}) \approx (1.001, 2.00099975)$

Slope $\approx \dfrac{2.00099975 - 2}{1.001 - 1} = 0.9997501248$

As we choose points increasingly close to $x = 1$, what do you observe about the slopes of the secant lines shown in Figure 2.32?

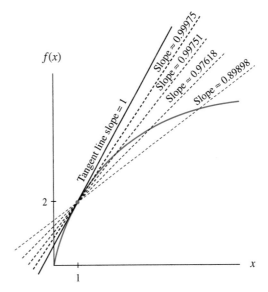

FIGURE 2.32

$x = 1.5$	Secant line slope ≈ 0.8989794856
$x = 1.1$	Secant line slope ≈ 0.9761769634
$x = 1.01$	Secant line slope ≈ 0.9975124224
$x = 1.001$	Secant line slope ≈ 0.9997501248

The pattern in the slope values continues as we choose closer points: for $x = 1.0001$, the slope to six decimal places is 0.999975, for $x = 1.00001$, the slope to seven decimal places is 0.9999975, and so on. Thus the slopes of the secant lines when we use points to the right of $x = 1$ appear to be approaching 1. You may have noticed by now that we are numerically estimating the limit of the slopes of secant lines. The fact that the limit of the slopes of the secant lines that approach the point from the left and the limit of the slopes of the secant lines that approach the point from the right is important in the context of finding the slope at a point. A limit exists only if the limit from the left and the limit from the right are equal. For this reason, in order to conclude that the slope of the tangent line at $x = 1$ is 1, we must also consider the limit of the slopes of secant lines using points to the left of $x = 1$. Choosing the x-values 0.5, 0.9, 0.99, and 0.999, we obtain the following slopes of secant lines between these x-values and $x = 1$:

$x = 0.5$	Secant line slope ≈ 1.171572875
$x = 0.9$	Secant line slope ≈ 1.026334039
$x = 0.99$	Secant line slope ≈ 1.002512579
$x = 0.999$	Secant line slope ≈ 1.000250125

Again, note the pattern in the slope values: for $x = 0.9999$, the slope to six decimal places is 1.000025. For $x = 0.99999$, the slope to seven decimal places is 1.0000025. Thus the slopes of secant lines using points to the left of $x = 1$ appear to be approaching 1. Because the limit of slopes using points to the left of $x = 1$ appears to be the same as the limit using points to the right of $x = 1$, we estimate that the slope of the line tangent to the graph of $f(x) = 2\sqrt{x}$ at $x = 1$ is 1. We use algebraic methods in the next section to verify that $f'(1) = 1$.

In this case, the graphical and numerical methods for estimating the slope of the tangent line yield similar results. However, Example 5 shows that calculating the slopes of nearby secant lines generally yields a much more precise result than sketching a tangent line and estimating its slope.

EXAMPLE 5   *Numerically Estimating a Rate of Change*

Investment   A multinational corporation invests $32 billion of its assets electronically in the global market, resulting in an investment with continuous compounding at 12% APY.

a.   How rapidly is the investment growing at the beginning of the fifth year?

b.   At what percentage rate of change is this investment growing?

Solution

a.   First, note that this is a compound interest function with accumulated amount given by

$$f(t) = 32(1.12^t) \text{ billion dollars}$$

after t years. A graph of this function is shown in Figure 2.33.

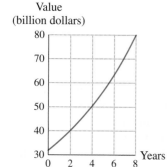

Value
(billion dollars)

Figure 2.33

One method of approximating the slope of the tangent line is to sketch the tangent line and estimate its slope. On the graph in Figure 2.33, draw the tangent line at $t = 4$, and estimate the slope. If you accurately sketched the tangent line and were careful in reading two points off that line, you should have found that the slope of the tangent line is some value between 5 and 6 billion dollars per year.

To obtain a more precise estimate of the slope of the tangent line, we calculate slopes of nearby secant lines. We choose increasingly close points to both the right and the left of the point where $t = 4$: (4, 50.3526195). We calculate slopes until they remain constant to one decimal place beyond the desired accuracy for two or three calculations. You should verify each of the computations in Table 2.3.

TABLE 2.3

Points to the left	Points to the right
Point at $t = 3.99$:(3.99, 50.2955879)	Point at $t = 4.001$:(4.001, 50.3583262)
Slope $= \dfrac{50.2955879 - 50.3526195}{3.99 - 4}$	Slope $= \dfrac{50.3583262 - 50.3526195}{4.001 - 4}$
Slope $\approx 5.\underline{70316}$	Slope $\approx 5.\underline{70672}$
Point at $t = 3.999$:(3.999, 50.3469135)	Point at $t = 4.0001$:(4.0001, 50.3531902)
Slope $= \dfrac{50.3469135 - 50.3526195}{3.999 - 4}$	Slope $= \dfrac{50.3531902 - 50.3526195}{4.0001 - 4}$
Slope $\approx 5.\underline{70607}$	Slope $\approx 5.\underline{70642}$
Point at $t = 3.9999$:(3.9999, 50.3520489)	Point at $t = 4.00001$:(4.00001, 50.3526766)
Slope $= \dfrac{50.3520489 - 50.3526195}{3.9999 - 4}$	Slope $= \dfrac{50.3526766 - 50.3526195}{4.00001 - 4}$
Slope $\approx 5.\underline{70636}$	Slope $\approx 5.\underline{70640}$
Point at $t = 3.99999$:(3.99999, 50.3525625)	Point at $t = 4.000001$:(4.000001, 50.3526252)
Slope $= \dfrac{50.3525625 - 50.3526195}{3.99999 - 4}$	Slope $= \dfrac{50.3526252 - 50.3526195}{4.000001 - 4}$
Slope $\approx 5.\underline{70639}$	Slope $\approx 5.\underline{70640}$

Whether points to the left or right of $t = 4$ are chosen, it seems clear that the slopes are approaching approximately 5.706. That is, the limit of slopes of secant lines using points to the left of $t = 4$ is approximately 5.706, and the limit of slopes of secant lines using points to the right of $t = 4$ is approximately 5.706. Thus we conclude that the slope of the line tangent to the graph at $t = 4$ is approximately 5.706 billion dollars per year.

Note that this numerical method of calculating slopes of nearby secant lines in order to estimate the slope of the tangent line at $t = 4$ gives a much more precise answer than graphically estimating the slope of the tangent line. (Be certain that you keep all decimal places in your calculations and enough decimal places in your recorded slope values to be able to see the limit.) We conclude that at the beginning of the fifth year, the accumulated amount of the investment is growing by 5.706 billion dollars per year.

b. The percentage rate of change at the beginning of the fifth year is

$$\frac{5.706 \text{ billion dollars/year}}{50.3526 \text{ billion dollars}} \cdot 100\% \approx 11.33\% \text{ per year.} \quad \bullet$$

Recall that for compound interest functions, the annual percentage change is constant and is the APY. In Example 5, we found the constant percentage rate of change of a continuous compounding. By rewriting this investment function, we obtain

$$f(t) = 32(1.12^t) \approx 32e^{0.1133t} \text{ billion dollars is the value of the investment}$$

after t years. The APR from this rewritten formula is 11.33%. It is no coincidence that the APR in this example is the constant percentage rate of change. Percentage rate of change is a measure of the percentage change at a point. Continuous compounding considers constant percentage change at a point.

Rate of change (or instantaneous rate of change) and percentage rate of change are measures of change occurring at a point. Rates of change (also known as derivatives) are the first concept of calculus that we will study in detail. In Chapter 4, we will use derivatives to answer questions concerning the maxima and minima of models.

2.3   Concept Inventory

- Derivative = rate of change = slope of tangent line
- Derivative notation
- Relationships between the graph of f and statements about f'
- Percentage rate of change
- Slope of a tangent line = the limiting value of slopes of secant lines
- Numerical method of estimating the slope of a tangent line

2.3   Activities

Getting Started

1. **Distance**   Suppose that $P(t)$ is the number of miles from an airport that a plane has flown after t hours.

   a. What are the units on $\frac{d}{dt}[P(t)]$?

   b. What common word do we use for $\frac{d}{dt}[P(t)]$?

2. **Mutual Fund**   Let $B(t)$ be the balance, in dollars, in a mutual fund t years after the initial investment. Assume that no deposits or withdrawals are made during the investment period.

   a. What are the units on $\frac{dB}{dt}$?

   b. What is the financial interpretation of $\frac{dB}{dt}$?

3. **Typing**   Let $W(t)$ be the number of words per minute that a student in a typing class can type after t weeks in the course.

   a. Is it possible for $W(t)$ to be negative? Explain.

   b. What are the units on $W'(t)$?

   c. Is it possible for $W'(t)$ to be negative? Explain.

4. **Corn Crop**   Suppose that $C(f)$ is the number of bushels of corn produced on a tract of farm land when f pounds of fertilizer are used.

   a. What are the units on $C'(f)$?

   b. Is it possible for $C'(f)$ to be negative? Explain.

   c. Is it possible for $C(f)$ to be negative? Explain.

5. **Profit**   Suppose that $F(p)$ is the weekly profit, in thousands of dollars, that an airline makes on its flights from Boston to Washington D.C. when the ticket price is p dollars. Interpret the following:

   a. $F(65) = 15$

   b. $F'(65) = 1.5$

   c. $\frac{dF}{dp} = -2$ when $p = 90$

6. **Sales**   Let $T(p)$ be the number of tickets from Boston to Washington D.C. that a certain airline sells in 1 week when the price of each ticket is p dollars. Interpret the following:

   a. $T(115) = 1750$

   b. $T'(115) = 220$

   c. $\frac{dT}{dp} = 22$ when $p = 125$

7. On the basis of the following information, sketch a possible graph of t with input x.

   - $t(3) = 7$

   - $t(4.4) = t(8) = 0$

- $\frac{dt}{dx} = 0$ at $x = 6.2$

- The graph of t has no concavity changes.

8. Using the information that follows, sketch a possible graph of m with input t.

- $m(0) = 3$

- $\frac{d}{dt}[m(t)] = 0.34$

9. **Weight Loss** Suppose that $W(t)$ is your weight t weeks after you begin a diet. Interpret the following:

   a. $W(0) = 167$

   b. $W(12) = 142$

   c. $\frac{dW}{dt} = -2$ when $t = 1$

   d. $\frac{dW}{dt} = -1$ when $t = 9$

   e. $W'(12) = 0$

   f. $W'(15) = 0.25$

   g. On the basis of the information in parts a through f, sketch a possible graph of W.

10. **Fuel Efficiency** Suppose that $G(v)$ equals the fuel efficiency, in miles per gallon, of a car going v miles per hour. Give the practical meaning of the following statements.

    a. $G(55) = 32.5$

    b. $\frac{dG}{dv} = -0.25$ when $v = 55$

    c. $G'(45) = 0.15$

    d. $\frac{d}{dv}[G(51)] = 0$

11. **Births** $P(b)$ is the percentage of all births to single mothers in the United States in year b from 1940 through 2000. Using the following information, sketch a graph of P.

    (Source: Based on data from L. Usdansky, "Single Motherhood: Stereotypes vs. Statistics," *New York Times*, February 11, 1996, Section 4, page E4, and on data from *Statistical Abstract*, 1998.)

    - $P(1940) \approx 4$

    - $P'(b)$ is never zero.

    - $P(b) \approx 12$, when $b = 1970$

    - $P(2000)$ is about 21 percentage points more than $P(1970)$.

- The average rate of change of P between 1970 and 1980 is 0.6 percentage point per year.

- Lines tangent to the graph of P lie below the graph at all points between 1940 and 1990 and above the graph between 1990 and 2000.

12. **Enrollment** $E(x)$ is the public secondary school enrollment, in millions of students, in the United States between 1940 and 2008 x years after 1940. Use the following information to sketch a graph of E.

    (Sources: Based on data appearing in *Datapedia of the United States*, Lanham, MD: Bernan Press, 1994; and in *Statistical Abstract*, 1998 and 2001.)

    - $E(40) = 13.2$

    - The graph of E is always concave down.

    - Between 1980 and 1990, enrollment declined at an average rate of 0.19 million students per year.

    - The projected enrollment for 2008 is 14,400,000 students.

    - It is not possible to draw a line tangent to the graph of E at $x = 50$.

13. **Profit** Let $P(x)$ be the profit in dollars that a fraternity makes selling x number of T-shirts.

    a. Is it possible for $P(x)$ to be negative? Explain.

    b. Is it possible for $P'(x)$ to be negative? Explain.

    c. If $P'(200) = -1.5$, is the fraternity losing money? Explain.

14. **Politics** Let $M(t)$ be the number of members in a political organization t years after its founding. What are the units on $\frac{d}{dt}[M(t)]$?

15. **Doubling Time** Let $D(r)$ be the time, in years, that it takes for an investment to double if interest is continuously compounded at an annual rate of $r\%$. (Here r is expressed as a percentage, not a decimal.)

    a. What are the units on $\frac{dD}{dr}$?

    b. Why does it make sense that $\frac{dD}{dr}$ is always negative?

    c. Give the practical interpretation of the following:

       i. $D(9) = 7.7$

       ii. $\frac{dD}{dr} = -2.77$ when $r = 5$

       iii. $\frac{dD}{dr} = -0.48$ when $r = 12$

16. Unemployment Let $U(t)$ be the number of people unemployed in a country t months after the election of a new president.

a. Draw and label an input/output diagram for U.

b. Is U a function? Why or why not?

c. Interpret the following facts about $U(t)$ in statements describing the unemployment situation:

   i. $U(0) = 3,000,000$

   ii. $U(12) = 2,800,000$

   iii. $U'(24) = 0$

   iv. $\dfrac{dU}{dt} = 100,000$ when $t = 36$

   v. $\dfrac{dU}{dt} = -200,000$ when $t = 48$

d. On the basis of the information in part c, sketch a possible graph of the number of people unemployed during the first 48 months of the president's term. Label numbers and units on the axes.

Applying Concepts

17. Raindrop The accompanying graph shows the terminal speed, in meters per second, of a raindrop as a function of the size of the drop measured in terms of its diameter.

a. Sketch a secant line connecting the points for diameters of 1 mm and 5 mm, and estimate its slope. What information does this secant line slope give?

b. Sketch a line tangent to the curve at a diameter of 4 mm. What information does the slope of this line give?

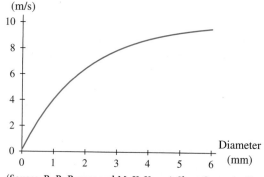

(Source: R. R. Rogers and M. K. Yau, *A Short Course in Cloud Physics*, White Plains, NY: Elsevier Science, 1989.)

c. Estimate the derivative of the speed for a diameter of 4 mm. Interpret your answer.

d. Estimate the rate at which the speed is rising for a raindrop with diameter 2 mm. Use this estimate to approximate the terminal speed of a raindrop with diameter 2.5 mm.

e. Find and interpret the percentage rate of change of speed for a raindrop with diameter 2 mm.

18. Customers The scatter plot and graph depict the number of customers that a certain fast-food restaurant serves each hour on a typical weekday.

a. Estimate the average rate of change of the number of customers between 7 A.M. and 11 A.M. Interpret your answer.

b. Estimate the instantaneous rate of change and percentage rate of change of the number of customers at 4 P.M. Interpret your answer.

c. List the factors that might affect the accuracy of your answers to parts a and b.

d. Use your estimate in part b to approximate the number of customers at 5 P.M.

19. Study Time Refer once more to the function G, your grade out of 100 points on the next calculus test when you study t hours during the week before the test. The graph of G is shown below.

a. Carefully draw tangent lines at 4 hours and 11 hours. Estimate the slope of each tangent line.

b. Estimate the average rate of change between 4 hours and 10 hours. Interpret your answer.

c. Estimate the percentage rate of change of the grade after 4 hours of studying. Interpret your answer.

d. Use $G'(4)$ to estimate your grade after 4.6 hours of studying.

20. Mortality   Consider the accompanying graph of rates of death from cancer among U.S. males.

Cancer death rates by site, males, United States, 1930–89

(Rates are adjusted to the 1970 U.S. census population.)

(Source: Figure courtesy of the American Cancer Society, Inc.)

a. Estimate how rapidly the number of deaths due to lung cancer was increasing in 1970 and in 1980.

b. Estimate the percentage rate of change of deaths due to liver cancer in 1980.

c. Estimate the slope of the stomach cancer curve in 1960.

d. Describe in detail the behavior of the lung cancer curve from 1930 to 1990. Explain why the lung cancer curve differs so radically from the other curves shown.

e. List as many factors as you can that might affect a cancer death rate curve.

21. a. Sketch a line tangent to the graph of $y = 2^x$ at the point corresponding to $x = 2$, and estimate its slope.

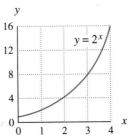

b. Use the equation $y = 2^x$ to estimate numerically the slope of the line tangent to the graph at $x = 2$.

22. a. Sketch a line tangent to the graph of $y = -x^2 + 4x$ at the point corresponding to $x = 3$, and estimate its slope.

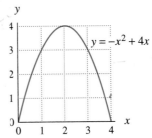

b. Use the equation $y = -x^2 + 4x$ to estimate numerically the slope of the line tangent to the graph at $x = 3$.

23. Airport Traffic   The number of passengers going through Hartsfield-Jackson International Airport in Atlanta, Georgia between 2001 and 2005 yearly, can be modeled as

$$P(t) = -0.29t^3 + 2.92t^2 - 6.1t + 79.4 \text{ million passengers}$$

where t is the number of years since 2000. A graph of the function is shown below.

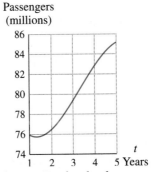

(Sources: Based on data from Airports Council International, www.airports.org)

a. Use the graph to estimate $\frac{dP}{dt}$ when $t = 4$.

b. Use the equation to investigate $P'(4)$ numerically. Interpret your answer.

c. Use the equation to determine the percentage rate of change of P at $t = 4$. Interpret your answer.

d. Discuss the advantages and disadvantages of using the two methods (in parts *a* and *b*) for finding derivatives.

24. Bank Account   The balance in a savings account is shown in the graph and is given by the equation Balance $= 1500(1.0407^t)$ dollars, where t is the number of years since the principal was invested.

Account balance
(dollars)

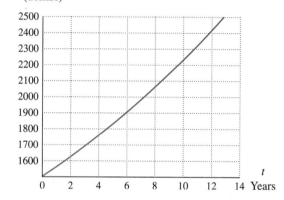

a. Using only the graph, estimate how rapidly the balance is growing after 10 years.

b. Use the equation to investigate numerically the rate of change of the balance when $t = 10$.

c. Which of the two methods (part *a* or part *b*) is more accurate? Support your answer by listing the different estimates that had to be made during each method.

d. Use the equation to determine the percentage rate of change of the balance when $t = 10$.

25. Swim Time   The time it takes an average athlete to swim 100 meters freestyle at age x years can be modeled by the equation

$$T(x) = 0.181x^2 - 8.463x + 147.376 \text{ seconds}$$

(Source: Based on data from *Swimming World*, August 1992.)

a. Use the numerical method to find the rate of change of the time for a 13-year-old swimmer to swim 100 meters freestyle.

b. Determine the percentage rate of change of swim time for a 13-year-old.

c. Is a 13-year-old swimmer's time improving or getting worse as the swimmer gets older?

26. Sales   Annual U.S. factory sales, in billions of dollars, of consumer electronics goods to dealers from 1990 through 2001 can be modeled by the equation

$$S(t) = 0.0388t^3 - 0.495t^2 + 5.698t + 43.6$$
$$\text{billion dollars}$$

where t is the number of years since 1990.

(Sources: Based on data from *Statistical Abstract*, 2001, and Consumer Electronics Association.)

a. Estimate the derivative of S when $t = 10$.

b. Interpret your answer to part *a*.

27. Profit   Let $P(x) = 1.02^x$ Canadian dollars be the profit from the sale of x mountain bikes. On November 25, 2002, P Canadian dollars were worth $C(P) = \frac{P}{1.5786}$ American dollars. Assume that this conversion applies today.

a. Write a function for profit in American dollars from the sale of x mountain bikes.

b. What is the profit in Canadian and in American dollars from the sale of 400 mountain bikes?

c. How quickly is profit (in American dollars) changing when 400 mountain bikes are sold?

28. Profit   Let $P(x) = 1.02^x$ Canadian dollars be the profit from the sale of x mountain bikes. On November 25, 2002, P Canadian dollars were worth $C(P) = \frac{P}{1.5786}$ American dollars. Assume that this conversion applies today.

a. Write a function giving average profit per mountain bike for the sale of x mountain bikes in Canadian dollars.

b. Write a function for average profit in American dollars.

c. How quickly is average profit (in American dollars) changing when 400 mountain bikes are sold?

Discussing Concepts

29. Explain how percentage change and percentage rate of change are related and how they differ.

30. Describe the process of using tangent lines to approximate function values. Include a discussion of when this technique is most accurate and when it is least accurate.

31. Discuss the advantages and disadvantages of finding rates of change graphically and numerically. Include in your discussion a brief description of when each method might be appropriate to use.

32. Explain why there may be differences between the numerical estimate of a rate of change of a modeled function at a point and the actual rate of change that occurred in the underlying real-world situation.

2.4 **Algebraically Finding Slopes**

When we have enough carefully chosen close points to observe the trend in the secant line slopes, the numerical method is a fairly good way to find a slope to a specified accuracy. For this reason, the process of numerically estimating slope is valuable, but keep in mind that it gives only an estimation of the actual slope. However, we can generalize the numerical method to develop an algebraic method that will give the exact slope of a tangent line at a point.

We saw in Sections 2.2 and 2.3 that the slope of a tangent line is the limiting value of the slopes of secant lines at a point. Before we proceed to evaluating slopes algebraically, we need to revisit in a little more detail the idea of the limiting value of a function at a point.

Limits and the Infinitesimally Small

In Section 1.4, we used the concept of limits to consider end behavior. In calculus we are also interested in the behavior of the output of a function as the input of that function gets closer and closer to a certain value. This type of behavior analysis is similar to looking at the function through a microscope and increasing the power of the magnification so as to zoom in on a very small portion of that function.

Concept Development: Limit at a Point Consider $r(t) = \frac{t^2 - 16}{t - 4}$. The graph of r appears to be a line, but as we zoom in on the graph near $t = 4$, a hole in the graph becomes evident. (See Figure 2.34).

FIGURE 2.34

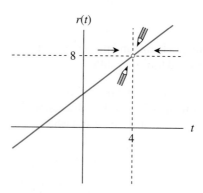

FIGURE 2.35

To graphically estimate the behavior of r as t gets closer and closer to 4, place the tips of two pencils on the graph in Figure 2.35 on either side of $t = 4$ and, keeping the pencils on the graph, move them toward each other. The pencil tips should move toward the hole in the function. Indeed, as the input becomes closer and closer to 4 from either direction, the graph becomes closer and closer to an output of 8. The fact that $r(t)$ is never actually 8 does not affect the limit, because when determining limits, we are interested in where the function is headed, not in whether it ever actually arrives there.

The output $r(t)$ is not actually 8 at $t = 4$ because the output is not defined for $t = 4$. However, we can say that as the input t approaches (gets closer and closer to) 4, the output $r(t)$ approaches 8. Mathematically, we say, "as t approaches 4, the limiting value of r is 8." Thus we write $\lim_{t \to 4} r(t) = 8$.

It is also possible to estimate this *limit* numerically. To do so, we evaluate the function at values increasingly close to, and on either side of, $t = 4$. Table 2.4 shows $r(t)$ values as t approaches 4 from the left (this is denoted $t \to 4^-$), and Table 2.5 shows $r(t)$ values as t approaches 4 from the right (this is denoted $t \to 4^+$).

TABLE 2.4

$t \to 4^-$	$r(t)$
3.8	7.8
3.9	7.9
3.99	7.99
3.999	7.999

TABLE 2.5

$t \to 4^+$	$r(t)$
4.2	8.2
4.1	8.1
4.01	8.01
4.001	8.001

Caution: Do not confuse the symbols used to indicate approaching an input value from the right or from the left with the statement "$x \to \pm c$" or "$x \to \pm\infty$." A plus or minus sign placed *in front of* a number or the infinity symbol indicates whether the number or infinity is positive or negative, whereas a plus or minus sign written *after* a number ($x \to c^+$ or $x \to c^-$) indicates a specific direction from which that number is to be approached.

In Table 2.4 it appears that as t approaches 4 from the left, the output is becoming closer and closer to 8. We symbolize this idea by writing

$$\lim_{t \to 4^-} r(t) = 8$$

This is read as "the limit of $r(t)$ as t approaches 4 from the left is 8." On the basis of Table 2.5, we make a similar statement: "The limit of $r(t)$ as t approaches 4 from the right is 8," which we write as

$$\lim_{t \to 4^+} r(t) = 8$$

Note that the input values near 4 in the tables were arbitrarily chosen. You should arrive at the same conclusion if you choose other values increasingly close to $t = 4$. Because the limits from the left and right of 4 are the same, we conclude that $\lim_{t \to 4} r = 8$; that is, the limit of $r(t)$ as t approaches 4 is 8.

Another function behavior that is possible is the outputs increasing or decreasing without bound as the inputs approach a specific value from the left or from the right. Consider Example 1.

EXAMPLE 1   *Numerically Estimating a Limit at a Point*

For $u(x) = \dfrac{3x}{8x + 2}$, numerically estimate $\lim_{x \to -0.25} u(x)$.

Solution
Note that $u(x)$ is not defined at $x = -0.25$ because the denominator is zero when $x = -0.25$. Consider values of x increasingly close to -0.25 from both the left and the right, as shown in Table 2.6.

2.4.1

TABLE 2.6

$x = -0.25^-$	$u(x)$	$x \to -0.25^+$	$u(x)$
-0.251	94.125	-0.249	-93.375
-0.2501	937.875	-0.2499	-937.125
-0.25001	9375.375	-0.24999	-9374.625
-0.250001	93750.375	-0.249999	-93749.625

It appears that the output values of u are becoming increasingly large as x moves closer and closer to -0.25 from the left. Also, the output values of u are negative, and their magnitudes seem to become increasingly large as x moves closer and closer to -0.25 from the right. On the basis of this numerical investigation, we conclude that the limits as x approaches -0.25 from the left and right do not exist. To indicate that $u(x)$ increases without bound as x approaches -0.25 from the left, we use the notation $\lim_{x \to -0.25^-} u(x) \to \infty$. We also write $\lim_{x \to -0.25^+} u(x) \to -\infty$ to indicate that $u(x)$ decreases without bound as x approaches -0.25 from the right.

Keep in mind that this numerical method gives only an estimate. Figure 2.36 shows a graph of the function u.

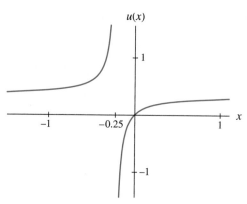

FIGURE 2.36

The graph seems to support our previous estimates that $\lim_{x \to -0.25^-} u(x) \to \infty$ and that $\lim_{x \to -0.25^+} u(x) \to -\infty$. You should recognize the numerical technique illustrated in Example 1 as being the same basic technique used in Section 2.3 to evaluate the slope of a tangent line. ●

Continuity Revisited

The functions r and u seen in this section are not continuous functions. Because calculus involves the study of continuous portions of functions, it is important to have a complete understanding of what makes a function *continuous* or discontinuous.

Let us first consider some functions that are not continuous and the types of situations that lead to a function's being discontinuous at a point. Consider the four functions shown in Figure 2.37. We observe that a function is not continuous at a point where a hole in the graph occurs (see f), the output becomes infinitely large (see g), or a break or jump occurs (see h and j).

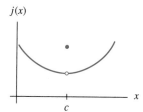

FIGURE 2.37

We say that a function is **continuous** on an (open) interval if the output of the function is defined at every point on the interval and there are no breaks or jumps in the function output.

Continuity

A function is continuous on an (open) interval if the output of the function is defined at every point on the interval and there are no breaks or jumps in the function output.

Limits give us the power to evaluate the behavior of a continuous function at a point. A special function that we have been working with in the chapter is the function that gives us the slope of the secant lines of another function. This slope function is continuous as long as the original function is continuous and smooth. We now use the power of limits algebraically in order to determine expressions for slope functions.

Finding Slopes Using the Algebraic Method

Consider finding the slope of $f(x) = 0.1x^2 + 3x$ at $x = 2$. We begin with the point $(2, 6.4)$. Instead of choosing close x-values such as 1.9, 2.1, 2.01, and so on, we simply call the close value $x = 2 + h$. (Note that if $h = 0.1$, then $x = 2.1$; if $h = 0.01$, $x = 2.01$; if $h = -0.01$, $x = 1.99$, and so on.) The output value that corresponds to $x = 2 + h$ is

$$f(2 + h) = 0.1(2 + h)^2 + 3(2 + h)$$
$$= 0.1(4 + 4h + h^2) + 6 + 3h = 6.4 + 3.4h + 0.1h^2$$

Next we find the slope of the secant line between the point of tangency $(2, 6.4)$ and the close point $(2 + h, 6.4 + 3.4h + 0.1h^2)$.

$$\text{Slope of secant line} = \frac{(6.4 + 3.4h + 0.1h^2) - 6.4}{(2 + h) - 2} = \frac{3.4h + 0.1h^2}{h}$$

We now have a formula for the slope of the secant line through the points at $x = 2$ and $x = 2 + h$. We can apply the formula to obtain slopes at points increasingly close to $x = 2$ (see Table 2.7).

The slopes become increasingly close to approximately 3.4.

Numerically evaluating the secant line slope formula for smaller and smaller values of h gives us a good picture of where the slopes are headed, but it does not give us the exact answer. By noting that h approaches zero as the close point approaches

We arbitrarily chose three-decimal-place accuracy for the answer in this illustration.

TABLE 2.7

Close point to left	h	Slope $= \dfrac{3.4h + 0.1h^2}{h}$	Close point to right	h	Slope $= \dfrac{3.4h + 0.1h^2}{h}$
1.9	−0.1	3.<u>39</u>	2.1	0.1	3.<u>41</u>
1.99	−0.01	3.<u>399</u>	2.01	0.01	3.<u>401</u>
1.999	−0.001	3.<u>3999</u>	2.001	0.001	3.<u>4001</u>
1.9999	−0.0001	3.<u>39999</u>	2.0001	0.0001	3.<u>40001</u>
1.99999	−0.00001	3.<u>399999</u>	2.00001	0.00001	3.<u>400001</u>

2, we can find the limit of the secant line slope formula as h approaches zero. That is, we need to find

$$\lim_{h \to 0} \frac{3.4h + 0.1h^2}{h}$$

The secant line slope formula is not continuous at $h = 0$ because it is not defined there. However, a rule called the Cancellation Rule for limits states:

> If the numerator and denominator of a rational function share a common factor, then the new function obtained by algebraically canceling the common factor has all limits identical to those of the original function.

If we factor h out of the numerator and cancel this common factor, then we can find the limit by evaluating the new expression at $h = 0$ because the new expression $(3.4 + 0.1h)$ is continuous at $h = 0$.

$$\lim_{h \to 0} \frac{h(3.4 + 0.1h)}{h} = \lim_{h \to 0}(3.4 + 0.1h) = 3.4 + 0.1(0) = 3.4$$

On the basis of this limit calculation, we state that the slope of the line tangent to $f(x) = 0.1x^2 + 3x$ at $x = 2$ is exactly 3.4.

This method of finding a formula for the slope of a secant line in terms of h and then determining the limiting value of the formula as h approaches zero is called the **algebraic method.** It is important because it always yields the *exact* slope of the tangent line.

EXAMPLE 2   *Using the Algebraic Method to Find the Slope at a Point*

Coal Production   The amount of coal used quarterly for synthetic-fuel plants in the United States between 2001 and 2004 can be modeled by

$$f(x) = -1.6x^2 + 15.6x - 6.4 \text{ million short tons}$$

where x is the number of years since the beginning of 2000.

a. Find $\frac{df}{dx}$ at $x = 3.5$ by writing an expression for the slope of a secant line in terms of h and then evaluating the limit as h approaches 0.

b. Interpret $\frac{df}{dx}$ at $x = 3.5$ in the context given.

Solution

a. First, we find the output of f when $x = 3.5$.

$$f(3.5) = 28.6$$

Second, we write an expression for $f(x)$ when $x = 3.5 + h$.

$$f(3.5 + h) = -1.6(3.5 + h)^2 + 15.6(3.5 + h) - 6.4$$

We simplify this expression as much as possible, using the fact that

$$(3.5 + h)^2 = 12.25 + 7h + h^2$$

Thus

$$f(3.5 + h) = 28.6 + 4.4h - 1.6h^2$$

Third, we find the slope of the secant line through the two close points $(3.5, f(3.5))$ and $(3.5 + h, f(3.5 + h))$ as

$$\text{Slope of secant line} = \frac{f(3.5 + h) - f(3.5)}{(3.5 + h) - 3.5}$$

$$= \frac{(28.6 + 4.4h - 1.6h^2) - (28.6)}{(3.5 + h) - 3.5}$$

Again, we simplify this as much as possible.

$$\text{Slope of secant line (continued)} = \frac{(28.6 + 4.4h - 1.6h^2) - (28.6)}{(3.5 + h) - 3.5}$$

$$= \frac{h(4.4 - 1.6h)}{h}$$

Finally, we find the slope of the tangent line (the derivative) at $x = 3.5$ by evaluating the limit of the slope of the secant line as h approaches 0.

$$\frac{df}{dx} = \text{slope of tangent line} = \lim_{h \to 0} \frac{h(4.4 - 1.6h)}{h}$$

$$= \lim_{h \to 0} (4.4 - 1.6h)$$

$$= 4.4$$

b. In the second quarter of 2003, the amount of coal being used for synthetic-fuel plants in the United States was increasing at a rate of 4.4 million short tons per year.   ●

A General Formula for Derivatives

The real value of the algebraic method is not in finding a slope at a particular point but in finding general formulas for derivatives. These rate-of-change (or slope) formulas can be used to find rates of change for many input values.

To illustrate, consider $y = x^2$. Because we desire a general equation for any x-value, we use (x, x^2) as the point of tangency. This is the same idea as the algebraic method in Example 2 and the preceding discussion, but there we worked with a numerical value for x. Next we choose a close point. We use $x + h$ as the x-value of the close point and find the y-value by substituting $x + h$ into the function: $y = (x + h)^2 = x^2 + 2xh + h^2$. Thus the original point is (x, x^2), and a close point is $(x + h, x^2 + 2xh + h^2)$. Now we find the slope of the secant line between these two points.

$$\text{Slope of the secant line} = \frac{(x^2 + 2xh + h^2) - x^2}{(x + h) - x} = \frac{2xh + h^2}{h}$$

Finally, we determine the limiting value of the secant line slope as h approaches 0.

$$\lim_{h \to 0} \frac{2xh + h^2}{h} = \lim_{h \to 0} (2x + h) = 2x + 0 = 2x$$

Therefore, the slope formula for $y = x^2$ is $\frac{dy}{dx} = 2x$. Using this formula, we find that the slope of the graph of $y = x^2$ is 6 at $x = 3$, -12 at $x = -6$, 0 at $x = 0$, 1 at $x = 0.5$, and so on.

This method can be generalized to obtain a formula for the derivative of an arbitrary function.

Four-Step Method to Find $f'(x)$

Given a function f, the equation for the derivative with respect to x can be found as follows:

1. Begin with a typical point $(x, f(x))$.
2. Choose a close point $(x + h, f(x + h))$.
3. Write a formula for the slope of the secant line between the two points.

$$\text{Slope} = \frac{f(x + h) - f(x)}{(x + h) - x} = \frac{f(x + h) - f(x)}{h}$$

It is important at this step to simplify the slope formula.

4. Evaluate the limit of the slope as h approaches 0.

$$\lim_{h \to 0} \frac{f(x + h) - f(x)}{h}$$

This limiting value is the derivative formula at each input where the limit exists.

Thus we have the following derivative formula (slope formula, rate-of-change formula) for an arbitrary function:

Derivative Formula

If $y = f(x)$, then the derivative $\frac{dy}{dx}$ is given by the formula

$$\frac{dy}{dx} = \lim_{h \to 0} \frac{f(x + h) - f(x)}{h}$$

provided that the limit exists.

Example 3 illustrates the Four-Step Method for finding a derivative formula.

EXAMPLE 3   *Using the Four-Step Method to Find a Slope Formula*

Coal Prices   The average price paid by the synfuel industry for coal between 2002 and 2005 can be modeled by

$$W(t) = 1.2t^2 - 6.1t + 39.5 \text{ dollars per short ton}$$

where t is the number of years since the beginning of 2000.

a. Use the limit definition of the derivative (the Four-Step Method) to develop a formula for the rate of change of the price of coal used by the synfuel industry.

b. How quickly was the price of coal used by the synfuel industry growing in the middle of 2003?

Solution

a. **Step 1.** A typical point is $(t, W(t)) = (t, 1.2t^2 - 6.1t + 39.5)$.
Step 2. A close point is $(t + h, W(t + h))$
$$= (t + h, 1.2(t + h)^2 - 6.1(t + h) + 39.5).$$

We rewrite the output of the close point before we proceed:

$$W(t + h) = 1.2(t + h)^2 - 6.1(t + h) + 39.5$$
$$= 1.2(t^2 + 2ht + h^2) - 6.1(t + h) + 39.5$$
$$= 1.2t^2 + 2.4ht + 1.2h^2 - 6.1t - 6.1h + 39.5$$

Step 3. Write the slope of the secant line between the two points from Steps 1 and 2.

$$\text{Slope} = \frac{W(t + h) - W(t)}{(t + h) - t}$$

$$= \frac{[(1.2t^2 + 2.4ht + 1.2h^2 - 6.1t - 6.1h + 39.5) - (1.2t^2 - 6.1t + 39.5)]}{(t + h) - t}$$

$$= \frac{2.4ht + 1.2h^2 - 6.1h}{h}$$

$$= \frac{h(2.4t + 1.2h - 6.1)}{h}$$

Step 4. Evaluate the limit of the secant line slope as h approaches 0.

$$W'(t) = \lim_{h \to 0} \frac{h(2.4t + 1.2h - 6.1)}{h} = \lim_{h \to 0} (2.4t + 1.2h - 6.1)$$

$$= 2.4t - 6.1$$

Thus the price of coal used by the synfuel industry was increasing by

$$W'(t) = 2.4t - 6.1 \text{ dollars per short ton per year}$$

t years after the beginning of 2000, $2 \le t \le 5$.

b. We find that $W'(3.5) \approx 2.3$ dollars per short ton per year. Thus the price of coal used by the synfuel industry was increasing by approximately 2.3 dollars per short ton per year in the middle of 2003. ●

Using the Four-Step Method to find a derivative formula for a nonpolynomial function may require more thoughtful algebra.

EXAMPLE 4 *Algebraically Finding a Slope Formula*

Consider the function $f(x) = 2\sqrt{x}$.

a. Use the Four-Step Method to find a formula for the slope graph of f.

b. Use the formula from part a to find the slope of the graph of f at $x = 1$.

Compare this answer with the one found by numerical estimation in Section 2.3.

Solution

a. To find a slope formula, begin with a general point $\left(x, 2\sqrt{x}\right)$ and a close point $\left(x + h, 2\sqrt{x + h}\right)$. Next find the slope between these two points:

$$\text{Secant line slope} = \frac{2\sqrt{x + h} - 2\sqrt{x}}{x + h - x} = \frac{2\sqrt{x + h} - 2\sqrt{x}}{h}$$

Now find the limit of this formula as h approaches zero:

$$\lim_{h \to 0} \frac{2\sqrt{x + h} - 2\sqrt{x}}{h}$$

Unlike the case for polynomial functions that always contain h as a common factor, we cannot cancel the h here without rewriting the numerator. The key to this cancellation is to rewrite the numerator by multiplying the numerator and denominator by the term $2\sqrt{x + h} + 2\sqrt{x}$. Observe how this multiplication enables us to cancel the h term:

$$\lim_{h \to 0} \frac{2\sqrt{x + h} - 2\sqrt{x}}{h} \cdot \frac{2\sqrt{x + h} + 2\sqrt{x}}{2\sqrt{x + h} + 2\sqrt{x}}$$

$$= \lim_{h \to 0} \frac{4(x + h) - 4x}{h\left(2\sqrt{x + h} + 2\sqrt{x}\right)}$$

$$= \lim_{h \to 0} \frac{4h}{h\left(2\sqrt{x + h} + 2\sqrt{x}\right)}$$

$$= \lim_{h \to 0} \frac{4}{2\sqrt{x + h} + 2\sqrt{x}}$$

$$= \frac{4}{2\sqrt{x + 0} + 2\sqrt{x}} = \frac{4}{4\sqrt{x}} = \frac{1}{\sqrt{x}}$$

Thus the slope formula is $f'(x) = \dfrac{1}{\sqrt{x}}$.

b. Using this slope formula, we find that $f'(1) = \dfrac{1}{\sqrt{1}} = 1$. That is, the slope of the line tangent to the graph of $f(x) = 2\sqrt{x}$ at $x = 1$ is 1. This calculation confirms that the numerical estimate in Section 2.3 is correct. ●

The definition of the derivative of a function gives us a formula for the slope graph of the function, which enables us to calculate exact rates of change quickly. Unfortunately, this method is primarily for polynomial functions and not for exponential, logarithmic, or logistic functions. However, in Chapter 3 we will use the algebraic method as a powerful tool to help us develop some general rules for derivative formulas.

2.4 Concept Inventory

- The algebraic method for determining the slope of a graph at a given point
- The Four-Step Method for determining a rate-of-change formula
- Limit definition of a derivative

2.4 Activities

Getting Started

For Activities 1 through 4, numerically determine the indicated limit if it exists.

1. $\lim\limits_{x \to 2} \dfrac{x^3}{x-2}$

2. $\lim\limits_{x \to 3} \dfrac{5x^2}{3x-9}$

3. $\lim\limits_{x \to 0} \dfrac{-2x^3 + 7x}{x}$

4. $\lim\limits_{x \to 0} \dfrac{e^{1+x} - e}{x}$

5. Consider the function $f(x) = 4x^2$. Use the algebraic method to find $f'(2)$ by evaluating the limit of an expression for the slope of a secant line.

6. Consider the function $s(t) = -2.3t^2$. Use the algebraic method to find $s'(1.5)$ by evaluating the limit of an expression for the slope of a secant line.

7. Consider the function $g(t) = -6t^2 + 7$. Use the algebraic method to find $\dfrac{dg}{dt}$ at $t = 4$ by evaluating the limit of an expression for the slope of a secant line.

8. Consider the function $m(p) = 4p + p^2$. Use the algebraic method to find $\dfrac{dm}{dp}$ at $p = -2$ by evaluating the limit of an expression for the slope of a secant line.

In Activities 9 through 14, use the Four-Step Method outlined in this section to show that each statement is true.

9. The derivative of $y = 3x - 2$ is $\dfrac{dy}{dx} = 3$.

10. The derivative of $y = 15x + 32$ is $\dfrac{dy}{dx} = 15$.

11. The derivative of $f(x) = 3x^2$ is $f'(x) = 6x$.

12. The derivative of $f(x) = -3x^2 - 5x$ is $f'(x) = -6x - 5$.

13. The derivative of $y = x^3$ is $\dfrac{dy}{dx} = 3x^2$.

   (*Hint:* $(x + h)^3 = x^3 + 3x^2h + 3xh^2 + h^3$)

14. The derivative of $f(x) = 2x^3 - 5x + 7$ is $\dfrac{df}{dx} = 6x^2 - 5$.

Applying Concepts

15. **Swim Time**   The time it takes an average athlete to swim 100 meters freestyle at age x years can be modeled by the equation
$$T(x) = 0.181x^2 - 8.463x + 147.376$$

   a. Find the swim time when $x = 13$.

   b. Write a formula for the average swim time when $x = 13 + h$.

   c. Write a simplified formula for the slope of the secant line connecting the points at $x = 13$ and $x = 13 + h$.

   d. What is the limiting value of the slope formula in part c as h approaches 0? Interpret your answer.

16. **Sales**   Annual U.S. factory sales of consumer electronics goods to dealers between 1990 and 2001 can be modeled by the equation
$$S(x) = 0.0388x^3 - 0.495x^2 + 5.698x + 43.6$$
$$\text{billion dollars}$$

   where x is the number of years since 1990.

   (Sources: Based on data from *Statistical Abstract*, 2001, and Consumer Electronics Association.)

   a. Find the sales when $x = 10$.

   b. Write an expression for the sales when $x = 10 + h$.

   c. Write a simplified formula for the slope of the secant line connecting the points at $x = 10$ and $x = 10 + h$.

   d. What is the limiting value of the slope formula in part c as h approaches 0? Interpret your answer.

17. **Airline Fuel**   The amount of airline fuel consumed by Northwest Airlines each year between 1998 and 2004 can be modeled as
$$f(t) = -0.042t^2 + 0.18t + 1.89 \text{ billion gallons}$$

   where t is the number of years since 1998.

   (Source: Northwest Airlines Corporation, Financial and Operating Statistics 5/27/05, **ir.nwa.com**)

   a. Find the amount of fuel consumed in 2001.

   b. Write a formula in terms of h for the consumption of fuel a little after 2001.

c. Write a simplified formula for the slope of the secant line connecting the points at 2001 and a little after 2001.

d. What is the limiting value for the slope formula as h approaches 0? Interpret your answer.

18. **Tuition CPI** The CPI for college tuition between 1990 and 2000 can be modeled by the equation

$$c(t) = -0.498t^2 + 20.603t + 174.458$$

where t is the number of years since 1990.

(Source: Based on data from *Statistical Abstract*, 2001.)

a. Find the consumer price index for college tuition in 1998.

b. Write a formula in terms of h for the consumer price index of college tuition a little after 1998.

c. Write a simplified formula for the slope of the secant line connecting the points at 1998 and a little after 1998.

d. What is the limiting value for the slope formula as h approaches 0? Interpret your answer.

19. **Falling Object** An object is dropped off a building. Ignoring air resistance, we know from physics that its height above the ground t seconds after being dropped is given by

$$\text{Height} = -16t^2 + 100 \text{ feet}$$

a. Use the Four-Step Method to find a rate-of-change equation for the height.

b. Use your answer to part a to determine how rapidly the object is falling after 1 second.

20. **Distance** Clinton County, Michigan, is mostly flat farmland partitioned by straight roads (often gravel) that run either north/south or east/west. A tractor driven north on Lowell Road from the Schafers' farm is

$$d(m) = 0.28m + 0.6 \text{ miles}$$

north of Howe Road m minutes after leaving the farm's drive.

a. How far is the Schafers' drive from Howe Road?

b. Use the Four-Step Method to show that the tractor is moving at a constant speed.

c. How quickly (in miles per hour) is the tractor moving?

21. **Drivers** The number of licensed drivers between the ages of 16 and 21 in 1997 is given below.

Age (years)	Number of drivers (millions)
16	0.85
17	1.24
18	1.41
19	1.47
20	1.54
21	1.51

(Source: U.S. Department of Labor and Transportation.)

a. Find a quadratic model for the number of licensed drivers as a function of age.

b. Use the limit definition of the derivative to develop a formula for the derivative of the rounded model.

c. Use the derivative formula in part b to find the rate of change of the function in part a for an age of 20 years. Interpret your answer.

d. Find the percentage rate of change in the number of licensed drivers 20 years old. Interpret this result.

22. **Drivers** The data below give the percentage of females of a certain age who were licensed drivers in 1997.

Age (years)	Licensed drivers (percent)
15	0.4
16	43.4
17	61.9
18	72.7
19	73.8

(Source: U.S. Department of Labor and Transportation.)

a. Find a quadratic model for these data.

b. Use the limit definition of the derivative to develop the derivative formula for the rounded equation.

c. Use the derivative formula in part *b* to find the rate of change of the equation in part *a* when the input is 16 years of age. Interpret your answer.

d. Find the percentage rate of change in the number of female licensed drivers 20 years old. Interpret this result.

Discussing Concepts

23. Discuss the advantages and disadvantages of finding rates of change graphically, numerically, and algebraically. Include in your discussion a brief description of when each method might be appropriate to use.

24. Explain from a graphical viewpoint how algebraically finding a slope formula is related to numerically estimating a rate of change.

SUMMARY

This chapter is devoted to describing change: the underlying concepts, the language, and proper interpretations.

Change, Average Rate of Change, and Percentage Change

The change in a quantity over an interval is a difference of output values. Apart from expressing the actual change in a quantity that occurs over an interval, change can be described as the average rate of change over an interval or as a percentage change. The numerical description of an average rate of change has an associated geometric interpretation—namely, the slope of the secant line joining two points on a graph.

Instantaneous Rates of Change

Whereas average rates of change indicate how rapidly a quantity changes (on average) over an interval, instantaneous rates of change indicate how rapidly a quantity is changing at a point. The instantaneous rate of change at a point on a graph is simply the slope of the line tangent to the graph at that point. It describes how quickly the output is increasing or decreasing at that point.

Tangent Lines

The principle known as local linearity guarantees that the graph of any continuous function looks like a line if you are close enough. A line tangent to a graph at a point is the line you see when you zoom in on the graph closer and closer to that point.

The line tangent to a graph at a point *P* can also be thought of as the limiting position of nearby secant lines—that is, secant lines through *P* and nearby points on the graph. It reflects the tilt, or slope, of the graph at the point of tangency. We can estimate the instantaneous rate of change at a point on a curve by sketching a tangent line at that point and approximating the tangent line's slope.

Derivatives and Percentage Rate of Change

Derivative is the calculus term for (instantaneous) rate of change. Accordingly, all of the following terms are synonymous: derivative, instantaneous rate of change, rate of change, slope of the curve, and slope of the line tangent to the curve.

Three common ways of symbolically referring to the derivative of a function *G* with respect to *x* are $\frac{dG}{dx}$, $\frac{d}{dx}[G(x)]$, and $G'(x)$. The proper units on derivatives are output units per input unit. Rates of change also can be expressed as percentages. A percentage rate of change describes the relative magnitude of the rate.

Numerically and Algebraically Finding Slopes

When we have an equation $y = f(x)$ to associate with the curve, we can improve our graphical approximations of the slope of the tangent line with numerical approximations of the limit of slopes of secant lines. The method of numerically estimating slopes can be generalized to provide a valuable algebraic method for finding exact slopes at points, as well as formulas for slopes at any input value. We call this method the Four-Step Method of finding derivatives. This method yields the formal definition of a derivative: If $y = f(x)$, then

$$\frac{dy}{dx} = f'(x) = \lim_{h \to 0} \frac{f(x + h) - f(x)}{h}$$

provided that the limit exists.

CONCEPT CHECK

Can you		To practice, try	
• Find and interpret change, percentage change, and average rates of change			
• using data?		Section 2.1	Activities 5, 7
• using graphs?		Section 2.1	Activities 9, 11
• using equations?		Section 2.1	Activities 17, 19
• Work with APR and APY?		Section 2.1	Activities 25, 28
• Illustrate the relationship between secant lines and tangent lines?		Section 2.2	Activities 3, 17
• Accurately sketch tangent lines?		Section 2.2	Activity 19
• Use tangent lines to estimate rates of change?		Section 2.2	Activities 21, 25
• Use and interpret derivative notation?		Section 2.3	Activities 5, 11
• Correctly interpret derivatives?		Section 2.3	Activities 13, 15, 23
• Find and interpret percentage rate of change?		Section 2.3	Activities 17, 25
• Graphically and numerically estimate rates of change?		Section 2.3	Activity 19
• Numerically estimate the limit of a function at a point?		Section 2.4	Activities 1, 3
• Use the algebraic method to find a rate of change at a point?		Section 2.4	Activities 7, 15
• Use the Four-Step Method to find a rate-of-change formula?		Section 2.4	Activities 11, 17

CONCEPT REVIEW

1. Answer the following questions about the graph:

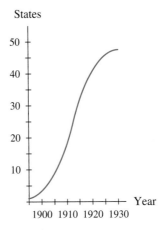

States

(Source: Based on data from Hamblin, Jacobson, and Miller, *A Mathematical Theory of Social Change,* New York: Wiley, 1973.)

a. List the labeled points at which the slope appears to be (i) negative, (ii) positive, and (iii) zero.

b. If B is the inflection point, what is the relationship between the steepness at B and the steepness at the points A, C, and D on the graph?

c. For each of the labeled points, will a tangent line at the point lie above or below the graph?

d. Sketch tangent lines at points A, B, and E.

2. Suppose the graph in Activity 1 represents the speed of a roller coaster (in feet per second) as a function of the number of seconds after the roller coaster reached the bottom of the first hill.

a. What are the units on the slopes of tangent lines? What common word is used to describe the quantity measured by the slope in this context?

b. When, according to the graph, was the roller coaster speeding up?

c. When was the roller coaster's speed the slowest?

d. When was the roller coaster slowing down most rapidly?

3. **P.T.A.**   The accompanying graph models the number of states associated with the national P.T.A. organization from 1895 through 1931. In 1915, 30 states were associated with the national organization. The association grew to 48 states by 1931.

a. Use the graph to approximate how rapidly (on average) the membership was growing from 1915 through 1931.

b. What was the percentage growth in membership from 1915 through 1931?

c. Approximately how rapidly (on average) was the membership growing from 1923 through 1927?

4. **Investment**   Suppose that to help pay for your college education, 15 years ago your parents invested a sum of money that has grown to $25,000 today.

a. How much did they originally invest if the investment earned 7.5% interest compounded monthly?

b. How much will $25,000 be worth 15 years from now, if it is invested in an account that earns 6.5% quarterly?

c. Write a formula for the accumulated amount in an account in which $25,000 is deposited for t years with interest being paid at 6.5% compounded quarterly.

d. Use the function in part c to determine the average rate of change of the amount in the account between the fifth and tenth years. What is the percentage change for this same time period?

5. **Employees**   The graph of a model for the number of Dell Computer Corporation employees between 1992 and 2002 is shown below.

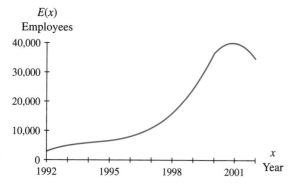

(Source: Based on data in Hoover's Online Guide Company Capsules.)

a. Sketch a secant line between the points with inputs 1993 and 1997. Describe the information that the slope of this line provides.

b. Sketch a tangent line at the point corresponding to 1998. Describe the information that the slope of this line provides.

c. Estimate the average rate of change in the number of employees between 1993 and 1997. Interpret your answer.

d. Estimate the rate of change and the percentage rate of change in the number of employees in 1998. Interpret your answers.

6. **Swim Time** $T(x)$ is the number of seconds that it takes an average athlete to swim 100 meters free style at age x years.

a. Write sentences interpreting $T(22) = 49$ and $T'(22) = -0.5$.

b. What does a negative derivative indicate about a swimmer's time?

7. **Airline Revenue**   Northwest Airlines revenues from passengers for selected years between 1991 and 2003 are given in the table.

Year	Passenger revenue (billion dollars)
2003	7.632
2001	8.207
1999	8.692
1997	8.822
1995	7.762
1993	6.620
1991	5.862

(Source: Northwest Airlines Corporation, Financial and Operating Statistics 5/27/05, ir.nwa.com)

a. Find a model for the data.

b. Numerically investigate the rate of change of the passenger revenue in 2001. Choose at least three increasingly close points. In table form, record the close points, the slopes with four decimal places, and the limiting value with two decimal places.

c. Interpret the limiting value in part *b*.

d. Give the formula for the derivative of the equation in part *a*. Evaluate the derivative in 2001.

8. In your own words, outline the Four-Step Method for calculating derivatives. Illustrate the method for the function $f(x) = 7x + 3$.

Project 2.1 Fee-Refund Schedules

Setting

Some students at many colleges and universities enroll in courses and then later withdraw from them. Such students may have part-time status upon withdrawing. Part-time students have begun questioning the fee-refund policy, and a public debate is taking place. Students who enrolled under full-time status are unable to receive a fee refund even if they have part-time status after dropping their classes. Recently, the student senate at one university passed a resolution condemning the current fee-refund schedule. Then, the associate vice president issued a statement claiming that further erosion of the university's ability to retain student fees would reduce course offerings. The Higher Education Commission has scheduled hearings on the issue. The Board of Trustees has hired your firm as consultants to help them prepare their presentation.

Tasks

1. Examine the current fee-refund schedule for your college or university. Present a graph and formula for the current fee-refund schedule. Critique the refund schedule.

   Create alternative fee-refund schedules that include at least two quadratic plans (one concave up and one concave down), an exponential plan, a logistic plan, a no-refund plan, and a complete-refund plan. (*Hint:* Linear models have constant first differences. What is true about quadratic and exponential models?) For each plan, present the refund schedule in a table, in a graph, and with an equation. Critique each plan from the students' viewpoint and from that of the administration.

   Select the nonlinear plan that you believe to be the best choice from both the students' and the administration's perspectives. Outline the reasons for your choice.

2. Estimate the rate of change of your selected equation for withdrawals after 1 week, 3 weeks, and 5 weeks. Include any other times that are indicated by your school's schedule. Interpret the rates of change in this context. How might the rate of change influence the administration's view of the model you chose? Would the administration consider a different model more advantageous? If so, why? Why did you not propose it as your model of choice?

Reporting

1. Prepare a written report of your results for the Board of Trustees. Include scatter plots, models, and graphs. Include in an appendix the reasoning that you used to develop each of your models.

2. Prepare a press release for the college or university to use when it announces the adoption of your plan. The press release should be succinct and should answer the questions *who, what, when, where,* and *why.* Include the press release in your report to the Board.

3. (Optional) Prepare a brief (15-minute) presentation on your work. You will be presenting it to members of the Board of Trustees of your college or university.

Project 2.2 Doubling Time

Setting

Doubling time is defined as the time it takes for an investment to double. Doubling time is calculated by using the compound interest formula $A = P\left(1 + \frac{r}{n}\right)^{nt}$ or the continuously compounded interest formula $A = Pe^{rt}$. An approximation to doubling time can be found by dividing 72 by 100r. This approximating technique is known as the **Rule of 72**.

    Dr. C. G. Bilkins, a nationally known financial guru, has been criticized for giving false information about doubling time and the Rule of 72 in seminars. Your team has been hired to provide mathematically correct information for Dr. Bilkins to use.

Tasks

1. Construct a table of doubling times for interest rates from 2% to 20% (in increments of 0.25%) when interest is compounded annually, semiannually, quarterly, monthly, weekly, and daily. Construct a table of doubling-time approximations for interest rates of 2% through 20% when using the Rule of 72. Devise similar rules for 71, 70, and 69. Then construct tables for these rules. Examine the tables and determine the best approximating rule for interest compounded semiannually, quarterly, monthly, weekly, and daily. Justify your choices.

For each interest compounding listed above, compare percent errors when using the Rule of 72 and when using the rule you choose. Percent error is $\frac{\text{estimate} - \text{true value}}{\text{true value}} \cdot 100\%$. Comment on when the rules overestimate, when they underestimate, and which is preferable.

2. Dr. Bilkins is interested in knowing how sensitive doubling time is to changes in interest rates. Estimate rates of change of doubling times at 2%, 8%, 14%, and 20% when interest is compounded quarterly. Interpret your answers in a way that would be meaningful to Dr. Bilkins.

Reporting

1. Prepare a written report for Dr. Bilkins in which you discuss your results in Tasks 1 and 2. Be sure to discuss whether Dr. Bilkins should continue to present the Rule of 72 or should present other rules that depend on the number of times interest is compounded.

2. Prepare a summary document for Dr. Bilkins. It should include (a) a brief summary of how to estimate doubling time using an approximation rule and (b) a statement about the error involved in using the approximation. Also include a brief statement summarizing the sensitivity of doubling time to fluctuations in interest rates. Include the document in your written report.

3. (Optional) Prepare a brief (15-minute) presentation of your study. You will be presenting it to Dr. Bilkins. Your presentation should be only a summary, but you need to be prepared to answer any technical questions that may arise.

Determining Change: Derivatives

3

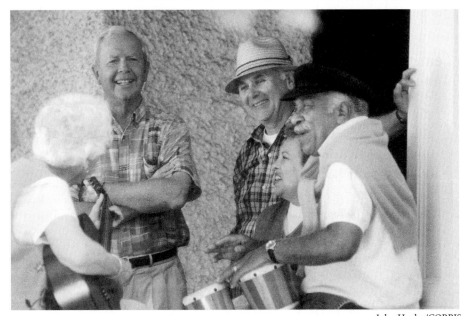

John Henley/CORBIS

Concept Application

The aging of the American population may be one of the demographic changes that has the greatest impact on our society over the next several decades. Given a model for the projected number of senior Americans (65 years of age or older), the function and its derivative can be used to answer questions such as the following:

• What is the projected number of senior Americans in 2030?

• How rapidly will that number be changing in 2030?

• What is the estimated percentage rate of change in the number of senior Americans in 2030?

You will be able to answer these questions by using the model given in Activity 30 of Section 3.2 and the derivative rules presented in this chapter.

Chapter Introduction

We have described change in terms of rates: average rates, instantaneous rates, and percentage rates. Of these three, instantaneous rates are the most important in our study of calculus. In Chapter 2 we presented a method, using the definition of the derivative, that enables us to find derivative models for certain functions.

In this chapter, we consider some rules for derivatives: the Simple Power Rule, the Constant Multiplier Rule, the Sum and Difference Rules, the Chain Rule, the Product Rule, and the Quotient Rule. These rules provide the foundation needed to work with more complicated functions that we often encounter in the course of real-life investigations of change.

Concepts You Will Be Learning

- Drawing rate-of-change graphs or slope graphs (3.1)
- Identifying points of undefined slope (3.1)
- Using simple derivative rules for power, exponential, and log functions (3.2, 3.3)
- Using the Chain Rule for derivatives (3.4)
- Using the Product and Quotient Rules for derivatives (3.5)
- Applying derivative rules to find rate-of-change formulas (3.2, 3.3, 3.4, 3.5)
- Determining the rate of change of a function at a point (3.2, 3.3, 3.4, 3.5)
- Using L'Hôpital's Rule to determine limits of ratios (3.6)

3.1   Drawing Rate-of-Change Graphs

In Chapter 2 we considered the rate of change of a function at a given point. We learned how to express the instantaneous rate of change verbally as well as estimate it graphically, numerically, and algebraically. At the end of Section 2.4 we saw that the algebraic method for determining the rate of change at a specific point can be generalized to a formula. The limit definition of the derivative is a key concept of calculus. In Section 3.2 we develop general rules about slope formulas. However, it is important that we have a good intuitive understanding of the relationship between functions and their slope formulas before we begin using derivative rules. To enhance this understanding, we consider the relationship between the graph of a function and its slope graph.

Extracting Rate-of-Change Information from a Function Graph

Every smooth, continuous curve with no vertical tangent lines has a slope associated with each point on the curve. When these slopes are plotted, they also form a smooth, continuous curve. We call the resulting curve a **slope graph, rate-of-change graph,** or **derivative graph.**

Consider the smooth, continuous curve shown in Figure 3.1. What do we know about the slopes of this graph? Sketch lines tangent to the curve at the points where $x = A$ and $x = C$ and at several other points on the curve, as shown in Figure 3.2.

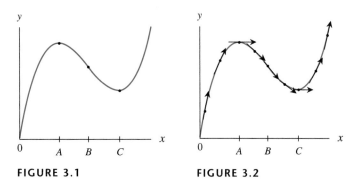

FIGURE 3.1   FIGURE 3.2

The graph is smooth and continuous so we deduce the following facts:

- The tangent lines at the points with inputs A and C are horizontal, so the slope is zero at those points.

- Between 0 and A, the graph is increasing, so the slopes are positive. The tangent lines become less steep moving from 0 to A, so the slopes start off large and become smaller as we approach A from the left.

- Between A and C, the graph is decreasing, so the slopes are negative.

- At B the graph has an inflection point. This is the point at which the graph is decreasing most rapidly—that is, the point at which the slope is most negative.

- To the right of C, the graph is again increasing, so the slopes are positive. The tangent lines become steeper as we move to the right of C, so the slopes become larger as the input increases beyond C.

Because the vertical-axis units of the slope graph are different from those of the function graph, we do not draw the slope graph on the same set of axes as the original graph.

We record the above information in Figure 3.3. Then, we sketch a continuous slope graph, as shown in Figure 3.4.

FIGURE 3.3

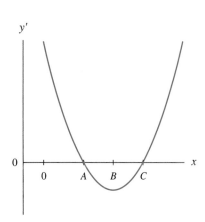

FIGURE 3.4

We do not know the specifics of the slope graph—how far below the horizontal axis it dips, where it crosses the vertical axis, how steeply it rises to the right of *C*, and so on. However, we do know its basic shape.

EXAMPLE 1 *Sketching a Slope Graph*

A Logistic Curve The graph in Figure 3.5 is a logistic curve. Sketch its slope graph.

FIGURE 3.5

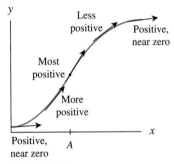

FIGURE 3.6

Solution
We note that the logistic curve in Figure 3.5 is always increasing. Thus its slope graph is always positive (above the horizontal axis). Even though there is no relative maximum or relative minimum, the logistic curve does level off at both ends. Thus its slope graph will be near zero at both ends. (See Figure 3.6.)

We note that the logistic curve has its steepest slope at *A* because this is the location of the inflection point. Therefore, the slope graph is greatest (has a maximum) at this point. (See Figure 3.7.) We sketch the continuous slope graph in Figure 3.8.

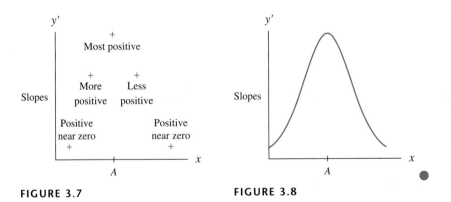

FIGURE 3.7

FIGURE 3.8

Example 1 illustrated using information from the graph of a function to sketch the slope graph. In Example 2, we use information concerning the slopes of a function to sketch both the graph of the function and its slope graph.

EXAMPLE 2   *Relating Function and Rate-of-Change Graphs*

Decreasing Functions

The graphs in parts *a* and *b* are decreasing but with different slopes.

a. Sketch a graph that is always decreasing but has slopes that are always increasing. Also sketch its slope graph.

b. Sketch a graph that is always decreasing with slopes that are always decreasing. Also sketch its slope graph.

Solution

a. If a graph is decreasing, it is falling from left to right and has negative slopes. If the negative slopes are increasing, they are becoming less negative (moving toward zero) as the input increases. The graph is becoming less steep. Such a graph must be concave up, as shown in Figure 3.9.

The slopes of this graph are always negative, so a slope graph must lie completely below the input axis. As Figure 3.10 shows, the negative slopes are approaching zero. They will never be positive. (See Figure 3.11.)

FIGURE 3.9

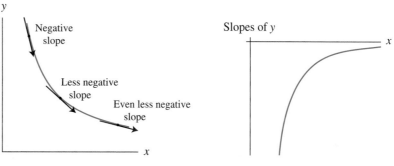

FIGURE 3.10   **FIGURE 3.11**

b. Like the graph in part *a*, this graph is falling from left to right and has negative slopes. However, the slopes are becoming more negative. They become more and more negative. This means the graph becomes more steep as input increases.

A declining graph that becomes increasingly steep looks like the one shown in Figure 3.12. The slopes are always negative, so the slope graph will lie completely below and will move farther away from the input axis as the input increases. See Figures 3.13 and 3.14.

FIGURE 3.12

FIGURE 3.13   **FIGURE 3.14**

In the preceding discussion and example, the graphs we used had no labeled tick marks on the horizontal or vertical axes. In such cases, it is not possible to estimate the value of the slope of the graph at any given point. Instead, we sketch the general shape of the slope graph by observing the important points and general behavior of the original graph, such as

- Points at which a tangent line is horizontal
- The intervals over which the graph is increasing or decreasing
- Points of inflection
- Places at which the graph appears to be horizontal or leveling off

As the previous examples indicate, sketching lines tangent to a curve helps us determine the relative magnitude of the slopes. As this process becomes more familiar, you should be able to visualize the tangent lines. This technique is illustrated in Example 3.

EXAMPLE 3   *Using Relative Magnitudes to Sketch Slope Graphs*

Growth Rate   The height (in centimeters) of a plant often follows the general trend shown in Figure 3.15. Draw a graph depicting the growth rate of the plant.

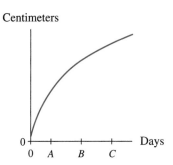

FIGURE 3.15

Solution
The slopes at *A*, *B*, and *C* are all positive. Is the slope at *A* smaller or larger than that at *B*? It is larger, so the slope graph at *A* should be higher than it is at *B*. The graph at *C* is not as steep as it is at either *A* or *B*, so the slope graph should be lower at *C* than at *B*. (See Figure 3.16.)

The slope is steepest near the left endpoint and least steep near the right endpoint. Adding these observations to your plot yields Figure 3.17.

Now we sketch the slope graph according to the plot. (See Figure 3.18.)

FIGURE 3.16

FIGURE 3.17

FIGURE 3.18

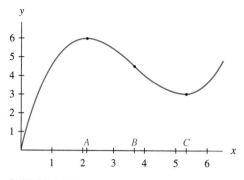

FIGURE 3.19

A Detailed Look at the Slope Graph

When a graph has labeled tick marks on both the horizontal and the vertical axes or an equation for the graph is known, it is possible to estimate the values of slopes at certain points on the graph. However, it would be tedious to calculate the slope graphically or numerically for every point on the graph. Instead, we calculate the slope at a few points including inflection points and relative extremes.

Consider again a graph with a maximum, an inflection point, and a minimum similar to the one we saw at the beginning of this section in Figure 3.1. Figure 3.19 shows such a graph, but this time the graph has labeled tick marks on both the horizontal and the vertical axes.

We know that the slope graph crosses the horizontal axis at A and C and that a minimum occurs on the slope graph below the horizontal axis at B. Before, we did not know how far below the axis to draw this minimum. Now that there is a numerical scale on the axes, we can graphically estimate the slope at the inflection point and use that estimate to help us sketch the slope graph.

By drawing the tangent line at B and estimating its slope, we find that the minimum of the slope graph is approximately 1.4 units below the horizontal axis. (See Figure 3.20.)

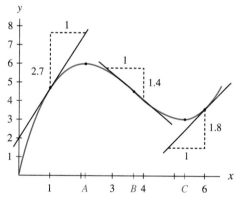

FIGURE 3.20

If we estimate the slopes at two additional points, say at $x = 1$ and $x = 6$, then we can produce a fairly accurate sketch of the slope graph. Table 3.1 shows a list of estimated slope values. Plotting these points and sketching the slope graph give us the graph in Figure 3.21.

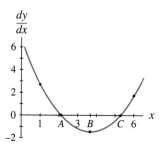

FIGURE 3.21

TABLE 3.1

x	1	A	B	C	6
Slope	2.7	0	−1.4	0	1.8

If we do not have a continuous curve but have only a scatter plot, then we can sketch a rate-of-change graph after first sketching a smooth curve that fits the scatter plot. Then we can draw the slope graph of that smooth curve. We show this technique in Example 4.

EXAMPLE 4 *Using a Curve Through Data to Sketch a Slope Graph*

Population In 1797, the Lorenzo Carter family built a cabin on Lake Erie where today the city of Cleveland, Ohio, is located. Table 3.2 gives population data for Cleveland from 1810 through 1990.

TABLE 3.2

Year	Population	Year	Population
1810	57	1910	560,663
1820	606	1920	796,841
1830	1076	1930	900,429
1840	6071	1940	878,336
1850	17,034	1950	914,808
1860	43,417	1960	876,050
1870	92,829	1970	750,879
1880	160,146	1980	573,822
1890	261,353	1990	505,616
1900	381,768		

(Source: U.S. Department of Commerce, Bureau of the Census.)

a. Sketch a smooth curve representing population. Your curve should have no more inflection points than the number suggested by the scatter plot.

b. Sketch a graph representing the rate of change of population.

Solution

a. Draw a scatter plot of the population data, and sketch the smooth curve. (See Figure 3.22.)

b. The population graph is fairly level in the early 1800s, so the slope graph will begin near zero. The smooth sketched curve increases during the 1800s and early 1900s until it peaks in the 1940s. Thus the slope graph will be positive until the mid-1940s, at which time it will cross the horizontal axis and become negative. Population decreased from the mid-1940s onward.

There appear to be two inflection points. The point of most rapid growth appears near 1910, and the point of most rapid decline appears near 1975. These are the years in which the slope graph will be at its maximum and at its minimum, respectively.

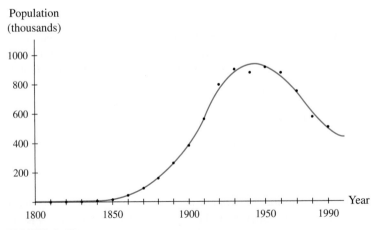

FIGURE 3.22

By drawing tangent lines at 1910 and at 1975 and estimating their slopes, we find that population was increasing by approximately 22,500 people per year in 1910 and was decreasing by about 12,500 people per year in 1975. See Figure 3.23.

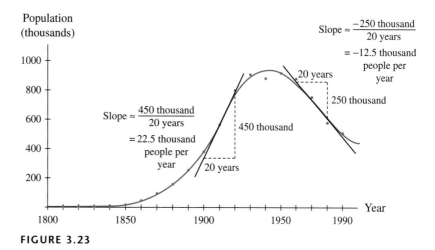

FIGURE 3.23

Now we use all the information from this analysis to sketch the slope graph shown in Figure 3.24.

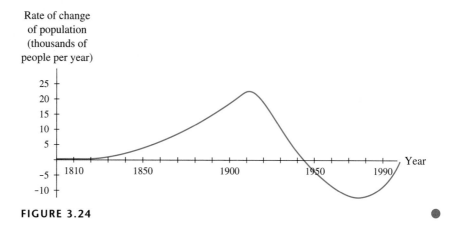

FIGURE 3.24

Of course, if we had a formula for the graph, we could estimate the slope numerically at a few points instead of graphically estimating it with tangent lines. Even so, we still need to understand curvature and horizontal-axis intercepts to sketch the rate-of-change graph adequately.

Points of Undefined Slope

It is possible for the graph of a continuous function to have a point at which the slope does not exist. Remember that the slope of a tangent line is the limit of slopes of approximating secant lines and that we should be able to use secant lines through points either to the left or to the right of the point at which we are estimating the slope to find this limit. Recall that if the limits from the left and from the right are not the same, then the derivative does not exist at that point. We depict the nonexistence of the derivative at such points on the slope graph by drawing an open circle on each piece of the slope graph. This is illustrated in Figure 3.25a.

Also, points at which the tangent line is vertical (that is, the slope calculation results in a zero in the denominator) are considered to have an undefined slope. The graph of one such function is shown in Figure 3.25b.

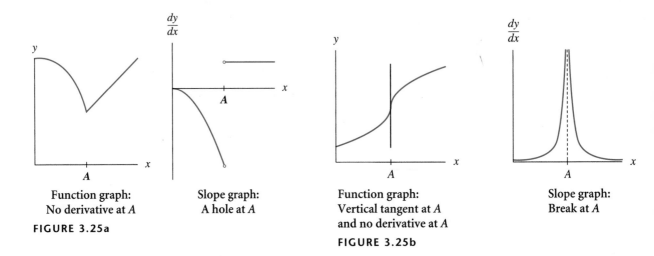

Function graph:
No derivative at *A*

FIGURE 3.25a

Slope graph:
A hole at *A*

Function graph:
Vertical tangent at *A*
and no derivative at *A*

FIGURE 3.25b

Slope graph:
Break at *A*

If a function is not continuous at a point, then its slope is undefined at that point even when the slope from the left and the slope from the right are the same.

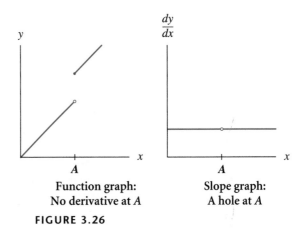

Function graph:
No derivative at *A*

Slope graph:
A hole at *A*

FIGURE 3.26

Most of the time when there is a break in the slope graph, it is because the original function is piecewise, as shown in Figures 3.25a and 3.26. You should be careful when drawing slope graphs of piecewise continuous functions. Figure 3.25b shows a smooth, continuous function with a point at which the derivative is undefined. We do not often encounter such phenomena in real-life applications, but they can happen.

3.1 Concept Inventory

- Slope graph, rate-of-change graph, derivative graph
- Increasing functions have positive slopes
- Decreasing functions have negative slopes
- Maxima and minima have zero slopes
- Inflection points are maxima or minima of slope graph or points of undefined slope

3.1 Activities

Getting Started

In Activities 1 through 10, list as many facts as you can about the slopes of the graphs. Then, on the basis of those facts, sketch the slope graph of each function.

1.

2.

3.

4.

5.

6.

7.

8.

9.

10.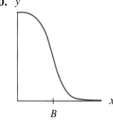

11. a. Sketch a graph that is increasing with increasing slopes. Also sketch its slope graph.

   b. Sketch a graph that is increasing with decreasing slopes. Also sketch its slope graph.

12. a. Sketch a graph that is decreasing with decreasing slopes. Also sketch its slope graph.

   b. Sketch a graph that is decreasing with increasing slopes. Also sketch its slope graph.

Applying Concepts

13. Phone Bill The graph shows the average monthly cell phone bill in the United States between 1987 and 2002.

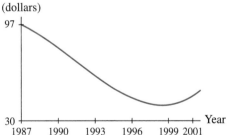

(Source: Based on data from the Cellular Telecommunication and Internet Association.)

   a. Estimate and record the slopes of tangent lines for the input values shown below.

Year	1991	1993	1997	1999	2001
Slope of tangent line					

   b. Use the information in part *a* to sketch an accurate rate-of-change graph for the average monthly cell phone bill. Label the axes with units as well as values.

14. Population The graph shows the population of Iowa between 1990 and 1999.

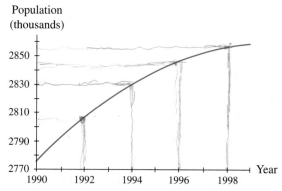

Population (thousands)

(Source: Based on data from U.S. Bureau of the Census.)

a. Sketch tangent lines for the input values of 1992, 1994, 1996, and 1998. Also sketch a tangent line for a point near 1990. Estimate the slopes of these five tangent lines.

b. Use the information in part *a* to sketch an accurate rate-of-change graph for the population of Iowa. Label the axes with units as well as values.

15. AIDS The graph shows the cumulative number of AIDS cases between 1985 and 2001 diagnosed in the United States since 1984.

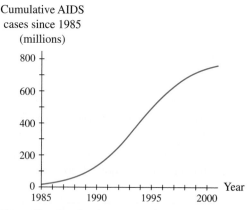

Cumulative AIDS cases since 1985 (millions)

(Source: Based on data from Centers for Disease Control.)

a. Sketch tangent lines for the input values of 1990, 1995, 1997, and 2000. Also estimate the slope of a tangent line for a point near 1985.

b. Use the information in part *a* to sketch an accurate rate-of-change graph for the cumulative number of AIDS cases diagnosed in the United States. Label the axes with units as well as values.

16. Fuel The graph shows the average annual fuel consumption of vehicles in the United States between 1970 and 1995.

Average fuel consumption (gallons per year)

(Source: Based on data from *Statistical Abstract*, 1998.)

a. Sketch tangent lines for the input values of 1975, 1980, 1985, and 1990. Also sketch tangent lines for a point near 1970 and a point near 1995. Estimate the slopes of these six tangent lines.

b. Use the information in part *a* to sketch an accurate rate-of-change graph for the average annual fuel consumption. Label the axes with units as well as values.

17. Membership The graph gives the membership in a campus organization during its first year.

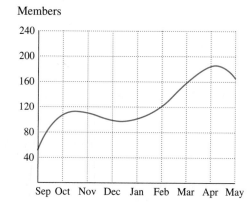

Members

a. Estimate the average rate of change in the membership during the academic year.

b. Estimate the instantaneous rates of change in mid-September, November, February, and April.

c. On the basis of your answers to part *b*, sketch a rate-of-change graph. Label the units on the axes.

d. The membership of the organization was growing most rapidly in September. Not including that month, when was the membership growing most rapidly? What is this point on the membership graph called?

e. Why was the result of the calculation in part *a* of no use in part *c*?

18. Police Calls The scatter plot depicts the number of calls placed each hour since 2 A.M. to a sheriff's department.

a. Sketch a smooth curve through the scatter plot with no more inflection points than the number suggested by the scatter plot.

(Source: Sheriff's Office of Greenville County, South Carolina.)

b. At what time(s) is the number of calls a minimum? a maximum?

c. Are there any other times when the graph appears to have a zero slope? If so, when?

d. Estimate the slope of your smooth curve at any inflection points.

e. Use the information in parts *a* through *d* to sketch a graph depicting the rate of change of calls placed each hour. Label the units on both axes of the rate-of-change graph.

19. Jails The capacity of jails in a southwestern state has been increasing since 1990. The average daily population of one jail between 1990 and 2000 is shown in the graph.

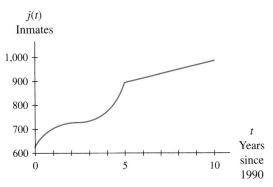

(Source: Based on data from Washoe County Jail, Reno, Nevada.)

a. Sketch the slope graph of *j*. (*Hint:* Estimate $j'(t)$ near $t = 0$ and $t = 4.5$ in order to sketch the slope graph accurately.)

b. Label both the horizontal and the vertical axes.

20. Price The graph shows cattle prices (for choice 450-pound steer calves) from October 1994 through May 1995. Input is the number of months since October 1994.

p(m)
Cattle price
(dollars per pound)

```
1.00
0.95
0.90                      /\
0.85 ·                   /    \                    m
0.80                    /        \·              Months
0.75 +--+--+--+--+--+--+--+                      since
     0  1  2  3  4  5  6  7                       October
                                                  1994
```

(Source: Based on data from the National Cattleman's Association.)

a. Sketch a slope graph of *p*. (*Hint:* Estimate $p'(m)$ near $m = 0$ and $m = 2.5$ in order to sketch the slope graph accurately.)

b. Label the horizontal and vertical axes.

21. Profit The accompanying graph depicts the average monthly profit for Slim's Used Car Sales for the previous year.

a. Estimate the average rate of change in Slim's average monthly profit if the number of cars he sells increases from 40 to 70 cars.

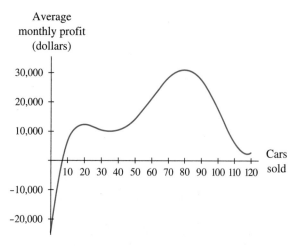

Average monthly profit (dollars)

b. Estimate the instantaneous rates of change at 20, 40, 60, 80, and 100 cars.

c. On the basis of your answers to part *b*, sketch a rate-of-change graph. Label the units on the axes.

d. For what number of cars sold between 20 and 100 is average monthly profit increasing most rapidly? For what number of cars sold is average monthly profit decreasing most rapidly? What is the mathematical term for these points?

e. Why was the result of the calculation in part *a* of no use in part *c*?

22. Mortality   The graph shows deaths of males due to different types of cancer.

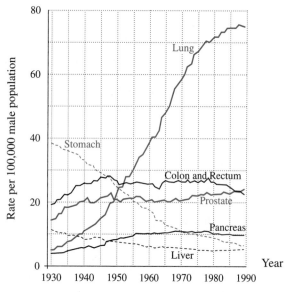

a. Use the graph to estimate carefully the rate of change in deaths of males due to lung cancer in 1940, 1960, and 1980.

b. Use this information to sketch an accurate rate-of-change graph for deaths of males due to lung cancer.

c. Label the units on both axes of the derivative graph.

In Activities 23 through 26, indicate the input values for which the graph has no derivative. Explain why the derivative does not exist at those points. Sketch a derivative graph for each of the function graphs.

23.

24.

25.

26.

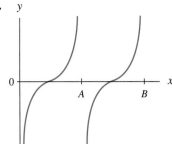

27. Sketch the slope graph of a function f with input t that meets these criteria: $f(-2) = 5$, the slope is positive for $t < 2$, the slope is negative for $t > 2$, and $f'(2)$ does not exist.

28. Sketch the slope graph of a function g with input x that meets these criteria: $g(3)$ does not exist, $g'(0) = -4$, $g'(x) < 0$ for $x < 3$, g is concave down for $x < 3$, $g'(x) > 0$ for $x > 3$, g is concave up for $x > 3$, $\lim_{x \to 3^+} g(x) \to \infty$, and $\lim_{x \to 3^-} g(x) \to -\infty$.

29. Construct the graphs of a function h and its slope h', with input x, such that $h'(1)$ is significantly different from the percentage rate of change of h at $x = 1$.

30. The figure shows a graph of the function $q(t) = \frac{1}{t}$.

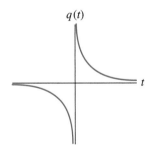

a. Sketch a slope graph of q.

b. Find a formula for the slope graph. [*Hint:* Multiply the numerator and denominator of the secant line slope formula by $t(t + h)$.] Compare a graph of this formula with the graph you sketched in part *a*.

31. The figure below shows a graph of the function $p(m) = m + \sqrt{m}$.

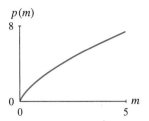

a. Sketch a slope graph of p.

b. Find a formula for the slope graph. Compare a graph of this formula with the graph you sketched in part *a*. (*Hint:* Multiply the numerator and denominator of the secant line slope formula by $\sqrt{m + h} + \sqrt{m}$.)

32. The figure below shows a graph of the function $k(x) = x + \frac{1}{x}$.

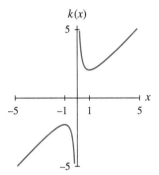

a. Sketch a slope graph of k.

b. Find a formula for the slope graph. [*Hint:* Multiply the numerator and denominator of the secant line slope formula by $x(x + h)$.] Compare a graph of this formula with the graph you sketched in part *a*.

Discussing Concepts

33. What elements of a function graph are of specific importance when sketching a rate-of-change graph for that function? Explain why these elements are important.

34. Why is it important to understand curvature and horizontal-axis intercepts in order to adequately sketch a rate-of-change graph?

3.2   Simple Rate-of-Change Formulas

By now you should have a thorough understanding of the concept of instantaneous rate of change as the slope of a line tangent to a curve at a point, where that slope is defined as a limiting value of slopes of secant lines. We now rely on this conceptual understanding in order to present formulas for rapid calculation of rates of change.

You already know two rate-of-change formulas from our study of linear functions in Chapter 1. A horizontal line has slope zero, and a nonhorizontal line of the form $y = ax + b$ has slope a. We know that the rate of change, or derivative, of a line is its slope, so we can state the following derivative formulas:

Constant Rule for Derivatives

If $y = b$, then $\dfrac{dy}{dx} = 0$.

Derivative of a Linear Function

If $y = ax + b$, then $\dfrac{dy}{dx} = a$.

EXAMPLE 1   *Finding the Derivative of a Linear Function*

Cricket's Chirping   The frequency of a cricket's chirp is affected by air temperature and can be modeled by

$$C(t) = 0.212t - 0.309 \text{ chirps per second}$$

when the temperature is $t°$F, $50 \le t \le 85$. Write a formula for the rate of change of a cricket's chirping speed with respect to a change in temperature.

Solution
The frequency of a cricket's chirp is changing by

$$C'(t) = 0.212 \text{ chirps per second per degree Fahrenheit}$$

when t is the temperature between 50°F and 85°F.   ●

The Simple Power Rule

Next, consider quadratic and cubic functions. In Section 2.4, we determined that the rate-of-change formula for $y = x^2$ is $\dfrac{dy}{dx} = 2x$. In Activity 13 of that same section, you were asked to show that the rate-of-change formula for $y = x^3$ is $\dfrac{dy}{dx} = 3x^2$. Note that these are two special cases of one of the most important rules that we use for quickly finding derivative formulas, the **Simple Power Rule.**

> ## Simple Power Rule for Derivatives
>
> If $y = x^n$, then $\dfrac{dy}{dx} = nx^{n-1}$, where n is any nonzero real number.

The Constant Multiplier and the Sum and Difference Rules

In order to find derivative formulas for any polynomial, we need two rules in addition to the Simple Power Rule. The first derivative rule we illustrate is the **Constant Multiplier Rule.** Each of the figures in Figure 3.27 shows the graph of a function and a graph of a constant multiple of that function, and the slope graphs of the function and the constant multiple of that function.

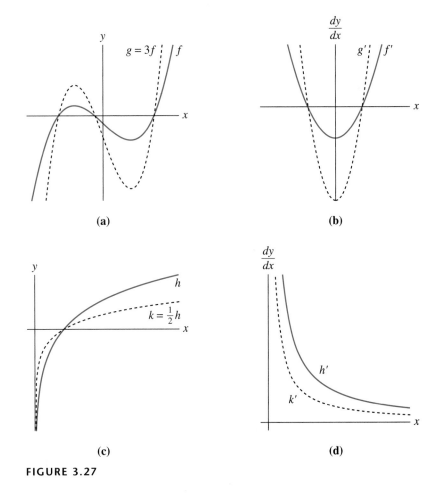

FIGURE 3.27

The effect of a constant multiplier is to amplify the output if the multiplier is greater than 1 or to diminish the output if the multiplier has magnitude between 0 and 1. The behavior of the rate of change of the function will be amplified or diminished by the same factor.

If the constant multiplier is negative, it has the additional effect of reflecting the function over the horizontal axis. The rate-of-change function is likewise reflected, as illustrated in Figures 3.28a and b.

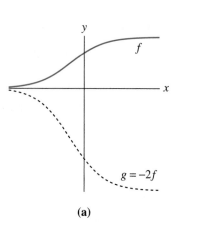

(a)   (b)

FIGURE 3.28

The graphs in Figures 3.27 and 3.28 are basic illustrations of the following general rule:

Constant Multiplier Rule for Derivatives

If $y = kf(x)$, then $\dfrac{dy}{dx} = kf'(x)$.

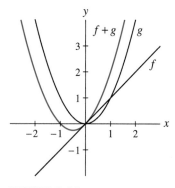

FIGURE 3.29

This rule enables us to calculate quickly the rate-of-change formula for a function such as $y = 5x^4$: leave the 5 alone, and apply the Simple Power Rule to x^4. This process gives $\frac{dy}{dx} = 5(4x^3) = 20x^3$.

The final rules needed for rapid calculation of the rate-of-change formula for any polynomial are the **Sum and Difference Rules.**

Concept Development: Sum and Difference Rules   We present two graphical illustrations of the Sum and Difference Rules. Figure 3.29 illustrates the graphs of $f(x) = x$, $g(x) = x^2$ and the graph of $(f + g)(x) = x + x^2$, the function that is the sum of f and g.

The minimum of the sum function $f + g$ appears to occur at $x = -\frac{1}{2}$, indicating that the slope graph of the sum function crosses the horizontal axis at $x = -\frac{1}{2}$. Moving from left to right along the horizontal axis, the outputs of $f + g$ are decreasing before $x = -\frac{1}{2}$ and increasing again after $x = -\frac{1}{2}$. Thus, the sum function slope graph is negative to the left of $x = -\frac{1}{2}$ and positive to the right of $x = -\frac{1}{2}$. Further, note that the graph of the sum function has the same basic shape as the function f, except that it is shifted.

We now investigate the basic shape and magnitude of the slope graph by looking at a few arbitrarily chosen inputs ($x = -2$, $x = 3$, and $x = 7$). By first using the Linear Function Rule and the Simple Power Rule to obtain the slopes of f and g, we complete the second and third rows of Table 3.3. Numerically investigating the slope of $f + g$ at the inputs given in the first row of Table 3.3 yields the estimates in the fourth row.

TABLE 3.3

x	-2	$-\frac{1}{2}$	0	3	7
$\frac{df}{dx} = 1$	1	1	1	1	1
$\frac{dg}{dx} = 2x$	-4	-1	0	6	14
$\frac{d(f + g)}{dx} \approx 1 + 2x$	-3	0	1	7	15

Figure 3.30 shows the slope graphs of f, g, and the sum function $f + g$ (in teal). The graph of the sum function was obtained by plotting the outputs in the fourth row of the table and connecting them with a smooth curve.

Note in both Table 3.3 and Figure 3.30, that the slopes of the sum function $f + g$ at a specific point can be obtained by summing the slopes of the functions f and g. A similar result is obtained if we investigate the difference function $f - g$. The slope of the difference function $f - g$ at a certain input can be obtained by subtracting the slope of g from the slope of f at that same input. See Figures 3.31a and b.

FIGURE 3.30

(a)

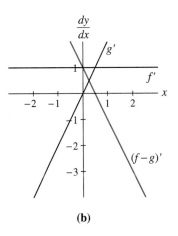

(b)

FIGURE 3.31

The second graphical illustration of the Sum and Difference Rules specifically illustrates the differences of two simple power functions, $k(x) = x^3$ and $h(x) = x^2$. Figure 3.32 shows graphs of these two functions and their difference function $(k - h)(x) = x^3 - x^2$.

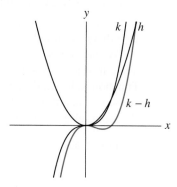

FIGURE 3.32

The difference function $k - h$ appears to have a minimum at $x = \frac{2}{3}$ and a maximum at $x = 0$. Therefore, the slope graph crosses the horizontal axis at these input values. Moving from left to right along the horizontal axis, the difference function is increasing before $x = 0$ and after $x = \frac{2}{3}$ and is decreasing between these two inputs. Thus the slope graph is positive to the left of $x = 0$ and to the right of $x = \frac{2}{3}$ and is negative between these values. Numerically evaluating the limiting value of the slope of $k - h$ at $x = -1$, $x = \frac{1}{3}$, and $x = 2$ yields the estimates in the second row of Table 3.4. Using these numerical estimates as additional points on the graph, we sketch the slope graph of $k - h$. See Figure 3.33.

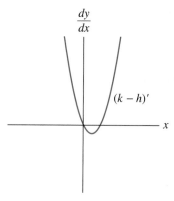

FIGURE 3.33

TABLE 3.4

x	-1	$\frac{1}{3}$	2
$\dfrac{d(k - h)}{dx}$	5	-0.33333	8

Table 3.5 and Figure 3.34 illustrate the relationship of the slopes of the functions k and h and the difference function $k - h$. Similar to the result we found with the sum

function, the slopes of the difference function are the differences of the slopes of the two individual functions.

TABLE 3.5

x	-1	0	$\frac{1}{3}$	$\frac{2}{3}$	2
$\frac{dk}{dx} = 3x^2$	3	0	$\frac{1}{3}$	$\frac{4}{3}$	12
$\frac{dh}{dx} = 2x$	-2	0	$\frac{2}{3}$	$\frac{4}{3}$	4
$\frac{d(k-h)}{dx} \approx$	5	0	$\frac{-1}{3}$	0	8

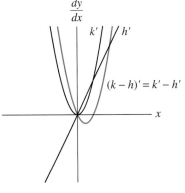

FIGURE 3.34

We state the following general rule:

The Sum and Difference Rules for Derivatives

If $j(x) = f(x) + g(x)$, then $\dfrac{dj}{dx} = \dfrac{df}{dx} + \dfrac{dg}{dx}$.

If $j(x) = f(x) - g(x)$, then $\dfrac{dj}{dx} = \dfrac{df}{dx} - \dfrac{dg}{dx}$.

The Sum and Difference Rules also apply to sums and/or differences of more than two functions. With the rules we now have, we can find the rate-of-change formula for any polynomial function. For example, if

$$p(x) = 3.22x^3 - 0.15x^2 + 9.98x - 30$$

we use the Constant Multiplier and the Simple Power Rules to find the derivative formula for each term, and then we combine the terms using the Sum and Difference Rules. The rate-of-change formula for p is

$$p'(x) = 3.22(3x^2) - 0.15(2x) + 9.98 - 0 = 9.66x^2 - 0.3x + 9.98$$

Example 2 is an application of the Sum and Difference Rules.

EXAMPLE 2   *Applying Derivative Rules*

Maintenance Costs   Table 3.6 gives the average yearly maintenance costs per vehicle for 15,000 miles of operation in the United States from 1993 through 2000.

TABLE 3.6

Year	1993	1994	1995	1996	1997	1998	1999	2000
Maintenance costs (cents per mile per vehicle)	2.4	2.5	2.6	2.8	2.8	3.1	3.6	3.9

(Source: Bureau of Transportation Statistics.)

Find a quadratic model for the data. Use it to approximate how rapidly maintenance costs were increasing in 1998.

Solution
A quadratic model for the data is

$$g(t) = 0.0304t^2 - 0.00417t + 2.446 \text{ cents per mile per vehicle}$$

gives the maintenance cost for a vehicle where t is the number of years after 1993, $0 \le t \le 7$. Applying the Sum and Difference, Power, Constant Multiplier, and Constant Rules, we find that the derivative of g with respect to t is

$$\frac{dg}{dt} = 0.0304(2t) - 0.00417(1) + 0$$

so

$$\frac{dg}{dt} = 0.0608t - 0.00417 \text{ cents per mile per vehicle per year}$$

gives the rate of change in the maintenance costs, t years after 1993, $0 < t < 7$.

Evaluating the derivative at $t = 5$ gives 0.2998 cent per mile per vehicle per year as the rate of change of maintenance costs in 1998. Thus we estimate that in 1998, the average maintenance cost per vehicle was increasing at a rate of approximately 0.30 cent per mile per year. ●

In summary, here is a list of the rate-of-change formulas you should know.

	Simple Derivative Rules	
Rule Name	**Function**	**Derivative**
Constant Rule	$y = b$	$\frac{dy}{dx} = 0$
Linear Function Rule	$y = ax + b$	$\frac{dy}{dx} = a$
Power Rule	$y = x^n$	$\frac{dy}{dx} = nx^{n-1}$
Constant Multiplier Rule	$y = kf(x)$	$\frac{dy}{dx} = kf'(x)$
Sum Rule	$y = f(x) + g(x)$	$\frac{dy}{dx} = f'(x) + g'(x)$
Difference Rule	$y = f(x) - g(x)$	$\frac{dy}{dx} = f'(x) - g'(x)$

3.2 Concept Inventory

- Derivative formulas
- For constants a, b, and n:

  If $y = b$, then $y' = 0$.

  If $y = ax + b$, then $y' = a$.

  If $y = x^n$, then $y' = nx^{n-1}$.

  If $y = kf(x)$, then $y' = kf'(x)$.

  If $y = f(x) \pm g(x)$, then $y' = f'(x) \pm g'(x)$.

3.2 Activities

Getting Started

For each of the functions whose graphs are given in Activities 1 through 6, first sketch the slope graph and then give the slope equation.

1.

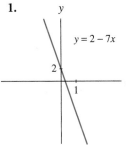

$y = 2 - 7x$

2.

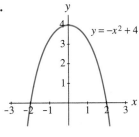

$y = -x^2 + 4$

3.

$y = x^4$

4.

$y = x^3$

5.

$y = \frac{3}{2}$

6.

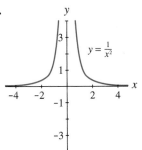

$y = \frac{1}{x^2}$

For each function in Activities 7 through 18,

  a. identify which simple derivative rules apply,

  b. write the formula for the derivative of the function.

7. $f(x) = x^5$ **8.** $f(x) = x^4$

9. $f(x) = 3x^3$ **10.** $f(x) = -0.5x^2$

11. $f(x) = -5x$ **12.** $f(x) = 7x$

13. $f(x) = 0.2$ **14.** $f(x) = 35$

15. $y = 12x + 13$

16. $f(x) = 7x^2 - 9.4x + 12$

17. $y = 5x^3 + 3x^2 - 2x - 5$

18. $y = -3.2x^3 + 6.1x - 5.3$

For each function in Activities 19 through 26,

  a. rewrite the expression in power notation if necessary, and

  b. write the derivative formula for the function.

19. $f(x) = \dfrac{1}{x^3}$ (*Hint:* $\dfrac{1}{x^n} = x^{-n}$.)

20. $f(x) = \dfrac{1}{x^{-3}}$ **21.** $y = \dfrac{-9}{x^2}$

22. $f(x) = \dfrac{3x^2}{x}$

23. $j(x) = \dfrac{3x^2 + 1}{x}$

  (*Hint:* Rewrite as two separate terms.)

24. $j(x) = \dfrac{4x^2 + 19x + 6}{x}$

  (*Hint:* Rewrite as three separate terms.)

25. $f(x) = \sqrt{x}$ (*Hint:* Rewrite as $\sqrt{x} = x^{1/2}$.)

26. $h(x) = 17 - 8\sqrt{x}$

Applying Concepts

27. ATM Fee The average ATM transaction fee charged by U.S. banks between 1996 and 1999 can be modeled by the equation $A(t) = 0.1333t + 0.17$ dollars t years after 1990.

(Source: Based on data from the U.S. Public Interest Research Group.)

  a. Write the derivative formula for A.

  b. Estimate the transaction fee in 2000.

  c. How quickly was the fee changing in 1999?

28. Population   The population of Hawaii between 1970 and 1990 can be modeled by

$$P(t) = 15.48t + 485.4 \text{ thousand people}$$

t years after 1950. A graph of this model is given.

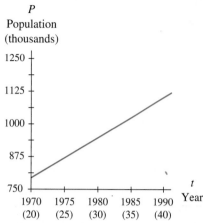

P
Population
(thousands)

(Source: Based on data from George T. Kurian, *Datapedia of the United States, 1790–2000*, Latham, MD: Bernan Press, 1994.)

a. Write the formula for P'.

b. How many people lived in Hawaii in 1970?

c. How quickly was Hawaii's population changing in 1990?

29. Temperature   The graph shows the temperature values (in °F) on a typical May day in a certain midwestern city.

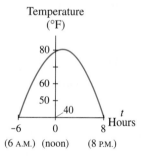

Temperature
(°F)

The equation of the graph is

$$\text{Temperature} = -0.8t^2 + 2t + 79°\text{F}$$

where t is the number of hours since noon. Use the derivative formula to verify each of the following statements.

a. The graph is not as steep at 1:30 P.M. as it is at 7 A.M.

b. The slope of the tangent line at 7 A.M. is 10°F per hour.

c. The instantaneous rate of change of the temperature at noon is 2°F per hour.

d. At 4 P.M. the temperature is falling by 4.4°F per hour.

30. Population   The projected number of Americans age 65 or older for the years 1995 through 2030 can be modeled by the equation

$$N(x) = 0.03x^2 + 0.315x + 34.23 \text{ million people}$$

where x is the number of years after 2000.

(Source: Based on data from John Greenwald, "Elder Care: Making the Right Choice," *Time*, August 30, 1999, p. 52.)

a. What is the projected number of Americans 65 years of age and older in 1995? in 2029? in 2030?

b. What is the rate of change of the projected number in 1996? in 2029?

c. Find the percentage rate of change in the projected number in 2029.

d. The Census Bureau predicts that in 2030, 20.1% of the U.S. population will be 65 years of age or older. Use this prediction and one of the unrounded answers to part *a* to estimate the total U.S. population in 2030.

31. Births   The number of live births to U.S. women 45 years and older between 1950 and 2000 can be modeled by the equation

$$B(x) = 0.2685x^3 - 15.6x^2 + 94.684x + 5378.03 \text{ births}$$

where x is the number of years since 1950.

(Source: Based on data from www.infoplease.com. Accessed 9/24/02.)

a. Was the number of live births rising or falling in 1970? in 1995?

b. How rapidly was the number of live births rising or falling in 1970? in 1995?

32. Study Time The graph represents a test grade (out of 100 points) as a function of hours studied.

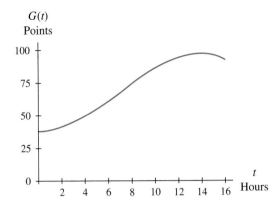

The equation of the graph is

$$G(t) = -0.044t^3 + 0.918t^2 + 38.001 \text{ points}$$

after t hours of study. Use the equation to verify each of the following statements.

a. $\frac{dG}{dt} = 1.704$ points per hour when $t = 1$ hour.

b. $G'(4) = 5.232$ points per hour.

c. The slope of the tangent line when $t = 15$ hours is approximately -2 points per hour.

33. Metabolic Rate The table shows the metabolic rate of a typical 18- to 30-year-old male according to his weight.

Weight (pounds)	Metabolic rate (kilocalories per day)
88	1291
110	1444
125	1551
140	1658
155	1750
170	1857
185	1964
200	2071

(Source: L. Smolin and M. Grosvenor, *Nutrition: Science and Applications*, Philadelphia, PA: Saunders College Publishing, 1994.)

a. Find a formula for a typical man's metabolic rate.

b. Write the derivative of the formula in part *a*.

c. What does the derivative in part *b* tell you about a man's metabolic rate if that man weighs 110 pounds? if he weighs 185 pounds?

34. Profit An artisan makes hand-crafted painted benches to sell at a craft mall. Her weekly revenue and costs (not including labor) are given in the table.

Number of benches sold each week	Weekly revenue (dollars)	Weekly cost (dollars)
1	300	57
3	875	85
5	1375	107
7	1750	121
9	1975	143
11	1950	185
13	1700	213

a. Find models for revenue, cost, and profit.

b. Write the derivative formula for profit.

c. Find and interpret the rates of change of profit when the artisan sells 6, 9, and 10 benches, respectively.

d. What does the information in part *c* tell you about the number of benches the artisan should produce each week?

35. Sales The accompanying table gives revenue from new-car sales and associated advertising expenditures for franchised new-car dealerships in the United States for selected years between 1980 and 2000.

Year	Advertising expenses (billions of dollars)	Revenue (billions of dollars)
1980	1.2	130.5
1985	2.8	251.6
1990	3.7	316.0
1995	4.6	456.2
1998	5.3	546.3
2000	6.4	646.8

(Source: *Statistical Abstract*, 2001.)

a. Find a model that describes revenue as a function of advertising expenditures.

b. Write the formula for the derivative of the equation in part *a*.

c. Use your equations from parts *a* and *b* to estimate the revenue and to find how rapidly the revenue was changing when $5 billion was spent on advertising.

d. What was the percentage rate of change in the revenue when $5 billion was spent on advertising?

36. Costs   Production costs (in dollars per hour) for a certain company to produce between 10 and 90 units per hour are given in the table.

Units	Cost (dollars per hour)
10	150
20	200
30	250
40	400
50	750
60	1400
70	2400
80	3850
90	5850

a. Consider the cost for producing 0 units to be $0. Include (0, 0) in the data and find a cubic model for production costs.

b. Convert the model in part *a* to one for the average cost per unit produced.

c. Find the slope formula for average cost.

d. How rapidly is the average cost changing when 15 units are being produced? 35 units? 85 units? Interpret your answers.

37. Profit   The managers of Windolux, Inc., have modeled some cost data and found that if they produce *x* storm windows each hour, the cost (in dollars) to produce one window is given by the function

$$C(x) = 0.015x^2 - 0.78x + 46 + \frac{49.6}{x}, \quad x > 0$$

Windolux sells its storm windows for $175 each. (You may assume that every window made will be sold.)

a. Write the formula for the profit made from the sale of one storm window when Windolux is producing *x* windows each hour.

b. Write the formula for the rate of change of profit.

c. What is the profit made from the sale of a window when Windolux is producing 80 windows each hour?

d. How rapidly is profit from the sale of a window changing when 80 windows are produced each hour? Interpret your answer.

38. Sales   A publishing company estimates that when a new book by a best-selling American author first hits the market, its sales can be predicted by the equation $n(x) = 68.95\sqrt{x}$, where $n(x)$ represents the total number (in thousands) of copies of the book sold in the United States by the end of the *x*th week. The number of copies of the book sold abroad by the end of the *x*th week can be modeled by

$$a(x) = 0.125x \text{ thousand copies of the book}$$

a. Write the formula for the total number of copies of the book sold in the United States and abroad by the end of the *x*th week.

b. Write the formula for the rate of change of the total number of books sold.

c. How many books will be sold by the end of the first year (that is, after 52 weeks)?

d. How rapidly are books selling at the end of the first year? Interpret your answer.

Discussing Concepts

39. Use your knowledge of the shape and end behavior of the graph of a cubic function to explain why the slope graph of a cubic function is the graph of a quadratic function. Use this argument to explain why the rate-of-change formula for a cubic function is the formula for a quadratic function.

40. Use the simple derivative rules presented in this section to explain why the rate-of-change formula for a cubic function of the form $y = ax^3 + bx^2 + cx + d$ is the formula for a quadratic function. Write your explanation in paragraph form.

3.3   Exponential and Logarithmic Rate-of-Change Formulas

In Section 3.2 we developed some general rules for rate-of-change formulas. In this section we will continue using those rules and develop others.

Exponential Rules

Our next formulas involve derivatives of exponential functions. Because the proof of these rules is beyond the scope of this book, we explore the functions graphically and numerically to develop an understanding of the behavior of the derivative of the function before stating the general derivative formula. We begin our exploration with the function $y = e^x$. First, we consider the concavity and end behavior of this function (see Figure 3.35).

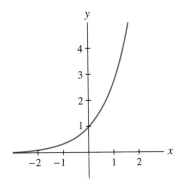

FIGURE 3.35

- $y = e^x$ approaches 0 as x decreases without bound, so the slope graph of $y = e^x$ seems to become horizontal (i.e., $y' \to 0$ as $x \to {}^-\infty$).

- $y = e^x$ increases without bound as x increases without bound ($x \to \infty$) and the graph of the function is concave up and has no vertical asymptotes. The graph of $y = e^x$ seems to become more and more vertical; so the slopes are increasing without bound (i.e., $y' \to \infty$ as $x \to \infty$).

Next, to obtain an idea of magnitude, we numerically investigate the slope at a few points. Table 3.7 shows function values and slope values (rounded to three decimal places) for several inputs.

TABLE 3.7

x	−2	0	1	3
$y = e^x$	0.135	1.000	2.718	20.086
$y' = \dfrac{dy}{dx}$	0.135	1.000	2.718	20.086

This function is surprising in that the rate-of-change values are precisely the same as the function values. *This function is its own derivative!* In other words, if $y = e^x$, then $\dfrac{dy}{dx} = y' = e^x$. The slope graph of $y = e^x$ coincides with the graph of the original function.

Derivative of e^x

If $y = e^x$, then $\dfrac{dy}{dx} = e^x$.

Does this rule apply to exponential functions that have bases different from e? In other words, if $y = b^x$, is $\dfrac{dy}{dx} = b^x$? Consider the functions $y = 2^x$ and $y = 3^x$. Graphically, the descriptions of end behavior and curvature lead to the same conclusions about the shape of the derivative graphs for these exponential functions as did the analysis of the shape and end behavior of $y = e^x$. (See Figures 3.36a and b.) Any differences that occur should appear in a numerical investigation of the magnitude of the slopes.

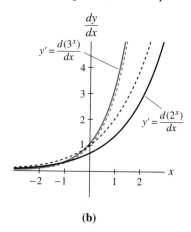

FIGURE 3.36

(a)

(b)

TABLE 3.8

x	$y = 2^x$	$y' = \dfrac{dy}{dx}$
−2	0.25	0.17329
0	1	0.69315
1	2	1.38629
3	8	5.54518

We begin by exploring the derivative of $y = 2^x$. See Table 3.8 (values are rounded to five decimal places for convenience). It is obvious from the table that the derivative of $y = 2^x$ is not $y' = 2^x$. If we use the definition of derivative for the function $f(x) = 2^x$, we obtain

$$f'(x) = \lim_{h \to 0} \frac{2^{x+h} - 2^x}{h}$$

You may recall that $2^{x+h} = 2^x 2^h$. Using this fact, we rewrite the derivative formula as

$$f'(x) = \lim_{h \to 0} \frac{2^x 2^h - 2^x}{h} = \lim_{h \to 0} \left[2^x \left(\frac{2^h - 1}{h} \right) \right]$$

Because the term 2^x is not affected by h approaching 0, we treat it as a constant:

$$f'(x) = 2^x \left[\lim_{h \to 0} \frac{2^h - 1}{h} \right]$$

This formula indicates that the derivative of $y = 2^x$ is $2x$ times a constant. In Table 3.9 we numerically estimate the limiting value of the multiplier $\lim_{h \to 0} \dfrac{2^h - 1}{h}$.

TABLE 3.9

$h \to 0^+$	$\dfrac{2^h - 1}{h}$	$h \to 0^-$	$\dfrac{2^h - 1}{h}$
0.1	0.717735	−0.1	0.669670
0.01	0.695555	−0.01	0.690750
0.001	0.693387	−0.001	0.692907
0.0001	0.693171	−0.0001	0.693123
0.00001	0.693150	−0.00001	0.693145
0.000001	0.693147	−0.000001	0.693147
Limit ≈ 0.693147		Limit ≈ 0.693147	

It may seem that the multiplier 0.693147 is arbitrary because it is not a familiar number, but that is not the case. You should verify that $0.693147 \approx \ln 2$. In fact, it can be proved that the limit of the multiplier in the derivative formula for $f(x) = 2^x$ is $\ln 2$. We state the formula for the derivative of $y = 2^x$ as $y' = (\ln 2)2^x$ A similar exploration suggests that the formula for the derivative of $y = 3^x$ is $y' = (\ln 3)3^x$.

The two derivative formulas $\frac{d}{dx}(2^x) = (\ln 2)2^x$ and $\frac{d}{dx}(3^x) = (\ln 3)3^x$ are special cases of the general derivative formula for exponential functions. The derivative of $y = b^x$ is $y' = (\ln b)b^x$ if $b > 0$. In fact, the rule $\frac{d}{dx}(e^x) = e^x$ is also a special case of this formula. You will be asked to verify this fact in the activities.

Derivative of b^x

If $y = b^x$, where the real number $b > 0$, then $\dfrac{dy}{dx} = (\ln b)b^x$.

EXAMPLE 1   *Using Exponential Derivative Formulas*

Credit Cards   If credit card purchases are not paid off by the due date on the credit card statement, finance charges are applied to the remaining unpaid balance. In July 2001, one major credit card company had a daily finance charge of 0.054% on unpaid balances. Assume that the unpaid balance is \$1 and that no new purchases are made.

a.   Find an exponential function for the balance owed d days after the due date.

b.   How much is owed after 30 days?

c.   Write the derivative formula for the function from part *a*.

d.   How quickly is the balance changing after 30 days?

e.   Repeat parts *a* through *d*, assuming that the unpaid balance is \$2000.

Solution

a.   Recall that the constant b in an exponential function $f(x) = ab^x$ is $(1 + \text{percentage growth})$ and that the constant a is the value of $f(0)$. Thus we use the function

$$f(d) = 1(1.00054^d) = 1.00054^d \text{ dollars}$$

to represent the balance due d days after the due date.

b.   Thirty days after the due date, the balance is $f(30) \approx \$1.02$.

c.   According to the derivative rules we have seen in this chapter, the derivative of $y = b^x$ is $y' = (\ln b)b^x$. Thus the derivative formula for our function f is

$$f'(d) = (\ln 1.00054)1.00054^d \text{ dollars per day}$$

after d days.

d.   We evaluate $f'(30)$. After 30 days, the balance is increasing at a rate of 0.0005 dollar per day.

e.　If the unpaid balance is \$2000, the balance-due function is

$$f(d) = 2000(1.00054^d) \text{ dollars}$$

after d days. The amount due after 30 days is $f(30) = \$2032.65$.

According to the Constant Multiplier and the Exponential Rules, the derivative of the balance function is

$$f'(d) = 2000(\ln 1.00054)1.00054^d \text{ dollars per day}$$

After 30 days, the balance is increasing at a rate of $f'(30) = \$1.10$ per day.　●

Natural Logarithm Rule

As with exponential functions, we motivate the derivative rule for the natural log function graphically and numerically.

The natural logarithm function is not defined for negative input values or for an input of zero. But as x approaches 0 from the right ($x \to 0^+$), the outputs of the natural log function decrease without bound. The tilt of the function appears to become vertical. As x increases without bound, $\ln x$ increases without bound, but more and more slowly. The slope never becomes zero. (See Figures 3.37a and b.)

TABLE 3.10

x	Derivative of $y = \ln x$
$\dfrac{1}{2}$	2.000
1	1.000
2	0.500
4	0.250
10	0.100

(a)

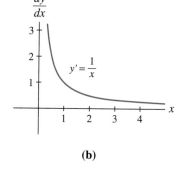

(b)

FIGURE 3.37

Numerically investigating the slope (to three decimal places) for a few input values (to three decimal places) once again helps to establish magnitude. (See Table 3.10.) Unlike the case for the exponential function, whose derivative at a certain input value is dependent on the corresponding output value, these derivatives are dependent on the input values. Note that each derivative value is the reciprocal of the input value—that is, it is 1 divided by the input value. The derivative of $y = \ln x$ at $x = 2$ is $\frac{1}{2}$, the derivative at $x = 4$ is $\frac{1}{4}$, the derivative at $x = 10$ is $\frac{1}{10}$, and so on.

Derivative of ln x

If $y = \ln x$, then $\dfrac{dy}{dx} = \dfrac{1}{x}$ for positive x-values.

Our next example illustrates the use of all of the derivative rules presented in this section and the previous section.

EXAMPLE 2   *Using Simple Derivative Rules*

Find the derivatives of the following functions:

a. $f(x) = 12.36 + 6.2 \ln x$ b. $g(t) = 4e^t + 19$

c. $m(r) = \dfrac{8}{r} - 12\sqrt{r}$ d. $j(y) = 17\left(1 + \dfrac{0.025}{12}\right)^{12y}$

Solution

a. Apply the Constant Rule to the first term and the Constant Multiplier and the Natural Log Rules to the second term. Use the Sum Rule to add the two derivatives together.

$$\frac{df}{dx} = f'(x) = 0 + 6.2\left(\frac{1}{x}\right) = \frac{6.2}{x}$$

b. Apply the Constant Multiplier and the e^x Rules to the first term and the Constant Rule to the second term. Again, use the Sum Rule to add the two derivatives.

$$\frac{dg}{dt} = g'(t) = 4e^t + 0 = 4e^t$$

c. The key to finding the derivative formula for this function is rewriting the two terms using algebra rules for exponents. Recall that a negative exponent is used to indicate that a term is in the denominator and that an exponent of $\frac{1}{2}$ indicates a square root. Using these facts, rewrite m as

$$m(r) = 8r^{-1} - 12r^{1/2}$$

Now apply the Constant Multiplier, the Power, and the Sum Rules to obtain

$$\frac{dm}{dr} = m'(r) = -(8)r^{-1-1} - \frac{1}{2}(12)r^{1/2-1} = -8r^{-2} - 6r^{-1/2} = \frac{-8}{r^2} - \frac{6}{\sqrt{r}}$$

d. Begin by calculating the number $\left(1 + \frac{0.025}{12}\right)^{12}$ in order to rewrite the formula in the form ab^x. We have rounded this number to three decimal places, but in using the derivative to calculate rates of change, you should keep all decimal places stored in your calculator.

$$j(y) = 17\left(1 + \frac{0.025}{12}\right)^{12y} \approx 17(1.025^y)$$

Now apply the Constant Multiplier and the Exponential Rules.

$$\frac{dj}{dy} = j'(y) \approx 17(\ln 1.025)(1.025^y) \approx 0.425(1.025^y) \quad \bullet$$

In summary, we present a list of the rate-of-change formulas you should know. (The list includes the formulas from Section 3.2.) The formulas are best learned through practice. Although you may need to refer to the table on page 194 for some of the beginning activities, you should attempt to work most of them without looking at this list.

Simple Derivative Rules

Rule Name	Function	Derivative
Constant Rule	$y = b$	$\dfrac{dy}{dx} = 0$
Linear Function Rule	$y = ax + b$	$\dfrac{dy}{dx} = a$
Power Rule	$y = x^n$	$\dfrac{dy}{dx} = nx^{n-1}$
Exponential Rule	$y = b^x, b > 0$	$\dfrac{dy}{dx} = (\ln b)b^x$
e^x Rule	$y = e^x$	$\dfrac{dy}{dx} = e^x$
Natural Log Rule	$y = \ln x, x > 0$	$\dfrac{dy}{dx} = \dfrac{1}{x}$
Constant Multiplier Rule	$y = kf(x)$	$\dfrac{dy}{dx} = kf'(x)$
Sum Rule	$y = f(x) + g(x)$	$\dfrac{dy}{dx} = f'(x) + g'(x)$
Difference Rule	$y = f(x) - g(x)$	$\dfrac{dy}{dx} = f'(x) - g'(x)$

3.3 Concept Inventory

• Derivative formulas

For constants a, b, k, and n,

If $y = b$, then $y' = 0$.

If $y = ax + b$, then $y' = a$.

If $y = x^n$, then $y' = nx^{n-1}$.

If $y = b^x$, then $y' = (\ln b)b^x$.

If $y = e^x$, then $y' = e^x$.

If $y = \ln x$, then $y' = \dfrac{1}{x}$.

If $y = kf(x)$, then $y' = kf'(x)$.

If $y = f(x) \pm g(x)$, then $y' = f'(x) \pm g'(x)$.

3.3 Activities

Getting Started

For each of the functions whose graphs are given in Activities 1 through 6, first sketch the slope graph and then give the slope equation.

1.

2.

3.

4.

5.

6.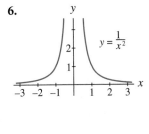

For each function in Activities 7 through 20, give the derivative formula.

7. $h(x) = 3 - 7e^x$ **8.** $y = 5e^x + 3$

9. $g(x) = 2.1^x$ **10.** $y = 3.5^x$

11. $h(x) = 12(1.6)^x$ **12.** $y = 6(0.8)^x$

13. $f(x) = 10\left(1 + \dfrac{0.05}{4}\right)^{4x}$ (*Hint:* Rewrite as ab^x.)

14. $f(x) = 24\left(1 + \dfrac{0.06}{12}\right)^{12x}$

15. $j(x) = 4.2(0.8^x) + 3.5$

16. $j(x) = 7(1.3^x) - e^x$ **17.** $j(x) = 4 \ln x$

18. $j(x) = -\ln x$ **19.** $y = 12 - 7 \ln x$

20. $k(x) = 3.7e^x - 2 \ln x$

Applying Concepts

21. Investment The value of a $1000 investment in an account with 4.3% interest compounded continuously can be modeled as

$$A = e^{0.043t} \text{ thousand dollars after } t \text{ years, } t > 0$$

a. Write the rate-of-change formula for the value of the investment. (*Hint:* Let $b = e^{0.043}$, and use the rule for $y = b^t$.)

b. How much is the investment worth after 5 years?

c. How quickly is the investment growing after 5 years?

d. What is the percentage rate of growth after 5 years?

22. Investment An individual has $45,000 to invest: $32,000 will be put into a low-risk mutual fund averaging 6.2% interest compounded monthly, and the remainder will be invested in a high-yield bond fund averaging 9.7% interest compounded continuously.

a. Find an equation for the total amount in the two investments.

b. Give the rate-of-change equation for the combined amount.

c. How rapidly is the combined amount of the investments growing after 6 months? after 15 months?

23. Investment The value of a $1000 investment after 10 years in an account whose interest rate is $100r\%$ compounded continuously is

$$A(r) = 1000e^{10r} \text{ dollars}$$

a. Write the rate-of-change function for the value of the investment.

b. Determine the rate of change of the value of the investment at 7% interest. Discuss why the rate of change is so large.

c. If the interest rate is input as a percentage instead of a decimal, the function for the value of a $1000 investment after 10 years in an account with interest compounded continuously is

$$A(r) = 1000e^{0.1r} \text{ dollars}$$

where $r = 1.00$ when the interest rate is 1%, $r = 1.25$ when the interest rate is 1.25%, etc. Write the rate-of-change function for the value of the investment. Compare this rate-of-change function with that in part *a*.

d. Using the function in part *c*, determine the rate of change of the value of the investment at 7% interest. Compare this answer to that of part *b*.

24. Rising Dough For the first couple of hours after yeast dough has been kneaded, it approximately doubles in volume every 42 minutes. If we prepare 1 quart of yeast dough and let it rise in a warm room, then its growth can be modeled by the function

$$V = e^h \text{ quarts}$$

where h is the number of hours the dough has been allowed to rise.

a. How many minutes will it take the dough to attain a volume of 2.5 quarts?

b. Write a formula for the rate of growth of the yeast dough.

c. How quickly is the dough expanding after 24 minutes, after 42 minutes, and after 55 minutes? Report your answers in quarts per minute.

25. **iPod** The cumulative sales of iPods can be modeled by the equation

$$s(x) = 0.14(4.106^x) \text{ million units}$$

where $x = 0$ is the fiscal year ending in September 2002, $0 \le x \le 3$.

(Source: Simplified model based on data from "Apple Reports Fourth Quarter Results," 2003–2005, Apple Computer, Inc.)

a. How long did it take Apple to sell 2.5 million iPods?

b. Write a formula for the rate at which iPods were selling x years after the end of fiscal year 2001–2002.

c. How quickly were iPods selling at the time the 2.5 millionth iPod was sold?

26. **Population** The population of Aurora, a Nevada ghost town, can be modeled as

$$p(t) = \begin{cases} -7.91t^3 + 121t^2 + 194t \\ \quad - 123 \text{ people} & \text{when } 0.7 \le t \le 13 \\ 45.5(0.847^t) \\ \quad \text{thousand people} & \text{when } 13 < t \le 55 \end{cases}$$

where t is the number of years since the beginning of 1860.

(Source: Simplified model based on data from Don Ashbaugh, *Nevada's Turbulent Yesterday: A Study in Ghost Towns,* Los Angeles: Westernlore Press, 1963.)

a. The population model is defined using two different functions over different time intervals. For what years is a cubic model used? For what years is an exponential model used?

b. Write a formula giving the rate of change of population before $t = 13$.

c. Write a formula giving the rate of change of population after $t = 13$.

d. How quickly was the population growing or declining in the beginning of the years 1870, 1873, and 1900?

27. **Weight** The weight of a laboratory mouse between 3 and 11 weeks of age can be modeled by the equation

$$w(t) = 11.3 + 7.37 \ln t \text{ grams}$$

where the age of the mouse is $(t + 2)$ weeks after birth (thus, for a 3-week-old mouse, $t = 1$).

a. What is the weight of a 9-week-old mouse, and how rapidly is its weight changing?

b. How rapidly on average does the mouse grow between ages 6 and 11 weeks?

c. What happens to the rate at which the mouse is growing as it gets older? Explain.

28. **Web TV** The projected number of homes with access to the Internet via cable television between 1998 and 2005 can be modeled by the equation

$$I(x) = -138.27 + 76.29 \ln x \text{ million homes}$$

x years after 1990.

(Source: Based on data from Paul Kagen Associates, Inc., Cable Television Technology.)

a. Give the rate-of-change formula for the projected number of such homes.

b. How many homes are projected to have Internet access via a cable TV system in 2004, and how rapidly is that number projected to be growing?

29. **Milk Storage** The temperature at which milk must be stored can be modeled by the equation

$$T(d) = -9.9\ln(d) + 60.5°F$$

where d is the number of days that the milk needs to remain fresh, $d \ge 0$.

(Source: Simplified model based on data from the back of a milk carton from Model Dairy.)

a. Write a formula for the rate of change of temperature.

b. Consider graphs of the temperature function and the rate-of-change function. What do the graphs of the temperature function and its rate of change tell us as the number of days increases?

30. Costs Suppose the managers of a dairy company have found that it costs them approximately $c(u) = 3250 + 75 \ln u$ dollars to produce u units of dairy products each week. They also know that it costs them approximately $s(u) = 50u + 1500$ dollars to ship u units. Assume that the company ships its products once each week.

a. Write the formula for the total weekly cost of producing and shipping u units.

b. Write the formula for the rate of change of the total weekly cost of producing and shipping u units.

c. How much does it cost the company to produce and ship 5000 units in 1 week?

d. What is the rate of change of total production and shipping costs at 5000 units? Interpret your answer.

31. Tuition CPI The consumer price index (CPI) for college tuition between 1990 and 2000 is shown in the table.

Year	CPI	Year	CPI	Year	CPI
1990	175.0	1994	249.8	1998	306.5
1991	192.8	1995	264.8	1999	318.7
1992	213.5	1996	279.8	2000	331.9
1993	233.5	1997	294.1		

(Source: *Statistical Abstract,* 2001.)

a. Align the data as the number of years since 1980, and find a log model for the CPI.

b. Use the model to find the rate of change of the CPI in 1998.

32. Income The Bureau of the Census reports the median family income since 1947 as shown in the table. (Median income means that half of American families make more than this value and half make less.)

Year	Median family income (constant 1997 dollars)
1947	20,102
1957	26,133
1967	35,076
1977	40,656
1987	43,756
1997	44,568

a. Find a model for the data.

b. Find a formula for the rate of change of the median family income.

c. Find the rates of change and percentage rates of change of the median family income in 1972, 1980, 1984, 1992, and 1996.

d. Do you think the above rates of change and percentage rates of change affected the reelection campaigns of Presidents Nixon (1972), Carter (1980), Reagan (1984), Bush (1992), and Clinton (1996)?

33. iPods The cumulative revenue realized by Apple on the sales of iPods is shown in the table.

Fiscal year (ending September)	iPod revenue (millions of dollars)
2002	53
2003	174
2004	711
2005	1923
2006*	9423

*projected
(Source: Based on data from "Apple Reports Fourth Quarter Results," 2003–2005, Apple Computer, Inc.)

a. Find an exponential model for the data.

b. Write the derivative formula for the model.

c. Determine the revenue, rate of change in revenue, and percentage rate of change in revenue in 2005. Interpret these values.

34. VCR Homes The percentage of households with TVs that also have VCRs from 1990 through 2001 is shown in the table.

Year	Households (percent)	Year	Households (percent)
1990	68.6	1996	82.2
1992	75.0	1998	84.6
1994	79.0	2001	86.2

(Sources: *Statistical Abstract,* 1998, and Television Bureau of Advertising.)

a. Align the input data as the number of years since 1987, and find a log model for the data.

b. Write the rate-of-change formula for the model in part *a*.

c. According to the model, what was the percentage of households with TVs that also had VCRs in 2000? How rapidly was the percentage growing in that year? Interpret your answers.

Discussing Concepts

35. We have seen that the derivative of $y = b^x$ is $\frac{dy}{dx} = (\ln b)b^x$ as long as $b > 0$. We have also seen that the derivative of $y = e^x$ is $\frac{dy}{dx} = e^x$.

a. Show that the derivative formula for $y = e^x$ is a special case of the derivative formula for $y = b^x$ by applying the formula for $y = b^x$ to $y = e^x$

and then reconciling the result with the known derivative formula for $y = e^x$.

b. Use the derivative formula for $y = b^x$ to find a formula for the derivative of an exponential function of the form $y = e^{kx}$, where k is some known constant.

36. Use your knowledge of the shape and end behavior of the graph of a log function of the form $y = a + b \ln x$, as well as your knowledge of the simple derivative rules in Sections 3.2 and 3.3, to describe the shape and end behavior of the graph and mathematical form of the rate-of-change function of a log model.

3.4 The Chain Rule

We now present derivative formulas for more complicated functions than those considered in Sections 3.2 and 3.3. In particular, we introduce the method used for finding derivative formulas for composite functions.

The First Form of the Chain Rule

It is well known that high levels of carbon dioxide (CO_2) in the atmosphere are linked to increasing populations in highly industrialized societies. This is because large urban environments consume enormous amounts of energy, and CO_2 is a natural byproduct of the (often incomplete) consumption of that energy. Imagine that in a certain large city, the level of CO_2 in the air is linked to the size of the population by the equation $C(p) = \sqrt{p}$, where the units of $C(p)$ are parts per million (ppm) and p is the population. Also suppose that the population is projected to grow quadratically between 2000 and 2015 according to the equation $p(t) = 400t^2 + 2500$ people, where t is the number of years since 2000. Note that C is a function of p, and p is a function of t. Thus, indirectly, C is also a function of t. Suppose we want to know the rate of change of the CO_2 concentration *with respect to time* in 2013—that is, how rapidly the CO_2 concentration is rising or falling in 2013. The mathematical notation for this rate of change is $\frac{dC}{dt}$, and the units are ppm per year.

The derivative of C is $\frac{dC}{dp} = \frac{1}{2\sqrt{p}}$ ppm per person. But this is not the rate of change that we want because $\frac{dC}{dp}$ is the rate of change *with respect to population,* not time. The question now becomes "How do we transform ppm per person to ppm per year?" If we knew the rate of change of population with respect to time (people per year), then we could multiply as indicated to get the desired units:

$$\left(\frac{\text{ppm}}{\text{person}}\right)\left(\frac{\text{people}}{\text{year}}\right) = \frac{\text{ppm}}{\text{year}}$$

Population is given as a function of time, so its derivative is the rate of change that we need: $\frac{dp}{dt} = 800t$ people per year. This motivates

$$\frac{dC}{dp}\frac{dp}{dt} = \frac{dC}{dt} \text{ or } \left(\frac{1}{2\sqrt{p}}\frac{\text{ppm}}{\text{person}}\right)\left(800t\frac{\text{people}}{\text{year}}\right) = \frac{dC}{dt}\frac{\text{ppm}}{\text{year}}$$

Because $\frac{dC}{dt}$ is a rate of change *with respect to time*, it is standard procedure to write the derivative formula in terms of t. Recall that $p(t) = 400t^2 + 2500$ people, where t is the number of years since 2000. Substituting $400t^2 + 2500$ for p in the equation for $\frac{dC}{dt}$, we have

$$\frac{dC}{dt} = \frac{1}{2\sqrt{400t^2 + 2500}}(800t) \text{ ppm/year}$$

Now we substitute $t = 13$ (for 2013) to obtain our desired result:

$$\frac{dC}{dt} = \frac{1}{2\sqrt{400(13)^2 + 2500}}[800(13)] \approx 19.64 \text{ ppm/year}$$

In 2013, the CO_2 concentration will be increasing by approximately 19.64 ppm per year. The method used to find $\frac{dC}{dt}$ in the situation above is called the **Chain Rule** because it links together the derivatives of two functions to obtain the derivative of their composite function.

The Chain Rule (Form 1)

If C is a function of p, and p is a function of t, then

$$\frac{dC}{dt} = \left(\frac{dC}{dp}\right)\left(\frac{dp}{dt}\right)$$

EXAMPLE 1   *Using the First Form of the Chain Rule*

Violin Production   Let $A(v)$ denote the average cost to produce a student violin when v violins are produced, and let $v(t)$ represent the number (in thousands) of student violins produced t years after 2000. Suppose that 10 thousand student violins are produced in 2008 and that the average cost to produce a violin at that time is $142.10. Also, suppose that in 2008 the production of violins is increasing by 100 violins per year and the average cost of production is decreasing by 15 cents per violin.

a.   Describe the meaning and give the value of each of the following in 2008:

   i. $v(t)$ ii. $v'(t)$ iii. $A(v)$ iv. $A'(v)$

b.   Calculate the rate of change with respect to time of the average cost for student violins in 2008.

Solution

a. i. There are $v(8) = 10{,}000$ violins produced in 2008.

    ii. The rate of change of violin production in 2008 is $v'(8) = 0.1$ thousand violins per year. That is, $\frac{dv}{dt} = 100$ violins per year.

    iii. The average cost to produce a violin is $A(10) = \$142.10$ when 10,000 violins are produced.

    iv. When 10,000 violins are produced, the average cost is changing at a rate of $A'(10) = -\$0.15$ per violin. That is, $\frac{dA}{dv} = -\$0.15$ per violin.

b. The rate of change with respect to time of the average cost to produce a student violin in 2008 is

$$\frac{dA}{dt} = \frac{dA}{dv} \cdot \frac{dv}{dt}$$

$$= (-\$0.15 \text{ per violin})(100 \text{ violins per year}) = -\$15 \text{ per year}$$

In 2008 the average cost to produce a violin is declining by \$15 per year. ●

The Second Form of the Chain Rule

Recall the discussion at the beginning of this section concerning CO_2 pollution and population. We were given two functions—p, with input t, and C, whose input corresponds to the output of p—and then asked to find the derivative $\frac{dC}{dt}$. You may wonder why we did not substitute the expression for population into the CO_2 equation before finding the derivative:

$$C(p) = \sqrt{p} \text{ with } p(t) = 400t^2 + 2500 \text{ so } C(p(t)) = \sqrt{400t^2 + 2500}$$

This process, which is called function composition (see Section 1.1), enables us to express C directly as a function of t. If we now take the derivative, we get $\frac{dC}{dt}$, which is exactly what we needed. The reason we did not do this before is that we did not know a formula for finding the derivative of a composite function. However, we can now use the Chain Rule to obtain a formula. First, we review some terminology from Section 1.1.

Because $p(t)$ was substituted into the formula for C to create the composite function $C \circ p$, we call p the inside function and C the outside function. Next, recall the Chain Rule process:

$$\frac{dC}{dt} = \left(\frac{dC}{dp}\right)\left(\frac{dp}{dt}\right)$$

$$= \left(\frac{1}{2\sqrt{p}}\right)(800t)$$

$$= \left(\frac{1}{2\sqrt{400t^2 + 2500}}\right)800t$$

The first term, $\frac{1}{2\sqrt{400t^2 + 2500}}$, is simply the derivative of $\sqrt{p}$ with p replaced by $400t^2 + 2500$. This is the derivative of the outside function with the inside function substituted for p. The second term, $800t$, is the derivative with respect to t of p, the inside function. This leads us to a second form of the Chain Rule. If a function is expressed as a result of function composition (that is, if it is a combination of an inside function and an outside function), then its slope formula can be found as follows:

$$\text{Slope formula of composite function} = \begin{pmatrix} \text{derivative of the} \\ \text{outside function} \\ \text{with the inside} \\ \text{function untouched} \end{pmatrix} \begin{pmatrix} \text{derivative} \\ \text{of the inside} \\ \text{function} \end{pmatrix}$$

Mathematically, we state this form of the Chain Rule as follows:

The Chain Rule (Form 2)

If a function f can be expressed as the composition of two functions h and g—that is, if

$$f(x) = (h \circ g)(x) = h(g(x))$$

then its slope formula is

$$\frac{df}{dx} = f'(x) = h'(g(x)) \cdot g'(x)$$

In Example 2, we consider three somewhat different forms of composite functions, identify the inside function and the outside function for each, and use the second form of the Chain Rule to find formulas for the derivatives.

EXAMPLE 2   *Using the Second Form of the Chain Rule*

Write the derivatives (with respect to x) for the following three functions.

a. $y = e^{x^2}$ b. $y = (x^3 + 2x^2 + 4)^{1/2}$ c. $y = \dfrac{3}{4 - 2x^2}$

Solution

a. We can consider $y = e^{x^2}$ as composed of an outside function $y = e^p$ and an inside function $p = x^2$. The derivative of the outside function is e^p. (This exponential function is its own derivative.) Form 2 of the Chain Rule instructs us to leave the inside function untouched (that is, in its original form), so instead of e^p appearing in the derivative, the first expression in the slope formula is e^{x^2}. The second expression in the slope formula is the derivative, $2x$, of the inside function. The final answer is the product of these two derivatives.

$$\frac{dy}{dx} = (e^{x^2})(2x) = 2xe^{x^2}$$

b. The inside function of $y = (x^3 + 2x^2 + 4)^{1/2}$ is $p = x^3 + 2x^2 + 4$, and the outside function is $y = p^{1/2}$. The derivative of the outside function is $\frac{1}{2}p^{-1/2}$;

with p untouched, this becomes $\frac{1}{2}(x^3 + 2x^2 + 4)^{-1/2}$. The derivative of the inside function is $3x^2 + 4x$. Thus the Chain Rule gives

$$\frac{dy}{dx} = \frac{1}{2}(x^3 + 2x^2 + 4)^{-1/2}(3x^2 + 4x)$$

c. The function $y = \dfrac{3}{4 - 2x^2}$ can be thought of as the composition of the outside function $y = \dfrac{3}{p}$ and the inside function $p = 4 - 2x^2$. The derivative of the outside function is $\dfrac{-3}{p^2}$, or $\dfrac{-3}{(4 - 2x^2)^2}$. The derivative of the inside function is $-4x$. The derivative of the composite function is then

$$\frac{dy}{dx} = \left(\frac{-3}{(4 - 2x^2)^2}\right)(-4x) = \frac{12x}{(4 - 2x^2)^2} \quad \bullet$$

As illustrated in Example 3, one common use of the Chain Rule is to find the derivative of a logistic function.

EXAMPLE 3   *Using the Chain Rule to Find a Logistic Function Derivative*

VCR Homes   The percentage of households between 1980 and 2001 with VCRs can be modeled* by

$$P(t) = \frac{84.4}{1 + 33.6e^{-0.484t}} \text{ percent}$$

where t is the number of years since 1900. Find the rate-of-change formula for P with respect to t.

Solution
The function P can be rewritten as

$$P(t) = 84.4(1 + 33.6e^{-0.484t})^{-1}$$

In this form, it is easy to see that $p = 84.4u^{-1}$ is the outside function and that the inside function is $u = 1 + 33.6e^{-0.484t}$. Further, we can split u into an outside and an inside function with $u = 1 + 33.6e^v$ as the outside function and $v = -0.484t$ as the inside function.

Now, the derivative of P with respect to t is

$$\begin{aligned}
P'(t) &= (\text{derivative of } 84.4u^{-1})(\text{derivative of } u) \\
&= (\text{derivative of } 84.4u^{-1})[(\text{derivative of } 1 + 33.6e^v)(\text{derivative of } v)] \\
&= (-84.4u^{-2})[(33.6e^v)(-0.484)] \\
&= \frac{-84.4(33.6e^v)(-0.484)}{u^2} \\
&\approx \frac{1372.547e^v}{u^2}
\end{aligned}$$

---

*Based on data from *Statistical Abstract*, 1998.

Next, substitute $u = 1 + 33.6e^{-0.484t}$ and $v = -0.484t$ back into the expression to obtain the derivative in terms of t.

$$\frac{dP}{dt} \approx \frac{1372.547e^{-0.484t}}{(1 + 33.6e^{-0.484t})^2} \text{ percentage points per year is the rate of change in the}$$

number of households with VCRs between 1980 and 2001

where t is the number of years since 1980. ●

3.4 Concept Inventory

- Function composition
- Inside and outside portions of a composite function
- Chain Rule:

$$\frac{dC}{dt} = \frac{dC}{dp} \cdot \frac{dp}{dt} \qquad \textbf{(Form 1)}$$

$$C'(t) = C'(p(t)) \cdot p'(t) \quad \textbf{(Form 2)}$$

3.4 Activities

Getting Started

1. Let x be a function of t, and let f be a function whose input corresponds to the output of x. If $x(2) = 6$, $f(6) = 140, x'(2) = 1.3$, and $f'(6) = -27$, give the values of

   a. $f(x(2))$

   b. $\frac{df}{dx}$ when $x = 6$

   c. $\frac{dx}{dt}$ when $t = 2$

   d. $\frac{df}{dt}$ when $t = 2$

2. Let v be a function of x, and let g be a function whose input corresponds to the output of v. If $v(88) = 17$, $v'(88) = 1.6$, $g(17) = 0.04$, and $g'(17) = 0.005$, give the values of

   a. $g(v(88))$

   b. $\frac{dv}{dx}$ when $x = 88$

   c. $\frac{dg}{dv}$ when $x = 88$

   d. $\frac{dg}{dx}$ when $x = 88$

3. **Investment** An investor has been buying gold at a constant rate of 0.2 troy ounce per day. The investor currently owns 400 troy ounces of gold. If gold is currently worth $323.10 per troy ounce, how quickly is the value of the investor's gold increasing per day?

4. **Leaking Tank** A gas station owner is unaware that one of the underground gasoline tanks is leaking. The leaking tank currently contains 600 gallons of gas and is losing 3.5 gallons per day. If the value of the gasoline is $1.51 per gallon, how much potential revenue is the station losing per day?

5. **Revenue** Let $R(x)$ be the revenue in Canadian dollars from the sale of x units of a commodity, and let $C(R)$ be the U.S. dollar value of R Canadian dollars. On November 25, 2002, $10,000 Canadian was worth $6334.70 U.S., and the rate of change of the U.S. dollar value was $0.63347 U.S. per Canadian dollar. On the same day, sales were 476 units, producing a revenue of $10,000 Canadian, and revenue was increasing by $2.6 Canadian per unit. Identify the following values on November 25, 2002, and write a sentence interpreting each value.

   a. $R(476)$

   b. $C(10,000)$

   c. $\frac{dR}{dx}$

   d. $\frac{dC}{dR}$

   e. $\frac{dC}{dx}$

6. **Mail** Suppose that $v(t)$ is the volume of mail (in thousands of pieces) processed at a post office on the tth day of the current year and that $E(v)$ is the number of employee-hours needed to process v thousand pieces of mail. On January 1 of this year, 150 thousand pieces of mail were processed, and that number was decreasing by 200 pieces per day. The rate of change of the number of employee-hours is a constant 12 hours per thousand pieces of mail. Identify the following quantities on January 1 of this year, and write a sentence interpreting each value.

   a. $v(1)$

   b. $\frac{dv}{dt}$

   c. $\frac{dE}{dv}$

   d. $\frac{dE}{dt}$

7. Refuse The population of a city in the Northeast is given by $p(t) = \frac{130}{1 + 12e^{0.02t}}$ thousand people, where t is the number of years since 2000. The number of garbage trucks needed by the city can be modeled by the equation $g(p) = 2p - 0.001p^3$, where p is the population in thousands. Find the value of the following in 2010:

a. $p(t)$ b. $g(p)$

c. $\frac{dp}{dt}$ d. $\frac{dg}{dp}$ e. $\frac{dg}{dt}$

f. Interpret the answers to parts a through e.

8. Profit Let $p(x) = 1.019^x$ Canadian dollars be the profit from the sale of x mountain bikes. On November 25, 2002, p Canadian dollars were worth $C(p) = \frac{p}{1.5786}$. On the same day, sales were 476 mountain bikes. Identify the following quantities on November 25, 2002:

a. $p(x)$ b. $C(p)$

c. $\frac{dp}{dx}$ d. $\frac{dC}{dp}$ e. $\frac{dC}{dx}$

f. Interpret the answers to parts a through e.

Rewrite each pair of functions in Activities 9 through 16 as a single composite function, and then find the derivative of the composite function.

9. $c(x) = 3x^2 - 2$ $x(t) = 4 - 6t$

10. $f(t) = 3e^t$ $t(p) = 4p^2$

11. $h(p) = \frac{4}{p}$ $p(t) = 1 + 3e^{-0.5t}$

12. $g(x) = \sqrt{7 + 5x}$ $x(w) = 4e^w$

13. $k(t) = 4.3t^3 - 2t^2 + 4t - 12$ $t(x) = \ln x$

14. $f(x) = \ln x$ $x(t) = 5t + 11$

15. $p(t) = 7.9(1.046^t)$ $t(k) = 14k^3 - 12k^2$

16. $r(m) = \frac{9.1}{m^2} + 3m$ $m(f) = f^4 - f^2$

For each of the composite functions in Activities 17 through 38, identify an inside function and an outside function, and find the derivative with respect to x of the composite function.

17. $f(x) = (3.2x + 5.7)^5$

18. $f(x) = (5x^2 + 3x + 7)^{-1}$

19. $f(x) = \frac{8}{(x - 1)^3}$ 20. $f(x) = \frac{350}{4x + 7}$

21. $f(x) = \sqrt{x^2 - 3x}$ 22. $f(x) = \sqrt{x^2 + 5x}$

23. $f(x) = \ln(35x)$ 24. $f(x) = (\ln 6x)^2$

25. $f(x) = \ln(16x^2 + 37x)$ 26. $f(x) = e^{3.7x}$

27. $f(x) = 72e^{0.6x}$ 28. $f(x) = e^{4x^2}$

29. $f(x) = 1 + 58e^{0.08x}$ 30. $f(x) = 1 + 58e^{(1 + 3x)}$

31. $f(x) = \frac{12}{1 + 18e^{0.6x}} + 7.3$

32. $f(x) = \frac{37.5}{1 + 8.9e^{-1.2x}} + 89$

33. $f(x) = \left(\sqrt{x} - 3x\right)^3$ 34. $f(x) = 3^{\sqrt{2x}}$

35. $f(x) = 2^{\ln x}$ 36. $f(x) = \ln(2^x)$

37. $f(x) = Ae^{-Bx}$ 38. $f(x) = \frac{L}{1 + Ae^{-Bx}}$

Applying Concepts

39. Advertising The marketing division of a large firm has found that it can model the effectiveness of an advertising campaign by $S(u) = 0.75\sqrt{u} + 1.8$, where $S(u)$ represents sales in millions of dollars when the firm invests u thousand dollars in advertising. The firm plans to invest $u(x) = -2.3x^2 + 53.2x + 249.8$ thousand dollars each year x years from now.

a. Write the formula for predicted sales x years from now.

b. Write the formula for the rate of change of predicted sales x years from now.

c. What will be the rate of change of sales in 2007?

40. Rearing Children The percentage of children living with their grandparents between 1970 and 2000 can be modeled by the equation

$$p(t) = 3 + 0.216e^{0.09263t} \text{ percent}$$

t years after 1970.

(Source: Based on data from the U.S. Bureau of the Census.)

a. Write the rate-of-change formula for p.

b. How rapidly was the percentage of children living with their grandparents growing in 1995?

c. How rapidly on average did the percentage of children living with their grandparents grow between 1970 and 1990?

d. Geometrically illustrate the answers to parts *b* and *c*.

41. Revenue In October of 1999, iGo Corp. offered 5 million shares of public stock at $9 per share. Revenue for the two years preceding the stock offering can be modeled by the equation

$$R(q) = 2.9 + 0.0314e^{0.62285q} \text{ million dollars}$$

q quarters after the beginning of 1998.

(Source: Based on data from the Securities and Exchange Commission.)

a. Write the rate-of-change formula of *R*.

b. Complete the table below.

Quarter ending	June 1998	June 1999	June 2000
Revenue			
Rate of change of revenue			
Percentage rate of change of revenue			

42. Cable TV The percentage of households with TVs that subscribed to cable in the years from 1970 through 2002 can be modeled by the logistic equation

$$P(t) = 6 + \frac{62.7}{1 + 38.7e^{-0.258t}} \text{ percent}$$

where *t* is the number of years since 1970.

(Source: Based on data from the Television Bureau of Advertising.)

a. Write the rate-of-change formula for the percentage of households with TVs who subscribe to cable.

b. How rapidly was the percentage growing in 2000?

c. According to the model, what will happen to the percentage of cable subscribers in the long run? Do you believe that the model is a correct predictor of the long-term behavior? Explain.

43. P.T.A. A model for the number of states associated with the national P.T.A. organization is

$$m(x) = \frac{49}{1 + 36.0660e^{-0.206743x}} \text{ states}$$

x years after 1895.

(Source: Based on data from Hamblin, Jacobsen, and Miller, *A Mathematical Theory of Social Change*, New York: Wiley, 1973.)

a. Write the derivative of *m*.

b. How many states had national P.T.A. membership in 1902?

c. How rapidly was the number of states joining the P.T.A. growing in 1915? in 1927?

44. Flu Civilian deaths due to the influenza epidemic in 1918 can be modeled as

$$c(t) = \frac{93,700}{1 + 5095.9634e^{-1.097175t}} \text{ deaths}$$

t weeks after August 31, 1918.

(Source: Based on data from A. W. Crosby, Jr., *Epidemic and Peace 1918*, Westport, CT: Greenwood Press, 1976.)

a. How rapidly was the number of deaths growing on September 28, 1918?

b. What percentage increase does the answer to part *a* represent?

c. Repeat parts *a* and *b* for October 26, 1918.

d. Why is the percentage change for parts *b* and *c* decreasing even though the rate of change is increasing?

45. Tuition The tuition at a private 4-year college from 2000 through 2010 is projected to grow as shown in the table.

Year	Tuition (dollars)	Year	Tuition (dollars)
2000	14,057	2006	16,918
2001	14,434	2007	17,561
2002	14,847	2008	18,264
2003	15,298	2009	19,033
2004	15,790	2010	19,873
2005	16,329		

a. Find an exponential equation of the form $f(x) = ab^x$ to fit the data.

b. Convert the equation you found in part a to one of the form $f(x) = ae^{kx}$.

c. Find rate-of-change formulas for both equations.

d. Use both equations to find the rate of change in 2008. How do your answers compare?

46. Police Calls   Dispatchers at a sheriff's office record the total number of calls received since 5 A.M. in 3-hour intervals. Total calls for a typical day are given in the table.

Time	Total calls since 5 A.M.
8 A.M.	81
11 A.M.	167
2 P.M.	301
5 P.M.	495
8 P.M.	738
11 P.M.	1020
2 A.M.	1180
5 A.M.	1225

(Source: Greenville County, South Carolina, Sheriff's Office.)

a. Is a cubic or a logistic model more appropriate for this data set? Explain.

b. Find the more appropriate model for the data.

c. Find the rate-of-change formula for the model.

d. Evaluate the rate of change at noon, 10 P.M., midnight, and 4 A.M. Interpret the rates of change.

e. Discuss how rates of change can help a sheriff's office schedule dispatchers for work each day.

47. Cost   A manufacturing company has found that it can stock no more than 1 week's worth of perishable raw material for its manufacturing process. When purchasing this material, however, the company receives a discount based on the size of the order. Company managers have modeled the cost data as $C(t) = 196.25 + 44.45 \ln t$ dollars to produce t units per week. Each quarter, improvements are made to the automated machinery to help boost production. The company has kept a record of the average units per week that were produced in each quarter since January 2000. These data are given in the table.

Quarter	Units per week
Jan–Mar 2000	2000
Apr–June 2000	2070
July–Sept 2000	2160
Oct–Dec 2000	2260
Jan–Mar 2001	2380
Apr–June 2001	2510
July–Sept 2001	2660
Oct–Dec 2001	2820
Jan–Mar 2002	3000
Apr–June 2002	3200
July–Sept 2002	3410
Oct–Dec 2002	3620
Jan–Mar 2003	3880
Apr–June 2003	4130
July–Sept 2003	4410
Oct–Dec 2003	4690

a. Find an appropriate model for production per week x quarters after January 2000.

b. Use the company cost model along with your production model to write an expression modeling cost per unit as a function of the number of quarters since January 2000.

c. Use your model to predict the company's cost per week for each quarter of 2004.

d. Carefully study a graph of the function in part b from January 2000 to January 2005. According to this graph, will cost ever decrease?

e. Find an expression for the rate of change of the cost function in part b. Look at the graph of the rate-of-change function. According to this graph, will cost ever decrease?

48. Cost   A dairy company's records reveal that it costs about $C(u) = 3250.23 + 74.95 \ln u$ dollars per week for the company to produce u units each week. Consumer demand has been increasing, so the company has been increasing production to keep up with demand. The accompanying table indicates the production of the company, in units per week, from 1990 through 2003.

Year	Production (units per week)
1990	5915
1991	5750
1992	5940
1993	6485
1994	7385
1995	8635
1996	10,245
1997	12,210
1998	14,530
1999	17,200
2000	20,230
2001	23,610
2002	27,345
2003	31,440

a. Describe the curvature of the scatter plot of the data in the table. What types of equations could be used to fit these data?

b. Find an appropriate model for production.

c. Use the company's cost model along with your production model to write an expression modeling cost per week as a function of the number of years since 1990.

d. Write the rate-of-change function of the cost function you found in part *c*.

e. Use your model to estimate the company's cost per week in 2002, 2003, 2004, and 2005. Also estimate the rates of change for those same years.

f. Carefully study the cost graph from 1990 to 2010. According to this graph, will cost ever decrease? Why or why not?

g. Look at the slope graph of the cost function from 1990 to 2010. According to this graph, will cost ever decrease? Why or why not?

Discussing Concepts

49. When you are composing functions, why is it important to make sure that the output of the inside function agrees with the input of the outside function?

50. Use your knowledge of the shape and end behavior of the graph of a shifted exponential function of the form $y = ae^{bx} + c$, as well as your knowledge of the simple derivative rules and the Chain Rule from Sections 3.2 through 3.4, to describe the shape and end behavior of the graph and the mathematical form of the rate-of-change function of a shifted exponential model.

3.5   The Product Rule

It is fairly common to construct a new function by multiplying two functions. For example, revenue is the number of units sold multiplied by price. If both units sold and price are given by functions, then revenue is given by the product of the two functions. How to find rates of change for product functions is the topic of this section.

Applying the Product Rule Without Equations

Suppose that the enrollment in a university is given by a function E and the percentage (expressed as a decimal) of students who are from out of state is given by a function P. In both functions, the input is t, the year corresponding to the beginning of the school year (that is, for the 2003–04 school year, t is 2003) because school enrollment figures are stated for the beginning of the fall term. Note that the product function $N(t) = E(t) \cdot P(t)$ gives the number of out-of-state students in year t. For example, if in the current year, enrollment began at 17,000 students with 30% of those from out of state, then the number of out-of-state students is calculated as $(17,000)(0.30) = 5100$.

Suppose that, in addition to enrollment being 17,000 with 30% from out of state, the enrollment is decreasing at a rate of 1420 students per year $\left(\frac{dE}{dt} = -1420\right)$, and the percentage of out-of-state students is increasing at a rate of 1.5 percentage points per year $\left(\frac{dP}{dt} = 0.015\right)$. How rapidly is the number of out-of-state students changing?

There are two rates to consider in determining $N'(t)$. First, we consider the rate at which the number of out-of-state students is changing because of the overall decline in enrollment. Of the 1420 students per year by which enrollment is declining, 30% are from out of state. The product $(-1420$ students per year$)(0.30) = -426$ gives the amount by which the number of out-of-state students is decreasing. Thus, as a consequence of the decline in enrollment, the number of out-of-state students is declining by 426 students per year.

Second, we consider the rate at which the number of out-of-state students is increasing. Of the 17,000 students enrolled, the percentage of out-of-state students is growing by 1.5% per year. Thus the product $(17,000$ students$) \cdot (0.015$ per year$) = 255$ gives the amount by which the number of out-of-state students is increasing. The increasing percentage of out-of-state students results in a rate of increase of 255 out-of-state students per year.

To find the overall rate of change in the number of out-of-state students, we add the rate of change due to decline in enrollment and the rate of change due to increase in percentage.

$$-426 \text{ students per year} + 255 \text{ students per year} = -171 \text{ students per year}$$

We interpret this result as follows: As a consequence of the declining enrollment and the increasing percentage of students from out of state, the number of out-of-state students is declining by 171 per year.

The steps to obtain this rate of change can be summarized in the equation

$$\frac{dN}{dt} = \left(\frac{dE}{dt}\right)P(t) + E(t)\left(\frac{dP}{dt}\right)$$

This result is known as the **Product Rule** and can be stated as follows: If a function is the product of two functions, that is,

$$\text{Product function} = \left(\begin{array}{c}\text{first}\\\text{function}\end{array}\right)\left(\begin{array}{c}\text{second}\\\text{function}\end{array}\right)$$

then

$$\begin{array}{c}\text{Derivative}\\\text{of product} =\\\text{function}\end{array}\left(\begin{array}{c}\text{derivative}\\\text{of first}\\\text{function}\end{array}\right)\left(\begin{array}{c}\text{second}\\\text{function}\end{array}\right) + \left(\begin{array}{c}\text{first}\\\text{function}\end{array}\right)\left(\begin{array}{c}\text{derivative}\\\text{of second}\\\text{function}\end{array}\right)$$

> ### The Product Rule
>
> If $f(x) = g(x) \cdot h(x)$, then $\dfrac{df}{dx} = \left(\dfrac{dg}{dx}\right) h(x) + g(x)\left(\dfrac{dh}{dx}\right).$

EXAMPLE 1   *Using the Product Rule Without an Equation*

Egg Production   The industrialization of chicken (and egg) farming brought improvements to the production rate of eggs. Consider a chicken farm that has 1000 laying hens, each of which lays an average of 24 eggs each month. By selling or buying hens, the farmer can decrease or increase production. Also, by selective breeding and genetic research, it is possible that over a period of time the farmer can increase the average number of eggs that each hen lays.

a. How many eggs does the farm produce in a month?

b. Suppose the farmer increases the number of hens by 12 hens per month and increases the average number of eggs laid by each hen by 1 egg per month. By how much will the farmer's production be increasing?

Solution

a. The monthly egg production is the product of h, the number of hens, and l, the number of eggs each hen lays in one month. Currently, $h = 1000$ hens and $l = 24$ eggs per month. The farmer's current monthly production is

$$h \cdot l = (1000 \text{ hens})(24 \text{ eggs per hen}) = 24{,}000 \text{ eggs}$$

b. Let t be the number of months from now. We are told that $\dfrac{dh}{dt} = 12$ hens per month and that $\dfrac{dl}{dt} = 1$ egg per hen per month. Applying the Product Rule yields

$$\frac{d(hl)}{dt} = \frac{dh}{dt}l + h\frac{dl}{dt}$$

$$= \left(12\,\frac{\text{hens}}{\text{month}}\right)\left(24\,\frac{\text{eggs}}{\text{hen}}\right) + (1000 \text{ hens})\left(1\,\frac{\text{egg/hen}}{\text{month}}\right)$$

$$= 1288\,\frac{\text{eggs}}{\text{month}}$$

The farmer's egg production will be increasing by 1288 eggs per month.   ●

Applying the Product Rule with Equations

The next example illustrates using the Product Rule for quantities that are represented by mathematical functions.

EXAMPLE 2   *Using the Product Rule in a Business Setting*

Sales   A music store has determined from a customer survey that when the price of each CD is x dollars, the number of CDs sold in a four-week period can be modeled by the function

$$N(x) = 6250\,(0.92985^x) \text{ CDs}$$

Find and interpret the rates of change of revenue when CDs are priced at $10, $12, $13.75, and $15.

Solution

Revenue is the number of units sold times the selling price. In this case, the monthly revenue R(x) is given by

$$R(x) = N(x) \cdot x = 6250\,(0.92985^x)\,x \text{ dollars}$$

where x dollars is the selling price. Using the Product Rule, we find that the rate-of-change equation is

$$\frac{dR}{dx} = \left[\frac{d}{dx}N(x)\right]x + N(x)\left[\frac{d}{dx}(x)\right]$$

$$= 6250\,(\ln 0.92985)(0.92985^x) \cdot x + 6250\,(0.92985^x)(1) \text{ dollars per dollar}$$

where x dollars is the selling price. The output unit on the derivative, dollars per dollar, indicates dollars of revenue per dollar of price.

Evaluating $\frac{dR}{dx}$ at the indicated values of x yields Table 3.11. At $10, revenue is increasing by $824 per $1 of CD price. In other words, increasing the price results in an increase in revenue. Similarly, at $12, revenue is increasing by $332 per $1 of CD price. At $13.75, revenue is neither increasing nor decreasing. This is the price at which revenue has reached its peak. Finally, at $15, revenue is declining by $191 per $1 of CD price.

The graph of the revenue function is shown in Figure 3.38. Review the statements above about how the revenue is changing as they are related to the graph.

TABLE 3.11

Price (dollars)	Rate of change of revenue (dollars per dollar)
10.00	824
12.00	332
13.75	0
15.00	−191

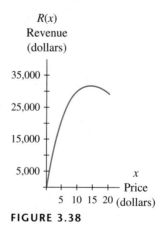

FIGURE 3.38

Often product functions are formed by multiplying a quantity function by a function that indicates the proportion of that quantity for which a certain statement is true. This is illustrated in Example 3.

EXAMPLE 3   *Using the Product Rule When the Product Involves a Proportion*

Tourists   Judging on the basis of data supplied by the Office of Travel and Tourism Industries at the U.S. Department of Commerce, the number of overseas international tourists who traveled to the United States between 1995 and 2000 can be modeled by the equation

$$f(t) = 0.148t^3 - 3.435t^2 + 26.673t - 45.44 \text{ million tourists}$$

where t is the number of years since 1990. Suppose that during the same time period, the proportion (percentage expressed as a decimal) of foreign travelers to the United States who were from Europe is given by

$$p(t) = -0.00179t^3 + 0.0395t^2 - 0.275t + 1.039$$

where t is the number of years since 1990.

a. Find a model for the number of European tourists traveling to the United States.

b. Find the derivative of the formula in part *a*.

c. Find the number of European tourists to the United States in 2000, and determine how rapidly that number was changing in that year.

Solution

a. The number $N(t)$ of European tourists to the United States is given by the product function $N(t) = f(t)\,p(t)$.

$$N(t) = (0.148t^3 - 3.435t^2 + 26.673t - 45.44)(-0.00179t^3 + 0.0395t^2 - 0.275t + 1.039) \text{ million European tourists}$$

t years after 1990, $5 \le t \le 10$.

b. To use the Product Rule, we need the derivatives f' and p':

$$f'(t) = 0.444t^2 - 6.87t + 26.673 \text{ million tourists per year, and}$$
$$p'(t) = -0.00537t^2 + 0.079t - 0.275$$

(Note that we did not label $p'(t)$ with units. If $p(t)$ had been expressed as a percentage, then the units would have been percentage points per year. Expressed as a decimal, $p(t)$ is actually a proportion, which is a unitless number. It would be possible to label $p'(t)$ as hundredths of a percentage point per year, but we choose to state the derivative of p without a label.)

Thus, by the Product Rule,

$$N'(t) = (0.444t^2 - 6.87t + 26.673)(-0.00179t^3 + 0.0395t^2 - 0.275t + 1.039)$$
$$+ (0.148t^3 - 3.435t^2 + 26.673t - 45.44)(-0.00537t^2 + 0.079t - 0.275)$$

European tourists per year t years after 1990; $5 \le t \le 10$.

c. The number of European tourists in 2000 is $N(10)$.

$$N(10) = (25.79)(0.449) \approx 11.6 \text{ million tourists}$$

The rate of change of the number of European tourists in 2000 is $N'(10)$.

$$N'(10) \approx (2.373)(0.449) + (25.79)(-0.022)$$
$$\approx 1.065 - 0.567$$
$$\approx 0.50 \text{ million European tourists per year}$$

In 2000, there were approximately 11.6 million tourists from Europe, and that number was growing by about 0.50 million tourists per year. ●

The Quotient Rule

Occasionally functions are constructed as the quotients of other functions—that is, functions of the form $f(x) = \frac{g(x)}{h(x)}$. You may wish to rewrite $f(x)$ as $f(x) = g(x)[h(x)]^{-1}$ and use the Chain and Product Rules to write the derivative formula for such functions. Another approach is to use the **Quotient Rule:**

$$f'(x) = \frac{g'(x) \cdot h(x) - h'(x) \cdot g(x)}{[h(x)]^2}$$

We present this rule without illustration because it is an algebraic consequence of the Product and the Chain Rules.

3.5   Concept Inventory

- **Product Rule**

  If $f(x) = g(x) \cdot h(x)$,

  then $\frac{df}{dx} = \frac{dg}{dx} \cdot h(x) + g(x) \cdot \frac{dh}{dx}$.

- **Quotient Rule**

3.5   Activities

Getting Started

1. Find $h'(2)$ if $h(x) = f(x) \cdot g(x)$, $f(2) = 6$, $f'(2) = -1.5$, $g(2) = 4$, and $g'(2) = 3$.

2. Find $r'(100)$ if $r(t) = p(t) \cdot q(t)$, $p(100) = 4.65$, $p'(100) = 0.5$, $q(100) = 160$, and $q'(100) = 12$.

3. **Computer Homes**   Let $h(t)$ be the number of households in a city, and let $c(t)$ be the proportion (expressed as a decimal) of households in that city that own a computer. In both functions, t is the number of years since 2005.

   a. Interpret the following mathematical statements:

   i. $h(2) = 75,000$ ii. $h'(2) = -1200$

   iii. $c(2) = 0.52$ iv. $c'(2) = 0.05$

   b. If $N(t) = h(t) \cdot c(t)$, what are the input and output of N?

   c. Find and interpret the values of $N(2)$ and $N'(2)$.

4. **Demand**   Let $D(x)$ be the demand (in units) for a new product when the price is x dollars.

   a. Interpret the following statements:

   i. $D(6.25) = 1000$ ii. $D'(6.25) = -50$

   b. Give a formula for the revenue $R(x)$ generated from the sale of the product when the price is x dollars. (Assume demand = number sold.)

   c. Find and interpret $R'(x)$ when $x = 6.25$.

5. **Stock Value**   The value of one share of a company's stock is given by $S(x) = 15 + \frac{2.6}{x+1}$ dollars x weeks after it is first offered. An investor buys some of the stock each week and owns $N(x) = 100 + 0.25x^2$ shares after x weeks. The value of the investor's stock after x weeks is given by $V(x) = S(x) \cdot N(x)$.

   a. Find and interpret the following:

   i. $S(10)$ and $S'(10)$ ii. $N(10)$ and $N'(10)$

   iii. $V(10)$ and $V'(10)$

   b. Give a formula for $V'(x)$.

6. **Education Cost**   The number of students in an elementary school t years after 2002 is given by

$S(t) = 100 \ln (t + 5)$ students. The yearly cost to educate one student can be modeled by $C(t) = 1500(1.05^t)$ dollars per student.

a. What are the input and output of the function $F(t) = S(t) \cdot C(t)$?

b. Find and interpret the following:

  i. $S(3)$ **ii.** $S'(3)$ **iii.** $C(3)$

  iv. $C'(3)$ **v.** $F(3)$ **vi.** $F'(3)$

c. Find a formula for $F'(t)$.

7. Farming A wheat farmer is converting to corn because he believes that corn is a more lucrative crop. It is not feasible for him to convert all his acreage to corn at once. He is farming 500 acres of corn in the current year and plans to increase that number by 50 acres per year. As he becomes more experienced in growing corn, his output increases. He currently harvests 130 bushels of corn per acre, but the yield is increasing by 5 bushels per acre per year. When both the increasing acreage and the increasing yield are considered, how rapidly is the total number of bushels of corn increasing per year?

8. Basketball A point guard for an NBA team averages 15 free-throw opportunities per game. He currently hits 72% of his free throws. As he improves, the number of free-throw opportunities decreases by 1 free throw per game, while his percentage of hits increases by 0.5 percentage point per game. When his decreasing free throws and increasing percentage are taken into account, what is the rate of change in the number of free-throw points that this point guard makes per game?

9. Politics Two candidates are running for mayor in a small town. The campaign committee for candidate A has been conducting weekly telephone polls to assess the progress of the campaign. Currently there are 17,000 registered voters, 48% of whom are planning to vote. Of those planning to vote, 57% will vote for candidate A. Candidate B has begun some serious mud slinging, which has resulted in increasing public interest in the election and decreasing support for candidate A. Polls show that the percentage of people who plan to vote is increasing by 7 percentage points per week, while the percentage who will vote for can-

didate A is declining by 3 percentage points per week.

a. If the election were held today, how many people would vote?

b. How many of those would vote for candidate A?

c. How rapidly is the number of votes that candidate A will receive changing?

10. Customers Suppose a new shop has been added in the O'Hare International Airport in Chicago. At the end of the first year it is able to attract 2% of the passengers passing by the store. The manager estimates that at that time, the percentage of passengers it attracts is increasing by 0.05% per year. Airport authorities estimate that 52 thousand passengers passed by the store each day at the end of the first year and that that number was increasing by approximately 114 passengers per day. What is the rate of change of customers at the shop?

Find derivative formulas for the functions in Activities 11 through 28.

11. $f(x) = (\ln x)\, e^x$ **12.** $f(x) = (x + 5)\, e^x$

13. $f(x) = (3x^2 + 15x + 7)(32x^3 + 49)$

14. $f(x) = 2.5\,(0.9^x)(\ln x)$

15. $f(x) = (12.8x^2 + 3.7x + 1.2)[29\,(1.7^x)]$

16. $f(x) = (5x + 29)^5(15x + 8)$

17. $f(x) = (5.7x^2 + 3.5x + 2.9)^3(3.8x^2 + 5.2x + 7)^{-2}$

18. $f(x) = \dfrac{2x^3 + 3}{2.7x + 15}$ **19.** $f(x) = \dfrac{12.6\,(4.8^x)}{x^2}$

20. $f(x) = (8x^2 + 13)\left(\dfrac{39}{1 + 15e^{-0.09x}}\right)$

21. $f(x) = (79x)\left(\dfrac{198}{1 + 7.68e^{-0.85x}} + 15\right)$

22. $f(x) = [\ln(15.7x^3)](e^{15.7x^3})$

23. $f(x) = \dfrac{430(0.62^x)}{6.42 + 3.3\,(1.46^x)}$

24. $f(x) = (19 + 12 \ln 2x)(17 - 3 \ln 4x)$

25. $f(x) = 4x\sqrt{3x + 2} + 93$

26. $f(x) = \dfrac{4(3^x)}{\sqrt{x}}$ **27.** $f(x) = \dfrac{14x}{1 + 12.6e^{-0.73x}}$

28. $f(x) = \dfrac{1}{(x-2)^2}(3x^2 - 17x + 4)$

Applying Concepts

29. Childbirth   On the basis of data from a study conducted by the University of Colorado School of Medicine at Denver, the percentage of women receiving regional analgesia (epidural pain relief) during childbirth at small hospitals between 1981 and 1997 can be modeled by the equation

$$p(x) = 0.73(1.2912^x) + 8 \text{ percent}$$

x years after 1980.

(Source: Based on data from "Healthfile," *Reno Gazette Journal*, Oct. 19, 1999, p. 4.)

Suppose that a small hospital in southern Arizona has seen the yearly number of women giving birth decline as described by the equation $b(x) = -0.026x^2 - 3.842x + 538.868$ women giving birth x years after 1980.

a. Give the equation and its derivative for the number of women receiving regional analgesia while giving birth at the Arizona hospital.

b. Was the percentage of women who received regional analgesia while giving birth increasing or decreasing in 1997?

c. Was the number of women who gave birth at the Arizona hospital increasing or decreasing in 1997?

d. Was the number of women who received regional analgesia during childbirth at the Arizona hospital increasing or decreasing in 1997?

e. If the Arizona hospital made a profit of $57 per woman for the use of regional analgesia, what was the profit for the hospital from this method of pain relief during childbirth in 1997?

30. Sales   During the first 8 months of last year, a grocery store raised the price of a certain brand of tissue paper from $1.14 per package at a rate of 4 cents per month. Consequently, sales declined. The sales of tissue can be modeled as

$$S(m) = -0.95m^2 + 0.24m + 279.91 \text{ packages}$$

during the mth month of the year.

a. Construct an equation for revenue.

b. Use the equation to find the revenue in August and the projected revenue in September. Would you expect the rate of change of revenue to be positive or negative in August? Why?

c. Give the rate-of-change formula for revenue.

d. How rapidly was revenue changing in February, August, and September?

31. Sales   A music store has determined that the number of CDs sold monthly is approximately

$$\text{Number} = 6250(0.9286^x) \text{ CDs}$$

where x is the price in dollars.

a. Give an equation for revenue as a function of price.

b. If each CD costs the store $7.50, find an equation for profit as a function of price.

c. Find formulas for the rates of change of revenue and profit.

d. Complete the table below.

Price	Rate of change of revenue	Rate of change of profit
$13		
$14		
$20		
$21		
$22		

e. What does the table tell the store manager about the price corresponding to the highest revenue?

f. What is the price corresponding to the highest profit?

32. Population   The population (in millions) of the United States as a function of the year is given by

$$P(d) = 99.9(1.108^d) \text{ million people}$$

d decades after 1970.

The percentage of people in the United States who live in the Midwest can be modeled by the equation $m(d) = 6.53(0.994^d) + 22$ percent, where d is the number of decades since 1970.

(Source: Simplified models based on data from *Statistical Abstract*, 2001.)

a. Write an expression for the number of people who live in the Midwest t years after 1970.

b. Find an expression for the rate of change of the population of the Midwest.

c. According to the model how rapidly was the population of the Midwest changing in 1990, 1995, and 2000?

33. **Costs** Costs for a company to produce between 10 and 90 units per hour are given in the table.

Units	Cost (dollars)	Units	Cost (dollars)
10	150	60	1400
20	200	70	2400
30	250	80	3850
40	400	90	5850
50	750		

a. Find an exponential model for production costs.

b. Find the slope formula for production costs.

c. Convert the model in part *a* to one for the average cost per unit produced.

d. Find the slope formula for average cost.

e. How rapidly is the average cost changing when 15 units are being produced? 35 units? 85 units?

f. Examine the slope graph for average cost. Is there an interval of production levels over which average cost is decreasing?

g. Determine the point at which average cost begins to increase. (That is, find the point at which the rate of change of average cost changes from negative to positive.) Explain how you found this point.

34. **Poverty** The accompanying table gives the number of men 65 years old or older in the United States and the percentage of men age 65 or older living below the poverty level.

Year	Men 65 years or older (millions)	Percentage below poverty level
1970	8.3	20.2
1980	10.3	11.1
1985	11.0	8.7
1990	12.6	7.8
1997	14.0	7.0
2000	14.4	7.5

(Sources: *Statistical Abstract*, 2001, and *Current Population Survey*, March 2001.)

a. Using time as the input, determine the best model for each set of data.

b. Write an expression for the number of men 65 years old or older who are living below the poverty level in the United States.

c. How rapidly was the number of male senior citizens living below the poverty level changing in 1990 and in 2000?

35. **VCR Homes** The first table gives the number of households with TVs in the United States for selected years between 1970 and 2002.

Year	Households (millions)	Year	Households (millions)
1970	59	1990	92
1975	69	1995	95
1980	76	2000	101
1985	85	2002	106

(Sources: *Statistical Abstract*, 2001, and Television Bureau of Advertising.)

a. Find a model for the data given in the table above.

b. The second table gives (for selected years between 1978 through 2002) the percentages of U.S. households with TVs that also have VCRs.

Year	Percentage	Year	Percentage
1978	0.3	1995	81.0
1980	1.1	2000	85.1
1985	20.9	2002	91.2
1990	68.6		

(Sources: *Statistical Abstract*, 2001, and Television Bureau of Advertising.)

Align the data so that the input values correspond with those in the model for part *a* (that is, if 1980 is $x = 10$ in part *a*, then you want 1980 to be $x = 10$ here also). Find a logistic model for the data.

c. Find a model for the number of U.S. households with VCRs.

d. Find an equation for the rate of change of the number of U.S. households with VCRs.

e. How rapidly was the number of U.S. households with VCRs growing in 1990? in 1995? in 2000?

36. Funding   The amount of federal funds spent for agricultural research and services from 1990 through 2002 in the United States is given in the first table.

Year	Amount (billions of dollars)
1990	2.197
1992	2.539
1994	2.695
1996	2.682
1998	2.909
2000	3.189
2002	4.252

(Source: U.S. Office of Management and Budget.)

The purchasing power of the dollar, as measured by producer prices from 1988 through 2000 is given in the second table. (In 1982, one dollar was worth $1.00.)

Year	Purchasing power of $1
1988	0.93
1990	0.84
1992	0.81
1994	0.80
1997	0.76
2000	0.73

(Source: *Statistical Abstract*, 1998, 2001.)

a. Find models for both sets of data. (Remember to align such that both models have the same input values.)

b. Use these models to determine a new model for the amount, measured in constant 1982 dollars, spent on agricultural research and services.

c. Use your new model to find the rates of change and the percentage rates of change of the amount spent on agricultural research and services in 1992 and 2000.

d. Why might it be of interest to consider an expenditure problem in constant dollars?

37. Dropouts   The table shows the number of students enrolled in the ninth through twelfth grades and the number of dropouts from those same grades in South Carolina for each school year from 1980–1981 through 1989–1990.

School year	Enrollment	Dropouts
1980–81	194,072	11,651
1981–82	190,372	10,599
1982–83	185,248	9314
1983–84	182,661	9659
1984–85	181,949	8605
1985–86	182,787	8048
1986–87	185,131	7466
1987–88	183,930	7740
1988–89	178,094	7466
1989–90	172,372	5768

(Source: Compiled from *Rankings of the Counties and School Districts of South Carolina.*)

a. Find a model for enrollment and a cubic model for the number of dropouts.

b. Use the two models that you found in part *a* to construct an equation for the percentage of high school students who dropped out each year.

c. Find the rate-of-change formula of the percentage of high school students who dropped out each year.

d. Look at the rate of change for each school year from 1980–1981 through 1989–1990. In which school year was the rate of change smallest? When was it greatest?

e. Are the rates of change positive or negative? What does this say about high school attrition in South Carolina during the 1980s?

38. Jobs   A house painter has found that the number of jobs that he has per year is decreasing in inverse proportion to the number of years he has been in business. That is, the number of jobs he has each year can be modeled by $j(x) = \dfrac{104.25}{x}$, where x is the number of years since 1997. He has also kept a ledger of how much, on average, he was paid for each job. His income per job is presented in the table

Year	Income per job (dollars)
1997	430
1998	559
1999	727
2000	945
2001	1228
2002	1597
2003	2075

a. Find an exponential model for his income per job.

b. Write the formula for the painter's total income per year.

c. Write the formula for the rate of change of the painter's income each year.

d. What was the painter's total income in 2003?

e. How rapidly was the painter's income changing in 2003?

Discussing Concepts

39. When you are working with products of models, why is it important to make sure that the input values of the two models correspond? (That is, why must you align both models in the same way?)

40. We have discussed three ways to find rates of change: graphically, numerically, and algebraically. Discuss the advantages and disadvantages of each method. Explain when it would be appropriate to use each method.

3.6 Limiting Behavior Revisited: L'Hôpital's Rule

In Chapter 1 we looked at the end behavior of the six models defined in this text. We noted that for a continuous, differentiable function f with input x, as x increases without bound f may increase (or decrease) without bound, approach a constant value k, or fluctuate so that the end behavior is undefined. We use the following limit notation in each case:

- $\lim_{x \to \infty} f(x) = \infty$ f increases without bound

- $\lim_{x \to \infty} f(x) = -\infty$ f decreases without bound

- $\lim_{x \to \infty} f(x) = k$ f approaches the value k

- $\lim_{x \to \infty} f(x)$ is undefined f continues to fluctuate

In Chapter 2 we considered the behavior of a function f as its input x approaches a specific value c from both the left and right sides. When f is continuous and differentiable (except possibly at $x = c$), then

- $\lim_{x \to c} f(x) = k$ if f approaches k as x approaches c from both the left and the right

- $\lim_{x \to c} f(x)$ is undefined   if f increases (or decreases) without bound as x approaches c

    or

    if f does not approach the same value as x approaches c from both the left and the right

Analyzing Limits Using Direct Substitution

One of the concepts of calculus tells us that when a function f is continuous over an open interval including a constant a, then as the inputs approach a, the outputs approach $f(a)$. This is known as the method of **direct substitution**: $\lim_{x \to a} f(x) = f(a)$. When the limits of f and g exist at $x = c$, three rules for limits are

- The sum rule: $$\lim_{x \to c} [f(x) + g(x)] = \lim_{x \to c} f(x) + \lim_{x \to c} g(x)$$

- The product rule: $$\lim_{x \to c} [f(x) \cdot g(x)] = [\lim_{x \to c} f(x)] \cdot [\lim_{x \to c} g(x)]$$

- The quotient rule: $$\lim_{x \to c} \left[\frac{f(x)}{g(x)} \right] = \frac{\lim_{x \to c} f(x)}{\lim_{x \to c} g(x)} \text{ as long as } \lim_{x \to c} g(x) \neq 0$$

These rules, as well as the method of direct substitution, are illustrated in Example 1.

EXAMPLE 1   *Using Direct Substitution for Limits*

Determine the following limits:

a. $\lim_{x \to 5} 3x^2 + 2$

b. $\lim_{x \to -4} 64(2^x)$

c. $\lim_{x \to -\infty} 3x^3 + 12x^2 + 4$

d. $\lim_{x \to \infty} \dfrac{542}{1 + 3e^{-4x}}$

Solution

a. $\lim_{x \to 5} 3x^2 + 2 = 3(5)^2 + 2 = 77$ b. $\lim_{x \to -4} 64(2^x) = 64(2^{-4}) = 4$

c. A polynomial function either increases or decreases without bound as its input increases or decreases without bound. Because the cubed term is the term of largest degree, it determines whether the function will increase or decrease without bound. Cubing any negative number will produce another negative number, and multiplying it by 3 will still produce a negative number. Therefore, the function is decreasing without bound as x decreases without bound:

$$\lim_{x \to -\infty} 3x^3 + 12x^2 + 4 = -\infty$$

d. The limit of the numerator is the constant 542. Next, we consider $\lim_{x \to \infty} 3e^{-4x}$. We know that $3e^{-4x}$ is a decreasing exponential that approaches 0 as x increases without bound. Therefore, the denominator $1 + 3e^{-4x}$ approaches 1 as x increases without bound, so

$$\lim_{x \to \infty} \frac{542}{1 + 3e^{-4x}} = \frac{542}{1} = 542 \quad \bullet$$

Indeterminate Forms and L'Hôpital's Rule

For our six models these basic definitions apply, but some interesting situations appear when we try to analyze the limiting behavior of functions that are constructed by division or multiplication of other functions. For example, using the substitution rule for limits, we find

- $\lim_{x \to 2} \dfrac{3x^2 - 4x - 4}{4x - 8} = \dfrac{0}{0}$

- $\displaystyle\lim_{x\to\infty} \frac{e^x}{5x^2} = \frac{\infty}{\infty}$

- $\displaystyle\lim_{x\to 0^+} (3x)(-2\ln x) = 0 \cdot \infty$

The forms $\dfrac{0}{0}, \dfrac{\infty}{\infty}$, and $0 \cdot \infty$, are known as *indeterminate* forms because without further analysis it is impossible to determine the actual limit. The forms $\dfrac{\infty}{\infty}$ and $0 \cdot \infty$ are both equivalent to the form $\dfrac{0}{0}$, so the following rule applies to all three forms.

In 1696 the French mathematician Guillaume de l'Hôpital first published the following result, which was discovered by Johann Bernoulli. This result is now known as L'Hôpital's Rule.

L'Hôpital's Rule

When functions f and g with input x are continuous and smooth (except possibly at $x = c$) and $\displaystyle\lim_{x\to c} f(x) = \lim_{x\to c} g(x) = 0$ then

$$\lim_{x\to c} \frac{f(x)}{g(x)} = \lim_{x\to c} \frac{f'(x)}{g'(x)}$$

This result says, "The ratio of the functions and the ratio of their slope functions have the same limiting value."

Note that L'Hôpital's Rule uses the quotient of derivatives, *not* the derivative of a quotient function as discussed in Section 3.5.

EXAMPLE 2 *Using L'Hôpital's Rule*

Determine the following limits:

a. $\displaystyle\lim_{x\to 2} \frac{3x^2 - 4x - 4}{4x - 8}$ b. $\displaystyle\lim_{x\to\infty} \frac{e^x}{5x^2}$

c. $\displaystyle\lim_{x\to 0^+} (3x)(-2\ln x)$

Solution

a. Before applying L'Hôpital's Rule, we check whether the limit of the ratio is an indeterminate form: $\displaystyle\lim_{x\to 2} 3x^2 - 4x - 4 = 3(2^2) - 4(2) - 4 = 0$ and $\displaystyle\lim_{x\to 2} 4x - 8 = 4(2) - 8 = 0$. Therefore,

$$\lim_{x\to 2} \frac{3x^2 - 4x - 4}{4x - 8} = \frac{0}{0} \text{ (i.e., an indeterminate form)}$$

We now apply L'Hôpital's Rule by writing the derivatives of the functions in the numerator and the denominator: $\dfrac{d}{dx}(3x^2 - 4x - 4) = 6x - 4$ and

$\dfrac{d}{dx}(4x - 8) = 4$. The limit of the ratios of these derivatives is

$$\lim_{x \to 2} \frac{6x - 4}{4} = \frac{6(2) - 4}{4} = \frac{8}{4} = 2$$

L'Hôpital's Rule gives us

$$\lim_{x \to 2} \frac{3x^2 - 4x - 4}{4x - 8} = \lim_{x \to 2} \frac{6x - 4}{4} = 2$$

b. We check $\lim\limits_{x \to \infty} e^x = \infty$ and $\lim\limits_{x \to \infty} 5x^2 = \infty$. Therefore,

$$\lim_{x \to \infty} \frac{e^x}{5x^2} = \frac{\infty}{\infty} \text{ (i.e., an indeterminate form)}$$

The derivatives of the functions in the numerator and denominator of this ratio are $\dfrac{d}{dx} e^x = e^x$ and $\dfrac{d}{dx} 5x^2 = 10x$. Applying L'Hôpital's Rule yields

$$\lim_{x \to \infty} \frac{e^x}{5x^2} = \lim_{x \to \infty} \frac{e^x}{10x}$$

Further analysis shows

$$\lim_{x \to \infty} \frac{e^x}{10x} = \frac{\infty}{\infty} \text{ (i.e., an indeterminate form)}$$

We again apply L'Hôpital's Rule: $\dfrac{d}{dx} e^x = e^x$ and $\dfrac{d}{dx} 10x = 10$. Thus

$$\lim_{x \to \infty} \frac{e^x}{10x} = \lim_{x \to \infty} \frac{e^x}{10}$$

Since e^x increases without bound as x increases without bound

$$\lim_{x \to \infty} \frac{e^x}{10} = \infty$$

Therefore, applying L'Hôpital's Rule twice we find

$$\lim_{x \to \infty} \frac{e^x}{5x^2} = \lim_{x \to \infty} \frac{e^x}{10x} = \lim_{x \to \infty} \frac{e^x}{10} = \infty$$

c. As x approaches 0 from the right, $\ln x$ decreases without bound, so $-2 \ln x$ increases without bound. At the same time $3x$ approaches 0. Thus,

$$\lim_{x \to 0^+} (3x)(-2 \ln x) = 0 \cdot \infty, \text{ (i.e., an indeterminate form)}$$

To apply L'Hôpital's Rule, we rewrite, $(3x)(-2 \ln x)$ as a ratio of functions:

$$(3x)(-2 \ln x) = \frac{-2 \ln x}{\left(\dfrac{1}{3x}\right)}$$

Evaluating $\lim\limits_{x \to 0^+} -2 \ln x = \infty$ and $\lim\limits_{x \to 0^+} \dfrac{1}{3x} = \dfrac{1}{0} = \infty$ yields

$$\lim_{x \to 0^+} \frac{-2 \ln x}{\left(\dfrac{1}{3x}\right)} = \frac{\infty}{\infty}$$

We apply L'Hôpital's Rule by finding the derivatives of the functions in the numerator and the denominator: $\frac{d}{dx}(-2\ln x) = -2\left(\frac{1}{x}\right) = \frac{-2}{x}$ and

$$\frac{d}{dx}\left(\frac{1}{3x}\right) = \frac{d}{dx}(3x)^{-1} = -1(3x)^{-2}(3) = -\frac{3}{(3x)^2} = -\frac{3}{9x^2} = -\frac{1}{3x^2}.$$

Writing the ratio of these derivatives yields $\dfrac{-\dfrac{2}{x}}{-\dfrac{1}{3x^2}}$.

We simplify this as $\dfrac{-\dfrac{2}{x}}{-\dfrac{1}{3x^2}} = \left(-\frac{2}{x}\right)\left(-\frac{3x^2}{1}\right) = \frac{6x^2}{x} = 6x.$

Applying the limit, we have $\displaystyle\lim_{x \to 0^+} \dfrac{-\dfrac{2}{x}}{-\dfrac{1}{3x^2}} = \lim_{x \to 0^+} 6x = 0.$

Therefore, L'Hôpital's Rule gives

$$\lim_{x \to 0^+} 3x(-2\ln x) = \lim_{x \to 0^+} \frac{-2\ln x}{\dfrac{1}{3x}} = \lim_{x \to 0^+} \dfrac{-\dfrac{2}{x}}{-\dfrac{1}{3x^2}} = \lim_{x \to 0^+} 6x = 0 \qquad \bullet$$

Evaluating limits using L'Hôpital's Rule can be relatively simple, as in part *a* of Example 2. Multiple applications of L'Hôpital's Rule may be necessary to evaluate a limit, as in part *b* of Example 2, or it may take some extra algebraic manipulation, as in part *c* of Example 2.

3.6 Concept Inventory

- Direct substitution for limits
- Indeterminate forms
- L'Hôpital's Rule

3.6 Activities

Getting Started

Use the method of direct substitution or end behavior analysis to determine the limits given in Activities 1 through 6.

1. $\displaystyle\lim_{x \to 2} 2x^3 - 3^x$

2. $\displaystyle\lim_{x \to -2} 3x^2 + e^x$

3. $\displaystyle\lim_{x \to 0} e^x - \ln(x + 1)$

4. $\displaystyle\lim_{x \to 3} \frac{9}{x}$

5. $\displaystyle\lim_{x \to 0^+} \frac{1}{\ln x}$

6. $\displaystyle\lim_{x \to 2} \frac{1}{x - 2}$

For each limit given in Activities 7 through 10, identify the indeterminate form. Use L'Hôpital's Rule to find the limit of indeterminate forms of type $\frac{0}{0}$ or $\frac{\infty}{\infty}$.

7. $\displaystyle\lim_{n \to 1} \frac{\ln n}{n - 1}$

8. $\displaystyle\lim_{t \to 1} \frac{e^{2t}}{2t}$

9. $\displaystyle\lim_{x \to 1} \frac{x^4 - 1}{x^3 - 1}$

10. $\displaystyle\lim_{x \to \infty} \frac{e^x}{x^2}$

For each limit given in Activities 11 through 14, rewrite the indeterminate form of type $0 \cdot \infty$ as either type $\frac{0}{0}$ or $\frac{\infty}{\infty}$. Use L'Hôpital's Rule to find the limit.

11. $\displaystyle\lim_{t \to 0^+} \sqrt{t} \cdot \ln t$

12. $\displaystyle\lim_{n \to -\infty} -2n^2 e^n$

13. $\displaystyle\lim_{x \to \infty} x^2 e^{-x}$

14. $\displaystyle\lim_{t \to 0^+} e^{-t} \ln t$

Applying Concepts

For Activities 15 through 28, determine the limit. If the limit is of an indeterminate form, indicate the form and then use L'Hôpital's Rule to determine the limit.

15. $\lim\limits_{x \to 2} \dfrac{3x - 6}{x + 2}$

16. $\lim\limits_{x \to 7} \dfrac{x^2 - 2x - 35}{7x - x^2}$

17. $\lim\limits_{x \to 5} \dfrac{\sqrt{x - 1} - 2}{x^2 - 25}$

18. $\lim\limits_{x \to 4} \dfrac{x - 4}{\sqrt[3]{x + 4} - 2}$

19. $\lim\limits_{x \to 2} \dfrac{2x^2 - 5x + 2}{5x^2 - 7x - 6}$

20. $\lim\limits_{x \to 3} \dfrac{3x^2 + 2}{2x^2 + 3}$

21. $\lim\limits_{x \to 0} (3x)\left(\dfrac{2}{e^x}\right)$

22. $\lim\limits_{x \to 0^+} (4x^2)(\ln x)$

23. $\lim\limits_{x \to \infty} (0.6^x)(\ln x)$

24. $\lim\limits_{x \to \infty} (3x)\left(\dfrac{2}{e^x}\right)$

25. $\lim\limits_{x \to \infty} \dfrac{3x^2 + 2x + 4}{5x^2 + x + 1}$

26. $\lim\limits_{x \to \infty} \dfrac{4x^2 + 7}{2x^3 + 3}$

27. $\lim\limits_{x \to \infty} \dfrac{3x^4}{5x^3 + 6}$

28. $\lim\limits_{x \to \infty} \dfrac{4x^3}{5x^3 + 6}$

Discussing Concepts

29. Explain why the forms $\dfrac{0}{0}$, $\dfrac{\infty}{\infty}$, and $0 \cdot \infty$ are considered indeterminate forms.

30. Show how the forms $\dfrac{\infty}{\infty}$ and $0 \cdot \infty$ are equivalent to the form $\dfrac{0}{0}$.

SUMMARY

Drawing Slope Graphs

The smooth, continuous graphs that we use to model real-life data have slopes (derivatives) at every point on the graph except at points that have vertical tangent lines. When these slopes (derivatives) are plotted, they usually form a smooth, continuous graph—the slope graph (rate-of-change graph, or derivative graph) of the original graph. Slope graphs tell us a great deal about the change that is occurring on the original graph.

Slope Formulas

The Four-Step Method of finding derivatives that was discussed in Chapter 2 is invaluable, but it is also cumbersome. For this reason, we desire formulas for derivatives of the most common functions we encounter. Here is a list of slope (derivative) formulas that you should know.

Function	Derivative
$y = b$	$\dfrac{dy}{dx} = 0$
$y = ax + b$	$\dfrac{dy}{dx} = a$
$y = x^n$	$\dfrac{dy}{dx} = nx^{n-1}$
$y = e^x$	$\dfrac{dy}{dx} = e^x$
$y = b^x$	$\dfrac{dy}{dx} = (\ln b)\, b^x$
$y = \ln x$	$\dfrac{dy}{dx} = \dfrac{1}{x}$
$y = kf(x)$	$\dfrac{dy}{dx} = kf'(x)$
$y = f(x) \pm g(x)$	$\dfrac{dy}{dx} = f'(x) \pm g'(x)$

The Chain Rule

The Chain Rule tells us how to calculate rates of change for a composite function. We present it in two forms. If

C is a function of p and p is a function of t, then C can be regarded as a function of t, and

Form 1 $\dfrac{dC}{dt} = \left(\dfrac{dC}{dp}\right)\left(\dfrac{dp}{dt}\right)$

Form 2 $\dfrac{dC}{dt} = C'(p(t))\, p'(t)$

The Product Rule

The Product Rule tells us how to calculate rates of change for a product function. If $f(x) = g(x) \cdot h(x)$, then

$$\frac{df}{dx} = \left(\frac{dg}{dx}\right) h(x) + g(x)\left(\frac{dh}{dx}\right)$$

If you need to calculate a rate of change for a general quotient function, say $h(x) = \dfrac{f(x)}{g(x)}$, simply view the quotient as a product

$$h(x) = f(x)[g(x)]^{-1}$$

and apply the Product and Chain Rules.

There are other formulas for derivatives that we have not given. However, we are providing the formulas that are most useful for the functions encountered in everyday situations associated with business, economics, finance, management, and the social and life sciences. If you ever need them, you can look up other formulas in a calculus book that emphasizes applications in science or engineering.

CONCEPT CHECK

Can you	To practice, try	
Sketch a general rate-of-change graph?	Section 3.1	Activities 3, 9
Use tangent lines to sketch an accurate slope graph?	Section 3.1	Activities 15, 17
Apply simple derivative rules?		
Power	Section 3.2	Activities 7, 13, 19
Constant Multiplier	Section 3.2	Activities 9, 11
Sum	Section 3.2	Activities 15, 17
Exponential	Section 3.3	Activities 5, 7, 11
Natural Log	Section 3.3	Activities 17, 19
Determine simple rate-of-change formulas?	Section 3.2	Activities 29, 31
	Section 3.3	Activities 25, 27
Use the Chain Rule (Form 1)?	Section 3.4	Activities 5, 7
Use the Chain Rule (Form 2)?	Section 3.4	Activities 17, 23, 27
Apply the Chain Rule?	Section 3.4	Activities 39, 41
Use the Product Rule?	Section 3.5	Activities 13, 15,19
Apply the Product Rule?	Section 3.5	Activities 29, 31
Use L'Hôpital's Rule?	Section 3.6	Activities 19, 23, 25

1. Consider the accompanying figure.

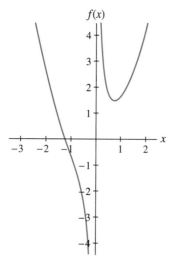

a. Note any input values for which the slope of the graph is zero.

b. For what input values is the slope of the graph positive? negative?

c. Are there any input values for which the slope of the graph does not exist?

d. Graphically estimate the slope of f at $x = -2$ and $x = 1$.

e. Sketch a slope graph for the function f.

2. **Turkey** The average annual per capita consumption of turkey in the United States between 1980 and 2002 can be modeled by the equation

$$D(t) = \frac{8.101}{1 + 214.8e^{-0.797t}} + 10 \text{ pounds per person}$$

t years after 1980.

(Source: Based on data from Economic Research Service/USDA.)

a. Find a formula for $\frac{dD}{dt}$.

b. Find the value of $D'(10)$. Interpret your answer.

c. How quickly was the consumption of turkey growing in 2001?

3. **Mortgage** The total amounts of outstanding mortgage debt in the United States for selected years between 1980 and 2000 are shown in the accompanying table. Below are a model for the data and a graph of the model.

$$A(t) = 0.173t^4 - 6.24t^3 + 71.06t^2$$
$$-32.2t + 1460.59 \text{ billion dollars}$$

t years after 1980.

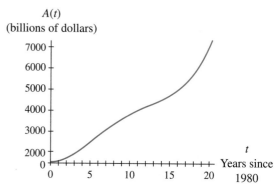

a. Use the graph to estimate how quickly the mortgage debt amount was changing in 1998.

b. Find the derivative of the equation in 1998. Interpret your answer.

4. **Mortgage** If $N(t)$ is the total amount of mortgage debt (in billions of dollars) attributable to new mortgages t years after 1980, we find the percentage of outstanding mortgage debt represented by new mortgages each year by dividing $N(t)$ by $A(t)$ in Activity 3 and multiplying by 100:

$$P(t) = \frac{N(t)}{A(t)} \cdot 100 \text{ percent } t \text{ years after 1980}$$

a. Discuss how you find a formula for the rate of change of the percentage of total mortgage debt represented by new mortgages each year.

b. What are the input and output units of measure for P'?

Year	1980	1985	1990	1992	1994	1996	1998	2000
Total outstanding debt (billions of dollars)	1465	2378	3808	4073	4380	4865	5698	6890

TABLE FOR ACTIVITY 3

(Source: *Statistical Abstract,* 2001.)

Project 3.1 Superhighway

Setting

The European Communities have decided to build a new superhighway that will run from Berlin through Paris and Madrid and end in Lisbon. This superhighway, like some others in Europe, will have no posted maximum speed so that motorists may drive as fast as they wish. There will be three toll stations installed, one at each border. Because these stations will be so far apart and motorists may not anticipate their need to stop, there has been widespread concern about the possibility of high-speed collisions at these stations. In response to the concern for safety, the Committee on Transportation has determined that flashing warning lights should be installed at an appropriate distance before each toll station. Your firm has been contracted to study known stopping distances and to develop a model for predicting where the warning lights should be installed and to suggest what other precautions could be taken to avoid accidents at the toll stations. (Bear in mind that you are a consultant to Europeans who wish to see all results in the metric system. However, because you work for an American-based company, you must also include the English equivalent.)

Tasks

1. Find data that give stopping distances as a function of speed, and cite the source for the data. Present the data in a table and as a graph. Find a model to fit the data. Justify your choice. Before using your model to extrapolate, consult someone who could be considered an authority to determine whether the model holds outside of the data range. Consult a reliable source to determine probable speeds driven on such a highway. On the basis of your model, make a recommendation about where the warning lights should be placed. Justify your recommendation.

2. Find rates of change of your model for at least three speeds, one of which should be the speed that you believe to be most likely. Interpret these rates of change in this context. Would underestimating the most likely speed have a serious adverse affect? Support your answer.

Reporting

1. Prepare a written report of your study for the Committee on Transportation.

2. Prepare a press release for the Committee on Transportation to use when it announces the implementation of your safety precautions. The press release should be succinct and should answer the questions who, what, when, where, and why.

Hint: Drivers' handbooks and Department of Transportation documents are possible sources of data on stopping distance.

Project 3.2 Fertility Rates

Setting

The *Statistical Abstract of the United States* (2001 edition) reports fertility rates in the United States. Data for three fertility rates are located on the *Calculus Concepts* website.

Tasks

1. Find a table of fertility rate data in a current edition of the *Statistical Abstract,* and summarize in your own words the meaning of "fertility rate." Assign units to the given fertility rate data.

2. Find a piecewise model consisting of at most three pieces that fits the given fertility rate data for whites. Write the derivative function for this model. Construct a table of fertility rates and the rate of change of fertility rates for all years from 1970 through 2000. Discuss any points at which the derivative of your model does not exist (and why it does not exist), and explain how you estimated the rates of change at these points.

3. Using the data in a current edition of the *Statistical Abstract,* complete the same analysis as in Task 2

for the fertility rates for blacks in the United States. (*Note:* The *Statistical Abstract* "Total Black" data for 1984 and earlier includes races other than black.)

4. Add any other recent data for the fertility rate of whites. (*Note:* Recent editions of the *Statistical Abstract* occasionally update older data points. Therefore, you should check the given data and change any updated values so that your data agree with the most recent *Statistical Abstract.*) Find a piecewise model for the updated data. Use this new model to calculate the rates of change that occurred in the years since 2000.

Reporting

Write a report discussing your findings and their demographic impact. Include your mathematical computations as an appendix.

Analyzing Change: Applications of Derivatives

4

James Leynse/CORBIS SABA

Concept Application

Businesses often experience growth or decline as a result of changes in the economy, turnover in management, introduction of new products, or even whims of consumers. A company measures its performance by measuring quantities such as revenue, profit, productivity, and stock prices. In analyzing its performance, a company may examine the past behavior of these quantities and seek the answers to such questions as

• When did the quantity exhibit highs and lows?

• Was there a time when the trend of the quantity changed?

• Is it possible to identify when the rate of change of the quantity was greatest?

   Such analysis may be helpful as the company seeks to improve its performance. You will find the tools in this chapter useful in answering questions such as these. One such exploration for the Polo Ralph Lauren Corporation's revenue is found in Activity 40 of Section 4.3.

Chapter Introduction

This chapter is devoted to exploring the ways in which rate-of-change information can be used to help analyze change. We begin by examining how a rate of change can be used to approximate change in a function's output.

Next, we consider the importance of those places at which the rate of change is zero. In many cases, these points correspond to local maximum or minimum function values. Absolute extrema may occur at these points.

Finally, we consider situations in which we find a rate of change of a function with respect to a variable that does not appear in the equation defining the function. The resulting equation, which is called a related-rates equation, is useful in describing how rates of change are interrelated.

Concepts You Will Be Learning

- Using tangent lines to approximate change (4.1)
- Using marginal analysis to estimate output (4.1)
- Using first derivatives to find relative and absolute extreme points (4.2)
- Interpreting extreme points (4.2)
- Writing second derivatives (4.3)
- Using second derivatives to find inflection points (4.3)
- Using second derivatives to determine concavity (4.3)
- Interpreting inflection points (4.3)
- Solving and interpreting related-rates equations (4.4)

4.1   Approximating Change

Recall from our discussion of linear models that the slope of a line $y = ax + b$ can be thought of as how much y changes when x changes by 1 unit. For example, the amount spent on pollution control in the United States during the 1980s can be described by the equation*

Amount $= 3.79t - 252.2$ billion dollars

where t is the number of years since 1900. The slope is $3.79 billion per year, so we can say that each year during the 1980s, an *additional* $3.79 billion was spent on pollution control. It follows that every 2 years spending increased by (2)($3.79) million, every 3 years spending increased by (3)($3.79) million, and so on.

Using Rates of Change to Approximate Change

Because rates of change are slopes, we can apply a similar type of reasoning to functions other than lines. However, we must be careful in doing so, for although the slope of a line is constant, the slopes of other functions can change at every point. Recall from the local linearity discussion in Section 2.2 that in a small enough interval around a point on a smooth, continuous function, the function and the line tangent to the function at

* Based on data from *Statistical Abstract*, 1992.

that point appear to be the same. We call upon this similarity when we use the rate of change (slope of the tangent) to approximate the actual change in the function.

Concept Development: Approximating Change   For example, consider the average retail price (cost to the consumer) during the 1990s of a pound of salted, grade AA butter, which can be modeled by the equation*

$$p(t) = 5.17t^2 - 28.7t + 195 \text{ cents}$$

where t is the number of years since the end of 1990. We calculate how rapidly the average price was increasing at the end of 1998 as follows:

$$\frac{dp}{dt} = 2(5.17)t - 28.7 = 10.34t - 28.7 \text{ cents per year}$$

When $t = 8$,

$$\frac{dp}{dt} = 10.34(8) - 28.7 = 54 \text{ cents per year}$$

Thus, at the end of 1998, the price of butter was rising by approximately 54 cents per year or $0.54 per year. On the basis of this rate of change and the fact that the average price at the end of 1998 was approximately $p(8) = 296$ cents $= \$2.96$, we estimate that during the following year (1999), the price increased by approximately $0.54 to a price of $3.50 and that during the first 6 months of 1999, the price increased by approximately $\frac{1}{2}(\$0.54) = \$0.27$ to a price of $3.23. Figure 4.1 illustrates these approximations. Note in Figure 4.1 that the approximation of price using the tangent line is relatively close to the actual price. Of course, because the price function p is not linear, the farther we are from the point of tangency, the less accurate is our tangent-line approximation.

Compare the 6-months and 1-year approximations, as well as approximations for time periods of 3 months, 9 months, and 2 years, with the actual values given by the model. These approximations and function values are listed in Table 4.1. In Table 4.1 we convert the price from the equation to dollars by multiplying $p(t)$ by 0.01 dollars per cents.

FIGURE 4.1

TABLE 4.1

Time from end of 1998	Approximated price	Price from equation	Difference between equation value and approximation
3 months	$2.96 + 0.25($0.54) = $3.10	$p(8.25) = \$3.10$	$0.00
6 months	$2.96 + 0.5($0.54) = $3.23	$p(8.5) = \$3.25$	$0.02
9 months	$2.96 + 0.75($0.54) = $3.37	$p(8.75) = \$3.40$	$0.03
1 year	$2.96 + 1($0.54) = $3.50	$p(9) = \$3.55$	$0.05
2 years	$2.96 + 2($0.54) = $4.04	$p(10) = \$4.25$	$0.21

* Simplified model based on data from *Statistical Abstract*, 1998.

Note that the shorter the time period, the closer the approximated price is to the price given by the model. This is no coincidence, because the rate of change is more likely to be nearly constant over a short time period than over a longer period of time. Rates of change can often be used to approximate changes in a function, and they generally give good approximations over small intervals.

To summarize, consider the following statements:

- The change in a function f from x to $x + h$ can be approximated by the change in the line tangent to the graph of the function at x from x to $x + h$ when h is a small number.

- The change in the tangent line from x to $x + h$ is

    (Slope of the tangent line at x) $\cdot h = f'(x) \cdot h$

The mathematical notation for the statement "The change in a function from x to $x + h$ is approximately the change of the tangent line at x from x to $x + h$" is

$$f(x + h) - f(x) \approx f'(x) \cdot h$$

for small values of h. We illustrate this statement geometrically in Figure 4.2.

FIGURE 4.2

Approximating Change

The approximate change in f is the rate of change of f times a small change in x. That is,

$$f(x + h) - f(x) \approx f'(x) \cdot h$$

where h represents the small change in x.

It follows from this formula for approximating change that we can approximate the function value $f(x + h)$ by adding the approximate change to $f(x)$.

Approximating the Result of Change

When x changes by a small amount to $x + h$, the output of f at $x + h$ is approximately the value of f at x plus the approximate change in f.

$$f(x + h) \approx f(x) + f'(x) \cdot h$$

It is the formula $f(x + h) \approx f(x) + f'(x) \cdot h$ that we used to obtain the approximated price column in Table 4.1 in the butter price example.

EXAMPLE 1   *Using a Tangent-Line Approximation to Estimate Outputs*

Temperature   The temperature for a 2-hour period during and after a thunderstorm can be modeled by

$$T(h) = 2.37h^4 - 5.163h^3 + 8.69h^2 - 9.87h + 78° \text{ Fahrenheit}$$

where h is the number of hours since the storm began.

a. Use the rate of change of $T(h)$ at $h = 0.25$ to estimate by how much the temperature changed between 15 and 20 minutes after the storm began.

b. Find the temperature and rate of change of temperature at $h = 1.5$ hours.

c. Using only the answers to part b, estimate the temperature 1 hour and 40 minutes after the storm began.

d. Sketch the graph of T from $h = 0$ to $h = 1.75$ with lines tangent to the graph at $h = 0.25$ and $h = 1.5$. On the basis of the graph, determine whether the answers to parts a and c are overestimates or underestimates of the temperature given by the model.

Solution

a. First we develop a rate-of-change formula for temperature:

$$T'(h) = 9.48h^3 - 15.489h^2 + 17.38h - 9.87°\text{F per hour}$$

Then we evaluate that rate-of-change formula at $h = 0.25$:

$$T'(0.25) = 9.48(0.25)^3 - 15.489(0.25)^2 + 17.38(0.25) - 9.87$$
$$\approx -6.34°\text{F per hour}$$

In order to calculate the change in input (hour) when minutes are given, we divide the change in input by the conversion factor 60 minutes per hour:

Interval given: "between 15 and 20 minutes"

Change in input: 5 minutes
$= \frac{5}{60}$ hour $= \frac{1}{12}$ hour

Interval given: "1.5 hours"...
"1 hour and 40 minutes"

Change in input: 10 minutes
$= \frac{10}{60}$ hour $= \frac{1}{6}$ hour

The change in the temperature between 15 and 20 minutes after the storm began is approximately $(-6.34°\text{F/hour})\left(\frac{1}{12} \text{ hour}\right) = -0.53°\text{F}$. The temperature fell approximately half a degree.

b. $T(1.5) \approx 77.3°\text{F}$ and $T'(1.5) \approx 13.3°\text{F}$ per hour

c. Note that 40 minutes $= \frac{40}{60}$ hour $= \frac{2}{3}$ hour, so 1 hour and 40 minutes $= 1\frac{2}{3}$ hours.

$$\begin{pmatrix} \text{Temperature at 1 hour} \\ \text{and 40 minutes} \end{pmatrix} = \begin{pmatrix} \text{temperature at} \\ 1\frac{1}{2} \text{ hours} \end{pmatrix} + \begin{pmatrix} \text{approximate change} \\ \text{in temperature} \end{pmatrix}$$

$$T\left(1\frac{2}{3}\right) \approx T(1.5) + T'(1.5)\left(\frac{1}{6}\right)$$

$$T\left(1\frac{2}{3}\right) \approx 77.3°\text{F} + (13.3°\text{F per hour})\left(\frac{1}{6} \text{ hour}\right)$$

$$\approx 77.3°\text{F} + 2.2°\text{F}$$

$$= 79.5°\text{F}$$

d.

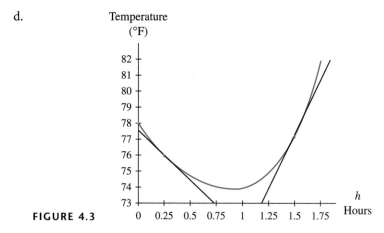

FIGURE 4.3

Because the tangent line at $h = 0.25$ hour is steeper and therefore, decreasing more quickly than the graph between $h = 0.25$ (15 minutes) and $h \approx 0.33$ (20 minutes), the approximate change in temperature overestimates the actual decreases (see Figure 4.3). Thus, using the approximate change to estimate the temperature at $h \approx 0.33$ gives a temperature that is lower than the temperature given by the model at $h \approx 0.33$. The tangent line at $h = 1.5$ is not as steep as the graph to the right of $h = 1.5$, so our temperature approximation for $h = 1.67$ is lower than the temperature given by the model.   ●

Sometimes it is necessary to use a tangent line to estimate a function output value because we do not have enough information available to develop a model. At other times, the tangent-line approximation is used for short-term extrapolation. This is illustrated in Example 2.

EXAMPLE 2   *Using Different Extrapolation Techniques*

Population (California)   The population of California from 1990 through 2000 can be modeled by

$$P(t) = 6.7t^3 - 89t^2 + 624t + 29{,}854 \text{ thousand people}$$

t years after July 1, 1990. Figure 4.4 shows the data and model in graphical form.

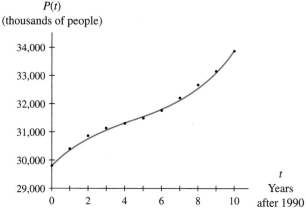

FIGURE 4.4

(Source: *Statistical Abstract*, 2001. The data are given for July 1 of each year.)

a. Use the fact that the population in 1999 was 33.145 million and in 2000 was 33.872 million to estimate the population on July 1, 2001.

b. Use the model to estimate the population on July 1, 2001.

c. Find the output of the model and the derivative of the model on July 1, 2000. Use these values to estimate the population on July 1, 2001.

d. Discuss the assumptions one makes when using each estimation technique in parts *a*, *b*, and *c*.

Solution

a. The average rate of change between 1999 and 2000 is

$$\frac{33.872 - 33.145 \text{ million people}}{1 \text{ year}} = 0.727 \text{ million people per year}$$

Adding this value to the population on July 1, 2000, we obtain an estimate of the July 1, 2001, population:

$$33.872 + 0.727 = 34.599 \text{ million people (that is, 34,599 thousand people)}$$

b. The model estimates the population on July 1, 2001, as

$$P(11) \approx 34{,}867 \text{ thousand people}$$

c. The derivative of *P* is

$$P'(t) = 20.1t^2 - 178t + 624 \text{ thousand people per year}$$

t years after July 1, 1990. On July 1, 2000, the rate of change of the population was approximately

$$P'(10) \approx 854 \text{ thousand people per year}$$

and the population according to the model was 33,894 thousand. Thus

$$P(11) \approx P(10) + P'(10)$$
$$\approx 33{,}894 + 854$$
$$\approx 34{,}748 \text{ thousand people}$$

d. To estimate using only the last two data points (part *a*) is to assume that the average rate of change in the population from July 1, 2000, through July 1, 2001, will be approximately the same as it was from July 1, 1999, through July 1, 2000. To estimate using only the model (part *b*) is to assume that future growth will continue in the manner of the cubic model. To estimate using the derivative of the model (part *c*) is to assume two things: that the model may be extended beyond 2000 and that the rate of change on July 1, 2000 (as estimated by the model) is a good predictor of the change in the population during the following year.

All three of these estimates are valid. If it were July 1, 2000, and someone needed an estimate for the population a year later, that person might use any one of these or many other techniques to make the prediction. ●

Marginal Analysis

In economics, it is customary to refer to the rates of change of cost, revenue, and profit with respect to the number of units produced or sold as **marginal cost, marginal**

revenue, and **marginal profit.** These rates are used to approximate actual change in cost, revenue, or profit when the number of units produced or sold is increased by one. The term **marginal analysis** is often applied to this type of approximation.

EXAMPLE 3   *Understanding Marginal Cost*

Cost   Suppose a manufacturer of toaster ovens currently produces 250 ovens per day with a total production cost of $12,000 and a marginal cost of $24 per oven.

a.   What information does the marginal cost value give the manufacturer?

b.   If $C(x)$ is the cost to produce x toaster ovens, what is the notation for marginal cost?

Solution

a.   The marginal cost is the rate of change of cost with respect to the number of units produced. It is the approximate increase in cost, $24, that will result if production is increased from 250 ovens per day to 251 ovens per day.

b.   The marginal cost is $C'(x)$, or $\frac{dC}{dx}$. In this example, $C'(250) = \$24$ per oven.   ●

We know that profit = revenue − cost. If $p(x)$, $r(x)$, and $c(x)$ are respectively the profit, revenue, and cost associated with x units, then we have the relationship $p(x) = r(x) - c(x)$. If we take the derivative of this expression, we have $p'(x) = r'(x) - c'(x)$, or

Marginal profit = marginal revenue − marginal cost

From this equation, we see that if marginal profit is to be positive, so that increased sales will increase profit, then marginal revenue must be greater than marginal cost. Example 4 explores these relationships.

EXAMPLE 4   *Using a Model for Marginal Analysis*

TABLE 4.2

Number of Customers	Buffet price (dollars)
86	7.70
83	7.90
80	8.20
78	8.30
76	8.50
73	8.70
70	9.00
68	9.10

Profit   A seafood restaurant has been keeping track of the price of its Monday night all-you-can-eat buffet and the corresponding number of nightly customers. These data are given in Table 4.2.

a.   Find a model for the data, and convert it into a model for revenue.

b.   If the cost to the restaurant is $4.50 per person regardless of the number of customers, find models for cost and profit.

c.   Find the marginal revenue, marginal cost, and marginal profit values for 50, 91, and 100 customers. Interpret the values in context.

Solution

a.   A linear model for these buffet price data is

$$B(x) = -0.0795x + 14.529 \text{ dollars price of one buffet meal}$$

where x is the number of customers, $68 \leq x \leq 86$. Revenue is equal to (price)(number of customers), so it is given by the equation

$$R(x) = -0.0795x^2 + 14.529x \text{ dollars revenue from } x \text{ buffet meals,}$$

where x is the number of customers, $68 \leq x \leq 86$.

b. The cost model is $c(x) = 4.5x$ dollars for x customers. The profit model is

$$\begin{aligned} p(x) = R(x) - c(x) &= -0.0795x^2 + 14.529x - 4.5x \\ &= -0.0795x^2 + 10.029x \text{ dollars cost for } x \text{ buffet meals} \end{aligned}$$

where x is the number of customers, $68 \leq x \leq 86$.

c. The derivatives of revenue, cost, and profit are, respectively,

$$R'(x) = -0.159x + 14.529 \text{ dollars revenue per customer}$$
$$c'(x) = \$4.50 \text{ cost per customer}$$
$$p'(x) = -0.159x + 10.029 \text{ dollars profit per customer}$$

where x is the number of customers. Evaluating the derivatives at 50, 91 and 100 customers gives the marginal values shown in Table 4.3.

TABLE 4.3

Demand (number of customers)	Marginal revenue (dollars per customer)	Marginal cost (dollars per customer)	Marginal profit (dollars per customer)
50	6.58	4.50	2.08
91	0.06	4.50	−4.44
100	−1.38	4.50	−5.88

What do these marginal values tell us? If the buffet price is set on the basis of 50 customers, then revenue is increasing by $6.58 per customer. Because this value is greater than marginal cost, we see a positive marginal profit. In other words, increasing the number of customers to 51 (by lowering the price) will increase nightly revenue by approximately $6.58 and nightly profit by $2.08. It would benefit the restaurant to increase the number of customers by lowering price.

Similarly, we estimate that if the number of customers is increased from 91 to 92, then revenue will not change significantly ($0.06 per customer) and profit will, therefore, decline. With 91 customers, stimulating sales by lowering the price will not benefit the restaurant.

Finally, note that when price is set so that the restaurant expects 100 customers, the marginal revenue and profit are negative. Increasing the number of customers (by decreasing price) to 101 will result in an approximate decrease in nightly revenue of $1.38 and a decrease in nightly profit of $5.88. That is clearly undesirable. ●

We have seen that the change in a quantity over a small interval can be approximated using the rate of change of that quantity over the corresponding interval. This tangent line approximation technique can be especially useful when there is insufficient data to calculate change directly or when it is desirable to make short-term extrapolations. The derivative is a useful tool in marginal analysis for business and marketing applications.

4.1 Concept Inventory

- Change in function ≈ change in tangent line close to the point of tangency

$$f(x + h) - f(x) \approx f'(x) \cdot h$$

- $f(x + h) \approx f(x) + f'(x) \cdot h$ for small values of h
- Marginal cost, marginal profit, marginal revenue

4.1 Activities

Getting Started

1. If the humidity is currently 32% and is falling at a rate of 4 percentage points per hour, estimate the humidity 20 minutes from now.

2. If an airplane is flying 300 mph and is accelerating at a rate of 200 mph per hour, estimate the airplane's speed in 5 minutes.

3. If $f(3) = 17$ and $f'(3) = 4.6$, estimate $f(3.5)$.

4. If $g(7) = 4$ and $g'(7) = -12.9$, estimate $g(7.25)$.

5. Interpret the following statements.
    a. At a production level of 500 units, marginal cost is $17 per unit.
    b. When weekly sales are 150 units, marginal profit is $4.75 per unit.

6. **Sales**   Interpret the marginal values given in the following statements.
    a. When weekly sales are 500 units, marginal revenue is $10 per unit and marginal cost is $13 per unit.
    b. When weekly sales are 10 units, marginal profit is −$3.46 per unit.

7. **Profit**   A fraternity currently realizes a profit of $400 selling T-shirts at the opening baseball game of the season. If its marginal profit is −$4 per shirt, what action should the fraternity consider taking to improve its profit?

8. **Profit**   If the marginal profit is negative for the sale of a certain number of units of a product, is the company that is marketing the item losing money on the sale? Explain.

9. **Insurance**   A graph showing the annual premium for a one-million-dollar term life insurance policy as a function of the age of the insured person is given in the figure.

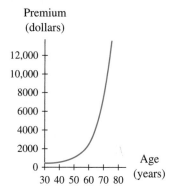

Sketch a tangent line at 70 years of age, and use it to predict the premium for a 72-year-old person.

10. **Life Expectancy**   A graph showing world life expectancy as a function of the number of decades since 1900 is given in the figure.

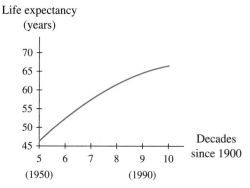

(Source: Based on data in *The True State of the Planet*, ed. Ronald Bailey, New York: The Free Press for the Competitive Enterprise Institute, 1995.)

Sketch the tangent line at 1990, and use it to estimate the world life expectancy in 2000.

Applying Concepts

11. **Sales**   A graph of revenue from new car sales and associated advertising expenditures for franchised new-car dealerships in the United States between 1980 (when advertising expenditures were $1.2 billion) and 2000 (when advertising expenditures were $6.4 billion) is shown in the figure.

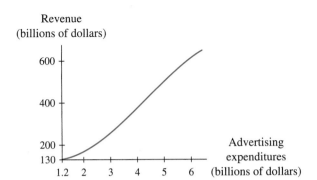

Revenue
(billions of dollars)

(Source: Based on data from *Statistical Abstract*, 2001.)

a. Sketch a tangent line at the point where advertising expenditures were $6 billion, and use it to estimate the revenue from new car sales when $6.5 billion was spent on advertising.

b. The model graphed in the figure is

$$R(x) = -3.68x^3 + 47.958x^2 - 80.759x$$
$$+ 166.98 \text{ billion dollars of revenue,}$$

when x billion dollars is spent on advertising, $1.2 \leq x \leq 6.5$. What does the model estimate as the revenue when $6.5 billion is spent on advertising?

c. Which estimate do you believe is the more reliable one? Why?

12. **Emissions**   In 1987, because of concern that CFCs (chlorofluorocarbons) have a detrimental effect on the stratospheric ozone layer, the Montreal Protocol calling for phasing out all CFC production was ratified. The accompanying graph shows estimated releases of CFC-11 between 1988 and 1993.

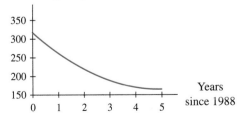

Release of
CFC-11
(millions of kilograms)

(Source: Based on data in *The True State of the Planet*, 1995.)

a. Sketch a tangent line at 1992, and use it to estimate CFC-11 releases in 1993.

b. The model whose graph is shown in the figure is

$$C(x) = 6.107x^2 - 60.799x + 315.994$$
million kilograms of CFC-11

where x is the number of years since 1988, $0 \leq x \leq 5$. What estimate does the model give for CFC-11 releases in 1993?

c. The actual amount of CFCs released into the atmosphere in 1993 was 149 million kilograms. Which estimate is the more accurate one?

13. **Population**   The population of South Carolina between 1790 and 2000 can be modeled by

$$P(x) = 268.79(1.013087^x) \text{ thousand people}$$

x years after 1790.

(Source: Based on data from *Statistical Abstract*, 2001.)

a. Find the rate of change of the population of South Carolina in 2000.

b. On the basis of your answer to part a, approximate by how much the population changed between 2000 and 2003.

c. Write an explanation of the procedure you used to find the approximate change in the population between 2000 and 2003.

14. **Investment**   The amount in an investment after t years is given by

$$A(t) = 120(1.126^t) \text{ thousand dollars}$$

a. Give the rate-of-change formula for the amount.

b. Find the rate of change of the amount after 10 years. Write a sentence interpreting the answer.

c. On the basis of your answer to part b, determine by approximately how much the investment will grow during the first half of the 11th year.

d. Find the percentage rate of change after 10 years. Given that A is exponential, what is the significance of your answer?

15. **Population**   The population of Mexico between 1921 and 2000 can be modeled by

$$P(t) = 7.567e^{0.026t} \text{ million people}$$

where t is the number of years since 1900.

(Source: Based on data from www.inegi.gob.mx, accessed 9/20/02.)

a. How rapidly was the population growing in 1998?

b. On the basis of your answer to part *a*, determine by approximately how much the population of Mexico should have increased between 1998 and 1999.

16. Study Time   Suppose your test grade out of 100 points as a function of the time that you spend studying can be modeled by

$$G(t) = -0.044t^3 + 0.92t^2 + 38 \text{ points}$$

where *t* is the number of hours spent studying, $0 \le t \le 15$.

a. Confirm the following assertions:

   i. After 11 hours of study, the slope is 4.2 points per hour, and the grade is 90.5 points.

   ii. The grade after 12 hours of study is 94.2 points.

b. Use the information in the first assertion of part *a* to estimate the grade after 12 hours. Is this an overestimate or an underestimate of the grade given by the model? Explain.

17. Mail   A model for the number of pieces of first-class mail handled by the U.S. Postal Service between 1980 and 2000 is

$$p(x) = 17.50 + 26.53 \ln x \text{ million pieces}$$

where *x* is the number of years since 1975.

(Source: Based on data from *Statistical Abstract*, 2000.)

a. How rapidly was the amount of first-class mail growing in 1998?

b. On the basis of the rate of change in 1998, what approximate increase would you expect between 1998 and 1999?

c. On the basis of the equation, what was the actual increase between 1998 and 1999?

d. According to the 2001 *Statistical Abstract*, the actual amounts of first-class mail handled by the U.S. Postal Service in 1998 and 1999 were 100.4 million pieces and 101.9 million pieces, respectively. What was the actual 1998-through-1999 increase?

e. Compare the increases given by the derivative in part *b*, by the model in part *c*, and by the data in part *d*. Which of the three answers is most accurate? Explain.

18. Costs   Suppose production costs for various hourly production levels of television sets are given by

$$c(p) = 0.16p^3 - 8.7p^2 + 172p + 69.4 \text{ dollars}$$

where *p* units are produced each hour.

a. Find and interpret marginal cost at production levels of 5, 20, and 30 units.

b. Find the cost to produce the 6th unit, the 21st unit, and the 31st unit.

c. Why is the cost to produce the 6th unit less than the marginal cost at a production level of 5 units? Why is the cost to produce the 21st unit greater than the marginal cost at a production level of 20 units? Why is the cost to produce the 31st unit greater than the marginal cost at a production level of 30 units?

d. Find a model for average cost.

e. Find and interpret the rate of change of average cost at production levels of 5, 20, and 30 units.

19. Bank Account   Three hundred dollars is invested in an account with an APR of 6.5% compounded monthly.

a. Find an equation for the balance in the account after *t* years.

b. Rewrite the equation in part *a* to be of the form $A = Pb^t$.

c. How much is in the account after 2 years?

d. How rapidly is the value of the account growing after 2 years?

e. Use the answer in part *d* to approximate how much the value of the account changes during the first quarter of the third year.

20. Bank Account   Two thousand dollars is invested in an account with an APR of 3.2% compounded monthly.

a. Write an equation for the balance in the account after *t* years.

b. Rewrite the equation in part *a* to be of the form $A = Pb^t$.

c. How much is in the account after 5 years?

d. How rapidly is the value of the account growing after 5 years?

e. Use the answer in part *d* to approximate how much the value of the account changes during the first month of the sixth year. How close is this approximation to the actual change?

21. Sales   The owner of a concession stand finds that if he prices hot dogs so as to sell a certain number at each sporting event, then the corresponding revenues are those given in the accompanying table.

Number of hot dogs sold	Revenue (dollars)
100	195
400	620
700	875
1000	1000
1200	1020
1500	975

Balls produced each hour (hundreds)	Cost (dollars)
2	248
5	356
8	432
11	499
14	532
17	567
20	625

a. Find a model for the data.

b. Each hot dog costs the owner of the concession stand $0.50. Use this fact and the model from part *a* to write models for cost and profit. Assume there are no fixed costs.

c. Find marginal revenue, marginal cost, and marginal profit for sales levels of 200, 800, 1100, and 1400 hot dogs. Interpret your answers.

d. Graph revenue, profit, and cost for sales values between 200 and 1400 hot dogs. How are the marginal values in part *c* related to the graphs?

22. **Production**   A golf ball manufacturer knows that the cost associated with various hourly production levels are as shown in the accompanying table.

a. Find a model for the data.

b. If 1000 balls are currently being produced each hour, find and interpret the marginal cost at that level of production.

c. Repeat part *b* for hourly production levels of 300 golf balls and of 2100 golf balls.

d. Convert the cost model in part *a* to one for average cost.

e. Find and interpret the rate of change of average cost for hourly production levels of 300 and of 1700 golf balls.

23. **CPI**   Rise in consumer prices is often used as a measure of inflation rate. The table shows the CPI during the 1980s for several different countries.

a. Find the best models for the data for the United States, Canada, Peru, and Brazil.

b. How rapidly were consumer prices rising in each of those four countries in 1987?

c. Considering part *b*, what would you expect the CPI to have been in the four countries in 1988?

24. **Revenue**   A pizza parlor has been experimenting with lowering the price of their large one-topping pizza to promote sales. The average revenues from the sale of large one-topping pizzas on a Friday night at various prices are given in the table.

Country	Year							
	1980	1981	1982	1983	1984	1985	1986	1987
United States	100	110.4	117.2	120.9	126.1	130.5	133.1	137.9
Canada	100	112.4	124.6	131.8	137.5	143.0	148.9	155.4
Mexico	100	127.9	203.3	410.2	679.0	1071.2	1994.9	4624.7
Japan	100	104.9	107.8	109.9	112.3	114.6	115.3	115.4
Israel	100	217	478	1174	5560	22,498	33,330	39,937
Peru	100	175.4	288.4	609	1280	3372	5999	11,150
Brazil	100	206	407	984	2924	9556	23,436	77,258
Argentina	100	204	541	2403	17,462	134,833	256,308	592,900

(Source: *International Marketing Data and Statistics, 1988–89.*)

Table for Activity 23

Price (dollars)	9.25	10.50	11.75	13.00	14.25
Revenue (dollars)	1202.50	1228.50	1210.25	1131.00	1054.50

a. Find a model for the data.

b. Find and interpret the rate of change of revenue at a price of $9.25.

c. Approximate the change in revenue if the price is increased from $9.25 to $10.25.

d. Find and interpret the rate of change of revenue at a price of $11.50.

e. Approximate the change in revenue if the price is increased from $11.50 to $12.50.

f. Explain why the approximate change is an overestimate of the change in price from $9.25 to $10.25 but an underestimate of the change in price from $11.50 to $12.50.

25. **Advertising**   A sporting goods company keeps track of how much it spends on advertising each month and of its corresponding monthly profit. From this information, the list of monthly advertising expenditures and the associated monthly profit shown in the accompanying table was compiled.

Advertising (thousands of dollars)	Profit (thousands of dollars)
5	150
7	200
9	250
11	325
13	400
15	450
17	500
19	525

a. Find a model for the data.

b. Find and interpret the rate of change of profit both as a rate of change and as an approximate change when the monthly advertising expenditure is $10,000.

c. Repeat part *b* for a monthly advertising expenditure of $18,000.

26. **Newspapers**   The circulation of daily English-language newspapers in the United States as of September 30 of each year between 1986 and 2000 is shown in the accompanying table.

Year	Circulation (millions)
1986	62.5
1988	62.7
1990	62.3
1992	60.1
1994	59.3
1996	57.0
1998	56.2
2000	55.8

(Source: *Statistical Abstract*, 1995, 2001.)

a. Find a model for the data. Why did you choose this model?

b. According to your model, what is the predicted circulation of daily English-language newspapers in 2007? Is this reasonable?

c. Estimate how rapidly the newspaper circulation was changing in 1998.

d. Use the derivative to approximate the change in the newspaper circulation between 1990 and 1991.

Discussing Concepts

27. Write a brief essay that explains why, when rates of change are used to approximate change in a function, approximations over shorter time intervals generally give better answers than approximations over longer time intervals. Include graphical illustrations in your discussion.

28. Write a brief essay that explains why, when rates of change are used to approximate the change in a concave-up portion of a function, the approximation is an underestimate and, when rates of change are used to approximate change in a concave-down portion of a function, the approximation is an overestimate. Include graphical illustrations in your discussion.

29. Recall that the derivative of a function f with input x is defined as

$$f'(x) = \lim_{h \to 0} \frac{f(x + h) - f(x)}{h}$$

provided that this limit exists. Starting with this equation, derive the formula for the approximation of change:

$$f(x + h) - f(x) \approx f'(x) \cdot h$$

4.2   Relative and Absolute Extreme Points

In this section, we turn our attention to finding high points (maxima) and low points (minima) on the graph of a function. Points at which maximum or minimum outputs occur are called **extreme points,** and the process of **optimization** involves techniques for finding them. Maxima and minima often can be found using derivatives, and such points have important applications to the world in which we live.

We use the terms *extreme points* to refer to maxima and minima (either relative or absolute, depending on the context) but not to inflection points.

Relative Extrema

We begin by examining a model for the population of Kentucky* from 1980 through 1993:

$$\text{Population} = p(x) = 0.395x^3 - 6.67x^2 + 30.3x + 3661 \text{ thousand people}$$

where x is the number of years since the end of 1980. It is evident from the graph in Figure 4.5 that between 1980 and 1993, the population indicated by the model was smallest in 1980 (3661 thousand people) and greatest in 1993 (3794 thousand people). However, there are two other points of interest on the graph. Sometime near 1983, the population reached a peak. We call the peak a **relative maximum.** It does not represent the highest overall point, but it is a point to which the population rises and after which it declines. Similarly, near 1988 the population reached a **relative minimum.** There are lower points on the graph, but the population decreases during a period of time immediately before this relative minimum and then increases during a time period immediately following this relative minimum.

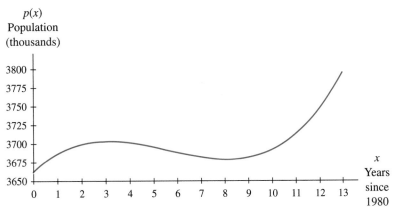

FIGURE 4.5

* Simplified model based on data from *Statistical Abstract,* 1994.

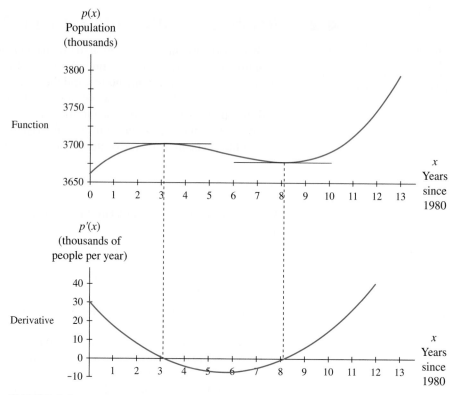

FIGURE 4.6

It should be intuitively clear from the discussions in Chapter 2 that at a point where the graph of a smooth, continuous function reaches a relative maximum or minimum, the tangent line is horizontal and the slope is 0. We can consider this important link between such a function and its derivative in more detail by examining the relationship between the Kentucky population function and its slope graph. Horizontal tangent lines on the population function graph correspond to the points at which the slope graph crosses the horizontal axis. Figure 4.6 shows the graphs of the population function and its derivative.

Note that near $x = 3$, the slope graph crosses the x-axis. This is the x-value for which $p(x)$ is at a local maximum. Likewise, the slope graph crosses the x-axis at the x-value near 8 for which $p(x)$ is at a local minimum. The connection between the graphical and algebraic views of this situation is a key feature of optimization techniques.

> Finding the point at which the slope graph of a function crosses or touches the input axis is the same as finding *the point at which the derivative of the function is zero*. That is, the slope graph of a function f crosses or touches the input x-axis where $f'(x) = 0$.

An extreme point is an ordered pair of the input value and the output value. Do not confuse extreme values with the inputs. The extreme value is always an output value.

The derivative of the population of Kentucky function is

$$\frac{dp}{dx} = 1.185x^2 - 13.34x + 30.3 \text{ thousand people per year}$$

where x is the number of years since 1980, $0 \leq x \leq 13$. Setting this expression equal to zero and solving for x results in two solutions: $x \approx 3.14$ and $x \approx 8.12$. This information, together with the graph of p shown in Figure 4.6, tells us that according to the model, the population peaked in early 1984 at approximately $p(3.14) = 3703$ thousand people. We also conclude that the population declined to a relative minimum in early 1989. The population at that time was approximately $p(8.12) = 3679$ thousand people.

It is important to note that relative extrema do not occur at the endpoints of an interval. A relative maximum is an output value that is larger than all other output values in some interval *around* the maximum. Similarly, a relative minimum is an output value that is smaller than all other output values in some interval *around* the minimum.

EXAMPLE 1   *Relating Zeros of a Derivative to Relative Extrema of the Function*

Baggage Complaints   The number of consumer complaints to the U.S. Department of Transportation about baggage* on U.S. airlines between 1989 and 2000 can be modeled by the function

$$B(x) = 55.15x^2 - 524.09x + 1768.65 \text{ complaints}$$

where x is the number of years after 1989.

a. Consider the function out of its modeling context. Find any relative maxima and minima of B on the interval $0 \leq x \leq 11$.

b. Graph the function and its derivative. On each graph, clearly mark the input value that corresponds to the minimum found in part *a*.

c. Find the year between 1989 and 2000 in which the number of baggage complaints was at a relative minimum.

Solution

a. Because the graph of B is continuous and smooth over the interval $0 \leq x \leq 11$, we know that the relative extrema occur where the derivative is zero. Thus we set the derivative equal to zero and solve for x:

$$B'(x) = 110.3x - 524.09 = 0$$

$$x \approx 4.8; \quad \text{The value of } B \text{ at } x \approx 4.8 \text{ is approximately } 523.5.$$

The equation for B is a quadratic with a positive leading coefficient; therefore, the graph of B is a concave-up parabola. Thus, we know that $(4.8, 523.5)$ is a relative minimum point. (We will see later in this section that this is also an absolute minimum.)

---

* Based on data from *Statistical Abstract*, 2001.

b.

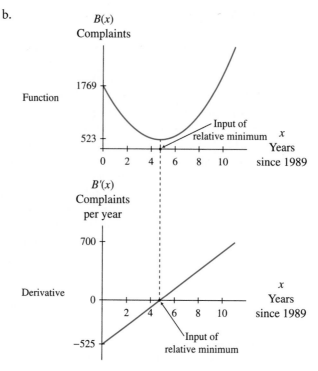

FIGURE 4.7

We see in Figure 4.7 that a relative minimum on the function graph corresponds to the point at which the derivative graph crosses the *x*-axis.

c. Because the model gives yearly complaint totals, it must be interpreted discretely. Thus the minimum number of complaints occurred in either 1993 (*x* = 4) or 1994 (*x* = 5). Checking the value of the function in each of these years, we find that the least number of complaints was approximately 527 in 1994. ●

Conditions When Relative Extrema Might Not Exist

We have just seen how derivatives can be used to locate relative maxima and minima. *You should use caution,* however, and not automatically assume that just because the derivative is zero at a point, there is a relative maximum or relative minimum at that point. When a function has a point at which the derivative of the function is zero (that is, when there is a horizontal tangent line on the graph of the function), one of the four situations depicted in Figure 4.8 occurs.

It is evident from Figures 4.8c and 4.8d that the graph of a function may have a horizontal tangent line at a point that is not an extreme point. It is therefore important that you graph the function when using derivatives to locate extreme points.

> Always begin the process of finding extreme points by graphing the function to see whether there are any relative maxima or minima before proceeding to work with derivatives.

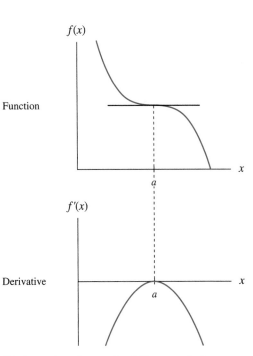

(a) Relative maximum:
To the left of input *a*,
slopes are positive, and
to the right of *a*, slopes
are negative.

(b) Relative minimum:
To the left of input *a*,
slopes are negative, and
to the right of *a*, slopes
are positive.

Function

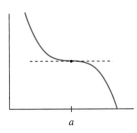

(c) Inflection point:
Slopes are positive to the
left and right of input *a*.

(d) Inflection point:
Slopes are negative to the
left and right of input *a*.

FIGURE 4.8

Derivative

$f'(a) = 0$ but the graph of *f* has no relative maximum or minimum at *a*.

FIGURE 4.9

Let us further investigate the graph shown in Figure 4.8d. Figure 4.9 shows the graph of the function that appears in Figure 4.8d and its slope (derivative) graph. If you carefully examine the slope graph, you will see that it touches the *x*-axis but does not cross it. Thus *f* does not have a relative maximum or minimum at *a*. You may notice that the derivative graph reaches its maximum at *a* as it touches the *x*-axis. Do not confuse maxima and minima on the derivative graph with maxima and minima of the original function. In Section 4.3, we will see that maxima and minima of the derivative graph have other important interpretations in terms of the original function.

EXAMPLE 2   *Relating Derivative Intercepts to Relative Extrema*

Revenue   Acme Cable Company actively promoted sales in a town that previously had no cable service. Once Acme saturated the market, it introduced a new 50-channel system and raised rates. As the company began to offer its expanded system, a different company, Bigtime Cable, began offering satellite service with more channels than Acme and at a lower price. A model for Acme's revenue for the 26 weeks after it began its sales campaign is

$$R(x) = -3x^4 + 160x^3 - 3000x^2 + 24{,}000x \text{ dollars}$$

where *x* is the number of weeks since Acme began sales. The graph of the model is shown in Figure 4.10. Some points on the graph of *R* are given in Table 4.4.

TABLE 4.4

Weeks	Revenue (dollars)
2	37,232
6	66,672
10	70,000
14	71,792
18	78,192
22	76,912
26	37,232

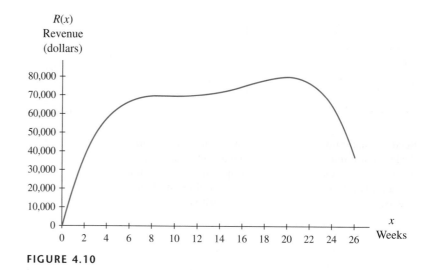

FIGURE 4.10

a. Determine the point at which Acme's revenue peaked during this 26-week interval.

b. At what other point is $R'(x) = 0$? Explain what happens to Acme's revenue at this point.

Solution

a. From the graph, we know that revenue peaks at the relative maximum. A closer examination of the graphs of R and its derivative (see Figure 4.11) locates this point near 20 weeks. Solving the equation

$$R'(x) = -12x^3 + 480x^2 - 6000x + 24{,}000 = 0$$

gives two solutions, $x = 10$ weeks and $x = 20$ weeks. Revenue peaked at 20 weeks, with a value of $R(20) = \$80{,}000$. This appears to correspond to the time immediately before Bigtime Cable's sales began negatively affecting the Acme company.

b. The other point at which $R'(x) = 0$ is (10, 70,000). The fact that the rate-of-change equation is zero at two places indicates that there are two places on the graph with horizontal tangent lines. Indeed, at $x = 10$ weeks, the line tangent to the curve is horizontal because the curve has leveled off. This corresponds to the time when Acme's revenue paused before beginning to increase again. No local maximum occurs at this point as the derivative is positive for values on either side of $x = 10$. The slope graph only touches but does not cross the input axis at $x = 10$. Note the relationships between the rate-of-change graph and the revenue graph shown in Figure 4.11 and how they connect to the slope descriptions given in Figure 4.8.

The maximum occurs where the derivative graph crosses the x-axis. The leveling-off point occurs where the derivative touches, but does not cross, the x-axis.

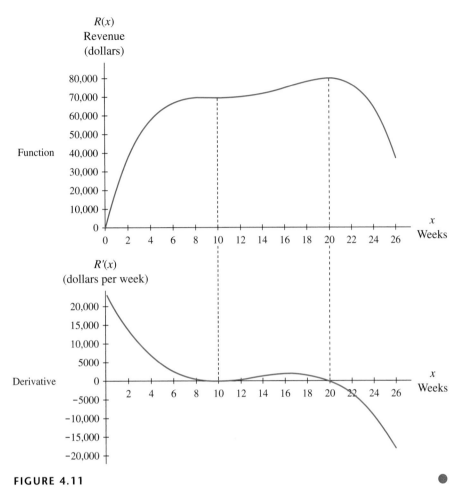

FIGURE 4.11

Relative Extrema on Functions That Are Not Smooth

Is it true for every continuous function that relative maxima and minima occur only where the derivative crosses the input axis? Although this seems to be the case for most of the functions we use, consider the piecewise continuous function describing the average concentration (in nanograms per milliliter) of a 360-mg dose of a blood pressure drug in a patient's blood during the 24 hours after the drug is given:

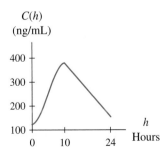

$C(h)$
(ng/mL)

FIGURE 4.12

$$C(h) = \begin{cases} -0.51h^3 + 7.65h^2 + 125 \text{ ng/mL} & \text{when } 0 \le h \le 10 \\ -16.07143h + 540.71430 \text{ ng/mL} & \text{when } 10 < h \le 24 \end{cases}$$

where h is the number of hours since the drug was given.

By calculating the left and right limits as h approaches 10 and comparing them with the function value at $h = 10$, we determine that C is continuous for all input values from 0 to 24. The two portions of the function join at the peak shown in Figure 4.12.

It is evident from the graph that the highest concentration of the drug occurs 10 hours after the patient receives the initial dose. Thus $C(10) = 380$ ng/mL is the maximum concentration. However, is $C'(10) = 0$? Does the slope graph for C cross the horizontal axis at $h = 10$? The slope at $h = 10$ exists only if the graph is smooth— that is, only if the one-sided slopes of the two portions of the graph of C are the same at $h = 10$. The one-sided slope of the graph on the left is zero at $h = 10$, but the one-sided slope of the graph on the right is -16.07143 at all points. These differing slopes cause the sharp point on the graph of C, resulting in a graph that is continuous but not smooth at $h = 10$. Thus $C'(10)$ does not exist. There is no line tangent to the graph of C at $h = 10$. That $C'(10)$ does not exist is illustrated in the graph of C' shown in Figure 4.13. It is therefore possible for an extreme point to occur where the derivative of the function does not exist, as long as the function has a value at that point.

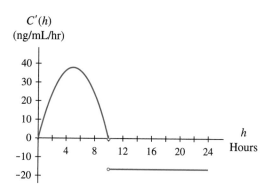

FIGURE 4.13

Conditions Where Extreme Points Exist

For a function f with input x, a relative extremum can occur at $x = c$ only if $f(c)$ exists (is defined). Furthermore,

1. A relative extremum exists where $f'(c) = 0$ and the graph of $f'(x)$ crosses (not just touches) the input axis at $x = c$.

2. A relative extremum can exist where $f(x)$ exists but $f'(c) = 0$ does not exist. (Further investigation is needed.)

Thus in order to find relative maxima and relative minima of a function f, first determine the input values for which the derivative of f is zero or undefined, and then examine a graph of f to determine which of these input values correspond to relative maxima or relative minima.

Absolute Extrema

Recall the example involving the population of Kentucky at the beginning of this section. The model for the population of Kentucky from 1980 through 1993 is

$$\text{Population} = p(x) = 0.395x^3 - 6.67x^2 + 30.3x + 3661 \text{ thousand people}$$

where x is the number of years since the end of 1980. Figure 4.14 shows a graph of p.

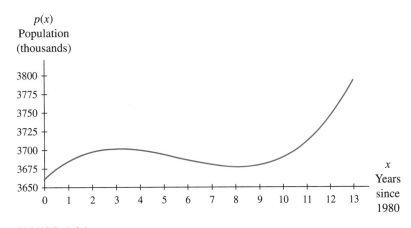

FIGURE 4.14

In the earlier discussion, it was noted that the population of Kentucky has a relative maximum of approximately 3703 thousand people in early 1984 ($x \approx 3.14$) and a relative minimum of approximately 3679 thousand people in early 1989 ($x \approx 8.12$). However, it is evident from the graph that between 1980 and 1993 there were years in which the population was greater than 3703 thousand (the relative maximum) and there was a time at which the population was less than 3679 thousand (the relative minimum).

   When considering maxima and minima over a closed interval, it is important to consider not only relative extrema but also **absolute extrema.** A function can have several different relative maxima (or minima) in a given closed interval. However, there can be only one absolute maximum value and one absolute minimum value for that interval. The absolute extremum can occur at more than one input value on the interval. An absolute extremum can occur at a relative extremum or it can occur at an endpoint of the interval. (In the trivial case of a linear function on a closed interval, all points in the interval are both absolute maxima and absolute minima.)

   In the case of the Kentucky population example, over the period between 1980 and 1993, the population of Kentucky reached its **absolute maximum** (the greatest output) in 1993. The **maximum value** of the population function is approximately 3794 thousand people. On the other hand, Kentucky's population between 1980 and 1993 was at its **absolute minimum** (the least output) in 1980 when its **minimum value** was approximately 3661 thousand people. Note that the absolute maximum and absolute minimum are stated in terms of the interval of years between 1980 and 1993. Obviously, there was a time before 1980 that the population was even lower, and it has probably risen since 1993. We discuss the idea of absolute extrema over the entire set of real numbers following Example 3.

EXAMPLE 3   *Finding Absolute Extrema on a Given Interval*

Baggage Complaints   Recall from Example 1 that the number of consumer complaints to the U.S. Department of Transportation about baggage* on U.S. airlines between 1989 and 2000 can be modeled by the function

$$B(x) = 55.15x^2 - 524.09x + 1768.65 \text{ complaints}$$

where x is the number of years after 1989. Consider the function out of its modeling context. Find the absolute maximum and the absolute minimum of B on the interval $0 \leq x \leq 11$.

Solution
As discussed in Example 1, the graph of B is a concave-up parabola with a minimum that occurs at $x \approx 4.8$ and is approximately 523.5.

To find the absolute maximum, we must determine the value of B at the endpoints of the given interval: $B(0) \approx 1768.7$ and $B(11) \approx 2676.8$. From our knowledge of the general shape of the graph of B and from these calculations, we conclude that the absolute maximum of B is approximately 2676.8 and occurs at the right endpoint when $x = 11$, and that the absolute minimum of B is approximately 523.5 and occurs at $x \approx 4.8$. ●

What if we do not have a specified input interval and are asked to find the absolute extrema? Let us again consider the function in Example 3 apart from its context and determine the absolute extrema of the function $B(x) = 55.15x^2 - 524.09x + 1768.65$ over all real number inputs. The limit $\lim_{x \to \pm\infty} B(x) \to \infty$ and the graph continues to increase infinitely in both directions. Thus there is no absolute maximum over all real number inputs. We know that the absolute minimum is the relative minimum because of the end behavior of the function. Therefore, the least output value is approximately 523.5 at $x \approx 4.8$. This value is the absolute minimum of the function over all real number inputs.

In general, in order to determine whether an absolute maximum or minimum exists for a function over all real number inputs, we must analyze the end behavior of the function as well as consider the outputs of the function at all of the input values for which the function is discontinuous or has relative extrema.

In order to help you be organized as you practice the concepts presented in this section, we conclude by outlining the steps for finding relative and absolute extrema.

---

* Based on data from *Statistical Abstract,* 2001.

Finding Extrema

To find the relative maxima and minima of a function f,

Step 1:   Determine the input values for which $f' = 0$ or f' is undefined.

Step 2:   Examine a graph of f to determine which input values found in Step 1 correspond to relative maxima or relative minima.

To find the absolute maximum and minimum of a function f on an interval from a to b,

Step 1:   Find all relative extrema of f in the interval.

Step 2:   Compare the relative extreme values in the interval with $f(a)$ and $f(b)$, the output values at the endpoints of the interval. The largest of these values is the absolute maximum, and the smallest of these values is the absolute minimum.

To find the absolute maximum and minimum of a continuous function f without a specified input interval,

Step 1:   Find all relative extrema of f.

Step 2:   Determine the end behavior of the function in both directions in order to consider a complete view of the function. The absolute extrema either do not exist or are among the relative extrema.

4.2   Concept Inventory

- Relative maximum
- Relative minimum
- An extreme point occurs at an input value
- The extreme value is an output value
- Conditions under which extreme points exist
- Absolute maximum
- Absolute minimum

4.2   Activities

Getting Started

1. Which of the six basic models (linear, exponential, logarithmic, logistic, quadratic, and cubic) could have relative maxima or minima?

2. Discuss in detail all of the options you have available for finding the relative maxima and relative minima of a function.

In Activities 3 through 8, mark the location of all relative maxima and minima with an X and the location of all absolute maxima and minima with an O. For each extreme point that is not an endpoint, indicate whether the derivative at that point is zero or does not exist.

3. *y*

4. *y*

5. *y*

6. *y*

7. y

8. y

9. Sketch a graph of a function whose derivative is zero at a point but that does not have a relative maximum or minimum at that point.

10. Sketch the graph of a function with a relative minimum at a point at which the derivative does not exist.

11. Identify for which of the graphs shown in parts *a* through *d* all of the following statements are true. For the other graphs, identify which statements are not true.

$$f'(x) > 0 \text{ for } x > 2$$
$$f'(x) > 0 \text{ for } x < 2$$
$$f'(x) = 0 \text{ for } x = 2$$

a. f(x)

b. f(x)

c. f(x)

d. f(x)

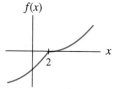

12. Identify for which of the graphs shown in parts *a* through *d* all of the following statements are true. For the other graphs, identify which statements are not true.

$$f'(x) > 0 \text{ for } x < 2$$
$$f'(x) < 0 \text{ for } x > 2$$
$$f'(x) = 0 \text{ for } x = 2$$

a. f(x)

b. f(x)

c. f(x)

d. f(x)

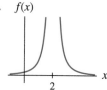

13. Sketch the graph of a function *f* such that all of the following statements are true.

$$f'(x) < 0 \text{ for } x < -1$$
$$f'(x) > 0 \text{ for } x > -1$$
$$f'(-1) \text{ does not exist.}$$

14. Sketch the graph of a function *f* such that all of the following statements are true.

$$f'(x) < 0 \text{ for } x < -1$$
$$f'(x) > 0 \text{ for } x > -1$$
$$f'(-1) = 0$$

15. Sketch the graph of a function *f* such that all of the following statements are true.

f has a relative minimum at $x = 3$.
f has a relative maximum at $x = -1$.
$f'(x) > 0$ for $x < -1$ and $x > 3$
$f'(x) < 0$ for $-1 < x < 3$
$f'(-1) = 0$ and $f'(3) = 0$

16. Sketch the graph of a function *f* such that all of the following statements are true.

$f'(x) > 0$ for $x < -1$ and $x > 3$
$f'(x) < 0$ for $-1 < x < 3$
$f'(-1) = 0$ and $f'(3) = 0$

For each function in Activities 17 through 22:

a. Write the derivative formula.

b. Locate any relative extrema and identify them as maxima or minima.

17. $f(x) = x^2 + 2.5x - 6$

18. $g(x) = -3x^2 + 14.1x - 16.2$

19. $h(x) = x^3 - 8x^2 - 6x$

20. $j(x) = 0.3x^3 + 1.2x^2 - 6x + 4$

21. $f(t) = 12(1.5^t) + 12(0.5^t)$

22. $j(t) = 5e^{-t} + \ln t$ with $t > 0$

23. Consider the function

$$g(x) = 0.04x^3 - 0.88x^2 + 4.81x + 12.11$$

a. Find the relative maximum and relative minimum of g.

b. Find the absolute maximum and the absolute minimum of g on the closed interval from $x = 0$ through $x = 14.5$.

c. Graph the function and its derivative. Indicate the relationship between the relative maximum and minimum of g and the corresponding points on the derivative graph.

24. Consider the function

$$g(x) = 5e^{-x} + \ln x - 0.2(1.5^x)$$

a. Find the relative maximum and relative minimum of g.

b. Find the absolute maximum and the absolute minimum of g on the closed interval from $x = 0$ through $x = 10$.

c. Graph the function and its derivative. Indicate the relationship between the relative maximum and minimum of g and the corresponding points on the derivative graph.

Applying Concepts

25. Grasshoppers The percentage of southern Australian grasshopper eggs that hatch as a function of temperature (for temperatures between 7°C and 25°C) can be modeled by

$$P(t) = -0.00645t^4 + 0.488t^3 - 12.991t^2$$
$$+ 136.560t - 395.154 \text{ percent}$$

where t is the temperature in °C, $7 \le t \le 25$.

(Source: Based on information in *Elements of Ecology*, George L. Clarke, New York: Wiley, 1954, p. 170.)

a. Find the temperature between 7°C and 25°C that corresponds to the greatest percentage of eggs hatching.

b. Use the equation $°F = \frac{9}{5}(°C) + 32$ to convert your answer to °F.

26. Population The U.S. Bureau of the Census prediction for the percentage of the population 65 to 74 years old from 2000 through 2050 can be modeled by

$$p(x) = (1.619 \cdot 10^{-5})x^4 - (1.675 \cdot 10^{-3})x^3$$
$$+ 0.050x^2 - 0.308x + 6.693 \text{ percent}$$

where x is the number of years after 2000, $0 \le x \le 50$. Find the absolute maximum and the absolute minimum percentages between 2000 and 2050. Give the years and the corresponding percentages.

(Source: Based on data from *Statistical Abstract*, 1998.)

27. River Rate Suppose the flow rate (in cubic feet per second, cfs) of a river in the first 11 hours after the beginning of a severe thunderstorm can be modeled by

$$C(h) = -0.865h^3 + 12.05h^2 - 8.95h + 123.02 \text{ cfs}$$

where h is the number of hours after the storm began.

a. What were the flow rates for $h = 0$ and $h = 11$?

b. Determine the absolute maximum and minimum flow rates on the closed interval from $h = 0$ through $h = 11$.

28. Lake Level Lake Tahoe lies on the California/ Nevada border, and its level is regulated by a 17-gate concrete dam at the lake's outlet. By federal court decree, the lake level must never be higher than 6229.1 feet above sea level. The lake level is monitored every midnight. The level of the lake from October 1, 1995, through July 31, 1996, can be modeled by

$$L(d) = (-5.345 \cdot 10^{-7})d^3 + (2.543 \cdot 10^{-4})d^2$$
$$- 0.0192d + 6226.192 \text{ feet above sea level}$$

d days after September 30, 1995.

(Source: Based on data from the Federal Watermaster, U.S. Department of the Interior.)

According to the model, did the lake remain below the federally mandated level from October 1, 1995 when $d = 1$, through July 31, 1996 when $d = 304$?

29. Swim Time *Swimming World* (August 1992) lists the time in seconds that an average athlete takes to swim 100 meters freestyle at age x years. The data are given in the accompanying table.

Age x (years)	Time (seconds)	Age x (years)	Time (seconds)
8	92	22	50
10	84	24	49
12	70	26	51
14	60	28	53
16	58	30	57
18	54	32	60
20	51		

a. Find the best model for the data.

b. Using the model, find the age at which the minimum swim time occurs. Also find the minimum swim time.

c. Compare the table values with the values in part *b*.

30. Costs A company analyzes the production costs for one of its products and determines the hourly operating costs when x units are produced each hour. The results are given in the accompanying table.

Production level, x (units per hour)	Hourly cost (dollars)
1	210
7	480
13	650
19	760
25	810
31	845
37	880
43	950
49	1070
55	1280
61	1590

a. Find a model for hourly cost in terms of production level.

b. Find and interpret the marginal cost when 40 units are produced.

c. On the basis of the model in part *a*, what is the equation for the average hourly cost per unit when x units are produced each hour?

d. Find the production level on the interval $7 \le x \le 61$, that minimizes average hourly cost. Give the average hourly cost and total cost at that level.

31. Sales *Consumer expenditure* and *revenue* are terms for the same thing from two perspectives. Consumer expenditure is the amount of money that consumers spend on a product, and revenue is the amount of money that businesses take in by selling the product. A street vendor constructs a table on the basis of sales data.

Price of a dozen roses (dollars)	Number of dozens sold per week
10	190
15	145
20	110
25	86
30	65
35	52

a. Find a model for quantity sold.

b. Convert the equation in part *a* into an equation for consumer expenditure.

c. What price should the street vendor charge to maximize consumer expenditure?

d. If each dozen roses costs $6, what price should the street vendor charge to maximize profit?

e. Why can the derivatives of the revenue and profit equations in this activity not be used to find the street vendor's marginal revenue and marginal profit from the sale of roses?

32. Demand An apartment complex has an exercise room and sauna, and tenants will be charged a yearly fee for the use of these facilities. A survey of tenants results in these demand/price data.

Quantity demanded	Price (dollars)
5	250
15	170
25	100
35	50
45	20
55	5

a. Find a model for price as a function of demand.

b. On the basis of the price model, give the equation for revenue.

c. Find the maximum point on the revenue model. What price and what demand give the highest revenue? What is the marginal revenue at the maximum point?

33. Refuse The yearly amount of garbage (in millions of tons) taken to a landfill outside a city during selected years from 1975 through 2005 is given in the table.

Year	Amount (millions of tons)
1975	81
1980	99
1985	117
1990	122
1995	132
2000	145
2005	180

a. Find a model for the data.

b. Give the slope formula for the model.

c. How rapidly was the amount of garbage taken to the landfill increasing in 2005?

d. Graph the derivative of your model, and determine whether your model has a relative maximum and/or minimum. Explain how you reached your conclusion.

34. Price Imagine that you have been hired as director of a performing arts center for a mid-sized community. The community orchestra gives monthly concerts in the 400-seat auditorium. To promote attendance, the former director lowered the ticket price every 2 months. The ticket prices and corresponding average attendance are given in the table.

Price (dollars)	Average attendance
35	165
30	200
25	240
20	280
15	335
10	400

a. Find quadratic and exponential models for the data. Which model better reflects the probable attendance beyond a $35 ticket price? Explain.

b. On the basis of the model that you believe is more appropriate, give the equation for revenue.

c. Find the maximum revenue and the corresponding ticket price and average attendance.

d. What other things besides the maximum revenue should you consider in setting the price?

Discussing Concepts

35. If they exist, find the absolute maxima and absolute minima of $y = \dfrac{2x^2 - x + 3}{x^2 + 2}$ over all real number inputs. If an absolute maximum or absolute minimum does not exist, explain why not.

36. If they exist, find the absolute maximum and absolute minimum of $y = (2 - 3x + x^2)(3.5 + x)^2$ over all real number inputs. If an absolute maximum or absolute minimum does not exist, explain why.

4.3   Inflection Points

Unlike relative extrema, which are output values, inflection points are coordinate points.

In Section 4.2, we discussed extreme points on a graph. Another important point that can occur on a graph is an **inflection point.**

Recall from our earlier work with cubic and logistic functions that an inflection point is a point where a graph changes concavity. On a smooth, continuous graph, the inflection point can also be thought of as the point of greatest or least slope in a region around the inflection point. In real-life applications, this point is interpreted as *the point of most rapid change or least rapid change.* (See Figure 4.15.)

(a) Inflection point: point of least slope, point of most rapid decrease

(b) Inflection point: point of greatest slope, point of most rapid increase

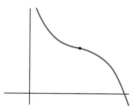

(c) Inflection point: point of greatest slope, point of least rapid decrease

(d) Inflection point: point of least slope, point of least rapid increase

FIGURE 4.15

Relative maxima and minima on a smooth, continuous graph can be found by locating the points at which the derivative graph crosses the horizontal axis. These points are among those where the original graph has horizontal tangent lines. Inflection points also can be found by examining the derivative graph and its relation to the function graph. To find the inflection point on a smooth, continuous graph, we must find the point where the slope (derivative) graph has a relative maximum or minimum. That is, we apply the method for finding maxima and minima to the *derivative graph.*

The Second Derivative

Consider, from the discussion in the previous section, the model for the population of Kentucky from 1980 through 1993:

$$\text{Population} = p(x) = 0.395x^3 - 6.67x^2 + 30.3x + 3661 \text{ thousand people}$$

where x is the number of years since the end of 1980. Graphs of the function and its derivative are the first two graphs shown in Figure 4.16.

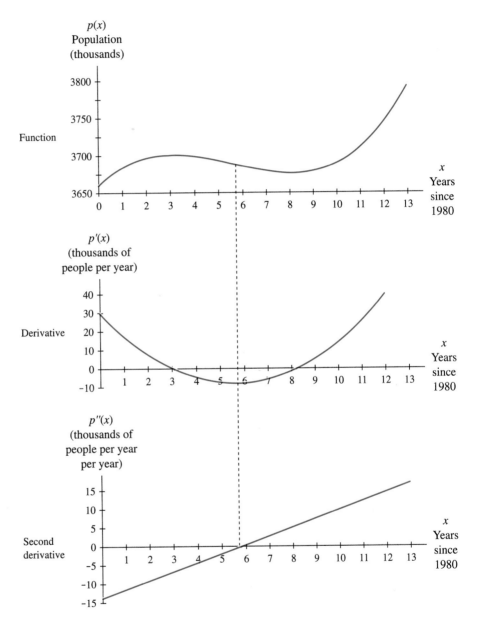

FIGURE 4.16

We wish to determine where the inflection point occurs—that is, where the population was declining most rapidly. It appears that p' has a minimum when p has an inflection point. In fact, this is exactly the case, so we can find the inflection point of p by finding the minimum of p'. To find the minimum of p' for this smooth, continuous function p, we must find where *its* derivative crosses the x-axis. The

Other notations for the second derivative of p with respect to x include $\dfrac{d^2p}{dx^2}$ and $\dfrac{d^2}{dx^2}[p(x)]$.

derivative of p' is called the **second derivative** of p, because it is the derivative of a derivative. The second derivative of p is denoted p''. In this case, the second derivative is given by

$$p''(x) = 2.37x - 13.34 \text{ thousand people per year per year}$$

where $x = 0$ in 1980.

Because the second derivative represents the rate of change of the first derivative, the output units of p'' are

$$\frac{\text{output units of } p'}{\text{input units of } p'}$$

An input/output diagram for this second derivative is shown in Figure 4.17.

The third graph in Figure 4.16 is a graph of the second derivative. The graph of p'' crosses the x-axis where the graph of p has an inflection point. Note that this identifies the minimum point on the graph of the derivative of p where the tangent line is horizontal.

Setting the second derivative equal to zero and solving for x give $x \approx 5.63$. According to the model, the population was declining most rapidly in mid-1986 at a rate of approximately $p'(5.63) \approx -7.3$ thousand people per year. At that time, the population was approximately $p(5.63) \approx 3690$ thousand people.

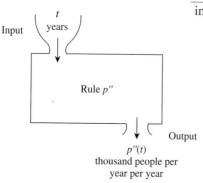

FIGURE 4.17

EXAMPLE 1   *Using the Second Derivative to Locate an Inflection Point*

Education   Consider a model for the percentage* of students graduating from high school in South Carolina from 1982 through 1990 who entered postsecondary institutions:

$$f(x) = -0.1057x^3 + 1.355x^2 - 3.672x + 50.792 \text{ percent}$$

where x is the number of years since 1982.

a. Find the inflection point of the function.

b. Determine the year between 1982 and 1990 in which the percentage was increasing most rapidly.

c. Determine the year between 1982 and 1990 in which the percentage was decreasing most rapidly.

Solution

a. Consider the point(s) at which the second derivative is zero. The first derivative formula for the percentage of students graduating from high school in South Carolina from 1982 through 1990 is

$$f'(x) = -0.3171x^2 + 2.71x - 3.672 \text{ percentage points per year}$$

---

* Based on data in *South Carolina Statistical Abstract, 1992.*

where x is the number of years since 1982. The second derivative is

$$f''(x) = -0.6342x + 2.71 \text{ percentage points per year per year}$$

where x is the number of years since 1982. The second derivative is zero when $x \approx 4.27$ years after 1982. Next, look at the graph of f shown in Figure 4.18. It does appear that $x = 4.27$ is the approximate input of the inflection point. The output is $f(4.27) \approx 51.6\%$, and the rate of change at that point is $f'(4.27) \approx 2.1$ percentage points per year.

b. Although f is a continuous function, and is increasing most rapidly at $x = 4.27$, we need to find $f'(4)$ and $f'(5)$ to determine whether enrollment was increasing faster in 1986 or 1987.

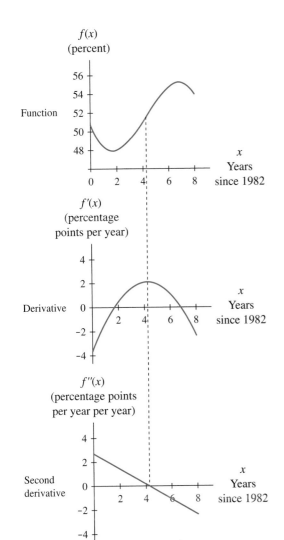

The rate of change of the model in 1986 is $f'(4) \approx 2.09$ percentage points per year. The rate of change in 1987 is $f'(5) \approx 1.95$ percentage points per year. We can say that according to the model, the percentage of South Carolina high school graduates who enter postsecondary institutions was increasing most rapidly in 1986. The percentage of graduates going on for postsecondary education in 1986 was approximately $f(4) = 51.0\%$. The percentage was increasing by about $f'(4) = 2.1$ percentage points per year at that time.

Figure 4.18 shows the function, its derivative, and its second derivative. Note again the relationship among the points at which the second derivative crosses the x-axis, at which the derivative has a maximum, and at which the function has an inflection point.

c. Observe from the graph of f shown in Figure 4.18 that the most rapid decrease appears to occur at one of the endpoints. We need to assume that the model can be extended to years before 1982. Then we evaluate $f'(0)$.

$$f'(0) = -3.672 \text{ percentage points per year}$$

The percentage was declining most rapidly in 1982 at a rate of approximately 3.7 percentage points per year. ●

You have just seen two examples of how the second derivative of a function can be used to find an inflection point. It is important to use the second derivative whenever possible, because it gives an exact answer. Sometimes, however, finding the second derivative of a function can be tedious. In such cases, you will have to decide how important extreme accuracy is. If a close approximation will suffice (as is often the case in real-world modeling), then you may wish to find the first derivative only and use appropriate technology to estimate where its maximum (or minimum) occurs.

FIGURE 4.18

EXAMPLE 2   *Using Technology to Locate an Inflection Point*

Epidemic   Consider the following model for the number of polio cases in the United States in 1949.

$$C(t) = \frac{42{,}183.911}{1 + 21{,}484.253e^{-1.248911t}} \text{ polio cases}$$

where $t = 1$ at the end of January, $t = 2$ at the end of February, and so forth. Find when the number of polio cases was increasing most rapidly, the rate of change of polio cases at the time, and the number of cases at that time.

Solution

The graphs of C, C', and C'' are shown in Figure 4.19. We seek the inflection point on the graph of C that corresponds to the maximum point on the graph of C' that corresponds to the point at which the graph of C'' crosses the t-axis.

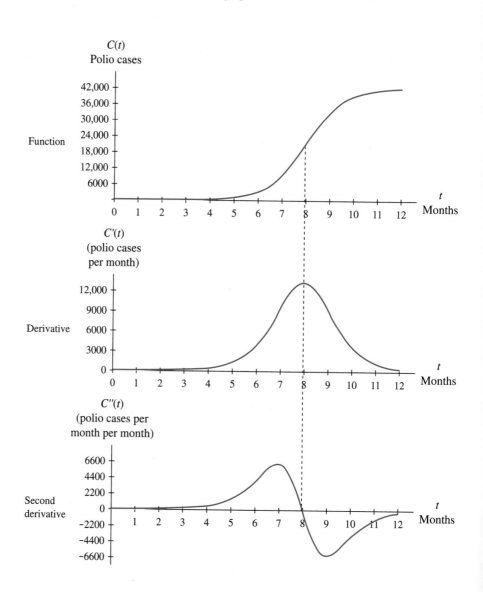

FIGURE 4.19

We choose to use technology to estimate the maximum point on the first derivative graph. It occurs at $t \approx 8$, where the output is approximately 13,171. It is important to understand what these numbers represent. The t-value tells us the month in which the greatest increase occurred: $t = 8$ corresponds to the end of August. The output value is a value on the first *derivative* graph with units cases per month. *This is the slope of the graph of C at the inflection point.* We can therefore say that polio was spreading most rapidly at the end of August 1949, at a rate of approximately 13,171 cases per month. To find the number of polio cases at the inflection point, substitute the unrounded t-value of the point into the original function to obtain approximately 21,092 cases. Note that to the right of the inflection point on the graph of C, the *number* of polio cases continued to increase, whereas the *rate* at which polio cases appeared was declining. ●

In some applications, the inflection point can be regarded as the **point of diminishing returns.** Consider the college student who studies for 8 hours without a break before a major exam. The percentage of new material that the student will retain after studying for t hours can be modeled as

$$P(t) = \frac{45}{1 + 5.94e^{-0.969125t}} \text{ percent}$$

This function has an inflection point at $t \approx 1.8$. That is, after approximately 1 hour and 48 minutes, the rate at which the student is retaining new material begins to diminish. Studying beyond that point will improve the student's knowledge, but not as quickly. This is the idea behind diminishing returns: Beyond the inflection point, you gain fewer percentage points per hour than you gain at the inflection point; that is, output increases at a decreasing rate. The existence of this point of diminishing returns is one factor that has led many educators and counselors to suggest studying in 2-hour increments with breaks in between.

We saw in Section 4.2 that for a smooth, continuous function, a relative maximum or minimum occurs where the derivative graph *crosses* the horizontal axis, but not where the first derivative graph touches the horizontal axis but does not cross it. A similar statement can be made about inflection points. If the second derivative graph *crosses* the horizontal axis, then an inflection point occurs on the graph of the function. The graphs in Figure 4.20 of a function, its derivative, and its second derivative illustrate this issue. Note that the point at which the second derivative graph touches, but does not cross, the horizontal axis actually corresponds to a relative maximum on the function graph, not to an inflection point.

Two other situations that could occur are illustrated in Figure 4.21 on page 262. Note that the graphs of both f and g have inflection points at $x = A$ because they change concavity at that point. However, the second derivatives of f and g never cross the horizontal axis. In fact, in each case, the second derivative does not exist at $x = A$, because the first derivative does not exist there. The function f has a vertical tangent line at $x = A$, and the function g is not smooth at $x = A$. Even though such situations as this do not often occur in real-world applications, you should be aware that they could happen. Keep in mind the following result:

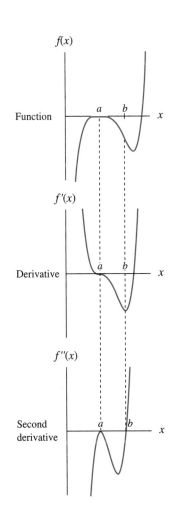

$f(x)$

Function

$f'(x)$

Derivative

$f''(x)$

Second derivative

FIGURE 4.20

> At a point of inflection on the graph of a function, the second derivative is either zero or does not exist. If the second derivative graph is negative on one side of an input value and positive on the other side of an input value, then an inflection point of the function graph occurs at that input value.

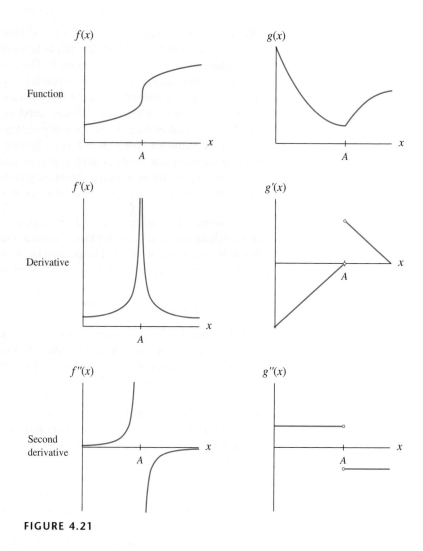

FIGURE 4.21

Concavity and the Second Derivative

Because the derivative of a function is simply the slope of the graph of that function, we know that a positive derivative indicates that the function output is increasing and a negative derivative indicates that the function output is decreasing. The second derivative provides similar information about where a function graph is concave up and where it is concave down.

In particular, if the second derivative is negative, it means that the first derivative graph is declining, which means that the original function graph is concave down. Similarly, a positive second derivative indicates that the first derivative is increasing, which means that the original function graph is concave up. And, as we have already seen, where the second derivative changes from positive to negative or from negative to positive, the function graph has an inflection point.

Consider, for example, the following information (see Table 4.5) about the second derivative of a function f. On the interval from $x = 0$ through $x = 6$, the second derivative f'' is continuous and has exactly 3 zeros. The values of the second derivative at the input values shown in the table provide information about the concavity of the graph of f at those points. We use "ccu" to indicate concave up and "ccd" to indicate concave down.

TABLE 4.5

x	0	1	2	3	4	5	6
f"(x)	15	0	−1	0	−1	0	15
Concavity of f	ccu	infl. pt.	ccd	not infl. pt.	ccd	infl. pt.	ccu

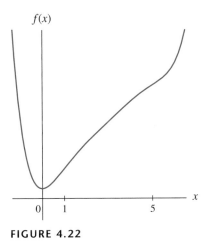

$f(x)$

FIGURE 4.22

We can conclude from this table that a graph of the function f has two inflection points at $x = 1$ and $x = 5$. Although the second derivative is zero at $x = 3$, the function graph does not change concavity at that value, so the corresponding point is not an inflection point.

Next, consider some values of the first derivative of f (see Table 4.6) on the closed interval from $x = -1$ through $x = 6$. Here we use the ↗ symbol to indicate increasing and the ↘ symbol to indicate decreasing.

TABLE 4.6

x	−1	0	1	2	3	4	5	6
f'(x)	−35.6	0	5.6	4.6	4.2	3.8	2.8	8.4
f(x)	↘	min.	↗	↗	↗	↗	↗	↗

We conclude that the graph of the function f decreases to a local minimum at zero and then increases to the right of zero. The graph is concave down between $x = 1$ and $x = 5$ and concave up to the left of $x = 1$ and to the right of $x = 5$. A possible graph of f, based on this information, is shown in Figure 4.22.

4.3 Concept Inventory

- Inflection point
- Second derivative
- Point of diminishing returns
- Conditions under which inflection points exist

4.3 Activities

Getting Started

1. **Production** The graph shows an estimate of the ultimate crude oil production recoverable from Earth.

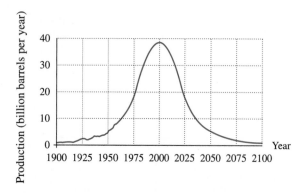

(Source: Adapted from François Ramade, *Ecology of Natural Resources*, New York: Wiley, 1984. Copyright 1984 by John Wiley & Sons, Inc. Reprinted by permission of the publishers.)

a. Estimate the two inflection points on the graph.

b. Explain the meaning of the inflection points in the context of crude oil production.

2. Advertising   The graph shows sales (in thousands of dollars) for a business as a function of the amount spent on advertising (in hundreds of dollars).

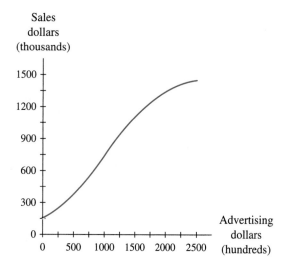

a. Mark the approximate location of the inflection point on the graph.

b. Explain the meaning of the inflection point in the context of this business.

c. Explain how knowledge of the inflection point might affect decisions made by the managers of this business.

In each of the Activities 3 through 6, identify each graph as a function, its derivative, or its second derivative. (Assume that the input is on the horizontal axis.) Give reasons for your choice.

3. a.

b.

c.

4. a.

b.

c.

5. a.

b.

c.

6. a.

-3.4 -2

b.

-3.4 -2

c.

-3.4 -2

For each function in Activities 7 through 18, write the first and second derivatives of the function.

7. $f(x) = -3x + 7$

8. $g(t) = e^t$

9. $c(u) = 3u^2 - 7u + 5$

10. $k(t) = -2.1t^2 + 7t$

11. $p(u) = -2.1u^3 + 3.5u^2 + 16$

12. $f(s) = 32s^3 - 2.1s^2 + 7s$

13. $g(t) = 37(1.05^t)$

14. $h(t) = 7 - 3(0.02^t)$

15. $f(x) = 3.2 \ln x + 7.1$

16. $g(x) = e^{3x} - \ln 3x$

17. $L(t) = \dfrac{16}{1 + 2.1e^{3.9t}}$

18. $L(t) = \dfrac{100}{1 + 99.6e^{-0.02t}}$

For each function in Activities 19 through 24, write the first and second derivatives of the function, and use the second derivative to determine inputs at which inflection points might exist.

19. $f(x) = x^3 - 6x^2 + 12x$

20. $g(t) = -0.1t^3 + 1.2t^2 + 3.6t + 4.5$

21. $f(x) = \dfrac{3.7}{1 + 20.5e^{-0.9x}}$

22. $g(t) = \dfrac{79}{1 + 36e^{0.2t}} + 13$

23. $f(t) = 98(1.2^t) + 120(0.2^t)$

24. $j(t) = 5e^{-t} + \ln t$ with $t > 0$

25. Consider the function

$$g(x) = 0.04x^3 - 0.88x^2 + 4.81x + 12.11$$

a. Graph g, g', and g'' between $x = 0$ and $x = 15$. Indicate the relationships among points on the three graphs that correspond to maxima, minima, and inflection points.

b. Find the inflection point on the graph of g. Is it a point of most rapid decline or least rapid decline?

26. Consider the function

$$f(x) = \dfrac{20}{1 + 19e^{-0.5x}}$$

a. Graph f, f', and f'' between $x = 0$ and $x = 15$. Indicate the points on the graphs of f' and f'' that correspond to the inflection point on the graph of f.

b. Find the inflection point on the graph of f. Is it a point of most rapid or least rapid increase?

Applying Concepts

27. Study Time   The percentage of new material that a student will retain after studying t hours without a break can be modeled by

$$P(t) = \dfrac{45}{1 + 5.94e^{-0.969125t}} \text{ percent}, \ 0 \le t \le 8$$

a. Find the inflection point on the graph of P, and interpret the answer.

b. Compare your answer with that given in the discussion at the end of this section.

28. Population   The U.S. Bureau of the Census prediction for the percentage of the population that is 65 to 74 years old from 2000 through 2050 can be modeled by

$$p(x) = (1.619 \cdot 10^{-5})x^4 - (1.675 \cdot 10^{-3})x^3$$
$$+ 0.050x^2 - 0.308x + 6.693 \text{ percent}$$

where x is the number of years after 2000.

(Source: Based on data from *Statistical Abstract*, 1998.)

a. Determine the year between 2000 and 2050 in which the percentage is predicted to be increasing most rapidly, the percentage at that time, and the rate of change of the percentage at that time.

b. Repeat part *a* for the most rapid decrease.

29. **Grasshoppers**   The percentage of southern Australian grasshopper eggs that hatch as a function of temperature (for temperatures between 7°C and 25°C) can be modeled by

$$P(t) = -0.00645t^4 + 0.488t^3 - 12.991t^2$$
$$+ 136.560t - 395.154 \text{ percent}$$

where *t* is the temperature in °C.

(Source: Based on information in *Elements of Ecology*, George L. Clarke. New York: Wiley, 1954, p. 170.)

a. Graph P, P', and P''.

b. Find the point of most rapid decrease on the graph of P. Interpret your answer.

30. **Home Sale**   The median size of a new single-family house built in the United States between 1987 and 2001 can be modeled by the equation

$$H(x) = 0.359x^3 - 15.198x^2 + 221.738x$$
$$+ 826.514 \text{ square feet}$$

where *x* is the number of years after 1980.

(Source: Based on data from the National Association of Home Builders Economics Division.)

a. Determine the time between 1987 and 2001 when the median house size was increasing least rapidly. Find the corresponding house size and rate of change in house size.

b. Graph H, H', and H'', indicating the relationships between the inflection point on the graph of H and the corresponding points on the graphs of H' and H''.

c. Determine the time between 1985 and 2001 when the median house size was increasing the most rapidly.

31. **Price**   The average price (per 1000 cubic feet) of natural gas for residential use from 1994 through 2000 is given by

$$p(x) = 0.03x^4 - 0.834x^3 + 8.45x^2 - 36.7x$$
$$+ 63.74 \text{ dollars}$$

where *x* is the number of years since 1990.

(Source: Based on data from *Statistical Abstract*, 1998, 2001.)

a. Sketch the graphs of *p* and its first and second derivatives. Label the vertical axes appropriately. Which points on the derivative graph correspond to the inflection points of the original function graph? Which point on the second derivative graph corresponds to the inflection point of the original function graph?

b. Find the *x*-intercepts of the second derivative graph, and interpret their meaning in context.

c. Determine when, according to the model, the average natural gas price was declining most rapidly and when it was increasing most rapidly, between 1990 and 2001.

d. Repeat part *c* for the interval 1995 through 1999.

32. **Cable TV**   The percentage of households with TVs that subscribed to cable can be modeled, for the years from 1970 through 2002, by

$$P(x) = 6 + \frac{62.7}{1 + 38.7e^{-0.258x}} \text{ percent}$$

where *x* is the number of years after 1970.

(Source: Based on data from the Television Bureau of Advertising.)

a. When was the percentage of households with TVs that subscribed to cable increasing the most rapidly from 1970 through 2002?

b. What were the percentage of households that subscribed to cable and the rate of change of the percentage of households that subscribed to cable at that time?

33. **Donors**   The number of people who donated to an organization supporting athletics at a certain university in the southeast from 1975 through 1992 can be modeled by

$$D(t) = -10.247t^3 + 208.114t^2$$
$$- 168.805t + 9775.035 \text{ donors}$$

t years after 1975.

(Source: Based on data from IPTAY Association at Clemson University.)

a. Find any relative maxima or minima that occur on a graph of the function from $t = 0$ through $t = 17$.

b. Find the inflection point(s) from $t = 0$ through $t = 17$.

c. How do the following events in the history of football at that college correspond with the curvature of the graph?

   i. In 1981, the team won the National Championship.

   ii. In 1988, Coach F was released and Coach H was hired.

34. **Cable TV** The amount spent on cable television per person per year from 1984 through 1992 can be modeled by

$$A(x) = -0.126x^3 + 1.596x^2$$
$$+ 1.802x + 40.930 \text{ dollars}$$

where x is the number of years since 1984.

(Source: Based on data from *Statistical Abstract*, 1994.)

a. Find the inflection point on the graph of A and the corresponding points on graphs of A' and A''.

b. Find the year between 1984 and 1992 in which the average amount spent per person per year on cable television was increasing most rapidly. What was the rate of change of the amount spent per person in that year?

35. **Labor** A college student works for 8 hours without a break assembling mechanical components. The cumulative number of components she has assembled after h hours can be modeled by

$$N(h) = \frac{62}{1 + 11.49e^{-0.654h}} \text{ components}$$

a. Determine when the rate at which she was assembling components was greatest.

b. How might her employer use the information in part *a* to increase the student's productivity?

36. **Lake Level** The lake level of Lake Tahoe from October 1, 1995, through July 31, 1996, can be modeled by

$$L(d) = (-5.345 \cdot 10^{-7})d^3 + (2.543 \cdot 10^{-4})d^2$$
$$- 0.0192d + 6226.192 \text{ feet above sea level}$$

d days after September 30, 1995.

(Source: Based on data from the Federal Watermaster, U.S. Department of the Interior.)

a. Determine when the lake level was rising most rapidly between October 1, 1995, and July 31, 1996.

b. What factors may have caused the inflection point to occur at the time you found in part *a*?

c. Would you expect the most rapid rise to occur at approximately the same time each year? Explain.

37. **Labor** The personnel manager for a construction company keeps track of the total number of labor hours spent on a construction job each week during the construction. Some of the weeks and the corresponding labor hours are given in the table.

Weeks after the start of a project	Cumulative labor hours
1	25
4	158
7	1254
10	5633
13	9280
16	10,010
19	10,100

a. Find a logistic model for the data.

b. Find the derivative of the model. What are the units on the derivative?

c. Graph the derivative, and discuss what information it gives the manager.

d. On the interval from week 1 through week 19, when is the maximum number of labor hours per week needed? How many labor hours are needed in that week?

e. Find the point of most rapid increase in the number of labor hours per week. How many weeks into the job does this occur? How rapidly is the number of labor hours per week increasing at this point?

f. Find the point of most rapid decrease in the number of labor hours per week. How many weeks into the job does this occur? How rapidly is the number of labor hours per week decreasing at this point?

g. Carefully explain how the exact values for the points in parts *e* and *f* can be obtained.

h. If the company has a second job requiring the same amount of time and the same number of labor hours, a good manager will schedule the second job to begin so that the time when the number of labor hours per week for the first job is declining most rapidly corresponds to the time when the number of labor hours per week for the second job is increasing most rapidly. How many weeks into the first job should the second job begin?

38. Advertising   A business owner's sole means of advertising is to put fliers on cars in a nearby shopping mall parking lot. The table shows the number of labor hours per month spent handing out fliers and the corresponding profit.

Labor hours each month	Profit (dollars)
0	2000
10	3500
20	8500
30	19,000
40	32,000
50	43,000
60	48,500
70	55,500
80	56,500
90	57,000

a. Find a model for profit.

b. For what number of labor hours is profit increasing most rapidly? Give the number of labor hours, the profit, and the rate of change of profit at that number.

c. In this context, the inflection point can be thought of as the point of diminishing returns. Discuss how knowing the point of diminishing returns could help the business owner make decisions related to employee tasks.

39. Refuse   The yearly amount of garbage (in millions of tons) taken to a landfill outside a city during selected years from 1970 through 2000 is given in the table.

Year	Amount (millions of tons)
1970	81
1975	99
1980	117
1985	122
1990	132
1995	145
2000	180

a. Using the table values only, determine during which 5-year period the amount of garbage showed the slowest increase. What was the average rate of change during that 5-year period?

b. Find a model for the data.

c. Give the second derivative formula for the equation.

d. Use the second derivative to find the point of slowest increase on a graph of the equation.

e. Graph the first and second derivatives, and explain how they support your answers to part *d*.

f. In what year was the rate of change of the yearly amount of garbage the smallest? What were the rate of increase and the amount of garbage in that year?

40. Revenue   The revenue (in millions of dollars) of the Polo Ralph Lauren Corporation from 1993 through 2001 is given in the table.

Year	Revenue (millions of dollars)
1993	767.3
1994	810.7
1995	846.6
1996	1,019.9
1997	1,180.4
1998	1,470.9
1999	1,713.1
2000	1,948.7
2001	1,982.4

(Source: Hoover's Online Guide.)

a. Use the data to estimate the year in which revenue was growing most rapidly.

b. Find a model for the data.

c. Find the first and second derivatives of the model in part *b*.

d. Determine the year in which revenue was growing most rapidly. Find the revenue and the rate of change of revenue in that year.

41. **Reaction** A chemical reaction begins when a certain mixture of chemicals reaches 95°C. The reaction activity is measured in Units (U) per 100 microliters (100 μL) of the mixture. Measurements at 4-minute intervals during the first 18 minutes after the mixture reaches 95°C are listed in the table.

Time (minutes)	2	6	10	14	18
Activity (U/100 μL)	0.10	0.60	1.40	1.75	1.95

(Source: David E. Birch et al., "Simplified Hot Start PCR," *Nature*, vol. 381, May 30, 1996, p. 445.)

a. According to the table, during what time interval was the activity increasing most rapidly?

b. Find a model for the data, and use the equation to find the inflection point. Interpret the inflection point in context.

42. **Emissions** The table gives the total emissions in millions of metric tons of nitrogen oxides, NO_x, in the United States from 1940 through 1990.

Year	NO_x (millions of metric tons)
1940	6.9
1950	9.4
1960	13.0
1970	18.5
1980	20.9
1990	19.6

(Source: *Statistical Abstract*, 1992.)

a. Find a cubic model for the data.

b. Give the slope formula for the equation.

c. Determine when emissions were increasing most rapidly between 1940 and 1990. Give the year, the amount of emissions, and how rapidly they were increasing.

43. For a function f, $f''(x) > 0$ for all real number input values. Describe the concavity of a graph of f, and sketch a function for which this condition is true.

44. Draw a graph of a function g such that $g''(x) = 0$ for all real number input values.

45. For a function f, the following statements are true:

$$f''(x) > 0 \quad \text{when } 0 \le x < 2$$
$$f''(x) = 0 \quad \text{when } x = 2$$
$$f''(x) < 0 \quad \text{when } 2 < x \le 4$$

a. Describe the concavity of a graph of f between $x = 0$ and $x = 4$.

b. Draw two completely different graphs that satisfy these second derivative conditions.

46. For a function h, the following statements are true:

$$h''(x) > 0 \quad \text{when } 0 < x < 2$$
$$h''(x) = 0 \quad \text{when } x = 2 \text{ and } x = 0$$
$$h''(x) < 0 \quad \text{when } x < 0 \text{ and } x > 2$$

a. Describe the concavity of a graph of h.

b. Draw a graph that satisfies all three of these second derivative conditions.

Discussing Concepts

47. Which of the six basic models (linear, exponential, logarithmic, logistic, quadratic, and exponential) could have inflection points?

48. Discuss in detail all of the options that are available for finding inflection points of a function.

4.4   Interconnected Change: Related Rates

We have seen that many situations in the world around us can be modeled mathematically. After a situation is modeled with a continuous function, we can use calculus to analyze changes that have taken place and possibly predict trends in the near future. So far we have considered how the rate of change of the output variable of a function is affected by a change in the input variable. We now consider the interaction of the rates of change of input and output variables with respect to a third variable. We shall see that the interconnection of the input and output variables is also reflected in an interaction between their rates of change with respect to a third variable.

Interconnected-Change Equations and Implicit Differentiation

An equation relating the volume V of a spherical balloon to its radius r is $V = \frac{4}{3}\pi r^3$. When the balloon is inflated (over time), its volume increases and its radius increases. Note that even though V and r depend on the amount of time since the balloon began to be inflated, no time variable appears in the volume equation. In such applications, we refer to both volume V and radius r as **dependent variables** because changes in their value depend on a third variable, time t. We refer to time, the "with respect to" variable, as the **independent variable.**

In order to develop an equation relating the rate of change of the balloon's volume with respect to time and the rate of change of its radius with respect to time, we differentiate both sides of the equation with respect to time t. This type of differentiation is known as **implicit differentiation.** We use the Chain Rule to differentiate the right side of the volume equation, considering $\frac{4}{3}\pi r^3$ as the outside function and r as the inside function. The derivative of the inside function with respect to t is $\frac{dr}{dt}$. Thus we get

$$\frac{dV}{dt} = \left[\frac{4}{3}\pi(3r^2)\right]\frac{dr}{dt} = 4\pi r^2 \frac{dr}{dt}$$

This equation shows how the rates of change of the volume and the radius of a sphere with respect to time are interconnected, and it can be used to answer questions about those rates. Such an equation is referred to as a **related-rates equation.** Example 1 demonstrates how to develop related-rates equations.

EXAMPLE 1   *Interconnecting Rates of Change*

Using each of the given equations, find an equation relating the indicated rates.

a. $p = 39x + 4$; relate $\frac{dp}{dt}$ and $\frac{dx}{dt}$.

b. $a = 4\ln t$; relate $\frac{da}{dx}$ and $\frac{dt}{dx}$.

c. $s = \pi r\sqrt{r^2 + h^2}$; relate $\frac{ds}{dx}$ and $\frac{dr}{dx}$, assuming that h is constant.

d. $v = \pi r^2 h$; relate $\frac{dr}{dt}$ and $\frac{dh}{dt}$, assuming that v is constant.

Solution

a. Differentiating the left side of $p = 39x + 4$ with respect to t gives $\frac{dp}{dt}$. We use the Chain Rule to differentiate the right side of the equation with respect to t, considering $39x + 4$ to be the outside function and x to be the inside function.

$$\frac{dp}{dt} = 39\frac{dx}{dt}$$

b. Applying the Chain Rule to the right side of $a = 4 \ln t$ yields

$$\frac{da}{dx} = 4\left(\frac{1}{t}\right)\frac{dt}{dx}$$

so

$$\frac{da}{dx} = \frac{4}{t}\frac{dt}{dx}$$

c. Differentiating the right side of $s = \pi r\sqrt{r^2 + h^2}$ requires both the Chain Rule and the Product Rule. Consider first the application of the Product Rule:

$$\frac{ds}{dx} = (\pi r)(\text{derivative of } \sqrt{r^2 + h^2} \text{ with respect to } x)$$

$$+ (\text{derivative of } \pi r \text{ with respect to } x)(\sqrt{r^2 + h^2})$$

In order to calculate the two derivatives with respect to x, remember to apply the Chain Rule.

$$\frac{ds}{dx} = (\pi r)\left[\frac{1}{2}(r^2 + h^2)^{-1/2}(2r)\left(\frac{dr}{dx}\right)\right] + \left(\pi\frac{dr}{dx}\right)(\sqrt{r^2 + h^2})$$

so

$$\frac{ds}{dx} = \pi\left(\frac{r^2}{\sqrt{r^2 + h^2}} + \sqrt{r^2 + h^2}\right)\frac{dr}{dx}$$

d. In order to develop a related-rates equation from $v = \pi r^2 h$ showing the interconnection between $\frac{dr}{dt}$ and $\frac{dh}{dt}$, we can isolate either r or h on one side and then find the derivative with respect to t, or we can find the derivative of both sides of the equation with respect to t and then solve for $\frac{dr}{dt}$. The two methods are equivalent, but sometimes one method has less-involved algebra than does the other method. We choose the second method because it leads to the immediate removal of v from the equation and thus does not require substitution later. Differentiating the left side of the equation with respect to t gives zero because v is constant. Applying the Product Rule and the Chain Rule to the right side of the equation gives

$$0 = (\pi r^2)\left(\frac{dh}{dt}\right) + 2\pi r\left(\frac{dr}{dt}\right)(h)$$

Now solve for $\frac{dr}{dt}$:

$$-2\pi rh\frac{dr}{dt} = \pi r^2\frac{dh}{dt}$$

$$-2rh\frac{dr}{dt} = r^2\frac{dh}{dt}$$

$$\frac{dr}{dt} = \frac{r^2}{-2rh}\frac{dh}{dt}$$

$$\frac{dr}{dt} = \frac{r}{-2h}\frac{dh}{dt}$$

Today's news often brings us stories of environmental pollution in one form or another. One serious form of pollution is groundwater contamination. If a hazardous chemical is introduced into the ground, it can contaminate the groundwater and make the water source unusable. The contaminant will be carried downstream via the flow of the groundwater. This movement of contaminant as a consequence of the flow of the groundwater is known as *avection*. As a result of *diffusion*, the chemical will also spread out perpendicularly to the direction of flow. The region that the contamination covers is known as a chemical *plume*.

Hydrologists who study groundwater contamination are sometimes able to model the area of a plume as a function of the distance away from the source that the chemical has traveled by avection. That is, they develop an equation showing the interconnection between A, the area of the plume, and r, the distance from the source that the chemical has spread because of the flow of the groundwater.

If A is a function of r, then the rate of change $\frac{dA}{dr}$ describes how quickly the area of the plume is increasing as the chemical travels farther from the source. However, of greater interest is the rate of change of A with respect to time, $\frac{dA}{dt}$, and how it is related to the rate of change of r with respect to time, $\frac{dr}{dt}$. These relationships are examined in Example 2.

EXAMPLE 2   *Using a Given Equation in a Related-Rates Problem*

Groundwater   In a certain part of Michigan, a hazardous chemical leaked from an underground storage facility. Because of the terrain surrounding the storage facility, the groundwater was flowing almost due south at a rate of approximately 2 feet per day. Hydrologists studying this plume drilled wells in order to sample the groundwater in the area and determine the extent of the plume. They found that the shape of the plume was fairly easy to predict and that the area of the plume could be modeled as

$$A = 0.9604r^2 + 1.960r + 1.124 - \ln(0.980r + 1) \text{ square feet}$$

when the chemical had spread r feet south of the storage facility.

a. How quickly was the area of the plume growing when the chemical had traveled 3 miles south of the storage facility?

b. How much area had the plume covered when the chemical had spread 3 miles south?

Solution

a. First, note that the question posed asks for the rate of change of area with respect to time. However, the equation does not contain a variable representing time. Second, note that we are given the rate of change of r with respect to time. If we represent the time in days since the leak began as t, then we know that $\frac{dr}{dt} = 2$ feet per day and we are trying to find $\frac{dA}{dt}$. We also have an equation that shows the interconnection between the dependent variables A and r.

Therefore, we differentiate with respect to t both sides of the equation that relates A and r.

$$\frac{dA}{dt} = 0.9604(2r)\frac{dr}{dt} + 1.960\frac{dr}{dt} + 0 - \left(\frac{1}{0.980r + 1}\right)\left(0.980\frac{dr}{dt}\right)$$

$$\frac{dA}{dt} = \left(1.9208r + 1.960 - \frac{0.980}{0.980r + 1}\right)\frac{dr}{dt}$$

Next, we substitute the known values $r = 3$ miles $= 15,840$ feet and $\frac{dr}{dt} = 2$ feet per day and then solve for the unknown rate.

$$\frac{dA}{dt} = \left(1.9208(15,840) + 1.960 - \frac{0.980}{0.980(15,840) + 1}\right)(2)$$

$$\approx 60,855 \text{ square feet per day}$$

When the chemical has spread 3 miles south, the plume is growing at a rate of 60,855 square feet per day.

b. The area of the plume is

$$A = 0.9604(15,840)^2 + 1.960(15,840) + 1.124 - \ln[0.980(15,840) + 1]$$

$$\approx 241,000,776 \text{ square feet}$$

$$\approx 8.6 \text{ square miles}$$

When the contamination has spread 3 miles south, the total contaminated area is approximately 8.6 square miles.   ●

Note the method we used to answer the question posed in Example 2. First, we determined which variables were involved. Second, we identified an equation that connected the dependent variables. Third, we determined which rates of change we needed to relate to one another. Next, we found the derivative of each side of the equation with respect to the independent variable. Finally, we substituted given quantities and rates into the related-rates equation and solved for the unknown rate. We summarize this method:

Method of Related Rates

Step 1:   Read the problem carefully and determine what variables are involved. Identify the independent variable (the "with respect to" variable) and all dependent variables.

Step 2:   Use the given equation or find an equation relating the dependent variables. The independent variable may or may not appear in the equation.

Step 3:   Differentiate both sides of the equation in Step 2 with respect to the independent variable to produce a related-rates equation. The Chain and/or the Product Rule(s) may be needed.

Step 4:   Substitute the known quantities and rates into the related-rates equation, and solve for the unknown rate.

Step 5:   Interpret in context the solution found in Step 4.

We illustrate this process in Example 3.

EXAMPLE 3   *Using Geometric Relationships in a Related-Rates Problem*

Baseball   A baseball diamond is a square with each side measuring 90 feet. A baseball team is participating in a publicity photo session, and a photographer at second base wants to photograph runners when they are halfway to first base. Suppose that the average speed at which a baseball player runs from home plate to first base is 20 feet per second. The photographer needs to set the shutter speed in terms of how fast the distance between the runner and the camera is changing. At what rate is the distance between the runner and second base changing when the runner is halfway to first base?

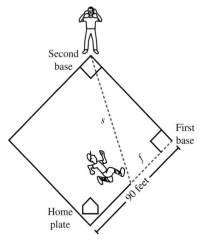

Second base

First base

Home plate

FIGURE 4.23

Solution

Step 1:   The three variables involved in this problem are time, the distance between the runner and first base, and the distance between the runner and the photographer at second base. Because speed is the rate of change of distance with respect to time, the independent variable is time, and the two distances are the dependent variables.

Step 2:   We need an equation that relates the distance between the runner and first base and the distance between the runner and the photographer at second base. A diagram can help us better understand the relationship between these distances. See Figure 4.23.

We consider the right triangle formed by the runner, first base, and second base. Using the Pythagorean Theorem, we know that the relationship between f and s in Figure 4.23 is

$$f^2 + 90^2 = s^2$$

Step 3:   Differentiating the equation in Step 2 with respect to t gives

$$2f\frac{df}{dt} + 0 = 2s\frac{ds}{dt}$$

$$\frac{ds}{dt} = \frac{f}{s}\frac{df}{dt}$$

Step 4:   Note that the rate we need to find is $\frac{ds}{dt}$. We are told that $f = 45$ feet (half of the way to first base) and $\frac{df}{dt} = -20$ feet per second (negative because the distance between first base and the runner is decreasing). Substitute these values into the related-rates equation to obtain $\frac{ds}{dt} = \frac{45}{s}(-20)$. Find the value of s using the equation $f^2 + 90^2 = s^2$ and the fact that $f = 45$ feet. Thus $s = \sqrt{10{,}125} \approx 100.62$ feet, and we have

$$\frac{ds}{dt} = \frac{45 \text{ feet}}{\sqrt{10{,}125} \text{ feet}}(-20 \text{ feet per second}) \approx -8.94 \text{ feet per second}$$

Step 5:   When a runner is halfway to first base, the distance between the runner and the photographer is decreasing by about 8.9 feet per second.   ●

Understanding that the change in one variable is connected to the change in another variable is important in a variety of applications. The independent variable is often—but not always—time. Being able to work with related rates can help you solve problems that occur in many real-world applications.

4.4 Concept Inventory

- Dependent and independent variables
- Related-rates equation
- Method of related rates

4.4 Activities

Getting Started

For each of the equations in Activities 1 through 14, write the indicated related-rates equation.

1. $f = 3x$; relate $\frac{df}{dt}$ and $\frac{dx}{dt}$.

2. $p^2 = 5s + 2$; relate $\frac{dp}{dx}$ and $\frac{ds}{dx}$.

3. $k = 6x^2 + 7$; relate $\frac{dk}{dy}$ and $\frac{dx}{dy}$.

4. $y = 9x^3 + 12x^2 + 4x + 3$; relate $\frac{dy}{dt}$ and $\frac{dx}{dt}$.

5. $g = e^{3x}$; relate $\frac{dg}{dt}$ and $\frac{dx}{dt}$.

6. $g = e^{15x^2}$; relate $\frac{dg}{dt}$ and $\frac{dx}{dt}$.

7. $f = 62(1.02^x)$; relate $\frac{df}{dt}$ and $\frac{dx}{dt}$.

8. $p = 5\ln(7 + s)$; relate $\frac{dp}{dx}$ and $\frac{ds}{dx}$.

9. $h = 6a\ln a$; relate $\frac{dh}{dy}$ and $\frac{da}{dy}$.

10. $v = \pi hw(x + w)$; relate $\frac{dv}{dt}$ and $\frac{dw}{dt}$, assuming that h and x are constant.

11. $s = \pi r\sqrt{r^2 + h^2}$; relate $\frac{ds}{dt}$ and $\frac{dh}{dt}$, assuming that r is constant.

12. $v = \frac{1}{3}\pi r^2 h$; relate $\frac{dh}{dt}$ and $\frac{dr}{dt}$, assuming that v is constant.

13. $s = \pi r\sqrt{r^2 + h^2}$; relate $\frac{dh}{dt}$ and $\frac{dr}{dt}$, assuming that s is constant.

14. $v = \pi hw(x + w)$; relate $\frac{dh}{dt}$ and $\frac{dw}{dt}$, assuming that v and x are constant.

Applying Concepts

15. **Trees** Trees do a lot more than provide oxygen and shade. They also help pump water out of the ground and transpire it into the atmosphere. The amount of water an oak tree can remove from the ground is related to the tree's size. Suppose that a tree transpires

$$w = 31.54 + 12.97\ln g \text{ gallons of water per day}$$

where g is the girth in feet of the tree trunk, measured 5 feet above the ground. A tree is currently 5 feet in girth and is gaining 2 inches of girth per year.

a. How much water does the tree currently transpire each day?

b. If t is the time in years, find and interpret $\frac{dw}{dt}$.

16. **BMI** The body-mass index of an individual who weighs w pounds and is h inches tall is given as

$$B = \frac{0.45w}{0.00064516h^2} \text{ points}$$

(Source: *New England Journal of Medicine*, September 14, 1995.)

a. Write an equation showing the relationship between the body-mass index and weight of a woman who is 5 feet 8 inches tall.

b. Find a related-rates equation showing the interconnection between the rates of change with respect to time of the weight and the body-mass index.

c. Consider a woman who weighs 160 pounds and is 5 feet 8 inches tall. If $\frac{dw}{dt} = 1$ pound per month, find and interpret $\frac{dB}{dt}$.

d. Suppose a woman who is 5 feet 8 inches tall has a body-mass index of 24 points. If her body-mass index is decreasing by 0.1 point per month, at what rate is her weight changing?

17. **BMI** Refer to the body-mass index equation in Activity 16.

a. Write an equation showing the relationship between the body-mass index and the height of a young teenager who weighs 100 pounds.

b. Find a related-rates equation showing the interconnection between the rates of change with respect to time of the body-mass index and the height.

c. If the weight of the teenager who is 5 feet 3 inches tall remains constant at 100 pounds while she is growing at a rate of $\frac{1}{2}$ inch per year, how quickly is her body-mass index changing?

18. Heat Index   The apparent temperature A in degrees Fahrenheit is related to the actual temperature $t°$F and the humidity $100h\%$ by the equation

$$A = 2.70 + 0.885t - 78.7h$$
$$+ 1.20ht \text{ degrees Fahrenheit}$$

(Source: W. Bosch and L. G. Cobb, "Temperature Humidity Indices," UMAP Module 691, *UMAP Journal,* vol. 10, no. 3, Fall 1989, pp. 237–256.)

a. If the humidity remains constant at 53% and the actual temperature is increasing from 80°F at a rate of 2°F per hour, what is the apparent temperature and how quickly is it changing with respect to time?

b. If the actual temperature remains constant at 100°F and the relative humidity is 30% but is dropping by 2 percentage points per hour, what is the apparent temperature and how quickly is it changing with respect to time?

19. Volume   The lumber industry is interested in being able to calculate the volume of wood in a tree trunk. The volume of wood contained in the trunk of a certain fir has been modeled as

$$V = 0.002198d^{1.739925}h^{1.133187} \text{ cubic feet}$$

where d is the diameter in feet of the tree, measured 5 feet above the ground, and h is the height of the tree in feet.

(Source: J. L. Clutter et al., *Timber Management: A Quantitative Approach,* New York: Wiley, 1983.)

a. If the height of a tree is 32 feet and its diameter is 10 inches, how quickly is the volume of the wood changing when the tree's height is increasing by half a foot per year? (Assume that the tree's diameter remains constant.)

b. If the tree's diameter is 12 inches and its height is 34 feet, how quickly is the volume of the wood changing when the tree's diameter is increasing by 2 inches per year? (Assume that the tree's height remains constant.)

20. Wheat Crop   The carrying capacity of a crop is measured in terms of the number of people for which it will provide. The carrying capacity of a certain wheat crop has been modeled as

$$K = \frac{11.56P}{D} \text{ people per hectare}$$

where P is the number of kilograms of wheat produced per hectare per year and D is the yearly energy requirement for one person in megajoules per person.

(Source: R. S. Loomis and D. J. Connor, *Crop Ecology: Productivity and Management in Agricultural Systems,* Cambridge, England: Cambridge University Press, 1982.)

a. Write an equation showing the yearly energy requirement of one person as a function of the production of the crop.

b. With time t as the independent variable, write a related-rates equation using your result from part *a.*

c. If the crop currently produces 10 kilograms of wheat per hectare per year and the yearly energy requirement for one person is increasing by megajoules per year, find and interpret $\frac{dP}{dt}$.

21. Production   A Cobb-Douglas function for the production of mattresses is

$$M = 48.10352L^{0.6}K^{0.4} \text{ mattresses produced}$$

where L is measured in thousands of worker hours and K is the capital investment in thousands of dollars.

a. Write an equation showing labor as a function of capital.

b. Write the related-rates equation for the equation in part *a,* using time as the independent variable and assuming that mattress production remains constant.

c. If there are currently 8000 worker hours, and if the capital investment is $47,000 and is increasing by $500 per year, how quickly must the number of worker hours be changing in order for mattress production to remain constant?

22. Ladder   A ladder 15 feet long leans against a tall stone wall. If the bottom of the ladder slides away from the building at a rate of 3 feet per second, how quickly is the ladder sliding down the wall when the top of the ladder is 6 feet from the ground? At what speed is the top of the ladder moving when it hits the ground?

23. **Height**   A hot-air balloon is taking off from the end zone of a football field. An observer is sitting at the other end of the field 100 yards away from the balloon. If the balloon is rising vertically at a rate of 2 feet per second, at what rate is the distance between the balloon and the observer changing when the balloon is 500 yards off the ground? How far is the balloon from the observer at this time?

24. **Kite**   A girl flying a kite holds the string 4 feet above ground level and lets out string at a rate of 2 feet per second as the kite moves horizontally at an altitude of 84 feet. Find the rate at which the kite is moving horizontally when 100 feet of string has been let out.

25. **Softball**   A softball diamond is a square with each side measuring 60 feet. Suppose a player is running from second base to third base at a rate of 22 feet per second. At what rate is the distance between the runner and home plate changing when the runner is halfway to third base? How far is the runner from home plate at this time?

26. **Volume**   Helium gas is being pumped into a spherical balloon at a rate of 5 cubic feet per minute. The pressure in the balloon remains constant.

   a. What is the volume of the balloon when its diameter is 20 inches?

   b. At what rate is the radius of the balloon changing when the diameter is 20 inches?

27. **Snowball**   A spherical snowball is melting, and its radius is decreasing at a constant rate. Its diameter decreased from 24 centimeters to 16 centimeters in 30 minutes.

   a. What is the volume of the snowball when its radius is 10 centimeters?

   b. How quickly is the volume of the snowball changing when its radius is 10 centimeters?

28. **Salt**   A leaking container of salt is sitting on a shelf in a kitchen cupboard. As salt leaks out of a hole in the side of the container, it forms a conical pile on the counter below. As the salt falls onto the pile, it slides down the sides of the pile so that the pile's radius is always equal to its height. If the height of the pile is increasing at a rate of 0.2 inch per day, how quickly is the salt leaking out of the container when the pile is 2 inches tall? How much salt has leaked out of the container by this time?

29. **Yogurt**   Soft-serve frozen yogurt is being dispensed into a waffle cone at a rate of 1 tablespoon per second. If the waffle cone has height $h = 15$ centimeters and radius $r = 2.5$ centimeters at the top, how quickly is the height of the yogurt in the cone rising when the height of the yogurt is 6 centimeters? (*Hint:* 1 cubic centimeter $= 0.06$ tablespoon and $r = \frac{h}{6}$.)

30. **Volume**   Boyle's Law for gases states that when the mass of a gas remains constant, the pressure p and the volume v of the gas are related by the equation $pv = c$, where c is a constant whose value depends on the gas. Assume that at a certain instant, the volume of a gas is 75 cubic inches and its pressure is 30 pounds per square inch. Because of compression of volume, the pressure of the gas is increasing by 2 pounds per square inch every minute. At what rate is the volume changing at this instant?

Discussing Concepts

31. Demonstrate that the two solution methods referred to in part *d* of Example 1 yield equivalent related-rates equations for the equation given in that part of the example.

32. In what fundamental aspect does the method of related rates differ from the other rate-of-change applications seen so far in this text? Explain.

33. Which step of the method of related rates do you consider to be most important? Support your answer.

SUMMARY

This chapter is devoted to analyzing change. The principal topics are approximating change, optimization, inflection points, and related rates.

Approximating Change

One of the most useful approximations of change in a function is to use the behavior of a tangent line to approximate the behavior of the function. Because of the Principle of Local Linearity, we know that tangent-line approximations are quite accurate over small intervals. We estimate the output $f(x + h)$ as $f(x) + f'(x) \cdot h$, where h represents the small change in input.

Optimization

The word *optimization* (as we used it in Section 4.2) refers to locating relative or absolute extreme points. A relative maximum is a point to which the graph rises and after which the graph falls. Similarly, a relative minimum is a point to which the graph falls and after which the graph rises. There may be several relative maxima and relative minima on a graph. The highest and lowest points on a graph over an interval or over all possible input values, are called the absolute maximum and absolute minimum points. These points may coincide with a relative maximum or minimum, or they may occur at the endpoints of a given interval.

Inflection Points

Inflection points are simply points where the concavity of the graph changes from concave up to concave down, or vice versa. Their importance, however, is that they identify the points of most rapid change or least rapid change in a region around the point.

Inflection points can be found where the graph of the second derivative of a function crosses the horizontal axis or, sometimes, where the second derivative fails to exist. In addition to locating input values of inflection points, the second derivative of a function can be used to determine the concavity of the function.

Related Rates

When the changes in one or more variables (called *dependent variables*) depend on a third variable (called the *independent variable*), a related-rates equation can be developed to show how the rates of change of these variables are interconnected. The Chain Rule plays an important role in the development of a related-rates equation, because the independent variable (which is often time) is not always expressed in the equation that relates the dependent variables.

CONCEPT CHECK

Can you

- Use derivatives to approximate change?

- Understand marginal analysis?

- Find relative and absolute extreme points?

- Interpret extrema?

To practice, try

Section 4.1	Activities 11, 17
Section 4.1	Activities 5, 21
Section 4.2	Activities 17, 21, 23
Section 4.2	Activities 25, 29

- Find inflection points?

- Interpret inflection points?

- Understand the relationship between second derivatives and concavity?

- Set up and solve related-rates equations?

CONCEPT REVIEW

1. **Tourists**   The number of tourists who visited Tahiti each year between 1988 and 1994 can be modeled by

$$T(x) = -0.4804x^4 + 6.635x^3 - 26.126x^2$$
$$+ \ 26.981x + 134.848 \text{ thousand tourists}$$

   x years after 1988.

   (Source: Stephen J. Page, "The Pacific Islands," *EIU International Reports*, vol. 1, 1996, p. 91.)

   a. Find any relative maxima and minima of $T(x)$ between $x = 0$ and $x = 6$. Explain how you found the value(s).

   b. Find any inflection points of the graph of T between $x = 0$ and $x = 6$. Explain how you found the value(s).

   c. Graph T, T', and T''. Clearly label on each graph the points corresponding to your answers to parts a and b.

   d. Between 1988 and 1994, when was the number of tourists the greatest and when was it the least? What were the corresponding numbers of tourists in those years?

   e. Between 1988 and 1994, when was the number of tourists increasing the most rapidly, and when was it declining the most rapidly? Give the rates of change in each of those years.

2. **Population**   Let $M(t)$ represent the population of French Polynesia (of which Tahiti is a part) at the middle of year t. If $M(2000) = 202$ thousand

people, and if $M'(2000) = 4.5$ thousand people per year, estimate the following:

(Source: *Statistical Abstract*, 2001.)

   a. How much did the population of French Polynesia increase during the third quarter of 2001?

   b. What was the population at the end of 2001?

3. **Gender Ratio**   The table shows the number of males per 100 females in the United States based on census data. This number is referred to as the gender ratio.

   a. Find a cubic model for the data.

   b. Write the second derivative of the equation you found in part a.

   c. In what year does the output of the model exhibit the most rapid decline? What was the gender ratio in that year, and how rapidly was it changing?

Year	Males per 100 females
1900	104.6
1910	106.2
1920	104.1
1930	102.6
1940	100.8
1950	98.7
1960	97.1
1970	94.8
1980	94.5
1990	95.1
2000	96.3

4. The graph of the derivative of a function h is shown.

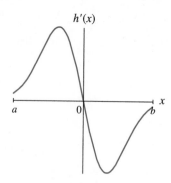

a. Does the graph of h have a relative maximum and/or minimum between a and b? If so, mark on the derivative graph the input location of each extreme point, and classify the type of extreme point at that location. If not, explain why not.

b. Does the graph of h have one or more inflection points between a and b? If so, mark and label on the derivative graph the input location(s) of the inflection point(s). If not, explain why not.

5. Skid Marks   The length of skid marks made on an asphalt road when a vehicle's brakes are applied quickly is given by

$$S = 0.000013wv^2 \text{ feet}$$

where the vehicle weighs w pounds and is traveling v mph when the brakes are applied. How quickly is the length of the skid marks changing when the velocity of a 4000-pound vehicle traveling at a speed of 60 mph is decreasing by 5 mph per second when the brakes are applied? (Assume that the vehicle's weight remains constant.)

Project 4.1 Hunting License Fees

Setting

In 1986, the state of California was trying to make a decision about raising the fee for a deer hunting license. Five hundred hunters were asked how much they would be willing to pay in excess of the current fee to hunt deer. The percentage of hunters to agree to a fee increase of x is given by the logistic model*

$$\text{Percentage} = \frac{1.221}{1 + 0.221e^{0.0116x}}$$

Suppose that in 1986 the license fee was $100, and 75,000 licenses were sold. Suppose that you are part of the 1986 Natural Resources Team presenting a proposed increase in the hunting license fee to the head of the California Department of Natural Resources.

Tasks

1. Illustrate how the model can be used by answering the following questions.

   a. What was the hunting license revenue in 1986?

   b. Suppose that in 1987 the fee increased to $150. What percentage of the 1986 hunters would

* Based on information in *Journal of Environmental Economics and Management*, vol. 24, no. 1, January 1993.

buy another license? How many hunters is that? What would be the 1987 revenue?

   c. What would be the answers to the questions in part *b* if the fee were increased to $300?

2. If the fee increase for 1987 were x dollars, find formulas for the following: (a) the percentage of hunters willing to pay the new fee, (b) the number of the 75,000 hunters willing to pay the new fee, (c) the new fee, and (d) the 1987 revenue.

3. Use your formulas to determine the optimal license fee. Also, find the optimal fee increase, the number of hunters who will buy licenses at the new fee, and the optimal revenue.

Reporting

1. Prepare a letter to the head of the California Department of Natural Resources. Your letter should address the fee increase and expectations for revenue. You should not make it technical but should give some support to back up your conclusions.

2. Prepare a technical written report outlining your findings as well as the mathematical methods you used to arrive at your conclusions.

Project 4.2 Fundraising Campaign

Setting

In order to raise funds, the mathematics department in your college or university is planning to sell T-shirts before next year's football game against the school's biggest rival. Your team has volunteered to conduct the fundraiser. Because several other student groups have also volunteered to head this project, your team is to present its proposal for the fund drive, as well as your predictions about its outcome, to a panel of mathematics faculty.

Task A

Follow the tasks for Project 1.2 on page 92. You will find a partial price listing for the T-shirt company on the *Calculus Concepts* website.

Task B

1. Review your work for Task A. If you wish to make any changes in your marketing scheme, you should do so now. If you decide to make any changes, make sure that the polling that was done is still applicable (for example, you will not be able to change your target market). Change (if necessary) any models from Task A to reflect any changes in your marketing scheme.

2. Use the models of demand, revenue, total cost, and profit developed in Task A to proceed with this section.

   Determine the selling price that generates maximum revenue. What is maximum revenue? Is the selling price that generates maximum revenue the same as the price that generates maximum profit? What is maximum profit? Which should you consider (maximum revenue or maximum profit) in order to get the best picture of the effectiveness of the drive?

   Re-evaluate the number of shirts you may wish to sell. Will this affect the cost you determined above?

If so, change your revenue, total cost, and profit functions to reflect this adjustment and re-analyze optimal values. Show and explain the mathematics that underlies your reasoning.

Discuss the sensitivity of the demand function to changes in price (check rates of change for $20, $14, and $8). Does the demand function have an inflection point? If so, find it. Find the rate of change of demand with respect to price at this point, and interpret its meaning and impact in this context. How would the sensitivity of the demand curve affect your decisions about raising or lowering your selling price?

On the basis of your findings, predict the optimal selling price, the number of T-shirts you intend to print, the costs involved, the number of T-shirts you expect to sell before realizing a profit (that is, the break-even point), and the expected profit.

Reporting

1. Write a report for the mathematics department concerning your proposed campaign. They will be interested in the business interpretation as well as in an accurate description of the mathematics involved. Be sure to include graphical as well as mathematical representations of your demand, revenue, cost, and profit functions. (Include graphs of any functions and derivatives that you use. Include your calculations and your survey as appendices.) Do not forget to also cover Task A in this report.

2. Make your proposal and present your findings to a panel of mathematics professors in a 15-minute presentation. Your presentation should be restricted to the business interpretation, and you should use overhead transparencies of graphs and equations of all models and derivatives, along with any other visual aids that you consider appropriate.

5

Accumulating Change: Limits of Sums and the Definite Integral

Concepts Outline

5.1 Results of Change and Area Approximations

5.2 Accumulation Functions

5.3 The Fundamental Theorem

5.4 The Definite Integral

5.5 Average Value and Average Rate of Change

5.6 Integration by Substitution or Algebraic Manipulation

James Leynse/CORBIS SABA

Concept Application

If crude oil is flowing into a holding tank through a pipe, the rate at which the oil is flowing determines how quickly the holding tank will fill. It is possible that the rate varies with time and can be mathematically modeled. Such a model could then be used to answer questions such as

• What is the change in the amount of oil in the tank during the first 10 minutes the oil is flowing into the tank?

• If the initial amount of oil in the tank was 5000 cubic feet, how much oil was in the tank after 10 minutes?

• How long can oil continue to flow into the tank before the tank is full?

Questions such as these can be answered using definite integrals. Examples of this type of problem appear in Activities 1 and 4 of the Chapter 5 Concept Review.

Chapter Introduction

Chapters 1 through 4 focused on the derivative, one of the fundamental concepts in calculus. Now we begin a study of another fundamental concept in calculus, the integral. As before, our approach is through the mathematics of change.

We start by analyzing the accumulated change in a quantity and how it is related to areas of regions between the graph of the rate-of-change function for that quantity and the horizontal axis. As we refine our thinking about area, we are led to consider limits of sums, which show us how to account for the results of change in terms of integrals. Integrals, as we shall see, are connected to derivatives by the Fundamental Theorem of Calculus.

We conclude by considering the difference of two accumulated changes and using integrals to calculate averages.

Concepts You Will Be Learning

- Approximating area using rectangles (5.1)
- Interpreting the area between a graph and the horizontal axis (5.1)
- Approximating area using a limiting value of sums of areas of rectangles (5.1)
- Sketching and interpreting accumulation graphs (5.2)
- Finding general antiderivatives (5.3)
- Finding and interpreting specific antiderivatives (5.3)
- Recovering a function from its rate-of-change equation (5.4)
- Evaluating and interpreting definite integrals (5.4)
- Calculating and interpreting the area between two curves (5.5)
- Calculating and interpreting the average value of a function and average rates of change (5.5)
- Using integration by substitution to write an accumulation function (5.6)

5.1   Results of Change and Area Approximations

In our study of calculus so far, we have concentrated on finding rates of change. We now consider the results of change.

Accumulated Change

Suppose that you have been driving on an interstate highway for 2 hours at a constant speed of 60 mph. Because velocity, v, is the rate of change of distance traveled, s, with respect to time, we write a function for velocity mathematically as $v(t) = s'(t) = 60$ mph, where t is the time in hours, $0 \le t \le 2$. A graph of this rate function over a 2-hour period of time appears in Figure 5.1.

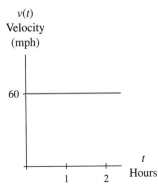

FIGURE 5.1

At a constant rate of 60 mph, the distance traveled during a time period of t hours is (rate)(time) $=$ (60 mph)(t hours) $=$ $60t$ miles. Geometrically, we view this multiplication as giving the area of the region between the rate-of-change graph and the horizontal axis over any time period of length t hours. Figure 5.2 illustrates this fact for the 1-hour time period between 0.5 hour and 1.5 hours, for the 15-minute time period between 1 hour 45 minutes and 2 hours, and for the first t hours of the trip.

Now, imagine that after a 2-hour drive at a constant speed of 60 mph, you accelerate at a constant rate to 75 mph over a 10-minute interval. You then maintain that constant 75-mph speed during the next half hour. A graph of your speed appears in Figure 5.3a.

We know that the distance traveled during the times when speed is constant is the speed multiplied by the amount of time driven at that speed (represented by regions

(a) Area $A =$ (60 mph) (1 hour)
$= 60$ miles
Distance traveled during 1 hour

(b) Area $B =$ (60 mph) (0.25 hour)
$= 15$ miles
Distance traveled during 15 minutes

(c) Area $C =$ (60 mph) (t hours)
$= 60t$ miles
Distance traveled during t hours

FIGURE 5.2

R_1 and R_3 in Figure 5.3b). But how can we calculate the distance driven between 2 hours and 2 hours 10 minutes when the speed is increasing linearly? If we knew the average speed over the 10-minute interval, then we could multiply that average speed by $\frac{1}{6}$ of an hour to obtain the distance traveled.

(a)

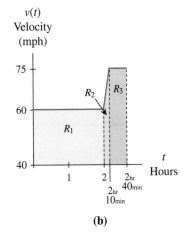

(b)

FIGURE 5.3

In this case, the average speed is simply the average of the beginning and ending speeds during the 10-minute interval. Thus we have

$$\begin{array}{l}\text{Distance traveled}\\\text{between 2 hours}\\\text{and 2 hours}\\\text{10 minutes}\end{array} = \begin{pmatrix}\text{average}\\\text{speed}\end{pmatrix}(\text{time}) = \left(\frac{60\text{ mph} + 75\text{ mph}}{2}\right)\left(\frac{1}{6}\text{ hour}\right)$$

We represent the distance traveled during the first 2 hours while the driver maintained a continuous speed of 60 mph as the area of a rectangle labeled R_1. Similarly, we represent the distance traveled during the next 10 minutes while the driver is accelerating from 60 mph to 75 mph as the area of the trapezoid $\left[\text{Area} = \frac{\text{side 1} + \text{side 2}}{2}(\text{base})\right]$ labeled R_2 in Figure 5.3b. We represent the distance traveled in the last 30 minutes while the driver maintained a continuous speed of 75 mph as the area of the rectangle labeled R_3. Thus, the distance traveled during the 2-hour 40-minute interval is calculated as

$$\begin{array}{l}\text{Distance}\\\text{traveled}\end{array} = \text{area of region } R_1 + \text{area of region } R_2 + \text{area of region } R_3$$

$$= (60\text{ mph})(2\text{ hr}) + \left(\frac{60\text{ mph} + 75\text{ mph}}{2}\right)\left(\frac{1}{6}\text{ hr}\right) + (75\text{ mph})\left(\frac{1}{2}\text{ hr}\right)$$

$$= 120\text{ miles} + 11.25\text{ miles} + 37.5\text{ miles}$$

$$= 168.75\text{ miles}$$

The distance traveled over a specific interval is given by the area of the region between the rate-of-change graph and the horizontal axis.

Recall that the rate of change of a continuous function is negative on any interval where the function is decreasing. In Example 1, we introduce the idea of signed area to indicate that an area trapped below the horizontal axis represents an accumulated decrease in the function.

EXAMPLE 1   *Relating Signed Area to Accumulated Change*

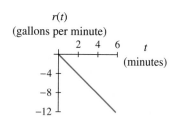

FIGURE 5.4

Draining Water

A water tank drains at a rate of $r(t) = -2t$ gallons per minute t minutes after the water begins draining. The graph of the rate-of-change function is shown in Figure 5.4.

a. What are the units on height, width, and area of the region between the time axis and the rate graph?

b. Determine the change in the volume of water in the tank during the first 4 minutes that the water was being drained.

Solution

a. The height corresponds to the output units, which are gallons per minute. The width is time (in minutes). In the calculation of area, the height and width are multiplied, giving area in gallons.

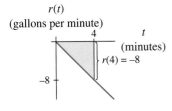

FIGURE 5.5

By *signed area* we mean the area of the region with a negative sign in front of the area value to indicate that the region lies below the input axis.

b. To find the change in the volume of the water, we find the area of the region between the time axis and the rate graph. This area is shaded in Figure 5.5.

The region is a triangle with base of length 4. The height is determined by the function value at $t = 4$. Note that the function value is negative: $r(4) = -8$. The negative sign indicates that the rate-of-change graph lies below the horizontal axis. We use the signed value for height to remind us that the region lies beneath the horizontal axis and represents a *decrease* in the amount of water in the tank. The *signed* area of the region is

$$\frac{1}{2} \cdot (4 \text{ minutes}) \cdot (-8 \text{ gallons per minute}) = -16 \text{ gallons}$$

Thus, during the first 4 minutes that the tank was being drained, the volume of water in the tank changed by -16 gallons. That is, the amount of water in the tank decreased by 16 gallons.   ●

Results of Change

If a rate-of-change function of a quantity is continuous over a closed interval $[a, b]$, the accumulated change in the quantity between input values of a and b is represented as the area or signed area of the region between the rate-of-change function for that quantity and the horizontal axis, provided the function does not cross the horizontal axis over the interval $[a, b]$.

Left- and Right-Rectangle Approximations

The functions in the preceding discussion and example were carefully chosen so that their rate-of-change graphs were easy to obtain and the areas of the desired regions were easy to calculate. But most real-life situations are not so simple. There are two issues that we must face:

- Obtaining the rate-of-change function for the quantity of interest
- Calculating the area of the desired region between the rate-of-change function and the horizontal axis

In many cases, we must resort to approximating both the rate-of-change function and the desired area. Consider the example of a store manager of a large department store who wishes to estimate the number of customers who came to a Saturday sale from 9 A.M. to 9 P.M. The manager stands by the entrance for 1-minute intervals at different times throughout the day and counts the number of people entering the store. He uses these data as an estimate of the number of customers who enter the store each minute. The manager's data may look something like Table 5.1.

The number of customers who attended the sale could be calculated by summing the number of customers who entered the store during each hour for every hour of the 12-hour sale. We do not have enough information to determine the exact number of customers who entered the store each hour; however, we can estimate the number. To build a model for the rate-of-change data, we choose to convert each of

TABLE 5.1

Time	Hours since 9 A.M.	Customers per minute	(est) Cust. per hour	Time	Hours since 9 A.M.	Customers per minute	(est) Cust. per hour
9:00 A.M.	0	1	60	2:30 P.M.	5.5	5	300
9:45 A.M.	0.75	2	120	3:10 P.M.	6.167	5	300
10:15 A.M.	1.25	3	180	4:00 P.M.	7	4	240
11:00 A.M.	2	4	240	5:15 P.M.	8.25	4	240
11:45 A.M.	2.75	4	240	6:30 P.M.	9.5	3	180
12:15 P.M.	3.25	5	300	7:30 P.M.	10.5	2	120
1:15 P.M.	4.25	5	300	8:15 P.M.	11.25	2	120

the above observation times to hours after 9:00 A.M. Thus $t = 0$ at 9:00 A.M. and $t = 11.25$ at 8:15 P.M. A model for the *estimated* number of customers per hour between 9 A.M. and 8:15 P.M. is

$$c(t) = (0.6)t^3 - 17t^2 + 119t + 53 \text{ customers per hour}$$

where t is the number of hours after 9:00 A.M. The graph of this model is shown in Figure 5.6.

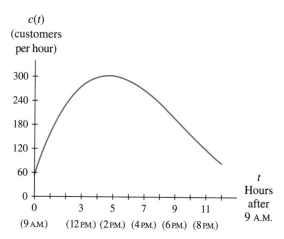

FIGURE 5.6

Concept Development: Left-Rectangle Approximation   To estimate the number of customers who attended the sale, we use the model to estimate the number of customers per hour entering the store at the beginning of each hour. Summing the estimates for each of the 12 hours results in an estimate for the total number of customers. This process is the same as drawing a set of 12 rectangles under the graph of c, one for each hour, and using the sum of their areas to estimate the total number of customers who came to the sale. (See Figure 5.7.)

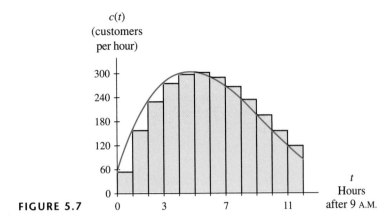

FIGURE 5.7

In Figure 5.7, the height of each rectangle is the function c evaluated at the left endpoint of the base of the rectangle. It is for this reason that we call these rectangles **left rectangles**. Because we are using 12 rectangles of equal width to span the 12-hour sale, the width of each rectangle is 1 hour. We use Table 5.2 to keep track of the areas that we are summing.

TABLE 5.2

Left endpoint of rectangle t hours since 9 A.M.	Height of rectangle $c(t)$ customers per hour	Area of rectangle* customers
9 A.M.: $t =$ 0	$c(0) \approx 53$	53
10 A.M.: $t =$ 1	$c(1) \approx 156$	156
11 A.M.: $t =$ 2	$c(2) \approx 229$	229
noon: $t =$ 3	$c(3) \approx 275$	275
1 P.M.: $t =$ 4	$c(4) \approx 298$	298
2 P.M.: $t =$ 5	$c(5) \approx 302$	302
3 P.M.: $t =$ 6	$c(6) \approx 290$	290
4 P.M.: $t =$ 7	$c(7) \approx 266$	266
5 P.M.: $t =$ 8	$c(8) \approx 233$	233
6 P.M.: $t =$ 9	$c(9) \approx 196$	196
7 P.M.: $t = 10$	$c(10) \approx 156$	156
8 P.M.: $t = 11$	$c(11) \approx 119$	119
	Sum of areas $\approx$ 2573 customers	
	Change in number of customers $\approx$ 2573 customers	

*These values were obtained using the unrounded model.

Thus, using 12 rectangles, we estimate that 2573 customers came to the Saturday sale.

   Note the importance in this example of estimating the number of customers entering the store per hour. If the number of customers counted per minute is *not* adjusted, then the area calculated by multiplying height (measured in customers per minute) by width (measured in hours) is not the number of customers. Make sure the units correspond so that the result of their multiplication gives the desired units. Also note that our decision to use time intervals of 1 hour was arbitrary.

The previous discussion illustrates a way to approximate accumulation using left-rectangle areas. In some situations, choosing rectangles whose heights are measured at the right endpoint of the base of each rectangle may be preferable. Such rectangles are called **right rectangles.** The use of right rectangles is illustrated in the following example.

EXAMPLE 2   *Using Right Rectangles to Approximate Change*

Medicine   A pharmaceutical company has tested the absorption rate of a drug that is given in 20-milligram doses for 20 days. Researchers have modeled the rate of change of the concentration of the drug, measured in micrograms per milliliter per day, $\mu g/mL/day$, in the bloodstream as

$$r(x) = \begin{cases} 1.7(0.8^x) \ \mu g/mL/day & \text{when } 0 \le x \le 20 \\ -10.2 + 3 \ln x \ \mu g/mL/day & \text{when } 20 < x \le 30 \end{cases}$$

where x is the number of days after the drug is first administered. Figure 5.8 illustrates a graph of this rate-of-change function. Note that $r(x)$ is defined with two equations, with each equation applying to a specific input interval. The amount of the drug in the bloodstream increases while the patient is taking the drug and decreases after the patient stops taking the drug. The function $r(x)$ is an example of a piecewise defined function.

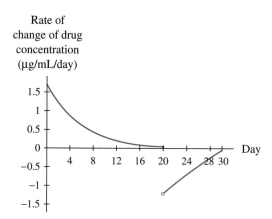

FIGURE 5.8

a. Use the model and right rectangles of width 2 days to estimate the change in the drug concentration in the bloodstream while the patient is taking the drug.

b. Use the model and right rectangles of width 2 days to estimate the change in the drug concentration in the bloodstream for the first 10 days after the patient stops taking the drug.

c. Combine your answers to parts *a* and *b* to estimate the change in the drug concentration in the bloodstream over the 30-day time period.

Solution

a. To determine the change in the drug concentration from the beginning of day 1 ($x = 0$) through the end of day 20 ($x = 20$), we use the exponential portion of the model and ten right rectangles, as shown in Figure 5.9 and Table 5.3.

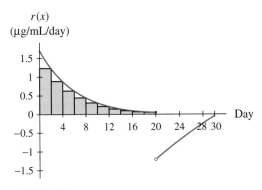

$r(x)$
(μg/mL/day)

FIGURE 5.9

TABLE 5.3

Right endpoint of rectangle x days	Height of the rectangle $r(x)$ (μg/mL/day)	Area of rectangle μg/mL
2	1.09	2.18
4	0.70	1.39
6	0.45	0.89
8	0.29	0.57
10	0.18	0.37
12	0.12	0.23
14	0.07	0.15
16	0.05	0.10
18	0.03	0.06
20	0.02	0.04
	Sum of areas $\approx$ 5.97 μg/mL	
	Change in concentration $\approx$ 5.97 μg/mL	

Over the 20 days that the patient took the drug, the drug concentration increased by approximately 6.0 micrograms per milliliter.

b. To determine the change in the concentration from the beginning of day 21 through the end of day 30, we use the log portion of the model and five right rectangles, as shown in Figure 5.10 and Table 5.4.

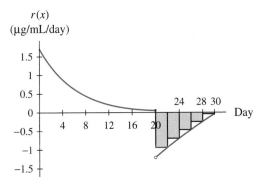

$r(x)$
(μg/mL/day)

FIGURE 5.10

TABLE 5.4

Right endpoint of rectangle x days	Signed height of the rectangle $r(x)$ (μg/mL/day)	Signed area of rectangle μg/mL
22	−0.93	−1.85
24	−0.67	−1.33
26	−0.43	−1.85
28	−0.20	−0.41
30	0	−0.01
	Sum of signed areas $\approx$ −4.44 μg/mL	
	Change in concentration $\approx$ −4.44 μg/mL	

From the beginning of day 21 through the end of day 30, the drug concentration decreased by approximately 4.4 μg/mL.

c. To determine the change in concentration from the beginning of day 1 through the end of day 30, we need only subtract the amount of decline from the amount of increase.

$$5.97 \ \mu g/mL - 4.44 \ \mu g/mL \approx 1.54 \ \mu g/mL$$

The drug concentration increased by approximately 1.5 μg/mL from the beginning of day 1 through the end of day 30. ●

Part c of Example 2 illustrates the results of change using signed areas. In general, if a function f gives the rate of change of a function F and if the function f is sometimes positive and sometimes negative between inputs a and b, then the accumulated (or net) change in F is equal to the area of the region lying under the graph of f and above the x-axis minus the area of the region lying above the graph of f and below the x-axis. (See Figure 5.11.) In other words, the accumulated change in a quantity is equal to the sum of the signed areas of the regions between the rate-of-change function for that quantity and the horizontal axis over the interval from a to b.

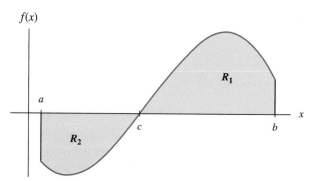

Accumulated change = area of R_1 − area of R_2
= sum of signed areas

FIGURE 5.11

Midpoint-Rectangle Approximation

It is often true that if a left-rectangle approximation is an overestimate, then a right-rectangle area will be an underestimate, and vice versa. For example, consider using four left and four right rectangles to approximate the area of the region between the function $f(x) = \sqrt{4 - x^2}$ and the x-axis between $x = 0$ and $x = 2$. Figure 5.12 shows the rectangles and the approximate areas.

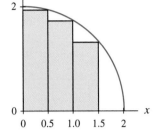

(a) Left-rectangle
approximation ≈ 3.5

(b) Right-rectangle
approximation ≈ 2.5

FIGURE 5.12

Note from Figure 5.12 that the left-rectangle approximation is an overestimate and the right-rectangle approximation is an underestimate.

We next consider approximating area using a third type of rectangle. The **midpoint-rectangle approximation** uses rectangles whose heights are calculated at the midpoints of the subintervals. Midpoint-rectangle approximation is illustrated in Example 3.

EXAMPLE 3   *Using Midpoint Rectangles to Approximate Change*

Consider again the region between the function $f(x) = \sqrt{4 - x^2}$ and the x-axis from $x = 0$ to $x = 2$. Use four midpoint rectangles to approximate the area of this region. (Note that we are actually seeking the area of one quarter of a circle that has a radius of 2. Using the formula for the area of a circle, $A = \pi r^2$, we find that the area of the entire circle is 4π. The area of one quarter of this circle is $\pi \approx 3.14$.)

Solution
Table 5.5 shows the calculations for the areas of the midpoint rectangles shown in Figure 5.13.

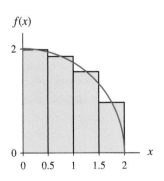

Four rectangles

FIGURE 5.13

TABLE 5.5

Rectangle number	Midpoint of interval	Height of rectangle	Width of rectangle	Area
1	0.25	$f(0.25) \approx 1.98$	0.5	0.99
2	0.75	$f(0.75) \approx 1.85$	0.5	0.93
3	1.25	$f(1.25) \approx 1.56$	0.5	0.78
4	1.75	$f(1.75) \approx 0.97$	0.5	0.48
			Total area of four midpoint rectangles ≈ 3.18	

The area of the region is approximately 3.18 (using four midpoint rectangles for estimation). ●

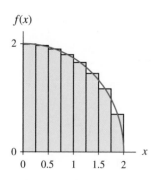

f(x)

Eight rectangles

FIGURE 5.14

Finding a Limit of Area Estimates

The midpoint-rectangle approximation is much closer to the actual area than are the two other approximations. This is often the case.

We can improve the estimate of the area using more rectangles (see Figure 5.14). In Table 5.6, we show the results when eight midpoint rectangles are used to estimate the area of one quarter of the circle. (Remember that we know this area is π.)

TABLE 5.6

Rectangle number	Midpoint of interval	Height of rectangle	Width of rectangle	Area
1	0.125	$f(0.125) \approx 1.996$	0.25	0.499
2	0.375	$f(0.375) \approx 1.965$	0.25	0.491
3	0.625	$f(0.625) \approx 1.900$	0.25	0.475
4	0.875	$f(0.875) \approx 1.798$	0.25	0.450
5	1.125	$f(1.125) \approx 1.654$	0.25	0.413
6	1.375	$f(1.375) \approx 1.452$	0.25	0.363
7	1.625	$f(1.625) \approx 1.166$	0.25	0.291
8	1.875	$f(1.875) \approx 0.696$	0.25	0.174
			Total area of eight midpoint rectangles $\approx$ 3.156	

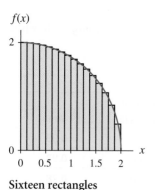

f(x)

Sixteen rectangles

FIGURE 5.15

Using eight midpoint rectangles gives a better estimate than using four midpoint rectangles. Sixteen midpoint rectangles appear to fit even better than eight midpoint rectangles. (See Figure 5.15).

In fact, if we let the number of rectangles increase without bound, the area of the rectangles will approach π. As we use more rectangles, the shaded region accounted for by the rectangles more closely approximates the region of interest. This fact will help us approximate the area. If we make a table of the approximations, we may be able to recognize a *limiting value*—that is, a value to which the approximations seem to be getting closer and closer as the number of rectangles becomes larger and larger.

> From now on, whenever we speak of approximating areas using rectangles, unless the type of rectangle is specified, we will use midpoint rectangles because they generally give the best approximations when compared with an equal number of either left or right rectangles.

Accumulated Change and the Definite Integral

Because the more rectangles we use to approximate area, the better we expect the approximation to be, we are led to consider area as the limiting value of the sums of areas of approximating midpoint rectangles as the number of rectangles increases without bound. Let f be a function that is continuous and non-negative over the interval from a to b. (See Figure 5.16.) Partition the interval from a to b into n subintervals of equal length $\Delta x = \dfrac{b - a}{n}$, and on each subinterval construct a rectangle of width Δx whose height is given by the value of f at the midpoint of the subinterval. Figures 5.17 through 5.20 show the rectangles when $n = 4, 8, 16,$ and 32.

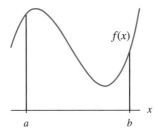

Regions under curve

FIGURE 5.16

Four rectangles

FIGURE 5.17

Eight rectangles

FIGURE 5.18

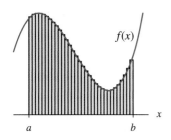

Sixteen rectangles

FIGURE 5.19

Thirty-two rectangles

FIGURE 5.20

The heights of the rectangles are given by the values

$$f(x_1), f(x_2), \ldots, f(x_n)$$

where $x_1, x_2, \ldots, x_n$ are the midpoints of the subintervals. Each rectangle has width Δx, so the areas of the rectangles are given by the values

$$f(x_1)\Delta x, f(x_2)\Delta x, \ldots, f(x_n)\Delta x$$

and the sum $[f(x_1) + f(x_2) + \ldots + f(x_n)]\Delta x$ is an approximation to the area of the region between the graph of f and the x-axis from a to b. As our examples have shown, the approximations generally improve as n increases. In mathematical terms, the area of the region between the graph of f and the x-axis from a to b is given by a limit of sums as n increases:

$$\text{Area} = \lim_{n \to \infty} [f(x_1) + f(x_2) + \cdots + f(x_n)]\Delta x$$

Area Beneath a Curve

Let f be a continuous non-negative bounded function from a to b. The area of the region between the graph of f and the x-axis from a to b is given by the limit

$$\text{Area} = \lim_{n \to \infty} [f(x_1) + f(x_2) + \cdots + f(x_n)]\Delta x$$

where $x_1, x_2, \ldots, x_n$ are the midpoints of n subintervals of length $\Delta x = \dfrac{b - a}{n}$ between a and b.

EXAMPLE 4   *Relating Accumulated Change to Signed Area*

Wine Consumption   The rate of change of the per capita consumption of wine in the United States from 1970 through 1990 can be modeled* as

$$W(x) = (1.243 \cdot 10^{-4})x^3 - 0.0314x^2 + 2.6174x - 71.977 \text{ gallons}$$

per person per year

where x is the number of years since the end of 1900. A graph of the function is shown in Figure 5.21.

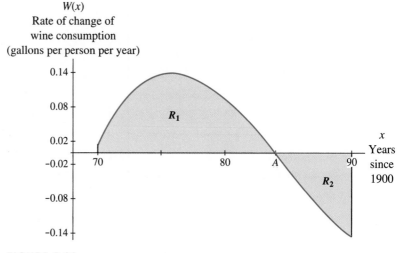

FIGURE 5.21

a.   Find the input value of the point labeled A.

b.   From 1970 through 1990, according to the model, when was wine consumption increasing and when was it decreasing?

c.   Use a limiting value of sums to estimate the areas, to two decimal places, of the regions labeled R_1 and R_2. Interpret your answers.

d.   According to the model, what was the change in the per capita consumption of wine from the end of 1970 through 1990?

Solution

a.   Solving $W(x) = 0$ gives $A \approx 83.97$, corresponding to the end of 1984.

b.   Wine consumption was increasing where the rate-of-change graph is positive—from 1970 through 1984 ($x \approx 83.97$)—and was decreasing from 1984 through 1990, where the rate-of-change graph is negative.

c.   In order to find the areas of the regions R_1 and R_2, we must know the lower limit and upper limit (that is, the endpoints) of each region. Because $W(x) = 0$ when

*Based on data from Statistical Abstract, 1994.

$x \approx 83.97$, we use lower limit $x = 70$ and upper limit $x \approx 83.97$ for R_1 and lower limit $x \approx 83.97$ and upper limit $x = 90$ for R_2.

The area of region R_1 is determined by examining sums of areas of midpoint rectangles for an increasing number of subintervals until a trend is observed, as shown in Table 5.7. The area of region R_1 is approximately 1.34 gallons per person. This indicates that wine consumption increased by approximately 1.34 gallons per person from the end of 1970 through 1984 ($x \approx 83.97$).

TABLE 5.7

Number of rectangles	Approximation of area of region R_1
5	1.35966
10	1.34130
20	1.33671
40	1.33556
80	1.33527
160	1.33520
	Limit $\approx$ 1.34

We calculate the signed area of region R_2 in a similar way, as shown in Table 5.8. The area of region R_2 is approximately 0.45 gallon per person. This is an estimate for the decrease in per capita wine consumption from 1984 ($x \approx 83.97$) through 1990.

TABLE 5.8

Number of rectangles	Approximation of signed area of region R_2
5	−0.44927
10	−0.44870
20	−0.44856
40	−0.44852
	Limit $\approx$ −0.45

d. To determine the net change in the per capita consumption of wine from the end of 1970 through 1990, we subtract the decrease (area of R_2) from the increase (area of R_1).

Net change $= 1.34 - 0.45 = 0.89$ gallon per person

We see an approximate net increase of 0.89 gallon per person from the end of 1970 through 1990. ●

In the previous example, we saw that when a rate-of-change function has both positive and negative outputs over a given input interval, the accumulated change in the quantity function is equal to the sum of the signed areas of the regions between the graph of the rate-of-change function and the horizontal axis. That is, we sum the signed areas of rectangles over the entire interval to calculate accumulated change. We illustrate this type of calculation using a limit of sums and the rate-of-change function $W(x) = (1.243 \cdot 10^{-4})x^3 - 0.0314x^2 + 2.6174x - 71.977$ gallons per person per year, where x is the number of years since the end of 1900, to estimate the net change in the per capita consumption of wine from the end of 1970 through 1990. Refer to Figure 5.22. Ignoring the horizontal-axis intercept, partition the interval from $x = 70$ to $x = 90$ into equal subintervals, and use the formula for W and midpoint rectangles to calculate the sums of signed-rectangle areas in Table 5.9.

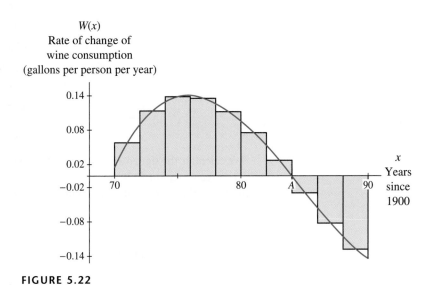

FIGURE 5.22

TABLE 5.9

Number of rectangles	Approximate accumulated change
5	0.92848
10	0.89712
20	0.88928
40	0.88732
80	0.88683
160	0.88671
320	0.88668
Limit $\approx$ 0.89 gallon per person	

The limit of sums $\lim\limits_{n\to\infty}[W(x_1) + W(x_2) + \cdots + W(x_n)]\Delta x$ from $x = 70$ to $x = 90$ yields the same net change as the subtraction of nonsigned areas in part d of Example 4.

It is tedious to write $\lim\limits_{n\to\infty}[W(x_1) + W(x_2) + \cdots + W(x_n)]\Delta x$ from $x = a$ to $x = b$ every time we want to denote the limit of sums. Mathematically, we use the shorthand notation $\int_a^b f(x)dx$. The sign $\int$ is called an *integral sign* and resembles an elongated S to remind us that we are finding the limit of sums. The values a and b identify the input interval, f is the function, and the symbol dx reminds us of the width Δx of each subinterval. When a and b are specific numbers, $\int_a^b f(x)dx$ is known as a **definite integral.** We now formally define the definite integral and accumulated change.

Accumulated Change and the Definite Integral

Let f be a continuous or piecewise continuous bounded function from a to b. The accumulated change in f from a to b is given by the limit

$$\lim_{n\to\infty}[f(x_1) + f(x_2) + \cdots + f(x_n)]\Delta x = \int_a^b f(x)dx$$

where $x_1, x_2, \ldots, x_n$ are the midpoints of n subintervals of length $\Delta x = \dfrac{b - a}{n}$ between a and b.

$\int_a^b f(x)dx$ is called the definite integral of f from a to b.

EXAMPLE 5   *Relating Accumulated Change and the Definite Integral*

Wine Consumption   Recall from Example 4 the function

$$W(x) = (1.243 \cdot 10^{-4})x^3 - 0.0314x^2 + 2.6174x - 71.977 \text{ gallons per person per year}$$

which gives the rate of change of per capita consumption of wine in gallons per person per year from 1970 through 1990, where x is the number of years since 1900.

a. Find the values of $\displaystyle\int_{70}^{83.97} W(x)dx$, $\displaystyle\int_{83.97}^{90} W(x)dx$, and $\displaystyle\int_{70}^{90} W(x)dx$.

b. What was the per capita wine consumption in 1990?

Solution

a. Refer to Figure 5.23. The area of region R_1, calculated in Example 4, is the value
    of the definite integral of W from 70 to 83.97.

$W(x)$
Rate of change of
wine consumption
(gallons per person per year)

FIGURE 5.23

$$\int_{70}^{83.97} W(x)dx \approx 1.34 \text{ gallons per person}$$

The signed area of region R_2, calculated in Example 4, is the value of the definite integral from 83.97 to 90.

$$\int_{83.97}^{90} W(x)dx \approx -0.45 \text{ gallon per person}$$

The limit of sums, calculated using Table 5.9, gives the accumulated change in
per capita wine consumption or the definite integral of W from 70 to 90.

$$\int_{70}^{90} W(x)dx \approx 0.89 \text{ gallon per person}$$

b. The definite integral tells us the change in a quantity over an interval, not the
    value of the quantity at the endpoint of the interval. We do not know the per
    capita wine consumption in 1990. ●

The first important concept in this section is that the accumulated change in a
quantity can be found by finding areas between rate-of-change graphs and the
horizontal axis. Sometimes we can calculate exact areas using geometric formulas. At
other times, we only approximate area using sums of areas of rectangles.

The other important concept in this section is the idea of finding the limiting
value of sums of areas of rectangles. We used the definite integral to indicate that we
were finding accumulated change in a quantity over an interval with specific numerical endpoints. In many cases, it is possible to find accumulation functions that will
give as output the accumulated change in a rate-of-change function. We explore these
accumulation functions graphically in Section 5.2 and algebraically in Section 5.3.

5.1   Concept Inventory

- Area or signed area of a region between a rate-of-change function and the horizontal axis between a and b = accumulated change in the amount function between a and b
- Left-rectangle approximation
- Right-rectangle approximation
- Midpoint-rectangle approximation
- Area = limiting value of sums of areas of midpoint rectangles
- $\int_a^b f(x)dx$ = accumulated change in F,

  where $F' = f$ for x between a and b

5.1   Activities

Getting Started

1. **Bacteria**   The growth rate of bacteria (in thousands per hour) in milk at room temperature is $B(t)$, where t is the number of hours that the milk has been at room temperature. We wish to use rectangles to estimate the area of the region between a graph of B and the t-axis. What are the units on

    a. the heights of the rectangles?

    b. the widths of the rectangles?

    c. the areas of the rectangles?

    d. the area of the region between the graph of B and the t-axis?

    e. the accumulated change in the number of bacteria in the milk during the first hour that the milk is at room temperature?

2. **Road Test**   The acceleration of a car (in feet per second per second) during a test conducted by a car manufacturer is given by $A(t)$, where t is the number of seconds since the beginning of the test.

    a. What does the area of the region between the portion of the graph of A lying above the t-axis and the t-axis tell us about the car?

    b. What are the units on

        i. the heights and widths of rectangles used to estimate area?

        ii. the area of the region between the graph of A and the t-axis?

3. **Braking**   The distance required for a car to stop is a function of the speed of the car when the brakes are applied. The rate of change of the stopping distance could be expressed in feet per mile per hour, where the input is the speed of the car, in miles per hour, when the brakes are applied.

    a. What does the area of the region between the rate-of-change graph and the input axis from 40 mph to 60 mph tell us about the car?

    b. What are the units on

        i. the heights and widths of rectangles used to estimate the area in part a?

        ii. the area in part a?

4. **Emissions**   The atmospheric concentration of CO_2 is growing exponentially. If the growth rate in ppm per year is $C(t)$, where t is the number of years since 1980, what are the units on

    a. the area of the region between the graph of C and the t-axis from $t = 0$ to $t = 20$?

    b. the heights and widths of rectangles used to estimate the area in part a?

    c. the change in the CO_2 concentration from 1980 through 2000?

5. **Population**   The rate of change of the population of a country, in thousands of people per year, is modeled by the function P with input t, where t is the number of years since 1995. What are the units on

    a. the area of the region between the graph of P and the t-axis from $t = 0$ to $t = 10$?

    b. $\int_{10}^{20} P(t)dt$?

    c. the change in the population from 1995 through 2000?

6. **Lake Level**   During the spring thaw a mountain lake rises by $L(d)$ feet per day, where d is the number of days since March 31. What are the units on

    a. the area of the region between the graph of L and the d-axis from $d = 0$ to $d = 15$?

    b. $\int_{16}^{30} L(d)dd$?

    c. the amount by which the lake rose from March 31 to May 31?

7. **Algae Growth**   When warm water is released into a river from a source such as a power plant, the increased temperature of the water causes some algae to grow and other algae to die. In particular, blue-green algae that can be toxic to some aquatic life thrive. If $A(c)$ is the growth rate of blue-green algae (in organisms per °C) and c is the temperature of the water in °C, interpret the following in context:

   a. $\displaystyle\int_{25}^{35} A(c)\,dc$

   b. The area of the region between the graph of A and the c-axis from $c = 30°C$ to $c = 40°C$

8. **Stock Value**   The value of a stock portfolio is growing by $V(t)$ dollars per day, where t is the number of days since the beginning of the year. Interpret the following in context:

   a. The area of the region between the graph of V and the t-axis from $t = 0$ to $t = 120$

   b. $\displaystyle\int_{120}^{240} V(t)\,dt$

9. **Production**   The graph in the figure shows the rate of change of profit at various production levels for a pencil manufacturer. Fill in the blanks in the following discussion of the profit. If it is not possible to determine a value, write NA in the corresponding blank.

Rate of change
of profit
(dollars per box)

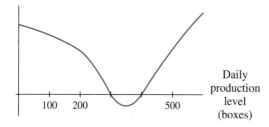

Profit is increasing when between (a) _____ and (b) _____ boxes of pencils are produced each day. The profit when 500 boxes of pencils are produced each day is (c) _____ dollars. Profit is higher than nearby profits at a production level of (d) _____ boxes each day, and it is lower than nearby profits at a production level of (e) _____ boxes of pencils each day. The profit is decreasing most rapidly

when (f) _____ boxes are produced each day. The area between the rate-of-change-of-profit function and the production-level axis between production levels of 100 and 200 boxes each day has units (g) _____. If $p'(b)$ represents the rate of change of profit (in dollars per box) at a daily production level of b boxes, would $\displaystyle\int_{300}^{400} p'(b)\,db$ be more than, less than, or the same value as $\displaystyle\int_{100}^{200} p'(b)\,db$? (h) _____

10. **Cost**   The graph shows the rate of change of cost for an orchard in Florida at various production levels during grapefruit season. Fill in the blanks in the following cost function discussion. If it is not possible to determine a value, write NA in the corresponding blank.

Rate of
change of cost
(dollars per carton)

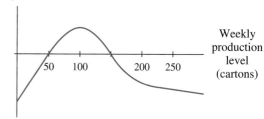

Cost is increasing when between (a) _____ and (b) _____ cartons of grapefruit are harvested each week. The cost to produce 100 cartons of grapefruit each week is (c) _____ dollars. The cost is lower than nearby costs at a production level of (d) _____ cartons, and it is higher than nearby costs at a production level of (e) _____ cartons of grapefruit each week. The cost is increasing most rapidly when (f) _____ cartons are produced each week. The area between the rate-of-change-of-cost function and the production-level axis between production levels of 50 and 150 cartons each week has units (g) _____. If $c'(p)$ represents the rate of change of cost (in dollars per carton) at a weekly production level of p cartons of grapefruit, would $\displaystyle\int_{200}^{250} c'(p)\,dp$ be greater than, less than, or the same value as $\displaystyle\int_{50}^{100} c'(p)\,dp$? (h) _____

11. The graph of a function g is shown.

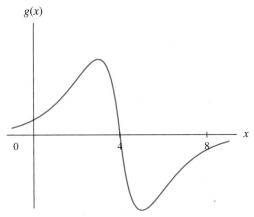

$g(x)$

a. Discuss how to approximate the area of the region between the graph of g and the x-axis between $x = 0$ and $x = 8$ with eight right rectangles that have the same width. Copy the graph, and draw the rectangles on the figure.

b. Repeat part a using eight left rectangles.

12. Stock Value   On January 4, 2000, DuPont stock was worth $65 per share.

a. Write a function for the value of x shares of stock. Graph this function. Note that this is a continuous model representing a discrete situation.

b. Write the function for the rate of change of the continuous model for the value of DuPont stock with respect to the number of shares held. Graph this rate-of-change function.

c. Find the change in the value of stock held if the number of shares held is increased from 250 to 300 shares. Depict this change as the area of a region on the rate-of-change graph.

13. The graph of a function f is shown.

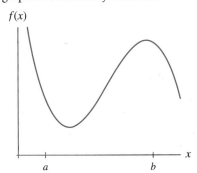

$f(x)$

Discuss how to approximate the area of the region beneath the graph of f from $x = a$ to $x = b$ with four midpoint rectangles that have the same width. Draw the rectangles.

14. Approximate the area of the region beneath the graph of $f(x) = e^{-x^2}$ from $x = -1$ to $x = 1$ using four left rectangles, four right rectangles, and four midpoint rectangles.

a. In each case,

   i. sketch the graph of f from $x = -1$ to $x = 1$.

   ii. label the points on the x-axis, and draw the rectangles.

   iii. calculate the approximate areas.

b. Proceed as in part a to approximate the area of the region beneath the graph of f from $x = -1$ to $x = 1$ using eight left rectangles, eight right rectangles, and eight midpoint rectangles.

c. The actual area, to nine decimal places, of the region beneath the graph of $f(x) = e^{-x^2}$ is 1.493648266. Which of the approximations found in part b is the most accurate?

Applying Concepts

15. Production   The graph shows two estimates, labeled A and B, of oil production rates (in billions of barrels per year).

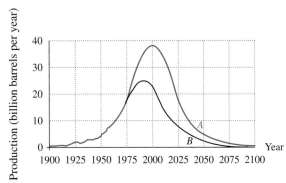

(Source: Adapted from *Ecology of Natural Resources* by François Ramade. Copyright 1984 by John Wiley & Sons, Inc. Reprinted by permission of the publisher.)

a. Use midpoint rectangles of width 25 years to estimate the total amount of oil produced from 1900 through 2100 using graph A.

b. Repeat part a for graph B.

c. On page 31 of *Ecology of Natural Resources*, the total oil production is estimated from graph A to be 2100 billion barrels and from graph B to be 1350 billion barrels. How close are your estimates?

16. Climate   Scientists have long been interested in studying global climatic changes and the effect of such changes on many aspects of the environment. From carefully controlled experiments, two scientists constructed a model to simulate daily snow depth in a region of the Northwest Territories in Canada. Rates of change (in equivalent centimeters of water per day) estimated from their model are shown as a scatter plot in the accompanying figure. Appropriate models have been sketched on the scatter plot. Note that both vertical and horizontal scales change after June 9.

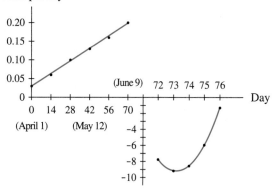

(Source: R. G. Gallimore and J. E. Kutzbach, "Role of Orbitally Induced Changes in Tundra Area in the Onset of Glaciation," *Nature,* vol. 381, June 6, 1996, pp. 503–505.)

a. What does the figure indicate occurred between June 9 and June 11?

b. Estimate the area of the region beneath the curve from April 1 through June 9. Interpret your answer.

c. Use four midpoint rectangles to estimate the area of the region from June 11 through June 15. Interpret your answer.

17. Robot Speed   A mechanical engineering graduate student designed a robot and is testing the ability of the robot to accelerate, decelerate, and maintain speed. The robot takes 1 minute to accelerate to 10 mph (880 feet per minute). The robot maintains that speed for 2 minutes and then takes half a minute to come to a complete stop. Assume that this robot's acceleration and deceleration are constant.

a. Draw a graph of the robot's speed during the experiment.

b. Find the area of the region between the graph in part *a* and the horizontal axis.

c. What is the practical interpretation of the area found in part *b*?

18. Expanding Gas   A certain gas expands as it is heated. The accompanying figure shows the rate of expansion of the gas measured at several temperatures.

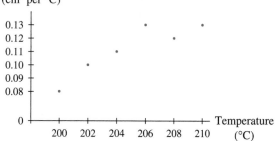

a. Use only the data and left rectangles to estimate by how much the gas expanded as it was heated from 200°C to 210°C. Sketch the rectangles on the scatter plot. Do you believe your approximation is an overestimate or an underestimate? Explain.

b. Repeat part *a* using right rectangles.

19. Energy Use   The graph shows the energy usage in megawatts for one day for a large university campus. The daily energy consumption for the campus is measured in megawatt-hours and is found by calculating the area of the region between the graph and the horizontal axis.

$m(t)$
Energy power usage
(megawatts)

a. Estimate the daily energy consumption using eight left rectangles.

b. Estimate the daily energy consumption using eight right rectangles.

c. Discuss whether your estimates in parts *a* and *b* are overestimates or underestimates of the actual daily energy consumption.

20. Population   The rate of change of the population of North Dakota from 1970 through 1990 can be modeled as

$$p(t) = \begin{cases} 3.87 \text{ thousand} \\ \quad \text{people per year} \quad \text{when } 0 \le t < 15 \\ -7.39 \text{ thousand} \\ \quad \text{people per year} \quad \text{when } 15 \le t \le 20 \end{cases}$$

where t represents the number of years since 1970.

(Source: Based on data from *Statistical Abstract*, 1994.)

a. Sketch a graph of the rate-of-change function.

b. Find the area of the region between the graph of p and the horizontal axis from 0 to 15. Interpret your answer.

c. Find the area of the region between the graph of p and the horizontal axis from 15 to 20. Interpret your answer.

d. Was the population of North Dakota in 1990 greater or less than the population in 1970? By how much did the population change between 1970 and 1990?

e. What information would you need to determine the population of North Dakota in 1990?

21. Cottage Cheese   The rate of change of the per capita consumption of cottage cheese in the United States between 1980 and 1999 can be modeled by the function

$$c(t) = \begin{cases} -0.01t - 0.058 \text{ pound} \\ \quad \text{per person per year} \quad \text{when } 0 \le t < 13 \\ -0.1 \text{ pound per person} \\ \quad \text{per year} \quad \text{when } 13 \le t < 15 \\ 0 \text{ pound per person per year} \quad \text{when } 15 \le t \le 19 \end{cases}$$

where t is the number of years since 1980.

(Source: Based on data from *Statistical Abstract*, 2001.)

a. Sketch a graph of the rate-of-change function.

b. Find the area of the region between the graph and the horizontal axis between $t = 0$ and $t = 19$.

c. Interpret the area in part b in the context of cottage cheese consumption.

d. Can you determine the per capita cottage cheese consumption in 1996? in 1999? Why or why not?

22. Hospital Stay   The rate of change of the length of the average hospital stay between 1993 and 2000 can be modeled by the equation

$$s(t) = \begin{cases} 0.82t - 0.39 \text{ days per year} \quad \text{when } 0 \le t < 5 \\ -0.1t \text{ days per year} \quad \text{when } 5 \le t \le 7 \end{cases}$$

where t is the number of years since 1993.

(Source: Based on data from *Statistical Abstract*, 2001.)

a. Graph s for the years between 1993 and 2000.

b. Judging on the basis of the graph, was the length of the average hospital stay increasing or decreasing between 1993 and 2000?

c. Find the area of the region lying above the axis between the graph and the t-axis.

d. Find the area of the region lying below the axis between the graph and the t-axis.

e. Judging on the basis of your answers to parts c and d, by how much did the average hospital stay change between 1993 and 2000? Can you determine the average stay in 2000? Why or why not?

23. Temperature   During a summer thunderstorm, the temperature drops and then rises again. The rate of change of the temperature during the hour and a half after the storm began is given by

$$T(h) = 9.5h^3 - 15.5h^2 + 17.4h - 10.12°\text{F per hour}$$

where h is the number of hours since the storm began.

a. Graph the function T from $h = 0$ to $h = 1.5$. Find the point A at which the graph crosses the horizontal axis.

b. Consider the portion of the graph of T lying below the horizontal axis. What does the area of the region between this portion of the graph of T and the horizontal axis represent?

c. What does the area of the region lying above the axis represent?

d. Consider the graph between 0 and 1.5 hours. Use three right rectangles to approximate the area of the region lying below the axis from 0 to 1.5 hours.

e. Repeat part d for the region lying above the axis.

f. Use a limit of sums to estimate $\int_0^A T(h)\, dh$.

g. Use a limit of sums to estimate $\int_A^{1.5} T(h)\, dh$.

h. Estimate $\int_0^{1.5} T(h)\, dh$. What information is needed to determine the temperature when $h = 1.5$? According to the model, one and a half hours after the storm began, was the temperature higher than, lower than, or the same as the temperature at the beginning of the storm? If it was higher or lower, by how many degrees?

24. Baby Boomers As the 76 million Americans born between 1946 and 1964 (the "baby boomers") continue to age, the United States will see an increasing proportion of Americans who are within one year of a retirement age of 66. The model

$$R(t) = \frac{1.9}{1 + 18e^{-0.04t}} + 0.1 \frac{\text{million retirees}}{\text{year}}$$

gives the projected rate of change in the number of people within one year of retirement, where t is the number of years since 1940, for years between 1940 and 2050. The model is based on data from the U.S. Bureau of the Census.

Use the equation and ten midpoint rectangles to estimate the change in the population within one year of retirement or older from the end of 2005 through the end of 2010.

25. Birthweight The rate of change of the percentage of low-birthweight babies (less than 5 pounds 8 ounces) in 2000 can be modeled by

$$P(w) = -11.5(0.86^w) \text{ percentage points per pound}$$

when the mother gains w pounds during pregnancy. The model is valid for weight gains between 18 and 43 pounds.

(Source: Based on data from *National Vital Statistics Reports,* vol. 50, no. 5, February 12, 2002.)

a. Sketch a graph of P from $w = 18$ to $w = 43$.

b. What does the fact that the graph of P lies below the t-axis from $w = 18$ to $w = 43$ tell you about the percentage of low-birthweight babies in 2000?

c. Use five midpoint rectangles to estimate the area of the region between the graph of P and the w-axis from $w = 18$ to $w = 43$. Interpret your answer.

26. Trust Fund The rate of change of the projected total assets in the Social Security trust fund for the years 2000 through 2033 can be modeled by the equation

$$S(x) = -0.46x^2 + 1.85x + 108.7 \text{ billion dollars per year}$$

x years after 2000.

(Source: Based on data from the Social Security Administration.)

a. Graph S between 2000 and 2033.

b. According to the graph of S, when will the trust fund assets be growing and when will they be declining?

c. Find the point on the graph of S that corresponds to the time when the amount in the trust fund will be greatest.

d. Using four midpoint rectangles, estimate the area lying above the axis and below the graph of S. Interpret your answer.

e. Using four midpoint rectangles, estimate the area lying below the axis and above the graph of S. Interpret your answer.

f. By how much will the trust fund amount change between 2000 and 2033? What information do we need to determine how much money is projected to be in the trust fund in 2033?

27. Life Expectancy Life expectancies in the United States are always rising because of advances in health care, increased education, and other factors. The rate of change (measured at the end of each year) of life expectancies for women in the United States between 1970 and 2010 can be modeled by

$$E(t) = 0.0004t^2 - 0.022t + 0.36 \text{ years per year}$$

where t is the number of years since 1970.

(Source: Based on data from *Statistical Abstract,* 1998.)

a. Graph E between 1970 and 2010.

b. Find the point on the graph of E that corresponds to the time between 1970 and 2010 when the life expectancy for women was growing least rapidly.

c. Using four midpoint rectangles, estimate the area lying between the graph of $E(t)$ and the horizontal axis.

d. By how much is the life expectancy for women projected to increase between 2000 and 2010? What information do we need to determine the projected life expectancy for women in 2010?

28. **Weight**   The rate of change of the weight of a laboratory mouse can be modeled by the equation

$$w(t) = \frac{13.785}{t} \text{ grams per week}$$

where t is the age of the mouse in weeks and $1 \le t \le 15$.

a. Use the idea of a limit of sums to estimate the value of $\int_{3}^{11} w(t)dt$.

b. Label units on the answer to part a. Interpret your answer.

c. If the mouse weighed 4 grams at 3 weeks, what was its weight at 11 weeks of age?

29. **Sales**   The rate of change of annual U.S. factory sales (in billions of dollars per year) of consumer electronic goods to dealers from 1990 through 2001 can be modeled by the equation

$$s(x) = 0.12x^2 - x + 5.7 \text{ billion dollars per year}$$

where x is the number of years since 1990.

(Sources: Based on data from *Statistical Abstract,* 2001, and Consumer Electronics Association.)

a. Use the idea of a limit of sums to estimate the change in factory sales from 1990 through 2001.

b. Write the definite integral symbol for this limit of sums.

c. If factory sales were $43.0 billion in 1990, what were they in 2001?

30. **Production**   On the basis of data obtained from a preliminary report by a geological survey team, it is estimated that for the first 10 years of production, a certain oil well can be expected to produce oil at the rate of $r(t) = 3.94t^{3.55}e^{-1.35t}$ thousand barrels per year t years after production begins.

a. Use the idea of a limit of sums to estimate the yield from this oil field during the first 5 years of production.

b. Use the idea of a limit of sums to estimate the yield during the first 10 years of production.

c. Write the definite integral symbols representing the limits of sums in parts a and b.

d. Estimate the percentage of the first 10 years' production that your answer to part a represents.

31. **Sales**   The table records the volume of sales (in thousands) of a popular movie for selected months during the first 18 months after it was released on DVD.

Months after release	Number of DVDs sold each month (thousands)
2	565
4	467
5	321
7	204
10	61
11	31
12	17
16	3
18	2

a. Find a logistic model for the data.

b. Use 5, 10, and 15 right rectangles to estimate the number of DVDs sold during the first 15 months after release.

c. Which of the following would give the most accurate value of the number of DVDs sold during the first 15 months after release?

  i. The answer to part b for 15 rectangles

  ii. The limiting value of the sums of midpoint rectangles using the model in part a

  iii. The sum of actual sales figures for the first 15 months

32. **Bank Account** The table gives rates of change of the amount in an interest-bearing account for which interest is compounded continuously.

At end of year	Rate of change (dollars per day)
1	2.06
3	2.37
5	2.72
7	3.13
9	3.60

a. Convert the input into days. Disregard leap years. Why is this conversion important for a definite integral calculation?

b. Find an exponential model for the converted data.

c. Use a limiting value of sums to estimate the change in the balance of the account from the day the money was invested to the last day of the ninth year after the investment was made. Again, disregard leap years.

d. Give the definite integral notation for your answer to part c.

33. **Labor**   The personnel manager for a large construction company keeps records of the number of labor hours per week spent on typical construction jobs handled by the company. He has developed the following model for a labor-power curve:

$$m(x) = \frac{6{,}608e^{-0.706x}}{(1 + 925e^{-0.706x})^2} \text{ million labor hours per week}$$

after the xth week of the construction job.

a. Use 5, 10, and 20 right rectangles to approximate the number of labor hours spent during the first 20 weeks of a typical construction job.

b. If the number of labor hours spent on a particular job exactly coincides with the model, which of the following would give the most accurate value of the number of labor hours spent during the first 20 weeks of the job?

  i. The 20-right-rectangle sum found in part a

  ii. The sum of 20 midpoint rectangles

  iii. The limiting value of the sums of midpoint rectangles

34. **Blood Pressure**   Blood pressure (BP) varies for individuals throughout the course of a day, typically being lowest at night and highest from late morning to early afternoon. The estimated rate of change in diastolic blood pressure for a patient with untreated hypertension is shown in the table.

Time	Rate of change of diastolic BP (mm Hg per hour)
8 A.M.	3.0
10 A.M.	1.8
12 P.M.	0.7
2 P.M.	−0.1
4 P.M.	−0.7
6 P.M.	−1.1
8 P.M.	−1.3
10 P.M.	−1.1
12 A.M.	−0.7
2 A.M.	0.1
4 A.M.	0.8
6 A.M.	1.9

a. During which time intervals was the patient's diastolic blood pressure rising? falling?

b. Estimate the times when diastolic blood pressure was rising and falling most rapidly.

c. Find a model for the data.

d. Find the times at which the output of the model is zero. Of what significance are these times in the context of blood pressure?

e. Use the idea of a limiting value of sums to estimate by how much the diastolic blood pressure changed from 8 A.M. to 8 P.M.

f. Write the definite integral notation for your answer to part e.

Discussing Concepts

35. Explain how area, accumulated change, and the definite integral are related and how they differ.

36. Why is it important to know whether, and if so where, a function has horizontal-axis intercepts before using a definite integral (limit of sums) to determine the area of the region(s) bounded by the function and the horizontal axis?

5.2 Accumulation Functions

In the previous section, we saw that when we have a rate-of-change function for a certain quantity, we approximate the accumulation of change in that quantity between two values of the input variable using the area between the rate-of-change curve and the horizontal axis. Area approximation methods are valuable, but in some situations it would be helpful to have a formula that would answer the question "What was the accumulated change in the quantity from a to t for any value of t?"

For instance, it is important for hydrogeologists studying a watershed to know how much water flowed through a river since a specific starting time. Typically, data on the rate of flow are gathered and used to create a flow rate model from which the accumulation of flow can be calculated.

EXAMPLE 1   *Estimating Accumulated Change*

Rising River   The flow rate past a sensor in the west fork of the Carson River in Nevada is measured periodically. Suppose the flow rates for a 28-hour period beginning at 12 A.M. Wednesday on a spring night can be modeled by the equation

$$f(t) = 0.018t^2 - 0.42t + 5.13 \text{ million cubic feet per hour}$$

where t is the number of hours after 12 A.M. Figure 5.24 shows a graph for the 28 hours between 12 A.M. Wednesday and 4 A.M. Thursday. A heavy rain began falling around 6 A.M. on Wednesday morning. Estimate to the nearest 10,000 cubic feet the amount of water that flowed past the sensor from 12 A.M. Wednesday until 4 A.M. Thursday. Make the estimate at 4-hour intervals.

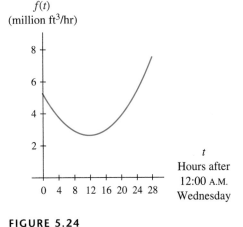

$f(t)$
(million ft³/hr)

t
Hours after
12:00 A.M.
Wednesday

FIGURE 5.24

Solution

The amount of water that flowed through the Carson River from 12 A.M. Wednesday ($t = 0$) and some ending time ($t = b$) can be estimated by the area between the graph of f and the horizontal axis from $t = 0$ to $t = b$. Table 5.10 shows the results of limits of sums for the various ending times.

TABLE 5.10

Ending time (input)	Area* approximation (output)	Ending time (input)	Area* approximation (output)
12 A.M. ($t = 0$)	$\int_0^0 f(t)dt \approx 0$	4 P.M. ($t = 16$)	$\int_0^{16} f(t)dt \approx 52.89$
4 A.M. ($t = 4$)	$\int_0^4 f(t)dt \approx 17.54$	8 P.M. ($t = 20$)	$\int_0^{20} f(t)dt \approx 66.6$
8 A.M. ($t = 8$)	$\int_0^8 f(t)dt \approx 30.67$	12 A.M. ($t = 24$)	$\int_0^{24} f(t)dt \approx 85.10$
12 P.M. ($t = 12$)	$\int_0^{12} f(t)dt \approx 41.69$	4 A.M. ($t = 28$)	$\int_0^{28} f(t)dt \approx 110.71$

*All area units are million cubic feet.

We see in Table 5.10 that changes in ending times lead to changes in the accumulation of area. As long as the starting time stays constant at some number a, we can represent the accumulated change in f from a to a variable ending time x as $\int_a^x f(t)dt$. This integral is called the **accumulation function of f from a to x.**

Accumulation Function

The accumulation function of a function f, denoted by $A(x) = \int_a^x f(t)dt$, gives the accumulation of the area between the horizontal axis and the graph of f from a to x.

Using Limits of Sums to Sketch Accumulation Graphs

When a function is continuous and bounded over a specific interval, the corresponding accumulation function will also be continuous over that same interval. For the rising river example, we can sketch an accumulation graph using the values in Table 5.10. A scatter plot of the area accumulations and a smooth curve representing river flow is given in Figure 5.25.

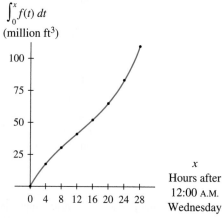

FIGURE 5.25

Using Estimated Areas to Sketch Accumulation Graphs

In Example 1, we sketched a graph of the accumulation function based on accumulated change, using the limits of sums. We were able to estimate the limits of sums because we had an equation for the flow rates past the sensor. If we have a graph of a rate-of-change function, we can sketch an accumulation function by estimating the signed areas trapped between the rate-of-change function and the horizontal axis. We use a graph of $f(t)$ sketched on a grid (see Figure 5.26).

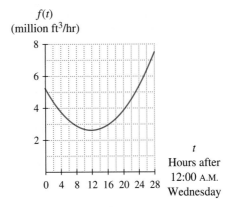

FIGURE 5.26

We begin by finding the area of a single box of the grid. The height of one box is 1 million cubic feet per hour. The width of one box is 2 hours. Thus the area of one box is (2 hours) 1 million cubic feet per hour = 2 million cubic feet.

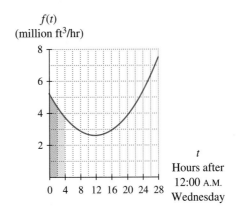

FIGURE 5.27

The area shaded under the curve from 0 to 2 is approximately $4\frac{3}{4}$ boxes or 9.5 million cubic feet. (See Figure 5.27.) The area shaded under the curve from 2 to 4 is approximately $4\frac{1}{4}$ boxes or 8.5 million cubic feet. Adding this to the area from 0 to 2, we find the area under the curve from 0 to 4 to be approximately 18 million cubic feet.

As we repeat this process, we approximate the area under the curve from 4 to 6 to be $3\frac{1}{2}$ boxes or 7 million cubic feet. Adding this to the area from 0 to 4, we estimate that the accumulated area from 0 to 6 is approximately 25 million cubic feet. There are approximately 3 boxes or 6 million cubic feet of area under the curve from 6 to 8, so the accumulated area from 0 to 8 is approximately 31 million cubic feet. See Figure 5.28a. We repeat this process until we have found the accumulated area for each successive interval. The results of our accumulation are given in Table 5.11.

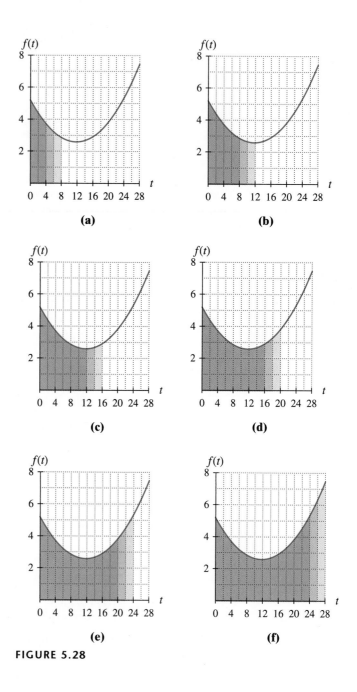

FIGURE 5.28

TABLE 5.11

Interval a to b	Number of boxes	Area* approximation	Accumulated area* from 0 to b
0 to 2	4.75	9.5	9.5
2 to 4	4.25	8.5	18.0
4 to 6	3.5	7.0	25.0
6 to 8	3.0	6.0	31.0
8 to 10	2.75	5.5	36.5
10 to 12	2.6	5.2	41.7
12 to 14	2.6	5.2	46.9
14 to 16	2.75	5.5	52.4
16 to 18	3.25	6.5	58.9
18 to 20	3.5	7.0	65.9
20 to 22	4.25	8.5	74.4
22 to 24	5.0	10.0	84.4
24 to 26	6.0	12.0	96.4
26 to 28	7.0	14.0	110.4

*Area approximations are measured in million cubic feet.

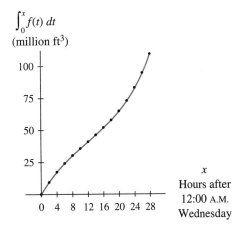

FIGURE 5.29

The accumulated change found in Example 1 is 110.71 million cubic feet, which is close to the estimated accumulation summarized in Table 5.11. Compare Figure 5.29 with Figure 5.25. Carefully counting areas using a grid is another method of drawing an accumulation function.

When a portion of a graph is negative, the area below the horizontal axis indicates a decrease in the accumulation. Example 2 illustrates how to sketch accumulation graphs for graphs that go below the horizontal axis.

EXAMPLE 2   *Using Estimated Grid Areas to Sketch Accumulation Functions*

Consider the graph of f shown in Figure 5.30.

a. Construct a table of accumulation function values for $x = -3, -2.5, \ldots, 2.5, 3$.

b. Sketch a scatter plot and continuous graph of the accumulation function $A(x) = \int_{-3}^{x} f(t)dt$.

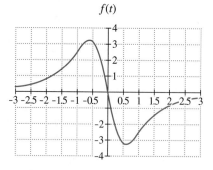

FIGURE 5.30

Solution

a. Begin estimating accumulated area from the far left side of the graph by counting the boxes between the graph of f and the horizontal axis from -3 to x. You should obtain values similar to those in the second and six throws of Table 5.12. Note that the boxes have height 1 unit and width 0.5 unit; thus the area of each box is $(1)(0.5) = 0.5$ unit^2. The fourth and eighth rows of Table 5.12 is the number of boxes multiplied by 0.5 to obtain the accumulated area value.

For values of x greater than zero, the boxes lie below the horizontal axis. The areas of these boxes should be subtracted from the accumulated area of boxes above the horizontal axis in order to obtain the net number of accumulated boxes. Because the number of boxes from -3 to 0 is the same as the number of boxes from 0 to 3, the net result of accumulated area from -3 to 3 is zero.

TABLE 5.12

Right endpoint	−3	−2.5	−2	−1.5	−1	−0.5	0
Additional number of boxes	0	0.5	0.5	1	2	3	2
Additional accumulated value	0	0.25	0.25	0.5	1	1.5	1
Total accumulated value	0	0.25	0.50	1.0	2	3.5	4.5
Right endpoint	0.5	1	1.5	2	2.5	3	
Additional number of boxes	2	3	2	1	0.5	0.5	
Additional accumulated value	−1.0	−1.5	−1	−0.5	−0.25	−0.25	
Total accumulated value	3.5	2.0	1.0	0.5	0.25	0	

b. A scatter plot and continuous graph for $A(x) = \int_{-3}^{x} f(t)dt$ are shown in Figure 5.31.

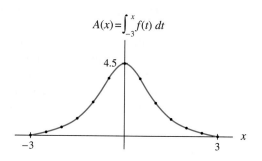

$$A(x) = \int_{-3}^{x} f(t)\, dt$$

FIGURE 5.31

Sketching Accumulation Graphs

Given the graph of a function, consider accumulation beginning at the far left, regardless of the location of the specified starting point. Sketch the accumulation graph starting at the far left, and then shift the graph up or down so that the output value at the specified starting point is zero.

EXAMPLE 3 *Sketching Accumulation Functions with Different Starting Points*

Consider again the function graph and accumulation graph from Example 2, redrawn here as Figures 5.32 and 5.33.

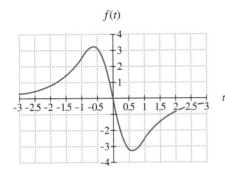

FIGURE 5.32   **FIGURE 5.33**

Use the graph in Figure 5.33 to sketch a graph of the accumulation function

$$B(x) = \int_0^x f(t)\,dt.$$

Solution

In order to sketch the accumulation graph with 0 as the starting point, we vertically shift the graph in Figure 5.33 so that the function value at the starting point is zero. In this example, we shift the graph down 4.5 units so that the peak of the graph is the point $(0, 0)$. (See Figure 5.34.)

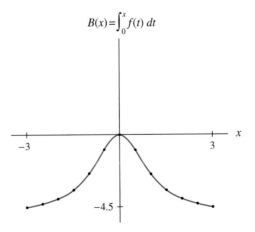

FIGURE 5.34

By now, you should have a good idea of what we mean by an accumulation function. The following information gives a procedure for sketching an accumulation function graph without making use of a grid.

Sketching Accumulation Functions

To sketch an accumulation function with starting value *a* given a graph of *f*,

Step 1: Choose as an initial starting value the input value at the left end of the horizontal axis shown in the graph.

Step 2: Sketch the accumulation of area from the far left such that

- Regions between the graph of *f* and the horizontal axis that lie above the axis contribute positive accumulation equal to the area of the region.
- Regions that lie beneath the horizontal axis contribute negative accumulation equal to the negative of the area of the region.
- Relative extrema on the accumulation graph occur at the same input values as the corresponding zeros on the rate-of-change graph.
- Inflection points on the accumulation graph occur at the same input values as the relative extrema on the rate-of-change graph.

Step 3: Vertically shift the accumulation graph in Step 2 so that the graph is zero at the actual starting value *a*.

In order to further refine the sketch of the graph of an accumulation function, it is necessary to understand how rapidly the accumulated area grows or declines.

Concavity and Accumulation

An important tool for accurately sketching accumulation function graphs is an understanding of how the increasing or decreasing nature of the rate-of-change function (as distinguished from the sign of the rate-of-change function) affects the shape of the associated accumulation function.

The circle in Figure 5.35 may be used as a quick indicator of the general shape that an accumulation function will take:

- An accumulation function showing slower increase will be shaped a bit like the upper-left arc of a circle. The accumulation function will be increasing and concave down.
- An accumulation function showing slower decrease will be shaped a bit like the lower-left arc of a circle. The accumulation function will be decreasing and concave up.
- An accumulation function showing faster decrease will be shaped a bit like the upper-right arc of a circle. The accumulation function will be decreasing and concave down.
- An accumulation function showing faster increase will be shaped a bit like the lower-right arc of a circle. The accumulation function will be increasing and concave up.

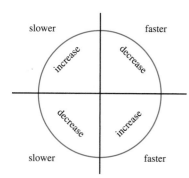

General shape of an accumulation function

FIGURE 5.35

Do not confuse the general shape of the accumulation function as shown by the circle diagram as an indication of whether the accumulation function is positive or negative over a given interval.

Example 4 demonstrates how the graph of a rate-of-change function can be analyzed to sketch the graph of an accumulation function.

EXAMPLE 4   *Sketching a General Accumulation Function Graph*

Consider the graph of y (a rate-of-change function) shown in Figure 5.36.

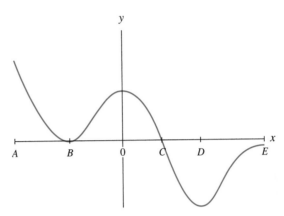

FIGURE 5.36

a.   Begin by identifying the x-intervals on which the accumulation function will be positive and those on which the accumulation function will be negative. The positive intervals on the rate-of-change function correspond to the intervals on the accumulation function where the accumulation function will be increasing. Similarly, the negative intervals on the rate-of-change function correspond to the intervals on the accumulation function where the accumulation function will be decreasing. Identify any relative extremes or x-intercepts on the rate-of-change graph. Classify each of these points as a relative maximum, a relative minimum, or an inflection point on the accumulation function.

b.   Sketch the accumulation function graph with $x = A$ as the starting point.

c.   Sketch the accumulation function graph with $x = 0$ as the starting point.

Solution

a.   The accumulation function will be increasing over (A, C) and decreasing over (C, E). There is a relative maximum on the rate-of-change graph at $x = 0$ so there is an inflection point on the accumulation function at $x = 0$. There is a relative minimum on the rate-of-change graph at $x = D$ so there is another inflection point on the accumulation function at $x = D$. There is a second relative minimum at $x = B$, so there is a third inflection point on the accumulation function at the point $x = B$. The slope of the accumulation graph at the point $x = B$ will be 0.

There is an x-intercept at the point $x = C$. The accumulation function will reach a relative maximum value at $x = C$.

FIGURE 5.37

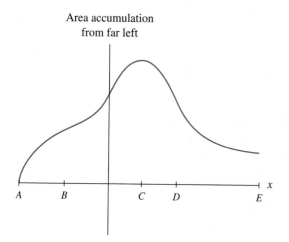

FIGURE 5.38

b. Consider the shape of the initial segment. We know that the function is increasing because the rate-of-change function is positive, but we see that the increase is slowing from the point $x = A$ to $x = B$. (See Figure 5.37.) Begin by drawing a concave-down shape to indicate that the rate of change of the accumulation function is slowing.

Note that the rate-of-change function is smooth and continuous. This means that the accumulation function will also be smooth and continuous. Draw your accumulation graph so that you can keep it smooth and continuous while incorporating inflection points (at points $x = B$, $x = 0$, and $x = D$) and a relative maximum at $x = C$. Use the connections to the shape of the accumulation function given in Figure 5.35.

A graph illustrating these properties is shown in Figure 5.38.

c. To obtain the accumulation function graph with zero as the starting point, shift the graph down so that it passes through $(0, 0)$. See Figure 5.39.

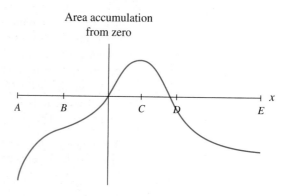

FIGURE 5.39

Recovering a Function

Recovering a function is the phrase we use for the process of beginning with a rate-of-change function for a quantity and obtaining a function for the quantity. An important part of recovering a quantity function from its rate of change is recovering the units of the quantity function from the units of its rate of change. We can recover the units of the amount function by recalling that the rate of change of a function is a slope of a tangent line. The units on slope are $\frac{\text{output units}}{\text{input units}}$, so the units of a rate-of-change function are the output units (of its quantity function) divided by the input units (of its quantity function). From the geometric viewpoint of area, we know that the output units of the quantity function are

$$(\text{Rate-of-change function units}) \cdot (\text{input units of quantity function})$$

$$= \left(\frac{\text{output units of quantity function}}{\text{input units of quantity function}} \right) \cdot (\text{input units of quantity function})$$

Suppose $\frac{dM}{dt}$ milliliters per hour is the rate-of-change function of the amount of insulin in a patient's body t hours after an injection. In the case of $\frac{dM}{dt}$, the units milliliters per hour can be rewritten as $\frac{\text{milliliters}}{\text{hour}}$. Now we can see that the output units of M are milliliters and the input units are hours. Figure 5.40 shows input/output diagrams for $\frac{dM}{dt}$ and M. When we recover the quantity function M, the output units will be milliliters and the input units will be hours.

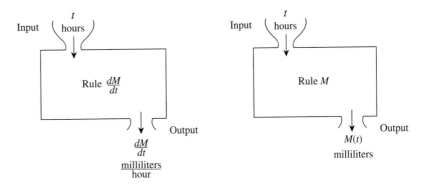

FIGURE 5.40

Occasionally, units of a rate of change are expressed in terms of a squared unit. For example, acceleration is often expressed in feet per second squared. Suppose $A(t)$ is acceleration of a vehicle in feet per second squared, where t is the number of seconds since the vehicle began accelerating. Again, this is obviously the rate of change of some function. In fact, it is the rate of change of velocity. However, the input and output units of that velocity function may not be immediately apparent because of the use of the word *squared*. Rewrite feet per second squared as

$$\frac{\text{feet}}{(\text{second})^2} = \frac{\text{feet}}{(\text{second})(\text{second})} = \frac{\text{feet}}{\text{second}} \div (\text{second})$$

$$= (\text{feet per second}) \text{ per second}$$

The output units of the velocity function are now identifiable as feet per second. Input/output diagrams for these functions are shown in Figure 5.41.

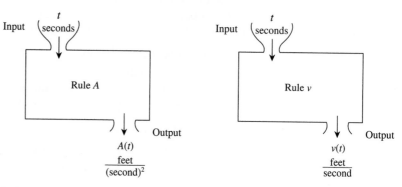

FIGURE 5.41

We have seen how to sketch an accumulated quantity function from a graph of its rate-of-change function and how to recover the quantity units from rate-of-change units. In the next section, we will see that the Fundamental Theorem of Calculus implies that we have a powerful algebraic tool for recovering the accumulated quantity formula from its rate-of-change formula.

5.2 Concept Inventory

- Accumulation and area
- Accumulation functions
- Sketching accumulation graphs
- Interpreting accumulation

5.2 Activities

Applying Concepts

1. **Velocity**   Refer to the velocity graph.

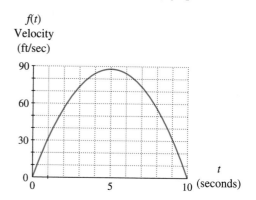

a. Sketch the accumulation function with 5 seconds as the starting point.

b. Give the mathematical notation for the function you sketched in part *a*.

c. In the context of the moving vehicle, what is the interpretation of the output values of the function in part *a*?

2. **Plant Growth**   Refer to the plant growth rate function graph.

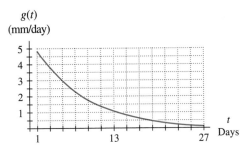

g(t)
(mm/day)

a. Sketch the accumulation function with day 13 as the starting point.

b. Give the mathematical notation for the function you sketched in part *a*.

c. In the context of plant growth, what is the interpretation of the output values of the accumulation function in part *a*?

3. **Stock Value**   Consider the graph of the rate of change in the price of a certain technology stock during the first 55 trading days of 2003.

a. What does the area of the region between the graph and the horizontal axis between days 0 and 18 represent?

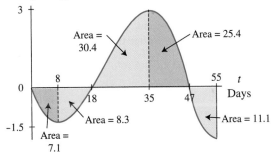

r(t)
Rate of change in price
(dollars per day)

Figure for Activities 3 and 4

b. What does the area of the region between the graph and the horizontal axis between days 18 and 47 represent?

c. Was the stock price higher or lower on day 47 than it was on day 0? How much higher or lower?

d. Was the stock price higher or lower on day 55 than it was on day 47? How much higher or lower?

e. Using the information presented in the graph, fill in the accumulation function values in the accompanying table.

x	0	8	18	35	47	55
$\int_0^x r(t)\,dt$						

f. Graph the function $R(x) = \int_0^x r(t)\,dt$ for values of *x* between 0 and 55, labeling the vertical axis as accurately as possible.

g. If the stock price was $127 on day 0, what was the price on day 55?

4. **Stock Value**   Consider the graph of the rate of change in the price of a certain technology stock during the first 55 trading days of 2003.

a. Label each of the shaded areas as representing positive or negative change in price. Also label each region as describing faster and faster or slower and slower change in stock price.

b. On the basis of your answers to part *a*, sketch a graph of the accumulation function

$$P(x) = \int_{18}^x r(t)\,dt$$

c. Sketch a graph of the accumulation function

$$Q(x) = \int_{35}^x r(t)\,dt$$

d. What differences do you notice among the three accumulation functions in part *f* of Activity 3 and parts *b* and *c* of this activity?

5. **Subscribers**   The accompanying graph shows the rate of change of the number of subscribers to an Internet service provider during its first year of business.

a. According to the graph, did the number of subscribers ever decline during the first year?

Subscribers per day

b. What is the significance of the peak in the rate-of-change graph at 20 weeks?

c. If $n(x)$ is the number of subscribers per day at the end of the xth day of the year, what does the function $N(t) = \int_{140}^{t} n(x)\,dx$ describe?

d. How many subscribers does each box in the figure represent?

e. Use the grid and graph in the figure to estimate the accumulation function values in the accompanying table.

Week	t (days)	$\int_0^t n(x)\,dx$	Week	t (days)	$\int_0^t n(x)\,dx$
4	28			28	196
8	56			36	252
12	84			44	308
16	112			52	364
20	140				

f. Sketch a graph of the accumulation function with 140 days as the starting value.

6. Profit   The graph shows the rate of change of profit for a new business during its first year. The input is the number of weeks since the business opened, and the output units are thousands of dollars per week.

a. What does the area of each box in the grid represent?

b. What is the interpretation, in context, of the accumulation function $P(x) = \int_0^x p(t)\,dt$?

c. Count boxes to estimate accumulation function values from 0 to x for the values of x given in the accompanying table.

x	Accumulation function value	x	Accumulation function value
0		28	
4		32	
8		36	
12		40	
16		44	
20		48	
24		52	

d. Use the data in part c to sketch an accurate graph of the accumulation function $P(x) = \int_0^x p(t)\,dt$. Label units and values on the horizontal and vertical axes.

7. Rainfall   The graph of $r(t)$ represents the rate of change of rainfall in Florida during a severe thunderstorm t hours after the rain began falling.

Draw a graph of the total amount of rain that fell during this storm, using the following facts:

- The rain started falling at noon and did not stop until 6 P.M.

- Three inches of rain fell between noon and 3 P.M.

- The total amount of rain that fell during the storm was 5.5 inches.

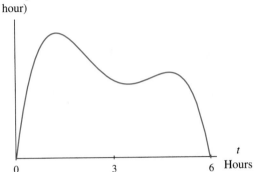

r(t)
(inches per hour)

0   3   6   Hours

8. Population   The Brazilian government has established a program to protect a certain species of endangered bird that lives in the Amazon rain forest. The program is to be phased out gradually by the year 2020. An environmental group believes that the government's program is destined to fail and has projected that the rate of change in the bird population between 2000 and 2050 will be as shown in the figure.

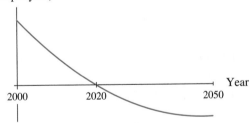

Rate of change
(birds per year)

2000   2020   2050   Year

Draw a graph of the bird population between 2000 and 2050, using the following:

- At the beginning of 2000 there were 1.3 million birds in existence.
- The species will be extinct by 2050.

In Activities 9 through 14, sketch the indicated accumulation function graphs.

9. a. $\int_A^x f(t)\,dt$

  b. $\int_B^x f(t)\,dt$

f(t)

B   A

10. a. $\int_0^x f(t)\,dt$

  b. $\int_A^x f(t)\,dt$

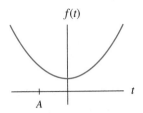

f(t)

A

11. a. $\int_0^x f(t)\,dt$

  b. $\int_A^x f(t)\,dt$

  c. $\int_B^x f(t)\,dt$

f(t)

A   B

12. $\int_0^x f(t)\,dt$

f(t)

13. $\int_0^x f(t)\,dt$

f(t)

14. $\int_A^x f(t)\,dt$

f(t)

A

In each of Activities 15 through 18, a graph is given. Identify, from graphs a through f, the derivative graph and the accumulation graph (with 0 as the starting point) of the given graph. Graphs a through f may be used more than once.

15.

A   B   C

16.

A   B

17.

18.

a.

b.

c.

d.

e.

f.

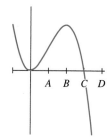

In each of Activities 19 and 20, a table of selected values for a function is given. Also shown are tables of values for the derivative and the accumulation function with 0 as the starting point. Determine which table contains values of the derivative and which contains values of the accumulation function. Justify your choice.

19.

t	f(t)	Input	Output	Input	Output
0	4	0	0	0	0
1	3	1	−2	1	3.667
2	0	2	−4	2	5.333
3	−5	3	−6	3	3
4	−12	4	−8	4	−5.333

20.

m	p(m)	Input	Output	Input	Output
0	0	0	0	0	0
1	−8	1	−12	1	−3
2	−16	2	0	2	−16
3	0	3	36	3	−27
4	64	4	96	4	0
5	200	5	180	5	125

For each of the rates of change in Activities 21 through 24:

   a. Write the units of the rate of change as a fraction.

   b. Draw an input/output diagram for the recovered function.

   c. Interpret the recovered function in a sentence.

21. When m thousand dollars is being spent on advertising, the annual revenue of a corporation is changing by $\frac{dR}{dm}$ million dollars per thousand dollars spent on advertising.

22. The percentage of households with washing machines was changing by $\frac{dW}{dt}$ percentage points per year, where t is the number of years since 1950.

23. The concentration of a drug in the bloodstream of a patient is changing by $\frac{dc}{dh}$ milligrams per liter per hour h hours after the drug was given.

24. The level of production at a tire manufacturer h hours after production began is increasing by $P'(h)$ tires per hour squared.

Discussing Concepts

25. Consider a rate-of-change graph that is increasing but negative over an interval. Explain why the accumulation graph decreases over this interval.

26. What behavior in a rate-of-change graph causes the following to occur in the accumulation graph: a minimum? a maximum? an inflection point? Explain.

5.3   The Fundamental Theorem

In Section 5.2 we graphed accumulation functions from graphs of rate-of-change functions. We saw that we could use numerical estimates of definite integrals to help us sketch accumulation graphs. In this section, we develop some algebraic tools to help us write formulas for accumulation functions.

The Slope Graph of an Accumulation Graph

We began Section 5.2 with the function shown here in Figure 5.42a and drew the accumulation function graph shown in Figure 5.42b.

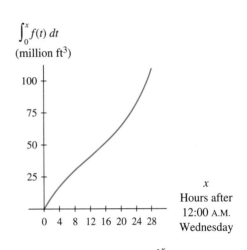

(a) Function $f(t)$

(b) Accumulation function $\int_0^x f(t)\, dt$

FIGURE 5.42

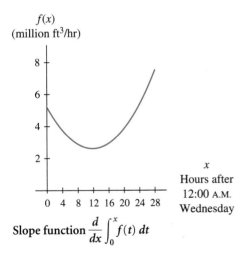

Slope function $\dfrac{d}{dx}\displaystyle\int_0^x f(t)\, dt$

FIGURE 5.43

Now we sketch the slope graph (derivative graph) of the accumulation function in Figure 5.42b. Note that the slopes are positive everywhere but become increasingly small as t goes from 0 to near 12. There appears to be a point of least slope near $t \approx 12$, after which the slopes increase. The slope graph appears in Figure 5.43. The slope graph is exactly the graph with which we began in Figure 5.42a (with the input variable labeled x instead of t).

In Examples 2 and 3 in Section 5.2, we began with the graph in Figure 5.44a and sketched the accumulation function shown in Figure 5.44b.

Again, let us sketch the slope graph of the accumulation function. To the left of zero, the graph has positive slopes. The slopes are near zero to the far left, and the graph becomes steeper until $-B$. Between $-B$ and 0, the slopes are still positive but are approaching 0 as the accumulation function

(a) Function $f(t)$

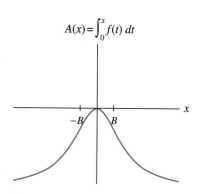

(b) Accumulation function $\displaystyle\int_0^x f(t)\, dt$

FIGURE 5.44

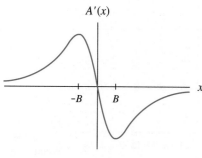

Slope function $\displaystyle\frac{d}{dx}\int_0^x f(t)\, dt$

FIGURE 5.45

approaches its maximum. At $x = 0$, the slope is zero. To the right of $x = 0$, the slopes are negative. They become more and more negative until B. To the right of B, the slopes are still negative but are getting closer and closer to zero as the graph levels off. The slope graph is shown in Figure 5.45. Again, this is exactly the graph with which we began in Figure 5.44a.

You may be noticing that if we begin with a function f with input t, graph or find a formula for the accumulation function $A(x) = \displaystyle\int_a^x f(t)\,dt$, and then take the derivative or draw the slope graph, we get f, the function with which we began, only in terms of x rather than t.

In order to explore this connection between accumulation functions and derivatives, consider the following argument:

Let A be the accumulation function of f from a to x. The graph in Figure 5.46a shows the function f and the area representing the accumulation function value from a to x. Figure 5.46b shows the region whose area is the accumulation value from a to $x + h$.

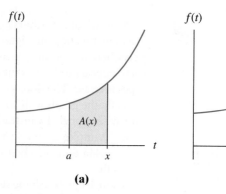

FIGURE 5.46

Next, consider the difference between the two areas. The small region with this area is shown in Figure 5.47a.

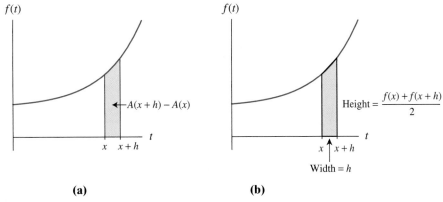

FIGURE 5.47

We can approximate the area of this region by using a trapezoid. Recall that the height of a trapezoid constructed over an interval is the average of the function value at the two endpoints. Figure 5.47b shows this trapezoid and its height and width.

The true area of the shaded region in Figure 5.47a is $A(x + h) - A(x)$, and it can be approximated by the area of the trapezoid. Thus we have

$$A(x + h) - A(x) \approx \left[\frac{f(x) + f(x + h)}{2} \right] h$$

We now divide each side of the expression by h. The reason for this division will be evident later.

$$\frac{A(x + h) - A(x)}{h} \approx \frac{f(x) + f(x + h)}{2}$$

Consider what happens as h becomes smaller and smaller. In other words, what happens when we take the limit of the above expression as h approaches zero?

$$\lim_{h \to 0} \frac{A(x + h) - A(x)}{h} \approx \lim_{h \to 0} \frac{f(x) + f(x + h)}{2}$$

You should recognize the term on the left as $\frac{dA}{dx}$, the derivative of A. The term on the right approaches $f(x)$ as h approaches 0, because $f(x + h)$ gets closer and closer to $f(x)$, so $\frac{f(x) + f(x)}{2} = \frac{2f(x)}{2} = f(x)$. Thus we have

$$\frac{dA}{dx} \approx f(x)$$

In fact, we can replace the approximation with an equality (although a discussion of why this is the case is beyond the scope of this book):

$$\frac{dA}{dx} = f(x)$$

This expression says that the derivative of the accumulation function is the original function. This is an important result because it links accumulation functions to derivatives. The importance of this connection is reflected in the name given the relation: the **Fundamental Theorem of Calculus.**

The Fundamental Theorem of Calculus

For any continuous function f with input t, the derivative of an accumulation function of f is the function f in terms of x. In symbols, we write

$$\frac{d}{dx}\int_a^x f(t)dt = f(x)$$

We can infer from the Fundamental Theorem that to find an accumulation formula, we need only reverse the process of finding a derivative. For this reason, the accumulation function $F(x) = \int_a^x f(t)dt$ is called an **antiderivative** of the function f.

Antiderivative

Let f be a function of x. A function F is called an antiderivative of f if $F'(x) = f(x)$; that is, the derivative of F is f.

Our motivation for developing accumulation functions (antiderivatives) is not only to have a formula for accumulated change but also (and more important) to develop a function for a quantity if we know a function for that quantity's rate of change.

Antiderivative Formulas

Given a function, how do we find an antiderivative? As we have seen, we must reverse the process of differentiation. Antidifferentiation starts with the known derivative and finds the unknown function. For example, consider the constant function $f(x) = 3$. To find an antiderivative of f, we need to find a function of x whose derivative is 3. One such function is $F(x) = 3x$. Other functions whose derivatives are 3 include $F(x) = 3x + 7$ and $F(x) = 3x - 24.9$.

In fact, having found one antiderivative F for a given function f, we can obtain infinitely many antiderivatives for that function by adding an arbitrary constant C to F. Thus we call $y = F(x) + C$ the **general antiderivative of f**. We use the notation

$$\int f(x)dx = F(x) + C$$

for the general antiderivative. The general antiderivative is a group of infinitely many functions. (A particular accumulation function is one specific function from that group.) Note that the integral sign has no upper and lower limits for general antiderivative notation. The dx in this notation is to remind us that we are finding the general antiderivative with respect to x, so our antiderivative formula will be in terms of x. For example, we say that the general antiderivative for $f(x) = 3$ is $F(x) = 3x + C$, and we write $\int 3dx = 3x + C$.

An antiderivative (accumulation formula) of any constant function will be a line because lines have constant derivatives. We can write this general rule as

$$\int kdx = kx + C$$

where k and C are any constants.

Now consider finding the general antiderivative of $f(x) = 2x$. We are seeking a function whose derivative is $2x$. The function is $F(x) = x^2 + C$, and we write

$$\int 2x \, dx = x^2 + C$$

It is more difficult to reverse the derivative process for $f(x) = x^2$. Recall that the power rule for derivatives $\left[\frac{d}{dx}(x^n) = nx^{n-1}\right]$ instructs us to

- Multiply by the power.
- Subtract 1 from the power to get the new power.

To reverse the process for antiderivatives, we
- *Add* 1 to the power to get the new power.
- *Divide* by that new power.

This formula is known as the **Simple Power Rule** for antiderivatives.

Simple Power Rule for Antiderivatives

$$\int x^n dx = \frac{x^{n+1}}{n+1} + C \text{ for any } n \neq -1$$

This rule requires that $n \neq -1$, because otherwise, we would be dividing by zero.

In the case of $f(x) = x^2$, where $n = 2$, the general antiderivative is

$$\int x^2 dx = \frac{x^3}{3} + C$$

EXAMPLE 1   *Using the Simple Power Rule to Find Antiderivatives*

Find the following general antiderivatives and their appropriate units.

a. $\int -7dx$ degrees per hour, where x is in hours

b. $\int h^{0.5} dh$ parts per million per day, where h is in days

Solution

a. $\int -7dx = -7x + C$ degrees

b. $\int h^{0.5} dh = \frac{h^{1.5}}{1.5} + C$ parts per million   ●

Recall the Constant Multiplier Rule for derivatives:

If $g(x) = kf(x)$, then $g'(x) = kf'(x)$, where k is a constant.

A similar rule applies for antiderivatives:

Constant Multiplier Rule for Antiderivatives

$$\int kf(x)dx = k\int f(x)dx$$

Thus, $\int 12x^6dx = 12\int x^6dx = 12\left(\dfrac{x^7}{7}\right) + C = \dfrac{12x^7}{7} + C.$

Another property of antiderivatives is the Sum Rule.

Sum Rule

$$\int [f(x) \pm g(x)]dx = \int f(x)dx \pm \int g(x)dx$$

The Sum Rule lets us find an antiderivative for a sum (or difference) of functions by operating on each function independently. For example,

$$\int (7x^3 + x)dx = \int 7x^3dx + \int xdx$$

$$= \left(\dfrac{7x^4}{4} + C_1\right) + \left(\dfrac{x^2}{2} + C_2\right)$$

$$= \dfrac{7x^4}{4} + \dfrac{x^2}{2} + C \quad \text{(Combine } C_1 \text{ and } C_2 \text{ into one constant } C.)$$

Repeated applications of the Simple Power Rule, the Constant Multiplier Rule, and the Sum Rule enable us to find an antiderivative of any polynomial function. We now have the tools we need to begin with a simple polynomial rate-of-change function for a quantity and recover an amount function for that quantity.

EXAMPLE 2   *Using Given Information to Find an Antiderivative*

Birth Rate An African country has an increasing population but a declining birth rate, a situation that results in the number of babies born each year increasing but at a slower rate. The rate of change in the number of babies born each year is given by

$$b(t) = 87,000 - 1600t \text{ births per year}$$

t years from the end of this year. Also, the number of babies born in the current year is 1,185,800.

a. Find a function describing the number of births each year t years from now.

b. Use the function in part a to estimate the number of babies that will be born next year.

Solution

a. A function B describing the number of births each year is found as

$$B(t) = \int b(t)dt = 87{,}000t - \frac{1600}{2}t^2 + C = 87{,}000t - 800t^2 + C \text{ births}$$

t years from now.

We also know that $B(0) = 1{,}185{,}800$, so $1{,}185{,}800 = 87{,}000 \cdot (0) - 800 \cdot (0^2) + C$, which gives $C = 1{,}185{,}800$. Thus we have

$$B(t) = 87{,}000t - 800t^2 + 1{,}185{,}800 \text{ births each year}$$

t years from now.

b. The number of babies born next year is estimated as $B(1) = 1{,}272{,}000$ babies. ●

We have just presented and applied three antiderivative rules: the Simple Power Rule, the Constant Multiplier Rule, and the Sum Rule. Now let us look at four more rules for finding antiderivatives.

Refer to the Simple Power Rule, and note that it does not apply for $n = -1$. The case where $n = -1$ is special. This results in the antiderivative $\int x^{-1}dx = \int \frac{1}{x}dx$. Recall that $\frac{d}{dx}(\ln x) = \frac{1}{x}$. This is valid only for $x > 0$, because $\ln x$ is not defined for $x \le 0$. When we are not certain that $x > 0$, we use $\ln|x|$.

Natural Log Rule

$$\int \frac{1}{x}dx = \ln|x| + C$$

The two final antiderivative formulas that we consider are for exponential functions. Recall that the derivative of $f(x) = e^x$ is e^x. Similarly, the general antiderivative of $f(x) = e^x$ is also e^x plus a constant.

---

e^x Rule

$$\int e^x dx = e^x + C$$

The other exponential function that we have encountered is $f(x) = b^x$. Its derivative was found by multiplying b^x by $\ln b$. To find the general antiderivative, we divide b^x by $\ln b$ and add a constant:

Exponential Rule

$$\int b^x dx = \frac{b^x}{\ln b} + C$$

Note that the e^x Rule is a special case of this Exponential Rule with $b = e$. If we use the Exponential Rule to find the antiderivative of e^x, we have $\int e^x dx = \frac{e^x}{\ln e} = e^x$ because $\ln e = 1$.

Because we often encounter functions of the form $f(x) = e^{ax}$, it is helpful to know this function's derivative formula. Recall that the Chain Rule for derivatives applied to $f(x) = e^{ax}$ gives $f'(x) = ae^{ax}$. Thus, to reverse the derivative process, we leave the e^{ax}-term and divide, rather than multiply, by a.

---

e^{ax} Rule

$$\int e^{ax} dx = \frac{1}{a} e^{ax} + C \quad \text{for any } a \neq 0$$

In summary, we now have the following antiderivative formulas, where k, n, b, and a are constants.

Antiderivative Formulas

	Function: f	General antiderivative: $\int f(x)dx$
Constant Rule	k	$kx + C$
Simple Power Rule	$x^n, n \neq -1$	$\left(\frac{1}{n+1}\right)x^{n+1} + C$
Natural Log Rule	$\frac{1}{x}$	$\ln |x| + C$
Exponential Rule	$b^x, b > 0$	$\left(\frac{1}{\ln b}\right)b^x + C$
e^x Rule	e^x	$e^x + C$
e^{ax} Rule	$e^{ax}, a \neq 0$	$\frac{1}{a}e^{ax} + C$
Constant Multiplier Rule	$kg(x)$	$k \int g(x)dx$
Sum Rule	$g(x) \pm h(x)$	$\int g(x)dx \pm \int h(x)dx$

EXAMPLE 3 *Using Antiderivative Formulas to Find General Antiderivatives*

Find the following general antiderivatives.

a. $\int \left(3^x - 7e^x + \dfrac{5}{x} \right) dx$ quarts per hour, where x is measured in hours

b. $\int (4\sqrt{x} + 100e^{0.06x} + 0.46) dx$ mpg per mph, where x is measured in mph

Solution

a. $\int \left(3^x - 7e^x + \dfrac{5}{x} \right) dx = \int 3^x dx - 7 \int e^x dx + 5 \int \dfrac{1}{x} dx$

$$= \dfrac{3^x}{\ln 3} - 7e^x + 5 \ln |x| + C \text{ quarts}$$

b. We must first rewrite $\sqrt{x}$ as $x^{1/2}$ and then apply the appropriate rules:

$$\int \left(4\sqrt{x} + 100e^{0.06x} + 0.46 \right) dx = \int [4x^{1/2} + 100e^{0.06x} + 0.46] dx$$

$$= 4 \int x^{1/2} dx + 100 \int e^{0.06x} dx + \int 0.46 dx$$

$$= 4 \dfrac{x^{3/2}}{3/2} + 100 \dfrac{e^{0.06x}}{0.06} + 0.46x + C$$

$$= \dfrac{8}{3} x^{3/2} + \dfrac{100}{0.06} e^{0.06x} + 0.46x + C \text{ mpg} \quad \bullet$$

Specific Antiderivatives

We have seen that any function has infinitely many antiderivatives, each differing by a constant. When we seek an antiderivative with a particular constant, the resulting function is a **specific antiderivative.** An example of a specific antiderivative is the function in Example 2 for the number of births in an African country. Using the information that in the current year the number of births is 1,185,800, we were able to solve for the constant to obtain the specific antiderivative $B(t) = 87,000t - 800t^2 + 1,185,800$ births each year t years from now.

In general, to find a specific antiderivative, you must be given additional information about the output quantity that the antiderivative describes. After finding a general antiderivative, you simply substitute the given input and corresponding output into the general antiderivative and solve for the constant. Then you replace the constant in the general antiderivative formula with the value you found to obtain the specific antiderivative. Example 4 illustrates this process.

EXAMPLE 4 *Finding a Specific Antiderivative*

Marginal Cost Suppose that a manufacturer of small toaster ovens has collected the data given in Table 5.13, which shows, at various production levels, the approximate cost to produce one more oven. Recall from Section 4.1 that this is marginal cost and can be interpreted as the rate of change of cost.

TABLE 5.13

Production level (ovens per day)	200	300	400	500	600	700
Cost to produce an additional oven	$29	$20	$15	$11	$9	$7

The manufacturer also knows that the total cost to produce 250 ovens is $12,000.

a. Find a model for the marginal cost data.

b. Recover a cost model from the model you found in part *a*.

c. Estimate the cost of producing 500 ovens.

Solution

a. Either a quadratic or an exponential model is a good fit to the data. We choose an exponential model:

$C'(x) = 47.6(0.997^x)$ dollars per oven (*Note:* We have rounded to simplify calculations.)

where x is the number of ovens produced.

b. To recover a model for cost, we need an antiderivative of C' satisfying the known condition that the cost to produce 250 ovens is $12,000. The general antiderivative is

$$C(x) = \frac{47.6(0.997^x)}{\ln 0.997} + K \approx -15,843 \cdot (0.997^x) + K$$

where K is a constant.

Using the fact that $C(250) = \$12,000$, we substitute 250 for x, set the antiderivative equal to 12,000, and solve for K.

$$-15,843(0.997^{250}) + K = 12,000$$
$$-7475 + K \approx 12,000$$
$$K \approx 19,475$$

Thus the specific antiderivative giving the approximate cost of producing x toaster ovens is

$$C(x) = -15,843(0.997^x) + 19,475 \text{ dollars}$$

c. You can readily determine that the cost of producing 500 toaster ovens is estimated by $C(500) \approx \$15,948$. ●

It is sometimes necessary to find an antiderivative twice in order to obtain the appropriate accumulation formula. For example, to obtain distance from acceleration, you must determine the specific antiderivative of the acceleration function to obtain a velocity function and then determine the specific antiderivative of the velocity function to obtain a function for distance traveled.

EXAMPLE 5   *Recovering Distance from Acceleration*

Falling Pianos   A mathematically inclined cartoonist wants to make sure his animated cartoons accurately portray the laws of physics. In a particular cartoon he is creating, a grand piano falls from the top of a 10-story building. How many seconds should he allow the piano to fall before it hits the ground? Assume that one story equals 12 feet and that acceleration due to gravity is -32 feet per second squared.

Solution
We begin with the equation for acceleration, $a(t) = -32$ feet per second squared t seconds after the piano falls. The antiderivative of acceleration gives an equation for velocity:

$$\int a(t)dt = v(t) = -32t + C \text{ feet per second after } t \text{ seconds of fall}$$

To find the specific velocity equation for this example, we need information about the velocity at a specific time. The fact that the piano falls (rather than being pushed with an initial force) tells us that the velocity is zero when the time is zero. Substituting zero for both t and v and solving for C give $C = 0$. Thus the specific antiderivative describing velocity is $v(t) = -32t$ feet per second after t seconds of fall.

From this velocity equation, we can derive an equation for position (the distance the piano is above the ground) by finding the antiderivative. In this case, the general antiderivative of v is

$$\int v(t)dt = s(t) = -16t^2 + K \text{ feet after } t \text{ seconds of fall}$$

Again, we find the specific position equation by using information given about the position of the piano at a certain time. In this example we know that when time is zero, the piano is 10 stories, or 120 feet, above the ground. We substitute this information into the position equation and solve for K, obtaining $K = 120$ feet. Substituting this value for K in the position equation yields the specific position equation

$$s(t) = -16t^2 + 120 \text{ feet after } t \text{ seconds of fall}$$

Now that we have equations for acceleration, velocity, and position, we can answer the question posed: How long will it be until the piano hits the ground? Let us phrase this question mathematically: When position is zero, what is time? To answer this question, we set the position equation equal to zero and solve for t.

$$0 = -16t^2 + 120$$
$$16t^2 = 120$$
$$t^2 = \frac{120}{16}$$
$$t \approx \pm 2.7 \text{ seconds}$$

Because negative time doesn't make sense in the context of the question, we conclude that the cartoonist should allow approximately 2.7 seconds for the piano to fall. ●

Let us summarize what we have learned thus far about integrals. The definite integral $\int_a^b f(x)dx$ is a limiting value of sums of areas of rectangles and gives us the area of the region between the graph of f and the x-axis if the graph lies above the horizontal axis from a to b. When the graph of f lies below the horizontal axis from a to b, the definite integral is the negative of the inscribed area. If $f(x)$ is a rate of change of some quantity, then $\int_a^b f(x)dx$ is the change in the quantity from a to b. The accumulation function $A(x) = \int_a^x f(t)dt$ is a formula in terms of x for the accumulated change in $f(t)$ from a to x. We use the integral symbol without the upper and lower limits, $\int f(x)dx$, to represent the general antiderivative of f. Although these three symbols are similar, it is important that you have a clear understanding of what each one represents. Their interpretations are summarized in Table 5.14.

TABLE 5.14

Symbol	Name	Interpretation
$\int_a^b f(x)dx$	definite integral	a number that can be thought of in terms of the accumulated change in f between the input values of a and b
$\int_a^x f(t)dt$	accumulation function, specific antiderivative	a formula for an accumulated amount between the starting input value of a and a general input value of x
$\int f(x)dx$	general antiderivative	a formula whose derivative is f

The Fundamental Theorem of Calculus tells us that accumulation functions are specific antiderivatives. As we shall see in Section 5.4, antiderivatives enable us to find areas algebraically by using accumulation formulas, rather than numerically as limiting values of sums of areas of rectangles.

Apart from helping us find areas or accumulated change, antiderivatives are useful in enabling us to recover functions from rates of change. We have seen several examples of that in this section. It may seem difficult to reverse your thinking from finding derivatives to finding antiderivatives, but with practice you will soon be proficient at both.

5.3 Concept Inventory

- Fundamental Theorem of Calculus
- Antiderivative
- Recovering a function from its rate of change
- $\int f(x)dx$ = general antiderivative
- Antiderivative formulas
- Specific antiderivative

5.3 Activities

Getting Started

In Activities 1 through 4, a and b are constants and x and t are variables. In these activities, label each notation as always representing:

   i. A function of x

   ii. A function of t

   iii. A number

1. a. $f'(t)$ **b.** $\dfrac{df}{dx}$ **c.** $f'(3)$

2. a. $\int f(t)dt$ **b.** $\int f(x)dx$ **c.** $\int_a^b f(t)dt$

3. a. $\int_a^b f(x)dx$ **b.** $\int_a^x f(t)dt$ **c.** $\int_b^t f(x)dx$

4. a. $\dfrac{d}{dx}\int_a^x f(t)dt$ **b.** $\dfrac{d}{dt}\int_a^t f(x)dx$ **c.** $\dfrac{d}{dx}\int_a^a f(t)dt$

5. Illustrate and explain the Fundamental Theorem of Calculus from a numerical viewpoint.

6. Write the Fundamental Theorem of Calculus from an algebraic viewpoint.

7. Write the Fundamental Theorem of Calculus from a verbal viewpoint. Do not include mathematical symbols or graphs.

8. Illustrate and explain the Fundamental Theorem of Calculus from a graphical viewpoint.

Find the general antiderivative as indicated in Activities 9 through 14. Check each of your antiderivatives by taking its derivative.

9. $\int 19.4(1.07^x)dx$

10. $\int 39e^{3.9x}dx$

11. $\int [6e^x + 4(2^x)]dx$

12. $\int (32.68x^3 + 3.28x - 15)dx$

13. $\int (10^x + 4\sqrt{x} + 8)dx$

14. $\int \left[\dfrac{1}{2}x + \dfrac{1}{2x} + \left(\dfrac{1}{2}\right)^x\right]dx$

For each of the rate-of-change functions in Activities 15 through 18, find the general antiderivative, and label the units on the antiderivative.

15. $s(m) = 600(0.93^m)$ CDs per month, m months since the beginning of the year

16. $p(x) = 0.04x^2 - 0.5x + 1.4$ dollars per 1000 cubic feet per year, x years since 1989

17. $c(x) = \dfrac{0.8}{x} + 0.38(0.01^x)$ dollars per unit squared, when x units are produced

18. $p(t) = 1.7e^{0.03t}$ millions of people per year, t years after 1990

In Activities 19 through 21, find F, the specific antiderivative of f.

19. $f(t) = t^2 + 2t;\ f(12) = 700$

20. $f(u) = \dfrac{2}{u} + u;\ f(1) = 5$

21. $f(z) = \dfrac{1}{z^2} + e^z;\ f(2) = 1$

Applying Concepts

22. Bond Yields   The rate of change of the average yield of short-term German bonds can be described by the equation $G(t) = \dfrac{0.57}{t}$ percentage points per year, for a bond with a maturity time of t years. The average 10-year bond has a yield of 4.95%. Find the specific antiderivative describing the average yield of short-term German bonds. How is this specific antiderivative related to an accumulation function of G?

23. **Weight**   The rate of change of the weight of a laboratory mouse can be modeled by the equation $W(t) = \dfrac{7.37}{t}$ grams per week, where t is the age of the mouse, in weeks, beyond 2 weeks. At an age of 9 weeks, a mouse weighed 26 grams. Find the specific antiderivative describing the weight of the mouse. How is this specific antiderivative related to an accumulation function of W?

24. **Fuel Use**   The rate of change of the average annual fuel consumption of passenger vehicles, buses, and trucks from 1970 through 2000 can be modeled by the equation $f(t) = 0.8t - 15.9$ gallons per vehicle per year, t years after 1970. The average annual fuel consumption was 712 gallons per vehicle in 1980.

    (Source: Based on data from Bureau of Transportation Statistics.)

    a. Find the specific antiderivative giving the average annual fuel consumption.

    b. How is this specific antiderivative related to an accumulation function of f?

25. **Gender Ratio**   The rate of change of the gender ratio for the United States during the twentieth century can be modeled as $g(t) = (1.67 \cdot 10^{-4})t^2 - 0.02t - 0.10$ males per 100 females per year, t years after 1900. In 1970 the gender ratio was 94.8 males per 100 females.

    (Source: Based on data from U.S. Bureau of the Census.)

    a. Find a specific antiderivative giving the gender ratio.

    b. How is this specific antiderivative related to an accumulation function of g?

26. **Investment**   An investment worth $1 million in 2000 has been growing at a rate of $f(t) = 0.140(1.15^t)$ million dollars per year, t years after 2000.

    a. Determine how much the investment has grown since 2000 and how much it is projected to grow over the next year.

    b. Recover the amount function, and determine the current value of the investment and its projected value next year.

27. **Dropped Coin**   The Washington Monument, located at one end of the Federal Mall in Washington, D.C., is the world's tallest obelisk at 555 feet. Suppose that a tourist drops a penny from the observation deck atop the monument. Let us assume that the penny falls from a height of 540 feet.

    a. Recover the velocity function for the penny using the following facts:

        i. Acceleration due to gravity near the surface of the earth is -32 feet per second squared.

        ii. Because the penny is dropped, velocity is 0 when time is 0.

    b. Recover the distance function for the penny using the velocity function from part a and the fact that distance is 540 feet when time is 0.

    c. When will the penny hit the ground?

28. **High Dive**   According to the *Guinness Book of Records*, the world's record high dive from a diving board is 176 feet, 10 inches. It was made by Olivier Favre (Switzerland) in 1987. Ignoring air resistance, approximate Favre's impact velocity (in miles per hour) from a height of 176 feet, 10 inches.

29.*Velocity   In the 1960s, Donald McDonald claimed in an article in *New Scientist* that plummeting cats never fall faster than 40 mph.

    a. What is the impact velocity (in feet per second and miles per hour) of a cat that accidentally falls off a building from a height of 66 feet $\left(5\tfrac{1}{2}\text{ stories}\right)$?

    b. What accounts for the difference between your answer to part a and McDonald's claim (assuming McDonald's claim is accurate)?

---

* McDonald's study was based on observations of veterinarians who treated cats that had fallen from buildings in New York City. None of the cats' falls were deliberately caused by the researchers.

30. Donors The table gives the increase or decrease in the number of donors to a college athletics support organization for selected years.

Year	Rate of change in donors (donors per year)
1985	−169
1988	803
1991	1222
1994	1087
1997	399
2000	−842

a. Find a model for the rate of change in the number of donors.

b. Find a model for the number of donors. Use the fact that in 1990 there were 10,706 donors.

c. Estimate the number of donors in 2002.

31. Employees From 1997 through 2002, an Internet company was hiring new employees at a rate of $n(x) = \dfrac{593}{x} + 138$ new employees per year, where x represents the number of years since 1996. By 2001 the company had hired 896 employees.

a. Write the function that gives the number of employees who had been hired by the xth year after 1996.

b. For what years will the function in part a apply?

c. Find the total number of employees the company had hired between 1997 and 2002. Would this figure necessarily be the same as the number of employees the company had at the end of 2002? Explain.

5.4   The Definite Integral

So far, we have been finding general and specific antiderivatives to recover functions from their rate-of-change functions. The Fundamental Theorem of Calculus tells us that accumulation functions are antiderivatives and leads to an algebraic method for finding an accumulation function. In general, we know that $\displaystyle\int_a^x f(t)dt = F(x) + C$, where F is an antiderivative of f. We also know that when $x = a$, the accumulation function is zero.

$$\int_a^a f(t)dt = F(a) + C = 0$$

This tells us that $C = -F(a)$. Thus we have

$$\int_a^x f(t)dt = F(x) - F(a)$$

To find the value of the accumulation function from a to b, we simply substitute b for x.

$$\int_a^b f(t)dt = F(b) - F(a)$$

We now have an efficient algebraic method for evaluating definite integrals:

Evaluating a Definite Integral

If f is a continuous function from a to b and F is any antiderivative of f, then

$$\int_a^b f(x)dx = F(b) - F(a)$$

Antiderivatives and Definite Integrals

Recall from Section 5.1 that we define the definite integral, $\int_a^b f(x)dx$, as the limiting value of sums of signed areas of rectangles. That is,

$$\int_a^b f(x)dx = \lim_{n \to \infty}[f(x_1) + f(x_2) + \cdots + f(x_n)]\Delta x$$

The antiderivative definition for a definite integral, $\int_a^b f(x)dx = F(b) - F(a)$, gives us a less tedious method for evaluating a definite integral for many functions. For example, we can calculate the area of the region between the graph of $f(x) = x^2 + 2$ and the x-axis from -2 to 4. (See Figure 5.48.)

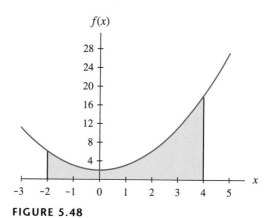

FIGURE 5.48

To find the area of this region in Section 5.1, we would have used sums of areas of rectangles. Now all we need to do is calculate the value of the definite integral, $\int_{-2}^4 (x^2 + 2)dx$, by simply finding an antiderivative and subtracting the value of the antiderivative at -2 from the value of the antiderivative at 4.

$$\int_{-2}^4 (x^2 + 2)dx = F(4) - F(-2)$$

where F is an antiderivative of $x^2 + 2$. Here are the details of this process:

1. Find an antiderivative: $\displaystyle\int_{-2}^{4}(x^2 + 2)dx = \left(\frac{x^3}{3} + 2x\right)\Big|_{-2}^{4}$

2. Evaluate at upper and lower limits and then subtract:

$$= \left[\frac{4^3}{3} + 2(4)\right] - \left[\frac{(-2)^3}{3} + 2(-2)\right]$$

$$= 29\tfrac{1}{3} - \left(-6\tfrac{2}{3}\right)$$

$$= 36$$

This notation is used to indicate that we have found an antiderivative and now must evaluate that antiderivative at 4 and -2 and then find the difference of the results.

Thus the area of the region depicted in Figure 5.48 is exactly 36.

EXAMPLE 1   *Evaluating and Interpreting a Definite Integral*

a. Find a formula for $\displaystyle\int 70(1.07^t)dt$.

b. Find a formula for the accumulation function $A(x) = \displaystyle\int_1^x 70(1.07^t)dt$.

c. Determine $\displaystyle\int_1^4 70(1.07^t)dt$. Interpret your answer graphically.

d. If $f(t) = 70(1.07^t)$ is the rate of change of the balance in a savings account given in dollars per year, and t is the number of years since the savings account was opened, what does your answer in part c represent?

Solution

a. $\displaystyle\int 70(1.07^t)dt = \frac{70(1.07)^t}{\ln 1.07} + C$

b. The accumulation function is the specific antiderivative (in terms of x) for which the antiderivative is zero when $x = 1$.

$$A(1) = \frac{70(1.07^1)}{\ln 1.07} + C = 0$$

$$C \approx {}^-1107.03$$

Thus we have

$$A(x) = \int_1^x 70(1.07^t)dt \approx \frac{70(1.07^x)}{\ln 1.07} - 1107.03$$

c. $\int_{1}^{4} 70(1.07^{t})dt = A(t)\Big|_{1}^{4}$

$= \dfrac{70(1.07^{t})}{\ln 1.07}\Big|_{1}^{4}$

$= \dfrac{70(1.07^{4})}{\ln 1.07} - \dfrac{70(1.07^{1})}{\ln 1.07}$

≈ 249.13

The graph of $f(t) = 70(1.07^{t})$ is always positive. This value is the area of the region between the graph of $f(t)$ and the horizontal axis from 1 to 4.

d. The answer to part c represents the change in the amount in the savings account between 1 and 4 years. The amount grew by $249.13.   ●

> The constant term in an antiderivative does not affect definite integral calculations. If you are concerned only with finding change in a quantity, finding the constant in the antiderivative is not necessary.

EXAMPLE 2   Using a Definite Integral to Find Accumulated Change

Marginal Cost   In Example 4 of Section 5.3 we modeled the marginal cost for toaster ovens using the exponential function

$C'(x) = 47.6(0.997^{x})$ dollars per oven

where x is the number of ovens produced per day. Suppose that the current production level is 300 ovens per day and that the manufacturer wishes to increase production to 500 ovens per day. How will this increase affect production cost?

Solution

The definite integral $\int_{300}^{500} C'(x)dx = C(500) - C(300)$ gives the change in cost as a result of this increase. Finding the change requires two steps. First, find an antiderivative of C'. Then evaluate the antiderivative at the two production levels and subtract the value at the lower limit of the integral from the value at the upper limit.

In Section 5.3 (using a rounded model), we found the general antiderivative for C' to be

$$C(x) = \int C'(x)dx \approx -15{,}843(0.997^{x}) + K$$

Because the constant K will not affect our calculations of change, we can ignore K. We illustrate this by finding $\int_{300}^{500} C'(x)dx = C(x)\Big|_{300}^{500}$ and including the value of $K = \$19{,}475$ that we found in Example 4 of Section 5.3.

The definite integral is

$$\int_{300}^{500} C'(x)dx \approx (-15{,}843(0.997^x) + 19{,}475)\Big|_{300}^{500}$$

$$= C(500) - C(300)$$

$$= [-15{,}843(0.997^{500}) + 19{,}475] - [-15{,}843(0.997^{300}) + 19{,}475]$$

$$\approx \$2905$$

Note that 19,475 will be added in and then subtracted. We ignore the constant when calculating a definite integral.

We conclude that when production is increased from 300 to 500 ovens per day, cost increases by approximately $2,905. ●

Piecewise Functions

Piecewise functions are defined using two or more separate continuous equations. The values of x where the specific equation that defines the function changes are called **break points**.

$$f(x) = \begin{cases} 18x^2 - 135x + 2{,}882 \text{ ft}^3/\text{hr} & \text{when } 0 \le x \le 20 \\ 12x^2 - 816x + 19{,}044 \text{ ft}^3/\text{hr} & \text{when } 20 < x \le 27 \end{cases}$$

is a piecewise function that describes flow rates of a river past a sensor in cubic feet per hour, for 27 hours following a storm. The break point for $f(x)$ occurs at $x = 20$. The graph of $f(x)$ is shown in Figure 5.49.

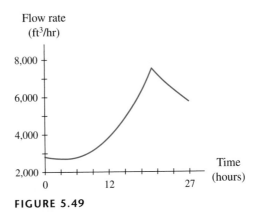

FIGURE 5.49

Calculations for definite integrals require special care. To calculate the area trapped between $f(x)$ and the horizontal axis for $0 \le x \le 27$, we must use two definite integrals.

Sums of Definite Integrals

To estimate the amount of water that flowed through the river over the 27-hour period, we calculate the value of the definite integral, $\int_0^{27} f(x)dx$. Note that the point of division for the model occurs in the interval from 0 to 27. For this reason, we cannot calculate the value of the definite integral simply by evaluating an antiderivative of f at 27 and 0 and subtracting.

Note that the area of the region from a to b shaded in Figure 5.50 is equal to the sum of the area of R_1 and the area of R_2.

This figure illustrates the following property of integrals:

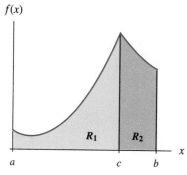

$f(x)$

R_1 R_2

a c b x

FIGURE 5.50

Sum Property of Integrals

$$\int_a^b f(x)\,dx = \int_a^c f(x)\,dx + \int_c^b f(x)\,dx$$

where c is between a and b.

It is this property that enables us to calculate definite integrals for piecewise continuous functions.

Returning to the river flow function, in order to calculate $\int_0^{27} f(x)\,dx$, we divide the integral into two pieces at the point where the model changes and sum the results.

$$\int_0^{27} f(x)\,dx = \int_0^{20} f(x)\,dx + \int_{20}^{27} f(x)\,dx$$

$$= \int_0^{20} (18x^2 - 135x + 2{,}882)\,dx$$

$$+ \int_{20}^{27} (12x^2 - 816x + 19{,}044)\,dx$$

$$= \left(\frac{18x^3}{3} - \frac{135x^2}{2} + 2{,}882x\right)\Big|_0^{20}$$

$$+ \left(\frac{12x^3}{3} - \frac{816x^2}{2} + 19{,}044x\right)\Big|_{20}^{27}$$

$$= (78{,}640 - 0) + (295{,}488 - 249{,}680)$$

$$= 78{,}640 + 45{,}808$$

$$= 124{,}448 \text{ cubic feet}$$

We estimate that during the first 20 hours, 78,640 thousand ft^3 of water flowed past the sensor. Between 20 and 27 hours, the volume of water was about 45,808 thousand ft^3. Summing these two values, we estimate that over the 27-hour period, 124,448 thousand ft^3 of water flowed past the sensor.

In order to calculate the change from a to b in a function whose graph is sometimes above and sometimes below the horizontal axis, it is necessary only to calculate $\int_a^b f(x)\,dx$; we need not calculate the change over separate intervals. This concept is illustrated in Example 3.

EXAMPLE 3   *Illustrating the Sum Property of Integrals*

Sea Level   Scientists believe that the average sea level is dropping and has been for some 4000 years. They also believe that this was not always the case. Estimated rates of change in the average sea level, in meters per year, during the past 7000 years are given in Table 5.15.

TABLE 5.15

Time, t (thousands of years before present)	−7	−6	−5	−4	−3	−2	−1
Rate of change of average sea level, $r(t)$ (meters/year)	3.8	2.6	1.0	0.1	−0.6	−0.9	−1.0

(Source: Estimated from information in François Ramade, *Ecology of Natural Resources*, New York: Wiley, 1981)

A quadratic model for the data is

$$r(t) = 0.148t^2 + 0.360t - 0.8 \text{ meters per yard}$$

t thousand years from the present (past years are represented by negative numbers). A graph of r is shown in Figure 5.51.

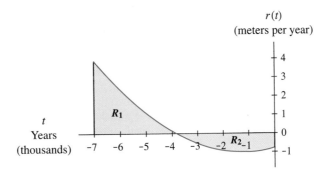

FIGURE 5.51

a.   Find the areas of the regions above and below the t-axis from $t = -7$ to $t = 0$. Interpret the areas in the context of sea level.

b.   Find $\displaystyle\int_{-7}^{0} r(t)\,dt$, and interpret your answer.

Solution

a.   The graph in Figure 5.51 crosses the t-axis at $t \approx -3.845$ thousand years. The area of region R_1 (above the t-axis) is

$$\int_{-7}^{-3.845} (0.148t^2 + 0.36t - 0.8)\,dt = \left(\frac{0.148}{3}t^3 + \frac{0.36}{2}t^2 - 0.8t\right)\Bigg|_{-7}^{-3.845}$$

$$\approx 2.933 - (-2.501) \approx 5.4 \text{ meters}$$

The area of region R_2 (below the t-axis) is

$$\int_{-3.845}^{0} (0.148t^2 + 0.36t - 0.8)dt = -\left(\frac{0.148}{3}t^3 + \frac{0.36}{2}t^2 - 0.8t\right)\Bigg|_{-3.845}^{0}$$

$$\approx -(0 - 2.933) \approx 2.9 \text{ meters}$$

From 7000 years ago through 3845 years ago, the average sea level rose by approximately 5.4 meters. From 3845 years ago to the present, the average sea level fell by approximately 2.9 meters.

b. $\displaystyle\int_{-7}^{0} r(t)dt = \int_{-7}^{0} (0.148t^2 + 0.36t - 0.8)dt$

$$= \left(\frac{0.148}{3}t^3 + \frac{0.36}{2}t^2 - 0.8t\right)\Bigg|_{-7}^{0}$$

$$\approx 0 - (-2.501) \approx 2.5 \text{ meters}$$

From 7000 years ago to the present, the average sea level has risen approximately 2.5 meters. This result is the same as that obtained by subtracting the amount that the average sea level has fallen from the amount that it has risen:

5.4 meters $-$ 2.9 meters $=$ 2.5 meters   ●

Differences of Accumulated Changes

Now we turn our attention to the difference of two accumulated changes. This difference can often be thought of as the area of a region between two curves. For example, suppose the number of patients admitted to a large inner-city hospital is changing by

$$a(h) = 0.0145h^3 - 0.549h^2 + 4.85h + 8.00 \text{ patients per hour}$$

h hours after 3 A.M. We find the approximate number of patients admitted to the hospital between 7 A.M. ($h = 4$) and 10 A.M. ($h = 7$) as

$$\int_4^7 a(h)dh = \int_4^7 (0.0145h^3 - 0.549h^2 + 4.85h + 8.00)dh$$

$$= \left(\frac{0.0145h^4}{4} - \frac{0.549h^3}{3} + \frac{4.85h^2}{2} + 8.00h\right)\Bigg|_4^7$$

$$\approx 120.760 - 60.016 \approx 61 \text{ patients}$$

Graphically, this value is the area of the region between the graph of a and the horizontal axis from 4 to 7. (See Figure 5.52.)

Now suppose that the rate at which patients are discharged is modeled by the equation

$$y(h) = \begin{cases} 0 \text{ patients/hour} & \text{when } 0 \leq h < 4 \\ -0.028h^3 + 0.528h^2 + 0.056h - 1.5 \text{ patients/hour} & \text{when } 4 \leq h \leq 17 \\ 0 \text{ patients/hour} & \text{when } 17 < h \leq 24 \end{cases}$$

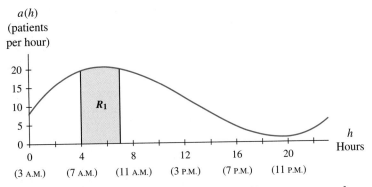

The area of R_1 is the number of patients admitted between 7 A.M. and 10 A.M.

FIGURE 5.52

where h is the number of hours after 3 A.M. The approximate number of patients discharged between 7 A.M. and 10 A.M. is calculated as

$$\int_4^7 y(h)dh = \int_4^7 (-0.028h^3 + 0.528h^2 + 0.056h - 1.5)dh$$
$$= (-0.007h^4 + 0.176h^3 + 0.028h^2 - 1.5h)\Big|_4^7$$
$$= 34.433 - 3.92 \approx 31 \text{ patients}$$

Graphically, this value is the area of the region between the graph of y and the horizontal axis from 4 to 7. (See Figure 5.53.)

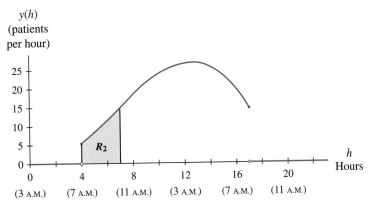

The area of R_2 is the number of patients discharged between 7 A.M. and 10 A.M.

FIGURE 5.53

The net change in the number of patients at the hospital from 7 A.M. to 10 A.M. is the difference between the number of patients admitted and the number discharged between 7 A.M. and 10 A.M. That is,

$$\text{Change in the number of patients from 7 A.M. to 10 A.M.} = \int_4^7 a(h)dh - \int_4^7 y(h)dh$$

$$\approx 60.744 - 30.513$$

$$\approx 30 \text{ patients}$$

Geometrically, we represent this value as the area of the region below the graph of a and above the graph of y from 4 to 7. (See Figure 5.54.)

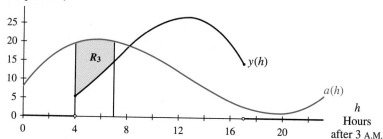

Patients admitted and discharged (patients per hour)

The area of R_3 is the net change in hospital patients between 7 A.M. and 10 A.M.

FIGURE 5.54

In general, when we want to find the area of a region that lies below one curve f and above another curve g from a to b (as in Figure 5.55), we calculate it as

$$\text{Area of the region between the graphs of } f \text{ and } g = \text{area beneath the graph of } f - \text{area beneath the graph of } g$$

$$= \int_a^b f(x)dx - \int_a^b g(x)dx$$

Using the Sum Rule for antiderivatives, we obtain

$$\text{Area of the region between the graphs } f \text{ and } g = \int_a^b [f(x) - g(x)]dx$$

Note that when f and g are obtained by fitting equations to data, the input variables of the functions must represent the same quantities measured in the same units.

FIGURE 5.55

If, while calculating the area of the region between two curves, you obtain the negative of the answer you expect, then it is likely that you have interchanged the positions of the functions in the integrand.

Area of the Region Between Two Curves

If the graph of f lies above the graph of g from a to b, then the area of the region between the two curves from a to b is given by

$$\int_a^b [f(x) - g(x)]dx$$

EXAMPLE 4   *Determining the Area of the Region Between Two Curves*

Tire Manufacturers   A major European tire manufacturer has seen its sales from tires skyrocket since 1989. A model for the rate of change of sales (in U.S. dollars) accumulated since 1989 is

$$s(t) = 3.7(1.194^t) \text{ million dollars per year}$$

where t is the number of years since the end of 1989.

At the same time, an American tire manufacturer's rate of change of sales accumulated since 1989 can be modeled by

$$a(t) = 0.04t^3 - 0.54t^2 + 2.5t + 4.47 \text{ million dollars per year}$$

where t is the number of years since the end of 1989. These models apply through the year 2010. By how much did the amounts of accumulated sales differ for these two companies from the end of 1999 through 2009?

Solution

First, determine whether one graph lies above the other on the entire interval in the question. The two rate-of-change functions are graphed in Figure 5.56.

Between the years 1999 and 2010, the graphs of the two rate-of-change functions $s(t)$ and $a(t)$ cross once near $t = 14$. If we set $s(t) = 3.7(1.194^t)$ equal to $a(t) = 0.04t^3 - 0.54t^2 + 2.5t + 4.47$ and solve for t, we find that on the interval $[10, 21]$, the two functions intersect when $t \approx 14.28$ (in 2004). (There are other intersections outside the given interval at $t \approx -0.37$, $t \approx 4.65$, *and* $t \approx 27.97$). Accumulated sales were greater for the European company than for the American company from $t \approx 4.65$ to $t \approx 14.28$. Between $t \approx 14.28$ and $t = 21$, the American company saw greater accumulated sales than the European company.

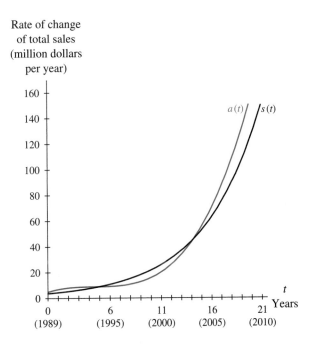

FIGURE 5.56

From the beginning of 2000 ($t \approx 10$) through most of the first quarter of 2004 ($t \approx 14.28$), the European company accumulated approximately

$$\int_{10}^{14.28} [s(t) - a(t)]dt = 18.88 \text{ million dollars}$$

more in sales than the American company. This is the area of region R_1 in Figure 5.57.

FIGURE 5.57

From close to the end of the first quarter of 2004 ($t \approx 14.28$) through 2009 ($t = 20$), the American company accumulated approximately

$$\int_{14.28}^{20} [a(t) - s(t)]dt \approx 77.77 \text{ million dollars}$$

more in sales than the European company. This is the area of region R_2 in Figure 5.57.

In order to calculate the estimated difference in accumulated sales between the two companies from 1999 through 2009, we subtract the portion where the American company's accumulated sales were greater from the portion where the European company's accumulated sales were greater. That is,

$$\text{Difference in accumulated sales} \approx \int_{10}^{14.28} [s(t) - a(t)]dt - \int_{14.28}^{20} [a(t) - s(t)]dt$$

$$\approx 18.88 \text{ million dollars} - 77.77 \text{ million dollars}$$

$$\approx -58.89 \text{ million dollars}$$

The European company's accumulated sales were nearly 59 million dollars less than the American company's accumulated sales over the years considered. ●

If we use the Constant Multiplier Rule and the Sum Rule for antiderivatives with the functions in Example 4, we see that we did not need to split the interval from 10 to 20 into two intervals.

$$\begin{aligned}
\text{Difference in} &= \int_{10}^{14.28} [s(t) - a(t)]dt - \int_{14.28}^{20} [a(t) - s(t)]dt \\
\text{accumulated sales} &\\
&= \int_{10}^{14.28} [s(t) - a(t)]dt + \int_{14.28}^{20} [-a(t) + s(t)]dt \\
&= \int_{10}^{14.28} [s(t) - a(t)]dt + \int_{14.28}^{20} [s(t) - a(t)]dt \\
&= \int_{10}^{20} [s(t) - a(t)]dt
\end{aligned}$$

This is true in general—when you wish to find the difference between accumulated change for two continuous rate-of-change functions, you can calculate the definite integral of the difference of the functions, regardless of where the functions intersect.

Difference of Two Accumulated Changes

If f and g are two continuous rate-of-change functions, then the difference between the accumulated change of f from a to b and the accumulated change of g from a to b is

$$\int_a^b [f(x) - g(x)]dx$$

It is important to note that $\int_a^b [f(x) - g(x)]dx$ may not represent the area between the graphs of f and g from a to b. In the tire sales example, the area of the regions between the two curves from 10 to 20 is $18.88 + 77.77 = 96.65$, whereas the difference in accumulated sales is $18.88 - 77.77 = -58.89$.

If two rate-of-change functions intersect in the interval from a to b, then the difference between their accumulated changes is *not* the same as the area of the regions between the two curves.

Most practical applications of the area between two curves involve the difference between two accumulated changes. However, if total area is to be calculated, remember the distinction between these quantities.

In this section, we have seen that the Fundamental Theorem of Calculus gives us a technique for evaluating definite integrals using antiderivatives. However, there are many antiderivative formulas not covered in this text, and there are some functions to which no antiderivative rule applies. It is important for you to understand that if you are ever unable to find an algebraic formula for the antiderivative of a function, you can still estimate the value of a definite integral of that function by using the limiting value of sums of areas of rectangles.

5.4   Concept Inventory

- $\int_a^b f(x)dx = F(b) - F(a)$, where F is an antiderivative of f

- $\int_a^b f(x)dx = \int_a^c f(x)dx + \int_c^b f(x)dx$

- Area(s) of region(s) between two curves

- Differences of accumulated changes

5.4   Activities

Getting Started

For each of Activities 1 through 7, determine which of the following processes you would use when answering the question posed. Note that a and b are constants.

   a. Finding a derivative

   b. Finding a general antiderivative (with unknown constant)

   c. Finding a specific antiderivative (solve for the constant)

1. Given a rate-of-change function for population and the population in a given year, find the population in year t.

2. Given a velocity function, determine the distance traveled from time a to time b.

3. Given a function, find its accumulation function from a to x.

4. Given a velocity function, determine acceleration at time t.

5. Given a rate-of-change function for population, find the change in population from year a to year b.

6. Given a function, find the area of the region between the function and the horizontal axis from a to b.

7. Given a function, find the slope of the tangent line at input a.

In Activities 8 through 11:

   a. Graph the function f from a to b.

   b. Find the area of the region between the graph of f and the x-axis from a to b. Is this area equal to $\int_a^b f(x)dx$? Explain.

   c. Find $\int_a^b f(x)dx$.

8. $f(x) = -4x^{-2}$; $a = 1, b = 4$

9. $f(x) = -1.3x^3 + 0.93x^2 + 0.49$; $a = -1, b = 2$

10. $f(x) = \dfrac{9.295}{x} - 1.472$; $a = 5, b = 10$

11. $f(x) = -965.27(1.079^x)$; $a = 0.5, b = 3.5$

Applying Concepts

12. **Air Speed**   The air speed of a small airplane during the first 25 seconds of takeoff and flight can be modeled by

$$v(t) = -940{,}602t^2 + 19{,}269.3t - 0.3 \text{ mph}$$

t hours after takeoff.

   a. Find the value of $\int_0^{0.005} v(t)dt$.

   b. Interpret your answer in context.

13. **Phone Calls**   The rate of change of the number of international telephone calls billed in the United States between 1980 and 2000 can be described by

$$P(x) = 32.432e^{0.1826x} \text{ million calls per year}$$

where x is the number of years after 1980. Find and interpret the value of $\int_5^{15} P(x)dx$.

(Source: Based on data from the Federal Communications Commission.)

14. **Weight**   The rate of change of the weight of a laboratory mouse t weeks (for $1 \le t \le 15$) after the beginning of an experiment can be modeled by the equation

$$w(t) = \dfrac{13.785}{t} \text{ grams per week}$$

Evaluate $\int_3^9 w(t)dt$, and interpret your answer.

15. Revenue   A corporation's revenue flow rate can be modeled by

$$r(x) = 9.907x^2 - 40.769x + 58.492$$
million dollars per year

x years after the end of 1987. Evaluate $\int_0^5 r(x)dx$, and interpret your answer.

16. Medicine   Consider the rate of change in the concentration of a drug modeled by

$$r(x) = \begin{cases} 1.708(0.845^x) \\ \quad \mu g/mL/day & \text{when } 0 \le x \le 20 \\ 0.11875x - 3.5854 \\ \quad \mu g/mL/day & \text{when } 20 < x \le 29 \end{cases}$$

where x is the number of days after the drug was administered. Determine the values of the following definite integrals, and interpret your answers.

a. $\int_0^{20} r(x)dx$ **b.** $\int_{20}^{29} r(x)dx$

c. $\int_0^{29} r(x)dx$

17. Snow Pack   The rate of change of the snow pack in an area in the Northwest Territories in Canada can be modeled by

$$s(t) = \begin{cases} 0.00241t + 0.02905 \text{ cm} \\ \quad \text{per day} & \text{when } 0 \le t \le 70 \\ 1.011t^2 - 147.971t + \\ \quad 5406.578 \text{ cm per day} & \text{when } 72 \le t \le 76 \end{cases}$$

where t is the number of days since April 1.

a. Evaluate $\int_0^{70} s(t)dt$, and interpret your answer.

b. Evaluate $\int_{72}^{76} s(t)dt$, and interpret your answer.

c. Explain why it is not possible to find the value of $\int_0^{76} s(t)dt$.

18. Temperature   The rate of change of the temperature during the hour and a half after the beginning of a thunderstorm is given by

$$T(h) = 9.48h^3 - 15.49h^2 + 17.38h - 9.87 \text{ °F per hour}$$

where h is the number of hours since the storm began.

a. Graph the function T from $h = 0$ to $h = 1.5$.

b. Calculate the value of $\int_0^{1.5} T(h)dh$. Interpret your answer.

19. Temperature   The rate of change of the temperature in a museum during a junior high school field trip can be modeled by

$$T(h) = 9.07h^3 - 24.69h^2 + 14.87h - 0.03$$
°F per hour

h hours after 8:30 A.M.

a. Find the area of the region that lies above the axis between the graph of T and the h-axis between 8:30 A.M. and 10:15 A.M. Interpret the answer.

b. Find the area of the region that lies below the axis between the graph of T and the h-axis between 8:30 A.M. and 10:15 A.M. Interpret the answer.

c. There are items in the museum that should not be exposed to temperatures greater than 73°F. If the temperature at 8:30 A.M. was 71°F, did the temperature exceed 73°F between 8:30 A.M. and 10:15 A.M.?

20. Road Test   The acceleration of a race car during the first 35 seconds of a road test is modeled by

$$a(t) = 0.024t^2 - 1.72t + 22.58 \text{ ft/sec}^2$$

where t is the number of seconds since the test began.

a. Graph the function a from $t = 0$ to $t = 35$.

b. Write the definite integral notation representing the amount by which the car's speed increased during the road test. Calculate the value of the definite integral.

21. Production   The estimated production rate of marketed natural gas, in trillion cubic feet per year, in the United States (excluding Alaska) from 1900 through 1960 is shown in the table.

Year	Estimated production rate (trillions of cubic feet per year)
1900	0.1
1910	0.5
1920	0.8
1930	2.0
1940	2.3
1950	6.0
1960	12.7

(Source: From information in *Resources and Man*, National Academy of Sciences, 1969, p. 165.)

a. Find a model for the data in the table.

b. Use the model to estimate the total production of natural gas from 1940 through 1960.

c. Give the definite integral notation for your answer to part b.

22. Advertising   Many businesses spend money each year on advertising in order to stimulate sales of their products. The data given show the approximate increase in sales (in thousands of dollars) that an additional $100 spent on advertising, at various levels, can be expected to generate.

Advertising expenditures (hundreds of dollars)	Revenue increase due to an extra $100 advertising (thousands of dollars)
25	5
50	60
75	95
100	105
125	104
150	79
175	34

a. Find a model for these data.

b. Use the model in part a to determine a model for the total sales revenue $R(x)$ as a function of the amount x spent on advertising. Use the fact that revenue is approximately 877 thousand dollars when $5000 is spent on advertising.

c. Find the point where returns begin to diminish for sales revenue.

d. The managers of the business are considering an increase in advertising expenditures from the current level of $8000 to $13,000. What effect could this decision have on sales revenue?

23. Production   The table shows the marginal cost to produce one more compact disc, given various hourly production levels.

Production (CDs per hour)	Cost of an additional CD
100	$5
150	$3.50
200	$2.50
250	$2
300	$1.60

a. Find an appropriate model for the data.

b. Use your model from part a to derive an equation that specifies production cost $C(x)$ as a function of the number x of CDs produced. Use the fact that it costs approximately $750 to produce 150 CDs in a 1-hour period.

c. Calculate the value of $\int_{200}^{300} C'(x)dx$. Interpret your answer.

For Activities 24 and 25:

a. Sketch graphs of the functions f and g on the same axes.

b. Shade the region between the graphs of f and g from a to b.

c. Calculate the area of the shaded region.

24. $f(x) = 10(0.85^x)$ $a = 2$

   $g(x) = 6(0.75^x)$ $b = 10$

25. $f(x) = x^2 - 4x + 10$ $a = 1$

   $g(x) = 2x^2 - 12x + 14$ $b = 7$

For Activities 26 and 27:

a. Sketch graphs of the functions f and g on the same axes.

b. Find the input value(s) at which the graphs of f and g intersect.

c. Shade the region(s) between the graphs of f and g from a to b.

d. Calculate the difference between the area of the region between the graph of f and the horizontal axis and the area of the region between the graph of g and the horizontal axis from a to b.

e. Calculate the total area of the shaded region(s).

26. $f(x) = 0.25x - 3$ $a = 15$

$g(x) = 14(0.93^x)$ $b = 50$

27. $f(x) = e^{0.5x}$ $a = 0.5$

$g(x) = \dfrac{2}{x}$ $b = 3$

28. Revenue/Cost   The figure depicts graphs of the rate of change of total revenue $R'(x)$ (in billions of dollars per year) and the rate of change of total cost $C'(x)$ (in billions of dollars per year) of a company in year x. The area of the shaded region is 126.5.

Rates of change of
revenue and cost
(billion dollars
per year)

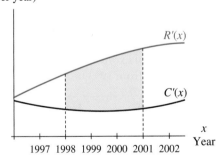

Year
1997 1998 1999 2000 2001 2002

a. Interpret the area in context.

b. Write an equation for the area of the shaded region.

29. Revenue/Cost   The figure shows graphs of $r'(x)$, the rate of change of revenue, and $c'(x)$, the rate of change of costs (both in thousands of dollars per thousand dollars of capital investment) associated with the production of solid wood furniture as functions of x, the amount (in thousands of

dollars) invested in capital. The area of the shaded region is 13.29.

Rates of change of
cost and revenue
(thousand dollars per
thousand dollars)

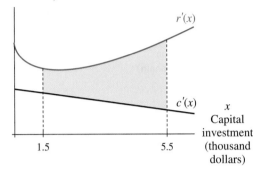

Capital
investment
(thousand
dollars)

a. Interpret the area in the context of furniture manufacturing.

b. Write an equation for the area of the shaded region.

30. Epidemic   The figure depicts graphs of $c(t)$, the rate at which people contract a virus during an epidemic, and $r(t)$, the rate at which people recover from the virus, where t is the number of days after the epidemic begins.

Rates of change of
contraction and recovery
(people per day)

Days
0   5   10   15   20   25

a. Interpret the area of region R_1 in the context of the epidemic.

b. Interpret the area of region R_2 in the context of the epidemic.

c. Explain how you could use a definite integral to find the number of people who have contracted the virus since day 0 and have not recovered by day 20.

31. Population   A country is in a state of civil war. As a consequence of deaths and people fleeing the country, its population is decreasing at a rate of $D(x)$ people per month. The rate of increase of the population as a result of births and immigration is $I(x)$ people per month. The variable x is the number of months since the beginning of the year. Graphs of D and I are shown in the figure. Region R_1 has area 3690, and region R_2 has area 9720.

a. Interpret the area of R_1 in context.

b. Interpret the area of R_2 in context.

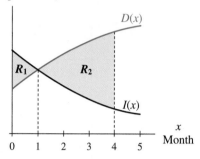

Rates of change of
population
(people per month)

c. Find the change in population from the beginning of January through the end of April.

d. Explain why the answer to part c is not the sum of the areas of the two regions.

32. Foreign Trade   The rate of change of the value of goods exported from the United States between 1990 and 2001 can be modeled as

$$E'(t) = -1.665t^2 + 16.475t + 7.632$$
billion dollars per year

t years after the end of 1990. Likewise, the rate of change of the value of goods imported into the United States during those years can be modeled as

$$I'(t) = 4.912t + 40.861 \text{ billion dollars per year}$$

t years after 1990.

(Source: Based on data from *World Almanac and Book of Facts*, ed. William A. McGeveran, Jr., New York: World Almanac Education Group, 2003.)

a. Find the difference between the accumulated value of imports and the accumulated value of exports from the end of 1990 through 2001.

b. Is your answer from part a the same as the area of the region(s) between the graphs of E' and I'? Explain.

33. Road Test   The accompanying table shows the time it takes for a Toyota Supra and a Porsche 911

Carerra to accelerate from 0 mph to the speeds given.

Toyota Supra		Porsche 911 Carerra	
Time (seconds)	Speed (mph)	Time (seconds)	Speed (mph)
2.2	30	1.9	30
2.9	40	3.0	40
4.0	50	4.1	50
5.0	60	5.2	60
6.5	70	6.8	70
8.0	80	8.6	80
9.9	90	10.7	90
11.8	100	13.3	100

(Source: *Road and Track.*)

a. Find models for the speed of each car, given the number of seconds after starting from 0 mph. (*Hint:* Add the point $(0, 0)$, and convert miles per hour into feet per second before modeling.)

b. How much farther than a Porsche 911 Carerra does a Toyota Supra travel during the first 10 seconds, assuming that both cars begin from a standing start?

c. How much farther than a Porsche 911 does a Toyota Supra travel between 5 seconds and 10 seconds of acceleration?

34. Postal Service   The table shows the approximate rates of change of revenue for the U.S. Postal Service (USPS), Federal Express (FedEx), and United Parcel Service (UPS) from 1993 to 2001.

Year	USPS (billions of dollars per year)	FedEx (billions of dollars per year)	UPS (billions of dollars per year)
1993	3.4	0.3	1.0
1994	3.3	0.6	1.2
1995	3.0	1.0	1.3
1996	2.6	1.5	1.5
1997	2.3	2.1	1.6
1998	2.0	2.3	1.8
1999	1.8	2.1	1.9
2000	1.7	1.4	2.1
2001	1.8	0	2.2

(Source: Based on data from Hoover's Online Guide.)

a. Using these data, find and graph equations for the rates of change of revenue for USPS and UPS.

b. Find and interpret the areas of the two regions bounded by the graphs in part *a* from 1993 through 2001.

35. **Postal Service**   Refer to the USPS, FedEx, and UPS data in the previous activity.

   a. Find and graph equations for the rates of change of revenue for FedEx and UPS.

   b. Find and interpret the areas of the three regions bounded by the graphs in part *a* between 1993 and 2001.

   c. Find the definite integral of the difference of the two equations in part *a* between 1993 and 2001. Interpret your answer.

36. **Mortality**   When modeling populations, biologists consider many factors that affect mortality. Some mortality factors (such as those that may be weather-related) are not dependent on the size of the population; that is, the proportion of the population killed by such factors remains constant regardless of the size of the population. Other mortality factors *are* dependent on the size of the population. In these cases, the proportion of a population killed by a certain mortality factor increases (or decreases) as the size of the population increases. Such factors are called *density-dependent mortality factors.*

   Varley and Gradwell studied the population size of a winter moth in a wooded area between 1950 and 1968. They found that predatory beetles represented the only density-dependent mortality factor in the life cycle of the winter moth. When the population of moths was small, the beetles ate few moths, searching elsewhere for food, but when the population was large, the beetles assembled in large clusters in the area of the moth population and laid eggs, thus increasing the proportion of moths eaten by the beetles.

   Suppose the annual number of winter moth larvae in Varley and Gradwell's study that survived winter kill and parasitism each year between 1961 and 1968 can be modeled by the equation

   $$l(t) = -0.0505 + 1.516 \ln t \text{ hundred moths}$$

   per square meter of tree canopy

and that the number of pupae surviving the predatory beetles each year during the same time period can be modeled by the equation

$$p(t) = 0.251 + 0.794 \ln t \text{ hundred moths}$$

per square meter of tree canopy

(Source: Adapted from P. J. denBoer and J. Reddingius, *Regulation and Stabilization Paradigms in Population Ecology,* London: Chapman and Hall, 1996.)

In both equations, *t* is the number of years since 1960. The area of the region below the graph of *l* and above the graph of *p* is referred to as the *accumulated density-dependent mortality* of pupae by predatory beetles. Use an integral to estimate this value between the years 1962 and 1965. Interpret your answer.

37. **Emissions**   In response to EPA regulations, a factory that produces carbon emissions plants 22 hectares of forest in 1990. The trees absorb carbon dioxide as they grow, thus reducing the carbon level in the atmosphere. The EPA requires that the trees absorb as much carbon in 20 years as the factory produces during that time. The trees absorb no carbon until they are 5 years old. Between 5 and 20 years of age, the trees absorb carbon at the rates indicated in the table.

Tree age (years)	5	10	15	20
Carbon absorption (tons per hectare per year)	0.2	6.0	14.0	22.0

(Source: Adapted from A. R. Ennos and S. E. R. Bailey, *Problem Solving in Environmental Biology,* Harlow, Essex, England: Longman House, 1995.)

   a. Find a model for the rate (in tons per year) at which carbon is absorbed by the 22 hectares of trees between 1990 and 2010.

   b. The factory produced carbon at a constant rate of 246 tons per year between 1990 and 1997. In 1997, the factory made some equipment changes that reduced the emissions to 190 tons per year. Graph, together with the model in part *a*, the rate of emissions produced by the factory between 1990 and 2010. Find and label the time in which the absorption rate equals the production rate.

c. Label the regions of the graph in part *b* whose areas correspond to the following quantities:

   i. The carbon emissions produced by the factory but not absorbed by the trees

   ii. The carbon emissions produced by the factory and absorbed by the trees

   iii. The carbon emissions absorbed by the trees from sources other than the factory

d. Determine the values of the three quantities in part *c*.

e. After 20 years, will the amount of carbon absorbed by the trees be at least as much as the amount produced by the factory during that time period, as required by the EPA?

Discussing Concepts

38. Consider the regions between *f* and *g* depicted in the figure.

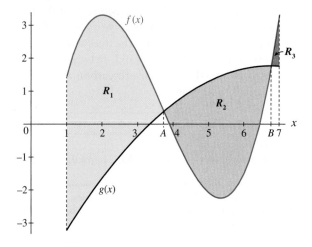

If *f* is the rate of change of the revenue of a small business and *g* is the rate of change of the costs of the business *x* years after its establishment (both quantities measured in thousands of dollars per year), interpret the areas of the regions R_1, R_2, and R_3 and the value of the definite integral $\int_{1}^{7} [f(x) - g(x)] dx$.

39. How are the heights of rectangles (between two curves) determined if one or both of the graphs lie below the horizontal axis? Consider the figure when giving an example.

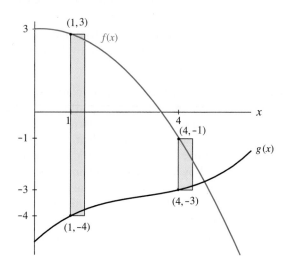

5.5   Average Value and Average Rate of Change

As a student, you are very familiar with grade averages and the method of calculating averages by adding grades and dividing by the number of them. Grades are discrete data. Let us consider a situation in which discrete averaging is not practical.

Concept Development: Averages of Continuous Functions   Consider calculating a person's average heart rate over 50 minutes of moderate activity. The actual heart rate is calculated as the number of times the person's heart beats during the time period divided by the time. However, without medical monitoring devices, it is impractical to count the number of heartbeats during a 50-minute period.

We could measure heart rate every 10 minutes and use these six data points to estimate the average over the entire 50-minute period. For example, by summing the heart rates in Table 5.16 and dividing by 6, we estimate that a person's heart rate over the time period represented by the table is 100.8 beats per minute.

TABLE 5.16

Time into test (minutes)	Heart rate (beats per minute)
0	95
10	105
20	100
30	94
40	101
50	110

Obviously, if the heart rate were measured every 5 minutes instead of every 10 minutes, a more accurate estimate of the average heart rate could be obtained. Averaging the data in Table 5.17 yields an estimate of 100.73 beats per minute.

TABLE 5.17

Time into test (minutes)	Heart rate (beats per minute)	Time into test (minutes)	Heart rate (beats per minute)
0	95	30	94
5	102	35	97
10	105	40	101
15	104	45	105
20	100	50	110
25	95		

The preceding averages use a discrete number of heart rates, whereas heart rate is constantly changing. In order to address this constantly changing situation, we use the data to model heart rate with a continuous function.

$$H(t) = (-4.802 \cdot 10^{-5})t^4 + 0.006t^3 - 0.229t^2$$
$$+ 2.813t + 94.371 \text{ beats per minute}$$

where t is the number of minutes since the test began.

Integrating this function over the 50-minute interval gives a close approximation of the total number of heart beats during that period:

$$\int_0^{50} H(t)dt \approx 5067 \text{ beats}$$

Dividing this total number of beats by 50 minutes yields the average heart rate of 101 beats per minute.

Caution: Using a continuous model for a discrete situation must be done with care. In this case, there are so many beats during the 50-minute interval (nearly 2 per second) that it is reasonable to model the heart rate with a continuous function.

Averaging is a balancing out of extremes. Figure 5.58 depicts a graph of the heart rate function. The average of that function's outputs, approximately 101 beats per minute, is shown as a dotted horizontal line on the graph.

FIGURE 5.58

The average value of a function over an interval can be graphically interpreted as the height (or signed height) of a rectangle whose area equals the area between the function and the horizontal axis over the interval. (Note that we do not show the vertical axis to zero in Figure 5.58; however, it is true that the area of the rectangle and the area between the graph and the line representing the horizontal axis shown in the figure are equal.)

Average Value of a Function

If $y = f(x)$ is a continuous function, then we can approximate the average value (or average) of the function over an interval from $x = a$ to $x = b$ by dividing the interval into n equally spaced subintervals, evaluating the function at a point in each subinterval, summing the function values, and dividing by n.

$$\text{Average value} \approx \frac{f(x_1) + f(x_2) \cdots f(x_{n-1}) + f(x_n)}{n}$$

We denote the length of each subinterval by Δx and calculate the length as $\Delta x = \frac{b - a}{n}$. Rewrite the average value estimate by multiplying the top and bottom terms by Δx. Then make the substitution $n \cdot \Delta x = b - a$ in the denominator.

$$\text{Average value} \approx \frac{[f(x_1) + f(x_2) + \cdots + f(x_{n-1}) + f(x_n)]\Delta x}{n \cdot \Delta x}$$

$$= \frac{[f(x_1) + f(x_2) + \cdots + f(x_{n-1}) + f(x_n)]\Delta x}{b - a}$$

As in the heart rate example, the estimate improves as the number of intervals increases. Thus we obtain the exact average value by finding the limit of the estimate as n approaches infinity:

$$\text{Average value} = \lim_{n \to \infty} \frac{[f(x_1) + f(x_2) + \cdots + f(x_{n-1}) + f(x_n)]\Delta x}{b - a}$$

which can be written as

$$\text{Average value} = \frac{\displaystyle\int_a^b f(x)dx}{b - a}$$

Thus we have

Average Value

If $y = f(x)$ is a smooth, continuous function from a to b, then the average value of $f(x)$ from a to b is

$$\begin{array}{c}\text{Average value of} \\ f(x) \text{ from } a \text{ to } b\end{array} = \frac{\displaystyle\int_a^b f(x)dx}{b - a}$$

EXAMPLE 1   *Finding Average Value and Average Rate of Change*

5.5.1

Temperature   Suppose that the hourly temperatures shown in Table 5.18 were recorded from 7 A.M. to 7 P.M. one day in September.

TABLE 5.18

Time	Temperature (°F)	Time	Temperature (°F)
7 A.M.	49	2 P.M.	80
8 A.M.	54	3 P.M.	80
9 A.M.	58	4 P.M.	78
10 A.M.	66	5 P.M.	74
11 A.M.	72	6 P.M.	69
noon	76	7 P.M.	62
1 P.M.	79		

a. Find a cubic model for this set of data.

b. Calculate the average temperature between 9 A.M. and 6 P.M.

c. Graph the equation together with the rectangle whose upper edge is determined by the average value.

d. Calculate the average rate of change of temperature from 9 A.M. to 6 P.M.

Solution

a. The temperature on this particular day can be modeled as

$$t(h) = -0.03526h^3 + 0.718h^2 + 1.58h + 13.69 \text{ degrees Fahrenheit}$$

h hours after midnight. This model applies only from $h = 7$ (7 A.M.) to $h = 19$ (7 P.M.).

b. The average temperature between 9 A.M. ($h = 9$) and 6 P.M. ($h = 18$) is

$$\text{Average temperature} = \frac{\displaystyle\int_9^{18} t(h)dh}{18 - 9} \approx 74.4° \text{ F}$$

c. Refer to Figure 5.59.

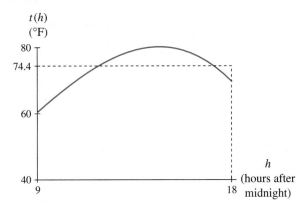

FIGURE 5.59

d. Recall that the average rate of change of a function on an interval is the change in output divided by the change in input. The average rate of change of temperature from 9 A.M. to 6 P.M. is

$$\text{Average rate of change of temperature} = \frac{t(18) - t(9)}{18 - 9} \approx 0.98 \text{ °F per hour} \quad \bullet$$

Average Rate of Change

The preceding example asked for an average rate of change. We know from Section 2.1 that the average rate of change of a continuous function $y = f(x)$ from $x = a$ to $x = b$ is calculated as $\frac{f(b) - f(a)}{b - a}$. However, consider what happens when you have a function that describes the rate of change of a quantity—that is, you have $y = f'(x)$—and you need to find the average rate of change of the quantity $f(x)$. In this case, you do not use the average rate-of-change formula but should instead use an integral to find the average value of the rate-of-change function. Note that we use the terms *average rate of change* and *average value of the rate of change* interchangeably.

> ### The Average Value of the Rate of Change
>
> If $y = f'(x)$ is a smooth, continuous rate-of-change function from a to b, then the average value of $f'(x)$ from a to b is
>
> $$\text{Average value of the rate of change of } f(x) \text{ from } a \text{ to } b = \frac{\int_a^b f'(x)\,dx}{b - a}$$
>
> $$= \frac{f(b) - f(a)}{b - a}$$
>
> where $f(x)$ is an antiderivative of $f'(x)$.

EXAMPLE 2   *Determining Which Quantity to Average*

Population Growth   The growth rate of the population of South Carolina between 1790 and 2000 can be modeled* as

$$p'(t) = 0.18t - 1.57 \text{ thousand people per year}$$

where t is the number of years since 1790. The population of South Carolina in 1990 was 3486 thousand people.

a.   What was the average rate of change in population from 1995 through 2000?

b.   What was the average size of the population from 1995 through 2000?

Solution

a.   The average rate of change in population between 1995 and 2000 is calculated directly from the rate-of-change function as

$$\frac{\int_{205}^{210} p'(t)\,dt \text{(thousand people/year)(years)}}{(210 - 205) \text{ years}} \approx 35.8 \text{ thousand people per year}$$

b.   In order to calculate the average population, we must have a function for population. That is, we need an antiderivative of the rate-of-change function:

$$p(t) = \int p'(t)\,dt$$

$$= 0.09t^2 - 1.57t + C \text{ thousand people}$$

We know that the population in 1990 was 3486 thousand people. Using this fact, we solve for C, so the function for population is

$$p(t) = 0.09t^2 - 1.57t + 200 \text{ thousand people}$$

where t is the number of years since 1790.

---

* Based on data from *Statistical Abstract,* 2001.

Now we calculate the average population between 1995 and 2000 as

$$\frac{\int_{205}^{210} p(t)dt}{210 - 205} \approx 3749 \text{ thousand people} \quad \bullet$$

Note in Example 2 that the average value of the population was found by integrating the population function, whereas the average rate of change was found by integrating the population rate-of-change function. This example illustrates an important principle:

> In using integrals to find average values, integrate the function whose output is the quantity you wish to average.

Note also that in part *a* of Example 2, we could have calculated the average rate of change by using the population function and the formula

$$\frac{p(210)-p(205)}{210 - 205} = \frac{178.9 \text{ thousand people}}{5 \text{ years}} \approx 35.8 \text{ thousand people per year}$$

Keeping units of measure attached to values can help you correctly calculate and label average values.

We summarize this discussion as follows:

Average Values and Average Rates of Change

If $y = f(x)$ is a continuous or piecewise continuous function describing a quantity from $x = a$ to $x = b$, then the average value of the quantity from a to b is calculated by using the quantity function and the formula

$$\text{Average value of } f(x) = \frac{\int_a^b f(x)dx}{b - a}$$

The average value has the same units as the output of the function f.

The average rate of change of the quantity, also called the average value of the rate of change, can be calculated from the quantity function as

$$\text{Average rate of change} = \frac{f(b)-f(a)}{b - a}$$

or from the rate-of-change function as

$$\text{Average rate of change} = \frac{\int_a^b f'(x)dx}{b - a}$$

The average rate of change has the same units as the rate of change of f.

EXAMPLE 3   *Graphically Illustrating Average Value*

Note that $a'(t) = r(t)$

Carbon-14   Scientists estimate that 100 milligrams of the isotope ^{14}C used in carbon dating methods decays at a rate of

$$r(t) = -0.0121(0.999879^t) \text{ milligrams per year}$$

where t is the number of years since the 100 milligrams of isotope began to decay. The amount of the isotope that remains after t years of decay is

$$a(t) = 100(0.999879^t) \text{ milligrams}$$

a.   What is the average amount of the remaining isotope during the first 1000 years?

b.   What is the average rate of decay during the first 1000 years?

c.   Graphically illustrate the answers to parts a and b.

Solution

a.   We calculate the average amount remaining during the first thousand years as

$$\frac{\int_0^{1000} a(t)dt}{1000 - 0} \approx 94.2 \text{ milligrams}$$

b.   We find the average rate of decay during the first 1000 years as

$$\frac{\int_0^{1000} r(t)dt}{1000 - 0} \approx -0.0114 \text{ milligram per year}$$

In other words, the amount of ^{14}C decreased by an average of 0.0114 milligram per year during the first 1000 years. Note that this average rate of change can also be calculated by using the amount function:

$$\frac{a(1000)-a(0)}{1000 - 0} \approx \frac{88.6 - 100 \text{ milligrams}}{1000 \text{ years}} = -0.0114 \text{ milligram per year}$$

c.   The average amount determines the top of the rectangle shown in Figure 5.60a. The average rate of decay determines the bottom of the rectangle shown in Figure 5.60b. The average decay rate also can be graphically illustrated as the slope of a secant line through two points on the amount function.

(a)

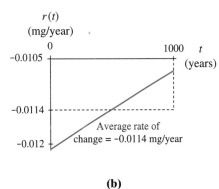

(b)

FIGURE 5.60

5.5 Concept Inventory

- Average value of a function
- Graphical illustration of average value
- Average rate of change of a function
- Average value of a rate-of-change function

5.5 Activities

Applying Concepts

1. **Traffic Speed** The Highway Department is concerned about the high speed of traffic during the weekday afternoon rush hours from 4 P.M. to 7 P.M. on a newly widened stretch of interstate highway that is just inside the city limits of a certain city. The Office of Traffic Studies has collected the data given in the table, which show typical weekday speeds during the 4 P.M. to 7 P.M. rush hours.

Time	Speed (mph)	Time	Speed (mph)
4:00	60	5:45	72.25
4:15	61	6:00	74
4:30	62.5	6:15	74.5
4:45	64	6:30	75
5:00	66.25	6:45	74.25
5:15	67.5	7:00	73
5:30	70		

a. Find a model for the data.
b. Use the equation to approximate the average weekday rush-hour speed from 4 P.M. to 7 P.M.
c. Use the equation to approximate the average weekday rush-hour speed from 5 P.M. to 7 P.M.

2. **Electronics Sales** U.S. factory sales of electronic goods to dealers from 1990 through 2001 can be modeled by the equation

$$\text{Sales} = 0.0388x^3 - 0.495x^2 + 5.698x + 43.6$$
billion dollars

where x is the number of years since 1990.

(Sources: Based on data from *Statistical Abstract*, 2001, and Consumer Electronics Association.)

a. Use a definite integral to approximate the average annual value of U.S. factory sales of electronic goods to dealers from 1990 through 2001.
b. Sketch the graph of sales from 1990 through 2001, and draw the horizontal line representing the average value.

3. **Phone Calls** The most expensive rates (in dollars per minute) for a 2-minute telephone call using a long-distance carrier are listed in the accompanying table.

Year	Rate (dollars per minute)
1982	1.32
1984	1.24
1985	1.14
1986	1.01
1987	0.83
1988	0.77
1989	0.65
1990	0.65
1995	0.40
2000	0.20

a. Find a model for the data.
b. Use a definite integral to estimate the average of the most expensive rates from 1982 through 1990.
c. Use a definite integral to estimate the average of the most expensive rates from 1982 through 2000.

4. **Ticket Price** The table gives the price (in dollars) of a round-trip flight from Denver to Chicago on a certain airline and the corresponding monthly profit (in millions of dollars) for that airline for that route.

Ticket price (dollars)	Profit (millions of dollars)
200	3.08
250	3.52
300	3.76
350	3.82
400	3.70
450	3.38

a. Find a model for the data.

b. Determine the average profit for ticket prices from \$325 to \$450.

c. Determine the average rate of change of profit when the ticket price rises from \$325 to \$450.

d. Graphically illustrate the answers to parts *b* and *c*.

5. **Population**   The population of Mexico between 1921 and 2000 is given by the model

Population = $7.567(1.02639^t)$ million people

where *t* is number of years since the end of 1900.

(Source: Based on data from www.inegi.gob.mx. Accessed 9/20/02.)

a. What was the average population of Mexico from the beginning of 1990 through the end of 1999?

b. In what year was the population of Mexico equal to its 1990s average?

c. What was the average rate of change of the population of Mexico during the 1990s?

6. **Veggies**   The per capita utilization of commercially produced fresh vegetables in the United States from 1980 through 2000 can be modeled by

$v(t) = 0.092t^2 + 0.720t + 149.554$ pounds per person

where *t* is the number of years after 1980.

(Sources: Based on data from *Statistical Abstract*, 2001, and www.ers.usda.gov. Accessed 9/25/02.)

a. Use a definite integral to estimate the average per capita utilization of commercially produced fresh vegetables in the United States between 1980 and 2000.

b. Find the average rate of change in per capita utilization between 1980 and 2000.

c. In which year was the per capita utilization closest to the average per capita utilization between 1980 and 2000?

7. **Air Accidents**   The number of general-aviation aircraft accidents from 1975 through 1997 can be modeled by

$a(x) = -100.6118x + 3967.5572$ accidents

where *x* is the number of years since 1975.

(Source: Based on data from *Statistical Abstract*, 1994 and 1998.)

a. Calculate the average rate of change in the yearly number of accidents from 1976 through 1997.

b. Use a definite integral to estimate the average number of accidents that occurred each year from 1976 through 1997.

c. Graphically illustrate the answers to parts *a* and *b*.

8. **Temperature**   During a certain summer thunderstorm, the temperature drops and then rises again. The rate of change of the temperature during the hour and a half after the storm began is given by

$T(h) = 9.48h^3 - 15.49h^2 + 17.38h - 9.87$ °F per hour

where *h* is the number of hours since the storm began.

a. Calculate the average rate of change of temperature from 0 to 1.5 hours after the storm began.

b. If the temperature was 85°F at the time the storm began, find the average temperature during the first 1.5 hours of the storm.

9. **Road Test**   The acceleration of a race car during the first 35 seconds of a road test is modeled by

$a(t) = 0.024t^2 - 1.72t + 22.58$ ft/sec^2

where *t* is the number of seconds since the test began. Assume that velocity and distance were both 0 at the beginning of the road test.

a. Calculate the average acceleration during the first 35 seconds of the road test.

b. Calculate the average velocity during the first 35 seconds of the road test.

c. Calculate the distance traveled during the first 35 seconds of the road test.

d. If the car had been traveling at its average velocity throughout the 35 seconds, how far would the car have traveled during that 35 seconds?

e. Graphically illustrate the answers to parts *a* and *b*. Explain how the answer to part *c* is related to the graphical illustration of the part *b* answer.

10. **Oil Production**   On the basis of data obtained from a preliminary report by a geological survey team, it is estimated that for the first 10 years of production, a certain oil well in Texas can be expected to produce oil at the rate of

$r(t) = 3.93546t^{3.55}e^{-1.35135t}$ thousand barrels per year

t years after production begins. Estimate the average annual yield from this oil well during the first 10 years of production.

11. **Velocity** An article in the May 23, 1996, issue of *Nature* addresses the interest some physicists have in studying cracks in order to answer the question "How fast do things break, and why?" Data given in the table are estimated from a graph in this article showing velocity of a crack during a 60-microsecond experiment.

Time (microseconds)	Velocity (meters per second)
10	148.2
20	159.3
30	169.5
40	180.7
50	189.8
60	200.0

a. Find a model for the data.

b. Determine the average speed at which a crack travels between 10 and 60 microseconds.

12. **Newspapers** The circulation (as of September 20 of each year) of daily English-language newspapers in the United States between 1986 and 2000 can be modeled as

$$n(x) = 0.00792x^3 - 0.32x^2 + 3.457x + 51.588$$
million newspapers

where x is the number of years since 1980.

(Source: Based on data from *Statistical Abstract*, 1995 and 2001.)

a. Estimate the average newspaper circulation from 1986 through 2000.

b. In what year was the newspaper circulation closest to the average circulation from 1986 through 2000?

c. Graphically illustrate the answer to part *a*.

13. **Blood Pressure** Blood pressure varies for individuals throughout the course of a day, typically being lowest at night and highest from late morning to early afternoon. The estimated rate of change in diastolic blood pressure for a patient with untreated hypertension is shown in the table.

a. Find a model for the data.

b. Estimate the average rate of change in diastolic blood pressure from 8 A.M. to 8 P.M.

c. Assuming that diastolic blood pressure was 95 mm Hg at 12 P.M., estimate the average diastolic blood pressure between 8 A.M. and 8 P.M.

Time	Diastolic BP (mm Hg per hour)
8 A.M.	3.0
10 A.M.	1.8
noon	0.7
2 P.M.	−0.1
4 P.M.	−0.7
6 P.M.	−1.1
8 P.M.	−1.3
10 P.M.	−1.1
midnight	−0.7
2 A.M.	0.1
4 A.M.	0.8
6 A.M.	1.9

14. **Air Speed** The air speed of a small airplane during the first 25 seconds of takeoff and flight can be modeled by

$$v(t) = -940,602t^2 + 19,269.3t - 0.3 \text{ mph}$$

t hours after takeoff.

a. Find the average air speed during the first 25 seconds of takeoff and flight.

b. Find the average acceleration during the first 25 seconds of takeoff and flight.

15. **Swim Time** The rate of change of the winning times for the 100-meter butterfly swimming competition at selected Summer Olympic Games between 1956 and 2000 can be described by $w(t) = 0.0106t - 1.148$ seconds per year, where t is the number of years after 1900. Find the average rate of change of the winning times for the competition from 1956 through 2000.

(Source: Based on data from *Statistical Abstract*, 2001.)

16. **Emissions** The federal government sets standards for toxic substances in the air. Often these standards are stated in the form of average pollutant levels over a period of time on the basis of the reasoning that exposure to high levels of toxic substances is harmful, but prolonged exposure to

moderate levels is equally harmful. For example, carbon monoxide (CO) levels may not exceed 35 ppm (parts per million) at any time, but they also must not exceed 9 ppm averaged over any 8-hour period.

(Source: Douglas J. Crawford-Brown, *Theoretical and Mathematical Foundations of Human Health Risk Analysis,* Boston: Kluwer Academic Publishers, 1997.)

The concentration of carbon monoxide in the air in a certain metropolitan area is measured and can be modeled as

$$c(h) = -0.004h^4 + 0.05h^3 - 0.27h^2 + 2.05h + 3.1 \text{ ppm}$$

h hours after 7 A.M.

a. Did the city exceed the 35-ppm maximum in the 8 hours between 7 A.M. and 3 P.M.?

b. Did the city exceed the 9-ppm maximum average between 7 A.M. and 3 P.M.?

17. **Emissions**   Refer to the discussion in Activity 16. The following table shows measured concentrations of carbon monoxide in the air of a city on a certain day between 6 A.M. and 10 P.M.

Time (hours since 6 A.M.)	CO concentration (ppm)
0	3
2	12
4	22
6	18
8	16
10	20
12	28
14	16
16	6

a. Consider a scatter plot of the data and determine (by examination of the data) over which 8-hour period the average CO concentration was greatest.

b. Model the data. Use the equation to calculate the average CO concentration during the 8-hour period determined in part *a.*

c. Use the equation in part *b* to estimate the average CO concentration in this city between 6 A.M. and

10 P.M. The city issues air quality warnings based on the daily average CO concentration of the previous day between 6 A.M. and 10 P.M. The warnings are as follows:

Average concentration	Warning
$0 < \text{CO} \le 9$	None
$9 < \text{CO} \le 12$	Moderate pollution. People with asthma and other respiratory problems should remain indoors if possible.
$12 < \text{CO} \le 16$	Serious pollution. Ban on all single-passenger vehicles. Everyone is encouraged to stay indoors.
$\text{CO} > 16$	Severe pollution. Mandatory school and business closures.

d. Judging on the basis of the data in the table and your answer to part *c*, which warning do you believe should be posted?

18. **Population**   Aurora, Nevada, was a mining boom town in the 1860s and 1870s. Its population can be modeled by the function

$$p(t) = \begin{cases} -7.91t^3 + 120.96t^2 + 193.92t \\ \quad - 123.21 \text{ people} & \text{when } 0.7 \le t \le 13 \\ 45{,}544(0.8474^t) \text{ people} & \text{when } 13 < t \le 55 \end{cases}$$

with rate-of-change function

$$p'(t) = \begin{cases} -23.73t^2 + 241.92t + 193.92 \\ \quad \text{people per year} & \text{when } 0.7 \le t < 13 \\ -7541.287(0.8474^t) \\ \quad \text{people per year} & \text{when } 13 < t \le 55 \end{cases}$$

In both functions, t is the number of years since 1860.

(Source: Based on data from Don Ashbaugh, *Nevada's Turbulent Yesterday: A Study in Ghost Towns,* Los Angeles: Westernlore Press, 1963.)

a. What was the average population of Aurora between 1861 and 1871? between 1871 and 1881?

b. Demonstrate two methods for calculating the average rate of change of the population of Aurora between 1861 and 1871.

Discussing Concepts

19. We know that the area of the region between the graph of a function and the horizontal axis from $x = a$ to $x = b$ is equal to the area of the rectangle whose height is the average value of the function from $x = a$ to $x = b$ and whose width is $b - a$. The graphs presented in this section show only a portion of the vertical axis. That is, in each graph, the vertical axis does not extend all the way to zero. Instead, the vertical axis is shown above (or below) a line $y = k$. However, on the interval from $x = a$ to $x = b$, the area of the region between the graph and the line $y = k$ and the area of the rectangle between the average value and the line $y = k$ are equal. Explain, illustrating with graphs, why this is true.

5.6 Integration by Substitution or Algebraic Manipulation

We have thus far examined situations in which it is useful to determine accumulated change in a quantity by finding or estimating the area of a region between the graph of a rate-of-change function and the horizontal axis. We estimated such areas by summing areas of rectangles until we discovered that the Fundamental Theorem of Calculus enables us to find areas using antiderivatives. Although there are limitations on our ability to find antiderivatives for functions, we explore two techniques that allow us to extend our ability to find antiderivatives.

The first technique is to use algebra to change the integrand into one that can be evaluated using the formulas from Section 5.4. We illustrate antiderivatives that involve simple products or quotients in Example 1.

EXAMPLE 1 *Finding Antiderivatives That Involve Products or Quotients of Functions*

Determine whether the following general antiderivatives involving products or quotients can be found using the techniques presented in this book. If so, find the antiderivative.

a. $\displaystyle\int x\sqrt{x}\, dx$

b. $\displaystyle\int 2x\sqrt{x^2 + 1}\, dx$

c. $\displaystyle\int e^{3x}(e^{4x} + 4)dx$

d. $\displaystyle\int \frac{4x^3 + 2x}{2x^2}dx$

Solution

a. Rewrite $x\sqrt{x}$ as $x(x^{1/2}) = x^{3/2}$. Then apply the Power Rule for antiderivatives to obtain $\displaystyle\int x\sqrt{x}\, dx = \frac{2x^{5/2}}{5} + C$.

b. Unlike the expression in part *a*, it is not possible to rewrite $2x\sqrt{x^2 + 1}$ in such a way that we can easily find its antiderivative.

c. Multiply the two factors to rewrite as $e^{7x} + 4e^{3x}$ and apply antiderivative rules to obtain

$$\int e^{3x}(e^{4x} + 4)dx = \int (e^{7x} + 4e^{3x})dx = \frac{e^{7x}}{7} + \frac{4e^{3x}}{3} + C$$

d. Rewrite $\dfrac{4x^3 + 2x}{2x^2}$ as $\dfrac{4x^3}{2x^2} + \dfrac{2x}{2x^2} = 2x + \dfrac{1}{x}$. Then apply the Sum Rule, the

Power Rule, and the Natural Log Rule for antiderivatives to obtain

$$\int \frac{4x^3 + 2x}{2x^2}dx = \int (2x + \frac{1}{x})\,dx = x^2 + \ln|x| + C. \quad \bullet$$

In part *b* of Example 1, we could not find $\displaystyle\int 2x\sqrt{x^2 + 1}\,dx$ using the antiderivative rules already presented in this text. The expression $2x\sqrt{x^2 + 1}$ involves function composition and function multiplication. The composite factor of the expression is $\sqrt{x^2 + 1}$. If we let $f(x) = x^2 + 1$ and $g(u) = \sqrt{u}$, we can write $\sqrt{x^2 + 1}$ as $\sqrt{f(x)} = g(f(x))$. The factor $2x$ is important because $f'(x) = 2x$. Changing the order of the factors in the expression and substituting f and g where appropriate, we get

$$2x\sqrt{x^2 + 1} = (\sqrt{x^2 + 1})\cdot 2x = g(f(x))\cdot f'(x).$$

The expression $g(f(x))\cdot f'(x)$ should look familiar to you. Recall that for a composite function $G(f(x))$ the derivative function is found using the Chain Rule:

$$\frac{d}{dx} G(f(x)) = g(f(x))\cdot f'(x) \text{ where } g = G'$$

Thus, $(\sqrt{x^2 + 1})\cdot 2x$ is in the form of the right side of the Chain Rule. Applying the Fundamental Theorem of Calculus to the Chain Rule (as stated here) yields

$$\int g(f(x))\cdot f'(x)dx = G(f(x)) + C$$

We shorten this notation by letting $u = f(x)$ and substituting du for $f'(x)dx$ to obtain $\displaystyle\int g(u)du = G(u) + C$. This method is known as **Integration by Substitution**.

Integration by Substitution

Given $\displaystyle\int g(f(x))\cdot f'(x)dx$, let $u = f(x)$ and $du = f'(x)dx$.

If G is an antiderivative of g, then

$$\int g(f(x))\cdot f'(x)dx = \int g(u)du = G(u) + C = G(f(x)) + C$$

Applying Integration by Substitution on $\int 2x\sqrt{x^2 + 1}\, dx$ yields

$$\int 2x\sqrt{x^2 + 1}\, dx = \int (\sqrt{x^2 + 1}) \cdot 2x\, dx$$

$$= \int \sqrt{u}\, du = \int u^{1/2}\, du \text{ where } u = x^2 + 1 \text{ and } du = 2x\, dx$$

$$= \frac{2}{3} u^{3/2} + C$$

$$= \frac{2}{3} (x^2 + 1)^{3/2} + C$$

The next example illustrates Integration by Substitution for other composite functions.

EXAMPLE 2   *Using Substitution to Find Antiderivatives That Involve Composite Functions*

Use Integration by Substitution to evaluate the following integrals.

a. $\int 6xe^{3x^2 - 7}\, dx$ b. $\int_0^2 6xe^{3x^2 - 7}\, dx$

c. $\int (3x - 7)^2\, dx$

Solution

a. Rewrite the expression with the factor involving composition to the left:

$$\int 6xe^{3x^2 - 7}\, dx = \int (e^{3x^2 - 7}) \cdot 6x\, dx$$

Let $u = 3x^2 - 7$ so that $du = 6x\, dx$, and rewrite the integral as $\int e^u\, du$.

Use the Exponent Rule for antiderivatives to obtain $\int e^u\, du = e^u + C$. Finally, replace u with $3x^2 - 7$ so that

$$\int 6xe^{3x^2 - 7}\, dx = e^{3x^2 - 7} + C$$

b. To determine $\int_0^2 6xe^{3x^2 - 7}\, dx$, evaluate the antiderivative from part a at 0 and 2.

$$\int_0^2 6xe^{3x^2 - 7}\, dx = e^{3x^2 - 7} \Big|_0^2 = e^5 - e^{-7}$$

c. For the integral $\int (3x - 7)^2\, dx$, let $u = 3x - 7$. The derivative of $3x - 7$

with respect to x is 3, so $du = 3dx$. Multiply the integral by $\frac{1}{3} \cdot 3$ to obtain the proper form.

$$\int (3x - 7)^2\, dx = \frac{1}{3} \cdot 3 \int (3x - 7)^2\, dx = \frac{1}{3} \int (3x - 7)^2 \cdot 3 dx$$

$$= \frac{1}{3} \int u^2 du \qquad \text{where } u = 3x - 7$$

$$= \frac{1}{3} \left(\frac{1}{3} u^3\right) + C = \frac{1}{9} u^3 + C$$

$$= \frac{1}{9} (3x - 7)^3 + C$$

Thus $\int (3x - 7)^2\, dx = \frac{1}{9} (3x - 7)^3 + C.$ ●

When finding antiderivatives, it is always a good idea to take the derivative of your answer in order to determine whether it is correct. Finding antiderivatives is one procedure for which there is a simple way to check the answer.

5.6   Concept Inventory

- Algebraic manipulation before integration
- Integration by substitution

5.6   Activities

In Activities 1 through 8, find the general antiderivative if possible.

1. $\int 2e^{2x}\, dx$

2. $\int 2xe^{x^2}\, dx$

3. $\int x^2 e^{x^2}\, dx$

4. $\int 3(\ln 2)2^x(1 + 2^x)^3\, dx$

5. $\int (1 + e^x)^2\, e^x\, dx$

6. $\int \sqrt{1 + e^x}\, e^x dx$

7. $\int \frac{2^x}{2^x + 2}\, dx$

8. $\int \frac{5e^x}{e^x + 2}\, dx$

In Activities 9 through 20, find the exact value of the integral by using antiderivative formulas if possible. If this is not possible, use technology to estimate the answer. In either case, state whether your answer is exact or an approximation.

9. $\int_1^4 \ln x\, dx$

10. $\int_1^4 x \ln x\, dx$

11. $\int_2^5 \frac{\ln x}{x}\, dx$

12. $\int_2^5 \frac{5(\ln x)^4}{x}\, dx$

13. $\int_1^2 2x \ln(x^2 + 1)\, dx$

14. $\int_1^2 \ln(x^2 + 1)\, dx$

15. $\int_3^4 \frac{2x}{x^2 + 1}\, dx$

16. $\int_3^4 \frac{1}{x^2 + 1}\, dx$

17. $\int_1^6 \frac{2x^2}{x^2 + 1}\, dx$

18. $\int_3^4 \frac{x^2 + 1}{2x}\, dx$

19. $\int_3^4 \frac{x^2 + 1}{x^2}\, dx$

20. $\int_0^1 -x\sqrt{x^2 + 1}\, dx$

SUMMARY

Approximating Results of Change

The accumulated results of change are best understood in geometric terms: Positive accumulation is the area of a region between the graph of a positive rate-of-change function and the horizontal axis, and negative accumu-lation is the signed area of a region between the graph of a negative rate-of-change function and the horizontal axis. We can approximate the areas of regions of interest by summing areas of rectangular regions.

Limits of Sums and Accumulation Functions

The area of a region between the graph of a continuous, non-negative function f and the horizontal axis from a to b is given by a limit of sums:

$$\text{Area} = \lim_{n \to \infty} [f(x_1) + f(x_2) + \cdots + f(x_n)]\Delta x$$

Here, the points $x_1, x_2, \ldots, x_n$ are the midpoints of n rectangles of width $\Delta x = \dfrac{b - a}{n}$ between a and b.

More generally, we consider the limit applied to an arbitrary continuous bounded function f over the interval from a to b and call this limit the definite integral of f from a to b. In symbols, we write

$$\int_a^b f(x)dx = \lim_{n \to \infty} [f(x_1) + f(x_2) + \cdots + f(x_n)]\Delta x$$

An accumulation function is an integral of the form $\int_a^x f(t)\,dt$, where the upper limit x is a variable. This function gives us a formula for calculating accumulated change in a quantity.

The Fundamental Theorem of Calculus

The Fundamental Theorem sets forth the fundamental connection between the two main concepts of calculus, the derivative and the integral. It tells us that for any continuous function f,

$$\frac{d}{dx} \int_a^x f(t)dt = f(x)$$

In other words, the derivative of an accumulation function of $y = f(t)$ is precisely $y = f(x)$.

If we reverse the order of these two processes and begin by differentiating first, then we obtain the starting function plus a constant.

$$\int_a^x f'(t)dt = f(x) + C$$

A function F is an antiderivative of f if $F'(x) = f(x)$.

Because the derivative of $y = \int_a^x f(t)dt$ is $y' = f(x)$, we see that $y = \int_a^x f(t)dt$ is an antiderivative of $y' = f(x)$.

Each continuous bounded function has infinitely many antiderivatives, but any two differ by only a constant.

The Fundamental Theorem enables us to find accumulation function formulas by finding antiderivatives.

The Definite Integral

The Fundamental Theorem of Calculus enabled us to show that when f is a smooth, continuous function, the definite integral $\int_a^b f(x)dx$ can be evaluated by

$$\int_a^b f(x)dx = F(b) - F(a)$$

where F is any antiderivative of f.

The Fundamental Theorem of Calculus ensures that each continuous bounded function does indeed have an antiderivative. Thus, to the extent that we can actually obtain an algebraic expression for an antiderivative, we can easily evaluate a definite integral. In situations where an antiderivative cannot be found, we use one of the approximation techniques discussed in Section 5.1 allowing technology to perform the calculations.

To compute the area between two curves, we used the fact that if the graph of f lies above the graph of g from a to b, then the integral $\int_a^b [f(x) - g(x)]dx$ is the area of the region between the two graphs from a to b.

Note that if the two functions intersect between a and b, then the difference between the accumulated changes of the functions is *not* the same as the total area of the regions between the two rate-of-change curves.

Average Values and Average Rates of Change

We use definite integrals to calculate the average value of a continuous function for a quantity:

$$\begin{array}{c} \text{Average value of} \\ f(x) \text{ from } a \text{ to } b \end{array} = \frac{\displaystyle\int_a^b f(x)dx}{b - a}$$

When we are given a rate-of-change function $y = f'(t)$, the average rate of change of $f(t)$ from $t = a$ to $t = b$ is

$$\begin{array}{c} \text{Average rate of change} \\ \text{of } f(x) \text{ from } a \text{ to } b \end{array} = \frac{\displaystyle\int_a^b f'(t)dt}{b - a}$$

CONCEPT CHECK

Can you

To practice, try

• Interpret accumulated change and area?	Section 5.1	Activity 3
• Approximate areas using rectangles?	Section 5.1	Activities 11, 13
• Interpret definite integrals?	Section 5.1	Activities 3, 5
• Approximate area using a limiting value?	Section 5.1	Activities 9, 11
• Sketch and interpret accumulation functions?	Section 5.2	Activities 3, 11
• Recover the units of a quantity function?	Section 5.2	Activity 21
• Find general antiderivatives?	Section 5.3	Activities 11, 15, 17
• Find and interpret specific antiderivatives?	Section 5.3	Activities 23, 25, 27
• Recover a function from its rate-of-change equation?	Section 5.3	Activity 29
• Use the Fundamental Theorem to evaluate definite integrals?	Section 5.4	Activities 13, 17
• Find and interpret areas between two curves?	Section 5.4	Activity 33
• Find average value and average rate of change?	Section 5.5	Activity 7
• Determine whether an approximation technique is necessary in order to estimate the value of a definite integral?	Section 5.6	Activities 13, 15

CONCEPT REVIEW

1. **Oil Flow**   The rate at which crude oil flows through a pipe into a holding tank can be modeled by

$$r(t) = 10(-3.2t^2 + 93.3t + 50.7) \text{ ft}^3/\text{minute}$$

where t is the number of minutes the oil has been flowing into the tank.

   a. Sketch a graph of r for t between 0 and 25 minutes.

   b. Use five midpoint rectangles to estimate the area of the region between the graph of r and the t-axis from 0 to 25 minutes. Sketch the rectangles on the graph you drew in part *a*.

   c. Interpret your answer to part *b*.

2. **Speed**   A hurricane is 300 miles off the east coast of Florida at 1 A.M. The speed at which the hurricane is

moving toward Florida is measured each hour. Speeds between 1 A.M. and 5 A.M. are recorded in the table.

Time	Speed (mph)	Time	Speed (mph)
1 A.M.	15	4 A.M.	38
2 A.M.	25	5 A.M.	40
3 A.M.	35		

a. Find a model for the data.

b. Use a limiting value of sums of areas of midpoint rectangles to estimate how far (to the nearest tenth of a mile) the hurricane traveled between 1 A.M. and 5 A.M. Begin with five rectangles, doubling the number each time until you are confident that you know the limiting value.

3. **Dieting** The accompanying graph depicts the rate of change in the weight of someone who diets for 20 weeks.

a. What does the area of the shaded region beneath the horizontal axis represent?

b. What does the area of the shaded region above the horizontal axis represent?

Rate of change in weight
(pounds per week)

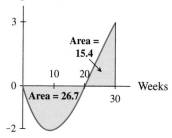

c. Is this person's weight at 30 weeks more or less than it was at 0 weeks? How much more or less?

d. If w is the function shown in the figure, sketch a graph of $W(t) = \int_0^x w(t)dt$. Label units and values on both axes of your graph.

e. What does the graph in part d represent?

4. **Oil Flow** Consider again the model for the flow rate of crude oil into a holding tank:

$$r(t) = 10(-3.2t^2 + 93.3t + 50.7)\text{ft}^3/\text{minute}$$

after t minutes.

a. If the holding tank contains 5000 ft³ of oil when $t = 0$, find a model for the amount of oil in the tank after t minutes.

b. Use your model in part a to find how much oil flowed into the tank during the first 10 minutes.

c. If the capacity of the tank is 150,000 ft³, according to the model, how long can the oil flow into the tank before the tank is full?

5. **Investment** Ten thousand dollars invested in a mutual fund is growing at a rate of

$$a(x) = 840(1.08763^x) \text{ dollars per year}$$

x years after it was invested.

a. Determine the value of $\int_0^{2.75} a(x)dx$.

b. Interpret your answer to part a.

c. What is the average rate of growth of the investment from $x = 0$ to $x = 2.75$?

6. **Earnings** Based on data provided by the U.S. Bureau of the Census for the years 1980 through 1988, the full-time average annual earnings of men and women in the United States can be modeled by the following equations:

Men: $m(t) = 0.0625t^2 - 10.38t$
$+ 466.8075$ thousand dollars

Women: $w(t) = -0.03125t^2 + 5.695t$
$- 234.89875$ thousand dollars

where t is the number of years since 1900. From the beginning of 1980 and through the end of 1988, by how much did the 9-year earnings of a man who earned the average wage exceed those of a woman who earned the average wage?

Project 5.1 Acceleration, Velocity, and Distance

Setting

According to tests conducted by *Road and Track*, a 1993 Toyota Supra Turbo accelerates from 0 to 30 mph in 2.2 seconds and travels 1.4 miles (1320 feet) in 13.5 seconds, reaching a speed of 107 mph. *Road and Track* reported the data given in the table.

Time (seconds)	Speed reached from rest (mph)
0	0
2.2	30
2.9	40
4.0	50
5.0	60
6.5	70
8.0	80
9.0	90
11.8	100

Tasks

1. Convert the speed data to feet per second, and find a quadratic model for velocity (in feet per second) as a function of time (in seconds). Discuss how close your model comes to predicting the 107 mph reached after 13.5 seconds.

2. Add the data point for 13.5 seconds, and find a quadratic model for velocity.

3. Use four rectangles and your model from Task 2 to estimate the distance traveled during acceleration from rest to a speed of 50 mph and the distance traveled during acceleration from a speed of 50 mph to a speed of 100 mph. Repeat the estimate using twice as many rectangles.

4. Use nine rectangles to approximate the distance traveled during the first 13.5 seconds. How close is your estimate to the reported value?

5. Find the distances traveled during

   a. Acceleration from rest to a speed of 50 mph

   b. Acceleration from a speed of 50 mph to a speed of 100 mph

   c. The first 13.5 seconds of acceleration

   Compare these answers to your estimates in Tasks 3 and 4. Explain how estimating with areas of rectangles is related to calculating the definite integral.

Reporting

Prepare a written report of your work. Include scatter plots, models, graphs, and discussions of each of the above tasks.

Project 5.2 Estimating Growth

Setting

A table based on data from the Berkeley Growth Study is located on the *Calculus Concepts* website. This table lists the rate of growth of a typical male from birth to 18 years.

Tasks

1. Use the data and right rectangles to approximate the height of a typical 18-year-old male.

2. Sketch a smooth, continuous curve over a scatter plot of the data. Find a piecewise model for the data. Use no more than three pieces.

3. Use your piecewise model and limits of sums to approximate the height of a typical 18-year-old male. Convert centimeters to feet and inches, and compare your answer to the estimate you obtained using right rectangles. Which is likely to be the more accurate approximation? Why?

4. Use your piecewise model and what you know about definite integrals to find the height of a typical 18-year-old male in feet and inches. Compare your answer with the better of the approximations you obtained in Task 3.

5. Randomly choose ten 18-year-old male students, and determine their heights. (Include your data—names are not necessary, only the heights.) Discuss your selection process and why you feel that it is random. Find the average height of the 18-year-old males in your sample. Compare this average height with your answer to Task 4. Discuss your results.

6. Refer to your sketch of the rate-of-growth graph in Task 2, and draw a possible graph of the height of a typical 18-year-old male from birth to age 18.

Reporting

Prepare a report that presents your findings in Tasks 1 through 6. Explain the different methods that you used, and discuss why these methods should all give similar results. Attach your mathematical work as an appendix to your report.

Analyzing Accumulated Change: Integrals in Action

6

Darama/CORBIS

Concepts Outline

6.1 Perpetual Accumulation and Improper Integrals

6.2 Streams in Business and Biology

6.3 Integrals in Economics

6.4 Probability Distributions and Density Functions

Concept Application

The CEO of a large corporation must concern himself or herself with many facets of the economy and the corporation's relationship to it. For example, the CEO may be interested in answering questions as diverse as

- What is the 5-year future value of an income stream that the corporation invests?

- What is the market equilibrium price for a particular product produced by the corporation?

- What is the probability that an entry-level employee will continue with the company at least 5 years?

In this chapter you will learn how to answer questions such as these.

Chapter Introduction

Chapter 5 established that the accumulated results of change are limiting values of approximating sums known as definite integrals. Magnitudes of accumulated change can be expressed as areas of regions between the graph of a rate-of-change function and the horizontal axis. The Fundamental Theorem of Calculus provides a simple method for evaluating definite integrals using antiderivatives.

In Chapter 6 we present several applications of integration. We use integrals to calculate perpetual accumulation, present and future values of income streams, and future values of biological streams. We discuss how integrals can be applied to economics topics and used to calculate economic quantities of interest to consumers and producers. We conclude by using integrals to calculate probabilities.

Concepts You Will Be Learning

- Evaluating and interpreting improper integrals (6.1)
- Recognizing when an improper integral diverges (6.1)
- Calculating and interpreting present and future values for income streams (6.2)
- Calculating and interpreting the following economic quantities: consumers' willingness and ability to spend, expenditure, and surplus; suppliers' willingness and ability to receive, revenue, and surplus; market equilibrium; total social gain (6.3)
- Calculating and interpreting elasticity (6.3)
- Calculating and interpreting probabilities, means, and standard deviations (6.4)
- Using probability and cumulative density functions (6.4)

6.1   Perpetual Accumulation and Improper Integrals

Definite integrals have specific numbers for both the upper limit and the lower limit. We now consider what happens to the accumulation of change when one or both of the limits of the integral are infinite. That is, we wish to evaluate integrals of the form $\int_a^\infty f(x)dx$, $\int_{-\infty}^b f(x)dx$, or $\int_{-\infty}^\infty f(x)dx$. We call integrals of this form **improper integrals.** Improper integrals play a role in economics and statistics, as well as in other fields of study.

Evaluating Improper Integrals

Consider evaluating the improper integral $\int_2^\infty 4.3e^{-0.06x}\,dx$. We can interpret this integral as the area of the region between the graph of $y = 4.3e^{-0.06x}$ and the x-axis from 2 to infinity. See Figure 6.1. One way to estimate this area is to consider the area between 2 and some large value. In Table 6.1 we show several area calculations for increasingly large values.

$y = 4.3e^{-0.06x}$

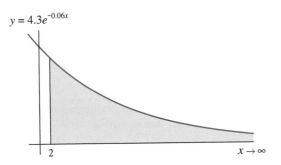

FIGURE 6.1

TABLE 6.1

	$\int_2^N 4.3e^{-0.06x}\,dx$
50	59.994558
100	63.384987
200	63.562191
400	63.562631
800	63.562631
1600	63.562631
Limit $\approx$ 63.56263	

Note that the area between 2 and 400 is not very different from the area between 2 and 1600. The difference is smaller than can be shown by the technology that we used. However, the limiting value seen in the table is still just an estimate of the value of the integral $\int_2^\infty 4.3e^{-0.06x}\,dx$. You should recognize that we are numerically investigating a limit in Table 6.1. We are investigating $\lim_{N\to\infty} \int_2^N 4.3e^{-0.06x}\,dx$. We can calculate this limit algebraically in order to obtain the exact answer. Begin by finding the general antiderivative of $4.3e^{-0.06x}$, evaluating it at 2 and N, and subtracting the results.

$$\int_2^N 4.3e^{-0.06x}dx = \frac{4.3}{-0.06}e^{-0.06x}\Big|_2^N = \frac{4.3}{-0.06}e^{-0.06N} - \left(\frac{4.3}{-0.06}e^{-0.06(2)}\right)$$

$$= \frac{4.3}{-0.06}e^{-0.06N} + \frac{4.3}{0.06}e^{-0.12}$$

An antiderivative must be found prior to using the limit process.

Next find the limit of this expression as N becomes infinitely large.

$$\lim_{N\to\infty}\left(\frac{4.3}{-0.06}e^{-0.06N} + \frac{4.3}{0.03}e^{-0.12}\right)$$

$$= \lim_{N\to\infty}\frac{4.3}{-0.06}e^{-0.06N} + \lim_{N\to\infty}\frac{4.3}{0.06}e^{-0.12}$$

The first term is a decreasing exponential function, so we know that as N approaches infinity, the value of this term approaches zero. The second term is a constant function and is not affected by the value of N.

$$\lim_{N\to\infty}\frac{4.3}{-0.06}e^{-0.06N} + \lim_{N\to\infty}\frac{4.3}{0.06}e^{-0.12}$$

$$= 0 + \frac{4.3}{0.06}e^{-0.12}$$

$$= \frac{4.3}{0.06}e^{-0.12}$$

We see that this answer confirms our former numerical estimate, because

$$\frac{4.3}{0.06}e^{-0.12} \approx 63.56263$$

The answer $\frac{4.3}{0.06} e^{-0.12}$ is exact, whereas the answer 63.56263 is not. Although an answer accurate to the fifth decimal place is sufficient for most applications, there are situations in which greater precision is necessary.

To summarize, an improper integral $\int_a^\infty f(x)dx$ is evaluated by replacing infinity with a variable, say N, and evaluating the limit of the integral $\int_a^N f(x)dx$ as N approaches infinity. That is, provided the limits exist,

$$\int_a^\infty f(x)dx = \lim_{N\to\infty} \int_a^N f(x)dx = \left[\lim_{N\to\infty} F(N)\right] - F(a)$$

$$\int_{-\infty}^b f(x)dx = \lim_{N\to\infty} \int_N^b f(x)dx = F(b) - \left[\lim_{N\to-\infty} F(N)\right]$$

where F is an antiderivative of f. We now have the tools we need to apply improper integrals to some real-world problems.

EXAMPLE 1   *Using a Limit to Evaluate an Improper Integral*

Decay   Carbon-14 dating methods are sometimes used by archeologists to determine the age of an artifact. The rate at which 100 milligrams of ^{14}C is decaying can be modeled by

$$r(t) = -0.01209(0.999879^t) \text{ milligrams per year}$$

where t is the number of years since the 100 milligrams began to decay.

a. How much of the ^{14}C will have decayed after 1000 years?

b. How much of the ^{14}C will eventually decay?

Solution

a. The amount of ^{14}C to decay during the first 1000 years is

$$\int_0^{1000} r(t)dt = \int_0^{1000} -0.01209(0.999879^t)dt \approx -11.4 \text{ milligrams}$$

Approximately 11.4 milligrams will decay during the first 1000 years. Note that -11.4 milligrams is the signed area of the shaded region in Figure 6.2.

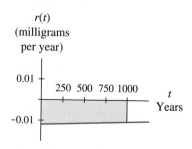

FIGURE 6.2

b.   In the long run, the amount that will decay is

$$\int_0^\infty r(t)dt = \lim_{N\to\infty} \int_0^N -0.01209(0.999879^t)dt$$

$$= \lim_{N\to\infty} \left[\frac{-0.01209(0.999879^t)}{\ln 0.0999879} \right]\Bigg|_0^N$$

$$= \lim_{N\to\infty} \left[\frac{-0.01209(0.999879^N)}{\ln 0.0999879} - \frac{-0.01209(0.999879^0)}{\ln 0.0999879} \right]\Bigg|_0^N$$

$$\approx 99.91131\left[\lim_{N\to\infty} (0.999879^N) \right] - 99.91131$$

$$= 99.91131(0) - 99.91131 \approx -100 \text{ milligrams}$$

Eventually all of the ^{14}C will decay. In terms of the graph shown in Figure 6.3, the area of the region between the graph of the function r and the horizontal axis gets closer and closer to 99.91131 as t gets larger and larger. Because the parameters in the equation are rounded, the area is getting closer and closer to 99.91131 rather than to 100, which is the amount that must ultimately decay. ●

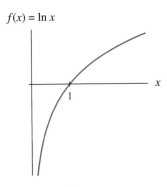

$r(t)$
(milligrams per year)

0.01

10,000   20,000 t
Years

-0.01

FIGURE 6.3

Divergence

It is possible that when we are evaluating an improper integral, the limit does not exist. (For example, as we numerically approximate the limit, the limit estimates become increasingly large.) In this case, we say that the improper integral **diverges.** Example 2 illustrates this situation.

EXAMPLE 2   *Recognizing That an Integral Diverges*

If possible, determine the value of $\int_1^\infty \frac{1}{x}dx$.

Solution
We begin by replacing ∞ with the variable N and finding the limit as $N \to \infty$.

$$\int_1^\infty \frac{1}{x}dx = \lim_{N\to\infty} \ln x \Bigg|_1^N$$

$$= \lim_{N\to\infty} (\ln N - \ln 1)$$

$$= \lim_{N\to\infty} \ln N - \lim_{N\to\infty} \ln 1$$

$f(x) = \ln x$

1

x

To evaluate these limits, recall the shape of the graph of $y = \ln x$ (see Figure 6.4). We see from the graph that $\ln 1 = 0$ and that as the input becomes increasingly large, the output also becomes increasingly large. Thus, the limiting value does not exist.

Because $\lim_{N\to\infty} \ln N \to \infty$, $\int_1^\infty \frac{1}{x}dx \to \infty$ and we say that this improper integral diverges. ●

FIGURE 6.4

6.1 Concept Inventory

- Improper integrals
- Divergence

6.1 Activities

Getting Started

For Activities 1 through 11, evaluate the indicated improper integral.

1. $\int_0^\infty 3e^{-0.2t}dt$

2. $\int_{15}^\infty 5(0.36^t)dt$

3. $\int_{10}^\infty 3x^{-2}dx$

4. $\int_{-\infty}^3 7e^{7x}dx$

5. $\int_{-\infty}^{-10} 4x^{-3}dx$

6. $\int_2^\infty \frac{1}{\sqrt{x}}dx$

7. $\int_{0.36}^\infty 9.6x^{-0.432}dx$

8. $\int_{-\infty}^{-2} \left(\frac{3}{x^2} + 1\right)dx$

9. $\int_2^\infty \frac{2x}{x^2 + 1}dx$

10. $\int_5^\infty [5(0.36^x) + 5]dx$

11. $\int_a^\infty [f(x) + k]\,dx$, where $\int_a^\infty f(x)dx = b$ and a, b, and k are constants

Applying Concepts

12. Decay The rate at which 15 grams of ^{14}C is decaying can be modeled by

$$r(t) = -0.027205(0.998188^t) \text{ grams per year}$$

where t is the number of years since the 15 grams began decaying.

a. How much of the ^{14}C will decay during the first 1000 years? during the fourth 1000 years?

b. How much of the ^{14}C will eventually decay?

13. Decay An isotope of uranium, ^{238}U, is commonly used in atomic weapons and nuclear power generators. Because of this isotope's radioactive nature, the United States government is concerned with safe ways of storing used uranium. The rate at which 100 milligrams of ^{238}U is decaying can be modeled by

$$r(t) = -1.55(0.9999999845^t)10^{-6} \text{ milligrams per year}$$

where t is the number of years since the 100 milligrams began decaying.

a. How much of the ^{238}U will decay during the first 100 years? during the first 1000 years?

b. How much of the ^{238}U will eventually decay?

The following information is used in Activities 14 and 15:

In the study of markets, economists define *consumers' willingness and ability to spend* as the maximum amount that consumers are willing and able to spend for a specific quantity of goods or services. If some consumers will purchase a product or service regardless of its price, then the consumers' willingness and ability to spend is defined by

$$C = qp_0 + \int_{p_0}^\infty D(p)dp$$

where q is a specific quantity, p_0 is the price associated with quantity q, and $D(p)$ is the demand for the commodity when the price is p. (Section 6.3 discusses these concepts in greater detail.)

14. Demand The weekly demand for a dozen roses is given by $D(p) = 316.765(0.949^p)$ dozen roses, where p is the price per dozen, in dollars.

a. Find the price that corresponds to a weekly demand of 80 dozen roses.

b. Use the price (p_0) found in part *a* to calculate how much consumers are willing and able to spend for 80 dozen roses per week.

15. Demand The yearly demand for a certain hardback science fiction novel is

$$D(p) = 499.589(0.958^p) \text{ thousand books}$$

where p is the price per book, in dollars.

a. Find the price that corresponds to a yearly demand of 150,000 books.

b. Use the price (p_0) found in part *a* to calculate how much consumers are willing and able to spend for 150,000 books each year.

16. Work The work required to propel a 10-ton rocket an unlimited distance from the surface of

Earth into space is defined in terms of force and is given by the improper integral

$$W = \int_{4000}^{\infty} \frac{160{,}000{,}000}{x^2}dx$$

The expression $\frac{160{,}000{,}000}{x^2}$ is force in tons. The variable x is the distance, measured in miles, between the rocket and the center of Earth.

a. What are the units on work in this context?

b. Calculate the work necessary to propel this rocket infinitely into space.

The following information is used in Activities 17 and 18:

A *probability density function* is defined as a nonnegative function f with the property that

$$\int_{-\infty}^{\infty} f(x)dx = 1$$

17. Consider the function

$$f(x) = \begin{cases} 0.1e^{-0.1x} & \text{when } x \geq 1 \\ 0 & \text{when } x < 1 \end{cases}$$

Show that f is a probability density function.

18. Consider the function

$$g(x) = \begin{cases} \dfrac{1}{x^2} & \text{when } x \geq 1 \\ 0 & \text{when } x < 1 \end{cases}$$

Show that g is a probability density function.

6.2 Streams in Business and Biology

Picture a stream flowing into a pond. You have probably just created a mental picture of water that is flowing continuously into the pond. We can also imagine moneys that are "flowing" continuously into an investment or new individuals that are "flowing" continuously into an existing population.

It is not unreasonable to consider the income of large financial institutions and major corporations as being received continuously over time in varying amounts. For instance, consider utility companies that receive payments at varying times throughout each month. Furthermore, with electronic transfer of funds, these payments can be made at any time during the day or night. Such a flow of money is called a **continuous income stream.** When you make payments to a bank or to some other financial institution for the purpose of investing money or repaying a loan, your payments are usually for the same fixed amount and are made at regular times that are separated by a specified interval. Such a flow of money is called a **discrete income stream.** Whether continuous or discrete, an income stream is usually described as a rate, $R(t)$, that varies with time t.

Determining Income Streams

Consider a business that currently posts a yearly profit of $4.3 million. The business allocates 5% of its profits in a continuous stream among several investments. There are several situations that could determine the flow rate into these investments. We consider the cases where the flow is constant or either increases or decreases by a constant or by a percentage.

If the company's profits remain constant, then the function that describes the income stream flowing into the investments is $R(t) = 0.05(\$4.3$ million per year$) = \$0.215$ million per year.

Suppose, however, that the company's profits increase by $0.2 million each year. In this case, the company's profit is linear, beginning with $4.3 million dollars the first year and increasing by a constant $0.2 million each year: $4.3 + 0.2t$ million dollars per year after t years. The investment stream is 5% of the profit, so $R(t) = 0.05(4.3 + 0.2t)$ million dollars per year t years after the company posted a profit of $4.3 million.

It is also possible that the company's profits could increase by a constant 7% each year. Recall that constant percentage change is modeled by an exponential equation. In this case, the function that describes the flow rate of the investment stream is

$$R(t) = 0.05[4.3(1.07^t)] \text{ million dollars per year}$$

t years after the company posted a profit of $4.3 million. Determining the rate at which income flows into an investment is the first step in answering questions about the present and future values of the invested income stream.

EXAMPLE 1   Writing Flow Rate Equations

Business Start-up

After you graduate from college, you start a small business that immediately becomes successful. When you establish the business, you determine that 10% of your profits will be invested each year. In the first year you post a profit of $579,000. Determine the income stream flow rate for your investments over the next several years if

a. The business's profit remains constant.

b. The profit grows by $50,000 each year.

c. The profit increases by 17% each year.

d. The profits for the first six years are as shown in Table 6.2 and are expected to follow the trend indicated by the data.

TABLE 6.2

Year	1	2	3	4	5	6
Profit (thousands of dollars)	579	600	610	618	623	627

Solution

a. If the profit remains constant, then the flow rate of the investment stream is constant, calculated as 10% of $579,000. Thus $R(t) = \$57,900$ per year.

b. Profit increasing by a constant amount each year indicates linear growth. In this case, the amount of profit that is invested is described by the linear function $R(t) = (0.10)(579,000 + 50,000t)$ dollars per year t years after the first year.

c. An increase in profit of 17% each year indicates exponential growth with a constant percentage change of 17%. In this case, the flow rate of the investment stream is described by the equation $R(t) = 0.10[579,000(1.17^t)]$ dollars per year t years after the first year of business.

d. A scatter plot of the data in Table 6.2 indicates an increasing, concave-down shape. (See Figure 6.5.) A quadratic model is a reasonably good fit, although the model indicates declining profits beyond the years given in the table. A better model for profit is the log model $P(t) = 580.117 + 26.8 \ln t$ thousand dollars per year after t years of business. Thus the investment flow rate is $R(t) = 0.10P(t) = 58.0117 + 2.68 \ln t$. Note that in parts a through c, the first year of business corresponds to an input value of 0. In this log model, the first year of business corresponds to an input value of 1.

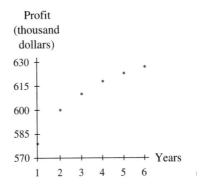

FIGURE 6.5

Future Value of a Continuous Stream

The **future value** of a continuous stream is the total accumulated value of the income stream and its earned interest. Suppose that an income stream flows continuously into an interest-bearing account at the rate of $R(t)$ dollars per year, where t is measured in years and the account earns interest at the annual rate of $100r\%$ compounded continuously. What is the future value of the account at the end of T years?

To answer this question, we begin by imagining the time interval from 0 to T years as being divided into n subintervals, each of length Δt.

$$0 \qquad\qquad t \quad t + \Delta t \qquad\qquad T = (\Delta t)(n)$$

We regard Δt as being small—so small that over a typical subinterval $[t, t + \Delta t]$, the rate $R(t)$ can be considered constant. Then the amount paid into the account during this subinterval can be approximated by

Amount paid in $\approx [R(t) \text{ dollars per year}](\Delta t \text{ years})$

$\approx R(t)\Delta t$ dollars

We consider this amount as being paid in at t, the beginning of the interval, and earning interest continuously for $(T - t)$ years. Using the continuously compounded interest formula $(A = Pe^{rt})$, we see that the amount grows to

$$[R(t)\Delta t]e^{r(T-t)} = R(t)e^{r(T-t)}\Delta t \text{ dollars}$$

at the end of T years. Summing over the n subintervals, we have the approximation

Future value $\approx [R(t_1)e^{r(T-t_1)} + R(t_2)e^{r(T-t_2)} + \cdots + R(t_n)e^{r(T-t_n)}] \Delta t$ dollars

where $t_1, t_2, \ldots, t_n$ are the left endpoints of the n subintervals. This sum should look familiar to you. If we simplify the expression by letting $f(t) = R(t)e^{r(T-t)}$ and rewrite the sum as $[f(t_1) + f(t_2) + \cdots + f(t_n)]\Delta t$, then you should recognize it as the type of sum we used in Section 5.1.

Because we are considering the income as a continuous stream and interest as being compounded continuously, we let the time interval Δt become extremely small ($\Delta t \to 0$). That is, we use an infinite number of intervals ($n \to \infty$). Thus

$$\text{Future value} = \lim_{n \to \infty} [f(t_1) + f(t_2) + \cdots + f(t_n)] \Delta t$$

$$= \int_0^T f(t)\,dt$$

$$= \int_0^T R(t)e^{r(T-t)}dt \text{ dollars}$$

Future Value of a Continuous Income Stream

Suppose that an income stream flows continuously into an interest-bearing account at the rate of $R(t)$ dollars per year, where t is measured in years and the account earns interest at the annual rate of $100r\%$ compounded continuously. The future value of the account at the end of T years is

$$\text{Future value} = \int_0^T R(t)e^{r(T-t)}dt \text{ dollars}$$

Using the Fundamental Theorem, we can find the rate-of-change function for future value:

$$\text{Rate of change of future value} = \frac{d}{dx}\int_0^x R(t)e^{r(T-t)}dt \quad \text{for } 0 \leq x \leq T$$

$$= R(x)e^{r(T-x)} \text{ dollars per year}$$

Thus the function $f(t) = R(t)e^{r(T-t)}$ gives the rate of change after t years of the future value (in T years) of an income stream whose income is flowing continuously in at a rate of $R(t)$ dollars per year. It is the rate-of-change function $f(t) = R(t)e^{r(T-t)}$, not the flow rate of the income stream $R(t)$, that we graph when depicting future value as the area of a region beneath a rate-of-change function.

EXAMPLE 2   *Finding the Future Value of a Continuous Income Stream*

Airline Expansion   The owners of a small airline are making big plans. They hope to be able to buy out a larger airline 10 years from now by investing into an account returning 9.4% APR. Assume a continuous income stream and continuous compounding of interest.

a. The owners have determined that they can afford to invest $3.3 million each year. How much will these investments be worth 10 years from now?

b. If the airline's profits increase so that the amount the owners invest each year increases by 8% per year, how much will their investments be worth in 10 years?

Solution

a. The flow rate of the income stream is $R(t) = 3.3$ million per year with $r = 0.094$ and $T = 10$ years. The value of these investments in 10 years is calculated as

$$\text{Future value} = \int_0^{10} 3.3 e^{0.094(10-t)} dt$$

$$= \int_0^{10} 3.3 e^{0.94} e^{-0.094t} dt$$

$$= \frac{3.3 e^{0.94}}{-0.094} e^{-0.094(10)} - \frac{3.3 e^{0.94}}{-0.094} e^{-0.094(0)}$$

$$\approx -35.106 + 89.872$$

$$\approx \$54.8 \text{ million}$$

b. The function modeling exponential growth of 8% per year in the investment stream is $R(t) = 3.3(1.08^t)$ million dollars per year after t years. The future value is calculated (using technology) as $\int_0^{10} 3.3(1.08^t) e^{0.094(10-t)} dt \approx \$77.7$ million. ●

Present Value of a Continuous Stream

The **present value** of a continuous income stream is the amount P that would have to be invested now in an interest-bearing account in order for the amount to grow to a given future value. Because P dollars earning continuously compounded interest would grow to a future value of Pe^{rT} dollars in T years, we have

$$Pe^{rT} = \int_0^T R(t) e^{r(T-t)} dt = \int_0^T R(t) e^{rT} e^{-rt} dt = e^{rT} \int_0^T R(t) e^{-rt} dt$$

Solving for P, we obtain

$$\text{Present value} = P = \int_0^T R(t) e^{-rt} dt$$

Present Value of a Continuous Income Stream

Suppose that an income stream flows continuously into an interest-bearing account at the rate of $R(t)$ dollars per year, where t is measured in years, and that the account earns interest at the annual rate of $100r\%$ compounded continuously. The present value of the account is

$$\text{Present value} = \int_0^T R(t) e^{-rt} dt \text{ dollars}$$

It is worth noting that once you have calculated future value, it is easy to calculate the associated present value by solving for P in the equation

$$Pe^{rt} = \text{Future value}$$

EXAMPLE 3   *Finding Present Value from Future Value*

Profit   Last year, profit for the HiTech Corporation was $17.2 million. Assuming that HiTech's profits increase continuously for the next 5 years at a rate of $1.3 million per year, what are the future and present values of the corporation's 5-year profits? Assume an interest rate of 12% compounded continuously.

Solution
We note that the rate of the stream is $R(t) = 17.2 + 1.3t$ million dollars per year in year t. In order to calculate the future value of this stream, we evaluate $\int_0^5 (17.2 + 1.3t)e^{0.12(5-t)}dt$. We have not developed a method for finding the antiderivative of $f(t) = (17.2 + 1.3t)e^{0.12(5-t)}$, so we numerically estimate the definite integral using a limiting value of sums or use technology to evaluate the integral.

$$\text{Future value} = \int_0^5 (17.2 + 1.3t)e^{0.12(5-t)}dt \approx \$137.9 \text{ million}$$

The invested revenue will be worth approximately $138 million in 5 years. Again, numerically estimate a limiting value of sums or use technology to find the present value.

$$\text{Present value} = \int_0^5 (17.2 + 1.3t)e^{-0.12t}dt \approx \$75.7 \text{ million}$$

This amount is the lump sum ($75.7 million) that would have to be invested at 12% compounded continuously in order to earn $137.9 million (the future value) in 5 years.

We could also use the future value ($137.9 million) to calculate the present value:

$$Pe^{(0.12)(5)} \approx \$137.9 \text{ million} \quad \text{so} \quad P \approx \$75.7 \text{ million}$$

The integral definition of the present value is useful in situations in which you do not know the future value.   ●

Discrete Income Streams

The assumptions that income is flowing continuously and that interest is compounded continuously make it possible to use calculus and are often imposed by economists. Unfortunately, they do not generally hold in the real world of business. It is much more realistic to consider an income stream that flows monthly into an account with monthly compounding of interest or a stream that flows quarterly with quarterly compoundings.

The process of finding the future value for discrete income streams begins in a similar way to that for continuous streams: Determine the rate-of-flow function for the income stream, and multiply by a term that accounts for compounding interest. In the discrete case, we base our interest calculations on the formula $A = P\left(1 + \dfrac{r}{n}\right)^{nt}$ where A is the dollar amount accumulated after t years when P dollars are invested at an annual interest rate of $100r\%$ compounded annually n times a year. Instead of integrating the resulting function, we sum a series of values.

Consider a small business that begins investing 7.5% of its monthly profit into an account that pays 10.3% annual interest compounded monthly. When the company begins investing, the monthly profit is $12,000 and is growing by $500 each month. We wish to determine the 2-year future value of the company's investment (assuming that profit continues to grow in the manner described).

The company will make a total of 24 deposits during the 2-year period. The first deposit is $(0.075)(\$12,000) = \$900$. This deposit earns interest each month for 24 months. The future value of this first deposit is $\$900\left(1 + \frac{0.103}{12}\right)^{24} = \$1104.91$.

The second deposit is $(0.075)(\$12,000 + \$500) = \$937.50$. This deposit earns interest each month for 23 months. The future value of the second deposit is $\$937.50\left(1 + \frac{0.103}{12}\right)^{23} = \$1141.15$.

The third deposit is $(0.075)(\$12,000 + \$1000) = \$975$. This deposit earns interest each month for 22 months. The future value of the third deposit is $\$975\left(1 + \frac{0.103}{12}\right)^{22} = \$1176.70$.

By now you should be able to see a pattern in the future values of these successive monthly deposits. (See Table 6.3.)

TABLE 6.3

Time d (months after first deposit)	Future value of monthly deposit $F(d)$
0	$F(0) = \$900.00\left(1 + \frac{0.103}{12}\right)^{24} = \$1104.91$
1	$F(1) = \$937.50\left(1 + \frac{0.103}{12}\right)^{23} = \$1141.15$
2	$F(2) = \$975.00\left(1 + \frac{0.103}{12}\right)^{22} = \$1176.70$
$\vdots$	$\vdots$
22	$F(22) = \$1725.00\left(1 + \frac{0.103}{12}\right)^{2} = \$1754.74$
23	$F(23) = \$1762.50\left(1 + \frac{0.103}{12}\right)^{1} = \$1777.63$
	Future value = sum of 24 values = \$35,204.03

The amount deposited each month is given by $R(d) = (0.075)(\$12,000 + \$500d)$, where d is the number of deposits after the first one. The deposit associated with input d accrues interest for $24 - d$ months. The future value of each month's deposit is given by the formula

$$F(d) = R(d)\left(1 + \frac{0.103}{12}\right)^{24-d} = (0.075)(12,000 + 500d)\left(1 + \frac{0.103}{12}\right)^{24-d}$$

To determine the 2-year future value, we add the future values of each month's deposit beginning with 0 (month 1) and ending with 23 (month 24). Using summation notation, we write

$$\text{Future value} = \sum_{d=0}^{23} F(d) = \sum_{d=0}^{23} (0.075)(12,000 + 500d)\left(1 + \frac{0.103}{12}\right)^{24-d}$$

The symbol $\sum_{d=0}^{23} F(d)$ is the notation used for the sum $F(0) + F(1) + F(2) +$ $\ldots + F(23)$. In this example, the future value of the deposits is \$35,204.03. We generalize the definition of future value for discrete income streams as follows:

Future Value of a Discrete Income Stream

Suppose that a deposit is made into an interest-bearing account at n equally spaced times throughout a year. The value of the dth deposit is $R(d)$ dollars per period, and it earns interest at an annual percentage rate of $100r\%$ compounded once in each deposit period. The future value of the deposits at the end of D deposit periods is

$$\text{Future value} = \sum_{d=0}^{D-1} R(d)\left(1 + \frac{r}{n}\right)^{D-d} \text{ dollars}$$

Once you have determined future value, present value can be found by solving for P in the equation

$$P\left(1 + \frac{r}{n}\right)^{D} = \text{Future value}$$

EXAMPLE 4 *Determining the Future Value of a Discrete Income Stream*

6.2.1

Savings

When you graduate from college (say, in 3 years), you would like to purchase a car. You have a job and can put \$75 into savings each month for this purchase. You choose a money market account that offers an APR of 6.2% compounded quarterly.

a. How much money will you have deposited in 3 years?

b. What will be the value of your savings in 3 years?

c. How much money would you have to deposit now (in one lump sum) to achieve the same future value in 3 years?

d. You are considering a second money market account that pays monthly interest of 0.5%. Will this account result in a greater future value than that calculated in part *b*?

Solution

a. The total amount deposited is $(36)(\$75) = \$2700$.

b. Because interest is compounded quarterly ($n = 4$), the monthly deposits each quarter do not earn interest until the end of the quarter in which they are deposited. We therefore consider three \$75 monthly deposits equivalent to one \$225 quarterly deposit, and this gives $R(d) = \$75(3) = \$225$ per quarter d

quarters after the first one. We assume that the first deposit is made at the beginning of a quarter. During the 3 years, there will be 12 quarters to consider ($D = 12$). Table 6.4 shows the pattern of the future values of each quarter's deposit.

The 3-year future value is given by

$$\text{Future value} = \sum_{d=0}^{12-1} R(d)\left(1 + \frac{0.062}{4}\right)^{12-d}$$

$$= \sum_{d=0}^{11} \$225\left(1 + \frac{0.062}{4}\right)^{12-d} = \$2988.10$$

TABLE 6.4

Time (quarters after first deposit)	Future value of quarterly deposit
0	$\$225\left(1 + \frac{0.062}{4}\right)^{12} = \$270.61$
1	$\$225\left(1 + \frac{0.062}{4}\right)^{11} = \$266.48$
2	$\$225\left(1 + \frac{0.062}{4}\right)^{10} = \$262.41$
$\vdots$	$\vdots$
10	$\$225\left(1 + \frac{0.062}{4}\right)^{2} = \$232.03$
11	$\$225\left(1 + \frac{0.062}{4}\right)^{1} = \$228.48$
Future value = sum of 12 values = $\$2988.10$	

c. Because we know the future value, we can solve $P\left(1 + \frac{0.062}{4}\right)^{12} \approx 2988.10$ for the present value P to obtain $P \approx \$2484.48$. This is the amount that you would need to deposit now to have \$2988.10 in 3 years.

d. Because the account pays interest monthly, we have the values $n = 12$ and $D = 3(12) = 36$. Also, because interest is compounded monthly, we consider the deposits being made monthly, so that $R(d) = \$75$. In this case, the interest rate is given in terms of a monthly rather than a yearly rate. In other words, we are given the term $\frac{r}{n} = \frac{r}{12} = 0.005$. Thus the 3-year future value of \$75 monthly deposits into this money market account is

$$\text{Future value} = \sum_{d=0}^{35} \$75(1.005)^{36-d} = \$2964.96$$

This is a smaller future value than for the account that pays 6.2% annual interest compounded quarterly. ●

Streams in Biology

Biology and other fields involve situations very similar to income streams. An example of this is the growth of populations of animals. As of 1978, there were approximately

1.5 million sperm whales[*] in the world's oceans. Each year approximately 0.06 million sperm whales are added to the population. Also each year, 4% of the sperm whale population either die of natural causes or are killed by hunters. Assuming that these rates (and percentage rates) have remained constant since 1978, we estimate the sperm whale population in 1998 using the same procedure as when determining future value of continuous income streams.

There are two aspects of the population that we must consider when estimating the population of sperm whales in 1998. First, we must determine the number of whales that were living in 1978 that will still be living in 1998. Because 4% of the sperm whales die each year, we calculate the number of whales that have survived the entire 20 years as $1.5(0.96^{20}) \approx 0.663$ million whales.

The second aspect that we must consider is the impact on the population made by the birth of new whales. We are told that 0.06 million whales are added to the population each year and that each year, 96% of those survive. Therefore, the growth rate of the population of sperm whales associated with those that were born t years after 1978 is

$$f(t) = 0.06(0.96)^{20-t} \text{ million whales per year}$$

Thus the sperm whale population in 1998 is calculated as

$$\text{Whale population} = 1.5(0.96^{20}) + \int_0^{20} 0.06(0.96)^{20-t}dt$$

$$\approx 0.663 + \int_0^{20} 0.06(0.96^{20})(0.96)^{-t}dt$$

$$= 0.663 + 0.06(0.96^{20}) \int_0^{20} (0.96^{-1})^t dt$$

$$= 0.663 + \left. \frac{0.06(0.96^{20})(0.96^{-1})^t}{\ln(0.96^{-1})} \right|_0^{20}$$

$$\approx 1.48 \text{ million sperm whales}$$

Functions that model such biological streams, in which new individuals are added to the population and the rate of survival of the individuals is known, are referred to as *survival and renewal functions*.

Future Value of a Biological Stream

The future value (in b years) of a biological stream with initial population size P, survival rate $100s\%$, and renewal rate $r(t)$, where t is the number of years, is

$$\text{Future value} \approx Ps^b + \int_0^b r(t)s^{b-t}dt$$

In the whale example, the initial population is $P = 1.5$ million. The survival rate is 96% per year, so $s = 0.96$. The renewal rate is $r(t) = 0.06$ million whales per year.

---

[*] Delphine Haley, *Marine Mammals*, Seattle, WA: Pacific Search Press, 1978.

EXAMPLE 5   *Determining the Future Value of a Biological Stream*

Flea Population   An example of a stream in entomology is the growth of a flea population. In cooler areas of the country, adult fleas die before winter, but flea eggs survive and hatch the following spring when temperatures again reach 70°F. Not all the eggs hatch at the same time, so part of the growth in the flea population is due to the hatching of the original eggs. Another part of the growth in the flea population is due to propagation. Suppose fleas propagate at the rate of 134% per day and that the original set of fleas (from the dormant eggs) become reproducing adults at the rate of 600 fleas per day. What will the flea population be 10 days after the first 600 fleas begin reproducing? Assume that none of the fleas die during the 10-day period and that all fleas become reproducing adults 24 hours after hatching and propagate every day thereafter at the rate of 134% per day.

Solution

We first note that because we begin counting when the first 600 fleas have become mature adults, we consider the initial population to be $P = 600$ fleas. The renewal rate is also 600 fleas per day, so $r(t) = 600$.

Because, in this case, the renewal rate function r does not account for renewal due to propagation, we must incorporate the propagation rate of 134% into the survival rate of 100%. Thus the survival/propagation rate is $s = 2.34$.

Because the renewal rate and survival/propagation rate are given in days, we let t be the input variable measured in days. The flea population will grow over 10 days to

$$\text{Flea population} \approx Ps^{10} + \int_0^{10} r(t)s^{10-t}dt = 600(2.34^{10}) + \int_0^{10} 600(2.34)^{10-t}dt$$

$$\approx 2{,}953{,}315 + 3{,}473{,}166 \approx 6.4 \text{ million fleas} \quad \bullet$$

6.2   Concept Inventory

- Income streams
- Flow rate of a stream
- Future and present value of a continuous stream
- Future and present value of a discrete stream
- Biological stream
- Future value of a biological stream

6.2   Activities

Applying Concepts

1. **Savings**   Suppose that after you graduate, you are hired by a company in the San Francisco Bay area. Housing prices in that region are the highest in the nation; however, you are determined to buy a house within 5 years of beginning your new job. Your starting salary is $47,000. After talking with fellow employees, you consider three possibilities for what might happen to your salary over the next 5 years:

   i.   Your salary remains at your starting level.

   ii. Your salary increases by $100 a month.

   iii. Your salary increases by 0.5% each month.

   a. You have decided to save 20% of your salary each month for a down payment on a house. Give the function describing your monthly investments for each of the three salary possibilities.

   b. You estimate that you will need $60,000 for a down payment, and you are unwilling to accept any investment risk. You will be investing your money monthly in a bank savings account that pays an annual interest rate of 5% compounded monthly. For which salary possibilities will the total amount saved in 5 years be at least $60,000?

2. **Investment** A company is hoping to expand its facilities but needs capital to do so. In an effort to position itself for expansion in 3 years, the company will direct half of its profits into investments in a continuous manner. The company's profits for the past 5 years are shown in the table.

Years ago	5	4	3	2	1
Profit (thousands of dollars)	860	890	930	990	1050

The company's current yearly profit is $1,130,000. Find the function that describes the flow of the company's investments for each of the following profit scenarios:

a. The profit for the next 3 years follows the trend shown in the table.

b. The profit increases each year for the next 3 years by the same percentage that it increased in the current year.

c. The profit remains constant at the current year's level.

d. The profit increases each year for the next 3 years by the same fixed amount that it increased this year.

e. If the company's investments can earn 16.4% annual interest compounded continuously, how much capital will it have saved after 3 years of investing for each of the profit scenarios given?

3. **Revenue** For the year ending June 30, 2002, the revenue of the Sara Lee Corporation was $17.628 billion. Assume that Sara Lee's revenue will increase by 5% per year and that beginning on July 1, 2002, 12.5% of the revenue was invested each year (continuously) at an APR of 7% compounded continuously. What is the future value of the investment at the end of the year 2006?
(Source: Hoover's Online Guide.)

4. **Savings** A high school student is trying to save money to help pay for her first-year college tuition. She plans to invest $300 each quarter for 3 years into an account that pays interest at an APR of 4% compounded quarterly. Her parents decide to lend her the money so that she can devote more time to her

studies while in high school. How much should they lend her so that she can invest the loaned amount now, as one lump sum, into the account and accumulate the same amount as if she had made the quarterly deposits for 3 years?

5. **Revenue** The revenue of General Motors Corporation (GM) in December 2001 was $177.26 billion. Assume that GM's revenue remains constant and that 3% of the revenue is invested continuously throughout each year, beginning at the end of December 2001, into an account that pays interest at a rate of 8.8% compounded continuously.
(Source: Hoover's Online Guide.)

a. Find the value of the account in December 2008.

b. How much would GM have had to invest at the end of December 2001, in one lump sum, into this account in order to build the same 7-year future value as the one found in part a?

6. **Revenue** For the year ending December 31, 2001, the General Electric Company's revenue was $125.68 billion. Assume that the revenue increases by 8% per year and that General Electric will (continuously) invest 10% of its profits each year at an APR of 8.5% compounded continuously for a period of 9 years beginning at the end of December of 2001. What is the present value of this 9-year investment?
(Source: Hoover's Online Guide.)

7. **Savings** To save for the purchase of your first home (in 6 years), suppose you begin investing $500 per month in an account with a fixed rate of return of 6.34%.

a. Assuming a continuous stream, what will the account be worth at the end of 6 years?

b. Assuming monthly activity (deposits and interest compounding), what will the account be worth at the end of 6 years?

c. Is the answer to part a or the answer to part b more likely to be the actual future value of the account? Explain.

8. **Investment** In preparing for your retirement (in 40 years), suppose you plan to invest 14% of your salary each month in an annuity with a fixed rate of return of 6.2%. You currently make $2800 per month and expect your income to increase by 3% per year.

a. Assuming a continuous stream, what will the annuity be worth at the end of 40 years?

b. Assuming monthly activity (deposits and interest compounding), what will the annuity be worth at the end of 40 years?

c. Is the answer to part *a* or the answer to part *b* more likely to be the actual future value of the annuity? Explain.

9. **Profit** Ticketmaster is the world's largest ticket retailer. Ticketmaster's 2002 third-quarter gross profits were $82.1 million. Assume that these profits will increase by 5% per quarter and that Ticketmaster will invest 15% of its quarterly profits in an investment with a quarterly return of 9%.
(Source: Hoover's Online Guide.)

a. Write a function for the rate at which money flows into this investment each quarter.

b. Write a function for the rate at which the 4-year future value of this investment is changing.

c. Find the value of this investment at the end of the year 2006. (Assume a quarterly stream beginning on January 1, 2003, with the investment of fourth-quarter 2002 profits.)

10. **Net Income** For the 2002 fiscal year, Lowe's Companies, Inc., reported an annual net income of $1,023,300,000. Assume the income can be reinvested continuously at an annual rate of return of 10% compounded continuously. Also assume that Lowe's will maintain this annual net income for the next 5 years.
(Source: Hoover's Online Guide.)

a. What is the future value of its 5-year net income?

b. What is the present value of its 5-year net income?

11. **Cola Sales** In 1993, PepsiCo installed a new soccer scoreboard for Alma College in Alma, Michigan. The terms of the installation were that Pepsi would have sole vending rights at Alma College for the next 7 years. It is estimated that in the 3 years after the scoreboard was installed, Pepsi sold 36.4 thousand liters of Pepsi products to Alma College students, faculty, staff, and visitors. Suppose that the average yearly sales and associated revenue remained constant and that the revenue from Alma College sales was reinvested at 4.5% APR. Also assume that PepsiCo makes a revenue of $0.80 per liter of Pepsi.

a. The vending of Pepsi products on campus can be considered a continuous process. Assuming that the revenue was invested in a continuous stream and that interest on that investment was compounded continuously, how much did Pepsi make from its 7 years of sales at Alma College?

b. Still assuming a continuous stream, find how much Pepsi would have had to invest in 1993 to create the same 7-year future value.

12. **Investment** Refer to Activity 8. How much would you have to invest now, in one lump sum instead of in a continuous stream, in order to build to the same future (40-year) value?

13. **Savings** Refer to Activity 7.

a. How much would you have to invest now, in one lump sum instead of in a continuous stream, in order to build to the same future (6-year) value? Assume that interest is compounded continuously.

b. How much would you have to invest now, in one lump sum instead of in a monthly stream, in order to build to the same future (6-year) value? Assume monthly compounding of interest.

c. Is the answer to part *a* or the answer to part *b* more likely to be the actual present value of the annuity? Explain.

14. **Revenue** Between 1995 and 2001, the revenue of Sears Roebuck and Co. can be modeled as

$$R(t) = \frac{11.24}{1 + 1.366e^{-1.55t}} + 30 \text{ billion dollars per year}$$

t years after 1995. Assume that the revenue can be reinvested at 9.5% compounded continuously.
(Source: Based on data from the Hoover's Online Guide.)

a. How much is Sears' revenue invested since 1995 worth in 2003?

b. How much was this accumulated investment worth in 1995?

15. **Buyout** In 1956, AT&T laid its first underwater phone line. By 1996, AT&T Submarine Systems, the division of AT&T that installs and maintains undersea communication lines, had seven cable ships and 1000 workers. On October 5, 1996, AT&T announced that it was seeking a buyer for its Submarine Systems division. The Submarine Systems

division of AT&T was posting a profit of $850 million per year.

(Source: "AT&T Seeking a Buyer for Cable-Ship Business," *Wall Street Journal*, October 5, 1996.)

a. If AT&T assumed that the Submarine Systems division's annual profit would remain constant and could be reinvested at an annual return of 15%, what would AT&T have considered to be the 20-year present value of its Submarine Systems division? (Assume a continuous stream.)

b. If prospective bidder A considered that the annual profits of this division would remain constant and could be reinvested at an annual return of 13%, what would bidder A consider to be the 20-year present value of AT&T's Submarine Systems? (Assume a continuous stream.)

c. If prospective bidder B considered that over a 20-year period, profits of the division would grow by 10% per year (after which it would be obsolete) and that profits could be reinvested at an annual return of 14%, what would bidder B consider to be the 20-year present value of AT&T's Submarine Systems? (Assume a continuous stream.)

16. **Buyout**   On October 4, 1996, Tenet Healthcare Corporation, the second-largest hospital company in the United States at that time, announced that it would buy Ornda Healthcorp.

(Source: "Tenet to Acquire Ornda," *Wall Street Journal*, October 5, 1996.)

a. If Tenet Healthcare Corporation assumed that Ornda's annual revenue of $0.273 billion would increase by 10% per year and that the revenues could be continuously reinvested at an annual return of 13%, what would Tenet Healthcare Corporation consider to be the 15-year present value of Ornda Healthcorp at the time of the buyout?

b. If Ornda Healthcorp's forecast for its financial future was that its $0.273 billion annual revenue would remain constant and that revenues could be continuously reinvested at an annual return of 15%, what would Ornda Healthcorp consider its 15-year present value to be at the time of the buyout?

c. Tenet Healthcare Corporation bought Ornda Healthcorp for $1.82 billion in stock. If the sale price was the 15-year present value, did either of the companies have to compromise on what it believed to be the value of Ornda Healthcorp?

17. **Buyout**   CSX Corporation, a railway company, announced in October of 1996 its intention to buy Conrail Inc. for $8.1 billion. The combined company, CSX-Conrail, would control 29,000 miles of track and have an annual revenue of $14 billion the first year after the merger, making it one of the largest railway companies in the country.

(Source: "Seeking Concessions from CSX-Conrail Is Seen as Most Likely Move by Norfolk," *Wall Street Journal*, October 5, 1996.)

a. If Conrail assumed that its $2 billion annual revenue would decrease by 5% each year for the next 10 years but that the annual revenue could be reinvested at an annual return of 20%, what would Conrail consider to be its 10-year present value at the time of CSX's offer? Is this more or less than the amount CSX offered?

b. CSX Corporation forecast that its Conrail acquisition would add $1.2 billion to its annual revenue the first year and that this added annual revenue would increase by 2% each year. Suppose CSX is able to reinvest that revenue at an annual return of 20%. What would CSX Corporation have considered to be the 10-year present value of the Conrail acquisition in October of 1996?

c. Why might CSX Corporation have forecast an increase in annual revenue when Conrail forecast a decrease?

18. **Buyout**   Company A is attempting to negotiate a buyout of Company B. Company B accountants project an annual income of 2.8 million dollars per year. Accountants for Company A project that with Company B's assets, Company A could produce an income starting at 1.4 million dollars per year and growing at a rate of 5% per year. The discount rate (the rate at which income can be reinvested) is 8% for both companies. Suppose that both companies consider their incomes over a 10-year period. Company A's top offer is equal to the present value of its projected income, and Company B's bottom price is equal to the present value of its projected income. Will the two companies come to an agreement for the buyout? Explain.

19. **Capital Value**   A company involved in videotape reproduction has just reported $1.2 million net income during its first year of operation. Projections are that net income will grow over the next 5 years at the rate of 6% per year. The *capital value* (present sales value) of the company has been set as its pres-

ent value over the next 5 years. If the rate of return on reinvested income can be compounded continuously for the next 5 years at 12% per year, what is the capital value of this company?

20. **Population**   There were once more than 1 million elephants in West Africa. Now, however, the elephant population has dwindled to 19,000. Each year 17.8% of West Africa elephants die or are killed by hunters. At the same time, elephant births are decreasing by 13% per year.

(Source: Douglas Chawick, *The Fate of the Elephant,* Sierra Club Books, 1992.)

a. How many of the current population of 19,000 elephants will still be alive 30 years from now?

b. Considering that 47 elephants were born in the wild this year, write a function for the number of elephants that will be born t years from now and will still be alive 30 years from now.

c. Estimate the elephant population of West Africa 30 years from now.

21. **Population**   In 1979 there were 12 million sooty terns in the world. Assume that the percentage of terns that survive from year to year has stayed constant at 83% and that approximately 2.04 million terns hatch each year.

(Source: Bryan Nelson, *Seabirds: Their Biology and Ecology,* New York: Hamlyn Publishing Group, 1979.)

a. How many of the terns that were alive in 1979 are still alive?

b. Write a function for the number of terns that hatched t years after 1979 and are still alive.

c. Estimate the present population of sooty terns.

22. **Population**   From 1936 through 1957, a population of 15,000 muskrats in Iowa bred at a rate of 468 new muskrats per year and had a survival rate of 75%.

(Source: Paul L. Errington, *Muskrat Population,* Ames, IA: Iowa State University Press, 1963.)

a. How many of the muskrats alive in 1936 were still alive in 1957?

b. Write a function for the number of muskrats that were born t years after 1936 and were still alive in 1957.

c. Estimate the muskrat population in 1957.

23. **Population**   There are approximately 200 thousand northern fur seals. Suppose the population is being renewed at a rate of $r(t) = 60 - 0.5t$ thousand seals per year and that the survival rate is 67%.

(Source: Delphine Haley, *Marine Mammals,* Seattle, WA: Pacific Search Press, 1978.)

a. How many of the current population of 200 thousand seals will still be alive 50 years from now?

b. Write a function for the number of seals that will be born t years from now and will still be alive 50 years from now.

c. Estimate the northern fur seal population 50 years from now.

Discussing Concepts

24. Explain, using related examples, the difference between a continuous income stream and a discrete income stream.

6.3 Integrals in Economics

This section uses improper integrals, which were discussed in Section 6.1

When you purchase an item in a store, you ordinarily have no control over the price that you pay. Your only choice is whether to buy or not to buy the item at the current price. In general, consumers hold to the view that price is a variable to which they can only respond. As the price per unit increases, consumers usually respond by purchasing (demanding) less. The typical relationship between the price per unit (as input) and the quantity in demand (as output) is shown in Figure 6.6a.

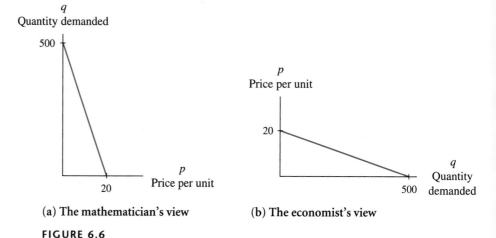

(a) The mathematician's view (b) The economist's view

FIGURE 6.6

The traditional approach to graphing in economic theory is to put the price per unit along the vertical axis and the quantity in demand along the horizontal axis. (See Figure 6.6b.) In general, we choose to graph price per unit as input along the horizontal axis. This will help us understand price as input and visualize the definite integrals used later in this section. However, occasionally we will present both the mathematician's and the economist's graphical viewpoints.

Demand Curves

The graph relating quantity in demand q to price per unit p is called a **demand curve.** In economic theory, demand is actually a function that has several input variables, such as price per unit, consumers' ability to buy, consumers' need, and so on. The demand curve we consider here is a simplified version. We assume that all the possible input variables are constant except price. We denote this demand function as D with input p.

Even though the demand function is not a rate-of-change function, there are economic interpretations for the areas of certain regions lying beneath the demand curve. In order to interpret the area of these regions, you must understand how to interpret the information the demand curve represents.

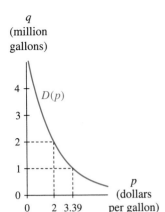

q
(million
gallons)

FIGURE 6.7

For instance, suppose the graph in Figure 6.7 represents the weekly demand for regular unleaded gasoline in a California city. A point on the demand curve indicates the quantity that consumers will purchase at a given price. For instance, at $3.39 per gallon, consumers will purchase 1 million gallons of gas. At $2.00 per gallon, consumers will purchase 2 million gallons of gas.

Consumers' Willingness and Ability to Spend

Even though points on the demand curve tell us how much consumers will actually purchase at certain prices, consumers are willing and able to pay more than this amount for the quantity they purchase. For instance, consumers are willing and able to spend approximately $3.39 million for the first million gallons of regular unleaded gasoline, but they are willing and able to spend only approximately $2.00 million for the second million gallons. Thus, in total, consumers are willing and able to spend approximately $5.39 million for 2 million gallons of gas.

If the price of gas is $1.19 a gallon, consumers are willing and able to buy the third million gallons. That is, consumers are willing and able to spend approximately

(1 million gallons)($3.39 per gallon) + (1 million gallons)($2.00 per gallon)

+ (1 million gallons)($1.19 per gallon) = $6.58 million

for 3 million gallons of gas, even though in actuality they spend only

(3 million gallons)($1.19 per gallon) = $3.57 million

Consumers' willingness and ability to spend can be approximated graphically as the areas of stacked horizontal rectangles. The amount that consumers actually spend is depicted as the area of a single vertical rectangle. (See Figures 6.8a and b.)

You should have noticed that the amount that consumers are willing and able to spend for 3 million gallons was given as *approximately* $6.58 million. We can make this approximation better by considering smaller increments for price. If we were to approximate consumers' willingness and ability to spend using price increments of

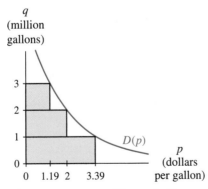

(a) Consumers are willing and able to spend about $6.58 million for 3 million gallons of gas.

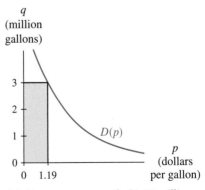

(b) Consumers pay only $3.57 million for 3 million gallons of gas.

FIGURE 6.8

$0.5 per gallon, $0.25 per gallon, $0.125 per gallon, and so on, we would see that the areas of the stacked rectangles representing these approximations would become closer to being the true area depicted in Figure 6.9.

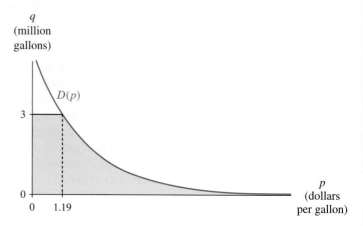

FIGURE 6.9

Thus consumers' willingness and ability to purchase 3 million gallons of gas can be visually represented by the sum of the area of the rectangle with width 1.19 under the horizontal line $D(p) = 3$ and the area under the demand curve from 1.19 to P, where P is the price above which consumers cannot and will not purchase any gas. We calculate the consumers' willingness and ability to spend as

$$3(1.19) + \int_{1.19}^{P} D(p) \, dp \text{ million dollars}$$

Suppose the demand for gas can be modeled by

$$D(p) = 5.43(0.607^p) \text{ million gallons}$$

where p dollars is the price per gallon. The only piece of information we still need is P, the price above which no gas will be purchased. You should notice that the demand function approaches 0 as p becomes large; however, it will never be exactly 0 for any p. Hence, we let P approach ∞. This is true for most demand functions in economics—some people will always want the product or service, regardless of the price. In this case, we consider the area under the demand curve as P becomes infinitely large. That is,

This limit can be viewed graphically as the limit of a decreasing exponential function.

$$3(1.19) + \int_{1.19}^{\infty} 5.43(0.607^p) dp$$

$$= 3.57 + \lim_{P \to \infty} \int_{1.19}^{P} 5.43(0.607^p) dp$$

$$= 3.57 + \lim_{P \to \infty} \left(\frac{5.43(0.607^p)}{\ln 0.607} \right) \Bigg|_{1.19}^{P}$$

$$= 3.57 + \left(\lim_{P \to \infty} \frac{5.43(0.607^p)}{\ln 0.607} \right) - \frac{5.43(0.607^{1.19})}{\ln 0.607}$$

$$\approx 3.57 + 0 + 6.00$$

$$\approx \$9.57 \text{ million}$$

Thus consumers are willing and able to spend $9.57 million in order to purchase 3 million gallons of gas.

In general, we make the following definition:

Consumers' Willingness and Ability to Spend

For a continuous demand function $q = D(p)$, the maximum amount that consumers are willing and able to spend for a certain quantity q_0 of goods or services is the area of the shaded region in Figure 6.10.

FIGURE 6.10

where p_0 is the market price at which q_0 units are in demand and P is the price above which consumers will purchase none of the goods or services. This area is calculated as

$$p_0 q_0 + \int_{p_0}^{P} D(p)\,dp$$

(Note that ∞ is used as the upper limit on the integral if the demand function approaches, but does not cross, the input axis.)

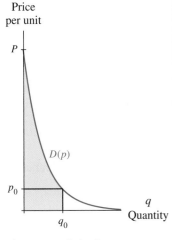

The economist's view
FIGURE 6.11

Because economists graph with the price on the vertical axis, in economics books the market price p_0 at which q_0 units are in demand and the price P above which consumers will purchase none of the goods or services both appear on the vertical axis, whereas q_0 is on the horizontal axis. The area depicting the maximum amount that consumers are willing and able to spend appears (from the economist's viewpoint) as the shaded area in Figure 6.11.

Consumers' Expenditure and Surplus

Now that we have considered what consumers are willing and able to spend for a certain quantity of a product, let us turn our attention to calculating what consumers *actually* spend for that quantity. We return to the discussion of gasoline demand.

As we said before, if the market price for gas is $1.19 per gallon, consumers will purchase 3 million gallons. The actual amount spent by consumers is (3 million gallons)($1.19 per gallon) = $3.57 million, even though they are willing and able to spend much more. This actual amount spent is (price)(quantity), which is the area of the rectangular region from the vertical axis to $p = 1.19$ with height 3, as shown in Figure 6.12. This amount is known as the **consumers' expenditure.** The amount that consumers are willing and able to spend but do not actually spend is known as the **consumers' surplus.**

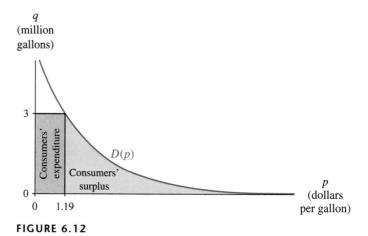

FIGURE 6.12

Earlier we found that consumers are willing and able to spend $9.57 million to purchase 3 million gallons of gas, so the consumers' surplus from buying 3 million gallons of gas at $1.19 per gallon is

$9.57 million − $3.57 million = $6 million

Consumers' surplus can also be computed as the area between the demand function and the horizontal axis as

$$\text{Consumers surplus} = \int_{1.19}^{\infty} 5.43(0.607^p)\,dp \approx \$6 \text{ million}$$

In general, we make the following definitions:

Consumers' Expenditure and Surplus

For a continuous demand function $q = D(p)$, the amount that consumers spend at a certain market price is called consumers' expenditure; it is represented by the rectangular area in Figure 6.13. Furthermore, the amount that consumers are willing and able to spend, but do not spend, for q_0 items at a market price p_0 is called consumers' surplus; it is represented by the area of the nonrectangular shaded region in Figure 6.13. The value P is the price above which consumers will purchase none of the goods or services.

FIGURE 6.13

These areas are calculated as follows:

$$\text{Consumers' expenditure} = p_0 q_0$$

$$\text{Consumers' surplus} = \int_{p_0}^{P} D(p)\,dp$$

(Note that ∞ is used as the upper limit on the integral if the demand function approaches, but does not cross, the input axis.)

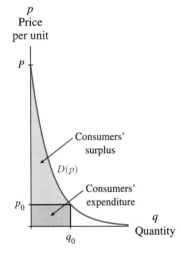

The economist's view

FIGURE 6.14

Again it is worth noting that because economists graph with the price on the vertical axis, graphs showing consumers' expenditure and surplus appear in economics books with the rectangle representing consumers' expenditure lying below the area representing consumers' surplus, as shown in Figure 6.14.

EXAMPLE 1   *Finding Areas Involving a Demand Curve*

Minivans   Suppose the demand for a certain model of minivan in the United States can be described as

$$D(p) = 14.12(0.933^p) - 0.25 \text{ million minivans}$$

when the market price is p thousand dollars per minivan.

a.   At what price per minivan will consumers purchase 2.5 million minivans?

b.   What is the consumers' expenditure when purchasing 2.5 million minivans?

c.   Does the model indicate a possible price above which consumers will purchase no minivans? If so, what is this price?

d.   When 2.5 million minivans are purchased, what is the consumers' surplus?

e.   What is the total amount that consumers are willing and able to spend on 2.5 million minivans?

Solution

a.   We solve $D(p) = 2.5$ to find the market price at which consumers will purchase 2.5 million minivans. The equation

$$14.12(0.933^p) - 0.25 = 2.5$$

is satisfied when $p \approx 23.59033$. That is, at a market price p_0 of approximately $23,600 per minivan, consumers will purchase $q_0 = 2.5$ million minivans.

b.   When they purchase 2.5 million minivans, consumers' expenditure will be

$$p_0 q_0 \approx (23.59033 \text{ thousand dollars per minivan})(2.5 \text{ million minivans})$$
$$\approx \$59.0 \text{ billion}$$

c.   If the demand function approaches but does not cross the horizontal axis as price per unit increases without bound, then there is no price above which consumers will not purchase minivans. However, in this case, the demand function crosses the horizontal axis near $p = 58.16701$ (found by solving $D(p) = 0$). According to the model, the price above which consumers will purchase no minivans is approximately $p = \$58.2$ thousand per minivan.

d.   Consumers' surplus is the area of the region shaded in Figure 6.15, calculated as

$$\int_{p_0}^{P} D(p)\,dp \approx \int_{23.59033}^{58.16701} [14.12(0.933^p) - 0.25]\,dp$$
$$\approx 27.40482$$

To determine the appropriate units for consumers' surplus, remember that we are finding the area of a region whose width is measured in thousand dollars per minivan and whose height is measured in million minivans. Thus the units on consumers' surplus are (thousand dollars per minivan)(million minivans), which simplify to billion dollars.

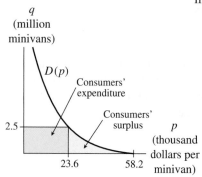

FIGURE 6.15

Therefore, we estimate the consumers' surplus when purchasing 2.5 million minivans to be $27.4 billion.

e.   The amount that consumers are willing and able to spend for 2.5 million minivans is the combined area of the two shaded regions in Figure 6.15. This area is approximately $59.0 + 27.4 = \$86.4$ billion.   ●

Elasticity of Demand

As the price per unit of a commodity increases, we expect the demand for that commodity to decrease. For instance, when the price per gallon of gasoline increases, the demand for gasoline decreases slightly. On the other hand, when the price per unit for minivans increases, the demand for minivans decreases substantially. A measure of the responsiveness of consumers to a change in the price of a commodity is **elasticity of demand**. Because the quantity of a commodity and the price per unit of that commodity normally have very different units of measure, **elasticity of demand** uses a ratio of percentage rates of change to compare relative changes. For a demand function D with input p price per unit, we define *elasticity of demand* as the absolute value of the percentage rate of change of the quantity demanded divided by the percentage rate of change of the price per unit. Algebraically elasticity of demand can be written as

$$\text{elasticity of demand} = \left| \frac{\text{percentage rate of change of } D(p)}{\text{percentage rate of change of } p} \right|$$

$$= \left| \frac{\dfrac{D'(p)}{D(p)} 100}{\dfrac{p'}{p} 100} \right|$$

Note that $\dfrac{p'}{p} = \dfrac{1}{p}$ because $\dfrac{d}{dp}(p) = 1$.

$$= \left| \frac{\dfrac{D'(p)}{D(p)}}{\dfrac{1}{p}} \right|$$

$$= \left| \frac{D'(p)}{D(p)} \cdot \frac{p}{1} \right|$$

$$= \left| \frac{p \cdot D'(p)}{D(p)} \right|$$

We will use the Greek letter eta, η, to represent elasticity of demand. When η is greater than 1 at a given price per unit k, a small change in price results in a relatively large response in the change of demand and we say that the demand is *elastic* at price k. When η is less than 1 at a given price per unit k, a small change in price results in a relatively small response in the change of demand and we say that the demand is *inelastic* at price k.

Elasticity of Demand

For a commodity with differentiable demand function, $q = D(p)$, where q is the quantity demanded when the price per unit is p, the *elasticity of demand* is

$$\eta = \left| \frac{\text{percentage rate of change of quantity}}{\text{percentage rate of change of price}} \right|$$

$$= \left| \frac{p \cdot D'(p)}{D(p)} \right|$$

Demand is *elastic* when $\eta > 1$ and *inelastic* when $\eta < 1$. Demand is at *unit elasticity* when $\eta = 1$.

EXAMPLE 2   *Finding Elasticity of Demand*

Minivans   Again consider the demand for a certain model of minivan in the United States as described in Example 1:

$$D(p) = 14.12(0.933^p) - 0.25 \text{ million minivans}$$

when the market price is p thousand dollars per minivan.

a. Find the point of unit elasticity.

b. For what prices is the demand elastic? For what prices is the demand inelastic?

Solution

a. First, we find an expression for elasticity:

$$\eta = \left| \frac{p \cdot D'(p)}{D(p)} \right|$$

$$= \left| \frac{p \cdot [14.12(\ln 0.933)(0.933^p)]}{14.12(0.933^p) - 0.25} \right|$$

Solving $\eta = 1$, we find that $p \approx 13.76$. That is, unit elasticity occurs when minivans are priced approximately 13.76 thousand dollars per minivan. At this price, demand is approximately 5.19 million minivans.

b. We begin by checking η for values of p on either side of 13.76. We choose to check η at $p = 10$ and $p = 20$.

When $p = 10$, $\eta = \left| \dfrac{10 \cdot [14.12(\ln 0.933)(0.933^{10})]}{14.12(0.933^{10}) - 0.25} \right| \approx 0.72$. So for prices less than 13.76 thousand dollars per minivan, demand is inelastic (not highly responsive to small increases in price.)

When $p = 20$, $\eta = \left| \dfrac{20 \cdot [14.12(\ln 0.933)(0.933^{20})]}{14.12(0.933^{20}) - 0.25} \right| \approx 1.49$. So for prices greater than 13.76 thousand dollars per minivan, demand is elastic (responsive to small increases in price). ●

A point of unit elasticity on a concave up, decreasing demand function $q = D(p)$ for a commodity equates to a maximum on the revenue function $R(p) = p \cdot D(p)$ for that commodity.

Supply Curves

We have seen that when prices go up, consumers usually respond by demanding less. However, manufacturers and producers respond to higher prices by supplying more. Thus a typical curve that relates the quantity supplied, S, to price per unit, p, is usually increasing and appears as shown in Figure 6.16.

The graph that expresses the quantity supplied in terms of the price per unit is called a **supply curve.** You should note from Figure 6.16 that there is a price p_1 below which producers are not willing or able to supply any quantity of the product. The point $(p_1, S(p_1))$ is known in economics as the **shutdown point.** If the market price (and the corresponding quantity) fall below this point, producers will shut down their production.

The supply function has an interpretation very similar to that of the demand function. Suppose the quantity of regular unleaded gasoline that producers will supply is modeled as

q
Quantity

$S(p)$

p_1

p
Price per unit

FIGURE 6.16

$$S(p) = \begin{cases} 0 \text{ million gallons} & \text{when } p < 1 \\ 0.792p^2 - 0.433p + 0.314 \text{ million gallons} & \text{when } p \geq 1 \end{cases}$$

where the market price of gas is p dollars per gallon. This function is graphed in teal in Figure 6.17. At \$1.24 a gallon, producers will supply 1 million gallons of gas. At \$1.78 per gallon, producers will supply 2 million gallons, and if the price is \$2.14 a gallon, producers will supply 3 million gallons.

q
(million gallons)

$S(p)$

p
(dollars per gallon)

1 1.24 1.78 2.14   3

FIGURE 6.17

Producers' Willingness and Ability to Receive

We approximate the minimum that producers are willing and able to receive for 3 million gallons of gas by summing the amount they are willing and able to receive for the first million gallons, for the second million gallons, and for the third million gallons:

($1.24 per gallon)(first 1 million gallons) + ($1.78 per gallon) ·

(second 1 million gallons) + ($2.14 per gallon)(third 1 million gallons)

= $1,240,000 + $1,780,000 + $2,140,000 = $5,160,000

Thus the minimum that producers are willing and able to receive for 3 million gallons of gas is approximately $5,160,000. This amount can be thought of as the sum of the areas of the three stacked rectangles shaded in Figure 6.17.

As we use more intervals, the area of stacked rectangles comes closer to the true area of the region above the $q = S(p)$ curve and below the $q = 3$ line shown in Figure 6.18. Because a portion of $S(p)$ is zero, we find the total area by dividing the region into a rectangular region and the region below $q = 3$ and above $q = S(p)$ to the right of the shutdown point.

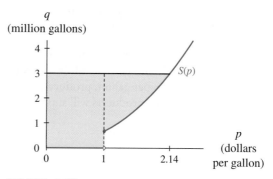

FIGURE 6.18

Therefore, the minimum amount that suppliers are willing and able to receive is calculated as

$$3(1) + \int_{1}^{2.14} [3 - S(p)]dp$$

$$= 3 + \int_{1}^{2.14} (-0.792p^2 + 0.433p + 2.686)dp$$

$$\approx \$4.5 \text{ million}$$

According to the supply model S, suppliers are willing and able to receive no less than $4.5 million for 3 million gallons of gas.

We make the following general definition:

Producers' Willingness and Ability to Receive

For a continuous or piecewise continuous supply function $q = S(p)$, the minimum amount that producers are willing and able to receive for a certain quantity q_0 of goods or services is the area of the shaded region in Figure 6.19.

FIGURE 6.19

where p_0 is the market price at which q_0 units are supplied and p_1 is the shutdown price. This area is calculated as

$$p_1 q_0 + \int_{p_1}^{p_0} [q_0 - S(p)] \, dp$$

If there is no shutdown price, then $p_1 = 0$.

The economist's view

FIGURE 6.20

In the economist's viewpoint (with price graphed on the vertical axis), the minimum amount that producers are willing and able to receive for a certain quantity q_0 of goods or services is the shaded region shown in Figure 6.20. The market price p_0 at which q_0 units are supplied and the shutdown price p_1 are both graphed on the vertical axis. However, because price is the input and quantity is the output, the area is still calculated as $p_1 q_0 + \int_{p_1}^{p_0} [q_0 - S(p)] \, dp$.

Producers' Revenue and Surplus

The market price that will lead to the supply of 3 million gallons of gas is $p \approx \$2.14$ per gallon. The **producers' revenue** is price times quantity, which is the area of the rectangle shown in Figure 6.21: ($\$2.14$ per gallon)(3 million gallons) $\approx \$6.4$ million. Producers will therefore receive $\$6.4$ million $- \$4.5$ million $\approx \$1.9$ million in excess of the minimum

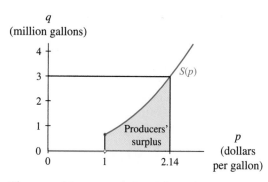

The area of the rectangle is producers' revenue.

FIGURE 6.21

they are willing and able to receive. This excess amount is known as the **producers' surplus** and is the area of the shaded region in Figure 6.21.

We calculate the producers' surplus from the sale of 3 million gallons of gas at the market price of approximately \$2.14 directly from the supply function as follows:

$$\int_{1}^{2.14} S(p)dp = \int_{1}^{2.14} (0.792p^2 - 0.433p + 0.314)dp$$

$$\approx \$1.9 \text{ million}$$

In general, we find the producers' total revenue and the producers' surplus as follows:

Producers' Revenue and Surplus

For a continuous or piecewise continuous supply function $q = S(p)$, the amount that producers receive at a certain market price is called the producers' revenue and is the area of the shaded rectangle in Figure 6.22a. Furthermore, the amount that producers receive above the minimum amount they are willing and able to receive for q_0 items at a market price p_0 is called the producers' surplus and is the area of the region between the supply function and the horizontal axis as shown in Figure 6.22b. The value p_1 is the price below which production shuts down. (If there is no shutdown price, then $p_1 = 0$.)

(a)   **(b)**

FIGURE 6.22

These areas are calculated as follows:

$$\text{Producers' revenue} = p_0 q_0$$

$$\text{Producers' surplus} = \int_{p_1}^{p_0} S(p)dp$$

Figure 6.23 is the economist's version of Figure 6.22. Because economists graph price vertically, producers' willingness and ability to receive and producers' surplus appear to be transposed, as shown in Figure 6.23b. However, because the supply function S uses price per unit p as input, the calculations for producers' revenue and producers' surplus are the same as given in the preceding box.

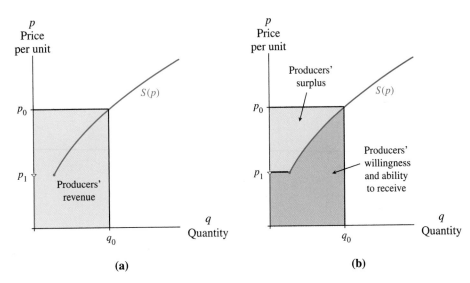

(a)   **(b)**

The economist's view

FIGURE 6.23

EXAMPLE 3   *Finding Areas Involving a Supply Curve*

Phones   Suppose the function for the average weekly supply of a certain brand of cellular phone can be modeled by the equation

$$S(p) = \begin{cases} 0 \text{ phones} & \text{when } p < 15 \\ 0.047p^2 + 9.38p + 150 \text{ phones} & \text{when } p \geq 15 \end{cases}$$

where p is the market price in dollars per phone.

a. How many phones (on average) will producers supply at a market price of $45.95?

b. What is the least amount that producers are willing and able to receive for the quantity of phones that corresponds to a market price of $45.95?

c. What is the producers' revenue when the market price is $45.95?

d. What is the producers' surplus when the market price is $45.95?

Solution

a. When the market price is $45.95, producers will supply an average of $S(45.95) \approx 680$ phones each week.

b. The minimum amount that producers are willing and able to receive is the area of the labeled region in Figure 6.24 and is calculated as

$$(15)(680.247) + \int_{15}^{45.95} [680.247 - S(p)]dp$$

$$= 10{,}203.704 + (-0.0157p^3 - 4.69p^2 + 530.247p)\big|_{15}^{45.95}$$

$$\approx \$16{,}300.53$$

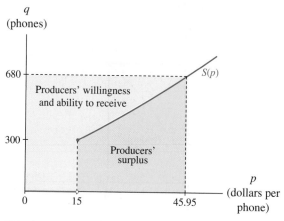

FIGURE 6.24

c. When the market price is $45.95, the producers' revenue is

(Quantity supplied at $45.95)($45.95 per phone)

$\approx$ (680.247 phones)($45.95 per phone)

$\approx \$31{,}257.35$

Graphically, the producers' revenue is the area of the rectangle in Figure 6.24.

d. When the market price is $45.95, the producers' surplus (see Figure 6.24) is

$$\int_{15}^{45.95} S(p)dp = (0.0157p^3 + 4.69p^2 + 150p)\big|_{15}^{45.95} \approx \$14{,}956.82$$

Note that the producers' surplus plus the minimum amount that the producers are willing and able to receive is equal to the producers' revenue. ●

Social Gain

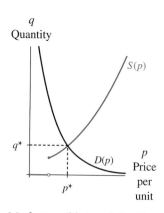

Market equilibrium (p^*, q^*) occurs when demand is equal to supply.

FIGURE 6.25

Consider the economic market for a particular item for which the demand and supply curves are shown in Figure 6.25. The point (p^*, q^*) where the demand curve and supply curve cross is called the **equilibrium point.** At the equilibrium price p^*, the quantity demanded by consumers coincides with the quantity supplied by producers. This quantity is q^*.

Economists consider that society is benefited whenever consumers and/or producers have surplus funds. When the market price of a product is the equilibrium price for that product, the total benefit to society is the consumers' surplus plus the producers' surplus. This amount is known as the **total social gain.**

Market Equilibrium and Social Gain

Market equilibrium occurs when the supply of a product is equal to the demand for that product. If $q = D(p)$ is the demand function and $q = S(p)$ is the supply function, then the equilibrium point is the point (p^*, q^*), where p^* is the price that satisfies the equation $D(p) = S(p)$ and $q^* = D(p^*) = S(p^*)$.

The total social gain for a product is the sum of the producers' surplus and the consumers' surplus. When q^* units are produced and sold at a market price of p^*, the total social gain is the area of the entire shaded region in Figure 6.26. The value p_1 is the price below which production shuts down, and P is the price above which consumers will not purchase.

FIGURE 6.26

The combined area is calculated as

Total social gain = producers' surplus + consumers' surplus

$$= \int_{p_1}^{p^*} S(p)\,dp + \int_{P}^{P} D(p)\,dp$$

The economist's view is shown in Figure 6.27. The visual representation does not change the manner in which the calculations are performed in order to find the equilibrium point and total social gain.

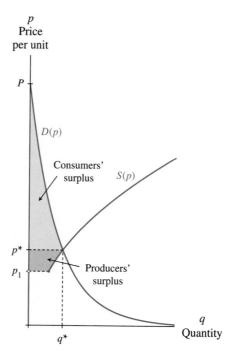

The economist's view

FIGURE 6.27

EXAMPLE 4   *Determining Market Equilibrium and Social Gain*

Gasoline   The demand and supply functions for the gasoline example given near the beginning of this section are

Demand $= D(p) = 5.43(0.607^p)$ million gallons

and

$$\text{Supply} \quad = S(p) = \begin{cases} 0 \text{ million gallons} & \text{when } p < 1 \\ 0.792p^2 - 0.433p + 0.314 \text{ gallons} & \text{when } p \geq 1 \end{cases}$$

where p is the market price in dollars per gallon.

a. Find the market equilibrium point for gasoline.

b. Find the total social gain when gasoline is sold at the market equilibrium price.

Solution

a. Solving

$$5.43(0.607^p) = 0.792p^2 - 0.433p + 0.314$$

for p yields $p^* \approx \$1.83$ per gallon. At this market price, $q^* \approx 2.2$ million gallons of gas will be purchased. [*Note:* q^* can be found as either $D(p^*)$ or $S(p^*)$.]

b. The total social gain at market equilibrium is the area of the shaded regions in Figure 6.28. We must find p_1, the shutdown price, and P, the price beyond which consumers will purchase no gasoline, before we can proceed.

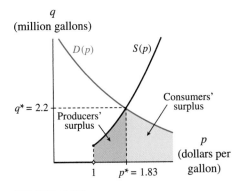

q
(million gallons)

$D(p)$ $S(p)$

$q^* = 2.2$

Producers'
surplus

Consumers'
surplus

p
(dollars per
gallon)

1     $p^* = 1.83$

FIGURE 6.28

The shutdown price is given in the statement of the supply function as $p_1 = 1$. The demand function indicates that there is no price beyond which consumers will not purchase. Thus, $P \to \infty$.

Now we proceed with our calculation of total social gain:

$$\text{Total social gain} \approx \int_{1.00}^{1.8311} (0.792p^2 - 0.433p + 0.314)dp$$

$$+ \int_{1.8311}^{\infty} 5.43(0.607^p)dp$$

$$\approx 1.108 + 4.360 \approx \$5.5 \text{ million}$$

At the market equilibrium price of $1.83 per gallon, the total social gain is approximately $5.5 million. ●

6.3 Concept Inventory

- Market price
- Demand curve
- Consumers' willingness and ability to spend
- Consumers' expenditure
- Consumers' surplus
- Elasticity of demand
- Supply curve
- Shutdown point
- Producers' revenue
- Producers' surplus
- Producers' willingness and ability to receive
- Market equilibrium
- Total social gain

6.3 Activities

Getting Started

1. Give the economic name by which we call each of the following:

   a. The function relating the number of items the consumer will purchase at a certain price and the price per item.

   b. The function relating the quantity of items the supplier of the items will sell at a certain price and the price per item.

   c. The area of the region below the supply curve between the shutdown price and the market price.

   d. The area of the region below the demand curve between the market price and the price above which consumers will cease to purchase.

2. For each of the following amounts:

   i. Describe the region whose area gives the specified amount.

   ii. Illustrate that region by sketching an example.

   a. The maximum amount that consumers are willing and able to spend.

   b. The minimum amount that producers are willing and able to receive.

   c. The consumers' expenditure.

   d. The total social gain at market equilibrium.

3. Explain how to find each of the following:

   a. The price P above which consumers will purchase none of the goods or services.

   b. The shutdown point.

   c. The point of market equilibrium.

4. **Demand**   The following two figures, drawn from the mathematician's and the economist's viewpoints, depict the same demand curve for a commodity. Consider p_0 to be the current market price of the commodity.

b. Sketch the supply curve from the economist's viewpoint. Include the shutdown price and the point (p_0, q_0) on the economist's graph.

c. Depict (by shading on each figure) the region representing producers' revenue.

6. Supply The following two figures, drawn from the mathematician's and the economist's viewpoints, depict the same supply curve for a commodity. Consider $p_0 = \$3$ per unit to be the current market price of the commodity.

a. Use $p_0 = \$20$ per unit and the demand curve to estimate q_0 on the figure showing the mathematician's view. Transfer the point (p_0, q_0) to the figure showing the economist's view.

b. Depict (by shading on each figure) the regions representing consumers' expenditure and consumers' surplus.

c. Outline on each figure the region representing the amount that consumers are willing and able to spend.

d. Write a formula for the calculation of consumers' willingness and ability to spend.

5. Supply The accompanying figure depicts a supply curve, drawn from the mathematician's viewpoint, for a commodity. Consider $p_0 = \$25$ per unit to be the current market price of the commodity and $p_1 = \$10$ per unit to be the shutdown price.

a. Use p_0 and the supply curve to estimate q_0 on the figure showing the mathematician's view.

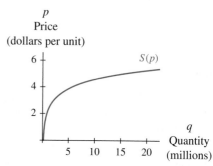

a. Use p_0 and the supply curve to estimate q_0 on the figure showing the mathematician's view. Transfer the point (p_0, q_0) to, and label the shutdown price on, the figure showing the economist's view.

b. Depict (by shading on each figure) the regions representing producers' willingness and ability to receive and producers' surplus.

c. Outline on each figure the region representing producers' revenue.

d. Write a formula for producers' willingness and ability to receive.

e. Write a formula for producers' surplus.

7. **Social Gain** The following two figures, drawn from the mathematician's and the economist's viewpoints, depict the same supply and demand curves for a product.

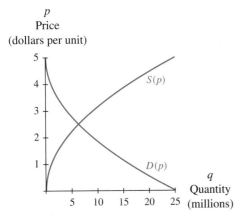

a. On both figures, mark the equilibrium point and label it (p^*, q^*). Estimate the values of p^* and q^* and label them on the axes in both

figures. Also estimate the value of, and label on both figures, the shutdown price p_1 and the price P above which consumers will not purchase the product.

b. Depict (by shading on each figure) the regions representing consumers' surplus and producers' surplus.

c. Outline on each figure the region representing total social gain.

d. Write a formula for the calculation of total social gain.

Applying Concepts

8. **Demand** The demand for wooden chairs can be modeled as

$$D(p) = -0.01p + 5.55 \text{ million chairs}$$

where p is the price (in dollars) of a chair.

a. According to the model, at what price will consumers no longer purchase chairs? Is this price guaranteed to be the highest price any consumer will pay for a wooden chair? Explain.

b. Find the quantity of wooden chairs that consumers will purchase when the market price is $99.95.

c. Determine the amount that consumers are willing and able to spend to purchase 3 million wooden chairs.

d. Find the consumers' surplus when consumers purchase 3 million wooden chairs.

9. **Demand** The demand for ceiling fans can be modeled as

$$D(p) = 25.92(0.996^p) \text{ thousand ceiling fans}$$

where p is the price (in dollars) of a ceiling fan.

a. According to the model, is there a price above which consumers will no longer purchase fans? If so, what is it? If not, explain why not.

b. Find the amount that consumers are willing and able to spend to purchase 18 thousand ceiling fans.

c. Find the quantity of fans that consumers will purchase when the market price is $100.

d. Find the consumers' surplus when the market price is $100.

10. **Demand**   The demand for a 12-ounce bottle of sparkling water is given in the accompanying table.

Price (dollars per bottle)	Demand (million bottles)
2.29	25
2.69	9
3.09	3
3.49	2
3.89	1
4.29	0.5

a. Find a model for demand as a function of price.

b. Does your model indicate a price above which consumers will purchase no bottles of water? If so, what is it? If not, explain.

c. Find the quantity of water that consumers will purchase when the market price is $2.59.

d. Find the amount that consumers are willing and able to spend to purchase the quantity you found in part c.

e. Find the consumers' surplus when the market price is $2.59.

11. **Demand**   The average daily demand for a new type of kerosene lantern in a certain hardware store is as shown in the table.

Price (dollars per lantern)	Average quantity demanded (lanterns)
21.52	1
17.11	3
14.00	5
11.45	7
9.23	9
7.25	11

a. Find a model giving the average quantity demanded as a function of the price.

b. How much are consumers willing and able to spend each day for these lanterns when the market price is $12.34 per lantern?

c. Find the consumers' surplus when the equilibrium price for these lanterns is $12.34 per lantern.

12. **Elasticity**   The demand for wooden chairs can be modeled as

$$D(p) = -0.01p + 5.55 \text{ million chairs}$$

where p is the price (in dollars) of a chair.

a. Find the point of unit elasticity.

b. For what prices is demand elastic? For what prices is demand inelastic?

13. **Elasticity**   The demand for ceiling fans can be modeled as

$$D(p) = 25.92(0.996^p) \text{ thousand ceiling fans}$$

where p is the price (in dollars) of a ceiling fan.

a. Find the point of unit elasticity.

b. For what prices is demand elastic? For what prices is demand inelastic?

14. **Elasticity**   In Activity 10 part a, you were asked to find a model for the demand for a 12-ounce bottle of sparkling water.

a. Use the model found in Activity 10 to find the point of unit elasticity.

b. For what prices is demand elastic? For what prices is demand inelastic?

15. **Elasticity**   In Activity 11 part a, you were asked to find a model for the average daily demand for a new type of kerosene lantern in a certain hardware store.

a. Use the model found in Activity 11 to find the point of unit elasticity.

b. For what prices is demand elastic? For what prices is demand inelastic?

16. **Supply**   The willingness of saddle producers to supply saddles can be modeled by the following function:

$$S(p) = \begin{cases} 0 \text{ thousand saddles} & \text{if } p < 5 \\ 2.194(1.295^p) \text{ thousand saddles} & \text{if } p \geq 5 \end{cases}$$

where saddles are sold for p thousand dollars.

a. How many saddles will producers supply when the market price is $4000? $8000?

b. At what price will producers supply 10 thousand saddles?

c. Find the producers' revenue when the market price is $7500.

d. Find the producers' surplus when the market price is $7500.

17. Supply The willingness of answering machine producers to supply can be modeled by the following function:

$$S(p) = \begin{cases} 0 \text{ thousand answering machines} & \text{if } p < 20 \\ 0.024p^2 - 2p + 60 \text{ thousand} \\ \quad \text{answering machines} & \text{if } p \geq 20 \end{cases}$$

where answering machines are sold for p dollars.

a. How many answering machines will producers supply when the market price is $40? $150?

b. Find the producers' revenue and the producers' surplus when the market price is $99.95.

18. Supply The table shows the number of CDs that producers will supply at the given prices.

Price per CD (dollars)	CDs supplied (millions)
5.00	1
7.50	1.5
10.00	2
15.00	3
20.00	4
25.00	5

a. Find a model giving the quantity supplied as a function of the price per CD. *Note:* Producers will not supply CDs when the market price falls below $4.99.

b. How many CDs will producers supply when the market price is $15.98?

c. At what price will producers supply 2.3 million CDs?

d. Find the producers' revenue and producers' surplus when the market price is $19.99.

19. Supply The table shows the average number of prints of a famous painting that producers will supply at the given prices.

Price per print (hundred dollars)	Prints supplied (hundreds)
5	2
6	2.2
7	3
8	4.3
9	6.3
10	8.9

a. Find a model giving the quantity supplied as a function of the price per print. *Note:* Producers will not supply prints when the market price falls below $500.

b. At what price will producers supply 5 hundred prints?

c. Find the producers' revenue and producers' surplus when the market price is $630.

20. Market Equilibrium The daily demand for beef can be modeled by

$$D(p) = \frac{40.007}{1 + 0.033e^{0.35382p}} \text{ million pounds}$$

where the price for beef is p dollars per pound. Likewise, the supply for beef can be modeled by

$$S(p) = \begin{cases} 0 \text{ million pounds} & \text{if } p < 0.5 \\ \dfrac{51}{1 + 53.98e^{-0.3949p}} \text{ million pounds} & \text{if } p \geq 0.5 \end{cases}$$

where the price for beef is p dollars per pound.

a. How much beef is supplied when the price is $1.50 per pound? Will supply exceed demand at this quantity?

b. Find the point of market equilibrium.

21. Social Gain The average quantity of sculptures that consumers will demand can be modeled as $D(p) = -1.003p^2 - 20.689p + 850.375$ sculptures, and the average quantity that producers will supply can be modeled as

$$S(p) = \begin{cases} 0 \text{ sculptures} & \text{when } p < 4.5 \\ 0.256p^2 + 8.132p \\ \quad + 250.097 \text{ sculptures} & \text{when } p \geq 4.5 \end{cases}$$

where the market price is p hundred dollars per sculpture.

a. How much are consumers willing and able to spend for 20 sculptures?

b. How many sculptures will producers supply at $500 per sculpture? Will supply exceed demand at this quantity?

c. Determine the total social gain when sculptures are sold at the equilibrium price.

22. Social Gain   A florist constructs a table on the basis of sales data for roses.

Price of 1 dozen roses (dollars)	Dozens sold per week
10	190
15	145
20	110
25	86
30	65
35	52

a. Find a model for the quantity demanded.

b. Determine how much money consumers will be willing and able to spend for 80 dozen roses each week.

c. If the actual market price of the roses is $22 per dozen, find the consumers' surplus.

Suppose the suppliers of roses collect the data shown in the following table.

Price of 1 dozen roses (dollars)	Dozens supplied per week
20	200
18	150
14	100
11	80
8	60
5	50

d. Find an equation that models the supply data. Suppliers will supply no roses for prices below $5 per dozen.

e. What is the producers' surplus when the market price is $17 per dozen?

f. For what price will roses be sold at the equilibrium point?

g. What is the total social gain from the sale of roses at market equilibrium?

23. Social Gain   The table gives both number of copies of a hardcover science fiction novel in demand and the number supplied at certain prices.

Price (dollars per book)	Books demanded (thousands)	Books supplied (thousands)
20	214	120
23	186	130
25	170	140
28	150	160
30	138	190
32	128	210

a. Find an exponential model for demand given the price per book.

b. Find a model for supply given the price per book. *Note:* Producers are not willing to supply any books when the market price is less than $18.97.

c. At what price will market equilibrium occur? How many books will be supplied and demanded at this price?

d. Find the total social gain from the sale of a hardcover science fiction novel at the market equilibrium price.

24. Social Gain   The table shows both the number of a certain type of graphing calculator in demand and the number supplied at certain prices.

Price (dollars per calculator)	Calculators demanded (millions)	Calculators supplied (millions)
60	35	10
90	31	32
120	15	50
150	5	80
180	4	100
210	3	120

a. Find a model for demand given the price per calculator.

b. Find a model for supply given the price per calculator. *Note:* Producers are not willing to supply any of these graphing calculators when the market price is less than $47.50.

c. At what price will market equilibrium occur? How many calculators will be supplied and demanded at this price?

d. Find the producers' surplus at market equilibrium.

e. Estimate the consumers' surplus at market equilibrium.

f. Estimate the total social gain from the sale of this type of graphing calculator at the market equilibrium price.

6.4 **Probability Distributions and Density Functions**

This section uses improper integrals, which were discussed in Section 6.1.

We have used derivatives to measure rates of change and integrals to measure accumulation of change. This section discusses another application of integrals—to measure the likelihood that certain events will occur in situations that involve some degree of chance or uncertainty. When all outcomes of a particular situation are considered, the pattern indicated by the variability in data is called the **distribution** of the quantity being studied. Consider, for instance, the distribution of scores for 2002 college-bound seniors on the mathematics portion of the SAT that is given in Table 6.5. This table shows the proportion of the 1,327,831 students taking the test whose math scores fell in each indicated interval.

TABLE 6.5

Math SAT score x (points)	Number of students in score interval	Proportion of students in score interval
$200 \leq x < 300$	32,593	0.02455
$300 \leq x < 400$	159,250	0.11993
$400 \leq x < 500$	381,339	0.28719
$500 \leq x < 600$	419,310	0.31579
$600 \leq x < 700$	251,650	0.18952
$700 \leq x \leq 800$	83,689	0.06303

(Source: "2002 College-Bound Seniors, A Profile of SAT Program Test Takers," College Entrance Examination Board and Educational Testing Service.)

This distribution of the SAT math scores can be viewed with a graph composed of rectangles called a **histogram**. We choose to construct the histogram so that the area of each rectangle is the proportion of students in the corresponding score interval. The intervals must be such that no score is in more than one interval and all possible scores are included. The height of each rectangle is calculated by dividing the area of the rectangle by the width of the score interval. (See Table 6.6)

TABLE 6.6

Math SAT score x (points)	Width of rectangle (points)	Area of rectangle (proportion of students	Height of rectangle (proportion of students) per point of score
$200 \leq x < 300$	100	0.02455	0.00025
$300 \leq x < 400$	100	0.11993	0.00120
$400 \leq x < 500$	100	0.28719	0.00287
$500 \leq x < 600$	100	0.31579	0.00316
$600 \leq x < 700$	100	0.18952	0.00190
$700 \leq x \leq 800$	100	0.06303	0.00063

A histogram based on the SAT score groupings in Table 6.6 is shown in Figure 6.29.

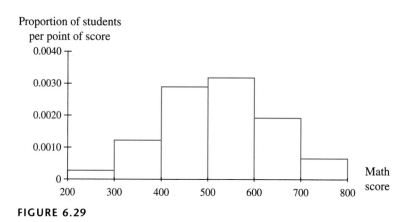

FIGURE 6.29

EXAMPLE 1   *Reading and Using a Histogram*

SAT Scores   Refer to Table 6.5 and the histogram of math SAT scores in Figure 6.29.

a. Describe the distribution of the scores.

b. Find the total area enclosed by the rectangles in the histogram.

c. What proportion of scores is between 300 and 600?

Solution

a. The distribution peaks near 500, and most students taking the test had math scores that ranged between 300 and 700.

b. The total area enclosed by the rectangles in the histogram equals 1:

$$\text{Area} = 0.02455 + 0.11993 + 0.28719 + 0.31579 + 0.18952 + 0.06303 = 1$$

c. From the third column in Table 6.5, we find that the proportion of scores between 300 and 600 is $0.11993 + 0.28719 + 0.31579 \approx 0.72$. ●

Area as Probability

The **probability** of an event is a measure of how likely it is to happen. Because there is no uncertainty associated with a known outcome, we assume that all variables for which probabilities are determined are **random variables**—that is, variables whose numerical values are determined by the results of an experiment involving chance. We intuitively consider the probability of an event to be the proportion of times the event occurs when the experiment associated with the event is repeated under similar conditions a large number of times.

To illustrate this concept, we return to the distribution of SAT I math scores given numerically in Table 6.5 and graphically in the histogram in Figure 6.29. What is the probability that a 2002 college-bound senior made a score between 400 and 600 on the mathematics portion of the SAT I? To answer this question, we first need to understand the terms involved and how they are related to probability.

- "Taking the math portion of the SAT I" is the experiment that was repeated, under similar conditions, a large number of times (1,327,831 students took the test).

- Assuming that the 2002 college-bound senior in the question is any of those taking the test, and assuming that we do not know any student's individual score, the random variable is the SAT I math score.

- The event being considered is the value of the SAT I math score lying in the interval of values between 400 and 600.

We can now compute the probability that a student's math score is between 400 and 600 by finding the proportion of scores that are in that score interval. From the information in Table 6.5, the proportion of students whose scores are between 400 and 600 is 0.60298, so the probability that a student's math score is between 400 and 600 is 0.60298.

Probabilities are proportions, so they are real numbers between 0 and 1. Suppose we want to know the probability that a student makes a math score between 200 and 800. Because all SAT math scores lie between 200 and 800, this event is known as a **certain** or **sure event,** so its probability should be 1. This was verified in part *b* of Example 1. What is the likelihood that a student makes an SAT math score of 950? The highest score is 800, so the probability that a student makes an SAT math score of 950 is 0. An event that has a probability of zero is known as an **impossible event.**

The histograms used in this section have been designed so that all rectangle heights are non-negative values, and the total area enclosed by the rectangles in each histogram is 1. When expressed as a proportion, each rectangle area gives the probability that the value of the random variable is in the interval that forms the base of the rectangle. For that reason, we also call these histograms **probability histograms.** The above discussions suggest the following statements:

Probability

The probability that any event occurs is a real number between 0 and 1. The probability of a certain (or sure) event is 1, and the probability of an impossible event is 0. Even though probabilities are real numbers between 0 and 1, they are often referred to as percentages between 0% and 100%.

When the distribution of a random variable is represented by a probability histogram, the probability that the value of the variable lies within certain intervals is given by the sum of the areas of the rectangles whose bases are those intervals.

If there are a large number of values very close together, then it often simplifies matters to approximate their behavior with a continuous function. Such an approximating function, shown in Figure 6.30, is overdrawn on a more detailed "SAT math scores for 2002 college-bound seniors" histogram. This continuous function is the familiar bell-shaped curve commonly called the **normal distribution.**

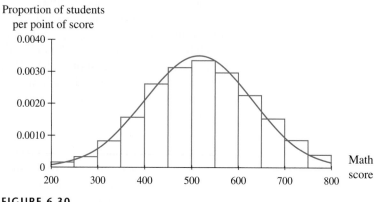

FIGURE 6.30

Instead of summing areas of rectangles in a histogram, we can estimate probabilities by finding areas under curves like the one shown in Figure 6.30. Such functions are called **probability density functions.** We do not discuss the interpretation of output values of probability density functions. Instead, we focus on the interpretation of areas of regions beneath these functions. Because probability density functions describe how probabilities are distributed over various intervals associated with random variables, they are also called **probability distributions.**

Probability Density Function

A probability density function is a continuous function or a piecewise continuous function with input consisting of some interval of real numbers and with output satisfying the following two conditions:

1. Each output value is greater than or equal to 0.

2. The area of the region between the function and the horizontal axis is 1.

Before proceeding further, we introduce a notation to simplify writing probability statements. We write the statement "the probability that the value of x is between a and b" using the notation $P(a \leq x \leq b)$. For instance, if x is the SAT math score, then $P(500 \leq x \leq 800)$ is read "the probability that the value of the SAT math score is between 500 and 800." Using this notation, we restate the definition of a probability density function and define probability for random variables having such density functions:

Probability and Probability Density Functions

A probability density function $y = f(x)$ for a random variable x is a continuous or piecewise continuous function such that

1. $f(x) \geq 0$ for each real number x, and

2. $\displaystyle\int_{-\infty}^{\infty} f(x)\,dx = 1$

The probability that a value of x lies in an interval with endpoints a and b, where $a \leq b$, is given by

$$P(a \leq x \leq b) = \int_{a}^{b} f(x)\,dx$$

It is possible for the interval from a through b to be the entire set of real numbers.

Probability density functions are constructed from experimental data and/or statistical theory using techniques you will probably study if you take a course in statistics. This section is not intended to discuss those statistical techniques. Rather, we are illustrating another use of integrals to find area under a curve.

EXAMPLE 2   *Finding Probabilities from a Probability Density Function*

Recovery Times   Suppose that the proportion of patients who recover from mild dehydration x hours after receiving treatment is given by

$$f(x) = \begin{cases} 12x^2 - 12x^3 & \text{when } 0 \leq x \leq 1 \\ 0 & \text{when } x < 0 \text{ or } x > 1 \end{cases}$$

a.   What is the random variable in this situation?

b.   Verify that f is a probability density function for this random variable.

c.   Find the probability that the recovery time is between 42 minutes and 48 minutes. Interpret your answer.

d.   Find the probability that recovery takes at least half an hour.

Solution

a.   The random variable x is the number of hours until recovery. After 1 hour all patients will have recovered.

b.   To verify that f is a probability density function for this random variable, we must show that the two properties of a probability density function are true.

 1.   As the graph in Figure 6.31 shows, all values of $f(x)$ are non-negative.

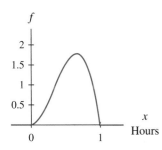

FIGURE 6.31

2. The area under the graph of f is 1 because

$$\int_{-\infty}^{\infty} f(x)dx = \int_{-\infty}^{0} 0dx + \int_{0}^{1}(12x^2 - 12x^3)dx + \int_{1}^{\infty} 0dx$$

$$= 0 + (4x^3 - 3x^4)\big|_{0}^{1} + 0$$

$$= 4 - 3 = 1$$

c. Because 42 minutes is 0.7 hour and 48 minutes is 0.8 hour, we find the probability that recovery time is between 42 minutes and 48 minutes by computing

$$P(0.7 \le x \le 0.8) = \int_{0.7}^{0.8}(12x^2 - 12x^3)dx$$

$$= (4x^3 - 3x^4)\big|_{0.7}^{0.8}$$

$$= (2.048 - 1.2288) - (1.372 - 0.7203)$$

$$= 0.1675$$

There is a 16.75% chance that the recovery time for a patient will be between 42 minutes and 48 minutes. (Note that 0.1675 is the area between the graph of f and the horizontal axis from $x = 0.7$ to $x = 0.8$.)

d. $P(x \ge 0.5) = \int_{0.5}^{\infty} f(x)dx = \int_{0.5}^{1}(12x^2 - 12x^3)dx + \int_{1}^{\infty} 0dx$

$$= (4x^3 - 3x^4)\big|_{0.5}^{1}$$

$$= 0.6875$$

There is a 68.75% chance that recovery takes at least a half hour. ●

It is important that you note the difference between the meanings of $f(x)$, the output of a probability density function, and $P(a \le x \le b)$, the probability that the random variable is within a certain interval. To see more clearly that the output of a probability density function is *not* a probability, look again at the graph of the density function shown in Figure 6.31. There are values of $f(x)$ that are obviously larger than 1, and we know that probabilities can never be greater than 1. Always keep in mind that whereas f is a function that shows how the probabilities associated with values of a random variable x are distributed over the input interval, $P(a \le x \le b)$ is a real number between 0 and 1. Figure 6.32 illustrates these ideas for a probability density function f.

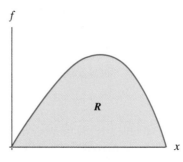

The area of R is 1.

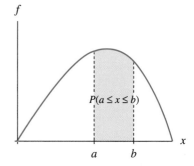

The area of the shaded region is the probability that x is between a and b.

FIGURE 6.32

The Uniform Probability Distribution

Even though probability density functions have a variety of shapes, some naturally occur so often that they have names. Perhaps the simplest density function is one that assumes a constant value between two specified inputs and is zero elsewhere. This probability distribution is called the **uniform density function** and has the equation

$$u(x) = \begin{cases} \dfrac{1}{b-a} & \text{when } a \leq x \leq b \\ \\ 0 & \text{when } x < a \text{ or } x > b \end{cases}$$

A graph of this piecewise continuous function is shown in Figure 6.33.

The uniform density function provides a good model for random variables that are evenly distributed over an interval. For instance, the distribution of winning numbers picked since the beginning of a state lottery is approximated by a uniform density function. The probability distribution that describes how tires wear (in terms of the remaining tread) on a properly aligned and balanced set of wheels is a uniform density function.

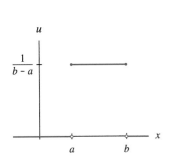

A uniform density function

FIGURE 6.33

EXAMPLE 3 *Using a Uniform Density Function*

Campus Bus Buses that transport students from one location to another on a large campus arrive at the student parking lot every 15 minutes between 7:30 A.M. and 4:30 P.M. If t is the number of minutes before the next bus arrives at the lot, then the distribution of waiting times is modeled by the density function

$$u(t) = \begin{cases} \dfrac{1}{15} & \text{when } 0 \leq t \leq 15 \\ \\ 0 & \text{when } t < 15 \text{ or } t > 0 \end{cases}$$

a. Explain, in the context of this situation, why it makes sense for $u(t)$ to equal 0 when $t > 15$ or $t < 0$.

b. Represent on a graph of u the probability that a student arriving at the parking lot will have to wait more than 5 minutes for the next bus.

c. Find $P(t \geq 5)$. Interpret the result.

Solution

a. If buses arrive every 15 minutes at the parking lot, no one will have to wait more than 15 minutes for a bus. Because time cannot be negative, the waiting time distribution is zero for $t < 0$. It therefore makes sense that $u(t) = 0$ when t is not in the interval with endpoints 0 and 15.

b. As shown in Figure 6.34, $P(t > 5)$ is the area of the shaded region between the graph of u and the t-axis to the right of $t = 5$.

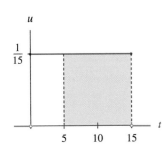

$P(t > 5)$ is the area of the shaded region.

FIGURE 6.34

c.   Because $P(t = 5) = 0$, $P(t \geq 5) = P(t > 5)$. This probability is represented by the area of the rectangle with height $\frac{1}{15}$ and width 10. (See Figure 6.34.) Thus

$$P(t \geq 5) = \frac{10}{15} \approx 0.667$$

Of course, this probability could have also been found using an integral:

$$P(t \geq 5) = \int_5^\infty u(t)dt = \int_5^{15} \frac{1}{15} \, dt + \int_{15}^\infty 0 \, dt = \frac{1}{15}(15 - 5) = \frac{10}{15} \approx 0.667$$

When a student arrives at the parking lot between 7:30 A.M. and 4:30 P.M., there is about a 66.7% chance that he or she will have to wait at least 5 minutes for a bus to arrive.   ●

Measures of Center and Variability

One important characteristic of a density function is its central value. The measure of central value that we consider is the mean (commonly referred to as the *average*). The **mean,** denoted by the Greek letter μ, is also called the *expected value* and is geometrically associated with the "balance point" of the region between the density function and the horizontal axis.

Another common measure of the center of a distribution is the median. The median is the input value such that half of the area under the density function lies to the left and half to the right of it.

Distributions can have the same mean but a completely different spread, or variability, about that center. One measure of how closely the values of the distribution cluster about its mean is the **standard deviation,** denoted by the Greek letter σ. If most of the values of the input variable are close to the mean, then the standard deviation is small. On the other hand, if it is likely that the input values are widely scattered about the mean, the standard deviation is large.

EXAMPLE 4   *Locating the Mean and Standard Deviation on a Graph*

SAT Scores   Refer to the continuous function that is overdrawn on the histogram of the 2002 college-bound seniors' SAT math scores in Figure 6.30 on page 426. The mean math SAT score is 516 points, and the standard deviation is 114 points.[*] Locate the mean and standard deviation on the graph of this continuous function that approximates the distribution of the SAT math scores.

Solution
Because the mean is an input value for this continuous function, μ is located on the horizontal axis. (See Figure 6.35.) The standard deviation tells us how the math scores are spread out around the mean. For instance, one standard deviation to the right of the mean would be $\mu + \sigma = 516 + 114 = 630$ points.

---

[*]"2002 College-Bound Seniors, A Profile of SAT Program Test takers," College Entrance Examination Board and Educational Testing Service.

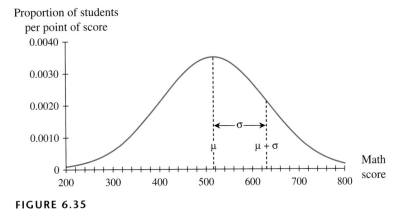

FIGURE 6.35

The mean and standard deviation of a known density function are determined using the following definitions:

Mean and Standard Deviation

For the density function $y = f(x)$, with x defined on the interval of real numbers,

- the mean is $\mu = \displaystyle\int_{-\infty}^{\infty} xf(x)\,dx$

- the standard deviation is $\sigma = \displaystyle\sqrt{\int_{-\infty}^{\infty} (x - \mu)^2 f(x)\,dx}$

provided that the integrals exist.

EXAMPLE 5   *Computing a Mean and Standard Deviation*

Campus Bus   Refer to the distribution of waiting times for campus transportation in Example 3:

$$u(t) = \begin{cases} \dfrac{1}{15} & \text{when } 0 \le t \le 15 \\[2mm] 0 & \text{when } t > 15 \text{ or } t < 0 \end{cases}$$

where t is the time in minutes until the next bus arrives.

a. Find the mean waiting time.

b. Find the standard deviation of the waiting times.

Solution

a. $\mu = \displaystyle\int_{-\infty}^{\infty} t\cdot u(t)dt = \int_{-\infty}^{0} t\cdot u(t)dt + \int_{0}^{15} t\cdot u(t)dt + \int_{15}^{\infty} t\cdot u(t)dt$

$= \displaystyle\int_{-\infty}^{0} t\cdot 0 dt + \int_{0}^{15} \frac{1}{15} t dt + \int_{15}^{\infty} t\cdot 0 dt$

$= 0 + \dfrac{1}{30} t^2 \Big|_{0}^{15} + 0 = \dfrac{1}{30}(225 - 0) = 7.5$

The average time spent waiting for a bus is 7.5 minutes.

b. $\sigma = \displaystyle\sqrt{\int_{-\infty}^{\infty} (t-\mu)^2 u(t)dt}$

$= \displaystyle\sqrt{\int_{-\infty}^{0} (t-7.5)^2 \cdot 0 dt + \int_{0}^{15} (t-7.5)^2 \cdot \frac{1}{15} dt + \int_{15}^{\infty} (t-7.5)^2 \cdot 0 dt}$

$= \displaystyle\sqrt{0 + \frac{1}{15}\int_{0}^{15}(t-7.5)^2 dt + 0} = \sqrt{\frac{1}{15}\cdot\frac{(t-7.5)^3}{3}\Big|_{0}^{15}}$

$= \displaystyle\sqrt{\frac{1}{15}\left(\frac{(15-7.5)^3}{3} - \frac{(0-7.5)^3}{3}\right)} = \sqrt{18.75} \approx 4.33$

The standard deviation of waiting times is about 4.33 minutes. ●

As illustrated in Example 5, a definite integral involving a density function f has a value of 0 if the height of the density function is 0. In these cases, we are finding the area of a rectangle with height 0 and width determined by the upper and lower limits on the integral:

Whenever $f(x) = 0$, area = (height)(width) = (0)(width) = 0.

Therefore, from this point on, we do not show the integrals involved in probability, mean, or standard deviation calculations for the portions of the horizontal axis where the value of a density function is 0.

The Exponential Probability Distribution

The amount of time it takes to learn a task, the duration of a phone call, the time you wait for service at a bank teller's window, the time between arrivals at the drive-through station of a fast-food restaurant—all are examples of random variables that are more likely to be small than large. With events such as these, we are interested in the time elapsed or space between any two occurrences of an event, rather than in the number of times the event happens. The likelihood of encountering certain intervals of time or space between consecutive occurrences of an event can be modeled by an **exponential density function,** with the general formula

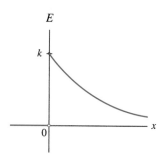

An exponential density function

FIGURE 6.36

$$E(x) = \begin{cases} ke^{-kx} & \text{when } x \geq 0 \\ 0 & \text{when } x < 0 \end{cases}$$

where k is some positive constant. The graph is shown in Figure 6.36.

The mean of the exponential distribution is $\frac{1}{k}$. When, on average, an event occurs at a rate of k arrivals per unit of time, the average gap between consecutive arrivals is $\frac{1}{k}$ time unit. For instance, suppose that you arrive at your local Burger King sometime between 11:30 A.M. and 12:30 P.M. and that the time you have to wait for service while in line at the drive-through window is an exponential random variable with a mean of 2.5 minutes. This means that there are 2.5 minutes between cars coming into the line, with cars arriving at the rate of 0.4 car per minute (that is, 4 cars every 10 minutes). When applying this distribution, remember that the values of the random variable x and the value of k must be in the same time units.

EXAMPLE 6   *Writing and Using an Exponential Density Function*

ER Arrivals   The distribution of the time between successive arrivals at an emergency room of a large city hospital on Saturday nights can be approximated by an exponential density function. Two patients arrive at the emergency room every 10 minutes.

a.   What is the equation for this exponential density function?

b.   What is the probability that the time between successive arrivals will be more than 1 minute? Interpret this result.

Solution

a.   The mean of the distribution is the time between consecutive events. Therefore, the mean is $\mu = \frac{1}{k} = \frac{10}{2} = 5$ minutes per arrival. Thus $k = \frac{1}{5}$, the average number of arrivals per minute. The equation of the exponential density function is

$$E(t) = \frac{1}{5} e^{-t/5} = 0.2e^{-0.2t} \quad \text{when } t \geq 0$$

where t is the time, in minutes, between successive arrivals. (In the context of time, it is assumed that $E(t) = 0$ when $t < 0$.)

b. $P(t > 1) = \displaystyle\int_{1}^{\infty} 0.2e^{-0.2t}\, dt = \lim_{T \to \infty} \int_{1}^{T} 0.2e^{-0.2t}\, dt$

$\qquad = \lim_{T \to \infty}\, [-e^{-0.2T} - (-e^{(-0.2)(1)})]$

$\qquad = 0 + e^{-0.2} \approx 0.819$

There is an 81.9% chance that the time between successive arrivals will be more than 1 minute. This event is likely to occur.   ●

The Normal Distribution

We now turn our attention to the single most important density function in statistics, the **normal density function,** which is also called the *normal distribution.* The equation of the normal density function with mean μ and standard deviation σ is

$$f(x) = \frac{1}{\sigma\sqrt{2\pi}}\, e^{\frac{-(x-\mu)^2}{2\sigma^2}} \quad \text{where } -\infty < x < \infty$$

The graph of a normal distribution is called a *normal curve*. The mean controls the location of a normal curve, and the standard deviation controls its spread. Figure 6.37 gives us a good idea of some of the features of any normal distribution.

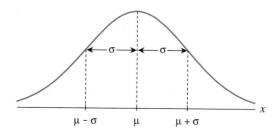

A normal curve

FIGURE 6.37

Note these important properties of any normal curve:

- The curve is bell-shaped with the absolute maximum occurring at the mean μ.
- The curve is symmetric about a vertical line through μ.
- The curve approaches the horizontal axis but never touches or crosses it.
- The inflection points occur at $\mu - \sigma$ and $\mu + \sigma$.

EXAMPLE 7   *Comparing Normal Curves*

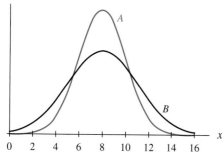

FIGURE 6.38

Consider the two normal curves shown in Figure 6.38.

a. Compare the means of the two normal distributions.

b. One of the curves has $\sigma = 3$, and the other curve has an inflection point at $x = 10$. Compare the spreads of the two curves.

c. What percentage of the total area under each normal curve lies to the right of $x = 8$?

Solution

a. The means of the two density functions are the same, because each curve has a maximum at $x = 8$.

b. From Figure 6.38, we see that the rightmost inflection point on normal curve A occurs around 10. Thus $8 + \sigma = 10$, and the standard deviation of curve A is approximately 2. Curve B is more spread out from its center than curve A, so it has the larger standard deviation, $\sigma = 3$.

c. Because a normal curve is the graph of a density function, the area between each normal curve and the horizontal axis must be 1. Each normal curve is symmetric about its mean, so 50% of the total area is to the right of μ for each normal curve. ●

The normal curve rises gradually to its absolute maximum and then decreases in a symmetric manner. Although it is not unique in exhibiting this form, it has been

found to provide a reasonable approximation to certain other distributions that occur in many real-life situations. Also, many naturally occurring phenomena, as well
as various mental and physical characteristics of human beings, can be described by
normal distributions.

EXAMPLE 8   *Using a Normal Density Function*

6.4.1

Light Bulb   A manufacturer of light bulbs advertises that the average life of these
bulbs is 900 hours with a standard deviation of 100 hours. Suppose the distribution
of the length of life of these light bulbs, with the life span measured in hundreds of
hours, is modeled by a normal density function.

a. Write the definite integral that represents the probability that a light bulb lasts
    between 900 and 1000 hours.

b. Approximate the value of the integral in part *a*, and interpret the result in context.

Solution

a. Note that the input for the normal density function is measured in hundreds of
    hours. The integral that gives $P(9 \leq x \leq 10)$ is $\int_9^{10} f(x)dx$, where f is the normal
    density function with $\mu = 9$ and $\sigma = 1$. That is,

$$P(9 \leq x \leq 10) = \int_9^{10} \frac{1}{\sqrt{2\pi}} e^{\frac{-(x-9)^2}{2}} dx$$

b. There is no antiderivative formula that can be used to find the exact value of an
    integral of the normal density function. However, the value of the definite
    integral can be numerically approximated using technology:

$$\int_9^{10} \frac{1}{\sqrt{2\pi}} e^{-0.5(x-9)^2} dx \approx 0.34$$

Thus the chance that any one of these light bulbs will last between 900 and 1000
hours is about 34%.   ●

Cumulative Density Functions

Suppose that the length of time a student waits for a computer terminal with which
to preregister for next term's classes is described by the uniform density function

$$f(x) = \begin{cases} \dfrac{1}{25} & \text{when } 0 \leq x \leq 25 \\[2mm] 0 & \text{when } x > 25 \end{cases}$$

FIGURE 6.39

where the value of the random variable x is measured in minutes. The probability that
the waiting time is less than or equal to 5 minutes is found by computing the area of
the shaded region in Figure 6.39.

TABLE 6.7

Time interval	Probability that waiting time is in time interval
Between 0 and 2 minutes	$P(0 \leq x \leq 2) = 0.08$
Between 0 and 5 minutes	$P(0 \leq x \leq 5) = 0.20$
Between 0 and 12.5 minutes	$P(0 \leq x \leq 12.5) = 0.5$
Between 0 and 20.38 minutes	$P(0 \leq x \leq 20.38) = 0.8152$
Between 0 and 25 minutes	$P(0 \leq x \leq 25) = 1$
Between 0 and 33 minutes	$P(0 \leq x \leq 33) = P(0 \leq x \leq 25) + P(25 < x \leq 33) = 1 + 0 = 1$
Between 0 and 40.2 minutes	$P(0 \leq x \leq 40.2) = P(0 \leq x \leq 25) + P(25 < x \leq 40.2) = 1 + 0 = 1$

Because the event that the waiting time is more than 25 minutes is impossible by the definition of this density function, $P(x > 25) = 0$. Also, $P(0 \leq x \leq a)$, when a is a waiting time between 0 and 25 minutes, is computed by finding the area of a rectangle with height $\frac{1}{25}$ and width a. Table 6.7 gives the results of some of these probability computations.

(a)

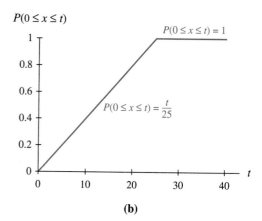

(b)

FIGURE 6.40

Note that when the waiting time x is between 0 and 25 minutes, the probability that a student waits between 0 minutes and t minutes seems to be a function of the upper endpoint of the interval. Also, the probability that a student waits between 0 minutes and t minutes, where $t > 25$, is 1 because 25 minutes is the maximum waiting time. A scatter plot of the points $(t, P(0 \leq x \leq t))$ that appear in Table 6.7 is shown in Figure 6.40a. If all probabilities $P(0 < x < t)$, where $0 < t < \infty$, were computed and plotted, then the graph shown in Figure 6.40b would result.

A function that shows how probabilities accumulate as the value of the random variable increases is called a **cumulative density function.** For instance, if $y = F(x)$ is a cumulative density function for waiting times, where x is measured in minutes, then the output $F(5) = 0.2$ represents the probability that the waiting time is less than or equal to 5 minutes. That is, $F(5) = P(x \leq 5)$. Similarly, $F(12.5) = P(x \leq 12.5)$, and so forth. In general, for a random variable x with probability density function f, where c is some constant, the cumulative density function of f at c is

$$F(c) = P(x \le c) = \int_{-\infty}^{c} f(x)dx$$

The left end behavior of any cumulative density function will be 0, corresponding to impossible events, and the right end behavior of any cumulative density function will be 1, corresponding to sure events. Cumulative density functions are always nondecreasing. Outputs of cumulative density functions are the areas between the corresponding probability density functions and the horizontal axis.

Does the link between probability density functions and cumulative density functions sound familiar? It should—it is the same as the relationship between functions and their accumulation functions, which we discussed in Chapter 5.

Cumulative Density Function

The cumulative density function for a random variable x defined on the interval of real numbers with probability density function f is

$$F(x) = \int_{-\infty}^{x} f(t)dt \quad \text{for all real numbers } x$$

For any value of the random variable x, say c, $F(c) = P(x \le c)$. The cumulative density function F is an accumulation function of the probability density function f.

EXAMPLE 9   *Graphing a Cumulative Density Function*

The graph in Figure 6.41 shows the probability density function for a random variable x.

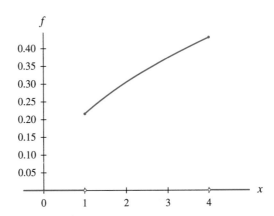

FIGURE 6.41

a. Sketch the graph of the cumulative density function for x.

b. Express $P(2 \le x < 3.4)$ using the probability density function f.

c. Express $P(2 \le x < 3.4)$ using the cumulative density function.

Solution

a. Because $f(x) = 0$ for $x < 1$, no area is accumulated when $x < 1$. Thus $f(x) = 0$ when $x < 1$. Note too that the accumulation of nonzero area under the graph of f begins at $x = 1$. Also, all accumulated area is positive because the graph of f is above the horizontal axis. As x moves to the right of the starting point $(x = 1)$, area is accumulating faster and faster. Thus the cumulative density function is increasing and concave up until $x = 4$. At this point, no more area is accumulated, because the value of the density function is once again 0. Because f is a probability density function, the total accumulated area must be 1.

Thus $F(4) = \int_{-\infty}^{4} f(x)dx = 1$. No area is added or subtracted past $x = 4$, so $F(x) = 1$ for $x > 4$. Combining all of this information, we can draw a possible graph of the cumulative density function F. (See Figure 6.42.)

b. $P(2 \leq x < 3.4) = \int_{2}^{3.4} f(x)dx$

c. $P(2 \leq x < 3.4) = F(3.4) - F(2)$ ●

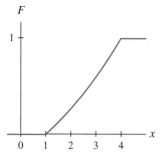

FIGURE 6.42

The Fundamental Theorem guarantees the equivalence of the results of parts b and c of Example 9. It also tells us that the derivative of a cumulative density function is the corresponding probability density function at all points where the derivative exists. That is, $\frac{d}{dx}[F(x)] = f(x)$.

EXAMPLE 10   *Finding Probabilities from a Cumulative Density Function*

Temperature   The graph in Figure 6.43 shows the cumulative density function for the distribution of temperatures in a southwestern city during a 24-hour period in May. The random variable x measures the temperature recorded in degrees Fahrenheit (beginning at midnight), and the output $T(x)$ is the proportion of the time that the temperature is less than or equal to $x°F$.

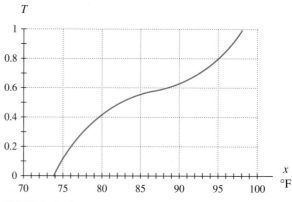

FIGURE 6.43

a. What proportion of the time do you expect the temperature to be at most 80°F? Interpret this result in a probability context.

b. Estimate the high and low temperatures.

c. Estimate the probability that the temperature will be above 90°F.

d. Sketch a graph of the probability density function for the distribution of May temperatures in this location.

Solution

a. The proportion of the time that the temperature will be at most (less than or equal to) 80°F is $P(x \leq 80) = T(80) \approx 0.41$. In a southwestern city during any 24-hour period in May, the temperature will be less than or equal to 80°F about 41% of the time.

b. $T(x)$ appears to be 0 at approximately 74°F. Because $T(x)$ is a proportion, it cannot be negative. Thus, the cumulative proportion to the left of 74°F must also be 0, and the minimum temperature is 74°F. The cumulative probability has a maximum of 1 at a temperature of about 98°F, so the maximum temperature is approximately 98°F.

c. The temperature on any day must be either less than 90°F or greater than or equal to 90°F. Thus the probability that the temperature is less than 90°F added to the probability that the temperature is 90°F or greater must equal 1.

$$T(90) + P(x \geq 90) = 1$$
$$P(x \geq 90) = 1 - T(90)$$
$$\approx 1 - 0.63$$
$$= 0.37$$

d. We know that the probability density function is the slope function of the cumulative density function. Note that because the graph of T is always increasing for temperatures between 74°F and 98°F, its slope graph is positive over this interval. (Recall that no output of a density function can be negative.) Also, the graph of T appears to have an inflection point (point of least slope) located at approximately 87°F, so there is a minimum on the slope graph at this temperature.

Using 74°F as the minimum temperature and 98°F as the maximum temperature, we know that $P(x < 74)$ and $P(x > 98)$ are both 0. Thus the value of the probability density function for temperatures less than 74°F and greater than 98°F is 0.

A possible graph of the probability density function is shown in Figure 6.44.   ●

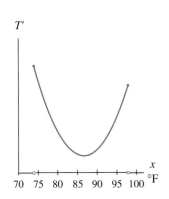

FIGURE 6.44

The connection between probability density functions and cumulative density functions lies at the very heart of calculus, for it is the relationship between a function and its accumulation function.

6.4 Concept Inventory

- Probability
  - Histogram
  - Random variable
  - Notation, computation, and interpretation
- Probability density function
- Probability distribution
  - Uniform probability distribution
  - Exponential probability distribution
  - Normal distribution
  - Mean and standard deviation
- Cumulative density function

6.4 Activities

Getting Started

1. Interpret each of the following probability statements in the context of the given situation.

   a. Suppose the random variable x is the length, in minutes, of a telephone call made on a computer software technical support line. Interpret $P(x \geq 5) = 0.46$.

   b. Suppose the random variable x is the distance in feet between cars on a certain two-lane highway. Interpret $P(x < 7) \approx 0.25$.

   c. The probability that New Orleans will receive between 2 and 4 inches of rain during the month of March is 0.15.

2. Figures a through d show the shapes of some probability distributions. Match each given situation to a possible graph of its density function. Give reasons for each of your choices.

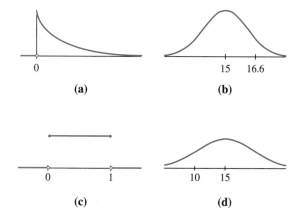

(a) (b)

(c) (d)

a. The amount of cereal put into a box is normally distributed with $\mu = 15$ ounces and $\sigma = 1.6$ ounces.

b. The height of a certain species of plant is normally distributed with a mean of 15 inches and a standard deviation of 5 inches.

c. You use a random number generator to choose a number between 0 and 1. The random variable x is the number that is chosen.

d. The time, in minutes, that a customer waits to pay for items at a department store is exponentially distributed.

3. Which of the following could be probability density functions? Explain.

   a. $f(x) = \begin{cases} 1.5(1 - x^2) & \text{when } 0 \leq x \leq 1 \\ 0 & \text{when } x < 0 \text{ or } x > 1 \end{cases}$

   b. $h(x) = \begin{cases} 6(x - x^2) & \text{when } 0 \leq x \leq 1 \\ 0 & \text{when } x < 0 \text{ or } x > 1 \end{cases}$

   c.

   d.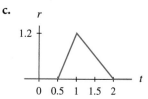

4. Which of the following could be probability density functions? Give reasons.

   a. $g(x) = \begin{cases} 3x(1 - x^2) & \text{when } 0 \leq x \leq 1 \\ 0 & \text{when } x < 0 \text{ or } x > 1 \end{cases}$

   b. $h(y) = \begin{cases} 0.625e^{-1.6y} & \text{when } y > 0 \\ 0 & \text{when } y \leq 0 \end{cases}$

   c.

d.

Applying Concepts

5. **Sales** Let x represent the amount of frozen yogurt (in hundreds of gallons) sold by the G&T restaurant on any day during the summer. Storage limitations dictate that the maximum amount of frozen yogurt that can be kept at G&T on any given day is 250 gallons. Records of past sales indicate that the probability density function for x is approximated by $y(x) = 0.32x$ for $0 \leq x \leq 2.5$.

   a. What is the probability that on some summer day, G&T will sell less than 100 gallons of frozen yogurt?

   b. What is the mean number of gallons of frozen yogurt that G&T expects to sell on a summer day?

   c. Sketch a graph of y, and locate the mean on the graph. Also, shade the region that the answer to part a represents.

6. **Waiting Time** Suppose that a traffic light on your campus remains red for 30 seconds at a time. You arrive at that light and find it red. Assume that your waiting time t (in seconds) at the light follows a uniform density function $y = u(t)$.

   a. Why does it make sense that $u(t) = 0$ for $t < 0$ and $t > 30$?

   b. Sketch a graph of u.

   c. Find your chances of waiting at least 10 seconds at the red light. What does this value represent on the graph of u?

   d. Find the probability of waiting no more than 20 seconds at the red light.

   e. What is the average time you would expect to wait at the light?

7. Explain, using the definition of a density function, why the definite integral calculation of a probability must result in a value between 0 and 1.

8. **Waiting Time** At a certain grocery checkout counter, the average waiting time is 2.5 minutes.

Suppose the waiting times follow an exponential density function.

   a. Why would customers prefer the waiting times at the grocery checkout to follow an exponential distribution rather than a uniform distribution with the same mean?

   b. Write the equation for the exponential distribution of waiting times. Graph the equation and locate the mean waiting time on the graph. Does $\mu = 2.5$ seem reasonable for the graph?

   c. What is the likelihood that a customer waits less than 2 minutes to check out?

   d. What is the probability of waiting between 2 and 4 minutes to check out?

   e. What is the probability of waiting more than 5 minutes to check out?

9. **ER Arrivals** Consider the exponential density function discussed in Example 6:

$$e(t) = 0.2e^{-0.2t} \quad \text{when } t \geq 0$$

where t is the time in minutes between successive arrivals at an emergency room in a large hospital on Saturday nights.

   a. Find the probability that successive arrivals are between 20 and 30 minutes apart.

   b. Find the probability that 10 minutes or less elapses between successive arrivals.

   c. Find the probability that successive arrivals will be more than 15 minutes apart.

10. a. Graph the exponential density function for $k = 0.5, 1, 1.5, 2,$ and 4.

   b. Comment on how changing the value of k affects the shape of the graph.

   c. How does the mean of the exponential density function change as k increases?

11. **Learning Time** The manufacturer of a new board game believes that the time it takes a child between the ages of 8 and 10 to learn the rules of its new board game has the probability density function

$$P(t) = \begin{cases} \dfrac{3}{32}(4t - t^2) & \text{when } 0 \leq t \leq 4 \\ \\ 0 & \text{when } t > 4 \end{cases}$$

where t is time measured in minutes.

a. Find the mean time that it takes a child age 8 to 10 to learn the rules of the game.

b. Find the standard deviation of the learning times.

c. Find $P(0 \leq t \leq 1.5)$. Interpret this result.

d. Find $P(t \geq 3)$. Interpret this result.

12. **Weight**   Suppose the weight of pieces of passenger luggage for domestic airline flights follows a normal distribution with $\mu = 40$ pounds and $\sigma = 10.63$ pounds.

a. Find the probability that a piece of luggage weighs less than 45 pounds.

b. Find the probability that the total weight of the luggage for 80 passengers on a particular flight is between 1200 and 2400 pounds. (Assume each passenger has one piece of luggage.)

c. Find the probability that the total weight of the luggage for 125 passengers on a particular flight is more than 5600 pounds. (Assume each passenger has one piece of luggage.)

d. Find where the probability density function for the weight of passenger luggage is decreasing most rapidly.

13. **Customers**   The number of customers served daily by the ATM machines for a certain bank follows a normal distribution with a mean of 167 customers and a standard deviation of 30 customers.

a. Find where the probability density function for the number of customers who require daily ATM service at this bank is increasing the fastest.

b. Give a specific reason why it would benefit a bank to know the probability distribution of its customers who are served daily by the ATM machines.

c. Sketch a graph of this normal distribution. In parts *i*, *ii*, and *iii*, shade on the graph the area representing the probability. Remembering that the area to the left (or right) of the mean of any normal distribution is 0.5, find the likelihood that, on a particular day,

    i. between 150 and 200 customers require service at the ATM machines.

    ii. fewer than 220 customers require service.

    iii. more than 235 customers require service.

14. **SAT Scores**   The accompanying figures are probability histograms of math SAT scores for 2002 male and female college-bound seniors, respectively. All scores are based on a recentered scale. (See Activity 15.) Overdraw, on the histograms, continuous curves representing normal density functions that approximate the distributions of scores. Discuss any similarities and/or differences between the two normal distributions.

(a)

(b)

Figures for Activity 14

(Source: Based on data from "2002 College-Bound Seniors, A Profile of SAT Program Test Takers," College Entrance Examination Board and Educational Testing Service.)

15. **SAT Scores** For all test dates on or after April 1, 1995, SAT Reasoning Test scores have been reported on a new, "recentered" scale. Over the years, the average score on the math portion of the SAT moved away from 500, the midpoint of the original 200-to-800 scale. This change reestablished the average score near the midpoint of the scale and realigned the verbal and math scores so that a student with a score of 450 on each test can conclude that his or her math and verbal scores are equal. The previous scales showed the average verbal score to be about 425 and the average math score to be about 475, which made comparison between the two difficult.

(Source: Used by permission from *Peterson's Guide to Four-Year Colleges, 1997*, 27th edition. Princeton, NJ: Peterson's Guides, Inc., 1996. © 1996 by Peterson's, Princeton, NJ.)

a. If the interval between 200 and 800 included all scores within three standard deviations of the mean score on the original scale, what was the standard deviation of the original math SAT distribution?

b. Is the realigned mean score for verbal scores more or less than 425? Is the realigned mean score for math scores more or less than 475? Explain.

c. Most standardized test scores follow a normal distribution. Using the fact that the probability of a score falling in a particular interval is the same as the percentage of students expected to score in that interval, determine what percentage of students were expected to make a math score of at least 475 under the "old" score scale.

d. Assuming that the SAT math and verbal scores follow a normal distribution, do you have enough information to draw a graph of the density function for either of the recentered SAT scores?

e. Do you think that recentering the SAT scores moved only the mean of the distribution or did it also change the standard deviation? Give reasons for your answer.

f. Why do the recentered "higher" scores not translate into improved performance?

16. As we have previously noted, a quick approximation is sometimes useful when an exact answer is not required. For a distribution that is symmetric and bell-shaped (in particular, for a normal distribution), the *Empirical Rule* states that

- Approximately 68% of the data values lie between $\mu - \sigma$ and $\mu + \sigma$.

- Approximately 95% of the data values lie between $\mu - 2\sigma$ and $\mu + 2\sigma$.

- Approximately 99.7% of the data values lie between $\mu - 3\sigma$ and $\mu + 3\sigma$.

a. Verify the statements in the Empirical Rule for the normal probability density function with $\mu = 5.3$ and $\sigma = 8.372$.

b. Estimate $P(-11.444 < x \le 13.672)$ using the Empirical Rule if x has a normal probability distribution with $\mu = 5.3$ and $\sigma = 8.372$.

c. Use the normal probability density function to find the probability in part b.

17. **Test Scores** Scores on a 100-point final exam administered to all calculus classes at a large university are normally distributed with a mean of 72.3 and a standard deviation of 28.65. What percentage of students taking the test made

a. a score between 60 and 80?

b. a score of at least 90?

c. a score that was more than one standard deviation away from the mean?

d. At what score was the rate of change of the probability density function for the scores a maximum?

18. Another measure of the center of a probability distribution is the *median*. The median is the value m such that $\int_{a}^{m} f(x)dx = \int_{m}^{b} f(x)dx$, where $f(x) > 0$ for $a \le x \le b$.

a. Refer to the distribution of waiting times in Example 5:

$$u(t) = \begin{cases} \dfrac{1}{15} & \text{when } 0 \le t \le 15 \\ 0 & \text{when } t > 15 \end{cases}$$

where t is the time until the next bus. Find the median time to wait for the next bus.

b. How does the median compare to the mean for a probability distribution that is symmetric about a vertical line drawn through its mean?

c. For the density function $y = f(x)$, where $f(x) > 0$ for $a \le x \le b$, explain why the statement

"The median is the value m such that

$$\int_a^m f(x)dx = \frac{1}{2}\text{,"}$$

is equivalent to saying

"The median is the value m such that

$$\int_a^m f(x)dx = \int_m^b f(x)dx\text{."}$$

d. Verify that the median of the general exponential density function is $x = \frac{\ln 2}{k}$.

19. Verify the following statements for the uniform density function

$$u(x) = \begin{cases} \frac{1}{b-a} & \text{when } a \le x \le b \\ 0 & \text{when } x < a \text{ or } x > b \end{cases}$$

a. The mean is $\mu = \frac{a+b}{2}$.

b. The standard deviation is $\sigma = \frac{b-a}{\sqrt{12}}$.

c. The cumulative density function is

$$F(x) = \begin{cases} 0 & \text{when } x < 0 \\ \frac{x-a}{b-a} & \text{when } a \le x \le b \\ 1 & \text{when } x > b \end{cases}$$

20. The graph of a cumulative density function is shown. Sketch the graph of the corresponding probability density function if the input set for both functions is all real numbers.

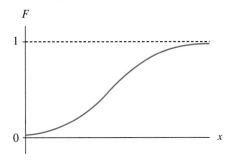

21. Population   The graph shows a probability distribution of the United States population at the time of the 2000 census.

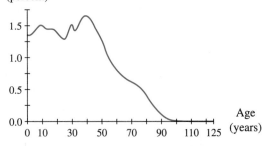

U.S. population
per year of age
(percent)

(Source: Based on data from the U.S. Bureau of the Census.)

a. Sketch the graph of the corresponding cumulative density function.

b. Locate, on the graph of the cumulative density function you sketched in part *a* and on the graph of the probability density function, the probability that a person is between 20 and 40 years old.

22. Suppose that $y = f(x)$ is the exponential density function with $k = 2$.

a. Find F, the corresponding cumulative density function.

b. Use both f and F to find the probability that $x \le 0.35$.

c. Use F to find the probability that $x > 0.86$.

d. Sketch graphs of f and F.

23. Consider the density function

$$f(x) = \begin{cases} 2x & \text{when } 0 \le x < 1 \\ 0 & \text{when } x < 0 \text{ or } x \ge 1 \end{cases}$$

a. Find F, the corresponding cumulative density function.

b. Use both f and F to find the probability that $x < 0.67$.

c. Use F to find the probability that $x > 0.25$.

d. Sketch graphs of f and F.

24. Population   In mid-1992 the U.S. resident population was about 255 million, with only approximately 45,000 persons aged 100 or older. The accompanying table gives the distribution of ages of those persons less than 100 years old. $F'(x)$ is the percentage of U.S. residents less than x years of age. (Assume that no one is more than 100 years old.)

a. Fill in the value for $F(0)$.

b. If possible, give the units of the corresponding probability density function. Use symmetric difference quotients to estimate $F'(x)$ at $x = 10, 25, 30, 35, 45, 50, 70,$ and 90 years of age.

c. The accompanying scatter plot shows some approximate values of the continuous density function. Label the axes and draw a smooth curve through the points so that there are no more concavity changes in your curve than those indicated by the given points. What is the demographic significance of the large bump on the graph?

x (years)	F(x) (percent)	x (years)	F(x) (percent)
0		55	79.2
5	7.6	60	83.3
10	14.8	65	87.4
15	21.9	70	91.3
20	28.6	75	94.7
25	36.1	80	97.2
30	44.0	85	98.8
35	52.8	90	99.7
40	61.1	95	99.9
45	68.4	100	100.0
50	74.5		

(Source: Based on data from the U.S. Bureau of the Census.)

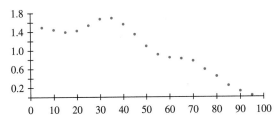

d. Use the cumulative density function F to find the percentage and number of 1992 U.S. residents who were age 20 or more but under age 50.

e. Use the density function F' to write an integral expression for the percentage of residents who were age 20 or more but under age 50.

f. Use three midpoint rectangles and the appropriate $F'(x)$ estimates from part b to estimate the value of the integral in part e. Sketch the rectangles you use on the scatter plot in part c.

g. Use the appropriate $F'(x)$ estimates calculated in part b and five midpoint rectangles to estimate $\int_0^{100} xF'(x)\,dx$. What does this integral represent, and what are its units?

25. **Income** The accompanying table shows income intervals (in thousands of dollars) and the percentage of Texas households with 1990 income in each interval. For instance, 9.6% of Texas households had income greater than or equal to $5000 but less than $10,000 in 1990.

Income interval (thousands of dollars)	Percent of households
0–5	8.2
5–10	9.6
10–15	9.8
15–25	18.8
25–35	15.8
35–50	16.6
50–75	13.3
75–100	4.3

(Source: U.S. Bureau of the Census.)

a. Complete the following table, which shows the cumulative percent $F(x)$ of households with incomes less than x thousand dollars.

x	F(x)	x	F(x)
5		35	
10		50	
15		75	
25		100	

b. Comment on the value $F(100)$. Why is it not 100%?

c. Examine a plot of the data in part a. Does it appear that the continuous density function f would have an inflection point or limiting value?

d. An approximate model for the density function is

$$f(x) = 0.85403395x^{0.56}e^{-0.0437980796x}$$
percentage points per thousand dollars

where x is household income in thousands of dollars. Examine a graph of this model on the plot of density function estimates that you constructed in part *c*. Comment on the fit.

e. Use the equation in part *d* to estimate the percentage of households with 1990 annual income less than $100,000. Compare your result with *F*(100) from part *a*.

f. Use the equation in part *d* to estimate the mean 1990 income for Texas households with incomes less than $100,000.

26. Accidents A study of serious accidents in British coal mines focused on the time interval between successive accidents. If, for example, successive accidents were observed on August 2 and August 5, then the time interval between these accidents was recorded as 3 days. During the study period, there were 34 serious accidents separated by 33 time intervals. The table gives some of the data. *A*(*x*) is the number of time intervals that were greater than or equal to *x* days.

x	A(x)	x	A(x)
1	31	13	7
4	19	16	4
7	13	19	3
10	9		

(Source: B. A. Maguire, E. S. Person, and A. W. Wynn, "The Time Interval Between Industrial Accidents," *Biometrika*, vol. 39, 1952, 168–180.)

a. Find *A*(0). Was there a day on which two accidents occurred? Was there a day on which more than three accidents occurred?

b. Explain why $F(x) = 1 - \dfrac{A(x)}{33}$ is the distribution of the time intervals observed between successive accidents.

c. Find an exponential model for *A*(*x*).

d. Use the model from part *c* to write a model for the distribution *F*, and then write a model for the density function *F'*.

e. What does the integral $\int_0^\infty xF'(x)dx$ represent, and what are its units?

27. Dinosaurs In Michael Crichton's novel *Jurassic Park*, dinosaur clones are alive and roaming about a remote jungle island intended to be a theme park. All the dinosaurs have been cloned female so that the populations can be controlled in Jurassic Park. Ian Malcolm, a cynical mathematician who is invited to the island, finds one of the first clues that all is not well when he examines one of the graphs given in the following figure. Both graphs show height distributions of the "compy" (Procompsognathid). (The park's computer that produced the graphs constructed them with straight lines connecting the data rather than using smooth curves.)

(Source: Michael Crichton, *Jurassic Park*, New York: Knopf, 1990.)

a. Malcolm claims that one of the graphs in the figure is characteristic of a breeding population and that the other graph is what would be expected from a controlled population in which the compys were introduced in three batches at six-month intervals. Which distribution corresponds to which population?

b. Which graph did Malcolm first see that indicated something was amiss?

c. Are the height distribution graphs in the figure graphs of probability density functions? Explain.

(a)

(b)

Height distribution (Procompsognathids)

Figure for Activity 27

SUMMARY

Improper Integrals

Improper integrals of the forms $\int_a^\infty f(x)dx$, $\int_{-\infty}^a f(x)dx$,

and $\int_{-\infty}^\infty f(x)dx$ can be evaluated by substituting a constant for each infinity symbol, finding an antiderivative and evaluating it to determine an expression in terms of x and the constant(s), and then determining the limit of the resulting expression as the constant approaches infinity or negative infinity. If the limit does not exist, we say the integral diverges.

Streams in Business and Biology

An income stream is a flow of money into an interest-bearing account over a period of time. If the stream flows continuously into an account at a rate of $R(t)$ dollars per year and the account earns annual interest at the rate of $100r\%$ compounded continuously, then the future value of the account at the end of T years is given by

$$\text{Future value} = \int_0^T R(t)e^{r(T-t)}dt \text{ dollars}$$

The present value of an income stream is the amount that would have to be invested now in order for the account to grow to a given future value. The present value of a continuous income stream whose future value is given by the previous equation is

$$\text{Present value} = \int_0^T R(t)e^{-rt}dt \text{ dollars}$$

When the income stream comes into the account discretely, we determine future value by summing rather than integrating:

$$\text{Future value} = \sum_{d=0}^{D-1} R(d)\left(1 + \frac{r}{n}\right)^{D-d} \text{ dollars}$$

where n is the number of deposits made each year, $R(d)$ is the value of the dth deposit, $100r\%$ is the annual interest rate, and D is the total number of deposits made. Once the future value of a discrete income stream is

calculated, the present value is determined by solving for P in the formula

$$P\left(1 + \frac{r}{n}\right)^D = \text{future value}$$

Streams also have applications in biology and related fields. The future value (in b years) of a biological stream with initial population size P, survival rate s (in decimals), and renewal rate $r(t)$, where t is the number of years of the stream, is

$$\text{Future value} \approx Ps^b + \int_0^b r(t)s^{b-t}dt$$

Integrals in Economics

A demand curve and a supply curve for a commodity are determined by economic factors. The interaction between supply and demand usually determines the quantity of an item that is available. Areas of special interest that are determined as areas associated with supply and demand curves are consumers' expenditure, consumers' surplus, consumers' willingness and ability to spend, producers' willingness and ability to receive, producers' surplus, producers' revenue, and total social gain.

Probability Distributions and Density Functions

The probability $P(a \le x \le b)$ is a measure of the likelihood that an outcome of an experiment involving a random quantity x will lie between a and b. Functions that describe how the probabilities associated with a random variable are distributed over various intervals of numbers are called probability density functions (or probability distributions).

Integrals of a probability density function f have the following meanings:

- The likelihood that x is between a and b is

$$P(a \le x \le b) = \int_a^b f(x)dx$$

- A measure of the center of the distribution is the mean:

$$\mu = \int_{-\infty}^{\infty} x f(x) dx$$

- A measure of the spread of the distribution is the standard deviation:

$$\sigma = \sqrt{\int_{-\infty}^{\infty} (x - \mu)^2 f(x) dx}$$

Three types of probability distributions that show up often in real-world applications are the uniform density function, the exponential density function, and the (bell-shaped) normal distribution.

A cumulative density function is an accumulation function of a probability density function. Outputs of cumulative density functions are the areas between the corresponding probability density functions and the horizontal axis. Probabilities can be determined by using either probability density functions or cumulative density functions.

CONCEPT CHECK

Can you

- Evaluate improper integrals?
- Recognize that an improper integral diverges?
- Determine income flow rate functions?
- Calculate and interpret present and future values of discrete and continuous income streams?
- Find various quantities related to a demand function?
- Calculate elasticity?
- Find various quantities related to a supply function?
- Find the market equilibrium point and total social gain?
- Find and interpret probability, mean, and standard deviation?
- Understand and use probability density functions?
- Work with cumulative density functions?

To practice, try

Section 6.1	Activities 1, 5
Section 6.1	Activities 7, 13
Section 6.2	Activities 1, 2
Section 6.2	Activities 7, 13
Section 6.3	Activities 9, 11
Section 6.3	Activities 13, 15
Section 6.3	Activities 17, 19
Section 6.3	Activities 21, 23
Section 6.4	Activities 11, 15
Section 6.4	Activities 3, 5
Section 6.4	Activities 23, 24

CONCEPT REVIEW

1. **Investment**   In preparing to start your own business (in 6 years), you plan to invest 10% of your salary each month in an account with a fixed rate of return of 5.3%. You currently make $3000 per month and expect your income to increase by $500 per year.

   a. Find a function for the yearly rate at which you will invest money in the account.

   b. If you start investing now, to what amount will your account grow in 6 years? (Consider a continuous stream.)

   c. How much would you have to invest now in one lump sum, instead of in a continuous stream, in order to build to the same 6-year future value?

2. **Investment**   A teacher is planning to retire in 8 years. To supplement her state retirement income, she plans to invest 7% of her salary each month until retirement in an annuity with a fixed rate of return of 5.2% compounded monthly. She currently makes $3100 per month and expects her income to increase, thanks to consulting work, by 0.4% per month.

   a. How much will be in the annuity at the end of 8 years?

   b. How much would she have to invest now, in one lump sum, to accumulate the same amount as the 8-year future value found in part a?

3. **Population**   Suppose a 1990 population of 10,000 foxes breeds at a rate of 500 pups per year and has a survival rate of 63%.

   a. Assuming that the survival and renewal rates remain constant, determine how many of the foxes alive in 1990 will still be alive in 2010.

   b. Write a function for the number of foxes that were born t years after 1990 and will still be alive in 2010.

   c. Estimate the fox population in the year 2010.

4. **Social Gain**   The average quantity of marble fountains that consumers will demand can be modeled as

   $$D(p) = -1.0p^2 - 20.6p + 900 \text{ fountains}$$

   and the average quantity that producers will supply can be modeled as

   $$S(p) = \begin{cases} 0 \text{ fountains} & \text{if } p < 2 \\ 0.3p^2 + 8.1p + 300 \text{ fountains} & \text{if } p \geq 2 \end{cases}$$

   when the market price is p hundred dollars per fountain.

   a. How much are consumers willing to spend for 30 fountains?

   b. How many fountains will producers supply at $1000 per fountain? Will supply exceed demand at this quantity?

   c. Determine the total social gain when fountains are sold at the equilibrium price.

5. The density function for a random variable x is

   $$f(x) = \begin{cases} 0.125x & \text{when } 0 \leq x \leq 4 \\ 0 & \text{when } x < 0 \text{ or } x > 4 \end{cases}$$

   a. Find the probability that x is less than 3.8. Interpret this result.

   b. Find the probability that x is between 1.3 and 5. Indicate, on a graph of f, what this answer represents.

   c. Find the mean value of x. Locate the mean on the graph you drew in part b.

   d. Find and graph $y = F(x)$, the cumulative density function for x.

   e. Use F to find the answer to part b. Show all work involved in your calculation.

Project 6.1 Arch Art

Setting

A popular historical site in Missouri is the Gateway Arch. Designed by Eero Saarinen, it is located on the original riverfront town site of St. Louis and symbolizes the city's role as gateway to the West. The stainless steel Gateway Arch (also called the St. Louis Arch) is 630 feet (192 meters) high and has an equal span.

In honor of the 200th anniversary of the Louisiana Purchase, which made St. Louis a part of the United States, the city has commissioned an artist to design a work of art at the Jefferson National Expansion Memorial which is a National Historic Site The artist plans to construct a hill beneath the Gateway Arch, located at the Historic Site, and hang strips of Mylar from the arch to the hill so as to completely fill the space. (See Figure 6.45.) The artist has asked for your help in determining the amount of Mylar needed.

Tasks

1. If the hill is to be 30 feet tall at its highest point, find an equation for the height of the cross section of the hill at its peak. Refer to the figure.

2. Estimate the height of the arch in at least ten different places. Use the estimated heights to construct a model for the height of the arch. (You need not consider only the models presented in this text.)

3. Estimate the area between the arch and the hill.

4. The artist plans to use strips of Mylar 60 inches wide. What is the minimum number of yards of Mylar that the artist will need to purchase?

5. Repeat Task 4 for strips 30 inches wide.

6. If the 30-inch strips cost half as much as the 60-inch strips, is there any cost benefit to using one width instead of the other? If so, which width? Explain.

Reporting

Write a memo telling the artist the minimum amount of Mylar necessary. Explain how you came to your conclusions. Include your mathematical work as an attachment.

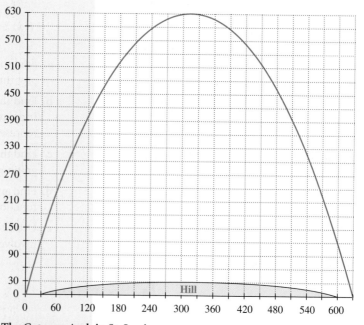

The Gateway Arch in St. Louis

Figure 6.45

Repetitive Change: Cyclic Functions

Joseph Sohm/Chromo Sohm Media, Inc./Photo Researchers Inc.

Concept Application

The levels of carbon dioxide (CO_2) in the atmosphere fluctuate in a periodic manner throughout the year, the lowest levels occurring in the summer when plants absorb significant amounts of CO_2. The amount of CO_2 in the atmosphere has been increasing for decades, and by using a model constructed from a trigonometric function and a quadratic function, we can model the carbon dioxide level over time. The model can then be used to answer questions such as

• How quickly is the level of carbon dioxide changing in a given month?

• What are the maximum and minimum levels of CO_2 in a given year, and when do those levels occur?

• When during a year is the amount of carbon dioxide increasing most rapidly?

You will be given an opportunity to answer questions such as these in Examples 2 and 3 of Section 7.3 and Activities 10 and 18 of Section 7.4.

451

Chapter Introduction

Many things change and then return to repeat the same change. This creates a repetitive pattern and forms a cycle. Patterns of repeating cycles occur in nature as well as in business applications.

Many cycles are best described with the functions from an area of mathematics called trigonometry. This term has its roots in the Greek word for "triangle measurement." Most of early trigonometry was centered on using ratios in similar triangles to determine indirect measurements. However, the trigonometric functions are now widely used to describe cyclic patterns of change.

Understanding the repetitive process in cycles and the mathematical models used to describe such cycles is the goal of the first part of this chapter. The second part of the chapter shows how calculus concepts can be applied to cyclic functions.

Concepts You Will Be Learning

- Identifying the amplitude, reflection, period, and horizontal and vertical shifts of a sine function (7.1, 7.2)
- Using data to construct and graph a sine model without the aid of technology (7.2)
- Using technology to construct a sine model (7.2)
- Writing rate-of-change formulas for sine and cosine functions (7.3)
- Calculating and interpreting derivatives of sine and cosine functions (7.3)
- Locating and interpreting extrema of sine and cosine functions (7.4)
- Locating and interpreting inflection points of sine and cosine functions (7.4)
- Writing antiderivatives of sine and cosine functions (7.5)
- Calculating and interpreting definite integrals of sine and cosine functions (7.5)
- Determining the expected value of a cyclic function (7.5)

7.1   Cycles and Sine Functions

A study of functions would not be complete without an examination of functions that repeat a pattern. If a function repeats itself and the length between the repetitions is constant, then we say the function is **periodic.** The shortest interval over which the function repeats itself is called the **period.** Furthermore, when a function is periodic and varies continuously between two extremes, we say the function is **cyclic.**

Cyclic Function

A cyclic function is a periodic, continuous function that varies between two extremes.

Sine and Cosine Functions

The most common periodic functions are the trigonometric (or trig) functions. There are six trig functions, all of them periodic. However, we restrict our study to the two cyclic trig functions: the sine function (abbreviated sin) and the cosine function (abbreviated cos). The basic sine function is of the form $y = \sin x$; its graph is shown in Figure 7.1.

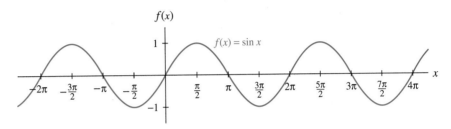

FIGURE 7.1

This graph extends infinitely in both horizontal directions. Note from the graph that the sine function is *periodic* with a period of 2π. That is, it starts at $y = 0$ when $x = 0$ and then rises to a maximum, falls to a minimum, and returns to $y = 0$ again when $x = 2\pi$. This pattern repeats itself every 2π input units. The sine function is also *cyclic* because it varies continuously, alternating between -1 and 1.

If you studied trigonometric functions in a previous math course, you probably considered the input of the sine function to be measured in degrees and may have also related this function to angles on a unit circle. However, it is important to note that in this course, we use the sine function simply as a model for situations that exhibit cyclic behavior with the input measured in real numbers (radians, not degrees).

It is important that you make sure that your technology is set to radian mode while performing all trig function calculations in this text. **7.1.1**

Another trig function that we make use of is $g(x) = \cos x$. (See Figure 7.2.)

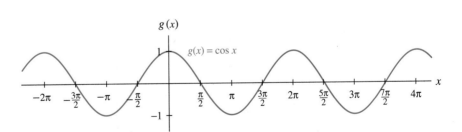

FIGURE 7.2

The connection between the sine and cosine functions and the unit circle can be used to show that for any input x measured in radians, $\cos^2 x + \sin^2 x = 1$. The cosine function can also be considered as a horizontal shift of the sine function by the relationship $\cos x = \sin(x + \frac{\pi}{2})$. We therefore restrict the trigonometric models we develop to those involving only the sine function.

Variations of the Sine Function

The sine function can be modified to vary between extremes other than -1 and 1, to shift up or down, to repeat itself more or less often than 2π, and to shift right or left. The ability to modify the sine function in these ways will be essential when we use a sine function to model data.

Multiplying the function $y = \sin x$ by a constant changes the extremes between which the output values of the function vary. In particular, the function $y = a \sin x$ varies between $-a$ and a. The magnitude of a, $|a|$, is called the **amplitude**, and its effect is illustrated in Figure 7.3. A negative value of a indicates that the graph is reflected across the horizontal axis.

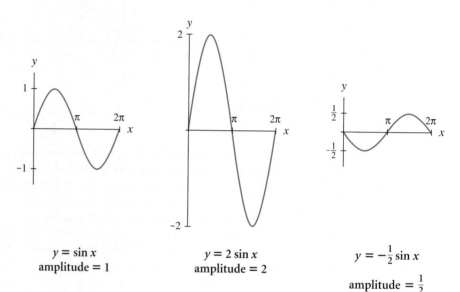

$$y = \sin x$$
$$\text{amplitude} = 1$$

$$y = 2 \sin x$$
$$\text{amplitude} = 2$$

$$y = -\tfrac{1}{2} \sin x$$
$$\text{amplitude} = \tfrac{1}{2}$$

FIGURE 7.3

Adding a constant to, or subtracting a constant from, the sine function shifts the graph up or down. This constant can be thought of as the **average** or **expected value** of one cycle because it is the midpoint between the high and low values of the function. Figure 7.4 illustrates the effect of adding or subtracting a constant to or from a sine function.

$$y = \sin x$$

$$y = \sin x + 4$$

$$y = \sin x - \tfrac{1}{2}$$

$$y = 2 \sin x + 4$$

$$y = 2 \sin x - \tfrac{1}{2}$$

FIGURE 7.4

The graph of a sine function repeats its cycle over an interval of a specific length. The basic sine function $y = \sin x$ repeats over an interval of length 2π units. When the input x is multiplied by a constant b ($b > 0$) the number of times the cycle repeats over an interval of 2π units changes. When x is multiplied by 2, the graph cycles twice over an interval of 2π units, or we say it cycles once over an interval of π units. When x is multiplied by $\frac{1}{2}$, the graph cycles once over an interval of 4π units. The interval over which a graph of a cyclic function completes one cycle is called the **period**. For a sine function of the form $y = \sin bx$, the constant b dictates the period. To find the period of $y = \sin bx$, we simply divide 2π by b:

$$\text{Period} = \frac{2\pi}{b}$$

Similarly, if we know the period, then we can find b by using the equation

$$b = \frac{2\pi}{\text{period}}$$

Figure 7.5 illustrates several functions of the form $y = \sin bx$.

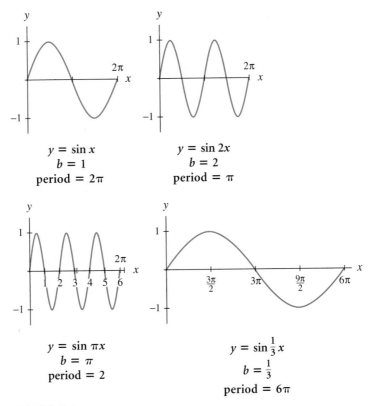

$$y = \sin x$$
$$b = 1$$
$$\text{period} = 2\pi$$

$$y = \sin 2x$$
$$b = 2$$
$$\text{period} = \pi$$

$$y = \sin \pi x$$
$$b = \pi$$
$$\text{period} = 2$$

$$y = \sin \tfrac{1}{3} x$$
$$b = \tfrac{1}{3}$$
$$\text{period} = 6\pi$$

FIGURE 7.5

Finally, we can shift a sine function left or right by adding a constant to the input. Specifically, for $y = \sin(bx + h)$, the graph is shifted horizontally by $\frac{|h|}{b}$ units. If h is negative, the shift is to the right. If h is positive, the shift is to the left. One way to identify the horizontal shift of a graph is to find an input at which the function attains its average value and is increasing. Because the function is cyclic, such a point on the function is not unique. The function $y = \sin x$ is increasing and attains its average value at $x = 0$, and $y = \sin(bx + h)$ reaches such a point at $x = \frac{-h}{b}$. Figure 7.6 illustrates several functions with horizontal shifts.

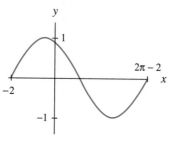

$y = \sin(x + 2)$

shift: 2 left and period $= 2\pi$

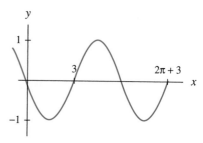

$y = \sin(x - 3)$

shift: 3 right and period $= 2\pi$

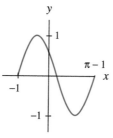

$y = \sin(2x + 2)$

shift: 1 left and period $= \pi$

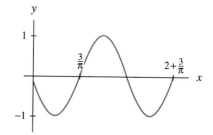

$y = \sin(\pi x - 3)$

shift: $\frac{3}{\pi} \approx 0.955$ right and period $= 2$

FIGURE 7.6

There is one final variation of the sine function to consider. The functions $y = \sin(-x)$ and $y = -\sin x$ are equivalent functions. That is, $\sin(-x) = -\sin x$. The graph of each of these functions appears to be the reflection of the graph of $y = \sin x$ across the horizontal axis. See Figure 7.7.

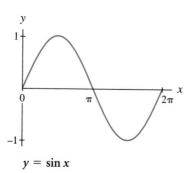

$y = \sin x$

FIGURE 7.7

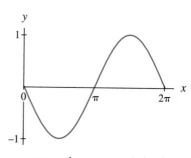

$y = -\sin x$ or $y = \sin(-x)$

We earlier stated that we assume b is positive. This restriction does not limit the functions we consider, because a negative value for either a or b in $y = a \sin(bx + h) + k$ indicates reflection. If we encounter a function in which b is negative, we simply factor the negative 1 out of the $(bx + h)$ term and use the fact that $\sin(-x) = -\sin x$ to rewrite the function with a positive b. For example, $y = 2 \sin(-3x + 4) + 6$ can be rewritten as

$$y = 2 \sin[-(3x - 4)] + 6 = -2 \sin(3x - 4)] + 6 = -2 \sin(3x - 4) + 6$$

Consider the cycle of the graph $y = a \sin(bx + h) + k$ that begins at $x = \frac{-h}{b}$. The output value is always k at the point with this input. If a is positive, this cycle will first increase and then decrease. If a is negative, this cycle is reflected across the line $y = k$, so it will first decrease and then increase.

We summarize the effects of the constants a, b, h, and k:

<table>
<tr><td>

Instead of the equation $y = a \sin(bx + h) + k$, some technologies use $y = a \sin b(x - h) + k$. The advantage in this alternative form is that the quantities influenced by the parameter have direct readouts. That is, in the equation $y = a \sin b(x - h) + k$, h is precisely the horizontal shift. In the first formulation, the one used in the text, $\frac{|h|}{b}$ is the horizontal shift.

</td><td>

Variations of the Sine Function

The constants of the sine function

$$f(x) = a \sin(bx + h) + k$$

are interpreted as follows (we assume $b > 0$):

$|a|$ is the amplitude, where $a < 0$ denotes reflection across the horizontal axis.

$\frac{2\pi}{b}$ is the period.

$\frac{|h|}{b}$ is the horizontal shift, right if $h < 0$ and left if $h > 0$.
k is the vertical shift, up if $k > 0$ and down if $k < 0$.

</td></tr>
</table>

EXAMPLE 1 *Graphing Variations of the Sine Function*

For each of the following sine functions, specify the amplitude, period, horizontal shift, and vertical shift. Graph one cycle of each function.

a. $y = 3 \sin x - 4$

b. $y = \sin(-2x - 6)$

c. $y = 0.5 \sin(0.2x - 1) + 2.5$

Solution

a.   The parameters of $y = 3 \sin x - 4$ are $a = 3$, $b = 1$, $h = 0$, and $k = -4$. Thus the amplitude of this function is 3, and the graph is shifted down 4 units. Without the shift down, the function would vary between -3 and 3. Subtracting 4 from each of these values, we see that the graph of $y = 3 \sin x - 4$ varies between -7 and -1. The period is 2π. We choose to graph the cycle that begins at 0 and ends at 2π. Because a is positive, this cycle begins with the graph increasing. The graph is shown in Figure 7.8.

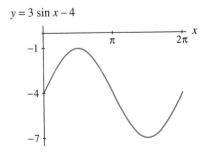

$y = 3 \sin x - 4$

FIGURE 7.8

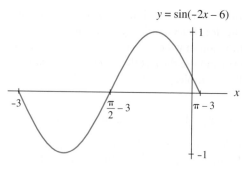

$y = \sin(-2x - 6)$

FIGURE 7.9

b.   Because b is negative in this function, we factor out the negative 1 and use the property that $\sin(-x) = -\sin x$:

$$\sin(-2x - 6) = \sin[-(2x + 6)] = -\sin(2x + 6)$$

Thus we consider the function in the form $y = -\sin(2x + 6)$. For this function $a = -1$, $b = 2$, $h = 6$, and $k = 0$. The amplitude of $y = -\sin(2x + 6)$ is 1. There is no vertical shift, so the function varies between -1 and 1. The constant b is 2, so the period is $\frac{2\pi}{2} = \pi$. The graph is shifted horizontally $\frac{|6|}{2} = 3$ units, and the shift is to the left because 6 is positive. Without the horizontal shift, one cycle would begin at 0 and end at π. With a horizontal shift of 3 units to the left, one cycle begins at -3 and ends at $\pi - 3$.

Because a is negative, this cycle begins by declining rather than rising. (See Figure 7.9.)

c.   For the function $y = 0.5 \sin(0.2x - 1) + 2.5$, the parameters are $a = 0.5$, $b = 0.2$, $h = -1$, and $k = 2.5$. The graph has amplitude 0.5 and is shifted up 2.5 units. Thus the function varies between 2 and 3. The constant b of the function is 0.2, so the period is $\frac{2\pi}{0.2} = 10\pi$. The graph is shifted horizontally $\frac{|-1|}{0.2} = 5$ units, and the shift is to the right because -1 is negative. Without the horizontal shift, one cycle begins at 0 and ends at 10π. With the horizontal shift 5 units to the right, one cycle begins at 5 and ends at $10\pi + 5$. Because a is positive, this cycle begins with the graph increasing. The graph is shown in Figure 7.10.

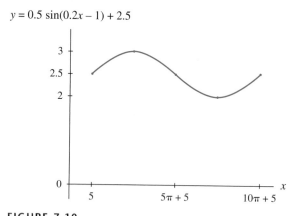

$y = 0.5 \sin(0.2x - 1) + 2.5$

FIGURE 7.10

Now that we have seen the basic form of the sine function $f(x) = a \sin(bx + h) + k$ and understand how the constants a, b, h, and k are related to the shape of a graph of the function, we can consider the usefulness of the sine function when modeling cyclic data. In the next section, we look at modeling various sets of cyclic data with sine functions.

7.1   Concept Inventory

- Periodic function
- Cyclic function
- Sine and cosine functions
- Sine function graph
- Sine function variations: $y = a \sin(bx + h) + k$
    - Amplitude
    - Horizontal shift
    - Vertical shift
    - Period
    - Expected value
    - Cycle
    - Reflection

For each of the functions in Activities 6 through 10, state the amplitude, period, vertical shift, and horizontal shift. Also state whether the function is reflected across the horizontal axis and whether the graph is increasing or decreasing at $x = \frac{-h}{b}$.

6. $f(x) = 0.1 \sin(2x - 4) - 0.5$

7. $g(x) = -\sin(x - \pi)$

8. $g(x) = 3.62 \sin(0.22x + 4.81) + 7.32$

9. $p(x) = 235 \sin(-300x + 100) - 65$

10. $p(x) = \sin(-x + 4) + 0.7$

11. Match functions a through f with graphs i through vi.

a. $y = 3 \sin x + 8$ b. $y = 3 \sin x - 3$

c. $y = 3 \sin x + 2$ d. $y = 4 \sin x + 8$

e. $y = 2 \sin x - 3$ f. $y = 2 \sin x + 2$

7.1   Activities

Getting Started

1. Construct an input/output diagram for the function $s(x) = \sin x$.

2. Construct an input/output diagram for the function $c(x) = \cos x$.

3. a. For x-values from 0 to 2π, what is the largest value that $s(x) = \sin x$ achieves? Also find the value(s) of x at which the maximum occurs.

   b. For any real number x, what is the largest value that $s(x) = \sin x$ achieves? Also find the value(s) of x at which the maximum occurs.

   c. For x-values from 0 to 2π, what is the smallest value that $s(x) = \sin x$ achieves? Also find the value(s) of x at which the minimum occurs.

   d. For any real number x, what is the smallest value that $s(x) = \sin x$ achieves? Also find the value(s) of x at which the minimum occurs.

4. Repeat Activity 3 for the cosine function.

5. a. Graph $c(x) = \cos x$ and $s(x) = \sin x$ on the same axes for $0 \leq x \leq 2\pi$.

   b. Find where $c(x) = s(x)$.

   c. On the basis of your answer to part b, what are the x-coordinates of all the points of intersection for the sine and cosine functions over all real numbers?

(i)

(ii)

(iii)

(iv)

(v)

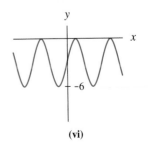

(vi)

12. **a.** What is the distance between two consecutive repeating maxima of the function $f(x) = \sin(2x)$? of the function $g(x) = \sin(0.5x)$?

   b. For the function $h(x) = \sin\left(\frac{1}{3}x + \frac{2}{3}\right)$ and the function $j(x) = \sin\left(\frac{1}{3}x - \frac{1}{3}\right)$, estimate the locations of the points of greatest slope closest to $x = 0$.

   c. Match the four functions given in this activity with graphs vii through x.

(i)

(ii)

(iii)

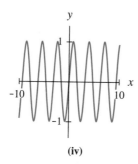

(iv)

Without the aid of technology, graph one cycle of each of the functions in Activities 13 through 18.

13. $f(x) = \sin 2x + 3$

14. $f(x) = -2 \sin x + 3$

15. $f(x) = 2 \sin(x + 3)$

16. $f(x) = \sin(-2x + 3)$

17. $f(x) = 2 \sin(-2x + 3)$

18. $f(x) = -2 \sin(-2x + 3) + 3$

19. Compare the graph of $y = -2 \sin x$ with the graph of $y = 2 \sin(x - \pi)$. Also compare the graphs of $y = -0.5 \sin x$ and $y = 0.5 \sin(x + 3\pi)$. What generalization can you make from your observations?

20. Sketch a graph of $y = \sin x$ from $x = 0$ to $x = 2\pi$.

   a. On the same axes, plot points for $y = -\sin x$ for $x = 0, \pi/2, \pi, 3\pi/2,$ and 2π. Draw arrows from the points on the graph of $y = \sin x$ to the corresponding points you plotted for $y = -\sin x$. Across which axis (vertical or horizontal) does the function $y = \sin x$ appear to have been reflected to give the points for $y = -\sin x$?

   b. On another set of axes, sketch a graph of the function $y = \sin x$ from $x = 0$ to $x = 2\pi$. On this new graph, plot points for $y = \sin(-x)$ for $x = 0, \pi/2, \pi, 3\pi/2,$ and 2π. Draw arrows from the points on the graph of $y = \sin x$ to the corresponding points you plotted for $y = \sin(-x)$. Across which axis (vertical or horizontal) does the function $y = \sin x$ appear to have been reflected to give the points for $y = \sin(-x)$?

   c. On a third set of axes, sketch a graph of $y = -\sin x$ from $x = 0$ to $x = 2\pi$. Extend the graph to the left to $x = -2\pi$. In a second color but on the same set of axes, sketch a graph of $y = \sin(-x)$ from $x = -2\pi$ to $x = 0$. Extend the graph to the right to $x = 2\pi$. In a third color, graph $y = \sin x$ from $x = -2\pi$ to $x = 2\pi$. How are the functions $y = \sin x, y = -\sin x,$ and $y = \sin(-x)$ related?

21. Sketch a graph of $y = \cos x$ from $x = 0$ to $x = 2\pi$.

   a. On the same axes, plot points for $y = -\cos x$ for $x = 0, \pi/2, \pi, 3\pi/2,$ and 2π. Draw arrows from the points on the graph of $y = \cos x$ to the corresponding points you plotted for $y = -\cos x$. Across which axis (vertical or horizontal) does the function $y = \cos x$ appear to have been reflected to give the points for $y = -\cos x$?

   b. On another set of axes, sketch a graph of the function $y = \cos x$ from $x = 0$ to $x = 2\pi$. On this new graph, plot points for $y = \cos(-x)$ for $x = 0, \pi/2, \pi, 3\pi/2,$ and 2π. Draw arrows from the points on the graph of $y = \cos x$ to the corresponding points you plotted for $y = \cos(-x)$. Across which axis (vertical or horizontal) does the function $y = \cos x$ appear to have been reflected to give the points for $y = \cos(-x)$?

   c. On a third set of axes, sketch a graph of $y = -\cos x$ from $x = 0$ to $x = 2\pi$. Extend the graph to the left to $x = -2\pi$. In a second color but on the same set of axes, sketch a graph of

$y = \cos(-x)$ from $x = -2\pi$ to $x = 0$. Extend the graph to the right to $x = 2\pi$. In a third color, graph $y = \cos x$ from $x = -2\pi$ to $x = 2\pi$. How are the functions $y = \cos x$, $y = -\cos x$, and $y = \cos(-x)$ related? Does $\cos x = \cos(-x)$?

Discussing Concepts

22. Explain how to find the amplitude and vertical shift of a sine function given its graph and/or data.

23. Explain how to find the period and horizontal shift of a sine function given its graph and/or data.

7.2 Sine Functions as Models

Be aware that not all technologies have a built-in sine regression routine. See the *Excel Instruction Guide* to obtain a sine curve-fitting procedure.

The world is full of cyclic data that repeatedly return to the same maximum and minimum. If we learn to model these data, then we can use calculus and the model to obtain special insight into the changing nature of the data. The sine and cosine functions are cyclic, and they are useful in modeling data that exhibit cyclic behavior. Because these two functions are similar (one can be obtained from the other by a horizontal shift), we choose to use only the sine function when modeling cyclic data.

In Section 7.1 we examined the sine function of the form $y = a \sin(bx + h) + k$. We saw that the constant a determines the height and reflection of the curve, the constant b determines the period as $\frac{2\pi}{b}$, the constant h influences the horizontal shift, and the constant k is the vertical shift. We now consider using this function to model data in real-life situations.

The monthly amount of ultraviolet (UV) radiation (in watts per square centimeter) received by a horizontal surface of area 1 cm^2 in Auckland, New Zealand, is given in Table 7.1, and a scatter plot of these data is shown in Figure 7.11.

TABLE 7.1

Month	Jan	Feb	Mar	Apr	May	Jun	Jul	Aug	Sep	Oct	Nov	Dec
UV radiation (watts per cm^2)	55	46	32	19	10	7	8	15	27	40	52	58

(Source: W. Rudloff, *World-Climates*, Stuttgart, Germany: Wissenschaftliche Verlagsgesellschaft, 1981.)

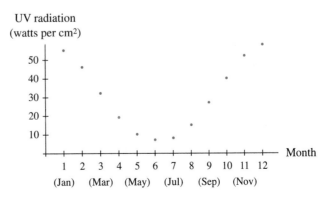

FIGURE 7.11

We see from the data and scatter plot that the data have a minimum and a maximum. We assume that the amount of UV radiation reaches this same maximum and minimum each year; hence the data are cyclic. Because the repetitions occur on a yearly basis, the period is 12 months. Thus it makes sense to fit a sine function to the data. Before using technology to fit the function $f(x) = a \sin(bx + h) + k$, let us inspect the data more carefully to see if we can estimate the constants a, b, h, and k.

The Constants of a Sine Function

We begin our inspection by looking for k. The vertical shift of the sine function is the value of k. It tells us how high (or low) the middle value of the output range is. This is the average (or expected) value of the cycle. In order to determine k, we must know the maximum output and the minimum output. The maximum (max) of the data occurs in December at 58 watts per cm^2, and the minimum (min) occurs in June at 7 watts per cm^2. To find the middle value of the output, we average the maximum and minimum values.

$$k = \frac{\text{max} + \text{min}}{2} = \frac{58 + 7}{2} = 32.5 \text{ watts per } cm^2$$

In other words, if we did not take into account the cyclic fluctuations in the amount of UV radiation, we would expect the average amount to be 32.5 watts per cm^2 for any given month. However, there are monthly variations in the amount. The amplitude tells us by how much the amount may vary from the expected (or average) value.

We find the amplitude a of the sine model by calculating half the difference between the maximum and minimum values.

$$a = \frac{\text{max} - \text{min}}{2} = \frac{58 - 7}{2} = 25.5 \text{ watts per } cm^2$$

That is, UV radiation varies by $\pm$ 25.5 watts per cm^2 away from the expected value of 32.5 watts per cm^2.

Because the data are periodic with a cycle that we assume to repeat each year, the period is 12 months. We calculate the constant b using the equation

$$\text{Period} = \frac{2\pi}{b}$$

Thus $12 = \frac{2\pi}{b}$, or $b = \frac{\pi}{6} \approx 0.52$.

Finally, we look for the constant h, which is an indication of the horizontal shift of the sine function. When looking for the horizontal shift of a function of the form $f(x) = a \sin(bx + h) + k$, we seek an input value x_0 at which the sine function f behaves the same way $g(x) = \sin x$ behaves at $x = 0$. At $x = 0$, a graph of $g(x) = \sin x$ is increasing and attains its average value, so we are looking for an input value x_0 at which the graph of $f(x) = a \sin(bx + h) + k$ is increasing and attains its average value.

On a function of the form $f(x) = a \sin(bx + h) + k$, such an input value x_0 occurs exactly halfway between the x-value at which $f(x)$ is lowest and the x-value at which $f(x)$ is highest. Thus for the UV radiation data in Table 7.1, we find that a candidate for the horizontal shift x_0 is halfway between June and December. If we align so that $x = 1$ in January and $x = 6$ in June, then $x = 12$ in December, and $x_0 = \frac{12 + 6}{2} = 9$ (September). This shift is to the right, indicating that h is negative. To calculate h from x_0, we use the equation

$$x_0 = \text{horizontal shift} = \frac{|h|}{b}$$

with $b = \frac{\pi}{6}$ as previously calculated. Thus $9 = \frac{|h|}{\pi/6}$, or $h = -(\frac{\pi}{6})(9) \approx -4.71$.

Now we can write a model to approximate the amount of ultraviolet radiation received in Auckland, New Zealand, as

$$r(m) = 25.5 \sin(0.52m - 4.71) + 32.5 \text{ watts per cm}^2$$

when $m = 1$ in January, $m = 2$ in February, and so on. Figure 7.12 shows this equation graphed on the scatter plot of the data.

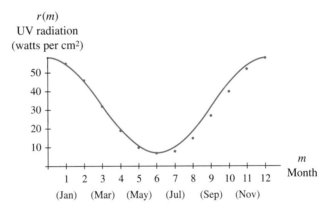

FIGURE 7.12

As we have seen, the context of a real-life situation often indicates reasonable estimates for the constants of a sine model. Knowing the interpretation of the constants a, b, h, and k in the general sine model $f(x) = a \sin(bx + h) + k$ enables us to calculate an equation by hand. We again illustrate these ideas in Example 1 by using the sine function to model the number of daylight hours at a location on the Arctic Circle.

EXAMPLE 1   *Constructing a Sine Model Without Using Technology*

Daylight Hours   On the Arctic Circle there are 24 hours of daylight on the summer solstice, June 21, and 24 hours of darkness on the winter solstice, December 21. We use this information, along with the fact that there are 12 hours of daylight and 12 hours of darkness midway between the summer and winter solstices, to construct a model that approximates the number of hours of daylight throughout the year on the Arctic Circle. We use as input the number of days since the beginning of the year and show just over 2 years of data so that the pattern in the data can be easily seen. Note that if January 1 is day 1, then December 21 of the previous year is day −10 and

December 21 of the current year is day 355. The data are given in Table 7.2, and a scatter plot of the data is shown in Figure 7.13

TABLE 7.2

Date	12/21		6/21		12/21		6/21		12/21	
Day of the year	−10	81.5	173	264	355	446.5	538	629	720	811.5
Hours of daylight	0	12	24	12	0	12	24	12	0	12

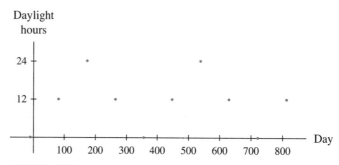

FIGURE 7.13

Use the data in Table 7.2 to calculate the constants a, b, h, and k of a model of the form $f(x) = a \sin(bx + h) + k$.

Solution

The scatter plot suggests that a sine model is appropriate. The output values of the data range from 0 to 24 hours; therefore, we expect the amplitude of our model to be $\frac{24}{2} = 12$ hours. However, without a vertical shift, the output of a sine model with amplitude 12 is between -12 and $+12$ hours. Because the data are between 0 and 24, we expect a vertical shift upward of 12 hours. We also expect the model to repeat itself every 365 days. To find the horizontal shift, we need to locate where the number of hours of daylight is the average value of the cycle (12 hours) and is first increasing. This occurs at 81.5 days, so 81.5 is the horizontal shift to the right. Thus in the sine function $f(x) = a \sin(bx + h) + k$, we expect

Amplitude $= a = 12$

Period $= \dfrac{2\pi}{b} = 365$, so $b \approx 0.01721$

Horizontal shift to the right $= \dfrac{|h|}{b} = 81.5$, so $h \approx -1.40296$

Vertical shift $= k = 12$

A model for the number of hours of daylight on the Arctic Circle is

$$h(t) = 12 \sin(0.01721t - 1.40296) + 12 \text{ hours}$$

where t is the number of days since December 31 of the previous year. Figure 7.14 shows this model graphed on the scatter plot.

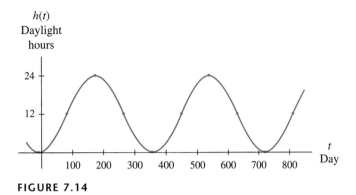

FIGURE 7.14

Fitting a Sine Model to Data

It may be the case that the data and information provided are not sufficient to predict accurately the maximum, minimum, or period of the cycle, or you may wish to find a model quickly. In such cases, you can use a calculator or computer to fit a sine function to the data. It is still important to understand the role of the constants a, b, h, and k of the equation so that you can interpret the model.

At the beginning of this section we calculated a model of the data for the amount of ultraviolet radiation in Auckland, New Zealand. However, our estimates of the maximum and minimum of the function were not exact. The minimum of the function probably occurs somewhere between the June and the July data, and the maximum probably occurs somewhere between the December and the January data. A sine function fitted by technology to the data in Table 7.1 is

$$A(m) = 27.1 \sin(0.485m + 1.707) + 32.9 \text{ watts per cm}^2$$

when $m = 1$ in January, $m = 2$ in February, and so on.

Let us examine this model and compare the constants to those we calculated earlier. The function A gives the average value of UV radiation as approximately 32.9 watts per cm^2 instead of the 32.5 watts per cm^2 previously calculated from the data. Ultraviolet radiation fluctuates as much as 27.1 watts per cm^2 above and below this average, according to the function A, giving a slightly larger amplitude than that calculated earlier. The period of the function A is $\frac{2\pi}{b} \approx \frac{2\pi}{0.485} \approx 13.0$. Thus the equation found using technology has a period of more than 12 months.

Finally, the horizontal shift of A is $\frac{|h|}{b} \approx \frac{|1.707|}{0.485} \approx 3.5$ to the left. Because this value is outside the data interval, we add one period (approximately 13) to it in order to interpret it correctly. In this case, adding the period to the horizontal shift gives approximately 9.4. This number is within the range of our data and can be interpreted as halfway between the September data and the October data. Thus UV radiation hits its average value and is increasing halfway between the September data and the October data. (The horizontal shift calculated earlier was 9, or September.) This supports our analysis that the minimum probably occurs halfway between the June and the July data and that the maximum probably occurs halfway between the December and the January data.

In this text, all sine models found using technology were constructed on a TI-84 Plus. If you use a different technology, your model may vary.

7.2.1

When we compare the two models, we see that the graph of the model calculated via technology is a better fit to the data (see Figure 7.15a). However, because the period of the technology-generated model is more than 1 year (the period we expect from the context), the two models will begin to differ by more and more after the first cycle (see Figure 7.15b). Thus the technology-generated model should be used only for inputs between 0 and 12.

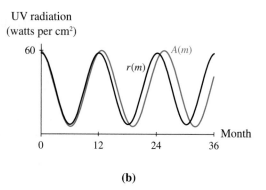

(a)   (b)

FIGURE 7.15

EXAMPLE 2   *Using Technology to Find a Sine Model*

Daylight Hours   Use technology to find a sine model for the Arctic Circle hours-of-daylight data. Compare the equation with the one calculated in Example 1.

Solution
A technology-determined model is

$$y = 12.00011 \sin(0.01721x - 1.40296) + 12 \text{ hours}$$

where x is the number of days since December 31 of the previous year. We see that the amplitude coefficient of this equation agrees to three decimal places with that of the equation found in Example 1. The other coefficients agree to at least the number of decimal places shown here. ●

We now have the ability to use a sine function to model data that exhibit a wave pattern. A sine model may also be used if the data do not show more than one complete cycle but the context indicates that the situation is cyclic in nature. It is also possible to use a sine model if a situation is not cyclic but the curvature of the data matches that of a sine function. In such cases the model would be useless for extrapolation, but it could be used for interpolation.

7.2 Concept Inventory

- The sine function: $f(x) = a \sin(bx + h) + k$
- Determining sine function constants $a, b, h,$ and k from data without the aid of technology
- Finding a sine function using technology

7.2 Activities

Applying Concepts

1. **Gas Usage** The table shows the average number of gas thermal units per day used by a residential gas customer in Reno, Nevada. (The data represent 15 months.)

Month	Gas usage (therms per day)	Month	Gas usage (therms per day)
Nov	1.2	July	0.4
Dec	1.7	Aug	0.3
Jan	3.2	Sept	0.3
Feb	3.3	Oct	0.4
Mar	3.3	Nov	1.4
Apr	2.5	Dec	2.3
May	1.5	Jan	2.9
June	0.9		

a. Plot the data for gas usage. Explain why the data should be cyclic.

b. Use the data to estimate the amplitude and the vertical shift.

c. Align the first January to $x = 1$, and approximate the period and horizontal shift from the data.

d. Construct, without the aid of technology and using the alignment in part c, a sine model for the

average number of gas thermal units per day used during the xth month of the year.

2. **Minimum Wage** The federal minimum wage rates, in constant 2000 dollars, between 1950 and 2000 are shown in the table.

Year	Mininum wage (dollars)	Year	Minimum wage (dollars)
1950	5.36	1980	6.48
1955	4.82	1985	5.36
1960	5.82	1990	5.01
1965	6.83	1995	4.80
1970	7.10	2000	5.15
1975	6.72		

(Source: U.S. Employment Standards Administration.)

a. Renumber the input as the number of years after 1950, and use the data to determine the amplitude and the vertical shift.

b. Approximate the period and the horizontal shift from the data.

c. Construct, without the aid of technology, a sine model for the aligned data.

d. Graph the function in part c on a scatter plot of the aligned data. Is the fit reasonable?

e. If the federal minimum wage data had been given in current dollars rather than in constant 2000 dollars, would a cyclic function fit the data? Explain.

3. **Temperature** The accompanying table on page 468 gives the normal daily mean temperatures, based on the 30-year period 1961 through 1990, for Omaha, Nebraska.

a. Plot these daily mean temperatures. Explain why the data should be cyclic.

b. Use the data to determine the amplitude and the vertical shift.

c. Approximate the period and the horizontal shift from the data.

Month	Daily mean temperature (°F)	Month	Daily mean temperature (°F)
Jan	21.1	July	76.9
Feb	26.9	Aug	74.1
Mar	38.6	Sep	65.1
Apr	51.9	Oct	53.4
May	62.4	Nov	39.0
June	72.1	Dec	25.1

(Source: U.S. National Oceanic and Atmospheric Administration, *Climatography of the United States,* No. 81.)

d. Construct, without the aid of technology, a sine model for mean daily temperature during the *x*th month of the year.

e. Graph your function on the plot of the data. Is the fit reasonable?

f. Use your function to predict the mean daily temperature in Omaha in July of this year. Discuss the reasonableness of the prediction.

4. **Beetles** Some populations of animals exhibit periodic behavior over time. During the 1960s and 1970s, two scientists carefully studied the population of the Carabid beetle in a region of the Netherlands. The table shows data from their study. The output data are log (base 10) data for the number of beetles not surviving in a given year. These values are referred to as the *reduction* in the number of beetles. The number of beetles not surviving in a given year is found by raising 10 to the reduction value in the table corresponding to that year.

Year	log (base 10) reduction	Year	log (base 10) reduction
1965	2.7	1971	2.7
1966	2.8	1972	2.9
1967	4.5	1973	3.7
1968	4.4	1974	4.5
1969	3.3	1975	4.4
1970	2.8	1976	2.7

(Source: P. J. denBoer and J. Reddingius, *Regulation and Stabilization Paradigms in Population Ecology,* London: Chapman & Hall, 1996.)

a. Renumber the input data as years since 1965. Using only the data, estimate the amplitude and vertical shift.

b. Using only the data, estimate the period and the horizontal shift.

c. On the basis of the values calculated in parts *a* and *b*, give a sine model for the reduction data. Sketch a graph of the function on a scatter plot of the data.

d. Use the equation in part *c* to construct a model for the number of beetles not surviving in a given year. Sketch a graph of this function, and compare it with the graph in part *c*.

5. **Temperature** The table shows the normal daily low temperatures, based on the 30-year period 1961 through 1990, for Omaha, Nebraska.

Month	Daily minimum temperature (°F)	Month	Daily minimum temperature (°F)
Jan	10.9	July	65.9
Feb	16.7	Aug	62.9
Mar	27.7	Sep	53.6
Apr	39.9	Oct	41.2
May	50.9	Nov	28.7
June	60.4	Dec	15.6

(Source: U.S. National Oceanic and Atmospheric Administration, *Climatography of the United States,* No. 81.)

a. How would you expect the scatter plot and model for the normal daily low temperatures in Omaha to be related to the scatter plot and model for the normal daily mean temperatures in Omaha?

b. Use the data for the normal daily low temperatures to determine the amplitude and the vertical shift. Plot the daily low temperatures, and use the plot to approximate the period and horizontal shift. Compare these results with those you found for the daily mean temperature in Activity 3. Are the findings what you expected?

c. On the basis of your answers to parts *a* and *b*, write a model for the normal daily low temperatures.

6. Temperature The normal daily high temperatures for the 30-year period 1961 through 1990 in New Orleans, Louisiana, and Boston, Massachusetts, are given in the table.

Month	New Orleans daily high temperature (°F)	Boston daily high temperature (°F)
January	60.8	35.7
February	64.1	37.5
March	71.6	45.8
April	78.5	55.9
May	84.4	66.6
June	89.2	76.3
July	90.6	81.8
August	90.2	79.8
September	86.6	72.8
October	79.4	62.7
November	71.1	52.2
December	64.3	40.4

(Source: U.S. National Oceanic and Atmospheric Administration, *Climatography of the United States,* No. 81.)

a. Would you expect these normal daily high temperature data to be cyclic? Explain.

b. Use the data to find the difference between high temperatures in January and July for these two cities. What do these differences tell you about how the climates of the cities compare?

7. Gas Usage Refer to the data for the average number of gas thermal units per day used by a residential gas customer in Reno, Nevada, given in Activity 1.

a. Align the data so that the first January is $x = 1$. Use technology to find a sine function to fit the data. State the amplitude, period, and the horizontal and vertical shifts of the equation.

b. According to the function, what is the average value (or expected value) of the number of therms per day?

c. Assuming that a billing period has 30 days and that the cost per therm is $0.5632, estimate the average gas bill for this customer.

8. Minimum Wage Consider the data in Activity 2.

a. Aligning the input as the number of years after 1950, use technology to find a sine function that fits the aligned minimum-wage data.

b. Compare and contrast the equation found in Activity 2 with the one found with technology in this activity.

c. Use the model found in Activity 2 and the one found in this activity to predict the federal minimum wage, in constant 2000 dollars, in the current year. Do these predictions seem reasonable?

9. Temperature Use your calculator or computer to find a sine function that fits the data in Activity 3. Compare and contrast the equation found in Activity 3 with the one found with technology in this activity.

10. Beetles Refer to the data in Activity 4.

a. Use technology to find a sine equation that fits the data. Compare and contrast the constants of the equation in part c of Activity 4 with those of the technology-derived equation.

b. Compare the graph of the technology-derived equation in part a with the graph in part c of Activity 4. Judging on the basis of these graphs, which model do you believe is the more appropriate one?

11. Temperature Refer to the data in Activity 5.

a. Use your calculator or computer to find a sine equation that fits the Omaha daily low-temperature data. Graph this equation and the one found in Activity 5 on a plot of the data, and examine the plot and the graphs. Discuss any differences you observe.

b. What, if any, are the advantages of using technology to find this equation?

12. Temperature Refer to the data in Activity 6.

a. Discuss any differences and similarities you would expect in the models for the normal daily high temperature on the basis of the 30-year period 1961 through 1990 for New Orleans and Boston.

b. Find sine models for each set of data. Compare the amplitude, vertical shift, horizontal shift, and period of these functions. What do these values indicate about the climates of the two cities?

c. Use the models to estimate the differences in normal maximum daily temperatures for the cities between April 15 and May 1. What do these values indicate about the climates of the two cities during the last half of April?

13. **Mass Transit**   In 1945, when gasoline was rationed because of World War II, Americans took 23.4 billion trips on mass transportation. Trips on mass transit reached a low of 6.5 billion by 1972. Now, growing congestion is sending people back to public transit. The table shows annual trips on U.S. mass transportations systems between 1992 and 2000.

Year	Mass transit trips (billions)	Year	Mass transit trips (billions)
1992	8.50	1997	8.23
1993	8.20	1998	8.60
1994	7.93	1999	9.08
1995	7.80	2000	9.40
1996	7.87		

(Source: American Public Transportation Association.)

a. Find a sine model for mass transit trips between 1992 and 2000.

b. Find a polynomial model for the data in the table.

c. Discuss how well the functions in parts a and b fit the data.

d. If you were to select one of these two models to predict mass transit use in 2006, which would you choose? Explain.

14. **Sales**   The data describe the monthly sales for an ice cream company.

Month	Monthly sales (thousand dollars)	Month	Monthly sales (thousand dollars)
Jan	50	July	167
Feb	60	Aug	159
Mar	77	Sept	108
Apr	96	Oct	75
May	137	Nov	61
June	158	Dec	54

a. Find the change in sales between January and June and between July and December.

b. Find a model for the ice cream data, and use it to estimate the changes in part a. Compare your answers with those in part a.

15. **Temperature**   A model fit to the normal mean air temperature at Fairbanks, Alaska, is

$$f(x) = 37 \sin[0.0172(x - 101)] + 25$$
$$\text{degrees Fahrenheit}$$

where x is the number of days since the last day of the previous year.

(Source: B. Lando and C. Lando, "Is the Curve of Temperature Variation a Sine Curve?" *The Mathematics Teacher*, vol. 7, no. 6, September 1977, p. 535.)

a. Estimate the highest and lowest mean daily temperatures.

b. Find the average of the highest and lowest mean daily temperatures. Relate this value to the vertical shift of the graph of f.

16. **Fever**   The table gives a patient's temperature during a 6-day illness, as recorded at noon each day.

Day	Temperature (°F)
1	103.9
2	104.4
3	102.8
4	100.2
5	98.6
6	99.2

a. Use the data to find the average rate of change of the temperature between day 2 and day 5.

b. Find a sine model for these data.

c. Judging by the graph of the model, what is your prognosis for this patient? Discuss the implications of extrapolating in this situation.

17. **Production**   The accompanying table shows the approximate numbers of large, civil-transport aircraft produced in the United States from 1949 through 1963.

Year	Aircraft	Year	Aircraft
1949	185	1957	230
1950	165	1958	235
1951	155	1959	225
1952	160	1960	210
1953	160	1961	180
1954	180	1962	160
1955	215	1963	155
1956	220		

(Source: Data estimated from J. J. Van Duijn, *The Long Wave in Economic Life,* London: Allen & Unwin, 1983.)

Date	1/5	2/2	3/1	3/29	4/26
Soup (millions of 16-oz cans)	200	215	180	160	150
Drink (millions of pints)	375	425	430	460	570
Date	5/24	6/21	7/19	8/16	9/13
Soup (millions of 16-oz cans)	120	110	100	110	130
Drink (millions of pints)	720	740	800	740	600
Date	10/11	11/8	12/6	1/3	
Soup (millions of 16-oz cans)	155	200	210	200	
Drink (millions of pints)	500	410	375	350	

(Source: *Wall Street Journal,* July 7, 1993, p. B1.)

a. Examine a scatter plot, and describe the curvature of the graph.

b. Which of the models that we have studied could be used to model these data?

c. Find a sine model for the data.

d. What does the equation give as the number of large, civil-transport aircraft produced in the United States in 1964?

e. Do you think the periodic nature of a sine model is a good description of aircraft production beyond 1963? Explain.

18. **Sales**   In order to smooth out seasonal work loads, the Campbell Soup Company produces both canned soup and powdered drink mix. Estimated sales for 1992 are shown in the table. The accompanying table values are in millions of reconstituted pints or millions of 16-ounce cans sold in a 4-week period beginning on the date indicated.

a. Find a model for the soup sales.

b. Find a model for the drink sales.

c. Compare and contrast the amplitudes, periods, and the vertical and horizontal shifts of the equations in parts *a* and *b*.

d. How do you suppose management would use the two models that you have found in their production scheduling?

19. **Temperature**   Utility needs are dynamic, and electric companies have to plan for base and peak loads carefully. Forecasting is fundamental to their management operations. A regular pattern of supply from the coal and nuclear plants is preplanned, and hydroelectric units are on standby to pick up the slack. The reason for this program is that coal and nuclear plants are slow to react, and their efficiency is lost without a regular, consistent pattern of operation. Hydroelectric facilities can come on line immediately, but their resources are limited and must be used sparingly. Pump storage may be used to restore hydroelectric resources during times of excess.

In the summer, high temperatures affect air conditioning energy requirements; in the winter, low temperatures affect heat requirements. The weather bureau's forecast for the high and low temperatures for the next 5 days will be used as the information base for a temperature model from which the planners can anticipate power load requirements. A 5-day forecast is shown on page 472.

Wednesday	Thursday	Friday
52/37	56/42	60/42

Saturday	Sunday
56/34	54/37

a. Construct a table using as input the number of hours since midnight on Wednesday, assuming that the high temperatures occur at 5 P.M. and the low temperatures occur at 5 A.M. Also assume that the midrange temperatures between the highs and lows occur at 11 A.M. and 11 P.M.

b. Find a sine model for the data. What is the period of the function?

c. What are the high and low temperatures given by the equation?

20. **Temperature** Activity 19 gives a 5-day forecast for temperatures. The actual highs and lows are given in the following table.

Weekday	High (°F)	Low (°F)
Wednesday	56	35
Thursday	59	40
Friday	71	52
Saturday	66	53
Sunday	56	33

Compare the actual high and low temperatures to the highest and lowest temperatures predicted by the equation in Activity 19. Assuming that the coal and nuclear power generators can supply enough energy for the highs and lows predicted by the model, when will the hydroelectric plant's energy be needed?

21. **Utilities** Consider electricity production.

a. Why do electric production facilities have to operate in sync with power demands?

b. Note your local temperature forecast, and build a power demand model for your area. During the next several days, keep a record of the daily highs and lows, and comment on how well your model forecasts the demand.

c. Imagine limits on your hydroelectric facilities that would make them inadequate to meet the residual demands. Explain how increasing the amplitude constant on the model could reduce the calls on the hydroelectric facilities.

22. **Daylight Hours** Find local information, and build a mathematical model for the hours of daylight in the town or city where your school is located.

23. **Darkness Hours** Use two different methods to build a sine model for the hours of darkness in Anchorage, Alaska, using the data in the table.

Day of the year	Hours of darkness	Day of the year	Hours of darkness
1	18	211	7
31	16	241	9.5
61	13	271	11.5
91	10.5	301	15.5
121	7.5	331	17.5
151	5	361	18.5
181	4.5		

24. **Daylight Hours** Locate appropriate data, and build a mathematical model for the hours of daylight at

a. The Tropic of Capricorn

b. The Equator

25. **Neurons** To study the rhythmic synchronization of neurons, a team of scientists exposed locusts to odors and measured the firing patterns of pairs of

neurons in response to those odors. The table located on the *Calculus Concepts* website gives the number of times per millisecond that the pair of neurons simultaneously fired during the experiment when exposed to cherry odor, apple odor, and a combination of the two.

The scientists claim that the period of neuron activity is not influenced by a particular odor. Find models for the data for cherry odor, apple odor, and combined odor, and report the period of each model. Do your models seem to support the scientists' claim? Explain.

26. **Fishing** An exclusive fishing club on the Restigouche River in Canada kept detailed records on the numbers of fish caught by its members between 1880 and 1930. Approximate data for the number of salmon caught per rod per day are located on the *Calculus Concepts* website. In *Cycles: The Science of Prediction*, Dewey and Dakin assert that the salmon data are periodic with a period of $9\frac{2}{3}$ years. Find a sine model for the salmon data. Does your equation agree with the assertion that the period is $9\frac{2}{3}$ years?

27. **Lizards** In desert areas of the western United States, lizards and other reptiles are harvested for sale as pets. Because reptiles hibernate during the winter months, the number of reptiles gathered is periodic. The table located on the *Calculus Concepts* website shows the number of lizards gathered during two consecutive years in a certain western state.

a. From an examination of the data, estimate the amplitude, period, and vertical shift.

b. Use technology to find a sine function that fits the 2-year data. Compare the amplitude, period, and vertical shift of the equation with those you estimated in part *a*.

c. Examine a graph of the equation on a scatter plot of the data. Discuss how well the graph fits the data.

d. Remove the months in which no lizards were harvested, and renumber the remaining months from 1 to 16. Find a sine model for the modified data. Compare the amplitude, period, and vertical shift of this equation with those of the equation in part *b*. Does the graph of this equation fit the data significantly better than the one in part *b*?

7.3   Rates of Change and Derivatives

As something moves through a cycle, we are often interested in following the change that takes place. Derivatives are one of the tools that can be used to measure how rapidly change occurs.

Derivative Formulas

As we seek a function to describe the rate of change of the sine function, we note that because the sine curve is periodic, we would expect the rate-of-change function to be periodic as well. We know that the rate of change of a sine graph is zero at the high and low points on the graph. The values in the sine curve repeat in a regular manner, so the zero slopes occur repeatedly. Thus the rate-of-change function of $y = \sin x$ has a sequence of repeating x-intercepts at $\frac{-\pi}{2}, \frac{\pi}{2}, \frac{3\pi}{2}, \frac{5\pi}{2}$, and so on.

Consider the slopes between the high and low points of $y = \sin x$. Figure 7.16 indicates where the slopes are positive and where they are negative. In addition, the blue dots in the figure mark the location of the inflection points. These are points of greatest or least slope and correspond to high or low points on the derivative graph.

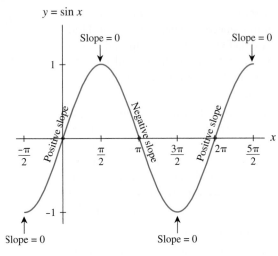

FIGURE 7.16

Sketching the slope graph results in the graph shown in Figure 7.17a.

(a)

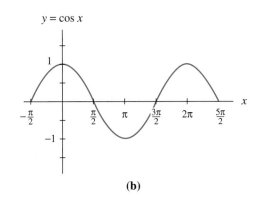

(b)

FIGURE 7.17

The rate-of-change graph of $y = \sin x$ is periodic with amplitude 1 and period 2π. A careful numerical investigation reveals that the output is 1 at $x = 0$, -1 at $x = \pi$, and 0 at $x = \dfrac{\pi}{2}$ and at $x = \dfrac{3\pi}{2}$. The graph of the cosine function is shown in Figure 7.17b. Note that it has the same characteristics as those previously stated for the rate-of-change graph of the sine function. In fact, it can be shown mathematically that the derivative of the sine function, $y = \sin x$, is the cosine function, $y' = \cos x$.

> ## Derivative of the Sine Function
>
> When x is a real number, the rate of change of the sine function is the cosine function.
>
> $$\text{If } f(x) = \sin x, \text{ then } \frac{df}{dx} = \cos x.$$

Derivative Rules

Now that we have a derivative formula for $y = \sin x$, we can apply the Constant Multiplier Rule, the Chain Rule, and the Sum Rule given in Chapter 3 to find slope formulas for functions of the form $f(x) = a \sin(bx + h) + k$.

To illustrate the use of these rules, we consider the temperatures in Philadelphia on August 27, 1993, as shown in Table 7.3.

TABLE 7.3

Time	1 A.M.	2 A.M.	3 A.M.	4 A.M.	5 A.M.	6 A.M.
Temperature (°F)	78	77	77	76	76	75
Time	7 A.M.	8 A.M.	9 A.M.	10 A.M.	11 A.M.	12 P.M.
Temperature (°F)	75	77	79	83	87	90
Time	1 P.M.	2 P.M.	3 P.M.	4 P.M.	5 P.M.	6 P.M.
Temperature (°F)	91	93	94	95	93	92
Time	7 P.M.	8 P.M.	9 P.M.	10 P.M.	11 P.M.	12 A.M.
Temperature (°F)	89	86	84	83	81	79

(Source: *Philadelphia Inquirer,* August 28, 1993.)

The data in Table 7.3 can be modeled as

$$t(x) = 9.6 \sin(0.285x - 2.93) + 84.2°F$$

x hours after midnight on August 26, 1993. Using the Constant Multiplier Rule (with 9.6 as the constant multiplier) and the Sum Rule (with the derivative of 84.2 being zero), we find that a rate-of-change formula for this function is

$$t'(x) = 9.6 \frac{d}{dx}[\sin(0.285x - 2.93)] + 0$$

Now, consider $u = 0.285x - 2.93$ to be an inside function with the sine function being the outside function. Using the Chain Rule, we have

$$t'(x) = 9.6 \frac{d}{du}(\sin u) \frac{d}{dx}(0.285x - 2.93)$$

$$= 9.6(\cos u)(0.285)$$

$$\approx 2.736 \cos(0.285x - 2.93)°F \text{ per hour}$$

x hours after midnight.

According to the model and its rate-of-change formula, the temperature at noon on August 27, 1993, was $t(12) \approx 89°F$, and it was increasing by $t'(12) \approx 2.4°F$ per hour.

EXAMPLE 1   *Writing and Interpreting a Sine Function Derivative*

Police Calls   The calls for service made to a county sheriff's department in a certain rural/suburban county can be modeled as

$$c(t) = 2.8 \sin(0.262t + 2.5) + 5.38 \text{ calls}$$

during the tth hour after midnight.

a. What is the average number of calls that the department receives each hour?

b. Find a formula for $c'(t)$.

c. How quickly is the number of calls received each hour changing at noon? at midnight?

Solution

a. The constant k of a sine model $f(x) = a \sin(bx + h) + k$ tells us the average (or expected) value of the cycle. Thus the department receives an average of 5.38 calls each hour during a day.

b. A rate-of-change model for calls received each hour can be found by using the Constant Multiplier Rule, the Chain Rule, and the Sum Rule:

$$c'(t) = 2.8 \frac{d}{dt}[\sin(0.262t + 2.5)] + 0$$

Now, let $u = 0.262t + 2.5$, and proceed using the Chain Rule.

$$c'(t) = 2.8 \frac{d}{du}(\sin u)\frac{d}{dt}(0.262t + 2.5)$$

$$= 2.8(\cos u)(0.262)$$

$$= 0.7336 \cos(0.262t + 2.5) \text{ calls per hour}$$

t hours after midnight.

c. At noon the number of calls received each hour is changing by $c'(12) \approx 0.6$ call per hour. At midnight the number of calls received each hour is changing by $c'(0) \approx -0.6$ call per hour. [*Note:* You could use $t = 24$ for midnight. If the cycle has close to a 24-hour period, then $c'(0)$ should be approximately the same as $c'(24)$.] ●

The Sum Rule is useful when we are finding the derivative of a sine function that is added to another function. This type of function occurs when a phenomenon creates cycles of the same period and amplitude but the expected value of each cycle changes according to some other function. Example 2 illustrates this type of model in the context of atmospheric carbon dioxide.

EXAMPLE 2   *Using the Product and Chain Rules with a Sine Function*

Carbon Dioxide   Figure 7.18 appeared in a *Scientific American* article in July of 1990.

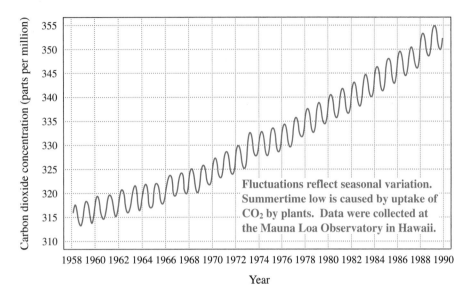

FIGURE 7.18
(Source: R. M. White, "The Great Climate Debate," *Scientific American*, vol. 263, no. 1, July 1990, pp. 36–43. Copyright © 1990 by Scientific American, Inc. All rights reserved. Reprinted with permission.)

This figure illustrates the rise in the amount of atmospheric carbon dioxide (CO_2) along with the seasonal fluctuations. We wish to find a model for the CO_2 concentration. An examination of the data from 1959 to the present (readily available on the Web) reveals that the data are cyclic with period 1 year. Using the equation $\frac{2\pi}{b} = 1$, we find that $b \approx 6.283$. The data show that the approximate location of the increasing inflection point of each cycle is the beginning of each year; thus there is no horizontal shift for each cycle. On the basis of these approximations, a model for the yearly fluctuation in the amount of atmospheric CO_2 is $f(x) = a\sin(6.283x) + d$ parts per million, where x is the time in years measured from the beginning of any year, a is the amplitude, and d is the vertical shift.

The amplitude of each cycle is slightly different, but using the data to estimate amplitudes for the years between 1959 and 1989, we observe that there is a general rise in amplitude. Modeling the amplitudes gives the equation

$a = 0.010345x + 2.105676$ parts per million

x years after the beginning of 1900.

We also note that the average amount of carbon dioxide (the constant d) is increasing each year. The average value of a cycle of a sine function that is not shifted horizontally occurs at an input of zero. By fitting a quadratic model to the CO_2 concentration in January of each year for the years between 1959 and 1989, we find that the average amount of CO_2 can be described by the equation

$$d(x) = 0.013783x^2 - 0.844566x + 316.913080 \text{ parts per million}$$

x years after the beginning of 1900. Adding this equation to the fluctuation cycle as the expected value and substituting the amplitude function for the constant a give the model for atmospheric CO_2 concentration as

$$c(x) = (0.010345x + 2.105676) \sin(6.283x) + 0.013783x^2 - 0.844566x$$
$$+ 316.913080 \text{ parts per million}$$

x years after the beginning of 1900. The model applies for years between 1959 and 1999.

a. Use the model to estimate the amount of atmospheric CO_2 in July of 1989.

b. Write a formula for the rate of change of the amount of atmospheric CO_2.

c. Use the formula from part b to estimate the rate of change of the amount of atmospheric CO_2 in July of 1989.

Solution

a. There were approximately $c(89.5) \approx 351.8$ parts per million of CO_2 in the atmosphere in July of 1989.

b. The derivative of c is

$$c'(x) = (0.010345x + 2.105676)(6.283) \cos(6.283x) + 0.010345 \sin(6.283x)$$
$$+ 2(0.013783)x - 0.844566 \text{ parts per million per year}$$

x years after the beginning of 1900.

c. $c'(89.5) \approx -17.4$ parts per million per year. The amount of atmospheric CO_2 was decreasing by approximately 17.4 parts per million per year in July of 1989. ●

Finally, let us consider finding a formula for the derivative of a rate-of-change formula for the sine model. This is the second derivative of the sine model. Because the derivative of $y = \sin x$ is $y' = \cos x$, we must know the derivative of $\cos x$ in order to find the second derivative of $y = \sin x$.

If we were to sketch the slope graph of the cosine function, the result would be the solid graph shown in Figure 7.19.

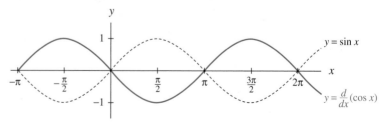

FIGURE 7.19

This solid graph appears to be a reflection of $y = \sin x$ across the horizontal axis. That is, the slope graph of $y = \cos x$ appears to be $y' = -\sin x$. In fact, using more rigorous mathematics, it can be proved that if $f(x) = \cos x$, then its derivative is $f'(x) = -\sin x$.

Derivative of the Cosine Function

When x is a real number, the rate of change of the cosine function is the negative of the sine function.

$$\text{If } g(x) = \cos x, \text{ then } \frac{dg}{dx} = -\sin x.$$

We use this fact when writing the second derivative of a sine function. For example, the model for Philadelphia temperatures x hours after midnight,

$$t(x) = 9.6 \sin(0.285x - 2.93) + 84.2°F$$

has the derivative

$$t'(x) = 2.736 \cos(0.285x - 2.93)°F \text{ per hour}$$

and its second derivative is

$$t''(x) = -0.77976 \sin(0.285x - 2.93)°F \text{ per hour per hour}$$

Note that in the first and second derivatives of t, the period and horizontal shift are the same as for t, whereas the amplitude and vertical shift are different.

EXAMPLE 3   *Writing and Interpreting a Cosine Function Derivative*

Carbon Dioxide   Recall from Example 2 that a model for the amount of atmospheric carbon dioxide is

$$c(x) = (0.010345x + 2.105676) \sin(6.283x) + 0.013783x^2 - 0.844566x$$
$$+ 316.913080 \text{ parts per million}$$

x years after the beginning of 1900. The model applies for years between 1959 and 1989.

a.   Write a formula for the second derivative of this function.

b.   Find and interpret $c''(80)$.

Solution

a.   The derivative of c was found in Example 2 to be

$$c'(x) = (0.010345x + 2.105676)(6.283) \cos(6.283x) + 0.010345 \sin(6.283x)$$
$$+ 2(0.013783)x - 0.844566 \text{ parts per million per year}$$

x years after the beginning of 1900. This derivative was found using the Product Rule, and the Product Rule is also required for the second derivative.

$$c''(x) = (0.010345x + 2.105676)(6.283)(6.283)[-\sin(6.283x)]$$
$$+ (0.010345)(6.283)\cos(6.283x)$$
$$+ 0.010345(6.283)\cos(6.283x) + 2(0.013783)$$
$$= (0.010345x + 2.105676)(6.283)(6.283)[-\sin(6.283x)]$$
$$+ 2(0.010345)(6.283)\cos(6.283x)$$
$$+ 2(0.013783) \text{ parts per million per year per year}$$

x years after the beginning of 1900.

b. $c''(80) \approx 1.87$ parts per million per year per year. At the beginning of 1980, the rate of change of the amount of atmospheric carbon dioxide was increasing by about 1.9 parts per million per year per year. ●

Even though in this section we have illustrated only some of the general derivative rules, any previously developed rule for derivatives of functions applies to the sine and cosine functions. Recall also that if you have a graph and not a function formula, then you can estimate rates of change by sketching tangent lines. This is illustrated in Example 4.

EXAMPLE 4 *Estimating Rates of Change from a Graph*

Temperature   Figure 7.20 shows the graph of a function *m* giving the normal daily mean temperature, based on the 30-year period 1961 through 1990, for Omaha, Nebraska.

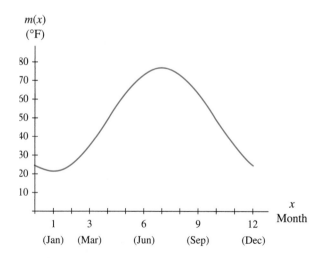

FIGURE 7.20

(Source: Based on data from U.S. National Oceanic and Atmospheric Administration, *Climatography of the United States,* No. 81.)

a.   Estimate the maximum difference in daily mean temperature. Estimate the average rate of change between the lowest daily mean temperature and the highest
daily mean temperature.

b.   Estimate where the daily mean temperature is increasing most rapidly.

c.   Estimate the rate of change of the daily mean temperature at the point where the
temperature is increasing most rapidly.

d.   Interpret each of the following:

    i. $m(9) - m(2) = 38.1$

    ii. $m'(8) = -7.3$

Solution

a.   The maximum difference in daily mean temperature is the difference between the
highest daily mean temperature and the lowest daily mean temperature.
According to Figure 7.20, the highest temperature is approximately 77°F (in July),
and the lowest temperature is approximately 21°F (in January). The maximum
difference is approximately 56°F. The average rate of change of daily mean
temperature between January and July is $\frac{77 - 21}{7 - 1} \approx 9.3°F$ per month.

b.   The daily mean temperature is increasing most rapidly at the inflection point of
this graph. This (according to Figure 7.20) occurs near $x = 4$, which corresponds
to April.

c.   We estimate the rate of change of daily mean temperature in April by carefully
drawing the tangent line to the graph at $x = 4$ and approximating its slope. (See
Figure 7.21.)

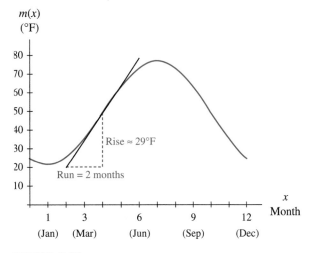

FIGURE 7.21

The daily mean temperature during April was increasing by approximately
$\frac{29°F}{2 \text{ months}} = 14.5°F$ per month.

   d.   i. The change in the daily mean temperature between February and September was 38.1°F.

        ii. In August, the daily mean temperature was decreasing by 7.3°F per month. ●

We now have the tools we need not only to find rates of change of a sine model but also to use rates of change to locate maxima, minima, and inflection points on sine models. This is the topic of the next section.

7.3   Concept Inventory

- Derivatives: If $y = \sin x$, then $y' = \cos x$.
  If $y = \cos x$, then $y' = -\sin x$.
- Second derivatives: If $y = \sin x$, then $y'' = -\sin x$.
  If $y = \cos x$, then $y'' = -\cos x$.

7.3   Activities

Getting Started

In Activities 1 through 6, find formulas for the indicated rates of change.

1. $f(x) = \sin 3x + 10.456, f'(x)$

2. $g(x) = \cos 0.45x - 3.763, \dfrac{dg}{dx}$

3. $t(r) = 5.2 \cos(0.45r + \pi) + 80r - 6.34, \dfrac{dt}{dr}$

4. $f(t) = 3 \sin(-0.45t + 3\pi) - 12.8t^3 + 4.6t, f''(t)$

5. $h(x) = 2.08 \sin(-0.16x + 12.3)$
    $\qquad + 3.58 \cos[1.35(2x + 6)] - 4.79,$
    $\qquad h'(x)$ and $h''(x)$

6. $y(x) = -0.023 \sin(2x + 7) + 4 \cos[3(0.5 - x)],$
    $\qquad y'(x)$ and $y''(x)$

Applying Concepts

7. **Satellite**   The graph shows a model of the distance in kilometers that a weather satellite is north or

south of the equator at time x minutes since the satellite was launched.

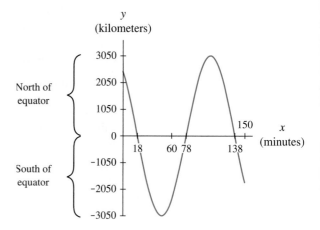

a. How long does it take the satellite to complete one orbit of Earth?

b. What is the greatest distance south of the equator that the satellite ever reaches?

c. Carefully draw the tangent line at the time the satellite has been in orbit for 1 hour.

d. Use the tangent line to estimate the rate of change of the satellite's distance from the equator after it has been in orbit for 1 hour.

e. Is the answer to part d the speed of the satellite after it has been in orbit for 1 hour? Explain.

8. **Turbine Power**   The accompanying figure shows the power output of a diesel engine in an irrigation pumping system that is supplemented by a wind turbine when the wind speeds are sufficient.

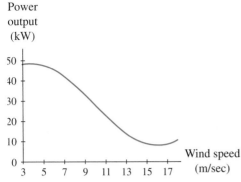

(Source: Based on data from B. A. Stout, *Handbook of Energy for World Agriculture*, London: Elsevier Applied Science, 1990.)

a. Estimate the change in power output when the wind speed changes from 5 m/sec to 10 m/sec and from 10 m/sec to 15 m/sec.

b. Report the estimates in part *a* as percentage changes and average rates of change.

c. Estimate the instantaneous rate of change in power output for wind speeds of 5, 10, and 15 m/sec. Convert your answers to percentage rates of change. Interpret your answers.

d. Why are the rates of change negative? What would you expect the rates of change to be for the power output of the wind turbine as a function of wind speed?

e. The graph was generated from a sine function, which is an excellent fit for the power output data. Comment on the appropriateness and limitations of using a sine model in this context.

9. Mass Transit   Consider the accompanying graph showing the number of trips on U.S. mass transportation systems each year between 1992 and 2000.

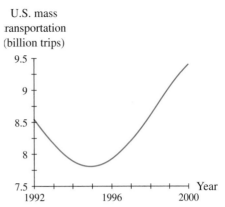

(Source: Based on data from the American Public Transportation Association.)

a. Use tangent lines to estimate the rates of change of the number of trips in 1992, 1996, and 2000.

b. Use a tangent line approximation to estimate the number of trips in 2001.

10. Temperature   The accompanying figure shows a temperature graph for a location in the south Gobi Desert over a period of 2 years.

a. Estimate average rates of change in temperature from

   i. July through July

   ii. February through February

   iii. July through December of the first year

b. Estimate during which month the temperature

   i. increased most rapidly

   ii. decreased most rapidly

   iii. increased most slowly

   iv. decreased most slowly

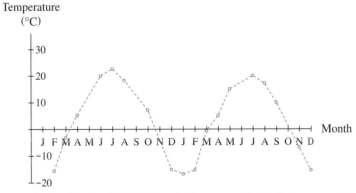

(Source: Based on data from Neil E. West, ed., *Ecosystems of the World: Temperate Deserts and Semi-Deserts*, Amsterdam: Elsevier Scientific Publishing Company, 1983.)

Figure for Activity 10

11. Radiation   A graph of the average amount of extraterrestrial radiation in Amarillo, Texas, for each month of the year is shown. The amount is measured in equivalent millimeters of water evaporation per day. Month 1 corresponds to January, month 12 to December.

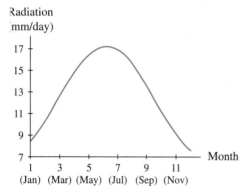

(Source: Based on data from A. A. Hanson, ed., *Practical Handbook of Agricultural Science*, Boca Raton, FL: CRC Press, 1990.)

a. Use the graph to estimate the change in the amount of radiation from June through November.

b. Report the change in part *a* as a percentage change and an average rate of change.

c. Use the graph to estimate the rate of change in March.

d. Convert the rate of change in part *c* to a percentage rate of change.

12. Profit Rate   The after-tax profit rate on investment is defined as the ratio of after-tax corporate profits to corporate stock of plant and equipment. The after-tax profit rate on investment in the United States between 1988 and 2002 can be approximated by $T(x) = 1.204 \sin(0.469x - 2.293) + 6.352$ percent, where x is the number of years after 1988.

(Source: Based on data from Bureau of Economic Analysis, *Business Week*, November 4, 2002, p. 107.)

a. Find a function that gives the rate of change of the profit rate.

b. Estimate the rate of change of the profit rate in 2000 and 2002.

c. Estimate the profit rate in 2003, assuming that the rate of change of the profit rate remained constant in 2002.

13. Sales   In order to smooth out seasonal work loads, the Campbell Soup Company produces both canned soup and powdered drink mix. The 1992 daily sales can be modeled by

$$c(x) = 1.8961 \sin(0.0186x + 1.1801) + 5.4660$$
$$\text{million cans (16 ounce) of soup}$$

$$p(x) = 7.3026 \cos(0.0197x - 3.7526) + 20.3728$$
$$\text{million pints (reconstituted) of drink mix}$$

where x is the day of the year. Assume that soup is sold at an average price of \$0.70 per can and drink mix is sold at \$0.20 per pint.

(Source: Based on information in *Wall Street Journal*, July 7, 1993, p. B1.)

a. Find a function giving the revenue from the combined 1992 daily sales as a function of the day of the year on which soup and powdered drink mix are produced.

b. Give a function that models the rate of change of revenue from combined 1992 sales.

c. How quickly was revenue changing on February 15, 1992?

d. At what other times during 1992 was revenue decreasing at the same rate as that found in part *c*?

e. Give one time during 1992 at which revenue was increasing at the same rate at which it was decreasing in part *c*.

14. Temperature   A model for the normal mean air temperature in Fairbanks, Alaska, is

$$f(x) = 37 \sin[0.0172(x - 101)] + 25°F$$

where x is the number of days since the last day of last year. Estimate how rapidly the normal mean temperature in Fairbanks is changing on March 15 and on December 31.

(Source: B. Lando and C. Lando, "Is the Curve of Temperature Variation a Sine Curve?" *The Mathematics Teacher*, vol. 7, no. 6, September 1977, p. 535.)

15. Temperature   The normal daily high temperature in Boston can be modeled by

$$B(m) = 22.926 \sin(0.510m - 2.151) + 58.502°F$$

at the end of the mth month of the year. Estimate how rapidly the normal daily high temperature in

Boston is changing at the end of November and in the middle of May.

(Source: Based on data from U.S. National Oceanic and Atmospheric Administration, *Climatography of the United States,* no. 81.)

16. **Sales**   Ice cream cones are sold at a county fair. The total number of cones sold since the booth opened at 8 A.M. is approximated by

$$c(t) = 80.153 \sin(0.511t - 1.680) + 87.564 \text{ cones}$$

where t is the number of hours since 8 A.M. Estimate how rapidly the number of cones sold is changing at 12 P.M. and 8 P.M.

17. **Turbine Power**   The power output of a diesel engine in an irrigation pumping system that is supplemented by a wind turbine can be modeled by

$$P(s) = 20.204 \sin(0.258s + 0.570) + 28.119 \text{ kilowatts}$$

when the wind speed is s meters per second.

(Source: Based on data from U.S. National Oceanic and Atmospheric Administration, *Climatography of the United States,* no. 81.)

a. Find the change in power output when the wind speed changes from 6 m/sec to 10 m/sec, from 10 m/sec to 14 m/sec, and from 14 m/sec to 18 m/sec.

b. Report the answers to part *a* as percentage changes and average rates of change.

c. Find a formula for $P'(s)$.

d. Find $P'(s)$ for $s = 6$, $s = 10$, $s = 14$, and $s = 18$. Interpret your answers.

e. Convert the answers to part *d* to percentage rates of change.

18. **Radiation**   The average amount of extraterrestrial radiation in Amarillo, Texas, can be modeled by

$$R(t) = 5.059 \sin(0.461t - 1.287) + 12.151$$
equivalent mm of water evaporation per day

where $t = 1$ in January and $t = 12$ in December.

(Source: Based on data in A. A. Hanson, ed., *Practical Handbook of Agricultural Science*, Boca Raton, FL: CRC Press, 1990.)

a. By how much does the amount of extraterrestrial radiation change between April and October? What is the percentage change?

b. How quickly (on average) is the amount of extraterrestrial radiation changing from April through October? Is this value an accurate representation of how extraterrestrial radiation changed during these months? Explain.

c. Find $R'(t)$ for $t = 4$ and $t = 10$. Also express your answers as percentage rates of change. Interpret your answers.

19. **Mortality**   The table shows the weekly pneumonia death rate (number of deaths per 100,000 people per week) in the United States from 1923 through 1925.

Weeks since Jan. 1, 1923	Pneumonia death rate	Weeks since Jan. 1, 1923	Pneumonia death rate
0	100	80	60
10	210	90	45
20	95	100	95
30	35	110	160
40	55	120	140
50	85	130	80
60	140	140	40
70	160	150	90

(Source: Estimated from E. R. Dewey and E. F. Dakin, *Cycles: The Science of Prediction,* New York: Holt, 1947.)

a. Find a sine model for the pneumonia death rate data. Why would such data be periodic?

b. Use the sine model to estimate the rate of change of the pneumonia death rate in the middle of 1924 and at the end of 1924.

20. **Tides**   The February 1995 tide chart for the Savannah River entrance notes the times of high and low tides. A portion of the tide chart is shown in the table on page 486. Assume that the tidal variation is 4 feet; that is, it varies from -2 to $+2$ feet around mean sea level.

(Source: *Sea Island Scene of Beaufort,* Beaufort, SC: Sands Publishing Co., 1995.)

a. On the basis of the data with mean sea level at 0 feet, what would you expect the period, amplitude, and average water height to be if the data are modeled by a sine function?

b. Use the data for March 2 through March 4 to find a sine model for the height of the water as a function of time.

c. How fast is the water falling at noon on March 2?

	Feb 26	Feb 27	Feb 28	Mar 1	Mar 2	Mar 3	Mar 4
Savannah River Entrance Tidal Chart	HI 0522	LO 0003	LO 0056	LO 0145	LO 0231	LO 0313	LO 0353
	LO 1146	HI 0619	HI 0708	HI 0753	HI 0835	HI 0915	HI 0955
	HI 1739	LO 1238	LO 1326	LO 1411	LO 1453	LO 1532	LO 1609
		HI 1833	HI 1922	HI 2006	HI 2047	HI 2128	HI 2209
	Mar 5	**Mar 6**	**Mar 7**	**Mar 8**	**Mar 9**	**Mar 10**	**Mar 11**
	LO 0431	LO 0509	LO 0549	HI 0024	HI 0115	HI 0208	HI 0304
	HI 1036	HI 1120	HI 1206	LO 0634	LO 0728	LO 0831	LO 0934
	LO 1646	LO 1724	LO 1805	HI 1255	HI 1347	HI 1442	HI 1539
	HI 2251	HI 2336		LO 1853	LO 1950	LO 2053	LO 2154

Table for Activity 20

d. How fast is the water falling at noon on March 4?

e. If a boat needs at least 1 foot of water above mean sea level in order to float away from being grounded at low tide, at what times is it possible for this boat to float away on March 3?

21. **Sun Declination**   The declination of the sun is the angle of the sun as measured from the equator. The table shows the angle of declination of the sun in Greenwich, England, for selected days throughout the year. These values vary slightly from year to year.

Day of the year	Declination of sun	Day of the year	Declination of sun
1	23.02° S	182	23.05° N
32	17.15° S	213	17.82° N
60	7.17° S	244	8.00° N
91	4.83° N	273	3.48° S
121	15.30° N	304	14.67° S
152	22.09° N	334	21.92° S

(Source: *Old Farmer's Almanac*, 1996.)

a. Considering southern declinations to be negative and northern declinations positive, find a sine model for the data. State and interpret the amplitude and period of the function.

b. Use the equation to find the rate of change of the declination of the sun at the two equinoxes (when the sun is directly on the equator).

c. What is the relationship between the rate of change of the declination of the sun and the summer and winter solstices?

The functions in Activities 22 through 27 are composite functions. For each function, determine the inside and outside function, and give the formula for the derivative.

22. $y = 2.43 \sin x - 12$

23. $y = \sin(2.4^x)$

24. $y = \sqrt{\sin(2x + 3)}$

25. $y = 4(\sin x - 7)^2 + 8(\sin x - 7) + 13$

26. $y = \sin(3x^2 + 19x)$

27. $y = \ln(\sin x)$

28. **Sales**   The sales for a retail women's clothing store for 5 years are given in the table located on the *Calculus Concepts* website.

a. Why should the December data be omitted?

b. Find a model for the 5-year data set (omitting the December data).

c. Use the model to estimate the rate of change of sales in April of both years.

29. **Sales**   The table located on the *Calculus Concepts* website shows the monthly sales for an ice cream company for a 4-year time period.

a. Find a sine model for the data. Comment on how well it fits the data.

b. Use the data in the table to find the average of the high and low sales each year.

c. Find a model for the average sales found in part *b*. Use as input the first month of each year in which sales would be expected to reach the average value.

d. Replace the constant d in the function in part a with the function for average value found in part c. Comment on how well this new function fits the data compared with the function in part a.

e. Use the model in part d to estimate the rate of change of sales in September of the third year and January of the fourth year. Interpret your answers.

Discussing Concepts

30. What happens to the slope of a graph of the sine function $f(x) = a \sin(bx + c) + d$ when f is at a maximum? at a minimum? equal to its expected (average) value?

7.4 Extrema and Points of Inflection

When describing a cycle, we must note the height of its peaks and the depth of its valleys. The height and depth between which a cycle oscillates determine its amplitude. How often the maximum values and minimum values repeat depends on how often the cycle repeats. We might also want to find the points at which the concavity of a cycle changes, because inflection points often have interesting interpretations in context.

Determining Extreme Points

Recall from Section 4.2 that if a function has a relative maximum or a relative minimum at an input c, then either $f'(c) = 0$ or $f'(c)$ does not exist but $f(c)$ does exist. We also know that if the derivative is zero and the slope graph crosses (not just touches) the horizontal axis at a certain input, then a relative maximum or a relative minimum exists at that input. When we are using sine or cosine functions of the forms discussed in this chapter, the derivative exists at all input values, so in our search for extreme points, we need consider only the inputs where the derivative of the function crosses the input axis.

EXAMPLE 1 *Locating Extreme Points Using Calculus*

Sales Weekly sales of heating oil are cyclic with a winter peak and a summer lull. A model for the weekly heating oil sales for a certain company is

$$f(t) = 2000 \sin(0.1208t + 1.5707) + 3000 \text{ gallons}$$

t weeks after the beginning of the year.

a. Find the period of the heating oil sales model.

b. Sketch a graph of one cycle of f, and mark the locations of maximum and minimum heating oil sales.

c. Use derivatives to find the maximum and minimum of a cycle.

Solution

a. The period of the heating oil sales model is $\frac{2\pi}{0.1208} \approx 52$ weeks.

b. A graph of the weekly heating oil sales for a 1-year period is shown in Figure 7.22.

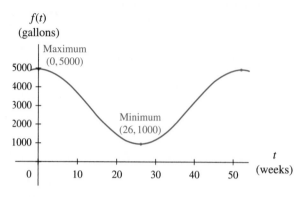

FIGURE 7.22

c. The derivative of f is

$$f'(t) = 241.6 \cos(0.1208t + 1.5707) \text{ gallons per week}$$

t weeks after the beginning of the year. By setting the derivative equal to zero and solving for t, we find that $f'(t) = 0$ when $t \approx 0$ and again when $t \approx 26$. The graph in Figure 7.22 shows that the second solution gives the minimum. Heating oil sales reach a maximum of $f(0) \approx 5000$ gallons at the beginning of January and reach a minimum of $f(26) \approx 1000$ gallons at the beginning of July. Sales again reach the maximum at 52 weeks. ●

Being able to solve for the values at which the first derivative of a sine or cosine function is zero helps us locate maxima and minima. We use a similar technique when we are looking for inflection points.

Inflection Points

Recall from Section 4.3 that at a point of inflection on the graph of a function, the second derivative is zero or does not exist. If the second derivative graph crosses the horizontal axis, then an inflection point occurs on the graph of the function at that input value. Let us again consider the model for heating oil sales.

EXAMPLE 2   *Locating Inflection Points Using Calculus*

Sales   A model for weekly heating oil sales is

$$f(t) = 2000 \sin(0.1208t + 1.5707) + 3000 \text{ gallons}$$

t weeks after the beginning of the year. A graph of f is shown in Figure 7.22 in Example 1.

a. Use the graph in Figure 7.22 to estimate the locations of the inflection points.

b. Use derivatives to find the inflection points.

c. What would be the best course of action for the sales manager during the time before and after each of the inflection points?

Solution

a. The graph of weekly heating oil sales appears to be concave down from week 0 through week 13, concave up from week 13 through week 39, and concave down from week 39 through week 52. Thus we estimate that inflection points occur at the beginning of April (week 13) and at the beginning of October (week 39).

b. In order for inflection points to occur on a sine or cosine graph of the forms used in this chapter, the second derivative of the function must be zero. The second derivative of the heating oil function is

$$f''(t) = -29.18528 \sin(0.1208t + 1.5707) \text{ gallons per week per week}$$

t weeks after the beginning of the year. By setting $f''(t) = 0$ and solving for t, we find that inflection points occur at $t \approx 13.0$ and $t \approx 39.0$. In both cases, 3000 gallons of heating oil are sold, so the inflection points are $(13, 3000)$ and $(39, 3000)$. The point of most rapid decrease occurs at the 13th week, and the point of most rapid increase occurs at the 39th week. (See Figure 7.22.)

c. Between January 1 and April 1, the oil manager should be concentrating on maintaining supply, making timely deliveries, and advertising the product. From April 1 until October 1, heating fuel demand is in the summer doldrums, and the company should be running promotion specials to move the product. Between October 1 and December 31, the manager should focus on ensuring that there is enough heating oil available to meet the demand. ●

Of course, in the real world there are rarely such idealized models as that in the previous example, but managers routinely talk about changes in the rate of increase or rate of decrease. Through those observations, they try to determine when fundamental shifts in demand occur. In mathematical terms, they are looking for the inflection points.

The connection between relative maxima and minima and inflection points of a function and the zero values of the first and second derivatives is what makes the use of calculus concepts so powerful in the analysis of cycles.

7.4 Concept Inventory

- Maxima and minima of sine and cosine models
- Inflection points of sine and cosine models

7.4 Activities

Applying Concepts

1. **Mass Transit** The number of trips on U.S. mass transportation systems each year between 1992 and 2000 can be modeled by

$$M(x) = 0.932 \sin(0.467x - 2.94) + 8.737 \text{ billion trips}$$

x years after 1992.

(Source: Based on data from the American Public Transportation Association.)

a. Temporarily ignoring the context, find the maximum and minimum values of the function M and the inputs at which those values occur for one period of the function beginning at $x = 0$.

b. Find the maximum and minimum values of the function M and the years between 1992 and 2000 when they occur. Interpret your answers.

2. **Fishing** An exclusive fishing club on the Restigouche River in Canada kept detailed records of the number of fish caught by its members. A model for the number of salmon caught per rod per day between 1880 and 1905 is

$$s(y) = 0.327 \sin(0.675y - 2.122) + 1.267$$
$$\text{salmon per rod per day}$$

y years after 1880.

(Source: Based on data estimated from E. R. Dewey and E. F. Dakin, *Cycles: The Science of Prediction*, New York: Holt, 1947.)

a. Find the nearest year after 1905 in which, according to the model, the number of salmon is expected to peak.

b. Find the nearest year after 1905 in which, according to the model, the number of salmon is expected to be at a minimum.

c. How might the manager of the fishing club have used the information in parts *a* and *b* to benefit the club?

3. Temperature   The table gives the normal daily mean temperatures, based on the 30-year period 1961 through 1990, for Omaha, Nebraska.

(Source: U.S. National Oceanic and Atmospheric Administration, *Climatography of the United States,* No. 81.)

Month	Daily mean temperature (°F)	Month	Daily mean temperature (°F)
Jan	21.1	July	76.9
Feb	26.9	Aug	74.1
Mar	38.6	Sept	65.1
Apr	51.9	Oct	53.4
May	62.4	Nov	39.0
June	72.1	Dec	25.0

a. Use only these data to estimate the maximum and minimum daily mean temperatures for Omaha.

b. Find a sine model for the data, and determine the highest and lowest points on the graph. Interpret these points in the context of Omaha's weather.

c. How do the answers obtained with the equation compare with those found using the data? What relationship is there between the maximum and minimum daily mean temperatures for Omaha found in parts *a* and *b* and the actual yearly high and low temperatures in a given year?

4. Radiation   The average amount of extraterrestrial radiation in Amarillo, Texas, for each month of the year is given in the table. The amount is measured in equivalent millimeters of water evaporation per day.

Month	Radiation (mm of H_2O per day)	Month	Radiation (mm of H_2O per day)
Jan	8.3	July	16.8
Feb	10.2	Aug	15.6
Mar	12.8	Sep	13.6
Apr	15.0	Oct	11.2
May	16.5	Nov	9.0
June	17.0	Dec	7.8

(Source: A. A. Hanson, ed., *Practical Handbook of Agricultural Science,* Boca Raton, FL: CRC Press, 1990.)

a. Use only these data to estimate the maximum and minimum radiation levels and when those levels occur.

b. Find a sine model for the data, and determine the highest and lowest points on the graph. Interpret these points in the context of radiation.

c. How might knowledge of high and low radiation levels be useful to someone living in Amarillo?

5. Price Index   The accompanying figure shows graphs of *w*, the indexed price of wheat in the United Kingdom, and a sine function, *i*, for the index.

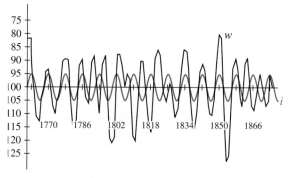

Eight-year cycle in Poynting's index numbers of the price of wheat (scale inverted)

(Source: From H. L. Moore, *Generating Economic Cycles,* New York: Macmillan, 1923; repr. 1967, Augustus M. Kelley Publishers, p. 75. Reprinted by permission.)

a. How many of the maxima of the sine graph coincide with a relative maximum in the wheat price index? Note that the vertical axis is inverted.

b. How many of the minima of the sine graph coincide with a relative minimum in the wheat price index?

c. An equation for the sine graph is $y = 100.2 + 0.4\sin\left(\frac{\pi}{4}t + \frac{62}{45}\right)$, where t is the number of years since 1761. Use this equation to find the years in which the next maximum and minimum occur after 1874.

d. On the basis of the graph and your answers to parts *a* and *b*, how accurately do you think the years you found in part *c* predict when the next maximum and minimum wheat price indices occurred? Do you think the sine model should be used to predict the next maximum and minimum price index?

6. Price Index A model for the Sauerbeck index of general wholesale prices in England between 1818 and 1914 is

$$p(x) = 3.1\sin\left(\frac{\pi}{3.69}x + \frac{23}{45}\right) + 100$$

x years after 1818. Use the model to estimate the years in which the next high and low wholesale prices occurred after 1914.

(Source: From H. L. Moore, *Generating Economic Cycles*, New York: Macmillan, 1923; repr. 1967, Augustus M. Kelley Publishers, p. 75.)

7. Daylight Hours The *Anchorage Daily News* in Anchorage, Alaska, includes in its weather section a chart of the hours of daylight. A copy of the newspaper chart is shown.

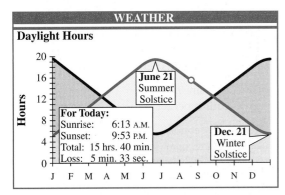

(Source: Used with the permission of the *Anchorage Daily News*.)

a. There are two graphs shown in the chart. Which graph represents daylight hours, and what does the other graph represent?

b. On the basis of the graph of daylight hours, estimate the period, amplitude, and vertical shift.

c. Reading carefully from the chart, estimate the hours of daylight at the beginning of each month, and create a scatter plot of these data. Explain why it makes sense to use a sine model for this data set.

d. Find a sine function to fit the data. Compare the period, amplitude, and vertical shift of the function to your estimates in part *b*.

8. Daylight Hours Refer to the chart of the hours of daylight in Anchorage, Alaska, given in Activity 7. (A function was found in part *d*.)

a. The amount of daylight contributes to one's moods. In particular, less daylight has been known to cause "winter blues." Also important to mood is a person's perception of future change. For example, when the number of hours of daylight is increasing rapidly, some people may develop an optimistic outlook, whereas a pessimistic outlook may result when the number of hours of daylight is declining rapidly. Use the sine model to find when the number of hours of daylight is increasing most rapidly and when it is decreasing most rapidly in Anchorage.

b. If you were directing a public campaign, you would not want to introduce the campaign when the public was in a pessimistic winter mood. Use your answers to part *a* to estimate when politicians in Alaska should begin a new campaign.

9. Daylight Hours Consider the number of daylight hours in your hometown.

a. Find a function (or find data and create a function) for the number of daylight hours in your hometown.

b. Repeat Activity 8 for your hometown.

10. Carbon Dioxide A sine model for the amount of carbon dioxide in the atmosphere was given in Section 7.3. We could also have used the following cosine model:

$$c(x) = (0.010345x + 2.105676)\cos\left(6.283x - \frac{\pi}{2}\right)$$
$$+ 0.013783x^2 - 0.844566x + 316.913080$$
parts per million

x years after the beginning of 1900. The model applies for years between 1959 and 1999.

(Source: Based on data from R. M. White, "The Great Climate Debate," *Scientific American*, vol. 263, no. 1, 1990, pp. 36–43.)

a. Graph the sine function given in Example 3 in Section 7.3 and the cosine function here. Are there any differences between these two graphs? Why can either a sine function or a cosine function be used?

b. Write a formula for the derivative of the cosine function.

c. Use c and its derivative to find the maximum and minimum carbon dioxide levels in 1960, 1970, 1980, and 1990. In what months do these maximum and minimum levels occur?

d. Why are the maxima different for each year?

11. **Radiation**   A model of the data for the amount of ultraviolet radiation in Auckland, New Zealand, is

$$a(m) = 27.1 \sin(0.485m - 1.707) + 32.9$$
watts per cm^2

when $m = 1$ in January, $m = 2$ in February, and so on.

(Source: Based on data from W. Rudloff, *World-Climates*, Stuttgart, Germany: Wissenschaftliche Verlagsgesellschaft, 1981.)

a. Write a function for the rate of change of the amount of ultraviolet radiation.

b. Estimate the time when ultraviolet radiation is at its highest level and the time when it is at its lowest level.

c. How much ultraviolet radiation is received at the times found in part b?

12. **Beetles**   Based on data for 1965 through 1976, the reduction in the number of beetles in a certain geographical area in the Netherlands can be modeled by the equation

$$R(x) = 100.9 \sin\left(\frac{\pi}{3}x - \frac{6.5\pi}{3}\right) + 3.6 \text{ beetles}$$

x years after 1960.

(Source: Based on data from P. J. denBoer and R. Reddingius, *Regulation and Stabilization Paradigms in Population Ecology*, London: Chapman & Hall, 1996.)

a. What is the period of this function?

b. Use calculus to find the extrema of this function over one period. Interpret your answers.

13. **Profit Rate**   The after-tax profit rate on investment is defined as the ratio of after-tax corporate profits to corporate stock of plant and equipment.

The after-tax profit rate on investment in the United States between 1988 and 2002 can be approximated by $T(x) = 1.204 \sin(0.469x - 2.293) + 6.352$ percent, where x is the number of years after 1988.

(Source: Based on data from the Bureau of Economic Analysis, *BusinessWeek*, November 4, 2002, p. 107.)

a. Write a function for the rate of change of the after-tax profit rate on investment.

b. Use calculus to find the inflection points and absolute extrema over one period of the function T. Interpret your answers.

c. Graph the function T for x between 0 and 14. Use the graph and the results of part b to explain the meaning of the phrase *profit boom of the 1990s*.

14. **Gender Ratio**   The number of males per 100 females in the United States between 1900 and 2000 can be modeled by

$$m(t) = 5.334 \sin(0.0426t + 1.265) + 99.94$$
males per 100 females

t years after 1900.

(Source: Based on data from the U.S. Bureau of the Census.)

a. Find the maximum and minimum values of the function and the years between 1900 and 2000 in which they occur. Interpret your answers.

b. Determine when the graph is decreasing most rapidly and how rapidly it is decreasing at that time. Interpret your answers.

15. **Star Pulses**   On December 15, 1995, a team of astronomers discovered X-ray pulses emitting from what they believe to be a neutron star. The speed of the pulses (in counts per second) can be modeled by

$$p(s) = 40.5 \sin(0.01345s - 1.5708) + 186.5$$
counts per second

after s milliseconds.

(Source: Based on information in M. H. Finger et al., "Discovery of Hard X-ray Pulsations from the Transient Source GRO J1744–28," *Nature*, vol. 381, May 23, 1996, pp. 291–292.)

a. What is the period of the pulsations?

b. Determine two times when the pulse speed was highest and two times when it was lowest. What were the pulse speeds at those times?

c. Find and interpret one inflection point where the function is increasing and one inflection point where the function is decreasing.

16. Turbine Power The combined power output of a diesel engine and wind turbine in an irrigation pumping system can be modeled by

$$P(s) = 20.204 \sin(0.258s + 0.570) +$$
$$19.026 \sin(0.247s - 2.549) + 44.952 \text{ kilowatts}$$

when the wind speed is s meters per second. The model should be used for wind speeds between 6 and 18 meters per second, because the wind turbine produces power only if wind speeds exceed 6 meters per second.

(Source: Based on information in B. A. Stout, *Handbook of Energy for World Agriculture*, London: Elsevier Applied Science, 1990.)

a. Find the wind speeds associated with the greatest and the least power output for this pumping system.

b. On the basis of your answer to part *a*, what do you believe is the benefit of having a wind turbine in this pumping system?

c. Find all inflection points of P between $s = 6$ and $s = 18$. Interpret your answers.

17. Mortality The table shows the weekly pneumonia death rate (number of deaths per 100,000 people per week) in the United States from 1923 through 1925.

Weeks since Jan 1, 1923	Pneumonia death rate	Weeks since Jan 1, 1923	Pneumonia death rate
0	100	80	60
10	210	90	45
20	95	100	95
30	35	110	160
40	55	120	140
50	85	130	80
60	140	140	40
70	160	150	90

(Source: Estimated from E. R. Dewey and E. F. Dakin, *Cycles: The Science of Prediction*, New York: Holt, 1947.)

a. Find a sine function to fit the pneumonia death rate data.

b. Use the sine equation to predict the next peak in the pneumonia death rate beyond the data given. How might this information have been useful to health care providers in 1926? What factors

might cause the actual peak to differ from the one found by the equation?

c. Find and interpret the first inflection point located beyond the data given.

18. Carbon Dioxide Refer to the cosine model given in Activity 10 for the amount of carbon dioxide in the atmosphere to answer the following questions.

a. Write a formula for c''.

b. Determine in what months of 1960, 1970, 1980, and 1990 the carbon dioxide level was increasing most rapidly.

c. According to the function c, what was the carbon dioxide level at the time of most rapid increase in 1960, 1970, 1980, and 1990? Explain why these values are increasing from 1960 through 1990.

19. Radiation Refer to the model given in Activity 11 for the amount of ultraviolet radiation in Auckland, New Zealand, to answer the following questions.

a. Write a function for the second derivative of the ultraviolet radiation model.

b. Estimate the time when ultraviolet radiation is increasing most rapidly and the time when it is decreasing most rapidly.

c. How much ultraviolet radiation is received at the times found in part *b*?

20. Sun Declination The declination of the Sun in Greenwich, England, can be described by the equation

$$D(d) = 23.677 \sin(0.0168x - 1.312) - 0.292 \text{ degrees}$$

on the xth day of the year. Negative output values correspond to southern declinations, and positive output values correspond to northern declinations.

(Source: Based on data from the *Old Farmer's Almanac*, 1996.)

a. Use calculus to find the inflection points and extrema over one period of the function. Interpret your answers.

b. Relate your answers in part *a* to Earth's equinoxes and solstices.

21. Sales The Campbell Soup Company produces both canned soup and powdered drink mix. The 1992 daily sales can be modeled by

$$c(x) = 1.8961 \sin(0.0186x + 1.1801) + 5.4660$$
$$\text{million cans (16 ounce) of soup}$$

$p(x) = 7.3026 \cos(0.0197x - 3.7526) + 20.3728$
million pints (reconstituted) of drink mix

where x is the day of the year. Assume that soup sold at an average price of 70 cents per can and that drink mix sold at an average price of 20 cents per pint.

(Source: Based on data from the *Wall Street Journal*, July 7, 1993, p. B1.)

a. Write a function giving the revenue from the combined 1992 daily sales as a function of the day of the year on which soup and powdered drink mix are produced.

b. Write a function that models the rate of change of the revenue from the combined 1992 sales.

c. Use the model and derivative to estimate the highest revenue and the day(s) on which this maximum occurred.

d. Use the model and derivative to estimate the lowest revenue and the day(s) on which this minimum occurred.

Discussing Concepts

22. Explain how you could determine without using derivatives the maximum, minimum, and inflection points (both output and input) on a graph of $f(x) = a \sin(bx + h) + k$.

7.5 Accumulation in Cycles

The first four sections of this chapter discussed sine and cosine functions and rates of change of sine and cosine functions. We now consider the accumulated change in sine and cosine functions and also investigate applications of integration using these functions.

We begin by stating general antiderivative formulas for the sine and cosine functions. Because $\frac{d}{dx}(-\cos x) = -1 \cdot \frac{d}{dx}(\cos x) = -1(-\sin x) = \sin x$, the Fundamental Theorem of Calculus tells us that a general antiderivative of the sine function is the negative of the cosine function. Also, because $\frac{d}{dx}(\sin x) = \cos x$, a general antiderivative of the cosine function is the sine function.

Antiderivatives of Sine and Cosine Functions

When x is a real number,

$$\int \sin x dx = -\cos x + C$$

$$\int \cos x dx = \sin x + C$$

To find the general antiderivative of the sine function $f(x) = a \sin(bx + h) + k$, we need only apply the antiderivative rules we used in Chapter 5. We begin by applying the Constant Multiplier Rule and the Constant Rule for antiderivatives:

$$\int [a \sin(bx + h) + k]dx = a\int \sin(bx + h)dx + \int k dx$$

$$= a\int \sin(bx + h)dx + kx + C_1$$

Now we need to find the general antiderivative of $y = \sin(bx + h)$. Recall that the antiderivative process reverses the derivative process. In using the Chain Rule to find the derivative of $y = \sin(bx + h)$, we would multiply by b, the derivative of the inside function, to obtain $y' = b\cos(bx + h)$. For the antiderivative, we *divide* by b:

$$\int [a\sin(bx + h) + k]dx = a\left[\frac{-\cos(bx + h)}{b}\right] + C_2 + kx + C_1$$

$$= \frac{-a}{b}\cos(bx + h) + kx + C$$

Similarly, we have

$$\int [a\cos(bx + h) + k]dx = a\left[\frac{\sin(bx + h)}{b}\right] + C_2 + kx + C_1$$

$$= \frac{a}{b}\sin(bx + h) + kx + C$$

Antiderivatives of Trigonometric Models

When x is a real number,

$$\int [a\sin(bx + h) + k]dx = \frac{-a}{b}\cos(bx + h) + kx + C$$

$$\int [a\cos(bx + h) + k]dx = \frac{a}{b}\sin(bx + h) + kx + C$$

Accumulated Change for Sine Models

With these formulas, we can find accumulated change for sine models. For example, tides in 1995 for the Savannah River entrance changed according to the rate-of-change model[*]

$$t(x) = 1.00934\sin(0.50467x + 2.5633) \text{ feet per hour}$$

x hours after midnight February 7, 1995. The height of the water x hours after midnight is the accumulated change in the rate of change from 0 to x. Thus we can find a function for the height of the water x hours after midnight on February 7 by writing the general antiderivative T of the rate-of-change function t:

$$T(x) = \frac{-1.00934}{0.50467}\cos(0.50467x + 2.5633) + C \text{ feet above sea level}$$

Suppose we know that midtide occurs at 4:16 A.M. That is, $T(4.26667) \approx 0$. Using this fact, we solve for C and obtain $C \approx 0.008$. Thus the height of the water x hours after midnight on February 7 can be modeled as

$$T(x) \approx -2\cos(0.50467x + 2.5633) + 0.008 \text{ feet above sea level}$$

[*Note:* Negative values of $T(x)$ denote tides that are lower than the average sea level.]

As illustrated in the tide example, when we have functions for rates of change, we find the accumulation of that rate of change by using the antiderivative of the function. Example 1 again illustrates this principle.

---

[*]Based on data in *Sea Island Scene of Beaufort* (Beaufort, SC: Sands Publishing Co., 1995).

EXAMPLE 1 *Determining Accumulated Change*

Temperature Earlier in this chapter, we saw that the rate of change of the temperature in Philadelphia on August 27, 1993, can be modeled as

$$t(x) = 2.733 \cos(0.285x - 2.93) \text{ °F per hour}$$

x hours after midnight. Use this rate-of-change model for temperature to find the accumulated change in the temperature between 9 A.M. and 3 P.M. on August 27, 1993.

Solution
The accumulated change in the temperature between 9 A.M. and 3 P.M. is given by the definite integral

$$\int_9^{15} 2.733 \cos(0.285x - 2.93)dx = \frac{2.733}{0.285} \sin(0.285x - 2.93)\Big|_9^{15}$$

$$= \left(\frac{2.733}{0.285} \sin[0.285(15) - 2.93]\right) - \left(\frac{2.733}{0.285} \sin[0.285(9) - 2.93]\right)$$

$$\approx 9.34606 - (-3.42296)$$

$$\approx 12.769°F$$

The temperature increased by approximately 13°F between 9 A.M. and 3 P.M. ●

Average Values and Sine Models

Throughout this chapter, we have referred to the constant k of the function $f(x) = a \sin(bx + h) + k$ as the average (or expected) value of a cycle. This is the value we would expect the function to take on if it were not for the fluctuations that occur. In Chapter 5 we defined the average value of a function f from c to d as

$$\text{Average value} = \frac{\int_c^d f(x)dx}{d - c}$$

Example 2 illustrates that the constant k of a sine function is its average value over one cycle, according to the definition in Chapter 5.

EXAMPLE 2 *Calculating Average Value*

Radiation A model for the amount of ultraviolet radiation received in Auckland, New Zealand, is

$$r(m) = 25.5 \sin(0.52m - 1.57) + 32.5 \text{ watts per cm}^2$$

during the mth month of the year.

a. Calculate the average value for one cycle of this model beginning at $m = 1$.

b. Calculate the average value for one cycle of this model between two successive minima. Interpret the result.

Solution

a. The function r has period $\frac{2\pi}{0.52} \approx 12.083$ months. Thus the cycle beginning at $m = 1$ ends at $m \approx 13.083$, so the average value of the cycle can be calculated as

$$\frac{\int_1^{13.083} [25.5 \sin(0.52m - 1.57) + 32.5]dm}{13.083 - 1}$$

$$= \frac{\left(\frac{-25.5}{0.52} \cos(0.52m - 1.57) + 32.5m\right)\Big|_1^{13.083}}{12.083}$$

$$\approx \frac{400.798 - (8.100)}{12.083}$$

$$\approx 32.5 \text{ watts per cm}^2$$

That is, discounting seasonal fluctuation, we expect the UV radiation over a period of approximately 1 year in Auckland to be 32.5 watts per cm². Note that this average value is the constant k in the function r.

b. The cycle between the first two consecutive minima starts at $m \approx -0.002$ and ends at $m \approx 12.081$. The average value of the cycle is calculated as

$$\frac{\int_{-0.002}^{12.081} [25.5 \sin(0.52m - 1.57) + 32.5]dm}{12.081 - (-0.002)}$$

$$= \frac{\left(\frac{-25.5}{0.52} \cos(0.52m - 1.57) + 32.5m\right)\Big|_{-0.002}^{12.081}}{12.083}$$

$$\approx \frac{392.6457 - (-0.0531)}{12.083}$$

$$\approx 32.5 \text{ watts per cm}^2$$

That is, discounting seasonal fluctuation, we expect the UV radiation in Auckland to be 32.5 watts per cm². This is, again, the constant k of the function r.   ●

No matter which cycle you use to compute the average value of a sine function, the average value of that cycle will always be the constant k of that sine function.

7.5 Concept Inventory

- The antiderivative of the sine function
- The antiderivative of the cosine function
- Average value of a sine or cosine function

7.5 Activities

Getting Started

For Activities 1 and 2, use the graph of f to sketch the indicated accumulation function graphs.

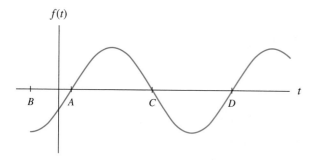

$f(t)$

$$\textbf{1. } \int_A^x f(t)\,dt \qquad\qquad \textbf{2. } \int_B^x f(t)\,dt$$

For Activities 3 through 6, consider the cyclic function f in the figure. The area of the shaded region is 2. Using the symmetry indicated by the graph, find each of the following:

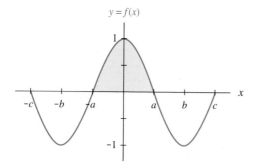

$y = f(x)$

$$\textbf{3. } \int_0^a f(x)\,dx \qquad\qquad \textbf{4. } \int_{-a}^c f(x)\,dx$$

$$\textbf{5. } \int_{-a}^a [f(x) + 1]\,dx \qquad \textbf{6. } \int_{-c}^a 3\,f(x)\,dx$$

For Activities 7 through 10, find the indicated general antiderivative.

$$\textbf{7. } \int (7.3\sin x + 12)\,dx \qquad \textbf{8. } \int 7.3\sin(x + 12)\,dx$$

$$\textbf{9. } \int \sin(7.3x + 12)\,dx$$

$$\textbf{10. } \int [7.3\sin(7.3x + 12) + 12]\,dx$$

11. Find the general antiderivative of
$$f(x) = 4.67\sin(0.024x + 3.211) + 14.63$$

12. Find the general antiderivative of
$$f(t) = 49.88\cos(3.54t - 4.86) + 7.02$$

Applying Concepts

13. Minimum Wage   When the wage is expressed in constant 2000 dollars rather than in current dollars, the rate of change of the federal minimum wage between 1950 and 2000 can be described by

$$w(t) = 0.1615\cos(0.145t - 1.582) \text{ dollars per year}$$

t years after 1950.
(Source: Based on data from the U.S. Employment Standards Administration.)

a. What are the units on the heights and widths of midpoint rectangles constructed between the graph of w and the t-axis? What are the units on the area of those midpoint rectangles?

b. Using 50 midpoint rectangles for each calculation, approximate the area of the region between the graph of w and the t-axis from $t = 7$ to $t = 50$.

c. Compare the result of part b and the value of $\int_7^{50} w(t)\,dt$. Interpret this value.

d. Shade on a graph of w the region represented by $\int_{20}^{45} w(t)\,dt$.

e. Find and interpret the value of $\int_{20}^{45} w(t)\,dt$.

14. Sales   The rate of change of sales for a store specializing in swimming pools in the summer and ski gear in the winter can be modeled by

$$S'(t) = 23.944\cos(0.987t + 1.276)$$

thousand dollars per month

where $t = 1$ in January, $t = 2$ in February, and so on.

a. Find a model for sales in month t if sales in January are $54,000.

b. Use the model to estimate when peak sales occur each year. Also estimate when sales will be lowest.

c. Find and interpret the value of $\int_1^6 S'(t)dt$.

d. Find the area of the region between the graph of S' and the t-axis from $t = 1$ to $t = 6$.

e. Find the average sales between January and June.

15. Profit Rate The after-tax profit rate on investment is defined as the ratio of after-tax corporate profits to corporate stock of plant and equipment. The rate of change of the after-tax profit rate on investment in the United States between 1988 and 2002 can be approximated by the function $T'(x) = 0.565 \sin(0.469x - 0.722)$ percent per year, where x is the number of years after 1988. (Source: Based on data from Bureau of Economic Analysis, *BusinessWeek*, November 4, 2002, p. 107.)

a. Find a model for the after-tax profit rate if the rate in 1988 was 5.5%.

b. Use the model to estimate when the after-tax profit rate was highest and when it was lowest between 1988 and 2002.

c. According to the model in part a, what was the average after-tax profit rate between 1988 and 2002?

d. The average after-tax profit rate between 1960 and 2000 was approximately 6.5%. Compare this value with the result of part c.

16. Temperature The rate of change of the average temperature in New York from 1873 through 1923 can be modeled by

$$T'(x) = 42.059 \cos(0.524x - 2.27) \text{ °F per month}$$

where $x = 1$ in January, $x = 2$ in February, and so on.

a. Find a model for the average temperature in New York. The average temperature in July is 73.5°F.

b. What does the model give as the average temperature in December?

c. Find and interpret the value of $\int_2^8 T'(x)dx$.

d. Find the area of the region between the graph of T' and the x-axis from $x = 2$ to $x = 8$.

17. Lizards The number of lizards legally gathered from a western state for selected months during a 2-year time period can be modeled by the equation

$$L(x) = 15.388 \sin(0.787x - 1.667) + 16.346$$
thousand lizards per month

where x is a number assigned to each month. The numbers 1 through 8 represent each of the eight consecutive months in which lizards are harvested in the first year, and the numbers 9 through 16 represent each of the eight consecutive harvesting months of the second year. In the months during the 2-year period not defined by the model, there were no lizards gathered. (Source: Based on information from the Nevada Division of Wildlife.)

a. Use a definite integral to estimate the number of lizards harvested during the 2-year harvesting period.

b. Because this model was formed from count data, you could also estimate the number of lizards harvested during the 2-year time period by summing each of the output values for the 16 months. Calculate this sum, and compare it to the estimate in part a.

c. Which method (the one in part a or the one in part b) do you prefer?

18. Sun Declination The rate of change of the declination of the Sun for Greenwich, England, can be described by the equation

$$S(d) = 0.398 \sin(0.0168d + 0.259) \text{ degrees per day}$$

on the dth day of the year. Use a definite integral to determine by how many degrees the declination changes between January 1 and March 1. (Source: Based on data from the *Old Farmer's Almanac*, 1996.)

19. Gender Ratio The rate of change of the ratio of males to females in the United States from 1900 through 2000 can be modeled by

$$r(t) = 0.2274 \sin(0.0426t + 2.836) \text{ males per 100}$$
females per year

t years after 1900. Find and interpret the values of

$$\int_0^{40} r(t)dt, \int_{50}^{100} r(t)dt, \text{ and } \int_0^{100} r(t)dt$$

(Source: Based on data from the U.S. Bureau of the Census.)

20. Daylight Hours   The rate of change of the number of hours of daylight in Honolulu, Hawaii, can be modeled by

$$d'(m) = 1.18 \cos(0.514m - 1.616) \text{ hours per month}$$

m months after the beginning of each year.

a. Find the area beneath the graph of d' that lies above the m-axis between $m = 0$ and $m = 12$. Interpret your answer.

b. Find the area above the graph of d' that lies below the m-axis between $m = 0$ and $m = 12$. Interpret your answer.

21. Star Pulses   On December 15, 1995, a team of astronomers discovered X-ray pulses being emitted from what they believe to be a neutron star. The speed of the pulses can be modeled by

$$p(s) = 40.5 \sin(0.01345s - 1.5708) + 186.5$$
$$\text{counts per second}$$

after s milliseconds.

(Source: Based on information in M. H. Finger et al., "Discovery of Hard X-ray Pulsations from the Transient Source GRO J1744–28," *Nature*, vol. 381, May 23, 1996, pp. 291–292.)

a. What will the units be on the heights and widths of midpoint rectangles constructed between the graph of p and the s-axis? What will the units be on the area of such midpoint rectangles?

b. Using the fact that there are 1000 milliseconds in 1 second, convert $p(s)$ to counts per millisecond.

c. Find and interpret the area between the graph of p and the s-axis for one period of the function, beginning at $s = 0$.

Discussing Concepts

22. Why do the inflection points of a sine function of the form $f(x) = a \sin(bx + h) + k$ occur at the inputs where the function attains its average value?

SUMMARY

Trigonometry has been an important topic in mathematics for centuries. We consider two trigonometric functions, sin x and cos x. When we use sine functions to model data, we consider the input as a real number with an interpretation determined by the context.

The Sine Model

Many types of data exhibit a cyclic pattern that can be modeled by a sine function of the form

$$f(x) = a \sin(bx + h) + k$$

The constants of the sine function correspond to certain physical properties of the data. The constant k is the average value of a cycle. The constant a is the amplitude of the fluctuation. The constant b (considered positive) is associated with the period of the cycle by the equation

$$\text{Period} = \frac{2\pi}{b}$$

The constant h is associated with the horizontal shift of the function by the equation

$$\text{Horizontal shift} = \frac{|h|}{b}$$

where the shift is to the left if $h > 0$ and to the right if $h < 0$. Understanding these constants and their interpretations in the context of the model helps us to understand the model itself.

Rates of Change

As with all the other functions that we have seen in this text, we are able to use calculus to analyze the rate of change that is occurring in a sine or cosine model. The derivative of the sine function is simply the cosine function, and using derivative rules developed in Chapter 3, we have

$$\frac{d}{dx}[a \sin(bx + h) + k] = ab \cos(bx + h)$$

We also saw that the derivative of the cosine function is the negative of the sine function, which enables us to find second derivatives for sine models.

Accumulation of Change

The antiderivative formulas for sine and cosine models are

$$\int [a \sin(bx + h) + k] \, dx = \frac{-a}{b} \cos(bx + h) + kx + C$$

$$\int [a \cos(bx + h) + k] \, dx = \frac{a}{b} \sin(bx + h) + kx + C$$

We use these antiderivatives to answer questions about the accumulated change in cyclic models.

CONCEPT CHECK

Can you	To practice, try	
• Identify the amplitude, reflection, period, vertical shift, and horizontal shift of a sine function?	Section 7.1	Activity 7
• Graph a sine function?	Section 7.1	Activity 15
• Construct a sine model with and without the use of technology?	Section 7.2	Activities 3, 9
• Calculate and interpret derivatives of sine and cosine functions?	Section 7.3	Activity 17
• Use derivatives to find extrema and inflection points of sine and cosine functions?	Section 7.4	Activity 14
• Find and interpret definite integrals of sine and cosine functions?	Section 7.5	Activity 19
• Find the expected (average) value of a cyclic function?	Section 7.5	Activity 15

CONCEPT REVIEW

1. Sales Lawn mower sales for a certain manufacturer are cyclic, with a low in the winter months, an increase in the spring, and a decline in the fall. Orders at this company for a 1-year period are shown in the table.

Month	Lawn mowers	Month	Lawn mowers
Jan	97	July	1400
Feb	450	Aug	1050
Mar	800	Sept	795
Apr	1150	Oct	400
May	1406	Nov	190
June	1500	Dec	75

  a. Use the data to determine the amplitude, vertical shift, period, and horizontal shift for the lawn mower orders.

  b. Use your calculator or computer to find a sine function for the number of lawn mowers ordered in terms of the month of the year. How do the function constants compare to those you gave in part *a*?

  c. Use the equation to predict lawn mower orders in April of the following year. Under what conditions should this estimate be used as a prediction?

  d. Use the equation to determine when lawn mower orders are greatest.

  e. When is the number of lawn mowers ordered increasing most rapidly?

2. Price Index The graph shows the Sauerbeck Index of general wholesale prices between 1818 and 1913.

Price index

(Source: Based on data from H. L. Moore, *Generating Economic Cycles*, New York: Augustus M. Kelley, 1967.)

  a. Estimate the average rate of change of the price index between 1860 and 1890.

  b. Estimate how quickly the price index was changing in 1860.

3. Price Index The equation for the graph in Activity 2 is

$$S(t) = 88.6 + 11.2 \sin\left(\frac{\pi}{48}t + \frac{19\pi}{10}\right)$$

$$+ 13.8 \sin\left(\frac{\pi}{24}t + \frac{11\pi}{36}\right) + 5.3 \sin\left(\frac{\pi}{9.6}t + \frac{13\pi}{45}\right)$$

t years after 1818.

  a. Use the equation to estimate the average rate of change of the price index between 1860 and 1890.

  b. Find and interpret $S'(42)$.

  c. Find the average price index between 1860 and 1890.

4. Sales The rate of change of the daily sales of powdered drink mix produced in 1992 by the Campbell Soup Company can be modeled by

$$r(t) = -0.1439 \sin(0.0197t - 3.7526)$$
million (reconstituted) pints per day

t days after January 1, 1992.

(Source: Based on data in the *Wall Street Journal*, July 7, 1993, p. B1.)

  a. Determine when the rate of change of the sales model was greatest in 1992.

  b. Find a model for the sales if the sales were 14.4 million pints on January 1, 1992.

  c. How is the answer to part *a* related to the graph of the function in part *b*?

5. Sales Find and interpret the value of $\int_{32}^{61} r(t)dt$, where *r* is the rate-of-change function in Activity 4.

Project 7.1 Seasonal Sales

Setting

Some companies sell products or offer services that are seasonal in nature. Summer or winter sports equipment is one example of a seasonal product, and swimming pool cleaning is an example of a seasonal service. Sometimes companies specialize in two different products or services for which the demand peaks in different seasons. For example, a snow ski shop may sell patio furniture in the summer.

Find a company that specializes in a seasonal product or service and that is willing to release sales data. Obtain data from the company. The data should span at least 1 year. If the company specializes in two different seasonal products, you may need to consider sales for the two products separately.

Consider your position as being that of a consultant. You are to make suggestions that will improve the company's sales. If the company sells only one product or offers only one service, you should suggest another product or service to offset the minimum sales created by the current product or service. You should also suggest when the company should begin advertising each product or service.

If the company already sells two products or offers two services, analyze whether the peak sales of one offset the low sales of the other. If you believe the company might benefit from offering a third product or service or from increasing advertising at particular times during the year, offer suggestions in your letter.

Tasks

1. Find a sine function for the data. Do you believe a sine model is the most appropriate model for the data you found? Give the period, amplitude, and vertical shift of the sine model. Interpret these values in the context of the company's sales.

2. Find the maximum and minimum sales for the model. When do these sales occur? Compare the extreme points of the sine function with the highest and lowest data values and corresponding times. According to the function, when are sales increasing most rapidly? When are they decreasing most rapidly?

3. If a sine function is not a good fit for the data, find a more appropriate function. Explain your reasons for choosing a different function.

Reporting

1. Write a letter addressed to the company. The letter should include your suggestions and brief reasons for those suggestions.

2. Write a report for your files, containing all the mathematics you used in performing Tasks 1 through 3, to refer to if the sales manager for the company calls to ask you questions.

Project 7.2 Lake Tahoe Levels

Setting

Lake Tahoe lies on the California-Nevada border. Its level is regulated by a 17-gate concrete dam at the lake's outlet. By federal court decree, the lake level must never be higher than 6229.1 feet above sea level. The lake level is monitored every midnight. A table showing the lake level on the first day of each month, as reported by the United States Department of the Interior, is located on the *Calculus Concepts* website.

Tasks

1. Examine a scatter plot of this set of data. Discuss why a sine function might be appropriate. If a sine function were used to describe these data, estimate what would be its period, amplitude, and vertical shift. Find a sine model to fit the data. What are the function's period, amplitude, and vertical shift? Compare these answers to your expectations, and discuss any discrepancies. Rewrite your model so that its output is in feet above sea level.

2. Is there a way to construct a better-fitting model by combining a sine function with some other type of function using function addition, multiplication, or composition, or by constructing a piecewise model? If so, construct such a model and explain why it makes sense to do so.

3. Carefully sketch a graph of the function you chose to model these data for the lake level. Use the sketch to estimate the lake level in January 2003 and the rate at which the level of the lake was changing at that time.

4. Use the model to estimate the lake level in January 2003 and to estimate numerically how quickly the level of the lake was changing at that time.

5. Use the derivative of the function to find the rate at which the level of the lake was changing in January 2003.

6. According to the data, when was the lake at its lowest level? When was it at its highest level? On a sketch of the function for lake level, draw lines that are tangent to the graph of the model at the model's minimum and maximum points. What is important about the tangent lines at these points?

Lake Tahoe Levels, *Continued*

7. Use the derivative of the function to estimate the month and day between October 1, 2002, and September 1, 2003, when the lake was at its lowest level. Also determine when the lake was at its highest level between these dates. According to the model, did the lake remain below the federally mandated level between October 1, 2002, and September 1, 2003?

8. When (between October 1, 2002, and September 1, 2003) was the level of the lake changing most rapidly? At that time, what was the level of the lake and how quickly was it changing?

Reporting

1. Write a report addressed to the U.S. Department of the Interior to communicate your findings on Lake Tahoe levels. Keep in mind that this should be a nonmathematical report of your conclusions. Use graphs in your report as appropriate. Include mathematical support for your conclusions as an appendix. Refer to your appendix in the body of your report as appropriate.

2. Prepare a 10-minute presentation of your conclusions to be given to the Department of the Interior. You should be prepared to discuss the mathematics if questioned, but keep in mind that your target audience is not expecting a math talk. Use overhead transparencies and/or other visual aids to enhance your presentation.

3. Prepare a poster to display your conclusions. The poster should be self-explanatory, attractive, and easily readable from 3 feet away. Show enough mathematics on the poster to support your conclusions.

8

Dynamics of Change: Differential Equations and Proportionality

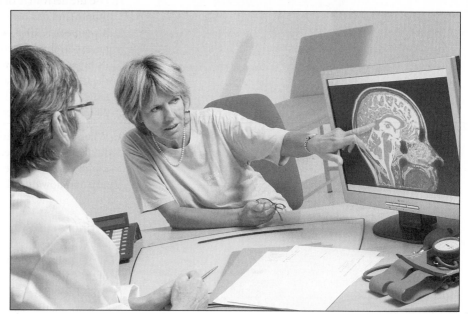

T & L/Image Point/CORBIS

Concept Application

The rate of decay that a radioisotope undergoes dictates the amount of that isotope left after a certain amount of time. It is this relationship that makes it possible for archeologists, geologists, and environmental engineers to use radioisotopes to help establish the age of artifacts and geological samples and to determine how much of a threat certain radioactive substances are to the environment. Activities 26 and 27 in Section 8.2 deal with developing differential equations from information about the decay of radioisotopes.

Chapter Introduction

Most of the functions that we have seen in this text have been motivated by real-world phenomena. In many cases, it is the underlying rate of change that determines whether the equation describing a phenomenon should be linear, quadratic, logistic, and so forth.

In this chapter we look at some applications of calculus that use information about rates of change. We consider equations that describe the forces that drive certain rates of change. Equations stating the behavior of a rate of change (that is, equations involving derivatives) are called differential equations. We look at differential equations graphically using slope fields, numerically using Euler's method, and analytically using integration.

Concepts you will be learning

- Finding and graphing particular solutions to constant and linear differential equations (8.1)
- Setting up differential equations using information about direct and inverse proportionality (8.1)
- Using slope fields to graphically analyze a differential equation (8.1, 8.2)
- Finding and graphing particular solutions to separable differential equations (8.2)
- Setting up differential equations using information about joint proportionality (8.2)
- Using Euler's method to numerically analyze a differential equation (8.3)
- Solving second-order differential equations (8.4)

8.1   Differential Equations and Slope Fields

In Section 4.4 we saw how to use a known equation to develop a related-rates equation that shows us the interconnection between different rates of change. Now we consider the opposite process: using equations that describe rates of change to develop equations that describe the situation. Equations that involve rates of change (derivatives) are called **differential equations.** The following equations are examples of differential equations:

$$\frac{dc}{dp} = -0.16p \qquad \frac{dy}{dx} = 5.9x - 3.2y \qquad \frac{d^2s}{dt^2} = 2.1s$$

$$\frac{dS}{dt} = \frac{k}{\ln(t+1.2)} \qquad \frac{d^2y}{dx^2} = 3xy \qquad \frac{d^2y}{dx^2} = 4\frac{dy}{dx} + 2y$$

Differential Equations

Consider, for instance, the differential equation

$$\frac{dy}{dx} = 63 \text{ mph}$$

which describes the speed of a vehicle after x hours of traveling west on a straight stretch of interstate highway in North Dakota. Suppose we want an equation for the distance between the vehicle and the eastern border of the state after x hours. Because we are given a derivative $\frac{dy}{dx}$ and wish to find a function y, we simply write the general antiderivative:

$$y(x) = 63x + C \text{ miles}$$

after x hours, where C represents the distance from the border when $x = 0$. This equation is the solution to the differential equation given above.

It is important to note that the solution of a differential equation is a function with derivatives that satisfy the differential equation. The solution is not a numerical value. We define the function f to be a **general solution** to a differential equation $\frac{dy}{dx} = g(x, y)$ if the substitution of $f(x)$ for y gives an identity (that is, a true statement).

Differential Equation and General Solution

A differential equation involves one or more derivatives. A general solution for a differential equation is a function that has derivatives that satisfy the differential equation.

In the velocity example, we found $y(x) = 63x + C$ miles to be a solution to $\frac{dy}{dx} = 63$ mph. To verify that this is indeed a general solution, we substitute $y(x)$ into the differential equation and obtain

$$\frac{d}{dx}(63x + C) = 63$$

$$63 = 63$$

The statement $63 = 63$ is called an identity. This identity confirms that we have a solution. The C parameter in the solution is an arbitrary constant; it is used to designate the family of functions that, when differentiated, gives the differential equation. In practice, unique values for C will be determined by the initial conditions stated in the specific problem that we are solving. In those cases, we call the solution a **particular solution.**

The velocity example is a specific example of the simplest differential equation— a **constant differential equation** that has the form $\frac{dy}{dx} = k$, where k is a constant. To solve this differential equation, we used our understanding of the relationships among a rate-of-change function, the accumulation function of that rate of change, and the quantity function. That is, we found the solution to the differential equation by determining the general antiderivative of the rate-of-change function. Another simple differential equation, called a **linear differential equation,** has the form $\frac{dy}{dx} = ax + b$ and is given in Example 1.

EXAMPLE 1   *Finding Solutions for a Linear Differential Equation*

Population   Judging on the basis of data compiled from *Statistical Abstract,* 1993, 1998, and 2001, between 1900 and 2000 the population of the United States was growing at rate of $0.0181x + 1.129$ million people per year, where x is the number of years since 1900. In 1990 the population of the United States was 249.9 million people.

a. Write a differential equation expressing the growth rate of the population with respect to time.

b. Find a general solution for this differential equation.

c. Find a particular solution for this differential equation. Graph the differential equation and the particular solution.

d. Use the particular solution to estimate the population in the year 2005.

Solution

a. Let P represent the population of the United States x years after 1900. The growth rate of the population is expressed by the differential equation

$$\frac{dP}{dx} = 0.0181x + 1.129 \text{ million people per year}$$

x years after 1900.

b. The general solution is a function P describing the population. Because the differential equation $\frac{dP}{dx} = 0.0181x + 1.129$ is simply the derivative of the population function P written in terms of the input variable x, a general antiderivative of $\frac{dP}{dx}$ is a general solution for this differential equation. Thus we have as a general solution $P(x) = 0.00905x^2 + 1.129x + C$ million people x years after 1900.

c. We know the population in 1990, so we use the fact that $P(90) = 249.9$ to solve for C in the general solution. Thus we obtain the particular solution

$$P(x) = 0.00905x^2 + 1.129x + 74.985 \text{ million people}$$

x years after 1900. Figure 8.1 on page 510 shows graphs of the differential equation and the particular solution.

d. We estimate the population of the United States to be $P(105) \approx 293.3$ million people in the year 2005.   ●

In order for us to use antiderivatives as solutions, the differential equation must satisfy two criteria:

1. The rate of change must be in terms of the input variable only.

2. We must know an antiderivative formula for the given rate-of-change function.

Many differential equations satisfy these criteria. Some of these differential equations are based on the ideas of proportionality.

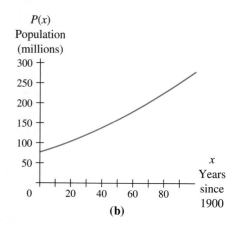

(a)   (b)

FIGURE 8.1

Proportionality

We have seen the two differential equations $\frac{dy}{dx} = k$ and $\frac{dy}{dx} = kx$, where k is a constant. The first differential equation states that the rate of change of y with respect to x is constant. The second differential equation, $\frac{dy}{dx} = kx$, states that the rate of change of y with respect to x is *proportional* to the input x.

The idea of *proportionality* is one that is often used in setting up differential equations. We say that a variable y is **directly proportional** to another variable x if there is a constant k such that $y = kx$. We call k the **constant of proportionality.** We use the terms *proportional* and *directly proportional* interchangeably.

Direct Proportionality

For input x and output y, y is directly proportional to x if there exists some constant k such that $y = kx$. The constant k is called the constant of proportionality.

For example, if $A(t) = 23.50t$ dollars represents the amount it costs to purchase t tickets to a concert, then we say that the cost is directly proportional to the number of tickets purchased. In this case, 23.50 is the constant of proportionality.

Another type of proportionality occurs when a quantity y is related to a quantity x by the equation $y = \frac{k}{x}$, where k is a constant. In this case, we say that y is **inversely proportional** to x.

Inverse Proportionality

For input x and output y, y is inversely proportional to x if there exists some constant of proportionality k such that $y = \frac{k}{x}$.

The German physiologist Gustav Fechner* said that the rate of change of the intensity of a response R with respect to the intensity of a stimulus s is inversely proportional to the intensity of the stimulus. That is, there is some constant k such that

$$\frac{dR}{ds} = \frac{k}{s}$$

This differential equation, known as Fechner's Law, says that if you are in a quiet environment and a small bell rings, you will perceive the sound from the bell as being rather loud, whereas if you are in a noisy environment and the same small bell rings, you will perceive the sound as being almost inaudible. Consider the following response differential equation:

$$\frac{dR}{ds} = \frac{2.94}{s}$$

where the stimulus (input s) is measured in decibels and the response (output R) is measured on a scale of sound intensity where 0 represents no sound and 10 represents unbearably loud sound. A general solution of this differential equation is simply a general antiderivative:

$$R(s) = 2.94 \ln s + C$$

where s is measured in decibels and is always positive.

If the smallest sound that can be detected is 10 decibels, then we can use the initial condition $R(10) = 0$ to find a particular solution to the differential equation. In this case, the particular solution is

$$R(s) = 2.94 \ln s - 6.77$$

where s is measured in decibels.

EXAMPLE 2   *Evaluating the Constant of Proportionality*

Sales   Suppose that the total sales (in billions of dollars) of a computer product are growing in inverse proportion to $\ln(t + 1.2)$, where t is the number of years since the product was introduced. Sales totaled $53.2 billion by the end of the first year.

a.   Write a differential equation representing the rate of change of sales with respect to time.

b.   At the end of the first year, total sales were growing by 8.3 billion dollars per year. Find the constant of proportionality.

c.   Can we write an explicit formula for the general solution of this differential equation?

* D. N. Burghes and M. S. Borrie, *Modelling with Differential Equations,* (Chichester, England: Ellis Horwood Limited, a division of Wiley, 1981.

Solution

a. Let $S(t)$ represent the total sales of the computer product t years after the product was introduced. A differential equation representing the information given is

$$\frac{dS}{dt} = \frac{k}{\ln(t + 1.2)} \text{ billion dollars per year}$$

where t is the number of years after the product was introduced.

b. We are told that $\frac{dS}{dt} = 8.3$ billion dollars per year when $t = 1$. Using this fact, we have

$$8.3 = \frac{k}{\ln(1 + 1.2)}$$

Thus the constant of proportionality is $k \approx 6.544$. The differential equation is

$$\frac{dS}{dt} \approx \frac{6.544}{\ln(t + 1.2)} \text{ billion dollars per year}$$

where t is the number of years after the product was introduced.

c. This differential equation expresses the derivative of S as a function of the input variable t. If we knew a formula for a general antiderivative of this function, then we could write a general solution of the differential equation. However, we do not know such a formula. ●

As in Example 2, even when the differential equation appears to be in a simple form, we may not be able to find an explicit formula for its general solution. However, we still can analyze such a differential equation graphically and numerically to develop useful insight into the nature of the function and to estimate the solution.

Slope Fields

One way to obtain a graphical representation of a solution to a differential equation is to draw a **slope field.** A slope field is constructed by placing a grid on a portion of the Cartesian plane and, at each point on the grid, drawing a short line segment whose slope is determined by the differential equation. For instance, consider the differential equation $\frac{dy}{dx} = 2x$. At the point $(1, 1)$, the slope of a solution to this equation is $2x = 2(1) = 2$, and at $(-0.5, 2)$, the slope is $2x = 2(-0.5) = -1$. Using the differential equation to determine the slopes at points on a grid on a plane where $-3 \le x \le 3$ and $-6 \le y \le 6$ and then sketching short line segments with those slopes at the appropriate points gives the slope field shown in Figure 8.2. (This construction is a tedious process and is usually done with computer software.)

Particular solutions for the differential equation can be sketched by following the line segments in such a way that the solution curves are tangent to each of the segments they meet. Figure 8.3 shows the graph of a particular solution for $\frac{dy}{dx} = 2x$. This particular solution goes through the point, or initial condition, $(0, -1)$. We use the term **initial condition** to refer to a known point on the graph of a particular solution. Knowing an initial condition allows us to find a particular, rather than a general, solution.

FIGURE 8.2   **FIGURE 8.3**

The slope field indicates that at the point $(0, -1)$, the derivative of the solution is zero. Thus the solution has a maximum, a minimum, or an inflection point at $(0, -1)$. The slopes to the left of $x = 0$ indicate that the solution is decreasing toward $(0, -1)$, and the slopes to the right of $x = 0$ indicate that the solution is increasing after it reaches $(0, -1)$. Therefore, $(0, -1)$ is a minimum point. We form the solution graph by following the general direction indicated by the slopes. You may find it helpful to consider this as a more sophisticated version of "connecting the dots." Remember, however, that slopes in a slope field graph are plotted at only some, not all, points on the plane.

Figure 8.4 shows the graphs of several particular solutions for $\frac{dy}{dx} = 2x$ drawn on the slope field. You should recognize the curves in Figure 8.4 as graphs of solutions of the form $y(x) = x^2 + C$, which we know is the general solution of $\frac{dy}{dx} = 2x$. The particular solution in Figure 8.4 with initial condition $(0, -1)$ is shown in teal. In this case, the particular solution is $y(x) = x^2 - 1$. The other particular solutions shown correspond to $C = -3, -2, 0, 1, 2, 3$.

Although this example of a slope field is for a differential equation with a known solution, slope fields are particularly helpful when we are graphing solutions for a differential equation for which we do not know solution formulas. A little practice looking at slope fields will assist you in sketching graphs of solutions and will help you understand how the forces that drive the rate of change of a quantity determine the shape of the graph of the quantity function.

Each of Figures 8.5 through 8.8 shows slope fields with three particular solutions sketched. On each figure, the particular solutions for the initial conditions $(-2, 2)$, $(1, 1)$, and $(1, -1)$ are shown for the quantity function y with input x.

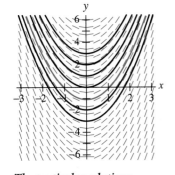

The particular solutions
$y = x^2 + C$ *for*
$C = -3, -2, -1, 0, 1, 2, 3$

FIGURE 8.4

FIGURE 8.5   **FIGURE 8.6**

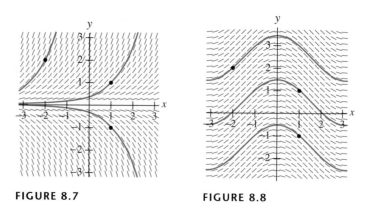

FIGURE 8.7   **FIGURE 8.8**

Now that we have seen a few examples of solution graphs drawn on slope fields, we use slope fields to help us determine a solution graph in an applied situation.

EXAMPLE 3   *Sketching Graphs of Particular Solutions on a Slope Field*

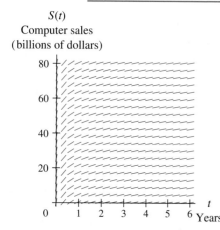

S(t)
Computer sales
(billions of dollars)

FIGURE 8.9

Sales   In Example 2 we derived a differential equation representing the rate of change of computer sales with respect to time:

$$\frac{dS}{dt} \approx \frac{6.544}{\ln(t + 1.2)} \text{ billion dollars per year}$$

where *t* is the number of years after the product was introduced.

a. Examine the slope field of this differential equation shown in Figure 8.9, and sketch three particular solutions on the slope field.

b. In Example 2 we were told that sales were $53.2 billion at the end of the first year. Sketch the particular solution corresponding to this initial condition, and use it to estimate sales after 3 years.

Solution

a. Figure 8.10 shows three particular solutions graphed on the slope field. You may have sketched different solutions, but they should all have the same general shape.

b. Figure 8.11 shows the particular solution when $S(t) = 53.2$ at $t = 1$. The point on the solution graph at $t = 3$ appears to be (3, 60). Thus we estimate sales after 3 years as approximately $60 billion. ●

So far we have seen only a few simple differential equations in which the derivative of some function *f* is given in terms of only the input variable *x*. In these cases, a general solution is the general antiderivative of the differential equation when one is known. Graphing the differential equation using slope fields can be helpful in obtaining insight into the nature of the function.

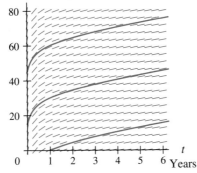

S(t)
Computer sales
(billions of dollars)

FIGURE 8.10

S(t)
Computer sales
(billions of dollars)

FIGURE 8.11

8.1 Concept Inventory

- Solutions to differential equations of the form
  $\frac{dy}{dx} = k$
- Solutions to differential equations of the form
  $\frac{dy}{dx} = f(x)$
- Direct proportionality
- Inverse proportionality
- Slope fields

8.1 Activities

Getting Started

For Activities 1 through 4, write an equation or differential equation for the given information.

1. The cost *c* to fill your gas tank is directly proportional to the number of gallons *g* your tank will hold.

2. The marginal cost of producing window panes (that is, the rate of change of cost *c* with respect to the number of units produced) is inversely proportional to the number of panes *p* produced.

3. Barometric pressure *p* is changing with respect to altitude *a* at a rate that is proportional to the altitude.

4. The rate of change of the cost *c* of mailing a first-class letter with respect to the weight of the letter is constant.

For each of the differential equations in Activities 5 through 11:

a. Use the corresponding slope field to sketch the graphs of three particular solutions.

b. Describe how the graphs of the solutions compare with each other.

c. Write a general solution for the differential equation.

5. $\frac{dy}{dx} = 0$

6. $\frac{dy}{dx} = 1$

7. $\dfrac{dy}{dx} = -1$

8. $\dfrac{dy}{dx} = \dfrac{1}{2}$

9. $\dfrac{dy}{dx} = \dfrac{1}{2}x$

10. $\dfrac{dy}{dx} = 2x$

11. $\dfrac{dy}{dx} = -x$

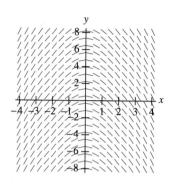

Discussing Concepts

12. For the differential equations in Activities 5 through 8, compare and contrast the particular solutions with initial condition $(0, 0)$.

13. For the differential equations in Activities 9 through 11, compare and contrast the particular solutions with initial condition $(0, 0)$.

Applying Concepts

14. Consider a function $y = f(x)$ whose rate of change with respect to x is constant.

   a. Write a differential equation describing the rate of change of this function.

   b. Write a general solution for the differential equation.

   c. Verify that the general solution you gave in part *b* is indeed a solution by substituting it into the differential equation and obtaining an identity.

15. **Energy** Between 1975 and 1980, energy production in the United States was increasing at an approximately constant rate of 0.98 quadrillion Btu per year. In 1980 the United States produced 64.8 quadrillion Btu.

(Source: Based on data from *Statistical Abstract,* 1994.)

   a. Write a differential equation for the rate of change of energy production.

   b. Write a general solution for the differential equation.

   c. Using the initial condition, determine the particular solution for energy production.

   d. Estimate the energy production in 1975, as well as the rate at which energy production was changing at that time.

   e. Use the slope field to sketch the graph of the particular solution indicated by the initial condition, and use this graph to estimate energy production in 1975. How close is your graphical estimate to your estimate in part *d*?

Energy production
(quadrillion Btu)

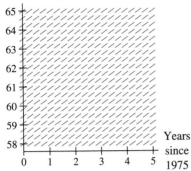

16. **Energy** Between 1975 and 1980, energy consumption in the United States was increasing at an approximately constant rate of 1.08 quadrillion Btu per year. In 1980 the United States consumed 76.0 quadrillion Btu.

(Source: Based on data from *Statistical Abstract*, 1994.)

a. Write a differential equation for the rate of change of energy consumption.

b. Write a general solution for the differential equation.

c. Determine the particular solution for energy consumption.

d. Estimate the energy consumption in 1975, as well as the rate at which energy consumption was changing at that time.

e. Use the slope field to sketch the graph of the particular solution indicated by the initial condition, and use this graph to estimate energy consumption in 1975. How close is your graphical estimate to your estimate in part *d*?

Energy consumption
(quadrillion Btu)

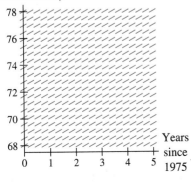

17. **Cropland** The amount of arable and permanent cropland worldwide increased at a slow but relatively steady rate of 0.0342 million square kilometers per year between 1970 and 1990). In 1980 there were 14.17 million square kilometers of cropland.

(Source: Ronald Bailey, ed., *The True State of the Planet*, New York: The Free Press for the Competitive Enterprise Institute, 1995.)

a. Write a differential equation representing the growth of cropland.

b. Write a general solution for the differential equation in part *a*.

c. Write the particular solution for the amount of cropland.

d. Use the equations to estimate the rate of change of cropland in 1970 and in 1990. Also estimate the amount of cropland in those years.

18. **Air Pressure** Barometric pressure *p* (measured in inches of mercury) decreases with respect to altitude *a* (measured in feet) at a rate that is directly proportional to the altitude. The constant of proportionality is $3.7 \cdot 10^{-5}$.

a. Write a differential equation representing the rate of change of barometric pressure.

b. Write a general solution for this differential equation.

c. Assume that barometric pressure at sea level is 30 inches of mercury. Find a particular solution for the differential equation.

d. Use the slope field to sketch the particular solution for the differential equation and initial condition given in part *c*.

$p(a)$
Barometric pressure
(inches of mercury)

19. **Falling Object** An object that has been dropped falls at a velocity *v* (in feet per second) that is

proportional to the number of seconds t after it has been dropped. The constant of proportionality depends on the force of gravity. On Earth, the proportionality constant is -32 feet per second squared.

a. Write an equation giving velocity as a function of time.

b. Rewrite the equation in part a as a differential equation giving the rate of change of distance as a function of time.

c. Find a general solution to the differential equation.

d. After how many seconds will the object hit the ground if it was dropped from a height of 35 feet? What is the terminal velocity of this object?

20. Falling Object   Refer to Activity 19. Use the slope field graph for $\frac{ds}{dt} = -32t$ that is given to answer the following questions.

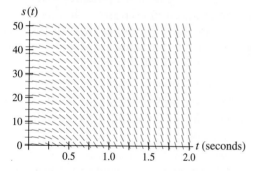

a. Sketch a graph of the particular solution for the initial condition $s = 35$ when $t = 0$.

b. Sketch a graph of the particular solution for the initial condition $s = 10$ when $t = 0$.

c. If v represents the velocity of a falling (or thrown) object in feet per second t seconds after the object is thrown or dropped, discuss what information is given by the graphs of the particular solutions in parts a and b.

21. Consider a function $y = f(x)$ whose rate of change with respect to x is directly proportional to the input.

a. Write a differential equation describing the rate of change of this function.

b. Write a general solution for the differential equation.

c. Verify that the general solution you gave in part b is indeed a solution by substituting it into the

differential equation and simplifying to obtain an identity.

22. Weight   For the first 9 months of life, the average weight w, in pounds, of a certain breed of dog increases at a rate that is inversely proportional to time t, in months. A 1-month-old puppy weighs 6 pounds, and a 9-month-old puppy weighs 80 pounds.

a. Write a differential equation describing the rate of change of the weight of the puppy.

b. Give the particular solution for this differential equation on the basis of the information given.

c. Estimate the weight of the puppy at 3 months and at 6 months.

d. Why does this differential equation describe weight gain for only 8 months instead of for the life span of the dog?

23. Height   The height h, in feet, of a certain tree increases at a rate that is inversely proportional to time t, in years. The height of the tree is 4 feet at the end of 2 years and reaches 30 feet at the end of 7 years.

a. Write a differential equation describing the rate of change of the height of the tree.

b. Give a particular solution for this differential equation.

c. How tall will the tree be in 15 years? What will happen to the height of this tree over time?

24. Weight   Refer to Activity 22. A slope field for the differential equation in part a of Activity 22 is shown.

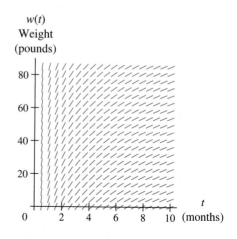

a. Sketch the graph of the particular solution in part *b* of Activity 22.

b. Use the graph to estimate the weight of the puppy at 3 months and at 6 months.

25. Height   Refer to Activity 23. A slope field for the differential equation in part *a* of Activity 23 is shown.

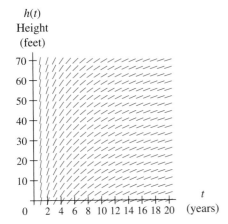

h(*t*)
Height
(feet)

a. Sketch the graph of the particular solution in part *b* of Activity 23.

b. Use the graph to estimate the height of the tree after 15 years of growth.

26. Consider a function $y = f(x)$ whose rate of change with respect to x is inversely proportional to the input.

a. Write a differential equation describing the rate of change of this function.

b. Write a general solution for the differential equation.

c. Verify that the general solution you gave in part *b* is indeed a solution by substituting it into the differential equation and simplifying to obtain an identity.

27. For each of the following differential equations and their slope fields:

  i. Sketch the graphs of three particular solutions.

  ii. Describe how the graphs of the solutions behave.

  iii. Compare and contrast the family of solutions for each of the differential equations.

a. $\dfrac{dy}{dx} = \dfrac{1}{x}$

b. $\dfrac{dy}{dx} = \dfrac{10}{x}$

c. $\dfrac{dy}{dx} = \dfrac{-1}{x}$

d. $\dfrac{dy}{dx} = \dfrac{1}{10x}$

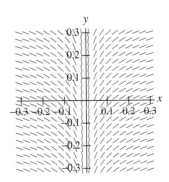

In Activities 28 through 31, use the slope fields given for the differential equations to sketch the particular solution for each given initial condition.

28. $\dfrac{dy}{dx} = 2x + 1$

 a. $x = 4, y = 11$

 b. $x = 2, y = -4$

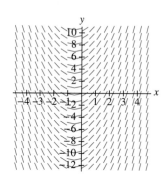

29. $\dfrac{dy}{dx} = -\sin x$

 a. $x = 3, y = 4$

 b. $x = 0, y = 0$

 c. $x = 2, y = -1$

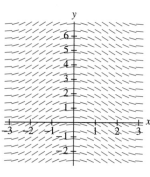

30. $\dfrac{dy}{dx} = \cos x$

 a. $x = 0, y = 0$

 b. $x = 2, y = 5$

 c. $x = -1, y = 2$

31. $\dfrac{dy}{dx} = 3x^2 + 2x$

 a. $x = 2, y = 5$

 b. $x = -3, y = 0$

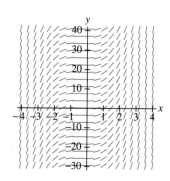

8.2   Separable Differential Equations

In Section 8.1 we considered differential equations of the form $\frac{dy}{dx} = f(x)$. In this section we consider differential equations of the forms $\frac{dy}{dx} = f(y)$ and $\frac{dy}{dx} = f(x, y)$. Because differential equations of these types give slope in terms of x and y, slope fields are useful in giving graphical insight into the behavior of the underlying function. For instance, a slope field for $\frac{dy}{dx} = \frac{32}{y}$ (see Figure 8.12) shows that the general solution for this differential equation appears to behave in a parabolic manner, with the parabola lying on its side.

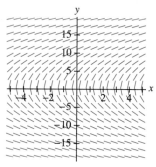

FIGURE 8.12

Separation of Variables

Because differential equations of the forms $\frac{dy}{dx} = f(y)$ and $\frac{dy}{dx} = f(x, y)$ are not in terms of only the input variable x, they cannot be solved directly by writing an antiderivative function. Instead, we use a technique known as **separation of variables** to solve such equations.

Let us again consider the differential equation $\frac{dy}{dx} = \frac{32}{y}$. Because we do not know what it means to find a general antiderivative of $\frac{32}{y}$ with respect to the variable x, we move all symbols containing y to one side of the equation and all symbols involving

Until now, we have considered $\frac{dy}{dx}$ as a single symbol denoting the rate of change of y with respect to x. In separating variables, we consider dy and dx to be two separate symbols, sometimes referred to as **differentials.**

x to the other side of the equation. This procedure is known as *separating the variables.* In this case, we have

$$ydy = 32dx$$

Now that the equation has the variables separated, we take antiderivatives of both sides of the equation.

$$\int ydy = \int 32dx$$

$$\frac{1}{2}y^2 + c_1 = 32x + c_2$$

where c_1 and c_2 are both constants. Combining the constants and solving for y^2 yields

$$y^2 = 64x + C$$

Finally, we write the solution equation giving y in terms of x by taking the square root of both sides of the equation.

$$y = \pm\sqrt{64x + C}$$

This equation does indeed yield the two sides of a horizontal parabola, as the slope field indicates. In this case, y is not a function of x because a single value of x could yield two different values of y.

Differential Equations Modeling Constant Percentage Change

Any time that percentage growth is constant, the situation can be described by the differential equation $\frac{dy}{dx} = ky$, where k is the constant percentage rate of change. Because constant percentage growth characterizes exponential functions, the solution to this differential equation is $y = ae^{kx}$. Example 1 illustrates the solution to differential equations of this form.

EXAMPLE 1   *Solving Differential Equations Using Separation of Variables*

Bank Account   Consider an account for which interest is compounded continuously at an annual interest rate of 7%.

a. Write a differential equation expressing the rate of change of the amount in the account with respect to time.

b. Examine the slope field of this differential equation, shown in Figure 8.13, and make a conjecture about the behavior of the function.

c. Find a general solution for this differential equation.

d. If the amount after 3 years is $1000, find the particular solution.

Solution

a. The rate of change of A, the amount in dollars in the account, can be expressed as the differential equation

$$\frac{dA}{dt} = 0.07A \text{ dollars per year}$$

after t years.

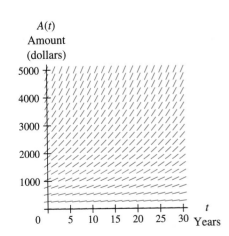

FIGURE 8.13

b. This slope field indicates a horizontal asymptote at $A = 0$ and growth that increases as t increases. This behavior is indicative of an exponential model.

c. To solve this equation, we use the technique of separating variables:

$$\frac{1}{A} \, dA = 0.07 \, dt$$

Determining general antiderivatives of both sides, we have

$$\int \frac{1}{A} \, dA = \int 0.07 \, dt$$

which gives

$$\ln A + c_1 = 0.07t + c_2$$

Combining the constants yields

$$\ln A = 0.07t + C$$

Recalling from algebra that $\ln x = y$ is equivalent to $x = e^y$, we have

$$A = e^{(0.07t + C)}$$
$$= e^{0.07t} e^C$$

Replacing the constant e^C with the constant a gives the general solution

$$A = ae^{0.07t} \text{ dollars}$$

after t years.

> We do not need to use $|A|$ in the antiderivative because we know that the amount in the account must be positive.

d. Because the amount after 3 years is $1000, we find the particular solution by substituting $t = 3$ and $A = 1000$ into the general solution and solving for a.

$$1000 = ae^{0.07(3)}$$
$$a \approx 810.584$$

The particular solution is

$$A \approx 810.584 e^{0.07t} \text{ dollars}$$

after t years. This solution can also be written in the form

$$A \approx 810.584(1.0725^t) \text{ dollars}$$

after t years. As Figure 8.14 shows, this particular solution fits the description in part b. ●

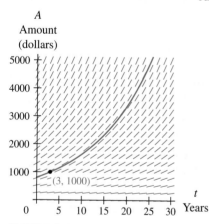

FIGURE 8.14

Example 2 illustrates the use of two different differential equations, one that requires separation of variables and one that can be solved by determining an antiderivative.

EXAMPLE 2   *Solving Differential Equations Using Various Techniques*

GNP   The gross national product (GNP) for a certain country has been increasing continuously at a rate of approximately 5% per year. The government has decided to keep the growth in the rate of deficit spending proportional to the GNP. Last year the GNP was $3 billion, and the country's national debt was $2.3 billion. The government has mandated that this year's national debt be held at $2.4 billion dollars.

a. Express the country's GNP growth as a differential equation, and find the solution.

b. Express the rate of change of the country's national debt as a differential equation, and find the solution.

c. Evaluate the solutions for $t = 2$, and interpret the answers.

Solution

a. Let G represent the GNP in billions of dollars. Then $\frac{dG}{dt} = 0.05G$ billion dollars per year represents the rate of change of the GNP after t years. The solution is found by separating variables.

$$\frac{1}{G}dG = 0.05 \, dt$$

yields

$$\ln G = 0.05t + C$$

which can be rewritten as

$$G = ae^{0.05t} \text{ billion dollars}$$

If we consider t to be the number of years since last year, then $a = 3$ because the GNP in year 0 (last year) was $3 billion. Thus the solution to the differential equation is

$$G = 3e^{0.05t} \text{ billion dollars}$$

after t years.

b. Let D be the national debt in billions of dollars. The statement "the growth rate of deficit spending is proportional to the GNP" can be translated into mathematical symbols as

$$\frac{dD}{dt} = kG \text{ billion dollars per year}$$

after t years, where k is the constant of proportionality. Note that at this point we do not have the information we need to solve for k. However, we have enough information to solve for k once we find a general solution. Knowing a function for G, we substitute this into the differential equation:

$$\frac{dD}{dt} = k(3e^{0.05t})$$

Because this differential equation gives the derivative of D in terms of only the input t, we do not need to use separation of variables but can proceed by writing a general antiderivative:

$$D(t) = \frac{3ke^{0.05t}}{0.05} + C = 60ke^{0.05t} + C \text{ billion dollars}$$

after t years. We now have two constants, k and C, to determine, so we must create a system of two equations that we can solve simultaneously. Because the national debt last year (when $t = 0$) was $2.3 billion, we substitute this information into D:

$$2.3 = 60ke^0 + C = 60k + C \tag{1}$$

Also, the national debt is $2.4 billion when $t = 1$, so

$$2.4 = 60ke^{0.05} + C \tag{2}$$

Solving equation 1 for C and substituting into equation 2 give the equation

$$2.4 = 60ke^{0.05} + (2.3 - 60k)$$

or

$$0.1 = (60e^{0.05} - 60)k$$

$$k = \frac{0.1}{60e^{0.05} - 60}$$

Thus $k \approx 0.0325$. Using this value of k in equation 1 gives

$$C \approx 2.3 - 60(0.0325) \approx 0.3496$$

Thus we have the particular solution

$$D(t) \approx 1.9504e^{0.05t} + 0.3496 \text{ billion dollars}$$

after t years.

c. When $t = 2$, $G(2) \approx \$3.3$ billion and $D(2) \approx \$2.5$ billion. In 2 years, the GNP will be approximately \$3.3 billion, and the national debt should be held to approximately \$2.5 billion. ●

Joint Proportionality

Section 8.1 introduced two forms of proportionality: direct and inverse. Now we consider a third form of proportionality. When a quantity y is proportional to the product of two other quantities x and z—that is, when there is some constant k such that $y = kxz$—we say the quantity y is **jointly proportional** to the quantities x and z.

Joint Proportionality

For inputs x and z and output y, y is jointly proportional to x and z if there exists some constant of proportionality k such that $y = kxz$.

Example 3 illustrates the concept of joint proportionality as it is used in psychology.

EXAMPLE 3 _Solving an Equation Involving Joint Proportionality_

Stimulus Response The Fechner Law relates response to stimulus. A different model that is used to describe this relationship is the Brentano-Stevens Law. This law says that the level of response R changes according to a joint proportionality between the level of the response and the inverse of s, the level of the stimulus. That is, $\frac{dR}{ds} = k\frac{R}{s}$ for some constant k.

Consider the following differential equation, which describes a person's perception of the intensity of sound:

$$\frac{dR}{ds} = \frac{2.94R}{s}$$

where the sound s is measured in decibels and intensity R is measured on a scale from 0 to 10, with 0 representing inaudible sound and 10 representing painfully intense sound.

a. Examine the slope field graph in Figure 8.15, and comment on the behavior of the graphs of the solutions to this differential equation.

b. Write an equation giving the response R in terms of stimulus s.

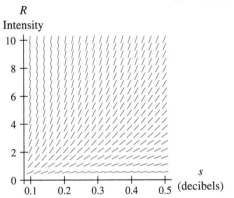

FIGURE 8.15

Solution

a. The slope field of $\frac{dR}{ds} = \frac{2.94R}{s}$ that is shown in Figure 8.15 suggests that the solutions are exponential.

b. Because the differential equation $\frac{dR}{ds} = \frac{2.94R}{s}$ gives the rate of change of R with respect to s in terms of both s and R, we use the method of separation of variables rather than simply writing an antiderivative formula. Separating the variables yields

$$\frac{1}{R} dR = \frac{2.94}{s} ds$$

Taking antiderivatives of both sides of the equation and realizing that $R > 0$ and $s > 0$ yield the equation $\ln R + c_1 = 2.94 \ln s + c_2$. Combining the constants c_1 and c_2 gives the equation $\ln R = 2.94 \ln s + C$. This equation is equivalent to

$$e^{\ln R} = e^{2.94 \ln s + C}$$

which we simplify as follows:

$$e^{\ln R} = e^{2.94 \ln s} e^C$$
$$e^{\ln R} = (e^{\ln s})^{2.94} e^C$$
$$R = s^{2.94} e^C$$

Replacing E^c with the constant a gives the general solution as

$$R = as^{2.94}$$

where s is measured in decibels and a is a constant. ●

Logistic Models and Their Differential Equations

We have seen differential equations that lead to linear, quadratic, logarithmic, and exponential models. What does a differential equation that yields a logistic model look like? To help us better understand the underlying differential equation, recall the role of the limiting value L in a logistic model:

$$y(x) = \frac{L}{1 + Ae^{-Bx}}$$

As we saw in Chapter 1, the logistic model may be used to study the spread of a virus in a network of computers. The virus initially spreads exponentially because the first computer infects another, then these two computers infect two others, then the four of them infect four others, and so on. At some point, the computers that have the virus contact only others that are also infected instead of uninfected computers, and the exponential sequence is broken. Eventually, the number of infected computers is close to the limiting value L.

The rate of change of the number of infected computers depends on two things: the number y of computers already infected and the number $L - y$ of computers not yet infected. Thus the rate of change is jointly proportional to the number of computers already infected and to the number of uninfected computers remaining. We can describe the spread of a virus with the differential equation

$$\frac{dy}{dx} = ky(L - y)$$

where L is the number of computers in the group and k is the constant of proportionality. It is also common to refer to the limiting value L as the **carrying capacity** of the system or as the **saturation level.**

A slope graph of a differential equation of the form $\frac{dy}{dx} = ky(L - y)$ gives us insight into the behavior of the function y. Figure 8.16 shows slope fields for differential equations of this form with different values of k and L.

In each case, the slope field of the differential equation appears to have an upper and a lower horizontal asymptote, and a solution between these limiting values

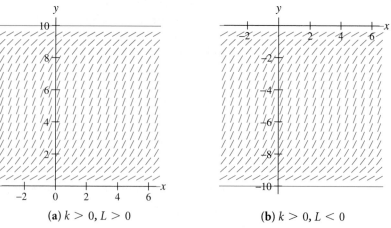

(a) $k > 0, L > 0$ (b) $k > 0, L < 0$

FIGURE 8.16   *Slope fields for* $\frac{dy}{dx} = ky(L - y)$

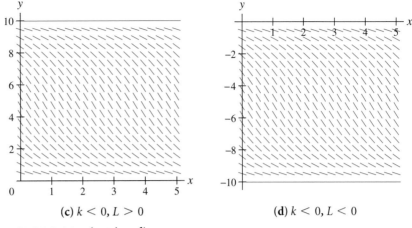

(c) $k < 0, L > 0$ **(d)** $k < 0, L < 0$

FIGURE 8.16   *(continued)*

appears to be logistic (either increasing or decreasing). In fact, it can be shown that the solution for $\frac{dy}{dx} = ky(L - y)$ is the logistic function

$$y = \frac{L}{1 + Ae^{-Lkx}}$$

Even though the logistic equation $y(x) = \frac{L}{1 + Ae^{-Bx}}$ (where A and L are constant and $B = Lk$) can be derived from the differential equation $\frac{dy}{dx} = ky(L - y)$ using separation of variables, partial fractions, and a lot of algebra, it is not within the scope of this text to go into this much detail. However, you will be asked in the activities to verify that $y(x) = \frac{L}{1 + Ae^{-Bx}}$, with $B = Lk$, is a general solution for $\frac{dy}{dx} = ky(L - y)$.

EXAMPLE 4   *Solving an Equation That Results in a Logistic Function*

Epidemic   In 1949 the United States experienced the second worst polio epidemic* in its history. (The worst was in 1952.) In January, 494 cases of polio were diagnosed, and by December, a total of 42,375 cases had been diagnosed. Assume that the spread of polio followed the general principle that the rate of spread is jointly proportional to the number of infected people and to the number of uninfected people. Also assume that the carrying capacity for polio in the United States in 1949 was approximately 43,000 people.

a. Write a differential equation describing the spread of polio.

b. Determine a particular solution for this differential equation.

---

* The National Foundation for Infantile Paralysis, *Twelfth Annual Report,* 1949.

Solution

a. Let $P(m)$ be the number of polio cases diagnosed by the end of the mth month of 1949, and let k be the constant of proportionality. A differential equation describing the spread of polio is

$$\frac{dP}{dm} = kP(43,000 - P) \text{ cases per month}$$

Because we are given information about the number of cases, not information concerning the rate of change of the number of cases, we cannot find the constant of proportionality at this point.

b. A general solution for this differential equation is the logistic equation

$$P(m) = \frac{43,000}{1 + Ae^{-43,000 \, km}} \text{ cases}$$

diagnosed by the end of the mth month of 1949. This equation contains two constants, A and k. We are given the two points $(1, 494)$ and $(12, 42,375)$. Substituting these into the logistic equation, we obtain a system of two equations that we can solve simultaneously for the constant, A and k. The equations are

$$494 = \frac{43,000}{1 + Ae^{-43,000k}} \tag{3}$$

$$42,375 = \frac{43,000}{1 + Ae^{-516,000k}} \tag{4}$$

Solving equation 3 for A and then substituting into equation 4 yields

$$42,375 = \frac{43,000}{1 + \left(\dfrac{42,506e^{43,000k}}{494}\right)e^{-516,000k}}$$

Solving this equation for k yields $k \approx 1.83328271 \cdot 10^{-5}$, or $B = Lk \approx 0.788312$. Substituting k into equation 3 and then solving for A yields $A \approx 189.2704$. Thus we have the particular solution

$$P(m) \approx \frac{43,000}{1 + 189.2704e^{-0.788312m}} \text{ cases}$$

diagnosed by the mth month of 1949.   ●

Separation of variables often yields a solution when we are considering differential equations of the form $\frac{dy}{dx} = f(y)$ or $\frac{dy}{dx} = f(x, y)$. Slope fields usually give graphical insight into the behavior of the underlying function, and in the case where $\frac{dy}{dx} = ky \, (L - y)$, we have a specific equation that gives the solution. However, there are many differential equations for which graphical and algebraic methods of determining particular solutions are beyond the scope of this book. In fact, there are many differential equations for which algebraic solution methods fail. In such cases, we rely on numerical techniques, one of which is discussed in the next section.

8.2   Concept Inventory

- Solutions to differential equations of the form
  $$\frac{dy}{dx} = f(x, y)$$
- Solutions to differential equations of the form
  $$\frac{dy}{dx} = ky$$
- Solutions to differential equations of the form
  $$\frac{dy}{dx} = ky(L - y)$$
- Separation of variables
- Joint proportionality

8.2   Activities

Getting Started

For Activities 1 through 5, write a differential equation for each of the statements. When possible, find a general solution to the differential equation.

1. Ice thickens with respect to time t at a rate that is inversely proportional to its thickness T.

2. The Verhulst population model assumes that a population P in a country will be increasing with respect to time t at a rate that is jointly proportional to the existing population and to the remaining amount of the carrying capacity C of that country.

3. The rate of change with respect to time t of the amount A that an investment is worth is proportional to the amount in the investment.

4. The rate of change in the height h of a tree with respect to its age a is inversely proportional to the tree's height.

5. In a community of N farmers, the number x of farmers who own a certain tractor changes with respect to time t at a rate that is jointly proportional to the number of farmers who own the tractor and to the number of farmers who do not own the tractor.

6. In mountainous country, snow accumulates at a rate proportional to time t and is packed down at a rate proportional to the depth S of the snowpack. Write a differential equation describing the rate of change in the depth of the snowpack with respect to time.

7. Water flows into a reservoir at a rate that is inversely proportional to the square root of the depth of water in the reservoir, and water flows out of the reservoir at a rate that is proportional to the depth of the water in the reservoir. Write a differential equation describing the rate of change in the depth D of water in the reservoir with respect to time t.

For Activities 8 through 17, sketch three particular solutions for each given slope field.

8.

9.

10.

11.

12.

13.

14.

15.

16.

17.

For Activities 18 through 24, identify the differential equation as one that can be solved using only antiderivatives or as one for which separation of variables is required. Then find a general solution for the differential equation.

18. $\dfrac{dy}{dx} = kx$

19. $\dfrac{dy}{dx} = ky$

20. $\dfrac{dy}{dx} = \dfrac{k}{y}$

21. $\dfrac{dy}{dx} = \dfrac{k}{x}$

22. $\dfrac{dy}{dx} = \dfrac{kx}{y}$

23. $\dfrac{dy}{dx} = \dfrac{ky}{x}$

24. $\dfrac{dy}{dx} = kxy$

Applying Concepts

25. Medicine   The rate of change with respect to time of the quantity q of pain reliever in a person's body t hours after the individual takes the medication is proportional to the quantity of medication remaining. Assume that 2 hours after a person takes 200 milligrams of a pain reliever, one-half of the original dose remains.

a. Write a differential equation for the rate of change of the quantity of pain reliever in the body.

b. Find a particular solution for this differential equation.

c. How much pain reliever will remain after 4 hours? after 8 hours?

26. Radioisotope   Technetium-99 is a radioisotope that has been used in humans to help doctors locate possible malignant tumors. Radioisotopes decay (over time) at a rate that is directly proportional to the amount of the radioisotope. Technetium-99 has a half-life of 210,000 years. Assume that 0.1 milligram of technetium-99 is injected into a person's bloodstream.

a. Write a differential equation for the rate at which the amount of technetium-99 decays.

b. Find a particular solution for this differential equation.

27. Radioisotope   Radon-232 is a colorless, odorless gas that undergoes radioactive decay with a half-life of 3.824 days. It is considered a health hazard, so new homebuyers often have their property tested for the presence of radon-232. Because radon-232 is a radioisotope, it decays (over time) at a rate that is directly proportional to the amount of the radioisotope.

a. Write a differential equation for the rate at which an amount of radon-232 decays.

b. Write a general solution for this differential equation.

c. If 1 gram of radon-232 is isolated, how much of it will remain after 12 hours? after 4 days? after 9 days? after 30 days?

28. Consider a function $y = f(x)$ whose rate of change is proportional to f.

a. Write a differential equation describing the rate of change of this function.

b. Write a general solution for the differential equation.

c. Verify that the general solution you gave in part *b* is indeed a solution by substituting it into the differential equation and simplifying to obtain an identity.

29. Postage   In 1880, 37 countries issued postage stamps. The rate of change (with respect to time) of the number of countries issuing postage stamps between 1836 and 1880 was jointly proportional to the number of countries that had already issued postage stamps and to the number of countries that had not yet issued postage stamps. The constant of proportionality was approximately 0.0049. By 1855, 16 countries had issued postage stamps.

(Source: "The Curve of Cultural Diffusion," *American Sociological Review,* August 1936, 547–556.)

a. Write a differential equation describing the rate of change in the number of countries issuing postage stamps with respect to the number of years since 1800.

b. Write a general solution for the differential equation.

c. Write the particular solution for the differential equation.

d. Estimate the number of countries that were issuing postage stamps in 1840 and in 1860.

e. Using the slope field, identify the upper and lower horizontal asymptotes.

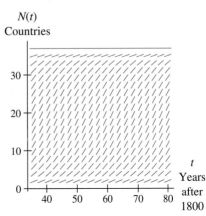

f. On the slope field, sketch the particular solution for the given initial condition.

30. Patents The number of patents issued for plow sulkies between 1865 and 1925 was increasing with respect to time at a rate jointly proportional to the number of patents already obtained and to the difference between the number of patents already obtained and the carrying capacity of the system. The carrying capacity was approximately 2700 patents, and the constant of proportionality was about $7.52 \cdot 10^{-5}$. By 1883, 980 patents had been obtained.

(Source: Hamblin, Jacobsen, and Miller, *A Mathematical Theory of Social Change*, New York: Wiley, 1973.)

a. Write a differential equation describing the rate of change in the number of patents with respect to the number of years since 1865.

b. Write a general solution for the differential equation.

c. Write the particular solution for the differential equation.

d. Estimate the number of patents obtained by 1900.

e. Using the slope field, identify the upper and lower horizontal asymptotes.

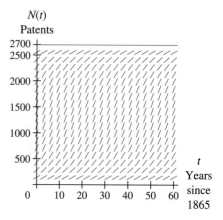

f. On the slope field, sketch the particular solution for the given initial condition.

31. Consider a function $y = f(x)$ whose rate of change is jointly proportional to f and to $L - f$.

a. Write a differential equation describing the rate of change of this function.

b. Write a general solution for the differential equation.

c. Verify that the general solution you gave in part b is indeed a solution by substituting it into the differential equation and simplifying to obtain an identity.

8.3   Numerically Estimating by Using Differential Equations: Euler's Method

There are differential equations that cannot be solved (or are difficult to solve) using the methods we have discussed. In these cases, you may wish to analyze the differential equation using a numerical method. One method we use for such an analysis is called Euler's method after the eighteenth-century Swiss mathematician Leonhard Euler (pronounced "oiler").

Euler's method relies on the use of the derivative function to approximate the change in the quantity function. Recall that if we know a point $(a, f(a))$ on a function f and we also know $f'(a)$, the slope at that point, then we can approximate the value of the function at a close point $(b, f(b))$ as $f(b) \approx f(a) + (b - a) f'(a)$. In using this approximation, we are using a point on the line tangent to the graph of f at $x = a$ to approximate a point on the function (see Figure 8.17).

We first illustrate the Euler method of approximating change for a differential equation we can solve. Judging on the basis of data compiled from *Statistical Abstract, 1993, 1998,* and *2001,* the growth rate of the population of the United States between 1900 and 2000 can be expressed as $\frac{dP}{dx} = 0.0181x + 1.129$ million people per year x years after 1900. In 1990 the population was 249.9 million people.

The initial condition gives us a starting point, (90, 249.9), and the differential equation gives us the slope of the line tangent to the graph of P at that point, $P'(90) = 2.758$ million people per year. If we use this information to estimate the population in the year 2005, then we obtain $P(105) \approx 249.9 + 15(2.758) = 291.27$ million people. Figure 8.18 illustrates the tangent-line estimate and the estimate given by the solution P.

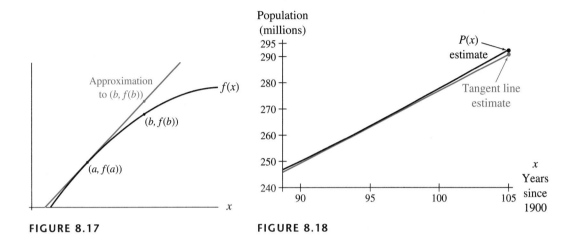

FIGURE 8.17   **FIGURE 8.18**

Euler's method says that we can obtain a better estimate by using many steps rather than using just one step in the approximation process. In this case, instead of approximating over 15 years all in one step, we obtain a better estimate by approximating over 1-year intervals 15 times. Using the initial condition (90, 249.9) and the differential equation evaluated at $x = 90$, $P'(90) = 2.758$, we approximate the population for the year 1991 as

$$P(91) \approx 249.9 + (1)(2.758) = 252.658 \text{ million people}$$

Now we have an estimate of a new point, (91, 252.658), and we use the differential equation to find the slope of the tangent line in 1991, $P'(91) = 2.7761$ million people per year. Using this new point and slope, we estimate the population in 1992 as

$$P(92) \approx 252.658 + (1)(2.7761) = 255.4341 \text{ million people}$$

Similarly, we estimate the population for each of the years from 1993 through 2005. Table 8.1 records these estimates, and Figure 8.19 illustrates the estimates and the line segments used to create them. (Note that even though the slopes found are those of tangent lines, the actual line segments may not be lines tangent to the graph of P but, rather, lines parallel to those tangent lines.)

Applying Euler's method using steps of size 1 year yields the estimate that the population in 2005 will be 293.17 million people. This estimate is slightly larger than our original estimate of 291.27 and is closer to the estimate of 293.3 that we obtained in Example 1 of Section 8.1 by finding a particular solution to the differential equation. (To obtain an estimate closer to that given by the particular solution, we could use Euler's method with 100 steps of size 0.1 to improve our results.)

The graph we obtain by plotting the Euler estimates (Figure 8.19) and drawing the appropriate line segments is not a smooth curve. However, it does resemble a portion of the quadratic curve that we expect to see for the solution of this differential equation and is an approximation to the graph of the population function described by the differential equation.

TABLE 8.1

x	Estimate of P(x)	Slope at x
90	249.9000	2.7580
91	252.6580	2.7761
92	255.4341	2.7942
93	258.2283	2.8123
94	261.0406	2.8304
95	263.8710	2.8485
96	266.7195	2.8666
97	269.5861	2.8847
98	272.4708	2.9028
99	275.3736	2.9209
100	278.2945	2.9390
101	281.2335	2.9571
102	284.1906	2.9752
103	287.1658	2.9933
104	290.1591	3.0114
105	293.1705	

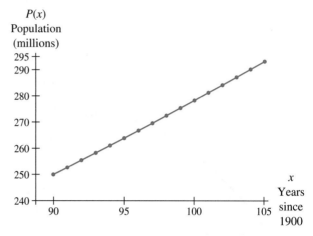

FIGURE 8.19

Euler's method is a fairly straightforward way of numerically estimating a solution to a differential equation. However, use caution. Because each step of Euler's method is built on an estimate made in the previous step, it can lead to very bad estimates when the step size is too large or when the slopes given by the differential equation change from very large to very small over a small interval. For these reasons, there are other methods of numerically estimating solutions that are taught in more advanced courses. However, because Euler's method is sufficient for our uses, we will not consider these other methods.

Example 1 illustrates the application of Euler's method to the differential equation given in Example 2 of Section 8.1.

EXAMPLE 1   *Applying Euler's Method to an Equation in One Variable*

Sales   In Example 2 of Section 8.1, we saw that the rate of change of the total sales of a computer product could be represented by the differential equation

$$\frac{dS}{dt} \approx \frac{6.544}{\ln(t + 1.2)} \text{ billion dollars per year}$$

where t is the number of years after the product was introduced. Also, we were told that at the end of the first year, sales totaled $53.2 billion. Use Euler's method to estimate the total sales at the end of the fifth year.

Solution

Our starting point (the total sales at the end of the first year) is given as (1, 53.2), we know that the rate of change at the end of the first year is $S'(1) = \frac{6.544}{\ln(1 + 1.2)} \approx 8.2998$, and we wish to estimate $S(5)$, the total sales at the end of the fifth year. We use Euler's method to estimate over an interval of 4 years. In order to keep the step sizes small, we choose to take 16 steps of size 0.25. The first step gives an estimate for $S(1.25)$:

$$S(1.25) \approx 53.2 + (0.25)(8.2998) \approx 55.275$$

The estimates (to three decimal places) from each step, as well as the slopes given by the differential equation, are recorded in Table 8.2.

TABLE 8.2

t	Estimate of $S(t)$ (billion dollars)	Slope at t (billion dollars per year)
1.0	53.200	8.2998
1.25	55.275	7.3029
1.5	57.101	6.5885
1.75	58.748	6.0491
2.0	60.260	5.6261
2.25	61.667	5.2843
2.5	62.988	5.0018
2.75	64.238	4.7637
3.0	65.429	4.5600
3.25	66.569	4.3834
3.5	67.665	4.2286
3.75	68.722	4.0916
4.0	69.745	3.9693
4.25	70.737	3.8594
4.5	71.702	3.7599
4.75	72.642	3.6694
5.0	73.559	

Euler's method with step sizes of 0.25 year yields the estimate that the total sales for this computer product will be $73.6 billion at the end of the fifth year. A graph (Figure 8.20) of the Euler estimates is an approximation of a graph of total sales.

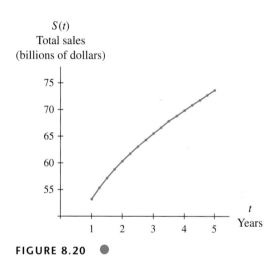

FIGURE 8.20 ●

Euler's method can be used on most first-order differential equations, even when separation of variables fails.

EXAMPLE 2   *Using Euler's Method with Two Variables*

Consider the differential equation $\frac{dy}{dx} = 5.9x - 3.2y$. Given an initial condition of $y(10) = 50$, estimate $y(12)$.

Solution

Because we know both x and y at $x = 10$, we can use the differential equation to calculate the slope at $x = 10$ and $y = 50$ as $\frac{dy}{dx} = 5.9(10) - 3.2(50) = -101$.

We choose to use Euler's method with ten steps of size 0.2. The first estimate is $y(10.2) \approx 50 + (0.2)(-101) = 29.8$.

TABLE 8.3

x	Estimate of y(x)	Slope at x
10	50	−101
10.2	29.8	−35.18
10.4	22.764	−11.485
10.6	20.467	−2.955
10.8	19.876	0.116
11	19.899	1.222
11.2	20.144	1.620
11.4	20.468	1.763
11.6	20.820	1.815
11.8	21.183	1.833
12	21.550	

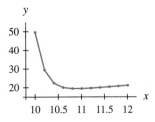

FIGURE 8.21

Because the formula for the slope $\left(\frac{dy}{dx} = 5.9x - 3.2y\right)$ relies on knowing both x and y to estimate the slope at $x = 10.2$, we must use our estimate $y(10.2) \approx 29.8$ in the slope formula. Thus, at $x = 10.2$,

$$\frac{dy}{dx} \approx 5.9(10.2) - 3.2(29.8) = -35.18$$

We now use the estimates $y(10.2) \approx 29.8$ and $\frac{dy}{dx} \approx -35.18$ at $x = 10.2$ to estimate the value of y at $x = 10.4$:

$$y(10.4) \approx 29.8 + (0.2)(-35.18) = 22.764$$

To find an estimate of $y(10.6)$, we need the slope $\frac{dy}{dx}$ at $x = 10.4$. Again we must estimate this slope at $x = 10.4$ using $y(10.4)$:

$$\frac{dy}{dx} \approx 5.9(10.4) - 3.2(22.764) = -11.4848$$

Thus the value of y at $x = 10.6$ is

$$y(10.6) \approx 22.764 + (0.2)(-11.4848) = 20.46704$$

Proceeding in this manner, we construct Table 8.3 of Euler estimates and find that $y(12) \approx 21.55$.

Graphing the Euler estimates gives us an idea of how the function y behaves (see Figure 8.21). There appears to be a minimum near $x = 10.8$. The minimum value is $y \approx 19.876$. ●

8.3 Concept Inventory

- Euler's method
- Step size versus number of steps
- Graph of Euler estimates

8.3 Activities

Getting Started

1. Use Euler's method and two steps to estimate the following values.

   a. Given $\frac{dy}{dx} = \frac{1}{2}$ with the initial condition $(0, 0)$, estimate y when $x = 4$.

   b. Given $\frac{dy}{dx} = 2x$ with the initial condition $(1, 4)$, estimate y when $x = 7$.

2. Are the answers to parts a and b of Activity 1 approximate or exact? In each case, explain why.

3. Use Euler's method and two steps to estimate the following values.

   a. Given $\frac{dy}{dx} = \frac{5}{y}$ with initial condition $(1, 1)$, estimate y when $x = 5$.

   b. Given $\frac{dy}{dx} = \frac{5}{x}$ with initial condition $(2, 2)$, estimate y when $x = 8$.

4. Consider the differential equations in parts a and b of Activity 3.

   a. Write the particular solution for the given initial condition.

b. Sketch the particular solution.

c. Sketch the Euler estimate.

d. Explain why the Euler estimate deviates from the true solution.

Applying Concepts

5. Weight For the first 9 months of life, the average weight w, in pounds, of a certain breed of dog increases at a rate that is inversely proportional to time t, in months. A 1-month-old puppy weighs 6 pounds. The constant of proportionality is 33.67885.

a. Write a differential equation describing the rate of change of the weight of the puppy.

b. Use Euler's method with a 0.25-month step length to estimate the weight of the puppy at 3 months and at 6 months.

c. Use Euler's method with a step length of 1 month to estimate the weight of the puppy at 3 months and at 6 months.

d. Do you expect the answer to part b or the answer to part c to be more accurate? Why?

6. Postage The rate of change (with respect to time) of the number of countries issuing postage stamps between 1836 and 1880 was jointly proportional to the number of countries that had already issued postage stamps and to the number of countries that had not yet issued postage stamps. The constant of proportionality was approximately 0.0049. By 1855, 16 countries had issued postage stamps.

(Source: "The Curve of Cultural Diffusion," *American Sociological Review*, August 1936, 547–556.)

a. Write a differential equation describing the rate of change in the number of countries issuing postage stamps with respect to the number of years since 1800.

b. Use Euler's method with five steps to estimate the number of countries issuing postage stamps in 1840.

c. Use Euler's method with a step length of 5 years to estimate the number of countries issuing postage stamps in 1840.

d. Do you expect the answer to part b or the answer to part c to be more accurate? Why?

7. Production It is estimated that for the first 10 years of production, a certain oil well can be expected to produce oil at a rate of

$$r(t) = 3.935t^{3.55}e^{-1.35135}$$

$$\text{thousand barrels per year}$$

t years after production begins.

a. Write a differential equation for the rate of change of the total amount of oil produced t years after production begins.

b. Use Euler's method with ten intervals to estimate the yield from this oil well during the first 5 years of production.

c. Graph the differential equation and the Euler estimates. Discuss how the shape of the graph of the differential equation is related to the shape of the graph of the Euler estimates.

8. Labor The personnel manager for a large construction company keeps records of the worker hours per week spent on typical construction jobs handled by the company. The manager has developed the following model for a worker hours curve:

$$r(x) = \frac{6{,}608{,}830e^{-0.705989x}}{(1 + 925.466e^{-0.705989x})^2}$$

$$\text{worker hours per week}$$

the xth week of the construction job.

a. Use this model to write a differential equation giving the rate of change of the total number of worker hours used by the end of the xth week.

b. Graph this differential equation, and discuss any critical points and trends that the differential equation suggests will occur.

c. Use Euler's method with 20 intervals to estimate the total number of worker hours used by the end of the 20th week.

d. Graph the Euler estimates, and discuss whether you believe the estimate is good. Refer to the points you discussed in part b. How could you improve the accuracy of your estimate?

9. Cooling Newton's Law of Cooling says that the rate of change (with respect to time t) of the temperature T of an object is proportional to the difference between the temperature of the object and the temperature A of the object's surroundings.

a. Write a differential equation describing this law.

b. Consider a room that has a constant temperature of $A = 70°F$. An object is placed in that room and allowed to cool. When the object is first placed in the room, the temperature of the object is $98°F$, and it is cooling at a rate of $1.8°F$ per minute. Determine the constant of proportionality for the differential equation.

c. Use Euler's method and 15 steps to estimate the temperature of the object after 15 minutes.

10. **Learning** A person learns a new task at a rate that is equal to the percentage of the task not yet learned. Let p represent the percentage of the task already learned at time t (in hours).

a. Write a differential equation describing the rate of change in the percentage of the task learned at time t.

b. Use Euler's method with eight steps of size 0.25 to estimate the percentage of the task that is learned in 2 hours.

c. Graph the Euler estimates, and discuss any critical points or trends.

11. Explain why you would expect Euler's method to have better accuracy when more steps of smaller size are used. Illustrate with graphs.

12. **Postage** Refer to the information given in Activity 6 about the rate of change of the number of countries issuing postage stamps.

a. Use Euler's method with 40 steps and with 80 steps to estimate the number of countries issuing postage stamps in 1840.

b. Graph the Euler estimates in part a.

c. Discuss your expectations for the accuracy of your answers.

13. **Production** Refer to the information given in Activity 7 about the rate of production of oil from an oil well.

a. Use Euler's method with intervals of 1 month, then with intervals of 1 week, and finally with daily intervals to estimate the yield from the well during the first 5 years of production.

b. Graph the Euler estimates in part a.

c. Discuss your expectations for the accuracy of your answers.

14. **Labor** Refer to the information given in Activity 8 about the labor power on a construction job.

a. Use Euler's method with 140 intervals to estimate the total number of worker hours used by the end of the 20th week.

b. Graph the Euler estimates in part a.

c. Discuss your expectations for the accuracy of your answers. Does an estimate using 140 intervals have any advantage over an estimate using 20 intervals? Explain.

15. **Cooling** Refer to the information given in Activity 9 about Newton's Law of Cooling. Consider particularly the specification given in part b of Activity 9.

a. Use Euler's method with intervals of length 1 second to estimate the temperature of the object after 15 minutes.

b. Graph the Euler estimates in part a.

c. How does this estimate compare with that found in part c of Activity 9? Discuss the accuracy of this method

8.4 Second-Order Differential Equations

Not all differential equations involve only the first derivative of a function. Some tell us about the second derivative. That is, they tell us about the rate at which the rate of change is changing.

Because acceleration is the derivative of velocity v with respect to time t, and velocity is the derivative of distance s with respect to time, we can write acceleration due to gravity near the surface of the Earth as the differential equation

$$\frac{d^2s}{dt^2} = -32 \text{ feet per second squared}$$

after t seconds. This differential equation is of the form $s''(t) = k$ for some constant k. (We saw these equations in Chapter 5 when working with antiderivatives.) This is a second derivative of a function, so a general solution can be found by finding the general antiderivative of $\frac{d^2s}{dt^2}$ twice. The general antiderivative of the differential equation for acceleration is

$$\frac{ds}{dt} = -32t + C \text{ feet per second}$$

Thus the general solution to the differential equation is

$$s(t) = -16t^2 + Ct + D \text{ feet}$$

after t seconds.

To confirm that this equation is a solution to the differential equation, we substitute for s in the differential equation:

$$\frac{d^2}{dt^2}(-16t^2 + Ct + D) = -32$$

Differentiating the left side of the equation twice yields the identity $-32 = -32$.

In the case where the object fell from a height of 40 feet ($s = 40$ and $v = 0$ at $t = 0$), we have the particular solution $s(t) = -16t^2 + 40$ feet after t seconds.

EXAMPLE 1 *Solving a Second-Order Linear Differential Equation*

Purchasing Power The rate of change in the purchasing power* of the U.S. dollar was changing at a linear rate between 1988 and 2000. A differential equation describing the rate at which the rate of change of the purchasing power was decreasing is

$$\frac{d^2P}{dx^2} = -0.00156x + 0.0115 \text{ dollars per year squared}$$

where x is the number of years since 1988. The purchasing power is based on 1982 dollars, making a 1982 dollar worth $0.93 in 1988 and $0.81 in 1992.

a. Write a general solution for the purchasing power of a dollar.

b. Write a particular solution for the purchasing power of a dollar.

c. Use the particular solution to determine how much a 1982 dollar was worth in 2000.

* Based on data from *Statistical Abstract,* 1994 and 2001.

Solution

a. By finding the antiderivative of the differential equation twice, we obtain the general solution

$$P(x) = -0.00026x^3 + 0.00575x^2 + Cx + D \text{ dollars}$$

where x is the number of years since 1988.

b. The conditions given are $P(4) = 0.81$ and $P(0) = 0.93$. The condition $P(0) = 0.93$ gives us the value for D as 0.93. Using $D = 0.93$ and $P(4) = 0.81$, we solve for C and find that $C \approx -0.0488$. Thus we have the particular solution

$$P(x) = -0.00026x^3 + 0.00575x^2 - 0.0488x + 0.93 \text{ dollars}$$

where x is the number of years since 1988.

c. By 2000, a 1982 dollar was worth only $P(12) \approx \$0.72$.   ●

Let us now consider situations in which the second derivative of an amount is proportional to the amount function—that is, the situation in which

$$\frac{d^2y}{dx^2} = ky$$

We consider the case where the constant of proportionality is negative:

$$\frac{d^2y}{dx^2} = -ky \text{ for } k > 0$$

Consider the differential equation $\frac{d^2y}{dx^2} = -y$. One function we have looked at that satisfies this equation is the function $y(x) = \sin x$. We verify this by differentiating the function twice:

$$y'(x) = \cos x$$
$$y''(x) = -\sin x = -y(x)$$

The cosine function is another function that satisfies $\frac{d^2y}{dx^2} = -y$.

For the more general case $\frac{d^2y}{dx^2} = -ky$, where $k > 0$, it can be shown that the general solution is

$$y(x) = a \sin(\sqrt{k}\, x + c)$$

where a and c are constants. You will be asked to verify this in the activities.

EXAMPLE 2   *Solving a Second-Order Differential Equation*

Fishing   An exclusive fishing club on the Restigouche River in Canada kept detailed records regarding the number of fish caught by its members.* Between 1880 and 1905, the rate of change (with respect to the year) in the number of fish per rod per day was changing at a rate proportional to the number of fish per rod per day. The constant of proportionality is approximately -0.455625.

---

* Based on information in E. R. Dewey and E. F. Dakin, *Cycles: The Science of Prediction*, New York: Holt, 1947.

The average number of fish per rod per day for the years between 1880 and 1905 was 1.267 fish per rod per day. In 1881, the catch was 0.9425 fish per rod per day, and in 1885, 1.5776 fish per rod per day were caught.

a.   Write a differential equation expressing the rate at which the rate of change in the number of fish per rod per day was changing with respect to the number of years since 1880.

b.   Write a particular solution to the differential equation.

c.   Write a model for the average number of fish per rod per day given the number of years since 1880.

Solution

a.   A differential equation expressing the rate at which the rate of change in g, the number of fish per rod per day, was changing is

$$\frac{d^2g}{dy^2} = -0.455625g \text{ fish per rod per day per year squared}$$

where y is the number of years since 1880.

b.   As previously stated, the general solution is $g(y) = a \sin(\sqrt{k}\,y + c)$, where $k = 0.455625$. Thus the general solution to this differential equation is

$$g(y) = a \sin (0.675y + c) \text{ fish per rod per day}$$

where y is the number of years since 1880, and a and c are constants. In order to determine the constants a and c for this equation, we must have two conditions. First, we note that the general solution does not include the parameter d giving the expected number of fish per rod per day that is normally included in a general sine model $f(x) = a \sin (bx + c) + d$. Thus we must write the conditions in terms of the difference from the expected value. That is, in 1881 the catch was 0.3245 fewer fish per rod per day than in an average year, and in 1885 the catch was 0.3106 more fish per rod per day than in an average year. Thus the two conditions are $g(1) = -0.3245$ and $g(5) = 0.3106$, resulting in the equations

$$-0.3245 = a \sin[0.675(1) + c] \tag{1}$$
$$0.3106 = a \sin[0.675(5) + c] \tag{2}$$

Solving for a in equation 1 and then substituting in equation 2 yields

$$0.3106 = \frac{-0.3245 \sin(3.375 + c)}{\sin(0.675 + c)}$$

which gives $c \approx 1.019$. Substituting this value of c into either equation 1 or equation 2 and then solving for a yields $a \approx -0.327$. Using these constants a and c, we have the particular solution for the differential equation as

$$g(y) = -0.327 \sin(0.675y + 1.019) \text{ fish per rod per day}$$

where y is the number of years since 1880.

c.   The general and particular solutions for the differential equation are both in terms of the difference from the expected value of fish per rod per day. To write the general sine model for this situation, we add the parameter d, the expected value of fish per day:

$$g(y) = -0.327 \sin(0.675y + 1.019) + 1.267 \text{ fish per rod per day}$$

where y is the number of years since 1880. ●

Before we leave this section, let us consider the differential equation of the form

$$\frac{d^2y}{dx^2} = ky, \text{ where } k > 0$$

In this case, the constant of proportionality is positive (rather than negative as in Example 2), and the general solution is

$$y(x) = ae^{\sqrt{kx}} + be^{-\sqrt{kx}}$$

where a and b are constants. Note that the general solution to this differential equation appears to be very different from the general solution in the negative case. The negative case leads to a model with which we are familiar; the positive case does not.

8.4 Concept Inventory

- Second-order differential equations
- Solutions to differential equations of the form $\frac{d^2y}{dx^2} = k$
- Solutions to differential equations of the form $\frac{d^2y}{dx^2} = f(x)$
- Solutions to differential equations of the form $\frac{d^2y}{dx^2} = ky$

8.4 Activities

Getting Started

For Activities 1 through 4, write a differential equation expressing the information given, and when possible, find a general solution for the differential equation.

1. The Rowan-Robinson model of the universe assumes that the universe is expanding with respect to time t at a rate that is decreasing in inverse proportion to the square of its current size S.

2. The rate of change with respect to time t of the demand D for a product is decreasing in proportion to the demand at time t.

3. The rate of change in year y of the population P of the United States is increasing with respect to the year at a constant rate.

4. The rate of growth of the height h of a young child with respect to the age y of the child decreases in inverse proportion to the age of the child.

Applying Concepts

5. **Jobs** The rate of change in the number of jobs for a Michigan roofing company is increasing by approximately 6.14 jobs per month squared. The number of jobs in January is decreasing at the rate of 0.87 job per month, and company records indicate that the company had 14 roofing jobs in February.

   a. Write a differential equation for the rate at which the rate of change in the number of roofing jobs for this company is changing.

   b. Find a particular solution to the differential equation in part a.

   c. Use the result of part b to estimate the number of roofing jobs in August and the number in November.

6. **Marriage** Between 1950 and 2000, the rate of change in the rate at which the median age of first marriage of females in the United States was changing was constant at 0.0042 year of age per year squared. The median age of first marriage for these females was increasing at the rate of 0.1713 year of

age per year in 1991, and females were first married at a median age of 25.1 in 2000.

(Source: Based on data from www.infoplease.com Accessed 9/20/02.)

a. Write a differential equation for the rate at which the rate of the median age of first marriage for United States females is changing.

b. Find a particular solution to the differential equation in part *a*.

c. Use the result of part *b* to estimate the median age of first marriage of United States females in the current year.

7. AIDS   Records of the number of AIDS cases diagnosed in the United States between 1988 and 1991 indicate that the rate at which the rate of change in the number of cases was changing was constant at −2099 cases per year squared. The number of AIDS cases diagnosed in 1988 was 33,590, and the number of cases was increasing at the rate of 5988.7 cases per year in 1988.

(Source: Based on data appearing in *HIV/AIDS Surveillance* 1992 Year End Edition.)

a. Write a differential equation for the rate of change in the rate of change of the number of AIDS cases diagnosed in year *t*, where *t* is the number of years after 1988.

b. Find a particular solution to the differential equation in part *a*.

c. Estimate how rapidly the number of AIDS cases diagnosed was changing in 1991 and the number of AIDS cases that were diagnosed in that year.

8. Postage   Between 1919 and 1995, the rate of change in the rate of change of the postage required to mail a first-class 1-ounce letter was approximately 0.022 cent per year squared. The postage was 2 cents in 1919, and it was increasing at the rate of approximately 0.393 cent per year in 1958.

(Source: Based on data from the United States Postal Service.)

a. Write a differential equation for the rate of change in the rate of change of the first-class postage for a 1-ounce letter in year *t*, where *t* is the number of years after 1900.

b. Find both a general and a particular solution to the differential equation in part *a*.

c. Use your previous results to estimate how rapidly the postage is changing in the current year and the

current first-class postage for a 1-ounce letter. Comment on the accuracy of your results. If they are not reasonable, give possible explanations.

9. Consider a function $y = f(x)$ whose rate of change with respect to *x* is changing at a constant rate.

a. Write a differential equation describing the rate of change in the rate of change for this function.

b. Write a general solution for the differential equation.

c. Verify that the general solution you gave in part *b* is indeed a solution by substituting it into the differential equation and simplifying to obtain an identity.

10. Motion Laws   When a spring is stretched and then released, it oscillates according to two laws of physics: Hooke's Law and Newton's Second Law. These two laws combine to form the following differential equation in the case of free, undamped oscillation:

$$m\frac{d^2x}{dt^2} + kx = 0$$

where *m* is the mass of an object attached to the spring, *x* is the distance the spring is stretched beyond its standard length with the object attached (its equilibrium point), *t* is time, and *k* is a constant associated with the strength of the spring. Consider a spring with $k = 15$ from which is hung a 30-pound weight. The spring with the weight attached stretches to its equilibrium point. The spring is then pulled 2 feet farther than its equilibrium and released.

a. Write a differential equation describing the acceleration of the spring with respect to time *t* measured in seconds. Use the fact that mass = $\frac{\text{weight}}{g}$, where *g* is the gravitational constant 32 feet per second per second.

b. Write a particular solution for this differential equation. Use the fact that when the spring is first released, its velocity is 0.

c. Graph this solution over several periods, and explain how to interpret the graph.

d. How quickly is the mass moving when it passes its equilibrium point?

11. Radiation   The rate of change in the rate at which the average amount of extraterrestrial radiation in Amarillo, Texas, for each month of the year is changing is proportional to the amount of extraterrestrial radiation received. The constant of proportionality is $k = -0.212531$. In any given month, the expected value of radiation is 12.5 mm per day. This expected value is actually obtained in March and September.

(Source: Based on data from A. A. Hanson, ed., *Practical Handbook of Agricultural Science*, Boca Raton, FL: CRC Press, 1990.)

a. Write a differential equation for the information given.

b. In June, the amount of radiation received is approximately 17.0 mm per day, and in December, the amount of radiation received is approximately 7.8 mm per day. Write a particular solution for this differential equation.

c. Change the particular solution into a function giving the average amount of extraterrestrial radiation in Amarillo.

d. How well does your model estimate the amounts of extraterrestrial radiation in March and September?

12. Consider a function $y = f(x)$ whose rate of change with respect to x is changing in proportion to f, where the constant of proportionality is negative.

a. Write a differential equation describing the rate of change in the rate of change for this function.

b. Write a general solution for the differential equation.

c. Verify that the general solution you gave in part *b* is indeed a solution by substituting it into the differential equation and obtaining an identity.

SUMMARY

In many situations (physical, sociological, psychological, and economic), there are certain laws that govern the dynamics of change. In these cases, differential equations often can be used to describe the change that occurs.

Differential Equations

Differential equations are equations involving derivatives. A solution for a differential equation is a function that, when substituted into the differential equation, results in an identity. A general solution contains arbitrary constants that can be determined if initial conditions are known. When the arbitrary constants are replaced by known constants, the solution is called a particular solution.

Some differential equations are of the simple form

$$\frac{dy}{dx} = f(x)$$

In this case, a general solution can be obtained by writing a general antiderivative for the given rate of change if an antiderivative is known.

Slope Fields

It is often helpful to view a graphical representation of a differential equation. This can be done in the form of a slope field. A slope field consists of line segments that represent the slopes given by the differential equation at different points on a grid placed on the coordinate plane.

Separable Differential Equations

Some differential equations are given as functions not only of the input variable but also of the output variable, so they are of the form

$$\frac{dy}{dx} = f(x, y)$$

In this case, a general solution might be obtained by using the method of separation of variables.

Euler's Method

Often, neither simple antidifferentiation nor separation of variables is sufficient for determining an explicit formula for a general solution of a differential equation. In these cases, we can numerically estimate a solution using Euler's method. Euler's method not only gives us a numerical method for estimating solutions but also, when the Euler estimates are graphed, can help us visualize how the solution function behaves.

Second-Order Differential Equations

Second-order differential equations involve the second derivative of a function. The simple cases we considered were the second-order differential equations that give rise to the quadratic, cubic, and sine models.

CONCEPT CHECK

Can you	To practice, try	
• Solve constant and linear differential equations?	Section 8.1	Activities 15, 19
• Set up an equation involving direct or inverse proportionality?	Section 8.1	Activities 19, 23
• Sketch a particular solution to a differential equation on a slope field?	Section 8.1 Section 8.2	Activities 7, 9 Activities 9, 13, 15
• Solve separable differential equations?	Section 8.2	Activity 25
• Set up an equation involving joint proportionality?	Section 8.2	Activity 29
• Estimate a solution to a differential equation using Euler's method?	Section 8.3	Activity 7
• Set up and solve second-order differential equations using antiderivatives?	Section 8.4	Activities 7, 11

CONCEPT REVIEW

1. **Accident Risk**   The relationship between the relative risk R (expressed as a percent) of having a car accident and the blood alcohol level of $100b\%$ of the driver is

$$\frac{dR}{db} = kR$$

   a. Write a statement interpreting this differential equation.

   b. Write a general solution for the differential equation.

   c. The risk of an accident is 1% when there is no alcohol in the blood and 20% when the blood alcohol level is 14%. Write a particular solution for the differential equation.

   d. At what blood alcohol level is a crash certain to occur?

e. Use the slope field to sketch the particular solution found in part *c*.

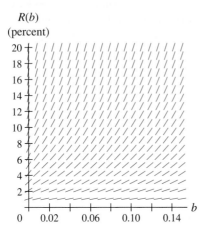

R(b)
(percent)

2. Famine   In Ireland in the 1840s, potato famines occurred. These famines are correlated with a drastic change in the dynamics of population growth and decline. The Verhulst model for population says that the rate of change in a population is jointly proportional to the current population and to the capacity remaining in the system.

a. From population data for 1780 through 1840, the carrying capacity of Ireland's population appears to have been 16.396 million people. The constant of proportionality for growth during this time was 0.001175. Write a differential equation expressing the rate of change of Ireland's population. Let *x* represent the number of years since 1800.

b. Write a general solution for the differential equation in part *a*.

c. Write a particular solution for the differential equation in part *a*. In 1780, there were 4.0 million people in Ireland.

d. Use the particular solution from part *c* to estimate the Irish population in 1840 and 1850.

3. Famine   Consider the differential equation from part *a* of Activity 2 and the initial condition that in 1780 there were 4.0 million people in Ireland.

a. Use Euler's method and 10-year steps to estimate the population of Ireland in 1840 and 1850.

b. Use Euler's method and 5-year steps to estimate the population of Ireland in 1840 and 1850.

c. How do your answers to parts *a* and *b* compare to those from part *d* of Activity 2?

4. Population   Population data for 1850 through 1920 show that Ireland's population was decreasing according to the Verhulst model with a constant of proportionality of 0.008307. Ireland reached a population low of 4.4 million people in 1910 and 1920. To use the Verhulst model for population change, we assume that the carrying capacity of Ireland was 7.154 million people above its 1910–1920 level.

a. Write a differential equation expressing the rate of change of Ireland's population between 1850 and 1920. Let *x* represent the number of years since 1800.

b. Using the fact that in 1900, there were 4.5 million people in Ireland (that is 0.1 million people above its 1910–1920 level), write a particular solution to the differential equation from part *a*.

c. Adjust the model for 1850 through 1920 by adding the base population level of 4.4 million people, and write a piecewise model for the population of Ireland from 1780 through 1920.

d. Use the piecewise model from part *c* to estimate the population of Ireland in 1850. How does this differ from the estimate you found in part *d* of Activity 2?

Project 8.1 On-the-Job Training

Setting

You are the personnel manager for a large manufacturing firm. The shareholders have asked you to estimate the cost for personnel training during the start-up of a new plant that will employee 56 workers. The firm has agreed to pay newly hired employees $10 per hour during their training. The firm has also agreed to pay current employees from another plant $45 per hour for each hour they spend training two new employees. It is estimated that for this job, the average newly hired employee will be able to learn his or her job at a rate that is equal to the percentage of the task not yet learned, where time is measured in 40-hour weeks.

Tasks

1. Write a differential equation describing the rate of change in the percentage of the task learned at time t.

2. Use Euler's method at least three times with decreasing step sizes to estimate the percentage of the task that is learned in 2 weeks.

3. Graph the Euler estimates, and discuss any critical points or trends.

4. Determine at what point the newly hired employees may be ready to handle the job on their own.

5. Formulate a budget for the training of the new personnel.

Reporting

Prepare a report that presents your findings in Tasks 1 through 5. Explain the method that you used to arrive at your conclusions. Attach your mathematical work as an appendix to your report.

9

Ingredients of Multivariable Change: Models, Graphs, Rates

Sonda Dawes/The Image Works

Concept Application

Competition is a fundamental element of a free-market society. Although many factors affect sales of competing products, the most obvious factor is the price of the product. If side-by-side vending machines sell competitive products, and if sales data are collected and modeled as a function of the two prices, then we can use the data and model to answer questions such as

• If one of the competitors lowers the price, what change can the other company expect in sales?

• How quickly are sales changing for two given prices?

• If one company lowers its price, how should the other company respond in order to maintain its current sales level?

You will have an opportunity to answer questions such as these in Activity 28 of Section 9.3 and Activity 21 of Section 9.4.

Chapter Introduction

The mathematics of change for functions of a single input variable was discussed in chapters 1 through 8 of this text. The mathematics of change for multivariable functions will be presented in Chapters 9 and 10. A multivariable function is a function with two or more input variables.

Graphs of functions with two input variables are three-dimensional and represent surfaces in space. We consider associated two-dimensional contour graphs and how they are related to the three-dimensional surfaces. Our understanding of any function and how it changes is greatly enhanced by a visual presentation.

We investigate change in a multivariable function by considering the rate of change with respect to any one of the input variables. We also discuss compensating for change in the context of an important consideration in any manufacturing process: the allocation of available resources to produce a fixed level of output.

Concepts you will be learning

- Constructing input/output diagrams for multivariable functions (9.1)
- Interpreting multivariable function inputs and outputs (9.1)
- Drawing contour curves (9.1)
- Interpreting contour graphs (9.1)
- Finding and interpreting cross-sectional models (9.2)
- Estimating partial rates of change from tables (9.2)
- Finding and interpreting first and second partial derivatives (9.3)
- Constructing a second-partials matrix (9.3)
- Calculating the slope on a contour curve at a specified point (9.3)
- Estimating the "compensation for a change" (9.4)

9.1   Multivariable Functions and Contour Graphs

In Chapters 1 through 8 we studied change using single-variable functions. Each function had one input variable and one output variable. We now consider multivariable functions. These functions have two or more input variables and one output variable.

Multivariable Functions

Many of the functions we encounter in everyday situations are multivariable functions. These are functions that depend on two or more input variables. A manufacturer's profit depends on sales, variable costs, fixed costs, and perhaps other input variables that are related to inventory costs, equipment failures, and labor strikes. In forestry, the volume of a tree is a function of its height and diameter. Crop yield is a function of temperature, rainfall, amount of fertilizer, and so forth.

The input of a multivariable function is denoted by $(x_1, x_2, x_3, \ldots, x_n)$. For each input of a function f, there is only one output $f(x_1, x_2, x_3, \ldots, x_n)$.

> A rule f that relates one output variable to several input variables $(x_1, x_2, x_3, \ldots, x_n)$ is called a **multivariable function** if for each input $(x_1, x_2, x_3, \ldots, x_n)$ there is exactly one output $f(x_1, x_2, x_3, \ldots, x_n)$.

A familiar example of a multivariable function is the value of an investment. The value of an investment is modeled by

$$A(P, r, n, t) = P\left(1 + \frac{r}{n}\right)^{nt} \text{ dollars}$$

where P dollars is the amount originally invested, r is the annual interest rate (written in decimal form), n is the number of times interest is paid each year, and t years is the time since the principal was deposited. An input/output diagram of this function is shown in Figure 9.1.

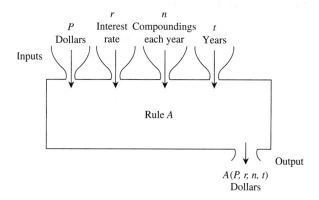

FIGURE 9.1

The **notation** $A(5000, 0.06, 4, 10)$ represents the accumulated value of a $5000 investment after 10 years when the annual interest rate is 6% compounded quarterly. We find this accumulated value to be

$$A(5000, 0.06, 4, 10) = 5000\left(1 + \frac{0.06}{4}\right)^{4(10)} \approx \$9070.09$$

and we say, "The value of a $5000 investment after 10 years with 6% interest paid quarterly is $9070.09."

A second example deals with the elevation of a plot of farmland. We do not have a multivariable equation that can be used to model this situation. However, it is possible to find the elevation of the land through various surveying methods. We do have a data table that presents the elevation at 0.1-mile intervals in two directions.

Elevation is a function whose output (distance above sea level) is determined by knowing the location of a point in terms of a reference point. Although we could locate each point in terms of its longitude and latitude, we simplify the numbers and let the southwest corner of the tract be our reference point. We measure distance from this point in miles from the southern fence and miles from the western fence. The two input variables are e and n, where e is the distance in miles east of the western fence and n is the distance in miles north of the southern fence. The output of the elevation function is $E(e, n)$, the elevation of the tract in feet above sea level at position (e, n). An input/output diagram for this function is shown in Figure 9.2. Graphically, $E(e, n)$ can be represented in three dimensions as shown in Figure 9.3.

Numerically, $E(e, n)$ can be represented by Table 9.1. From the table, we read the elevation at a position 0.3 mile east and 1 mile north of the southwest corner as $E(0.3, 1) = 799.7$ feet above sea level. Note that $e = 0.3$ because the position is 0.3 mile east of the western fence. Likewise, $n = 1$ because the position is 1 mile north of the southern fence.

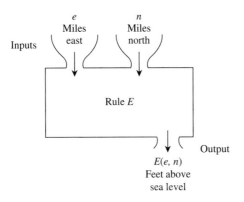

FIGURE 9.2

Three-dimensional graph of elevation
FIGURE 9.3

TABLE 9.1   Elevation $E(e, n)$ in feet above sea level on a tract of Missouri farmland measured e miles east of the western fence and n miles north of the southern fence

$e \rightarrow$	0	0.1	0.2	0.3	0.4	0.5	0.6	0.7	0.8	0.9	1.0	1.1	1.2	1.3	1.4	1.5
1.5	800.3	799.1	798.3	797.8	797.5	797.4	797.4	797.5	797.6	797.7	797.6	797.3	796.8	796.0	794.8	793.2
1.4	800.8	799.6	798.8	798.3	798.0	797.9	797.9	798.0	798.1	798.1	798.1	797.8	797.3	796.5	795.3	793.7
1.3	801.2	800.0	799.2	798.7	798.4	798.3	798.3	798.4	798.5	798.6	798.5	798.2	797.7	796.9	795.7	794.1
1.2	801.6	800.4	799.6	799.1	798.8	798.7	798.7	798.8	798.9	798.9	798.9	798.6	798.1	797.3	796.1	794.5
1.1	801.9	800.7	799.9	799.4	799.1	799.0	799.0	799.1	799.2	799.3	799.2	798.9	798.4	797.6	796.4	794.8
1.0	802.2	801.0	800.2	799.7	799.4	799.3	799.3	799.4	799.5	799.5	799.5	799.2	798.7	797.9	796.7	795.1
0.9	802.4	801.2	800.4	799.9	799.6	799.5	799.5	799.6	799.7	799.8	799.7	799.4	798.9	798.1	796.9	795.3
0.8	802.6	801.4	800.6	800.1	799.8	799.7	799.7	799.8	799.9	799.9	799.9	799.6	799.1	798.3	797.1	795.5
0.7	802.7	801.5	800.7	800.2	799.9	799.8	799.8	799.9	800.0	800.1	800.0	799.7	799.2	798.4	797.2	795.6
0.6	802.8	801.6	800.8	800.3	800.0	799.9	799.9	800.0	800.1	800.1	800.1	799.8	799.3	798.5	797.3	795.7
0.5	802.8	801.6	800.8	800.3	800.0	799.9	799.9	800.0	800.1	800.2	800.1	799.8	799.3	798.5	797.3	795.7
0.4	802.8	801.6	800.8	800.3	800.0	799.9	799.9	800.0	800.1	800.1	800.1	799.8	799.3	798.5	797.3	795.7
0.3	802.7	801.5	800.7	800.2	799.9	799.8	799.8	799.9	800.0	800.1	800.0	799.7	799.2	798.4	797.2	795.6
0.2	802.6	801.4	800.6	800.1	799.8	799.7	799.7	799.8	799.9	799.9	799.9	799.6	799.1	798.3	797.1	795.5
0.1	802.4	801.2	800.4	799.9	799.6	799.5	799.5	799.6	799.7	799.8	799.7	799.4	798.9	798.1	796.9	795.3
0	802.2	801.0	800.2	799.7	799.4	799.3	799.3	799.4	799.5	799.5	799.5	799.2	798.7	797.9	796.7	795.1
$n \uparrow$																

Sketching Contour Curves

A topographical map is a two-dimensional graph that shows the contour of the terrain by outlining different elevations. The curves that outline the land at different but constant elevations are known as **contour curves**. In general, a contour curve for a three-dimensional function is the collection of all points (x, y) for which $f(x, y) = K$, where K is a constant. A contour curve is a two-dimensional outline of a three-dimensional graph at a given output level. For a specific value of K, we sometimes call the contour curve the K contour curve.

> A **contour curve** for a three-dimensional function is the collection of all points (x, y) for which $f(x, y) = K$, where K is a constant. This curve is referred to as the K **contour curve**.
>
> Graphically, a contour curve is the two-dimensional outline of a three-dimensional graph at a given output level.

The teal contour curves shown in Figure 9.4 outline the shape of the land at an elevation of 800 feet above sea level. The contour curves we will sketch and the ones you will be asked to sketch should be smooth and should have as few concavity changes as possible.

$e\rightarrow$	0	0.1	0.2	0.3	0.4	0.5	0.6	0.7	0.8	0.9	1.0	1.1	1.2	1.3	1.4	1.5
1.5	800.3	799.1	798.3	797.8	797.5	797.4	797.4	797.5	797.6	797.7	797.6	797.3	796.8	796.0	794.8	793.2
1.4	800.8	799.6	798.8	798.3	798.0	797.9	797.9	798.0	798.1	798.1	798.1	797.8	797.3	796.5	795.3	793.7
1.3	801.2	800.0	799.2	798.7	798.4	798.3	798.3	798.4	798.5	798.6	798.5	798.2	797.7	796.9	795.7	794.1
1.2	801.6	800.4	799.6	799.1	798.8	798.7	798.7	798.8	798.9	798.9	798.9	798.6	798.1	797.3	796.1	794.5
1.1	801.9	800.7	799.9	799.4	799.1	799.0	799.0	799.1	799.2	799.3	799.2	798.9	798.4	797.6	796.4	794.8
1.0	802.2	801.0	800.2	799.7	799.4	799.3	799.3	799.4	799.5	799.5	799.5	799.2	798.7	797.9	796.7	795.1
0.9	802.4	801.2	800.4	799.9	799.6	799.5	799.5	799.6	799.7	799.8	799.7	799.4	798.9	798.1	796.9	795.3
0.8	802.6	801.4	800.6	800.1	799.8	799.7	799.7	799.8	799.9	799.9	799.9	799.6	799.1	798.3	797.1	795.5
0.7	802.7	801.5	800.7	800.2	799.9	799.8	799.8	799.9	800.0	800.1	800.0	799.7	799.2	798.4	797.2	795.6
0.6	802.8	801.6	800.8	800.3	800.0	799.9	799.9	800.0	800.1	800.1	800.1	799.8	799.3	798.5	797.3	795.7
0.5	802.8	801.6	800.8	800.3	800.0	799.9	799.9	800.0	800.1	800.2	800.1	799.8	799.3	798.5	797.3	795.7
0.4	802.8	801.6	800.8	800.3	800.0	799.9	799.9	800.0	800.1	800.1	800.1	799.8	799.3	798.5	797.3	795.7
0.3	802.7	801.5	800.7	800.2	799.9	799.8	799.8	799.9	800.0	800.1	800.0	799.7	799.2	798.4	797.2	795.6
0.2	802.6	801.4	800.6	800.1	799.8	799.7	799.7	799.8	799.9	799.9	799.9	799.6	799.1	798.3	797.1	795.5
0.1	802.4	801.2	800.4	799.9	799.6	799.5	799.5	799.6	799.7	799.8	799.7	799.4	798.9	798.1	796.9	795.3
0	802.2	801.0	800.2	799.7	799.4	799.3	799.3	799.4	799.5	799.5	799.5	799.2	798.7	797.9	796.7	795.1
$n\uparrow$																

FIGURE 9.4

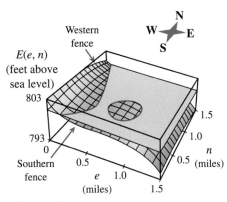

FIGURE 9.5

Note that there are two parts for the 800-feet contour curve. The 800-feet contour curves separate elevations that are above 800 feet from those elevations that are less than 800 feet. Elevations inside the egg-shaped curve are above 800 feet. Figure 9.5 shows the three-dimensional representation of the contour curve drawn in Figure 9.4.

Figure 9.6 gives a contour graph showing contour curves at elevations of 796, 797, 798, 799, 800, 801, and 802 feet above sea level. The contour curves at various elevations on the tract form the topographical map, or **contour graph,** that is shown in Figure 9.7a. Figure 9.7b shows the contour curves drawn on the three-dimensional graph. Because each contour curve represents all the points on the surface that correspond to a particular level of output, contour curves are sometimes called *level curves.*

In general, a **contour graph** is a graph of contour curves $f(x, y) = K$ for more than one value of K. Usually, the values of K are evenly spaced. When the values of K are evenly spaced, we can tell something about the steepness of the underlying three-dimensional surface by noting how close together the contour curves are. If the contour curves (for evenly spaced K) are close together, the surface is steeper in that region than in a portion of the graph where the contour curves are spaced farther apart.

e→	0	0.1	0.2	0.3	0.4	0.5	0.6	0.7	0.8	0.9	1.0	1.1	1.2	1.3	1.4	1.5
1.5	800.3	799.1	798.3	797.8	797.5	797.4	797.4	797.5	797.6	797.7	797.6	797.3	796.8	796.0	794.8	793.2
1.4	800.8	799.6	798.8	798.3	798.0	797.9	797.9	798.0	798.1	798.1	798.1	797.8	797.3	796.5	795.3	793.7
1.3	801.2	800.0	799.2	798.7	798.4	798.3	798.3	798.4	798.5	798.6	798.5	798.2	797.7	796.9	795.7	794.1
1.2	801.6	800.4	799.6	799.1	798.8	798.7	798.7	798.8	798.9	798.9	798.9	798.6	798.1	797.3	796.1	794.5
1.1	801.9	800.7	799.9	799.4	799.1	799.0	799.0	799.1	799.2	799.3	799.2	798.9	798.4	797.6	796.4	794.8
1.0	802.2	801.0	800.2	799.7	799.4	799.3	799.3	799.4	799.5	799.5	799.5	799.2	798.7	797.9	796.7	795.1
0.9	802.4	801.2	800.4	799.9	799.6	799.5	799.5	799.6	799.7	799.8	799.7	799.4	798.9	798.1	796.9	795.3
0.8	802.6	801.4	800.6	800.1	799.8	799.7	799.7	799.8	799.9	799.9	799.9	799.6	799.1	798.3	797.1	795.5
0.7	802.7	801.5	800.7	800.2	799.9	799.8	799.8	799.9	800.0	800.1	800.0	799.7	799.2	798.4	797.2	795.6
0.6	802.8	801.6	800.8	800.3	800.0	799.9	799.9	800.0	800.1	800.1	800.1	799.8	799.3	798.5	797.3	795.7
0.5	802.8	801.6	800.8	800.3	800.0	799.9	799.9	800.0	800.1	800.2	800.1	799.8	799.3	798.5	797.3	795.7
0.4	802.8	801.6	800.8	800.3	800.0	799.9	799.9	800.0	800.1	800.1	800.1	799.8	799.3	798.5	797.3	795.7
0.3	802.7	801.5	800.7	800.2	799.9	799.8	799.8	799.9	800.0	800.1	800.0	799.7	799.2	798.4	797.2	795.6
0.2	802.6	801.4	800.6	800.1	799.8	799.7	799.7	799.8	799.9	799.9	799.9	799.6	799.1	798.3	797.1	795.5
0.1	802.4	801.2	800.4	799.9	799.6	799.5	799.5	799.6	799.7	799.8	799.7	799.4	798.9	798.1	796.9	795.3
0	802.2	801.0	800.2	799.7	799.4	799.3	799.3	799.4	799.5	799.5	799.5	799.2	798.7	797.9	796.7	795.1
n↑	802	801	800									799		798	797	796

FIGURE 9.6

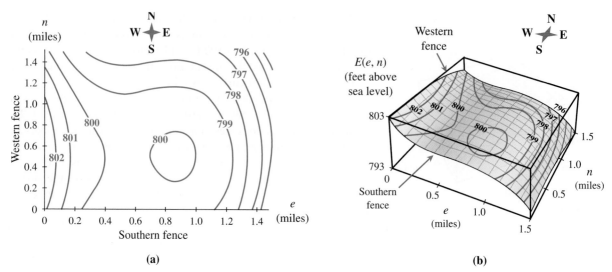

FIGURE 9.7

EXAMPLE 1   *Interpreting a Contour Curve Sketched on a Table of Data*

Payments   The data in the table shown in Figure 9.8 represent the monthly payments $M(t, A)$ required to pay off a mortgage of A thousand dollars over a period of t years when interest is paid on the loan at a rate of 7%.

		t, Period of loan (years)							
		10	**12.5**	**15**	**17.5**	**20**	**22.5**	**25**	**27.5**	**30**
	5	58.05	50.11	44.94	41.36	38.76	36.82	35.34	34.18	33.27
	10	116.11	100.22	89.88	82.72	77.53	73.65	70.68	68.36	66.53
	15	174.16	150.32	134.82	124.08	116.29	110.47	106.02	102.54	99.80
	20	232.22	200.43	179.76	165.44	155.06	147.30	141.36	136.72	133.06
	25	290.27	250.54	224.71	206.80	193.82	184.12	176.69	170.90	166.33
	30	348.32	300.65	269.65	248.16	232.59	220.95	212.03	205.08	199.59
	35	406.38	350.75	314.59	289.52	271.35	257.77	247.37	239.26	232.86
	40	464.43	400.86	359.53	330.88	310.12	294.60	282.71	273.45	266.12
	45	522.49	450.97	404.47	372.24	348.88	331.42	318.05	307.63	299.39
	50	580.54	501.08	449.41	413.60	387.65	368.24	353.39	341.81	332.65
	55	638.59	551.18	494.35	454.96	426.41	405.07	388.73	375.99	365.92
	60	696.65	601.29	539.29	496.31	465.18	441.89	424.07	410.17	399.18
	65	754.70	651.40	584.24	537.67	503.94	478.72	459.41	444.35	432.45
	70	812.76	701.51	629.18	579.03	542.71	515.54	494.74	478.53	465.71
	75	870.81	751.62	674.12	620.39	581.47	552.37	530.08	512.71	498.98
	80	928.86	801.72	719.06	661.75	620.24	589.19	565.42	546.89	532.24

A, Amount borrowed (thousand dollars)

FIGURE 9.8   *Contour curve for $520 payment*

a. Find and interpret $M(15, 50)$.

b. If a prospective house buyer can afford to pay only $520 each month, what are the options?

c. Explain how increasing the period of the loan affects the mortgage amount if the monthly payment remains constant.

Solution

a. We find the value that is in both the column for $t = 15$ and the row for $A = 50$: $M(15, 50) = 449.41$ dollars. The monthly payment is $449.41 on a $50,000, 15-year mortgage when the rate is fixed at 7%.

b. We answer this question by sketching a contour curve at the $520 level (as depicted in Figure 9.8) and identifying points on that curve. There are many available options. For instance, a buyer who wants to pay off the mortgage within 12 years can apply for a loan of around $50,000. If a buyer wants a 20-year mortgage, then the amount borrowed can be between $65,000 and $70,000. Similarly, if the buyer is willing to pay on the mortgage for 30 years, a mortgage slightly larger than $75,000 can be obtained.

c. If the loan period increases and the buyer wishes to remain on the contour curve (thus keeping the monthly payment constant), then the mortgage amount also increases.   ●

Data tables do not show every possible value for the input and output variables. For instance, in Example 1, you cannot determine from the data table the exact loan amount that can be obtained for a 20-year mortgage at 7% interest paid off with monthly payments of $520. If, however, a multivariable function is given, then exact values on a particular contour curve can be determined.

Given a function with two input variables, we draw contour graphs by plotting points that correspond to certain levels of output. We graph the K contour curve of a function by setting the function equal to K, picking values for one variable, solving for values of the other variable, and plotting the points generated. This three-step process is illustrated in the solution to part b of Example 2.

EXAMPLE 2   *Obtaining a More Accurate Contour Curve*

9.1.1

Heat Loss   Siple and Passel were two explorers who accompanied Admiral Byrd to the Antarctic and were among the first researchers to measure loss of body heat due to the wind. From their data, they obtained the equation*

$$H(v, t) = (10.45 + 10\sqrt{v} - v)(33 - t)$$

which gives the body's heat loss in kilogram-calories per square meter of body surface area per hour, for wind speed v, in meters per second, when the air temperature is $t°$C. Table 9.2 shows data generated from the model.

*W. Bosch and L. G. Cobb, "Windchill," UMAP Module 658, *The UMAP Journal*, vol. 5, no. 4, (Winter 1984), 477–492.

TABLE 9.2   A body's heat loss, in kilogram-calories per square meter of body surface area per hour

Air temperature (°F)	Wind speed (meters per second)					
	0	5	10	15	20	25
−20	554	1474	1700	1812	1864	1879
−25	606	1613	1860	1982	2040	2056
−30	658	1752	2021	2153	2216	2233
−35	711	1891	2181	2324	2392	2411
−40	763	2030	2341	2495	2568	2588

a. On the table, sketch a contour curve for a heat loss of 2000 kilogram-calories per square meter of body surface area per hour.

b. Use the equation to sketch this contour curve more accurately for wind speed values between 5 and 25 meters per second.

Solution

a. The 2000-kilogram-calories contour curve is shown on the table in Figure 9.9.

Air temperature (°F)	Wind speed (meters per second)					
	0	5	10	15	20	25
−20	554	1474	1700	1812	1864	1879
−25	606	1613	1860	1982	2040	2056
−30	658	1752	2021	2153	2216	2233
−35	711	1891	2181	2324	2392	2411
−40	763	2030	2341	2495	2568	2588

2000

FIGURE 9.9

b. We obtain a more accurate graph of this contour curve by setting the function H equal to 2000-kilogram-calories, choosing values for wind speed v, and solving for values of the temperature t. This process yields a set of points that can be used to sketch a contour curve.

Step 1. Set $H(v, t) = 2000$.

$$(10.45 + 10\sqrt{v} - v)(33 - t) = 2000$$

The values for v are chosen so that they are evenly spaced across the input interval. We choose enough points so that a pattern can be observed in the graph when the points are plotted.

Step 2. Let $v = 5$. Solving $(10.45 + 10\sqrt{5} - 5)(33 - t) = 2000$ for t yields $t \approx -38.9$ giving the point $(5, -38.9)$.

Then let $v = 10$. Solving $(10.45 + 10\sqrt{10} - 10)(33 - t) = 2000$ gives approximately $(10, -29.4)$.

We repeat Step 2 a few more times using 15, 20, and 25 for v. The set of points generated is

$$\{(5, -38.9), \quad (10, -29.4), \quad (15, -25.5), \quad (20, -23.9), \quad (25, -23.4)\}$$

Step 3. We plot the points and sketch the curve (see Figure 9.10).

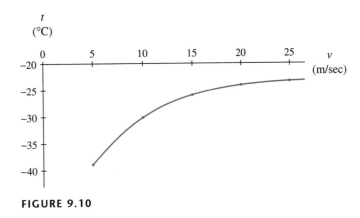

FIGURE 9.10

This curve has an increasing, concave-down shape similar to the one shown in Figure 9.9 but is more accurate. We can also use the equation to sketch contour curves for inputs other than those shown in the table. ●

Formulas for Contour Curves

Often it is helpful to be able to sketch a contour graph showing several contours. In this case, it is beneficial to find a formula to use to graph each contour curve. Because contour curves are generated by choosing a constant value K for output, we set the function equal to K and solve for one of the variables (whichever is easier). This gives a general formula that we can use to graph contour curves by replacing K with appropriate constants. In Example 3, we illustrate this approach to graphing contours.

EXAMPLE 3   *Using a Multivariable Function to Sketch a Contour Graph*

Heat Loss   Using the Siple and Passel heat-loss equation described in Example 2,

$$H(v, t) = (10.45 + 10\sqrt{v} - v)(33 - t)$$

find a general formula for the $H(v, t)$ contour curves, and use it to sketch a contour graph for heat-loss levels of 500, 1000, 1500, 2000, and 2500 kilogram-calories per square meter per hour.

Solution
Replacing $H(v, t)$ with K and then solving for t gives the general formula

$$t = 33 - \frac{K}{10.45 + 10\sqrt{v} - v}$$

We obtain the contour graph shown in Figure 9.11 by applying the three-step process (illustrated in Example 1) for each of the following values of K: 500, 1000, 1500, 2000, and 2500.

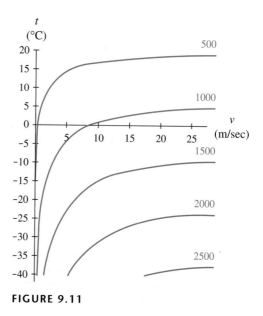

FIGURE 9.11

Estimating Output and Change in Output Using Contour Graphs

Figures 9.12a and 9.12b show a three-dimensional representation and a contour graph of the function $z = M(t, A)$, which gives the amount of the monthly payments necessary to pay off a loan of A thousand dollars over t years at a 7% interest rate.

(a)

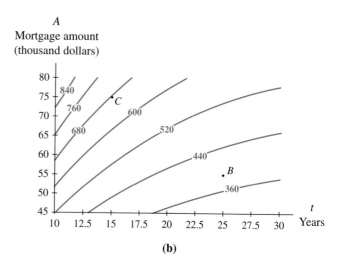

(b)

FIGURE 9.12

Note that in Figure 9.12a, it is possible to estimate that the input values corresponding to the point C are $t = 15$ years and $A = 75$ thousand dollars. It is difficult to estimate the output at that point. It is easier to use the contour graph when estimating the input and output values. Because C is located slightly below the $680 contour curve and is on the side closer to the $600 contour curve, we estimate that the output of C is slightly less than $680. We estimate that the output at C is approximately $675.

As illustrated in Example 4, we can use contour graphs to help estimate the change in outputs of a multivariable function.

EXAMPLE 4   *Estimating Change Using a Contour Graph*

Payments   Refer to Figure 9.12, which shows three-dimensional and contour graphs of the function $z = M(t, A)$. $M(t, A)$ is the monthly payment (in dollars) necessary to pay off a loan of A thousand dollars over t years at a 7% interest rate.

a.   How does the payment on a $55,000 mortgage change when the length of the loan is increased from 15 years to 25 years?

b.   Consider a $75,000, 15-year mortgage. Does the monthly payment change more when the amount of the mortgage is increased by $5000 or when the term of the mortgage is increased by 10 years?

Solution

a.   Refer to Figure 9.13. Locate the points $M(15, 55)$ and $M(25, 55)$ on the contour graph. Because $M(15, 55)$ is between the $520 and $440 contour curves but is closer to the $520 contour, we estimate the output to be $490. Because $M(25, 55)$ is between the $360 and $440 contours but is closer to the $360 contour, we estimate the output to be $390.

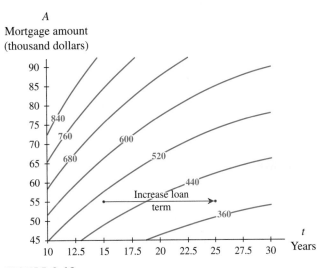

FIGURE 9.13

When the term of a $55,000 mortgage is increased from 15 years to 25 years, the monthly payment decreases by about $100.

b. Refer to Figure 9.14. $M(15, 75)$ is about $675.

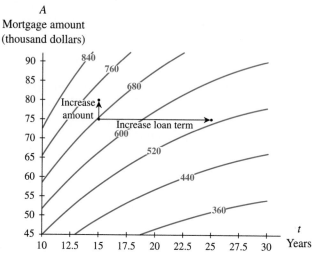

FIGURE 9.14

If the mortgage amount increases by $5000, the value of A increases by 5. $M(15, 80)$ is approximately $720. The monthly payment increases by about $45. If the length of the loan is increased by 10 years, we estimate $M(20, 75)$ as about $530. The monthly payment decreases by about $145.

The magnitude of the change (the absolute value of the change) is greater when the length of the loan is increased from 15 years to 20 years than when the amount borrowed is increased from $75,000 to $80,000. ●

Note that the vertical arrow in Figure 9.14 has length $5000, whereas the horizontal arrow has length 10 years. We do not use the arrow lengths when determining which change is greater, because the arrows have different units.

However, if the inputs of a function are comparable to each other, we can consider the idea of steepest descent.

EXAMPLE 5   Estimating Direction of Steepest Descent

Farmland   Again consider the elevation of the tract of Missouri farmland with the contour graph shown in Figure 9.15.

a. If you are standing at $(e, n) = (0.4, 1.0)$, will you be going downhill or uphill if you walk 0.4 mile north? south? east? west?

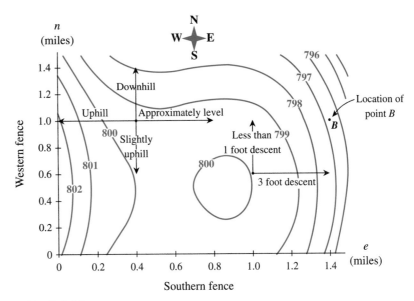

FIGURE 9.15

b. Starting at $(1.0, 0.6)$, which direction results in the steeper descent: east 0.4 mile or north 0.4 mile? Explain.

Solution

a. Refer to Figure 9.15. $E(0.4, 1.0)$ is about 799.4 feet above sea level. Walking 0.4 mile north takes you to $(0.4, 1.4)$. $E(0.4, 1.4)$ is about 798 feet above sea level. You have walked downhill.

Walking 0.4 mile south from $(0.4, 1.0)$ takes you to $(0.4, 0.6)$. $E(0.4, 0.6)$ is about 800 feet above sea level, so you have walked slightly uphill.

Walking 0.4 mile east takes you to $(0.8, 1.0)$. $E(0.8, 1.0)$ is slightly more than 799 feet above sea level. Any difference based on the contour graph is too small to mention.

Walking west, you will walk uphill to just over 802 feet above sea level.

b. Before looking for the steeper descent, we note that both inputs are given in miles. Because the input units are the same, we can compare steepness. Moving 0.4 mile east from $(1.0, 0.6)$ to $(1.4, 0.6)$ results in about a 3-foot descent from 800 feet to 797 feet. Moving north 0.4 mile results in less than a 1-foot descent. We conclude that movement 0.4 mile to the east results in a steeper descent than does movement 0.4 mile to the north. ●

We have seen in this section how to draw contour curves and how to estimate inputs and outputs at points on contour graphs and three-dimensional graphs. Being able to visualize a multivariable function often helps us better understand the function and the relationships between the variables in the function.

There are two ways to determine the direction of steepest descent or ascent. If the scales on the horizontal and vertical axes are the same, you can look for the direction in which the contours are closest together. A more deliberate approach is to move the same distance in each direction. You can determine the direction of steepest descent or ascent by comparing the change in output in each direction.

9.1 Concept Inventory

- Multivariable function
- Input/output diagram
- Contour curve
- Contour graph
- Three-dimensional graph
- Sketching contour curves
- Finding equations of contour curves
- Estimating output and change in output from a contour graph
- Estimating steeper direction

9.1 Activities

Getting Started

1. Let $P(c, s)$ be the profit in dollars from the sale of 1 yard of fabric when c dollars is the production cost per yard and s dollars is the selling price per yard. For parts a through c, write a sentence interpreting the mathematical notation.

   a. $P(1.2, s)$

   b. $P(c, 4.5)$

   c. $P(1.2, 4.5) = 3.0$

   d. Draw an input/output diagram for P.

2. Let $T(i, d)$ dollars be the amount of income tax owed by a household claiming d dependents with adjusted income of i dollars. For parts a through c, write a sentence interpreting the mathematical notation.

   a. $T(36,000, d)$

   b. $T(i, 4)$

   c. $T(36,000, 4) = 10,000$

   d. Draw an input/output diagram for T.

3. Let $P(l, m)$ be the probability that a certain senator votes in favor of a tobacco-ban bill when the senator receives l letters supporting the bill and m million dollars is invested by the tobacco industry lobbying against the bill. For parts a and b, write a sentence interpreting the mathematical notation.

   a. $P(100,000, m)$

   b. $P(l, 53)$

   c. Draw an input/output diagram for P.

4. Let $N(p, s)$ be the number of skiers on a Saturday at a ski resort in Utah when p dollars is the price of an all-day lift ticket and s is the number of inches of fresh snow that fell since the previous Saturday. For parts a and b, write a sentence interpreting the mathematical notation.

   a. $N(25, s)$

   b. $N(p, 6)$

   c. Draw an input/output diagram for N.

5. A multivariable function for the demand of a commodity is $D(i, p, r, c)$ million units, where i thousand dollars is the average household income, p dollars is the price of the commodity, r dollars is the price of a related commodity, and c people is the size of the consumer base. Draw an input/output diagram for the function.

6. A multivariable function for the volume of a rectangular packing container is $V(l, w, h) = lwh$ cubic feet, where the length, l, the width, w, and the height, h, of the container are all measured in feet. Draw an input/output diagram for the function.

7. A multivariable function for the principal on a loan is $A(m, r, n, t)$ dollars, where m dollars is paid n times a year for t years at an interest rate of $100r\%$. Draw an input/output diagram for the function.

8. A multivariable function for the monthly cost of owning a vehicle is $C(t, g, p, m, l)$ dollars, where t dollars is the cost of vehicle registration(s), g gallons is the amount of gas used, p dollars is the insurance premium, m dollars is the cost of maintenance, and l dollars is the loan payment. Draw an input/output diagram for the function.

Applying Concepts

9. **Heat Index** Your comfort in summer depends on the combined effects of air temperature and humidity. The apparent temperature table shows how hot it feels for a given air temperature and relative humidity.

   The National Weather Service has established the following guidelines for the health threat on the basis of the apparent temperature:

TABLE FOR ACTIVITY 9 **Apparent temperature (°F)**

Air temperature (°F)	Relative humidity (%)												
	40	45	50	55	60	65	70	75	80	85	90	95	100
110	135												
108	130	137											
106	124	130	137										
104	119	124	130	137									
102	114	119	124	130	137								
100	109	113	118	123	129	136							
98	105	108	113	117	122	128	134						
96	101	104	107	111	116	121	126	132					
94	97	100	103	106	110	114	119	124	129	135			
92	94	96	98	101	104	108	112	116	121	126	131		
90	91	92	94	97	99	102	106	109	113	117	122	126	131
88	88	89	91	93	95	97	100	103	106	109	113	117	121
86	85	86	88	89	91	93	95	97	99	102	105	108	111
84	83	84	85	86	87	89	90	92	94	96	98	100	102
82	81	82	83	83	84	85	86	87	88	90	91	93	94
80	80	80	81	81	82	82	83	83	84	85	85	86	87

(Source: National Oceanic and Atmospheric Administration.)

Apparent temperature	Health risk
80–90°F	Fatigue possible with prolonged exposure and/or physical activity
90–104°F	Heat exhaustion or heat cramps possible
105–130°F	Heat exhaustion or heat cramps likely
Above 130°F	Heat exhaustion or heat cramps highly likely

a. Draw contour curves on the table for apparent temperatures of 90°F, 105°F, and 130°F.

b. Shade in the region on the table corresponding to apparent temperatures that are likely to cause heat exhaustion or heat cramps.

10. **Temperature** The mean monthly temperature table shows temperatures for Halley Bay, Antarctica, at noon Greenwich Mean Time at heights where the air pressure was measured at the given value during the particular month. These data were collected during balloon ascents and reported in *Report of the Royal Society, IGY Antarctic Expedition to Halley Bay.* (Temperatures have been converted to °F.)

a. Draw contour curves on the data from −10°F to 20°F in increments of 10°F.

b. Interpret these contours in the context of the mean monthly temperature.

c. Why are the temperatures in December and January warmer than the temperatures in June and July?

d. In general, are temperatures higher at 30 millibars or at 850 millibars? Which air pressure represents elevation closer to the Earth's surface?

11. **Daylight Hours** The table shows the number of hours of daylight for a given month at a given latitude (measured in degrees away from the equator) for the Northern and Southern Hemispheres.

a. How many hours of daylight will there be at a location at latitude 25° north in March?

b. How many hours of daylight will there be at a location at latitude 25° south in September?

TABLE FOR ACTIVITY 10   Mean monthly temperature at noon (°F)

Pressure (millibars)	Month											
	Jan	Feb	Mar	Apr	May	Jun	Jul	Aug	Sep	Oct	Nov	Dec
30	12.9	8.5	2.6	−6.2	−11.7	−16.3	−18.9	−17.2	−13.9	−4.2	10.1	
40	12.3	8.4	2.6	−4.9	−11.3	−15.2	−18.1	−17.5	−15.3	−7.1	7.4	
50	11.6	8.4	3.3	−3.6	−11.2	−14.5	−17.3	−17.2	−15.2	−8.0	6.2	
60	11.2	8.2	3.7	−3.3	−10.3	−13.7	−16.3	−16.7	−14.6	−8.4	5.2	
80	10.6	8.1	4.3	−1.9	−7.9	−11.8	−14.8	−15.2	−19.6	−8.6	3.1	
100	10.0	7.8	4.4	−0.5	−6.7	−10.3	−13.1	−14.2	−13.6	−9.1	−1.2	
150	9.1	7.8	5.8	1.1	−3.8	−7.8	−10.7	−12.0	−11.8	−9.1	−1.4	
200	8.5	7.8	6.0	1.4	−3.0	−6.9	−9.7	−10.3	−10.2	−8.0	−2.8	
250	6.8	6.7	4.7	−0.4	−4.2	−5.0	−6.9	−7.9	−7.3	−5.6	−2.9	
300	4.1	4.4	1.6	0.3	−2.1	−2.2	−3.5	−4.3	−3.8	−2.2	−0.6	
400	8.1	8.3	6.3	5.8	3.7	4.2	3.1	2.8	3.6	4.3	6.2	
500	13.4	13.7	11.9	11.3	9.2	10.0	8.8	8.8	9.8	10.1	12.3	1
700	22.1	21.7	20.2	19.4	17.0	17.9	17.7	16.9	18.2	19.5	20.7	2
850	16.8	25.2	24.3	22.2	20.4	20.6	20.5	19.9	20.3	23.4	24.9	2

TABLE FOR ACTIVITY 11   Hours of daylight for a given month and latitude

Latitude north south	Month											
	Jan Jul	Feb Aug	Mar Sep	Apr Oct	May Nov	Jun Dec	Jul Jan	Aug Feb	Sep Mar	Oct Apr	Nov May	Dec Jun
0	12.12	12.12	12.12	12.12	12.12	12.12	12.12	12.10	12.11	12.12	12.12	12.12
5	11.87	11.96	12.08	12.22	12.35	12.41	12.38	12.28	12.16	12.02	11.90	11.83
10	11.61	11.81	12.06	12.35	12.57	12.70	12.64	12.45	12.17	11.91	11.67	11.55
15	11.34	11.66	12.04	12.47	12.82	13.00	12.92	12.62	12.22	11.81	11.44	11.25
20	11.07	11.50	12.01	12.60	13.07	13.32	13.22	12.81	12.26	11.70	11.20	10.94
25	10.78	11.33	11.97	12.74	13.34	13.66	13.53	13.02	12.31	11.58	10.94	10.62
30	10.45	11.14	11.97	12.88	13.65	14.05	13.88	13.23	12.35	11.47	10.67	10.26
35	10.09	10.95	11.95	13.06	13.98	14.47	14.27	13.47	12.42	11.33	10.36	9.86
40	9.68	10.71	11.91	13.25	14.36	14.96	14.71	13.76	12.48	11.18	10.00	9.39
45	9.19	10.45	11.87	13.48	14.82	15.55	15.25	14.09	12.55	11.01	9.60	8.85
50	8.61	10.13	11.84	13.78	15.38	16.29	15.91	14.48	12.66	10.80	9.07	8.17
55	7.83	9.73	11.79	14.10	16.14	17.28	16.78	14.99	12.76	10.55	8.45	7.28
60	6.79	9.21	11.74	14.62	17.10	18.70	18.01	15.67	12.92	10.22	7.60	6.04

(Source: A. A. Hanson, ed., *Practical Handbook of Agricultural Science*, Boca Raton, FL: CRC Press, 1990.)

c. How many hours of daylight will there be in January in the region where you attend school?

d. Draw contour curves representing 13, 14, 15, 16, 17, and 18 hours of daylight. In a different color, draw contour curves representing 12, 11, 10, and 9 hours of daylight.

12. Children The Hutterite Brethren live on communal farms in parts of Canada and the United States. They are a religious group that migrated from Europe to North America in the 1870s. Practically all marriages are within the group, and the data in the table give the number of the 1236 married Dariusleut or Lehrerleut Hutterite women born between 1879 and 1936 who had s sons and d daughters. For example, there were 28 women who had no sons and 1 daughter and 39 women with 4 sons and 4 daughters.

a. How many women had 2 daughters and 2 sons?

b. How many women had 5 children?

c. Draw contour curves at 34, 25, 16, and 7 women.

13. Draw the contour curves $g(s, k) = 200$, $g(s, k) = 400$, and $g(s, k) = 600$ for the multivariable function $g(s, k) = 100k(1.09^s)$ for $0 \le s \le 60$.

14. Draw the contour curves $f(L, K) = 50$, $f(L, K) = 55$, and $f(L, K) = 60$ for the multivariable function $f(L, K) = 38.9L^{0.5}K^{0.5}$ for $0.25 \le L \le 1$.

15. Draw the contour curves $P(s, u) = 40$, $P(s, u) = 60$, and $P(s, u) = 100$ for the multivariable function $P(s, u) = 38.6s - 2su + 13u + 0.99u^2$ for $0 \le u \le 5$.

16. Draw the contour curves $F(w, x) = 10$, $F(w, x) = 20$, and $F(w, x) = 30$ for the multivariable function $F(w, x) = 3wx$ for $0 \le w \le 10$

17. Capacity The function $C(d, h) = 0.0041d^2h^{1.4}$ gives the capacity of a settled unopened silo (in tons of corn or grass silage) at 68% moisture content when the silo has inside diameter of d feet and the silage is h feet deep. Draw the 117-tons contour curve for d between 12 and 30 feet.

18. Payments The function $M(t, A) = \dfrac{5.833333A}{1 - 0.932583^t}$ gives the amount (in dollars) of the monthly payments necessary to pay off a loan of A thousand dollars at 7% annual interest over t years. Draw the $400-monthly-payment contour curve for M for loans between 0 and 30 years.

TABLE FOR ACTIVITY 12 **Number of women with s sons and d daughters**

s, Sons	\multicolumn{13}{c}{d, Daughters}
	0	1	2	3	4	5	6	7	8	9	10	11	12
0		28	8	2	3	2	2	0	0	0	0	1	0
1	21	29	21	11	5	7	6	4	1	0	0	0	1
2	11	27	22	21	21	14	10	15	5	3	1	0	0
3	6	16	27	20	35	29	18	12	10	2	2	0	0
4	9	10	20	21	39	28	30	24	10	2	5	1	0
5	3	7	22	22	40	17	18	23	16	7	2	0	0
6	2	9	15	16	27	26	26	17	10	4	1	0	0
7	1	4	7	27	19	20	16	7	2	2	0	0	0
8	0	3	12	14	12	7	10	5	3	1	0	0	0
9	0	2	4	8	11	4	5	2	0	0	0	0	0
10	0	1	1	2	3	2	2	1	1	0	0	0	0
11	0	0	1	2	0	1	0	0	0	0	0	0	0
12	0	0	1	1	0	0	0	0	0	0	0	0	0

(Source: P. Guttorp, *Statistical Inference for Branching Processes*, New York: Wiley, 1991, p. 194.)

19. Price Index   In 1986, Cotterill developed a model for measuring the performance of supermarkets by considering their price index level. The price index level was an aggregate of 121 representative prices. The lowest-price supermarket was assigned a price index of 100. According to the Cotterill study, the price index level of an independent supermarket can be modeled by the function

$$P(c, d, p, s) = 109.168 - 0.730s + 0.027s^2$$
$$+ 0.002d - 0.041p + 0.175c$$

where the supermarket has s thousand square feet of sales space and is d miles from the warehouse, and the consumer base grew by p thousand people in 10 years and had a per capita income of c thousand dollars. Assume that the distance from a supermarket to its distribution warehouse is 100 miles and that the consumer base grew by 10,000 people in 10 years.
(Source: P. G. Helmberger and J. P. Chavas, *The Economics of Agricultural Prices*, Upper Saddle River, NJ: Prentice-Hall, 1996.)

a. Write an equation for $P(c, s) = P(c, 100, 10, s)$.

b. Draw the 110 contour curve for $P(c, s)$ for supermarkets containing between 5000 and 25,000 square feet of sales space.

20. Volume   In the timber industry, being able to predict the volume of wood in a tree stem is important, especially when one is trying to determine the number of boards a tree will yield. Several multivariable

models for total-stem volume for different varieties of trees have been developed. In 1973, Brackett developed the following model for predicting the total-stem (inside bark) volume for Douglas fir trees in British Columbia:

$$V(d, h) = 0.002198d^{1.739925} h^{1.133187} \text{ cubic feet}$$

where d is the diameter of the tree at breast height (4.5 feet above the ground), which is denoted by dbh and measured in inches, and h is the height of the tree in feet.
(Source: J. L. Clutter et al., *Timber Management: A Quantitative Approach*, New York: Wiley, 1983.)

a. Find the stem volume of a Douglas fir with a dbh of 1 foot and a height of 32 feet.

b. Draw a contour curve representing the volume you found in part *a* for diameters between 8 dbh and 18 dbh.

c. Explain how a change in dbh affects height if volume remains constant.

21. BMI   Your body-mass index (BMI) is a measure of how thin you are compared to your height. The body-mass index table shows BMI values for people between 5 and 6 feet tall who weigh between 90 and 200 pounds. For input units in inches and pounds, the body-mass index is calculated by the equation

$$B(h, w) = \frac{0.4536w}{0.00064516h^2} \text{ points}$$

TABLE FOR ACTIVITY 21   Body-mass index

Weight (pounds)	Height (inches)						
	60	62	64	66	68	70	72
90	17.6	16.5	15.4	14.5	13.7	12.9	12.2
100	19.5	18.3	17.2	16.1	15.2	14.3	13.6
110	21.5	20.1	18.9	17.8	16.7	15.8	14.9
120	23.4	21.9	20.6	19.4	18.2	17.2	16.3
130	25.4	23.8	22.3	21.0	19.8	18.7	17.6
140	27.3	25.6	24.0	22.6	21.3	20.1	19.0
150	29.3	27.4	25.7	24.2	22.8	21.5	20.3
160	31.2	29.3	27.5	25.8	24.3	23.0	21.7
170	33.2	31.1	29.2	27.4	25.8	24.4	23.1
180	35.2	32.9	30.9	29.1	27.4	25.8	24.4
190	37.1	34.8	32.6	30.7	28.9	27.3	25.8
200	39.1	36.6	34.3	32.3	30.4	28.7	27.1

(Source: Based on information obtained from www.shapeup.org (accessed on 6/27/00).)

where h is the person's height in inches and w is the person's weight in pounds.

a. Estimate your BMI from the table. Calculate your BMI using the equation. Use the chart that follows to assess your health risk on the basis of your BMI.

BMI	Health risk based solely on BMI
19−24	Minimal
25−26	Low
27−29	Moderate
30−34	High
35−39	Very high
above 40	Extremely high

b. On the table, sketch contour curves for index values of 15, 20, 25, 30, and 35 points.

c. Find a general equation for the contour curves of the function B.

d. Use the equation in part c to sketch a contour graph for index values of 15, 20, 25, 30, and 35 points. Compare this graph with the one sketched on the table.

22. Air Travel The demand for air travel between the United States and Europe between 1965 and 1978 can be modeled by the function

$$D(g, p) = \frac{15.44g^{1.905}}{p^{1.247}} \text{ thousand passengers}$$

where p is the yearly average airfare (in dollars) between New York City and London, adjusted for inflation, and g is the U.S. yearly gross national product (in billions of dollars), adjusted for inflation. The demand table shows selected values of this function.

a. On the table, sketch contour curves for demand values of 3000, 6000, 9000, 12,000, 15,000, 18,000, 21,000, and 24,000 thousand passengers.

b. Find a general equation for the contour curves of the function D.

c. Use the equation in part b to sketch a contour graph for demand values of 3000, 6000, 9000, 12,000, 15,000, 18,000, 21,000, and 24,000 thousand passengers. Compare this graph with the one sketched on the table.

23. Cooking The percentage cooking loss in sausage can be modeled by

$$P(w, s) = 10.65 + 1.13w + 1.04s - 5.83ws \text{ percent}$$

when w and s represent the proportions of whey protein and skim milk powder, respectively, used in the sausage.

(Source: M. R. Ellekjaer, T. Naes, and P. Baardseth, "Milk Proteins Affect Yield and Sensory Quality of Cooked Sausages," *Journal of Food Science*, vol. 61, no. 3 (1996), pp. 660–666.)

TABLE FOR ACTIVITY 22   Demand (thousands of passengers) for air travel between the United States and Europe from 1965 to 1978

Average yearly airfare (dollars)	Yearly U.S. gross national product (billions of dollars)					
	1400	1700	2000	2300	2600	2900
400	8655	12,529	17,075	22,284	28,146	34,655
500	6553	9485	12,927	16,871	21,309	26,237
600	5220	7556	10,298	13,440	16,976	20,902
700	4307	6235	8497	11,090	14,007	17,246
800	3647	5279	7194	9389	11,859	14,601
900	3148	4558	6211	8106	10,239	12,606
1000	2761	3996	5447	7108	8978	11,054
1100	2451	3549	4836	6312	7972	9816
1200	2199	3184	4339	5663	7152	8806
1300	1990	2881	3927	5125	6473	7970
1400	1815	2627	3580	4672	5902	7266

(Source: Based on information in J. M. Cigliano, "Price and Income Elasticities for Airline Travel: The North Atlantic Market," *Business Economics*, September 1980, pp. 17–21.)

a. Find a general formula for contour curves for *P*.

b. Sketch a contour graph for percentages of 10.6, 10.7, 10.8, 10.9, and 11.0. Note that because *w* and *s* are proportions, they should be graphed from 0 to 1.

24. Wheat Crop   The carrying capacity of a particular farm system is defined as the number of animals or people that can be supported by the crop production from a given land area. The carrying capacity of a wheat crop can be modeled by

$$K(P, D) = \frac{11.56P}{D} \text{ people per hectare}$$

where *P* is the number of kilograms of wheat produced per hectare per year and *D* is the yearly energy requirement for one person, measured in megajoules per person.

(Source: R. S. Loomis and D. J. Connor, *Crop Ecology: Productivity and Management in Agricultural Systems,* Cambridge, England: Cambridge University Press, 1992.)

a. Find a general formula for contour curves for *K*.

b. Sketch a contour graph for carrying capacities of 13, 15, 17, and 19 people per hectare.

25. Revenue   Refer to the contour graph and the three-dimensional graph representing the revenue *R*(*l, r*), in thousands of guilders, when *l* thousand tons of lower-fat (40%) cheese and *r* thousand tons of regular cheese are produced.

a. Use the contour graph to approximate the production levels that will maximize revenue. Why did you pick the production levels you chose?

b. Use the contour graph and the three-dimensional graph to approximate the maximum revenue. Explain how you arrived at this conclusion.

26. Sunflowers   A process to extract pectin and pigment from sunflower heads involves washing the sunflower heads in heated water. The three-dimensional graph and the associated contour graph on page 569, show the percentage of pigment that can be removed from a sunflower head by washing it for *t* minutes in *r* milliliters of water per gram of sunflower heads when the water temperature is 75°C.

(Source: X. Q. Shi et al., "Optimizing Water Washing Process for Sunflower Heads Before Pectin Extraction," *Journal of Food Science,* vol. 61, no. 3 (1996), pp. 608–612.)

a. Find and interpret the input and output values for point *A*.

b. Estimate the percentage of pigment removed from 15 grams of sunflower heads if the sunflower heads are washed for 10 minutes in 37.5 milliliters of 75°C water.

c. Estimate how much water would be necessary to remove 36% of the pigment from 9 grams of sunflower heads if they were washed for 15 minutes in 75°C water. Discuss why there are two answers.

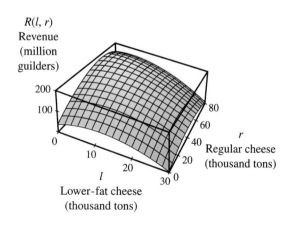

Contours of *R*(*l, r*)   3-D of *R*(*l, r*)

Figures for Activity 25

3-D of pigment function

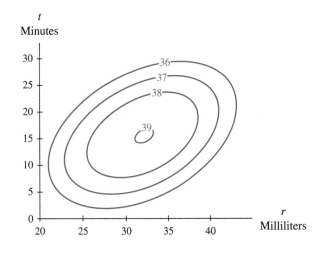

Contours of pigment function

Figures for Activity 26

3-D of parasitoid development

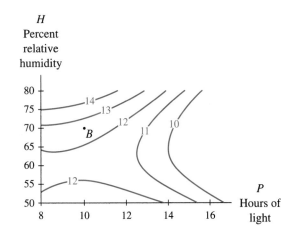

Contours of parasitoid development boll weevils

Figures for Activity 27

(Source: Based on information in J. A. Morales-Ramos, S. M. Greenberg, and E. G. King, "Selection of Optimal Physical Conditions for Mass Propagation of *Catolaccus grandis*," *Environmental Entomology*, vol. 25, no. 1 (February 1996), pp. 165–173.)

27. Parasites   Boll weevils have long presented a threat to cotton crops in the southern United States. Research has been done to determine the optimal conditions for reproduction of *Catolaccus grandis*, a parasitoid that attaches to boll weevils and kills them. The three-dimensional graph and an associated contour graph show the developmental time (in days) of *C. grandis* as a function of the relative humidity and the number of hours of light.

a. Estimate and interpret the input and output values at point *B*.

b. Estimate and interpret the input and output values at point *A*.

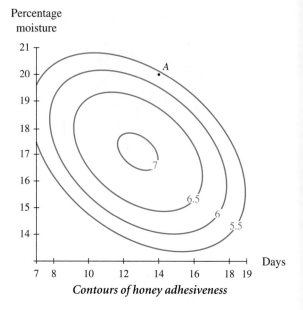

3-D of honey adhesiveness

Contours of honey adhesiveness

Figures for Activity 28

28. Honey   The ability of honey to attach to a surface on which it is spread is known as its adhesiveness. The adhesiveness of honey relies on several factors: the percentage of glucose and maltose (two sugars), the percentage of moisture, the percentage of crystallization in the honey before it begins to set, and the number of days the honey is allowed to set at 12°C. The three-dimensional graph and contour graph show a measure of the adhesiveness of

honey given the percentage of moisture and the number of days the honey is allowed to set when 40.9% of the honey is glucose and maltose and 12.5% of the honey was crystallized before setting began.

(Source: J. M. Shinn and S. L. Wang, "Textural Analysis of Crystallized Honey Using Response Surface Methodology," *Canadian Institute of Food Science and Technology Journal,* vol. 23, no. 4–5 (1990), pp. 178–182.)

Contours of f(x, y)

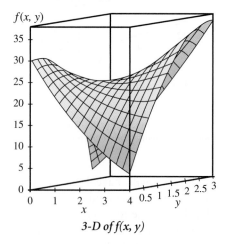

3-D of f(x, y)

Figures for Activity 29

(Source: M. R. Ellekjaer, T. Naes, and P. Baardseth, "Milk Proteins Affect Yield and Sensory Quality of Cooked Sausages," *Journal of Food Science,* vol. 61, no. 3 (1996), pp. 660–666.)

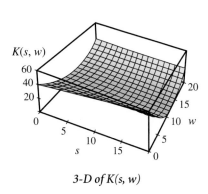

Contours of K(s, w)

3-D of K(s, w)

Figures for Activity 30

a. Estimate and interpret the input and output values at point *A*.

b. Estimate and interpret the input and output values at point *B*.

29. For the contour graph of $f(x, y)$ and its associated three-dimensional graph, answer the questions by analyzing the graphs. Explain in sentences why you answered as you did.

   a. At $(1.5, 2)$, does $f(x, y)$ increase when y increases or when y decreases?

   b. At $(2.5, 2.5)$, will $f(x, y)$ decrease more quickly as x decreases or as y decreases?

   c. Will the change in $f(x, y)$ be greater when $(2, 2)$ shifts to $(1, 2.5)$ or when $(1, 0)$ shifts to $(4, 1)$?

30. For each of the following questions, refer to the graphs of $K(s, w)$ and answer the questions by analyzing the graphs. Explain in sentences why you answered as you did.

   a. At $(10, 10)$, is $K(s, w)$ increasing when w increases or when s decreases?

   b. At $(15, 2.5)$, will $K(s, w)$ be decreasing more rapidly when w increases or when s decreases?

   c. Will the change in $K(s, w)$ be greater when the position is changed from $(5, 5)$ to $(6, 3)$ or when it changes from $(5, 5)$ to $(6, 7)$?

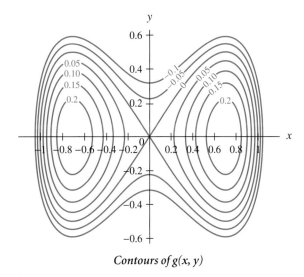

Contours of g(x, y)

Figure for Activity 31

31. Answer each of the following questions by analyzing the contour graph of $g(x, y)$ shown in the figure.

   a. Describe in as much detail as possible the three-dimensional graph that this contour graph represents.

   b. Is the descent greater when the position changes from $(0.7, 0.1)$ to $(0.4, 0.4)$ or when it changes from $(0.7, 0.1)$ to $(0, 0.3)$?

   c. At $(0, 0.1)$, does the function output increase as x increases or as y increases?

d. Locate a point with output approximately 0.15 unit greater than the output at $(-0.2, -0.3)$.

32. Answer each of the following questions by analyzing the contour graph of $h(x, y)$ shown in the figure.

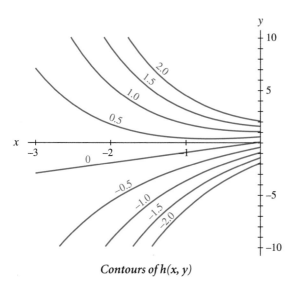

Contours of $h(x, y)$

Figure for Activity 32

a. Consider any point (x, y) on the graph. What happens to the function output when x remains constant and y increases?

b. Consider the point $(-1, 5)$. When x is decreased by 1/2, by what amount must y change in order for the point to remain on the same contour curve?

c. Consider the point $(-2, -2)$. When y is increased by 1.5, by what amount must x change in order for the output to remain constant?

33. **Temperature**   In meteorology, temperature contours are known as *isotherms*. The figure shows surface temperature isotherms[14] (in °F) on February 15, 1990. The shaded regions indicate the areas of precipitation.

(Source: Figure from R. R. Czys and R. W. Scott, "Forecasting Techniques: A Physically Based, Nondimensional Parameter for Discriminating Between Locations of Freezing Rain and Ice Pellets," *Weather and Forecasting*, vol. II (1996) p. 595. Used by permission of the American Meteorological Society.)

Figure for Activity 33

a. Label the regions most likely to have received snow, ice pellets, freezing rain, and rain.

b. How much of a change in temperature was experienced by a traveler who started in southern Kentucky and traveled to northern Missouri?

34. **Turbine Power**   Wind turbines can be used to harness the power of the wind and generate electricity. An optimally placed wind machine is located where wind power will generate the most electricity. The figure shows a contour map of average available wind power (measured in watts per square meter) over the contiguous United States.

(Source: Figure from D. M. Gates, *Energy and Ecology*, Sunderland, MA: Sinauer Associates, 1985. Copyright © 1985. Reprinted with permission of Sinauer Associates, Inc.)

a. Estimate four optimal wind machine placement sites in (or near the shore of) the United States.

b. What is the difference in average available wind power between mid-Texas and western Nebraska?

Discussing Concepts

35. Explain how to locate a relative maximum on a contour graph and on a table of data.

36. Discuss what is meant by the phrase *path of steepest descent*. Explain how you can sketch a path of steepest descent on a contour graph.

Contour map of wind power

Figure for Activity 34

9.2   Cross-Sectional Models and Rates of Change

In cases where the output is based on several different input variables, it is possible to model data using a technique called multiple regression. We will not explore modeling multivariable data in this text, but we will discuss cross-sectional modeling because it is a simple extension of the data-modeling techniques from Chapter 1.

Cross-Sectional Models from Data

The elevation $E(e, n)$ feet above sea level on a tract of farmland measured e miles east of the western fence and n miles north of the southern fence is given in Table 9.3. We can model the elevation along a line parallel to the western fence at a distance of $e = 0.8$ mile east of that fence by looking at only that one column of elevations.

We model part of the data in a table with two input variables by holding one input variable constant and finding an equation in terms of the other input variable.

The data that we are using to find the cross-sectional model is a portion of the larger table. We are interested in the elevation of points 0.8 mile east of the western fence, so we take our elevation data from that column for every available point north of the southern fence.

TABLE 9.3

e →	0	0.1	0.2	0.3	0.4	0.5	0.6	0.7	0.8	0.9	1.0	1.1	1.2	1.3	1.4	1.5
1.5	800.3	799.1	798.3	797.8	797.5	797.4	797.4	797.5	797.6	797.7	797.6	797.3	796.8	796.0	794.8	793.2
1.4	800.8	799.6	798.8	798.3	798.0	797.9	797.9	798.0	798.1	798.1	798.1	797.8	797.3	796.5	795.3	793.7
1.3	801.2	800.0	799.2	798.7	798.4	798.3	798.3	798.4	798.5	798.6	798.5	798.2	797.7	796.9	795.7	794.1
1.2	801.6	800.4	799.6	799.1	798.8	798.7	798.7	798.8	798.9	798.9	798.9	798.6	798.1	797.3	796.1	794.5
1.1	801.9	800.7	799.9	799.4	799.1	799.0	799.0	799.1	799.2	799.3	799.2	798.9	798.4	797.6	796.4	794.8
1.0	802.2	801.0	800.2	799.7	799.4	799.3	799.3	799.4	799.5	799.5	799.5	799.2	798.7	797.9	796.7	795.1
0.9	802.4	801.2	800.4	799.9	799.6	799.5	799.5	799.6	799.7	799.8	799.7	799.4	798.9	798.1	796.9	795.3
0.8	802.6	801.4	800.6	800.1	799.8	799.7	799.7	799.8	799.9	799.9	799.9	799.6	799.1	798.3	797.1	795.5
0.7	802.7	801.5	800.7	800.2	799.9	799.8	799.8	799.9	800.0	800.1	800.0	799.7	799.2	798.4	797.2	795.6
0.6	802.8	801.6	800.8	800.3	800.0	799.9	799.9	800.0	800.1	800.1	800.1	799.8	799.3	798.5	797.3	795.7
0.5	802.8	801.6	800.8	800.3	800.0	799.9	799.9	800.0	800.1	800.2	800.1	799.8	799.3	798.5	797.3	795.7
0.4	802.8	801.6	800.8	800.3	800.0	799.9	799.9	800.0	800.1	800.1	800.1	799.8	799.3	798.5	797.3	795.7
0.3	802.7	801.5	800.7	800.2	799.9	799.8	799.8	799.9	800.0	800.1	800.0	799.7	799.2	798.4	797.2	795.6
0.2	802.6	801.4	800.6	800.1	799.8	799.7	799.7	799.8	799.9	799.9	799.9	799.6	799.1	798.3	797.1	795.5
0.1	802.4	801.2	800.4	799.9	799.6	799.5	799.5	799.6	799.7	799.8	799.7	799.4	798.9	798.1	796.9	795.3
0	802.2	801.0	800.2	799.7	799.4	799.3	799.3	799.4	799.5	799.5	799.5	799.2	798.7	797.9	796.7	795.1
n ↑																

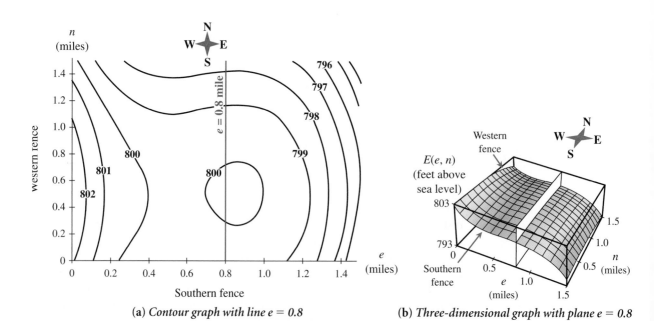

(a) *Contour graph with line e = 0.8*

(b) *Three-dimensional graph with plane e = 0.8*

FIGURE 9.16

TABLE 9.4

n	E(0.8,n)
0	799.5
0.1	799.7
0.2	799.9
0.3	800.0
0.4	800.1
0.5	800.1
0.6	800.1
0.7	800.0
0.8	799.9
0.9	799.7
1.0	799.5
1.1	799.2
1.2	798.9
1.3	798.5
1.4	798.1
1.5	797.6

We find that a model for the data set shown in Table 9.4 is

$$E(0.8,n) = -2.5n^2 + 2.497n + 799.490 \text{ feet above sea level}$$

where the distance east of the western fence is 0.8 mile and the distance north of the southern fence is n miles, $0 \leq n \leq 1.5$.

A model such as $E(0.8, n)$ is a **cross-sectional model**. For a function with two input variables, a **cross section** is the curve that results when the three-dimensional graph of the function is intersected with a plane. A cross section of a function has one less dimension (variable) than the function itself.

The equality $e = 0.8$ mile east of the western fence is depicted on the contour graph as a line (Figure 9.16a) and on the three-dimensional graph as a cross-sectional plane (Figure 9.16b). The curve resulting from the intersection of the plane $e = 0.8$ and the elevation function E is called a cross section of E and has output denoted by $E(0.8, n)$.

This model is only a partial description of all of the data. It tells us nothing about the elevations when the distance east of the western fence is something other than 0.8 mile. For this reason, we call it a **cross-sectional model**. Figure 9.17 shows a graph of this cross section of E with output $E(0.8,n)$.

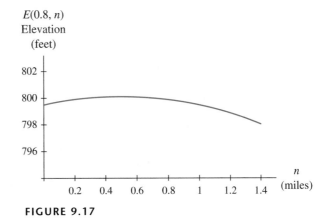

FIGURE 9.17

We can also find a cross-sectional model for the elevation when the distance north of the southern fence is held constant by modeling a specific row of data from the table. It is also possible to find cross-sectional models when we know an equation for a multivariable function.

Rates of Change of Cross-Sectional Models

As we have seen with the elevation example, we can use cross-sectional functions to help us understand the behavior of a multivariable function. And we can use a cross-sectional model to analyze the rate of change of the output with respect to one of the input variables.

When we are given a table of data for a function with two input variables, we approximate rates of change along one row or column by finding rates of change of cross sections. Consider again the elevation of a tract of farmland. We use cross-sectional models to help answer questions about the elevation and the steepness (that is, the magnitude of the rate of change of elevation) of the tract. When we are 0.8 mile

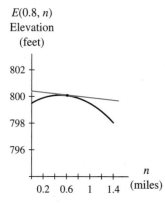

$E(0.8, n)$
Elevation
(feet)

Line tangent to E(0.8, n) at n = 0.6

FIGURE 9.18

east of the western fence and 0.6 mile north of the southern fence, how steep is the land? In other words, how rapidly is elevation changing, or what is the rate of change of elevation? To answer this question, we must first know in which direction to look: from south to north or from west to east.

Let us first look to the north. The question is "At $e = 0.8$ mile and $n = 0.6$ mile, what is the rate of change of elevation *with respect to the distance north of the southern fence?*" This cross-sectional rate of change is the slope of the tangent line that runs in the north-south direction at (0.8, 0.6). This tangent line is depicted in Figure 9.18 on the graph of the $E(0.8, n)$ cross section. Note that because movement is restricted to one direction, this rate of change gives us only a partial answer to the overall question of the steepness at this point. In Section 9.3, we will consider in detail the notion of a partial rate of change.

The cross-sectional model for $e = 0.8$ was found to be

$$E(0.8, n) = -2.5n^2 + 2.497n + 799.490 \text{ feet above sea level}$$

where n is the number of miles north of the southern fence. We find the derivative of the cross-sectional function with output $E(0.8, n)$ with respect to n (the distance from the southern fence) to be

$$\frac{dE(0.8, n)}{dn} = -5n + 2.497 \text{ feet per mile}$$

Evaluating $\frac{dE(0.8, n)}{dn}$ at $n = 0.6$ gives us approximately -0.5 foot per mile. This means that at the point located 0.8 mile east of the western fence and 0.6 mile north of the southern fence, the elevation is decreasing by 0.5 foot per mile as you go toward the north. It also means that the elevation is increasing by 0.5 foot per mile going toward the south.

Keep in mind that this rate of change is restricted to the north-south direction at a particular point. It does not tell us what is happening toward the east or west. In order to find the steepness in the east-west direction, we must look at the derivative of a cross-sectional function with respect to distance e miles east of the western fence.

EXAMPLE 1   *Finding a Rate of Change of a Cross Section from a Table*

Farmland   Refer to Table 9.3 on page 574. Estimate and interpret the rate of change of elevation with respect to distance from the western fence 0.8 mile east of the western fence and 0.6 mile north of the southern fence.

Solution
We need the cross-sectional model that has distance e miles east of the western fence as input with the distance 0.6 mile north of the southern fence held constant. Thus, we consider the row in Table 9.3 for $n = 0.6$ mile to obtain the data shown in Table 9.5.

A model for $E(e, 0.6)$, the elevation in feet above sea level of the land measured at $n = 0.6$ mile north of the southern fence, is

$$E(e, 0.6) = -10.124e^3 + 21.347e^2 - 13.972e + 802.809 \text{ feet above sea level}$$

TABLE 9.5

e	0	0.1	0.2	0.3	0.4	0.5	0.6	0.7
E(e, 0.6)	802.8	801.6	800.8	800.3	800.0	799.9	799.9	800.0
e	0.8	0.9	1.0	1.1	1.2	1.3	1.4	1.5
E(e, 0.6)	800.1	800.1	800.1	799.8	799.3	798.5	797.3	795.7

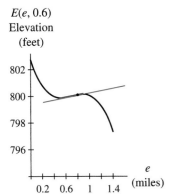

$E(e, 0.6)$
Elevation
(feet)

Line tangent to E(e, 0.6) at
e = 0.8

FIGURE 9.19

e miles east of the western fence and 0.6 mile north of the southern fence, $0 \le e \le 1.5$. The rate of change of $E(e, 0.6)$ with respect to distance e east of the western fence is

$$\frac{dE(e, 0.6)}{de} = -30.372e^2 + 42.694e - 13.972 \text{ feet per mile}$$

Evaluating $\dfrac{dE(e, 0.6)}{de}$ at $e = 0.8$ gives us approximately 0.75 foot per mile. This means that at the point located 0.8 mile east of the western fence and 0.6 mile north of the southern fence, the elevation is increasing by 0.75 foot per mile as you go toward the east. It also means that elevation is decreasing by 0.75 foot per mile going toward the west.

Figure 9.19 shows the line tangent to a graph of $E(e, 0.6)$ at $e = 0.8$. ●

Keep in mind that cross-sectional rates of change tell us only part of the story about the rate of change in output, because they are restricted to change in one input variable. They do not give us any information about what is happening with respect to other input variables.

9.2 Concept Inventory

- Cross-sectional models
- Derivatives of cross-sectional models

9.2 Activities

Getting Started

1. **Apparent Temperature** The table of apparent temperatures shows how comfortable it feels (the apparent temperature in degrees Fahrenheit) for

certain air temperatures and dew points. The dew point is the temperature to which the air needs to be cooled in order to achieve a relative humidity of 100%. The higher the dew point, the greater the amount of moisture in the air, and the muggier it feels.

a. In order to model the apparent temperature as a function of the dew point when the air temperature is 95°F, which variable must be held constant?

b. Is the cross section in part *a* represented by a row or a column of the table?

c. Find a cross-sectional model for the apparent temperature as a function of the dew point when the air temperature is 95°F.

TABLE FOR ACTIVITIES 1 AND 2   Apparent temperature (°F)

		Dew point (°F)							
		50	55	60	65	70	75	80	85
Air temperature (°F)	65	62.7	63.8	65.0	66.6				
	70	67.8	68.7	69.8	71.1	72.6			
	75	73.1	73.9	74.8	75.9	79.2	80.7		
	80	79.8	80.6	81.6	82.8	84.4	86.9	90.9	
	85	83.5	84.7	86.1	88.0	90.5	94.0	99.0	106.6
	90	87.9	89.4	91.2	93.6	96.9	101.2	107.2	115.6
	95	92.9	94.5	96.7	99.6	103.4	108.4	115.2	124.3
	100	98.1	99.9	102.4	105.6	109.8	115.3	122.7	132.3
	105	103.4	105.4	108.1	111.6	116.1	122.0	129.7	139.7
	110	108.7	110.9	113.8	117.5	122.3	128.4	136.3	146.5

(Source: www.nws.noaa.gov, accessed 12/28/02.)

2. **Apparent Temperature**   Consider the table of apparent temperatures, which shows apparent temperature (how hot it feels) given air temperature and dew point.

   a. In order to model the apparent temperature as a function of the air temperature when the dew point is 70°F, which variable must be held constant?

   b. Is the cross section in part *a* represented by a row or a column of the table?

   c. Find a cross-sectional model for the apparent temperature as a function of the air temperature when the dew point is 70°F.

3. **Cloud Cover**   The table showing the frequency of cloud cover over Minneapolis in January, given the fraction of the sky covered by clouds and the hour of the day, contains output that may be interpreted as the percentage of time that a certain situation occurs.

   a. What percentage of time is at least $\frac{8}{10}$ of the sky covered by clouds at noon?

TABLE FOR ACTIVITIES 3 AND 4   Frequency of cloud cover over Minneapolis in January

Fraction of sky covered	Hour of the day							
	Midnight	3:00 A.M.	6:00 A.M.	9:00 A.M.	Noon	3:00 P.M.	6:00 P.M.	9:00 P.M.
overcast	0.45	0.48	0.47	0.45	0.41	0.39	0.41	0.38
≥ 9/10	0.48	0.52	0.49	0.57	0.55	0.53	0.46	0.46
≥ 8/10	0.50	0.55	0.52	0.62	0.60	0.57	0.49	0.43
≥ 7/10	0.52	0.56	0.54	0.64	0.63	0.59	0.52	0.47
≥ 6/10	0.54	0.59	0.57	0.66	0.65	0.61	0.54	0.49
≥ 5/10	0.55	0.59	0.59	0.69	0.67	0.64	0.55	0.51
≥ 4/10	0.56	0.59	0.62	0.72	0.68	0.66	0.58	0.56
≥ 3/10	0.58	0.62	0.64	0.74	0.71	0.69	0.60	0.60
≥ 2/10	0.60	0.67	0.66	0.78	0.74	0.71	0.62	0.62
≥ 1/10	0.66	0.71	0.72	0.89	0.86	0.84	0.79	0.66

(Source: I. I. Gringorten, "Modelling Conditional Probability," *Journal of Applied Meteorology*, vol. 10, no. 4 (August 1971), pp. 646–657.)

b. In order to model the frequency of cloud cover at 9 A.M., which variable must be held constant? What will be the input variable of the cross-sectional model?

c. Is the cross section in part *b* represented by a row or a column of the table?

d. Find a cross-sectional model for the frequency of cloud cover at 9 A.M.

4. Cloud Cover The table showing the frequency of cloud cover over Minneapolis in January, given the fraction of the sky covered by clouds and the hour of the day, contains output that may be interpreted as the percentage of time that a certain situation occurs.

a. What percentage of time is at least half of the sky covered by clouds at 3 P.M.?

b. In order to model the frequency of an overcast sky given the time of day, which variable must be held constant?

c. Is the cross section in part *b* represented by a row or a column of the table?

d. Find a cubic cross-sectional model for the frequency of an overcast sky given the time of day.

5. Payments The table of monthly payments was taken from a magazine advertisement and shows monthly payments on a $1000 loan at different interest rates over different loan periods.

a. Is it possible to find a cross-sectional model for monthly payments for a 52-month loan? If so, would this cross section be represented by a row or a column of the table?

b. Is it possible to find a cross-sectional model for monthly payments for a loan at 9%? If so, would this cross section be represented by a row or a column of the table?

c. Find an appropriate cross-sectional model, and use it to estimate the monthly payments for a 52-month loan at 9%.

6. Payments The table of monthly payments was taken from a magazine advertisement and shows monthly payments on a $1000 loan at different interest rates over different loan periods.

a. Is it possible to find a cross-sectional model for monthly payments for a 42-month loan? If so, would this cross section be represented by a row or a column of the table?

b. Is it possible to find a cross-sectional model for monthly payments for a loan at 10.5%? If so, would this cross section be represented by a row or a column of the table?

c. Find an appropriate cross-sectional model, and use it to estimate the monthly payments for a 42-month loan at 10.5%.

7. Peaches The table for per capita peach consumption shows selected values of the average yearly consumption of peaches per person, based on the price of peaches and the yearly income of the person's family.

a. Find a cross-sectional model for a yearly income of $40,000.

TABLE FOR ACTIVITIES 5 AND 6 **Monthly payments per $1000 of loan amount**

Rate %	Months				
	24	36	42	48	60
5	43.87	29.97	26.00	23.03	18.87
6	44.32	30.42	26.46	23.49	19.33
7	44.77	30.88	26.91	23.95	19.80
8	45.23	31.34	27.38	24.41	20.28
9	45.68	31.80	27.84	24.89	20.76
10	46.14	32.27	28.32	25.36	21.25
11	46.61	32.74	28.79	25.85	21.74
12	47.07	33.21	29.28	26.33	22.24

(Source: *Automobile*, vol. 9, no. 4 (July 1994), p. 72.)

TABLE FOR ACTIVITIES 7 AND 8 **Per capita consumption of peaches (pounds per person per year)**

Yearly income (tens of thousands of dollars)	Price per pound above $1.50					
	0	0.10	0.20	0.30	0.40	0.50
1	5.0	4.9	4.8	4.7	4.7	4.6
2	6.4	6.3	6.2	6.1	6.1	6.0
3	7.2	7.1	7.0	6.9	6.9	6.8
4	7.8	7.7	7.6	7.5	7.4	7.4
5	8.2	8.1	8.0	8.0	7.9	7.8
6	8.6	8.5	8.4	8.3	8.3	8.2

b. Use the model to estimate the consumption for someone in a family with a yearly income of $40,000 when the price of peaches is $1.55 per pound.

8. Peaches   The table for per capita peach consumption shows selected values of the average yearly consumption of peaches per person, based on the price of peaches and the yearly income of the person's family.

   a. Find a cross-sectional model for a price of $1.80 per pound.

   b. Use the model to estimate consumption for a person in a family with a yearly income of $35,000 when the price is $1.80 per pound.

9. Sales   Two vending machines sit side by side in a college dorm. One machine sells Coke products, and the other sells Pepsi products. Daily sales of Coke products, based on the prices of the products in the two machines, are as shown in the table.

   a. In order to estimate sales of Coke products when the price of Coke products is $1.00 and the price of Pepsi products is $0.90, which variable should be held constant?

   b. Will the cross section from part *a* be represented by a row or column of the table?

   c. Find an appropriate cross-sectional model, and use it to estimate sales of Coke products when the price of Coke products is $1.00 and the price of Pepsi products is $0.90.

10. Sales   Two vending machines sit side by side in a college dorm. One machine sells Coke products, and the other sells Pepsi products. Daily sales of Coke products, based on the prices of the products in the two machines, are as shown in the table.

TABLE FOR ACTIVITIES 9 AND 10
Daily sales (number of cans) of Coke products from a vending machine

		Cost of Coke products			
		$0.50	$0.75	$1.00	$1.25	$1.50
Cost of Pepsi products	$0.50	157	143	123	98	65
	$0.75	206	192	172	146	114
	$1.00	255	241	221	195	163
	$1.25	304	290	270	244	211
	$1.50	353	339	319	293	260

a. In order to estimate sales of Coke products when the price of Coke products is $1.40 and the price of Pepsi products is $0.50, which variable should be held constant?

b. Will the cross-section from part *a* be represented by a row or a column of the table?

c. Find an appropriate cross-sectional model, and use it to estimate sales of Coke products when the price of Coke products is $1.40 and the price of Pepsi products is $0.50.

11. Population   The table gives the population (in millions) of the United States for residents from 15 to 50 years of age between 1990 and 2000, with projections through 2020.

   a. How many people of age 20 years were living in the United States in 2000?

   b. On the table, sketch the contour curve for a population of 4 million people passing through (50, 2020).

   c. How rapidly will the population be increasing with respect to age for residents who will be 35 years old in 2005? (*Hint:* Begin by finding an appropriate cross-sectional model.)

   d. How rapidly will the population be increasing with respect to the year for residents who will be 50 years old in 2020?

12. Population   The table gives the population (in millions) of the United States for residents from 15

TABLE FOR ACTIVITIES 11 AND 12
U.S. Population (in millions) by age

		Year						
		1990	1995	2000	2005	2010	2015	2020
Age	15	3.34	3.65	3.87	4.24	4.31	4.22	4.26
	20	4.04	3.51	3.88	4.10	4.48	4.55	4.45
	25	4.06	3.79	3.39	3.73	3.94	4.30	4.36
	30	4.50	4.38	3.92	3.52	3.86	4.08	4.44
	35	4.27	4.59	4.47	4.00	3.61	3.95	4.17
	40	3.80	4.28	4.65	4.54	4.07	3.68	4.02
	45	2.90	3.70	4.21	4.57	4.46	4.01	3.62
	50	2.43	2.93	3.69	4.19	4.55	4.44	4.00

(Source: U.S. Bureau of the Census.)

to 50 years of age between 1990 and 2000, with projections through 2020.

a. How many people of age 20 years will be living in the United States in 2010?

b. How rapidly will the population be increasing with respect to the year for residents who will be 20 years old in 2010?

c. Consider the specific group of people who are age 20 in 2010. Does the answer to part b describe the change in the size of this specific group of people as time increases? Explain.

13. **Weight**   The table shows average daily weight gain/loss of a pig $W(t, w)$ in kilograms per day as a function of weight and air temperature.

TABLE FOR ACTIVITIES 13 AND 14   Average daily weight gain/loss for a pig (kg/day)

		\multicolumn{5}{c}{**w, Mean live weight (kg)**}				

		68	**91**	**113**	**136**	**156**
	4.4	0.58	0.54	0.50	0.46	0.43
	10	0.67	0.71	0.76	0.80	0.85
	15.6	0.79	0.87	0.94	1.02	1.09
t, Air temperature (°C)	**21.1**	0.98	1.01	0.97	0.93	0.90
	26.7	0.83	0.76	0.68	0.62	0.55
	32.2	0.52	0.40	0.28	0.16	0.05
	37.8	−0.09	−0.35	−0.62	−0.88	−1.15

(Source: A. A. Hanson, ed., *Practical Handbook of Agricultural Science*, Boca Raton, FL: CRC Press, 1990.)

a. What is the average daily weight gain/loss for a 91-kg pig when the temperature is 37.8°C?

b. Find and interpret a model for $W(68, t)$.

c. Look at a graph of the model in part b, and describe its behavior. What does the behavior of the graph tell you about the weight gain of a pig?

14. **Weight**   The table shows average daily weight gain/loss of a pig $W(t, w)$ in kilograms per day as a function of weight and air temperature.

a. Find a model for the average daily weight gain/loss of a 68-kg pig as a function of the air temperature.

b. Find and interpret the rate of change of the average daily weight gain of a 68-kg pig with respect to a change in temperature when the temperature is 26.7°C.

c. Find a model for the average daily weight gain/loss of a pig as a function of the pig's weight when the air temperature is 26.7°C.

d. Find and interpret the rate of change of the average daily weight gain of a 68-kg pig with respect to the pig's weight when the air temperature is 26.7°C.

15. **Apparent Temperature**   The table of apparent temperatures shows how hot it feels, in degrees Fahrenheit, for certain air temperatures and dew points.

TABLE FOR ACTIVITIES 15 AND 16   Apparent temperature (°F)

		\multicolumn{8}{c}{**Dew point (°F)**}							

		50	**55**	**60**	**65**	**70**	**75**	**80**	**85**
	65	62.7	63.8	65.0	66.6				
	70	67.8	68.7	69.8	71.1	72.6			
	75	73.1	73.9	74.8	75.9	79.2	80.7		
	80	79.8	80.6	81.6	82.8	84.4	86.9	90.9	
Air temperature (°F)	**85**	83.5	84.7	86.1	88.0	90.5	94.0	99.0	106.6
	90	87.9	89.4	91.2	93.6	96.9	101.2	107.2	115.6
	95	92.9	94.5	96.7	99.6	103.4	108.4	115.2	124.3
	100	98.1	99.9	102.4	105.6	109.8	115.3	122.7	132.3
	105	103.4	105.4	108.1	111.6	116.1	122.0	129.7	139.7
	110	108.7	110.9	113.8	117.5	122.3	128.4	136.3	146.5

(Source: www.nws.noaa.gov (accessed 12/28/02.)

a. When the air temperature is 85°F and the dew point is 65°F, how rapidly is the apparent temperature increasing with respect to the dew point?

b. What steps were necessary in determining the answer to part *a*?

16. **Apparent Temperature**   The table of apparent temperatures shows how hot it feels in degrees Fahrenheit for certain air temperatures and dew points.

   a. When the air temperature is 85°F and the dew point is 65°F, how rapidly is the apparent temperature increasing with respect to air temperature?

   b. Consider the units on the rate of change given in part *a*. Even though the units of apparent temperature and air temperature cancel, why is it helpful to report the rate of change in degrees per degree?

17. **Investment**   The table gives the value $A(P, r)$ of an investment of P dollars after 2 years in an account whose annual percentage yield is r%.

   a. Find a model in terms of r for the value of a $14,000 investment after 2 years.

   b. Find and interpret $\dfrac{dA(14,000, r)}{dr}$ when the annual interest rate is 12.7%.

c. Repeat part *a*; however, instead of entering the interest rate in whole numbers, enter r in decimals so that $r = 0.02$ at 2%, $r = 0.03$ at 3%, and so on.

d. Use the model from part *c* to find $\dfrac{dA(14,000, r)}{dr}$ when the APY is 12.7%. Compare this answer to that of part *b*.

18. **Investment**   The table gives the value $A(t, r)$ of an initial investment of $1000 after t years in an account whose interest rate r% is compounded continuously.

   a. Find a cross-sectional model for the value of a $1000 investment in terms of r, assuming 10 years have elapsed since the initial investment.

   b. Use the model in part *a* to estimate the rate of change with respect to the interest rate of a $1000 investment after 10 years in an account paying 7% interest. Interpret the rate of change as an approximate change. Discuss why the rate of change appears to be 100 times as large as expected.

   c. Find a cross-sectional model for the value of a $1000 investment in terms of the interest rate expressed as a percentage, assuming 10 years have elapsed. Compare this equation with the one you found in part *a*.

TABLE FOR ACTIVITY 17   Amount (in dollars) after 2 years

Rate (%)	Initial investment				
	$10,000	$12,000	$14,000	$16,000	$18,000
2	10,404.00	12,484.80	14,565.60	16,646.40	18,727.20
3	10,609.00	12,730.80	14,852.60	16,974.40	19,096.20
4	10,816.00	12,979.20	15,142.40	17,305.60	19,468.80
5	11,025.00	13,230.00	15,435.00	17,640.00	19,845.00
6	11,236.00	13,483.20	15,730.40	17,977.60	20,224.80
7	11,449.00	13,738.80	16,028.60	18,318.40	20,608.20
8	11,664.00	13,996.80	16,329.60	18,662.40	20,995.20
9	11,881.00	14,257.20	16,633.40	19,009.60	21,385.80
10	12,100.00	14,520.00	16,940.00	19,360.00	21,780.00
11	12,321.00	14,785.20	17,249.40	19,713.60	22,177.80
12	12,544.00	15,052.80	17,561.60	20,070.40	22,579.20

TABLE FOR ACTIVITY 18
Value (in dollars) of $1000 investment

Rate (%)	Time (years)			
	5	7	10	12
2	1105.17	1150.27	1221.40	1271.25
3	1161.83	1233.68	1349.86	1433.33
4	1221.40	1323.13	1491.82	1616.07
5	1284.03	1419.07	1648.72	1822.12
6	1349.86	1521.96	1822.12	2054.43
7	1419.07	1632.32	2013.75	2316.37
8	1491.82	1750.67	2225.54	2611.70
9	1568.31	1877.61	2459.60	2944.68
10	1648.72	2013.75	2718.28	3320.12
11	1733.25	2159.77	3004.17	3743.42
12	1822.12	2316.37	3320.12	4220.70

d. Use the model in part c to estimate the rate of change with respect to the interest rate of a $1000 investment after 10 years in an account paying 7% interest. Interpret the rate of change as an approximate change. Compare these answers with those you found in part b, and reconcile any differences.

Discussing Concepts

19. Discuss the ways in which cross-sectional functions can be used to help estimate the input and output of optimal points on a three-dimensional function.

20. Discuss the drawbacks of using cross-sectional analysis to try to determine optimal points on a three-dimensional function.

9.3   Partial Rates of Change

In Section 9.2, we found rates of change for a cross-sectional function that we modeled from a given table of data. The rates of change allowed us some insight into the behavior of a multivariable function presented as a data table. In this section, we discuss rates of change found using a multivariable equation. This approach will enable us to choose a particular cross section and then to choose a particular point on that cross section. In this way, one general formula can be used as the basis for finding any cross-sectional rate of change.

Partial Derivatives

Because rates of change of a cross-sectional function give us only part of the picture, we refer to them as **partial rates of change** or **partial derivatives**. Suppose that we have a multivariable function F with input variables x and y. We use the notation $\frac{\partial F}{\partial x}$ and $\frac{\partial F}{\partial y}$ instead of $\frac{dF}{dx}$ and $\frac{dF}{dy}$ to remind ourselves that there is more than one input variable in the underlying function F. Another common notation for the partial derivative of F with respect to x is F_x.

The revenue generated by the sale of cheeses in the Netherlands can be modeled[*] as

$$R(l, r) = -0.04r^2 + 6r - 0.06lr + 10l - 0.4l^2 \text{ million guilders}$$

(a guilder is a Dutch monetary unit) when l thousand tons of lower-fat (40% fat) cheese and r thousand tons of regular cheese are sold.

Suppose that we want to find the rate of change of revenue with respect to the sales

[*]S. Louwes, J. Boot, and S. Wage, "A Quadratic-Programming Approach to the Problem of the Optimal Use of Milk in the Netherlands," *Journal of Farm Economics*, vol. 45, no. 2 (May 1963), pp. 309–317. The model is rounded to simplify calculation.

of regular cheese when 17 thousand tons of lower-fat cheese is sold. We can change $R(l, r)$ into a single-variable function by replacing l with 17. This replacement gives us the cross-sectional model $R(17, r) = -0.04r^2 + 4.98r + 54.4$ million guilders revenue when 17 thousand tons of lower-fat cheese and r thousand tons of regular cheese are sold (see Figure 9.20).

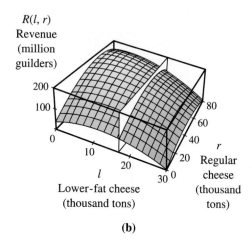

(a)   (b)

FIGURE 9.20

Taking the derivative of this cross-sectional model with respect to r, we get $\dfrac{dR(17, r)}{dr} = -0.08r + 4.98$ million guilders per thousand tons of regular cheese. In mathematical notation,* we say that $\dfrac{dR(17, r)}{dr} = \left.\dfrac{\partial R}{\partial r}\right|_{l=17}$. Evaluating this derivative of a cross-sectional model at $r = 40$ gives the slope of the tangent shown in Figure 9.21.

The derivative $\left.\dfrac{\partial R}{\partial r}\right|_{l=17} = \dfrac{dR(17, r)}{dr}$ gives us a picture of the rate of change for only only one cross section of the function R. It would be useful to develop a function that could be used to give us the rate of change for any cross section with respect to r. To do this, we treat r as a variable and l as a constant. We highlight r to help us remember that it is the variable that is changing and is not held at a constant value.

$$R(l, r) = -0.04r^2 + 6r - 0.06lr + 10l - 0.4l^2$$

---

*When writing the partial rate of change of a function $z = f(x, y)$ with respect to the variable x, we use the notation $\dfrac{\partial f}{\partial x}$ or f_x. The partial derivative of f with respect to x and evaluated at $y = b$ is denoted by $\left.\dfrac{\partial f}{\partial x}\right|_{y=b}$ or $f_x|_{y=b}$. This partial derivative gives the slope of a line tangent to the cross-sectional function for which $y = b$. The partial derivative of f with respect to y and evaluated at $x = a$ is denoted by $\left.\dfrac{\partial f}{\partial y}\right|_{x=a}$ or $f_y|_{x=a}$. This partial derivative gives the slope of a line tangent to the cross-sectional function for which $x = a$. We write $\left.\dfrac{\partial f}{\partial x}\right|_{(x, y)=(a, b)}$ or $f_x|_{(x, y)=(a, b)}$ when evaluating the partial derivative $\dfrac{\partial f}{\partial x}$ at the point where $x = a$ and $y = b$, where a and b are constants.

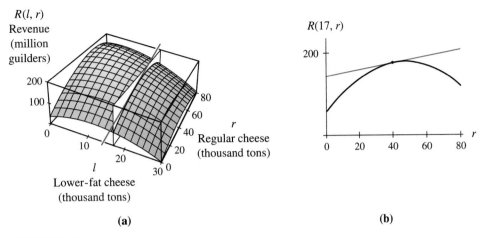

FIGURE 9.21

so finding the partial derivative of R with respect to r gives

$$R_r = \frac{\partial R}{\partial r} = -0.04 \cdot 2r + 6 \cdot 1 - 0.06l \cdot 1 + 0 - 0$$

$$= -0.08r + 6 - 0.06l \text{ million guilders per thousand tons of regular cheese}$$

Note that the derivatives of the first and second terms are straightforward. In the third term, $-0.06l$ acts as a constant multiple of r, so the derivative follows the Constant Multiplier Rule. Because l acts as a constant, the last two terms are both constants, and the derivative of any constant is 0.

The partial derivative of R with respect to r $\left(\text{denoted as either } R_r \text{ or } \frac{\partial R}{\partial r}\right)$ is a function of both r and l. If we evaluate $\frac{\partial R}{\partial r}$ at a particular value of l—say $l = 17$—we obtain a single-variable function with input r. This function gives the slope of any line tangent to the cross section $R(17, r)$. We use the notation $\frac{\partial R}{\partial r}\big|_{l=17}$ to represent this slope function. Evaluating $\frac{\partial R}{\partial r}\big|_{l=17}$, we have $-0.08r + 4.98$ million guilders per thosand tons of regular cheese.

The advantage of finding the partial derivative is that the formula for the partial derivative can be used to find rates of change at points on any cross section. The first method restricts us to points on one particular cross section.

Now we have a function that can be used to evaluate the rate of change of R with respect to r for any l. For example, estimate the partial rate of change of revenue with respect to regular cheese sales when 40 thousand tons of lower-fat fat cheese and 30 thousand tons of regular cheese are sold. Using $l = 40$ and $r = 30$, we find that

$$\frac{\partial R}{\partial r}\bigg|_{(40,30)} = -0.08 \cdot 30 + 6 - 0.06 \cdot 40$$

$$\approx 1.2 \text{ million guilders per thousand tons of regular cheese}$$

That is, when sales of lower-fat cheese remain constant at 40 thousand tons and regular cheese sales increase from 30 to 31 thousand tons, revenue increases by approximately 1.2 million guilders.

What would happen if the regular cheese sales were held constant and the sales of lower-fat cheese were varied? In this case, we could find a general formula for the partial rate of change of revenue with respect to the quantity of lower-fat cheese sold:

$$R(l, r) = -0.04r^2 + 6r - 0.06lr + 10l - 0.4l^2 \text{ million guilders}$$

so that

$$R_l = \frac{\partial R}{\partial l} = 0 + 0 - 0.06r + 10 - 0.8l$$

$$= -0.06r + 10 - 0.8l \text{ million guilders per thousand tons of lower-fat cheese}$$

when sales of regular cheese are held constant.

We now use the partial derivative $\frac{\partial R}{\partial l}$ to estimate the partial rate of change of revenue with respect to regular cheese sales when 40 thousand tons of lower-fat cheese and 30 thousand tons of regular cheese are sold. When $l = 40$ and $r = 30$,

$$\frac{\partial R}{\partial l}\bigg|_{(l, r) = (40, 30)} = -0.06 \cdot 30 + 10 - 0.8 \cdot 40$$

$$\approx -23.8 \text{ million guilders per thousand tons of lower-fat cheese}$$

That is, when regular cheese sales remain constant at 30 thousand tons and lower-fat cheese sales increase from 40 to 41 thousand tons, revenue decreases by approximately 23.8 million guilders. Again, this partial rate of change is the slope of the tangent line at $l = 40$ on the graph of the cross section with output $R(l, 30)$.

In general, we find the partial derivative of a multivariable function with respect to one input variable by treating all other input variables as constants and proceeding to take derivatives as functions of a single input variable. For a two-variable function, a partial rate of change can be visualized graphically as the slope of a line tangent to a cross section.

EXAMPLE 1   *Writing General Partial Derivative Formulas*

Investment   The formula for the accumulated value of an investment of P dollars over t years is

$$A(P, r, n, t) = P\left(1 + \frac{r}{n}\right)^{nt} \text{ dollars}$$

If the annual interest rate is 6% compounded quarterly, then the accumulated value formula is

$$A(P, t) = P\left(1 + \frac{0.06}{4}\right)^{4t} \approx P(1.0614^t) \text{ dollars}$$

a. Write a general formula for $\frac{\partial A}{\partial t}$. What notation is used to represent this general formula evaluated at $P = 1000$ and $t = 10$?

b. Write a general formula for $\frac{\partial A}{\partial P}$. Find and interpret $A_P\big|_{(P, t) = (7500, 10)}$.

Solution

a. Note that for each choice of principal P,

$$\frac{\partial A}{\partial t} = A_t = P(\ln 1.0614)(1.0614^t) \text{ dollars per year}$$

This result should not surprise you, because it follows the Constant Multiplier Rule for derivatives: When $f(x) = kg(x)$, then $f'(x) = kg'(x)$. In this case, P is the constant in the Constant Multiplier Rule. The general formula for $\frac{\partial A}{\partial t}$ evaluated at $P = 1000$ and $t = 10$ is denoted by

$$\frac{\partial A}{\partial t}\bigg|_{(P, t)} = (1000, 10) \quad \text{or} \quad A_t\big|_{(P, t) = (1000, 10)}$$

b. For any number of years t, $\dfrac{\partial A}{\partial P} = A_P = 1.0614^t$ dollars per dollar invested

$A_P\big|_{(P, t) = (7500, 10)} = 1.0614^{10} \approx \$1.81$ per dollar invested when \$7500 is invested for 10 years at 6% compounded quarterly. The accumulated value of the investment will increase by approximately \$1.81 if an additional dollar is invested. ●

Being able to calculate partial rates of change and evaluate these partial derivatives at various input values is important for the applications we will consider in subsequent sections.

Second Partial Derivatives

In Chapter 4 we considered the second derivative of a single-variable function and used the second derivative to locate inflection points. With multivariable functions, we can consider the second partial derivatives—that is, partial derivatives of partial derivatives. As we shall see in Chapter 10, these second partial derivatives are useful in identifying extrema and other interesting points on three-dimensional graphs. They also indicate how the partial rates of change of the function are changing.

Consider again the Example 1 investment function $A(P, t) = P(1.0614^t)$ giving the accumulated value (in dollars) of an investment of P dollars over t years when the interest rate is 6% compounded quarterly. The two partial derivatives are

$A_P = 1.0614^t$ dollars per dollar invested

$A_t = P(\ln 1.0614)(1.0614^t)$ dollars per year

What is happening to the rate of change of A with respect to t as t increases? Let us first look at this question graphically on one cross-sectional model, say $A(1000, t)$. Figure 9.22, on page 588, depicts $A(1000, t) = 1000(1.0614^t)$ along with tangent lines drawn at $t = 2$, $t = 10$, $t = 18$, and $t = 26$.

As t increases, the slope becomes larger. Thus the rate of change with respect to t, $A_t\big|_{P=1000}$, is increasing as t increases, so the second derivative must be positive. We can verify this by finding the derivative of $A_t\big|_{P=1000}$ with respect to t.

$$\frac{\partial}{\partial t}(A_t\big|_{P=1000}) = \frac{\partial}{\partial t}[1000(\ln 1.0614)(1.0614^t)]$$

$$= 1000(\ln 1.0614)^2(1.0614^t) \text{ dollars per year per year}$$

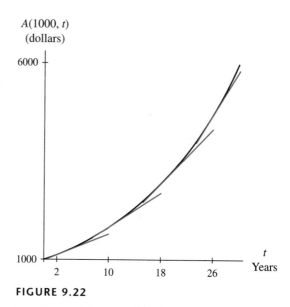

FIGURE 9.22

This second partial derivative is positive for all values of t, as Figure 9.22 suggests. Note also that because this partial derivative of the partial derivative $A_t|_{P=1000}$ is positive, the graph of the cross-sectional model with output $A(1000, t)$ is concave up. Before continuing with our interpretation of second partial derivatives, we find all second partial derivatives for A.

The partial derivative A_t is a function with two input variables, P and t. The partial derivatives of A_t are A_{tP} (the partial derivative of A_t with respect to P) and A_{tt} (the partial derivative of A_t with respect to t). Even though the partial derivative of A_P is a function of only one input variable, it is derived from a function with two input variables. For this reason, A_P also has two second partial derivatives: A_{PP} (the partial derivative of A_P with respect to P) and A_{Pt} (the partial derivative of A_P with respect to t).

The second partial derivatives for A are

The second partial derivative notation may also be written
$$A_{PP} = \frac{\partial^2 A}{\partial P^2}, \quad A_{Pt} = \frac{\partial^2 A}{\partial t \partial P},$$
$$A_{tP} = \frac{\partial^2 A}{\partial P \partial t}, \text{ and } A_{tt} = \frac{\partial^2 A}{\partial t^2}.$$

$A_{PP} = 0$ dollars per dollar invested per dollar invested

$A_{Pt} = (\ln 1.0614)(1.0614^t)$ dollars per dollar invested per year

$A_{tP} = (\ln 1.0614)(1.0614^t)$ dollars per year per dollar invested

$A_{tt} = P(\ln 1.0614)^2(1.0614^t)$ dollars per year per year

You may have noticed that $A_{Pt} = A_{tP}$. We refer to A_{Pt} and A_{tP} as mixed second partial derivatives. The mixed second partial derivatives of a multivariable function are equal whenever the function and its first and second partial derivatives are continuous. This is the case for all the multivariable functions in this book.

Concept Development: Interpreting Second Partials

We now further consider the interpretation of the second partial derivatives of $A(P, t)$. First, $A_{PP} = 0$ tells us that the rate of change of A with respect to P does not change when P changes. This can be seen by looking at the cross-sectional models of A for different values of t. Figure 9.23 shows graphs of the linear cross-sectional functions $A(P, 2)$, $A(P, 12)$, $A(P, 18)$, and $A(P, 26)$. In A_{PP} we consider P to be changing but consider t to be constant; that is, we look at what happens to the slope of each cross section as P changes. The cross sections are all lines, and as P increases, the slope of any cross section remains constant. Thus $A_{PP} = 0$, because the slopes do not change as P changes.

Now let us consider $A_{Pt} = (\ln 1.0614)(1.0614^t)$. No matter what t is, A_{Pt} is positive. This tells us that the rate of change (slope) of A in the P direction increases as we move in the t direction. To see this graphically, refer again to the cross sections in Figure 9.23. Now, however, instead of considering the effect on the slope of each cross section as P increases, we consider what happens at a particular value of P as t increases—that is, as we move from one cross section to another. Figure 9.24 depicts the cross-sectional models shown in Figure 9.23 with the slope of each cross section labeled at $P = 3000$. Note that as t increases, the slopes of the cross sections also increase. Hence $A_{Pt} > 0$. There are similar interpretations for A_{tt} and A_{tP}.

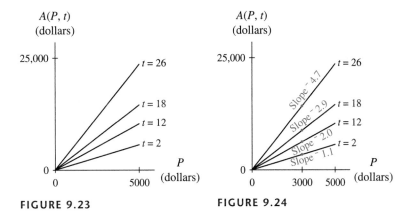

FIGURE 9.23   FIGURE 9.24

Keeping track of all the second partial derivatives for a particular function is easier with a mathematical array called a **matrix.** We write the second partial derivatives in a square matrix—that is, a table of rows and columns where the numbers of rows and columns are equal—with one of the second partial derivatives in each position.

We call this the **second partials matrix,*** and we use this matrix in the next chapter to help identify extreme points. A second partials matrix can be formed by labeling the rows with the input variables and labeling the columns with the input variables in the same order. For example, one possible setup for a second partials matrix for a multivariable function $z = f(x, y)$ is

$$\begin{matrix} & x & y \\ x & \left[\quad\quad \right. & \\ y & & \left. \quad \right] \end{matrix}$$

For convenience, we choose always to use the matrix with the input variables in the same order in which they appear in the notation used to represent the function. The labels on the rows and columns determine which second partial derivative we write in each position of the matrix. Using the function $z = f(x, y)$, we write f_{xx} in the

---

*This matrix is also called the *Hessian* of the function.

position corresponding to the row and column labeled x, we write f_{yx} in the row labeled y and the column labeled x, and so forth.

$$
\begin{array}{cc}
& \begin{array}{cc} x & y \end{array} \\
\begin{array}{c} x \\ y \end{array} & \begin{bmatrix} f_{xx} & f_{xy} \\ f_{yx} & f_{yy} \end{bmatrix}
\end{array}
$$

For the function $A(P, t) = P(1.0614^t)$, the second partials matrix is

$$
\begin{array}{cc}
& \begin{array}{cc} P & \quad\quad\quad\quad t \end{array} \\
\begin{array}{c} P \\ t \end{array} & \begin{bmatrix} 0 & (\ln 1.0614)(1.0614^t) \\ (\ln 1.0614)(1.0614^t) & P(\ln 1.0614)^2(1.0614^t) \end{bmatrix}
\end{array}
$$

Example 2 shows a function with three input variables. Because the function has three input variables, the process of finding its partials requires that two variables be considered as constants when finding each of the three partial derivatives.

EXAMPLE 2 *Working with Partial Derivatives*

Cheese Spread   A measure of the adhesiveness of cheese spread can be modeled[*] as a function of the percentage of glycerol, salt, and lactose used in preparation:

$$A(g, s, l) = 5600 - 3400s + 1600s^2 + 400l - 1800g + 140g^2 \\ + 1200sl - 500s^2l + 200sg$$

where g is the percentage of glycerol, s is the percentage of salt, and l is the percentage of lactose.

a. Write the partial derivatives of A.

b. Write the second partials matrix of A.

c. Interpret A_{gg} and A_{sl}.

d. Write the second partials matrix of A when $g = 10$, $s = 2$, and $l = 6$.

e. Interpret $A_{ls}\big|_{(g, s, l) = (10, 2, 6)}$.

Solution

a. The three partial derivatives are

$$\frac{\partial A}{\partial g} = -1800 + 280g + 200s \text{ units per percentage point of glycerol}$$

$$\frac{\partial A}{\partial s} = -3400 + 3200s + 1200l - 1000sl + 200g \text{ units per}$$

percentage point of salt

$$\frac{\partial A}{\partial l} = 400 + 1200s - 500s^2 \text{ units per percentage point of lactose}$$

[*]E. Kombila-Moundounga and C. Lacroix, "Effet des combinaisons de chloure de sodium, de lactose et de glycerol sur les caractéristiques rhéologiques et la couleur des fromages fondus à tartiner," *Canadian Institute of Food Science and Technology Journal*, vol. 24, no. 5 (1991), pp. 239–251.

b. The second partials matrix is

$$
\begin{array}{c}
 \\
\begin{array}{c} g \\ s \\ l \end{array}
\end{array}
\begin{array}{ccc}
g & s & l \\
\left[\begin{array}{ccc}
A_{gg} = 280 & A_{sg} = 200 & A_{lg} = 0 \\
A_{gs} = 200 & A_{ss} = 3200 - 1000l & A_{ls} = 1200 - 1000s \\
A_{gl} = 0 & A_{sl} = 1200 - 1000s & A_{ll} = 0
\end{array}\right]
\end{array}
$$

c. The second partial derivative $A_{gg} = 280$ is positive. This means that as g increases, the rate of change (slope) of A with respect to g (in the g direction) is increasing. When the percentage of glycerol increases by 1 percentage point, the rate of change of adhesiveness increases by approximately 280 units per percentage point of glycerol if salt and lactose percentages are held constant.

The second partial derivative $A_{sl} = 1200 - 1000s$ is positive when $s < 1.2$ and negative approximately when $s > 1.2$. Consider the percentage of glycerol as constant. If the percentage of salt is less than 1.2%, then the rate of change of adhesiveness with respect to salt is increasing as the percentage of lactose increases. Likewise, if the percentage of salt is more than 1.2%, then the rate of change of adhesiveness with respect to salt is decreasing as the percentage of lactose increases.

d. The second partials matrix of A at $(10, 2, 6)$ is

$$
\begin{array}{c}
\begin{array}{c} g \\ s \\ l \end{array}
\end{array}
\begin{array}{ccc}
g & s & l \\
\left[\begin{array}{ccc}
280 & 200 & 0 \\
200 & -2800 & -800 \\
0 & -800 & 0
\end{array}\right]
\end{array}
$$

e. We first note that $A_l\big|_{(g,\,s,\,l)=(10,\,2,\,6)} = 800$. This means that adhesiveness is increasing with respect to an increase in lactose above the 6% level. Because $A_{ls}\big|_{(g,\,s,\,l)=(10,\,2,\,6)} = -800$ is negative, as the percentage of salt increases above 2%, adhesiveness is increasing less rapidly (the rate of change A_l is decreasing) with respect to an increase in the percentage of lactose above the 6% level when the percentage of glycerol is held constant at 10%. ●

Partial rates of change and second partial derivatives will be important to us as we continue our study of multivariable functions.

9.3 Concept Inventory

- Partial derivatives/partial rates of change
- Partial derivative notation
- Second partial derivatives
- Second partials matrix
- Interpreting partial derivatives

9.3 Activities

Getting Started

In Activities 1 through 6, **a.** write the mathematical notation for the partial rate-of-change function needed to answer the question posed, and **b.** give the units of that rate-of-change function.

1. $W(a, h)$ is the weight (in pounds) of a person who is a years old and h inches tall. What is the rate of change of weight with respect to height?

2. $P(k, c)$ is the price (in dollars) of a diamond that weighs k karats and is of color code c. How quickly is the price of a diamond changing with respect to weight?

3. $T(g, t)$ is the mean daily temperature (in degrees Fahrenheit) at longitude g degrees and latitude t degrees. If longitude is $23°$ and latitude is changing, how rapidly is temperature changing?

4. $T(i, d)$ is the federal income tax (in dollars) owed by a person who made i dollars and can claim d dependents in a given year. When 4 dependents can be claimed and income is changing, how quickly is the amount of taxes owed changing?

5. $R(b, c)$ is the revenue (in dollars) a farmer makes from the sale of b bulls and c cows. When the farmer sells 2 bulls and 100 cows, how rapidly is revenue changing if the number of cows sold changes?

6. $G(h, s)$ is the expected grade-point average of a typical freshman college student who had a GPA of h in high school and made a combined score of s on the SAT. What is the rate of change of the expected GPA with respect to the SAT score when the high school GPA is 3.5 and the SAT score is 1048?

7. Let $P(l, m)$ be the probability that a certain senator votes in favor of a tobacco-ban bill when the senator receives l letters supporting the bill and m million dollars is invested by the tobacco industry lobbying against the bill.

   a. Interpret $\frac{\partial P}{\partial m}\Big|_{l=100,000}$.

   Would you expect $\frac{\partial P}{\partial m}\Big|_{l=100,000}$ to be positive or negative? Explain.

   b. Interpret $\frac{\partial P}{\partial l}\Big|_{m=53}$.

   Would you expect $\frac{\partial P}{\partial l}\Big|_{m=53}$ to be positive or negative? Explain.

8. Let $N(p, s)$ be the number of skiers on a Saturday at a ski resort in Utah when p dollars is the price of an all-day lift ticket and s is the number of inches of fresh snow received since the previous Saturday.

   a. Interpret $\frac{\partial N}{\partial s}\Big|_{p=25}$.

   Would you expect $\frac{\partial N}{\partial s}\Big|_{p=25}$ to be positive or negative? Explain.

   b. Interpret $\frac{\partial N}{\partial p}\Big|_{s=6}$.

   Would you expect $\frac{\partial N}{\partial p}\Big|_{s=6}$ to be positive or negative? Explain.

In Activities 9 through 18, find the indicated partial derivatives for each of the multivariable functions.

9. $f(x, y) = 3x^2 + 5xy + 2y^3$

   a. $\frac{\partial f}{\partial x}$ b. $\frac{\partial f}{\partial y}$ c. $\frac{\partial f}{\partial x}\Big|_{y=7}$

10. $g(k, m) = k^3 m^5 - 2km$

    a. g_k b. g_m c. $g_m\big|_{k=2}$

11. $f(x, y) = 5x^3 + 3x^2y^3 + 9xy + 14x + 8$

    a. $\frac{\partial f}{\partial x}$ b. $\frac{\partial f}{\partial y}$ c. $\frac{\partial f}{\partial x}\Big|_{y=2}$

12. $K(a, b) = 5ab^3 + 7(1.4^b)$

    a. $\frac{\partial K}{\partial a}$ b. $\frac{\partial K}{\partial b}$ c. $\frac{\partial K}{\partial b}\Big|_{a=6}$

13. $M(t, s) = s \ln t + 3.75s + 14.96$

    a. M_t b. M_s c. $M_s\big|_{t=3}$

14. $g(x, y, z) = 3.2x^2yz^2 + 2.9x^y + z$

    a. g_x b. g_y c. g_z

15. $h(s, t, r) = \frac{s}{t} + \frac{t}{r} - (st - tr)^2$

    a. $\frac{\partial h}{\partial s}$ b. $\frac{\partial h}{\partial t}$ c. $\frac{\partial h}{\partial r}$ d. $\frac{\partial h}{\partial r}\Big|_{(s, t, r)=(1, 2, -1)}$

16. $k(x, y) = x \ln(x + y)$

    a. $\frac{\partial k}{\partial x}$ b. $\frac{\partial k}{\partial y}$ c. $\frac{\partial k}{\partial y}\Big|_{x=3}$ d. $\frac{\partial k}{\partial y}\Big|_{(x, y)=(3, 2)}$

17. $f(x, y) = 2xy + 8x^2y^3 + 5e^{2y} + 10$

    a. f_x b. f_y
    c. $f_{xx} = \quad f_{xy} =$
    $\quad f_{yx} = \quad f_{yy} =$
    d. Write the second partials matrix.

18. $G(r, t) = t \ln r + 12rt^7 - 4(8^r) - tr$

    a. $\frac{\partial G}{\partial t}$ b. $\frac{\partial G}{\partial r}$

    c. $G_{rr} = \quad G_{rt} =$
    $\quad G_{tr} = \quad G_{tt} =$
    d. Write the second partials matrix.

Construct a second partials matrix for each of the functions in Activities 19 through 22.

19. $f(x, y) = \dfrac{x}{y} - \dfrac{y}{x}$

20. $g(x, y) = 6(3x - y + 4)^3$

21. $h(x, y) = e^{2x - 3y}$

22. $j(x, y) = y^2 \ln x$

Applying Concepts

23. Investment   The value $A(P, r)$ of an investment of P dollars after 2 years in an account with annual percentage yield $100r\%$ is given by the function $A(P, r) = P(1 + r)^2$ dollars.

   a. Find and interpret $A(14,000, r)$.

   b. Find and interpret $\dfrac{\partial A}{\partial r}\Big|_{(P, r) = (14,000, 0.127)}$.

   c. Explain how the rate of change in part b is related to a graph of the cross-sectional function in part a. Illustrate graphically.

24. Investment   The value $A(t, r)$ of an investment of $\$1000$ after t years in an account for which the interest rate is $100r\%$ compounded continuously is given by the function $A(t, r) = 1000e^{rt}$ dollars.

   a. Find and interpret $A(10, r)$.

   b. Find and interpret $\dfrac{\partial A}{\partial r}\Big|_{(t, r) = (10, 0.07)}$.

   c. Explain how the rate of change in part b is related to a graph of the cross-sectional function in part a. Illustrate graphically.

25. Radiation   Values of UV (ultraviolet) radiation are sometimes useful for the medical consultant, the chemist, and the technical engineer. The table below gives the amount of a certain type of UV radiation in watts per square meter per month.

   a. Find cross-sectional models for the amount of UV radiation at a given latitude in March and for the amount of radiation for a given month at a latitude of 50° south of the equator.

TABLE FOR ACTIVITY 25   Amount of UVA radiation (watts/m²/month)

	Jan	Feb	Mar	Apr	May	Jun	Jul	Aug	Sep	Oct	Nov	Dec	Year
North Pole	—	—	—	17	41	52	46	27	—	—	—	—	183
80°	—	—	3	19	42	52	47	28	8	—	—	—	179
70°	—	2	11	26	43	51	47	32	16	5	—	—	233
60°	3	8	20	34	46	53	49	39	24	12	4	2	294
50°	9	16	28	40	50	55	53	44	32	20	11	7	365
40°	19	25	35	45	53	56	54	49	39	29	20	15	439
30°	26	33	41	49	54	55	54	51	44	36	28	24	495
20°	34	40	47	51	53	53	53	52	48	42	36	32	541
10	42	46	50	51	50	50	50	50	50	47	43	40	569
Equator	49	50	52	50	47	45	46	48	50	50	49	47	583
10°	53	53	50	46	41	38	39	43	48	52	53	53	569
20°	56	54	49	42	34	31	32	38	45	51	55	56	543
30°	58	53	44	35	26	22	24	31	40	49	56	58	496
40°	57	50	39	27	18	13	15	23	34	45	55	59	435
50°	55	46	32	19	10	7	8	15	27	40	52	58	369
60°	52	40	24	11	5	1	2	7	18	33	47	56	296
70°	50	35	15	4	—	—	—	1	10	26	43	54	238
80°	49	27	8	—	—	—	—	—	3	19	41	56	203
South Pole	48	26	—	—	—	—	—	—	—	16	41	56	187

(Source: W. Rudloff, *World-Climates,* Stuttgart, Germany: Wissenschaftliche Verlagsgesellschaft, 1981.)

TABLE FOR ACTIVITY 26   Number of cars sold, $S(m, y)$

Year y	Month m											
	Jan	Feb	Mar	Apr	May	June	July	Aug	Sept	Oct	Nov	Dec
1960	6550	8728	12,026	14,395	14,587	13,791	9498	8251	7049	9545	9364	8456
1961	7237	9374	11,837	13,784	15,926	13,821	11,143	7975	7610	10,015	12,759	8816
1962	10,677	10,947	15,200	17,010	20,900	16,205	12,143	8997	5568	11,474	12,256	10,583
1963	10,862	10,965	14,405	20,379	20,128	17,816	12,268	8642	7962	13,932	15,936	12,628
1964	12,267	12,470	18,944	21,259	22,015	18,581	15,175	10,306	10,792	14,752	13,754	11,738
1965	12,181	12,965	19,990	23,125	23,541	21,247	15,189	14,767	10,895	17,130	17,697	16,611
1966	12,674	12,760	20,249	22,135	20,677	19,933	15,388	15,113	13,401	16,135	17,562	14,720
1967	12,225	11,608	20,985	19,692	24,081	22,114	14,220	13,434	13,598	17,187	16,119	13,713
1968	13,210	14,251	20,139	21,725	26,099	21,084	18,024	16,722	14,385	21,342	17,180	14,577

(Source: B. Abraham and J. Ledolter, *Statistical Methods for Forecasting*, New York: Wiley, 1983.)

  b. Estimate the rate of change of UV radiation at 50° south in March with respect to latitude.

  c. Estimate the rate of change of UV radiation at 50° south in March with respect to the month.

  d. Graph the cross-sectional functions in part *a*. On the graphs, illustrate the rates of change in parts *b* and *c*.

26. **Sales**   Refer to the table listing the number of cars sold in Québec from January 1960 through December 1968.

  a. Find cross-sectional models for car sales $S(m, y)$ in January and June as functions of the number of years *y* since 1960.

  b. Approximate the partial rates of change of car sales with respect to the year of the sales in January 1965 and in June 1965.

  c. Estimate and interpret $\frac{\partial S}{\partial y}$ at $m = 1$ (January) and $y = 2$.

27. **Peaches**   The per capita consumption table shows selected values of the average yearly consumption of peaches per person, based on the price of peaches and the yearly income of the person's family.

  a. Use a logarithmic cross-sectional model to estimate the rate of change of the per capita consumption of peaches with respect to yearly income when the yearly income is $30,000 and the price is $1.70 per pound.

TABLE FOR ACTIVITY 27   Per capita consumption of peaches (pounds per person per year)

Yearly income (tens of thousands of dollars)	Price per pound (dollars above $1.50)					
	0	0.10	0.20	0.30	0.40	0.50
1	5.0	4.9	4.8	4.7	4.7	4.6
2	6.4	6.3	6.2	6.1	6.1	6.0
3	7.2	7.1	7.0	6.9	6.9	6.8
4	7.8	7.7	7.6	7.5	7.4	7.4
5	8.2	8.1	8.0	8.0	7.9	7.8
6	8.6	8.5	8.4	8.3	8.3	8.2

  b. Use an exponential cross-sectional model to estimate the rate of change of the per capita consumption of peaches with respect to price when the yearly income is $30,000 and the price is $1.70 per pound.

  c. The data can be modeled by the equation

$$C(p, i) = 2\ln i + 2.7183^{-p} + 4$$
pounds per person per year

where the price of peaches is $(1.50 + p)$ per pound and the person lives in a family with annual income $10,000i$. Use this model to find the rates of change in parts *a* and *b*.

d. Compare the answers you found using the two methods in this activity. Which method was easier to use? Which answers do you believe are the more reliable?

28. Sales Two vending machines sit side by side in a college dorm. One machine sells Coke products, and the other sells Pepsi products. Daily sales of Coke products, based on the prices of the products in the two machines, are as shown.

TABLE FOR ACTIVITY 28 Daily sales (number of cans) of Coke products from a vending machine

Cost of Pepsi products	Cost of Coke products				
	$0.50	$0.75	$1.00	$1.25	$1.50
$0.50	157	143	123	98	65
$0.75	206	192	172	146	114
$1.00	255	241	221	195	163
$1.25	304	290	270	244	211
$1.50	353	339	319	293	260

a. Use a quadratic cross-sectional model to estimate the rate of change of the sale of Coke products with respect to the price of Coke products when Coke products cost $0.75 and Pepsi products cost $1.25.

b. Use a linear cross-sectional model to estimate the rate of change of the sale of Coke products with respect to the price of Pepsi products when Coke products cost $0.75 and Pepsi products cost $1.25.

c. The data can be modeled by the equation

$$S(c, p) = 196.42p - 50.2c^2 + 9.6c + 66.4 - 1.04cp$$
cans per day

when Coke products cost c and Pepsi products cost p. Use this model to find the rates of change in parts a and b.

d. Compare the answers you found using the two methods in this activity. Which method was easier to use? Which answers do you believe are the more reliable?

e. Use the equation in part c to find and interpret

$$\frac{\partial S}{\partial c}\bigg|_{(c,p)=(1.30,\,1.20)} \text{ and } \frac{\partial S}{\partial p}\bigg|_{(c,p)=(1.30,\,1.20)}.$$

29. Heat Loss Siple and Passel developed the equation

$$H(v, t) = (10.45 + 10\sqrt{v} - v)(33 - t)$$

giving the body's heat loss in kilogram-calories per square meter of body surface area per hour for wind speed v in meters per second when the air temperature is t degrees Celsius.

(Source: W. Bosch and L. G. Cobb, "Windchill," UMAP Module 658, *The UMAP Journal*, vol. 5, no. 4 (Winter 1984), pp. 477–492.)

a. Find the function expressing the partial rate of change of heat loss with respect to air temperature and the function expressing the partial rate of change of heat loss with respect to wind speed.

b. Would you expect $\frac{\partial H}{\partial v}$ at $(v, t) = (20, 12)$ to be positive or negative? Give reasons.

c. Find the value of $\frac{\partial H}{\partial v}$ at $(v, t) = (20, 12)$. Interpret your answer.

d. Would you expect $\frac{\partial H}{\partial t}$ at $(v, t) = (20, 12)$ to be positive or negative? Give reasons.

e. Find the value of $\frac{\partial H}{\partial t}$ at $(v, t) = (20, 12)$. Interpret your answer.

30. Livestock The carrying capacity of a particular farm system is defined as the number of animals or people that can be supported by the crop production from a given land area. The carrying capacity of a crop of rye grass when 70% of the crop is consumed and 80% of the amount consumed is digested as useful nutrients is

$$K(P, A) = \frac{9.52P}{A} \text{ animals per hectare}$$

where P is the net crop production (in kilograms per hectare per year) and A is the annual energy requirements of the animal (in megajoules per animal).

(Source: R. S. Loomis and D. J. Connor, *Crop Ecology: Productivity and Management in Agricultural Systems*, Cambridge, England: Cambridge University Press, 1992.)

a. Write a function for the partial rate of change of carrying capacity with respect to net crop production.

b. How quickly is carrying capacity changing with respect to net crop production when 15,000 kg of rye grass is produced per hectare annually and the crop is used to support milking cows that require approximately 64,000 megajoules of energy per cow each year?

c. Write a function for the partial rate of change of the carrying capacity with respect to the animal's energy requirements.

d. How quickly is the carrying capacity changing with respect to the animal's energy requirements when 15,000 kg of rye grass is produced per hectare annually and the crop is used to support milking cows that require approximately 64,000 megajoules of energy per cow each year?

e. Construct a second partials matrix for K, and interpret each of the second partial derivatives.

31. **Livestock**   The amount of organic matter that one beef cow grazing on the Northern Great Plains rangeland eats each day can be modeled by

$$I(s, m) = 8.62 - 1.24s + 0.09s^2 - 0.21m$$
$$+ 0.036m^2 + 0.21sm$$

kilograms per day when the cow produces m kilograms of milk per day and s is a number between -4 and 4 that describes the size of the cow.

(Source: E. E. Grings et al., "Efficiency of Production in Cattle of Two Growth Potentials on Northern Great Plains Rangelands During Spring-Summer Grazing," *Journal of Food Science*, vol. 74, no. 10 (1996), pp. 2317–2326.)

a. Would you expect $\frac{\partial I}{\partial s}$ and $\frac{\partial I}{\partial m}$ to be positive or negative? Explain.

b. Write and interpret functions for $\frac{\partial I}{\partial s}$ and $\frac{\partial I}{\partial m}$.

c. When a cow is of size 2 and produces 6 kg of milk per day, how quickly is the amount of organic matter consumed by the cow changing as its milk production increases?

d. When a cow is of size 2 and produces 6 kg of milk per day, how quickly is the amount of organic matter consumed by the cow changing as its size increases?

e. Construct a second partials matrix for I. What does this matrix indicate about the shape of the surface of I?

32. **Honey**   A measure of the adhesiveness of honey that is being seeded with crystals to cause controlled crystallization can be modeled by

$$A(g, m, s, h) = -151.78 + 4.26g + 5.69m$$
$$+ 0.67s + 2.48h - 0.05g^2 - 0.14m^2$$
$$- 0.03s^2 - 0.05h^2 - 0.07mh$$

where g is the percentage of glucose and maltose, m is the percentage of moisture, s is the percentage of seed, and h is the holding time in days.

(Source: J. M. Shinn and S. L. Wang, "Textural Analysis of Crystallized Honey Using Response Surface Methodology," *Canadian Institute of Food Science and Technology Journal*, vol. 23, nos. 4–5 (1990), pp. 178–182.)

a. Write functions for each of the partial derivatives of A.

b. Tell which partial derivative should be used to answer the question "How quickly is adhesiveness changing as the percentage of glucose and maltose changes?"

c. For which input variable(s) do you need a specific value in order to determine the actual rate at which adhesiveness is changing with respect to the percentage moisture?

d. Find a second partials matrix for A.

33. **Investment**   The value $A(t, r)$ of an investment of $1000 after t years in an account for which the interest rate $100r\%$ is compounded continuously is given by the function $A(t, r) = 1000e^{rt}$ dollars.

a. Write the partial derivatives $\frac{\partial A}{\partial t}$ and $\frac{\partial A}{\partial r}$.

b. Construct a second partials matrix for A, and interpret each of the second partial derivatives for $t = 30$ and $r = 0.047$.

34. **Investment**   The value $A(P, r)$ of an investment of P dollars after 2 years in an account with annual percentage yield $100r\%$ is given by the function $A(P, r) = P(1 + r)^2$ dollars.

a. Find the first partial derivatives of A.

b. Construct a second partials matrix for A, and interpret each of the second partial derivatives for $P = 10,000$ and $r = 0.09$.

35. **Investment**   The value $A(r, t)$ of an investment of 1 million dollars with an annual yield of $100r\%$ is given by the function $A(r, t) = (1 + r)^t$ million dollars.

a. Write the partial derivative $\frac{\partial A}{\partial t}$. What are the units on $\frac{\partial A}{\partial t}$?

b. Write the partial derivative $\frac{\partial A}{\partial r}$. What are the units on $\frac{\partial A}{\partial r}$?

c. How quickly will the value of the investment be changing with respect to time 5 years after the investment is made if the investment yields 15% annually?

d. Illustrate the answer to part c using a graph.

36. **Loan Amount** The following equation gives the amount of a loan A (in dollars) given the interest rate $100r\%$, the period n (in months), and the monthly payments m (in dollars).

$$A(r, n, m) = \frac{12m}{r}\left[1 - \left(1 + \frac{r}{12}\right)^{-n}\right]$$

a. Write an expression for the rate of change of the loan amount with respect to the amount of the monthly payments.

b. How quickly is the loan amount changing with respect to the amount of the monthly payments when $500 is paid monthly for 15 years on a loan with 12% interest?

c. Write the appropriate partial derivative, and calculate the rate of change of the loan amount when the interest rate and the monthly payment amount are fixed at 11% and $250, respectively, and the period is 3 years but may vary.

d. Use graphs to illustrate the rates of change in parts b and c.

Discussing Concepts

37. When finding a formula for the rate-of-change of a three-dimensional function f with respect to the variable x when the other variable y is held constant at c, does it matter whether you substitute the known constant $y = c$ before or after you algebraically find the partial derivative f_x? Explain.

38. What must be true about the partial derivatives of a three-dimensional function at a relative maximum? Explain from a graphical viewpoint why this is true.

9.4   Compensating for Change

The following question often arises in situations where output depends on two input variables: "If output must remain fixed at some constant level and one of the input variables changes, how must the other input variable change in order to compensate?" In other words, given a function of two variables $z = f(x, y)$, if x increases (or decreases), how must y change in order to guarantee that the output $f(x, y)$ remains the same?

Let us consider this question in the context of a manufacturing problem where production depends on more than one input. The number of units produced during a manufacturing process can often be regarded as depending on several different input variables, two of which are the size L of the labor force and the amount K invested in capital. Economists often use the Cobb-Douglas production function

$$f(L, K) = cL^a K^{1-a}$$

as a simple model for the number of units produced. The values c and a in the Cobb-Douglas production function are constants that depend on the particular manufacturing process. Furthermore, the model requires that a be greater than 0 but less than 1.

The Cobb-Douglas monthly production function for a certain mattress-manufacturing plant is

$$f(L, K) = 48.1L^{0.6}K^{0.4} \text{ mattresses}$$

where L represents the number of worker hours (in thousands) and K represents the amount invested in capital (in thousands of dollars). Let us suppose that currently each month the manufacturer spends \$47,000 in capital, has a labor force that works 8320 worker hours, and produces $f(8.32, 47) \approx 800$ mattresses.

A competing plant offering higher wages is hiring new employees. Management expects some of its employees to transfer to the new plant. Instead of replacing the employees, management decides to upgrade the equipment to improve efficiency. The number of lost worker hours is not yet known, so the information that is most beneficial to management is the rate of change of capital K with respect to worker hours L for the current production level. How do we find $\frac{dK}{dL}$?

Concept Development: Calculating Compensation for Change

To determine how to compensate for the change in the labor force, we look at the contour curve corresponding to 800 mattresses. This helps us understand the connection between the two input variables L and K. By solving

$$800 = 48.1L^{0.6}K^{0.4}$$

for K in terms of L, we obtain the equation of the contour curve shown in Figure 9.25.

$$K = \left(\frac{800}{48.1L^{0.6}}\right)^{\frac{1}{0.4}}$$

$$= \left(\frac{800L^{-0.6}}{48.1}\right)^{2.5}$$

$$= \left(\frac{800}{48.1}\right)^{2.5} L^{-1.5} \text{ thousand dollars}$$

A tangent line is drawn on the curve in Figure 9.25 at the current amount of capital and number of worker hours.

To find $\frac{dK}{dL}$, we simply differentiate the contour curve equation with respect to L to obtain

$$\frac{dK}{dL} = -1.5\left(\frac{800}{48.1}\right)^{2.5} L^{-2.5} \text{ thousand dollars per thousand worker hours}$$

Evaluating this derivative at the current number of worker hours ($L = 8.32$) gives $\frac{dK}{dL} \approx -8.475$ thousand dollars per thousand worker hours. This value is the slope of the tangent line shown in Figure 9.25.

Recall from Chapter 4 that we can use the slope of a tangent line to estimate by how much an output quantity will change if the input changes by a small amount. That is, for a function $y = f(x)$, if the slope of the tangent line is $\frac{dy}{dx}$ when $x = c$ and the input x changes by a small amount (Δx), then the corresponding change (Δy) in the output y can be approximated by

$$\Delta y \approx \frac{dy}{dx} \Delta x$$

This approximation is illustrated in Figure 9.26.

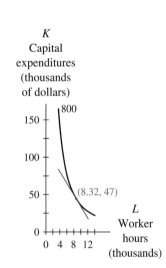

K
Capital expenditures (thousands of dollars)

FIGURE 9.25

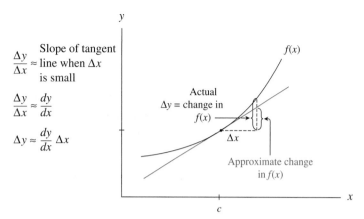

FIGURE 9.26

In the Cobb-Douglas example, the number of worker hours is currently $L = 8.32$ and $\frac{dK}{dL} \approx -8.475$ thousand dollars per thousand worker hours. That is, if the plant decreases the monthly labor force by 1000 worker hours, the amount spent on capital must increase by approximately \$8475 if the production level is to remain constant.

Suppose that the plant loses 500 worker hours as a result of employees leaving to work at the competing plant. In this case, the change in L is $\Delta L = -0.5$ thousand worker hours. Using the approximating-change equation just discussed, we estimate the corresponding change in capital K as

$$\Delta K \approx \frac{dK}{dL} \Delta L$$

$$\Delta K \approx (-\$8.475 \text{ thousand/thousand worker hours})$$

$$(-0.5 \text{ thousand worker hours})$$

$$\approx \$4.24 \text{ thousand}$$

Thus approximately \$4240 more will need to be spent on capital improvements in order to maintain the current production level and compensate for the loss of 500 worker hours. Figure 9.27 illustrates this approximation. As the figure shows, the approximation is an underestimate.

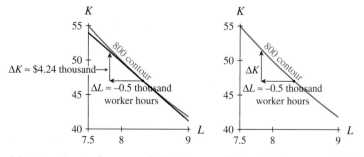

(a) *Approximate change needed in K*   **(b)** *Actual change needed in K*

FIGURE 9.27

Similarly, if the plant loses 2500 worker hours to the competing plant, then the change in capital is approximated as

$$\Delta K \approx \frac{dK}{dL} \Delta L$$

$$\Delta K \approx (-\$8.475 \text{ thousand/thousand worker hours})$$

$$(-2.5 \text{ thousand worker hours})$$

$$\approx \$21.2 \text{ thousand}$$

In order not to reduce production, an additional amount of approximately $21,200 in capital expenditures is needed to compensate for the loss of 2500 worker hours.

A General Formula

The preceding method of finding $\frac{dK}{dL}$ works only if we can solve the contour curve equation for one of the variables. How do we find a derivative of one input variable with respect to another input variable if we are not able to solve the contour curve equation algebraically for one of the variables?

Consider a function $z = f(x, y)$ and the contour curve equation $f(x, y) = c$. Even if we cannot solve for y in terms of x, it is true that we can consider y to be a function* of x. We replace y with $y(x)$ and write the contour curve equation as $f(x, y(x)) = c$. Note that the function f in this form is a composite function, where f is the outside function and y is the inside function. Recall from Chapter 3 the Chain Rule for the derivative of a composite function $f \circ g$. If we call g the inside function and f the outside function, then the derivative of f with respect to x is

$$\frac{df}{dx} = (\text{derivative of the outside function})(\text{derivative of the inside function})$$

$$= \left(\frac{df}{dg}\right)\left(\frac{dg}{dx}\right)$$

We use the Chain Rule as we develop the formula for the derivative of $z = f(x, y(x))$ with respect to x..

To take the derivative of $z = f(x, y(x))$ with respect to x, we consider the effect that a change in x has on the function f as well as the effect that a change in x has on y and the subsequent effect on the function f; that is,

$$\begin{pmatrix} \text{Rate of change } f(x, y(x)) \\ \text{with respect to } x \end{pmatrix} = \begin{pmatrix} \text{partial rate of change} \\ \text{of } f \text{ with respect to } x \end{pmatrix} + \begin{pmatrix} \text{partial rate of change} \\ \text{of } f \text{ with respect to } y \end{pmatrix}\begin{pmatrix} \text{rate of change of } y \\ \text{with respect to } x \end{pmatrix}$$

$$\frac{d}{dx}[f(x, y(x))] \qquad = \qquad \left(\frac{\partial f}{\partial x}\right) \qquad + \qquad \left(\frac{\partial f}{\partial y}\right) \qquad \cdot \qquad \left(\frac{dy}{dx}\right)$$

You may wonder why we use both derivative and partial derivative notation in the preceding equation. We use partial derivative notation when considering f to be a function of two variables, x and y, and we use derivative notation when considering f or y to be a function of the single variable x.

---

*When y is not a function of x, y can be broken into parts so that each part is a function of x.

With this formula, we return to the contour equation, differentiate both sides with respect to x, and solve for $\frac{dy}{dx}$.

$$f(x, y(x)) = c$$

$$\frac{d}{dx}[f(x, y(x))] = 0$$

$$\frac{\partial f}{\partial x} + \left(\frac{\partial f}{\partial y}\right)\left(\frac{dy}{dx}\right) = 0$$

$$\frac{dy}{dx} = \frac{-\left(\dfrac{\partial f}{\partial x}\right)}{\left(\dfrac{\partial f}{\partial y}\right)} = \frac{-f_x}{f_y}$$

This formula gives a method of finding a rate of change of one input variable with respect to another input variable at a point on a contour curve. It gives the slope of the tangent line at a point on a contour curve. This method is particularly useful when we cannot (or do not wish to) solve for one variable in terms of another.

The Slope of a Line Tangent to a Contour Curve

When a function of two variables $z = f(x, y)$ is held constant at a value c, the slope at any point on the contour curve $f(x, y) = c$ (that is, the slope of the line tangent to the c contour curve) is given by

$$\frac{dy}{dx} = \frac{-\left(\dfrac{\partial f}{\partial x}\right)}{\left(\dfrac{\partial f}{\partial y}\right)} = \frac{-f_x}{f_y}$$

whenever $f_y \neq 0$.

The rate of change $\frac{dy}{dx}$ tells us that if the value of the variable x changes by a small amount Δx, then the value of the variable y will change by a small amount that can be estimated as $\frac{dy}{dx}$ times Δx. Thus, as long as we remain on a constant level curve, we can compensate for a small change in one input variable x by making a comparable change in the other input variable determined by the approximation $\Delta y \approx \left(\frac{dy}{dx}\right)\Delta x$.

We have seen how to approximate the change needed in one variable to compensate for a change in another variable in order to maintain a constant function output in two ways: using a contour curve equation solved for one of the input variables to directly calculate a tangent line slope or using partial derivatives to calculate the needed slope. We summarize these two methods as follows:

Compensating for Change

In order to compensate for a small change Δx in x to keep $f(x, y)$ constant at c, y must change by approximately

$$\Delta y \approx \left(\frac{dy}{dx}\right)\Delta x$$

which can also be calculated as

$$\Delta y \approx \left(\frac{-f_x}{f_y}\right)\Delta x$$

EXAMPLE 1   *Finding the Slope of a Line Tangent to a Contour Curve*

9.4.1

BMI   Your body-mass index is a measure of how thin you are compared to your height. A person's body-mass index* is given by

$$B(h, w) = \frac{0.4536w}{0.00064516h^2} \text{ points}$$

where h is your height in inches and w is your weight in pounds. A teenage boy, in the middle of a growth spurt, has an appointment to see his doctor. He is 5 feet 7 inches tall and weighs 129 pounds. The doctor wants to ensure that the boy's body-mass index remains constant.

a. Find $\frac{dw}{dh}$ at the point (67, 129) on the contour curve corresponding to the boy's current body-mass index.

b. Use $\frac{dw}{dh}$ to estimate the weight change needed to compensate for growths of 0.5 inch, 1 inch, and 2 inches if the boy's body-mass index is to remain constant.

Solution

a. We begin by finding the two partial derivatives of B:

$$B_h = \frac{(-2)(0.4536w)}{0.00064516h^3} \text{ points per inch}$$

$$B_w = \frac{0.4536}{0.00064516h^2} \text{ points per pound}$$

where h is height in inches and w is weight in pounds. We evaluate these partial derivatives at $w = 129$ pounds and $h = 67$ inches and obtain

$$B_h \approx -0.60312 \text{ point per inch and } B_w \approx 0.15662 \text{ point per pound}$$

Thus,

$$\frac{dw}{dh} = \frac{-B_h}{B_w} \approx \frac{-(-0.60312) \text{ point per inch}}{0.15662 \text{ point per pound}}$$

$$\approx 3.85 \text{ pounds per inch}$$

New England Journal of Medicine, September 14, 1995.

b. We know that the change in weight needed to compensate for an increase in height can be approximated by $\Delta w \approx \frac{dw}{dh} \Delta h$. Thus,

For a 0.5-inch growth, $\Delta w \approx$ (3.85 pounds per inch) (0.5 inch) $\approx$ 1.9 pounds.

For a 1-inch growth, $\Delta w \approx$ (3.85 pounds per inch)(1 inch) $=$ 3.85 pounds.

For a 2-inch growth, $\Delta w \approx$ (3.85 pounds per inch)(2 inch) $=$ 7.7 pounds. ●

It is possible to estimate compensating change by using a table of data rather than a multivariable function. This is illustrated in Example 2.

EXAMPLE 2   *Compensating for Change Using a Table*

Tuition   A college wishes to keep its enrollment constant at 5600 students. From experience, the trustees know that the two factors that have the greatest influence on enrollment are tuition and the amount of available financial aid. Some research has been done at similar colleges, and Table 9.6 gives enrollment figures based on that research.

TABLE 9.6   College enrollment

				Tuition (thousand dollars)					
		16	**16.5**	**17.0**	**17.5**	**18.0**	**18.5**	**19**	**19.5**	**20.0**
Average financial aid per student (thousand dollars)	**1.50**	6358	6000	5662	5344	5043	4759	4491	4239	4000
	1.75	6722	6346	5990	5656	5339	5040	4757	4492	4240
	2.00	7086	6691	6318	5967	5634	5320	5024	4745	4480
	2.25	7451	7037	6647	6279	5930	5600	5290	4997	4720
	2.50	7815	7383	6975	6590	6226	5882	5557	5250	4960
	2.75	8179	7729	7303	6902	6522	6163	5823	5503	5200
	3.00	8543	8074	7631	7213	6817	6443	6089	5756	5440
	3.25	8907	8420	7959	7525	7113	6724	6356	6009	5680
	3.50	9272	8766	8288	7836	7409	7005	6622	6261	5920
	3.75	9636	9111	8616	8148	7704	7285	6889	6514	6160
	4.00	10,000	9457	8944	8459	8000	7566	7155	6767	6400

a. Using only the table values, estimate the change in the amount of financial aid the college should make available if it boosts tuition from $18.5 thousand to $19 thousand and wants to maintain an enrollment of 5600 students.

b. Use cross-sectional models to estimate the change in part *a*.

Solution

a. Reading in the column corresponding to a tuition of $18,500, we find that the enrollment of 5600 students occurs when the average financial aid is $2250 per student. If tuition is increased to $19,000, we must move one column to the right. Because the college wishes to keep enrollment constant, we seek a value of 5600 students in the $19,000 column. This is equivalent to staying on the 5600 contour curve (shown in teal in Figure 9.28), while increasing tuition to $19,000.

		Tuition (thousands of dollars)			
		18.0	18.5	19	19.5
Average financial aid per student (thousands of dollars)	1.50	5043	4759	4491	4239
	1.75	5339	5040	4757	4492
	2.00	5634	5320	5024	4745
	2.25	5930	5600	5290	4997
	2.50	6226	5882	5557	5250
	2.75	6522	6163	5823	5503
	3.00	6817	6443	6089	5736

5600

FIGURE 9.28

A look at the table shows that there is no 5600 entry in the $19,000 column. However, we know that 5600 occurs between 5557 (corresponding to financial aid of $2500) and 5823 (corresponding to financial aid of $2750). Thus the average financial aid will need to increase by a little more than $250 per student in order for tuition to increase to $19,000 and for enrollment to remain constant.

b. We choose to represent enrollment as $E(t, a)$ students, where tuition is t thousand dollars and average financial aid is a thousand dollars per student. Note that if $t = 18.5$ and $E = 5600$, then $a = 2.25$. We seek to estimate the change in financial aid a needed to compensate for an increase in tuition t using the equation

$$\Delta a \approx \frac{da}{dt}\Delta t = \frac{-E_t}{E_a}\Delta t$$

We begin by calculating rates of change of the appropriate cross-sectional models. To estimate E_a when $t = 18.5$ and $a = 2.25$, we find a cross-sectional model for $E(18.5, a)$. This is a linear model given by

$$E(18.5, a) = 1122.87a + 3074.55 \text{ students}$$

when a thousand dollars of financial aid is available and the tuition is $18,500. Now we find

$$\left.\frac{\partial E}{\partial a}\right|_{t=18.5} \approx \frac{dE(18.5, a)}{da} = 1122.87 \text{ students per thousand dollars of}$$
$$\text{financial aid}$$

Thus if $t = 18.5$ and $a = 2.25$, then $E_a \approx 1122.87$ students per thousand dollars.

Likewise, we find the cross-sectional model

$$E(t, 2.25) = 46{,}275.637 \, (0.892129^t) \text{ students}$$

when tuition is t thousand dollars and financial aid is $2250. Thus

$$\left.\frac{\partial E}{\partial t}\right|_{a=2.25} \approx \frac{dE(t, 2.25)}{dt} \approx -5282.10(0.892129^t) \text{ students per thousand}$$
$$\text{dollars of tuition}$$

Thus if $t = 18.5$ and $a = 2.25$, then $E_t \approx -639.3$ students per thousand dollars.

Because the change in tuition is $\Delta t = 0.5$ thousand dollars, we estimate the necessary change in financial aid as

$$\Delta a \approx \frac{-E_t}{E_a}\Delta t$$

$$\approx -\left(\frac{-639.3 \text{ students per } \$1000 \text{ of financial aid}}{1122.87 \text{ students per } \$1000 \text{ of tuition}}\right) \cdot$$

$$(0.5 \text{ thousand tuition dollars})$$

$$\approx 0.28 \text{ thousand dollars of financial aid}$$

The average financial aid available per student will need to increase by approximately \$280 in order to compensate for the increased tuition to maintain the current enrollment. (The estimate we made in part *a* using only table values, a little more than \$250, agrees with this result.) ●

In this section, we have seen examples of finding rates of change on contour curves and using them to compensate for a change in one input variable. Compensating for change is a valuable tool with many real-world applications.

9.4   Concept Inventory

- Approximating change
- Slope of a line tangent to a contour curve
- Compensating for change

9.4   Activities

Getting Started

For each of the functions in Activities 1 through 4, write a formula for the indicated rate of change.

1. $f(x, y) = 15x^2y^3; \dfrac{dx}{dy}$

2. $S(c, k) = c(39^k); \dfrac{dc}{dk}$

3. $g(m, n) = 59.3\ln m + 49nm + 16; \dfrac{dm}{dn}$

4. $A(r, t) = 83.2e^{rt}; \dfrac{dr}{dt}$

For each of the functions in Activities 5 through 8, sketch the contour curve indicated in the activity. Also sketch the tangent line indicated, and determine its slope.

5.* $g(x, y) = x(1.05^y)$

   $g(x, y) = 100$ for $0 \le y \le 10$

   tangent line at $y = 5$

6. $f(s, t) = s\ln(2t) + e^{-1.34t}$

   $f(s, t) = 2$ for $1 \le t \le 20$

   tangent line at $t = 10$

7. $f(a, b) = 2.8a^2b^3 - 1.8a^2 + 12b$

   $f(a, b) = 15$ for $0 \le a \le 10$ and $0.87 \le b \le 1.2$

   tangent line at $b = 0.9$

8. $f(m, n) = 10n(3.67 - m)^2e^{-0.2m}$

   $f(m, n) = 80$ for $1 \le m \le 10$ and $0 \le n \le 50$

   tangent lines at $n = 20$

For the functions in Activities 9 through 12, determine the output associated with the input given, and then approximate the change needed in one input variable to compensate for the given change in the other input variable.

9. $f(m, n) = 3m^2 + 2mn + 5n^2$ when $m = 2$, $n = 1$, and $\Delta m = 0.2$

10. $f(h, k) = (32h^3 + 15h^2 - 10h + 47)(43k + 15)$ when $h = 4.2$, $k = 3.7$, and $\Delta k = 0.6$

11. $f(h, s) = 0.00091s[0.103(2.5^h) + 1]$ when $h = 3.5$, $s = 1148$, and $\Delta h = -0.5$

12. $W(r, h) = 2.8r^2(1.08^h) + 59r(0.3h^2 - 3.3h + 72)$ when $r = 10$, $h = 60$, and $\Delta r = -1.3$

*In Activity 5 it is possible to consider the slope of the tangent line as $\dfrac{dy}{dx}$ or as $\dfrac{dx}{dy}$, depending on which input variable is placed on the horizontal axis. A similar note applies to Activities 6 through 12.

Applying Concepts

13. **Cost**   The cost of having specialty T-shirts made depends on the number of colors used in the T-shirt design and the number of T-shirts being ordered. A function giving A, the cost per T-shirt (the average cost), when c colors are used and n T-shirts are ordered is

$$A(c, n) = (-0.02c^2 + 0.35c + 0.99)(0.99897^n)$$
$$+ 0.46c + 2.57 \text{ dollars}$$

(Source: Based on data compiled from 1993 prices at Tigertown Graphics, Inc., Clemson, SC.)

a. Determine the average cost when 250 T-shirts are printed with six colors.

b. When 250 T-shirts are printed with six colors, how quickly is the average cost changing when more T-shirts are printed?

c. Find a formula for $\frac{dn}{dc}$. If average cost is to remain constant, would you expect $\frac{dn}{dc}$ to be positive or negative? Explain.

d. A fraternity is planning to buy 500 four-color shirts. One of the members has proposed several alternative designs, some using more and some fewer than four colors. Use $\frac{dn}{dc}$ to estimate the change in order size needed to compensate for an increase or decrease in the number of colors if the average cost per T-shirt is to remain constant.

14. **Heat Index**   A model for the apparent temperature (how hot or cold it feels) is

$$A(h, t) = 2.70 + 0.885t - 78.7h + 1.20th \text{ °F}$$

for an air temperature of t degrees Fahrenheit and a relative humidity of $100h\%$.

(Source: W. Bosch and L. G. Cobb, "Temperature Humidity Indices," UMAP Module 691, *The UMAP Journal*, vol. 10, no. 3 (Fall 1989), pp. 237–256.)

a. How hot does it feel when the relative humidity is 85% and the air temperature is 90°F?

b. Find a formula for $\frac{dh}{dt}$. If the apparent temperature is to remain constant, would you expect $\frac{dh}{dt}$ to be positive or negative? Explain.

c. Use $\frac{dh}{dt}$ to estimate the change in the relative humidity needed to compensate for a 2°F increase in temperature if the current conditions are those stated in part *a* and the apparent temperature is to remain constant.

d. Repeat part *c* for a 3.5°F decrease in temperature.

15. **Sunflowers**   A process to extract pectin and pigment from sunflower heads involves washing the sunflower heads in heated water. It has been shown that the percentage of pigment that can be removed from a sunflower head by washing for 20 minutes can be modeled as

$$p(t, r) = 306.761 - 9.6544t + 1.9836r$$
$$+ 0.07368t^2 - 0.02958r^2 \text{ percent}$$

where r milliliters of t°C water is used for each gram of sunflower heads.

(Source: X. Q. Shi et al., "Optimizing Water Washing Process for Sunflower Heads Before Pectin Extraction," *Journal of Food Science*, vol. 61, no. 3 (1996), pp. 608–612.)

a. Draw the 53% contour curve for $20 \leq r \leq 45$ and $85 \leq t \leq 88$.

b. Draw the line(s) tangent to the 53% contour curve when the temperature is 86.5°C.

c. Write a formula for the rate of change of temperature with respect to a change in the amount of water used when 53% of the pigment is removed.

d. Use the formula from part *c* to determine the slope(s) of the tangent line(s) drawn in part *b*.

16. **Free Volume**   In 1965, Honer developed a model for the total-stem volume of red pine trees in Canada. His model is

$$V(d, h) = \frac{d^2}{0.691 + 363.676h^{-1}} \text{ cubic feet}$$

where d is the diameter of the tree at breast height (4.5 feet above the ground), which is denoted by dbh and measured in inches, and the tree is h feet tall.

(Source: J. L. Clutter et al., *Timber Management: A Quantitative Approach*, New York: Wiley, 1983.)

a. Find the volume of a 40-foot tree with a 2-foot dbh and draw a contour curve corresponding to that volume.

b. On the contour curve, draw a line whose slope represents how quickly height is changing as dbh is changing if the volume does not change for a 40-foot tree with a 2-foot dbh.

c. Assuming a constant volume, find the rate at which height changes with respect to dbh for a 40-foot tree with a 2-foot dbh.

d. A logging company wishes to cut only trees that have a volume of at least 59 cubic feet. Use the answer to part *c* to estimate the height of a tree with dbh = 25.5 inches that satisfies the volume requirement. Repeat for a dbh of 23 inches.

e. How is your answer to part *c* related to the line you drew in part *b*?

17. **BMI**   Refer to the BMI function in Example 1.

a. Solve for *w* as a function of *h* for the body mass of the teenage boy in Example 1.

b. Use the formula in part *a* to find $\frac{dw}{dh}$ when $h = 67$ inches and $w = 129$ pounds.

c. Compare your answer in part *b* to the answer in part *a* of Example 1.

18. **Skin**   The amount of skin covering a person's body (in square feet) depends on the person's height and weight. One model for estimating this skin surface area is given by the multivariable function

$$A(w, h) = 0.6416w^{0.425}h^{0.725} \text{ square feet}$$

for a person weighing *w* pounds who is *h* feet tall. If a person 5 feet 11 inches tall who weighs 130 pounds grows 2 inches in height, by approximately how much must this person's weight change if the skin surface area is to remain the same?

19. **Payments**   The amount of a monthly payment on a loan with 6% interest compounded monthly can be calculated by using the function

$$m(A, t) = \frac{0.005A}{1 - 0.9419^t} \text{ dollars}$$

when the loan is for *A* dollars and is to be repaid over *t* years.

a. Suppose that you borrow $10,000 to buy a car and will repay the loan over a period of 5 years. What is your monthly payment?

b. Suppose that you decide to finance the car over a period of 4 years instead of 5. Approximate the amount you could borrow to buy a car without increasing or decreasing the monthly payment determined in part *a*.

20. **Tuition**   Refer to Table 9.6 on page 603, which shows a college's enrollment as a function of tuition and financial aid. The college now has enrollment of 7000 and average financial aid of $3500 per student.

a. Sketch the 7000 contour curve, and locate the approximate point on Table 9.6 corresponding to the college's current situation.

b. The board of trustees has decided to reduce the average financial aid by $500 per student in order to build a new dormitory. Use Table 9.6 to estimate the decrease in tuition that will be necessary to offset the cut in financial aid and allow enrollment to remain constant.

c. Use cross-sectional models to estimate the change in part *b*.

21. **Sales**   The table shows the sales of Coke products from a vending machine that is located next to a Pepsi vending machine. The current price of Coke products is $1.00, and Pepsi products cost $1.25.

TABLE FOR ACTIVITY 21   **Number of cans of Coke products sold daily from a vending machine**

Cost of Pepsi products	Cost of Coke products				
	$0.50	$0.75	$1.00	$1.25	$1.50
$0.50	157	143	123	98	65
$0.75	206	192	172	146	114
$1.00	255	241	221	195	163
$1.25	304	290	270	244	211
$1.50	353	339	319	293	260

a. Pepsi is planning to lower its price to $1.00. Use the table values to estimate by how much Coke would need to change its price in order to compensate for this change and retain current sales.

b. Using cross-sectional models, estimate the change in part *a*.

c. Judging on the basis of your estimates in parts *a* and *b*, what action do you think Coke should take when Pepsi lowers its prices?

22. **Peaches**   The table gives the per capita consumption of peaches as a function of annual family income and the price of peaches. The current average

annual family income in a community is $40,000, and the average price of peaches is $1.99 per pound.

TABLE FOR ACTIVITY 22   Per capita consumption of peaches (pounds per person per year)

Yearly income (tens of thousands of dollars)	Price per pound (dollars above $1.50)					
	0	0.10	0.20	0.30	0.40	0.50
1	5.0	4.9	4.8	4.7	4.7	4.6
2	6.4	6.3	6.2	6.1	6.1	6.0
3	7.2	7.1	7.0	6.9	6.9	6.8
4	7.8	7.7	7.6	7.5	7.4	7.4
5	8.2	8.1	8.0	8.0	7.9	7.8
6	8.6	8.5	8.4	8.3	8.3	8.2

a. Suppose that in the next year, a company that employs several thousand people in this community goes out of business, thereby increasing unemployment and lowering the average annual family income by $5000. Use the table to estimate the change in the price of peaches needed to compensate for the decrease in income.

b. Use cross-sectional models to estimate the change in part a.

c. The peach consumption data can be modeled by the equation

$$C(p, i) = 2\ln i + 2.718^{-p} + 4 \text{ pounds}$$
$$\text{per person per year}$$

where the price of peaches is $(1.50 + p)$ per pound and the person lives in a family with annual income $10,000i. Estimate the change in part a using this equation.

d. Compare and contrast the three methods of estimating change used in this activity in terms of ease of use and accuracy.

Discussing Concepts

23. For a function f with inputs x and y, explain from a graphical viewpoint what the algebraic ratio $\frac{f_x}{f_y}$ represents.

SUMMARY

Multivariable Functions and Contour Graphs

In applications where output depends on two or more input variables, multivariable functions occur. A multivariable function with two input variables is graphed using a three-dimensional coordinate system; it can also be graphed in two dimensions by contour curves representing constant values of output.

Multivariable Functions and Rates of Change

Cross-sectional models of a multivariable function with two input variables can be obtained by modeling one column (or row) of the data given in a multivariable table. Geometrically, cross-sectional models describe the curves that result when cross-sectional planes cut a three-dimensional graph of the function with two input variables parallel to one of the two input axes.

When considering the rate of change of a multivariable function, we must consider the direction of movement. Rates of change of cross-sectional models describe how the function is changing when moving on the three-dimensional graph of the function in directions parallel to the two input axes.

Partial Derivatives

When a function f has two input variables x and y, we use the symbols $\frac{\partial f}{\partial x}$ and $\frac{\partial f}{\partial y}$ to represent the partial rates of change and to indicate the direction of movement. Partial derivatives of multivariable functions with respect to a particular input variable are found by treating all the other input variables as constants and computing the derivative with respect to the changing variable.

Compensating for Change

In situations with fixed output and changing input, the adjustment needed in one input variable to compensate for small changes in the other input variable can be estimated using the slope of a line tangent to the fixed contour curve. Algebraically, for a function f with input variables x and y, the change is represented by the approximation formula

$$\Delta y \approx \frac{-f_x}{f_y} \Delta x$$

The partial derivatives in this formula are evaluated at the point from which the change occurs.

CONCEPT CHECK

Can you	To practice, try	
• Interpret multivariable function inputs and outputs?	Section 9.1	Activities 3, 5
• Draw contour graphs on tables?	Section 9.1	Activities 9, 11
• Draw contour graphs using equations?	Section 9.1	Activities 13, 17
• Answer questions using contour graphs?	Section 9.1	Activities 27, 29
• Find and interpret cross-sectional models?	Section 9.2	Activities 5, 9
• Find rates of change of cross-sectional models derived from tables?	Section 9.2	Activities 17, 19
• Interpret partial rates of change?	Section 9.3	Activities 5, 7
• Estimate partial rates of change using tables and cross-sectional models?	Section 9.3	Activities 11, 13, 17
• Calculate first and second partial derivatives using an equation?	Section 9.3	Activities 11,13,17
• Calculate the slope at a point on a contour curve?	Section 9.4	Activities 5, 15
• Estimate compensating change?	Section 9.4	Activities 19, 21

CONCEPT REVIEW

1. **Apples** The storage time of apples and the temperature at which they are blanched when making applesauce affect the consistency of the applesauce. The consistometer table gives the consistency values for applesauce as a function of the number of months the raw apples were stored and the temperature at which they were blanched. The consistometer value is a measure of how far (in centimeters) an amount of applesauce flows down a vertical surface in 30 seconds. $C(t, s)$ denotes the consistometer value for a storage time of s months and a blanch temperature of $t°C$.

Consistometer values (cm) for Rome applesauce

Storage time (months)	Temperature (Celsius)				
	35°	47°	59°	71°	83°
0	3.0	2.8	2.6	2.6	2.8
1	3.3	3.1	2.8	2.8	3.0
2	3.5	3.2	3.0	2.9	3.2
3	3.4	3.2	3.0	2.9	3.2
4	3.2	2.9	2.7	2.7	3.0

(Source: Based on information in A. M. Godfrey Usiak, M. C. Bourne, and M. A. Rao, "Blanch Temperature/Time Effects on Rheological Properties of Applesauce," *Journal of Food Science*, vol. 60, no. 6 (1995), pp. 1289–1291.)

a. Draw an input/output diagram for C.

b. Find and interpret $C(71, 3)$.

c. Find an appropriate cross-sectional model, and use it to estimate the consistometer value of applesauce made from apples that were stored for 2 weeks and blanched at 35°C.

d. Interpret the notation $\frac{\partial C}{\partial t}\big|_{s=4}$.

e. Use a cross-sectional model to estimate the value of the partial derivative in part *d* for $t = 45°C$. Interpret your answer.

f. Sketch contour curves on the table for consistometer values of 2.8, 3.0, and 3.2

2. **Insect Eggs** A model for the number of eggs laid per female in 30 days for a certain insect is

$$E(t, h) = -4191.6877 + 299.7038t + 23.1412h$$
$$- 5.2210t^2 - 0.0937h^2 - 0.4023th \text{ eggs}$$

where t is the temperature in degrees Celsius and h is the percentage relative humidity.

(Source: J. A. Morales-Ramos, S. M. Greenberg, and E. G. King, "Selection of Optimal Physical Conditions for Mass Propagation of *Catolaccus grandi*," *Environmental Entomology*, vol. 25, no. 1 (February 1996), pp. 165–173.)

a. Find and interpret $E(24, 60)$.

b. Find and interpret $\frac{\partial E}{\partial h}$ for a temperature of 27°C and relative humidity 77%.

c. A researcher wishes to hold the egg production constant but desires to investigate the change in humidity needed to compensate for an increase in temperature. Find a formula for the derivative that is most useful to this researcher.

d. If the researcher is currently conducting an experiment with temperature 25°C and humidity 63%, what approximate change in humidity will be needed to compensate for a decrease in temperature of 0.5°C while maintaining the current egg production level?

e. Discuss the graphical interpretation of the answer to part *d*.

3. **Insect Eggs** The figure shows a contour graph for the function described in Activity 2. Use the contour graph to answer the questions that follow.

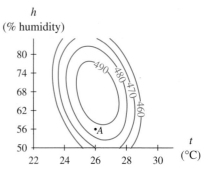

a. Estimate the inputs and output associated with point A. Interpret your answers.

b. At point A, which will result in a greater change in the number of eggs laid: an increase in temperature of 3°C or an increase in humidity of 3 percentage points?

c. At point A, will the number of eggs laid decrease more quickly when h decreases or when t decreases?

d. Estimate the slope of the line tangent to the contour graph at $t = 24$ and $h = 62$.

e. Calculate the answer to part d by using the equation given in Activity 2. Interpret your answer.

4. Insect Eggs Construct a second partials matrix for the function in Activity 2.

Project 9.1 Competitive and Complementary Products

Setting

Competitive and complementary products play an important role in today's business markets. Two commodities are called *competitive* if an increase in demand for one results in a decrease in demand for the other. Two different brands of the same item are competitive. For example, Pepsi and Coke products in side-by-side vending machines are competitive. In this case, when the demand for Pepsi increases, the demand for Coke decreases, and when the demand for Coke increases, the demand for Pepsi decreases. It is important to note that the driving force in the change in the demands for competitive products is often the increase (or decrease) in the prices of the products. That is, when the price of Pepsi increases, the demand for Pepsi will decrease and the demand for Coke will increase. Likewise, when the price of Coke increases, the demand for Coke will decrease and the demand for Pepsi will increase.

Sometimes products are used together because they complement each other (coffee and cream, computers and CDs, DVD players and DVDs). Two products are called *complementary* when both lose sales if one raises prices.

Tasks

1. Let $f(x, y)$ be the demand for a certain automobile sold for x dollars by Ford, and let $h(x, y)$ be the demand for a similar automobile sold for y dollars by Honda. If the total number of these two types of automobiles remains constant, explain why the automobiles are competitive if

$$\frac{\partial f}{\partial y} > 0 \text{ and } \frac{\partial h}{\partial x} > 0$$

2. Give four examples of commodities you believe would be competitive in today's market.

3. Let $D(a, b)$ be the demand for product A that sells for a dollars, and let $F(a, b)$ be the demand for product B that sells for b dollars. If products A and B are complementary, restate the definition of complementary products in terms of their demand functions, using partial derivative notation.

4. Give four examples of products you believe would be complementary in today's market.

Reporting

Prepare a written report containing detailed answers, including explanations, for the preceding tasks.

Project 9.2 Expert Witness

Setting

Investigators at accident scenes often wish to determine the speed at which a vehicle was traveling before the driver applied the brakes. Normally, all an investigator has to go on is the length of the skid marks and the weight of the vehicle that caused the skid marks. The investigator for an involuntary manslaughter lawsuit has called you as an expert witness to testify regarding the probable speed of the vehicle at the time of the accident.

Tasks

1. Under normal driving conditions, if a person driving a vehicle on an asphalt road slams on the brakes and skids to a stop, the length of the skid marks can be modeled by $S(v, w) = 0.000013wv^2$ feet, where the vehicle was traveling v miles per hour when the driver slammed on the brakes. The vehicle weighs w pounds.

   Suppose the investigator measures the skid marks and weighs the vehicle that made them. He finds that the skid marks are 112 feet long and the vehicle weighs 3145 pounds. Determine the velocity at which the vehicle must have been traveling if it was empty.

2. It is possible that when it was weighed, the vehicle did not contain everything that was in it when the skid marks were created. For instance, it is extremely unlikely that the driver and passengers were still in the vehicle. Therefore, the investigator's ability to predict the velocity of the vehicle accurately is affected by the rate of change of velocity with respect to weight. Find a formula for the rate of change of the velocity of a vehicle with respect to its weight. How quickly will the velocity of the 3145-pound vehicle that made skid marks 112 feet long be changing when its weight increases?

3. The investigator knows that the vehicle at the time of the accident contained one male driver 6 feet 1 inch tall and of average build, one female passenger 5 feet 5 inches tall and of average build, one 2-year-old child described as "chubby," and a child safety seat. Discuss whether the weight of the driver and passengers would significantly affect the calculation of the velocity of the vehicle in the case under investigation. Note that the accident occurred in a 50-mph zone.

Reporting

1. Prepare a document, to be introduced as evidence in court, summarizing your analysis of the vehicle's velocity. This report should be technical in nature, and your conclusions should be clearly stated.

2. Prepare a witness statement to be given under oath. You will be cross-examined by the defense attorney and should be prepared to justify your assumptions and conclusions.

10 Analyzing Multivariable Change: Optimization

Concepts Outline

10.1 Multivariable Critical Points

10.2 Multivariable Optimization

10.3 Optimization Under Constraints

10.4 Least-Squares Optimization

Philip and Karen Smith/Getty Images

Concept Application

Honey is composed of sugars (fructose, glucose, and maltose) and moisture content influenced by the floral source and variations in the climate where the honey was gathered. The percentages of sugars and moisture affect the texture of the honey. Measures of the texture of honey include cohesiveness and adhesiveness. With the ability to model multivariable data, food scientists are able to answer such questions as

- What is the minimum cohesiveness possible?

- What is the maximum adhesiveness possible?

- If the FDA restricts the percentage of sugars and moisture in Grade A honey, how does this affect the smallest cohesiveness and largest adhesiveness possible if honey is to be labeled Grade A?

You will have the opportunity to answer questions similar to these in Section 10.3.

Chapter Introduction

The optimization techniques for functions with a single input variable readily generalize to multivariable functions. In the same way that derivatives play an important role in determining critical points of a function with a single input variable, partial derivatives are used for locating critical points of multivariable functions. Critical points of functions of two input variables include maxima, minima, and saddle points.

We investigate methods for unconstrained optimization where the variables are free to change in any direction. We also consider constrained optimization, where there are limits on the values of the variables involved. We conclude with an application of optimization that is related to how we began: finding the equation of the line that best fits a set of data points.

Concepts You Will Be Learning

- Estimating critical points using tables and contour graphs (10.1)
- Estimating absolute extrema using tables and contour graphs (10.1)
- Finding critical points using equations (10.2)
- Classifying critical points using the Determinant Test (10.2)
- Solving constrained optimization using Lagrange multipliers (10.3)
- Classifying optimal points subject to a constraint (10.3)
- Interpreting the Lagrange multiplier (10.3)
- Using multivariable optimization to find a best-fit linear model (10.4)

10.1   Multivariable Critical Points

In Chapter 4 we considered relative maxima and minima of single-variable functions. Now we consider similar points on multivariable functions—maxima, minima, and saddle points.

Critical Points

Figure 10.1 shows a three-dimensional graph with a relative maximum (an output value greater than any of those around it). Figure 10.2 shows a three-dimensional graph with a relative minimum (an output value smaller than any of those around it).

FIGURE 10.1

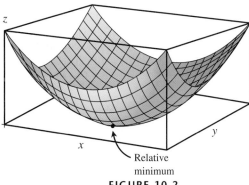

FIGURE 10.2

If for a given input region, there are no output values greater than a certain relative maximum, then we say that the relative maximum is also an **absolute maximum** in that region. Similarly, if for a given input region, there are no output values less than a certain relative minimum, then that relative minimum is called an **absolute minimum** in that region. Figure 10.3 shows a graph that contains relative maxima at points A and B and an absolute maximum at point B. A **saddle point** is a point that corresponds to a relative maximum of a cross section in one direction and to a relative minimum of a cross section in another. Figure 10.4 shows a function with a saddle point. A three-dimensional graph with a saddle point resembles a saddle in the area around that point. Note that the function in Figure 10.3 also has a saddle point in the valley between the points labeled A and B.

FIGURE 10.3

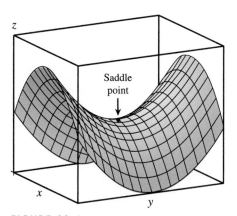

FIGURE 10.4

Saddle points and points corresponding to relative maxima and minima are called **critical points** (or stationary points). They are identified, as we will see in the next section, when partial rates of change are zero. Absolute extrema that occur on edges of tables or graphs may not fit this description.

Locating Critical Points on Contour Graphs

Contour graphs that correspond to the graphs in Figures 10.1 through 10.4 are shown in Figures 10.5 through 10.8, respectively.

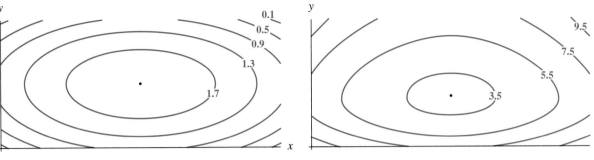

FIGURE 10.5 *A maximum point on a contour graph*   **FIGURE 10.6** *A minimum point on a contour graph*

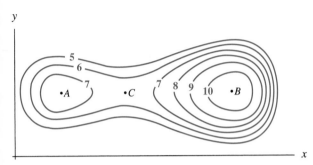

FIGURE 10.7 *Relative and absolute maxima and saddle point on a contour graph*   **FIGURE 10.8** *A saddle point on a contour graph*

Note that on the contour graph of a continuous function, relative maximum and minimum points lie within a *simple closed contour* (provided the contour graph is detailed enough). A simple closed contour is a contour that completely encloses a region but never crosses over itself. (See Figure 10.9.)

Three examples of simple closed contours   *Three curves that are not simple closed contours*

FIGURE 10.9

Relative maximum and minimum points lie in the center of a group of concentric simple closed contours. (See Figures 10.5, 10.6, and 10.7.)

Saddle points are also fairly easy to locate on contour graphs. The contour curves near the saddle point (but not through the saddle point) are all curved away from the point. (See Figure 10.8 and the contours near *C* in Figure 10.7). As we move away from the saddle point in certain directions, the contours we cross show increasing output levels; as we move away from the saddle point in other directions, the contours show decreasing output levels.

Locating Critical Points in Tables

When given only a table of data, we can use contour curves to identify critical points within the table. We simply sketch contour curves on the table for several equally spaced output values and then apply the methods for locating critical points on contour graphs.

Example 1 illustrates using contour curves to estimate a critical point in a table.

EXAMPLE 1   *Locating Extreme Points by Sketching Contour Curves*

Postal Rates   To receive "bound printed matter" rates from the U.S. Postal Service, items mailed must consist of advertising, promotional, directory, or editorial material. The maximum weight for bound printed matter is 15 pounds. Rates are based on weight, shape, and distance. The maximum size is 108 inches in combined length and distance around the thickest part. (For simplicity, we consider the distance around the thickest part of the package to be twice the width plus twice the height.) Table 10.1 shows some values of the volume of a rectangular package that contains the maximum amount of printed material according to the size requirement. All of the critical points lie within the region represented by the table.

TABLE 10.1   Volume of "Bound Printed Matter" Package

					Height (inches)				
		3	6	9	12	15	18	21	24	27
Width (inches)	3	864	1620	2268	2808	3240	3564	3780	3888	3888
	6	1620	3024	4212	5184	5940	6480	6804	6912	6804
	9	2268	4212	5832	7128	8100	8748	9072	9072	8748
	12	2808	5184	7128	8640	9720	10,368	10,584	10,368	9720
	15	3240	5940	8100	9720	10,800	11,340	11,340	10,800	9720
	18	3564	6480	8748	10,368	11,340	11,664	11,340	10,368	8748
	21	3780	6804	9072	10,584	11,340	11,340	10,584	9072	6804
	24	3888	6912	9072	10,368	10,800	10,368	9072	6912	3888
	27	3888	6804	8748	9720	9720	8748	6804	3888	0

(Source: Based on information at **www.usps.com,** accessed 1/4/2003.)

Sketch contours on the table at volumes of 8000, 9000, 10,000, and 11,000 cubic inches, and mark the location of any approximate critical points with an X. Identify each critical point as a relative maximum, a relative minimum, or a saddle point.

Solution

We sketch contour curves on the table as shown in Figure 10.10. From the contour graph and the given information, we conclude that there is only one critical point.

Height (inches)

	3	6	9	12	15	18	21	24	27
3	864	1620	2268	2808	3240	3564	3780	3888	3888
6	1620	3024	4212	5184	5940	6480	6804	6912	6804
9	2268	4212	5832	7128	8100	8748	9072	9072	8748
12	2808	5184	7128	8640	9720	10,368	10,584	10,368	9720
15	3240	5940	8100	9720	10,800	11,340	11,340	10,800	9720
18	3564	6480	8748	10,368	11,340	11,664	11,340	10,368	8748
21	3780	6804	9072	10,584	11,340	11,340	10,584	9072	6804
24	3888	6912	9072	10,368	10,800	10,368	9072	6912	3888
27	3888	6804	8748	9720	9720	8748	6804	3888	0

Width (inches)

FIGURE 10.10

Because this point (located near height $=$ 18 inches and width $=$ 18 inches) lies within concentric closed contours and the values of the contour curves decrease in all directions away from it, the point is the approximate location of a relative maximum. Note that this method gives 11,664 cubic inches as only an approximation of the maximum volume because the table does not show every possible input and output of the function. ●

Relative maxima and relative minima occur at the center of concentric closed contour curves. However, saddle points occur where the contours appear to bend outward away from a central point. Example 2 illustrates using contour curves to estimate a saddle point on a table.

EXAMPLE 2 *Locating Saddle Points by Sketching Contour Curves*

TV News The Nielsen Media Research ratings for television programs show the percentage of households in a certain broadcast market tuned to a specific program. Many television programs use the Nielsen ratings as a measure of how well they are doing in the market. The Project for Excellence in Journalism is an independent research project that has been set up to analyze the quality of local TV news broadcasts. Preliminary findings from this project show that several factors impact a local TV news broadcast's Nielsen rating. In addition to documenting the influence of the number of viewpoints presented, the amount of local news covered, the number of stories covered, the depth of the stories covered, the number and quality of the sources consulted, and the size of the news team, the project for Excellence in Journalism found that broadcasts with a mixture of tabloid news and serious news are not as likely to increase their Nielsen rating as broadcasts that are dedicated to one form of news. The preliminary findings also suggest that local news teams may be too understaffed to deliver quality reporting. Suppose that Table 10.2 shows the probability that a local news broadcast's Nielsen rating will be rising, given the proportion of tabloid news on the broadcast and the amount of time (on average) that a reporter has to research the story.

TABLE 10.2   Probability of rise in Nielsen ratings

		Research time (days)								
		0.6	0.8	1	1.2	1.4	1.6	1.8	2	2.2
Proportion of broadcast that is tabloid news	0.1	0.15	0.22	0.28	0.34	0.38	0.41	0.42	0.43	0.42
	0.2	0.12	0.19	0.25	0.30	0.33	0.35	0.36	0.36	0.35
	0.3	0.11	0.18	0.23	0.27	0.30	0.32	0.32	0.32	0.30
	0.4	0.12	0.18	0.23	0.26	0.29	0.30	0.30	0.29	0.26
	0.5	0.15	0.20	0.24	0.27	0.29	0.30	0.29	0.27	0.24
	0.6	0.19	0.24	0.27	0.30	0.31	0.31	0.30	0.27	0.24
	0.7	0.25	0.29	0.32	0.34	0.35	0.34	0.32	0.29	0.25
	0.8	0.33	0.36	0.39	0.40	0.40	0.39	0.36	0.33	0.28
	0.9	0.42	0.45	0.47	0.47	0.47	0.45	0.42	0.38	0.33

Use contour curves to help estimate the critical point in Table 10.2.

Solution
We sketch contour curves corresponding to probabilities of 0.20 through 0.40 at intervals of 0.05 on the table, as shown in Figure 10.11.

When two or more adjacent entries are equal, we estimate the location of the critical value.

FIGURE 10.11

There appears to be a saddle point just above and slightly to the right of the table entry 0.30 corresponding to 1.6 days of research and 50% tabloid news content. (See the X in Figure 10.11.) Note that the outputs on the contour curves decrease to the left and right of this value and increase above and below it. The value 0.30 is a maximum in the row in which it appears but is a relative minimum in its column. A table value that appears to be a relative maximum when approached from one direction and a relative minimum when approached from another direction is identified as a saddle point. ●

Note in Figure 10.11 that the entry 0.42 corresponding to 0.6 day research time and 90% tabloid news content in the broadcast is the largest value in the 0.6-day column and is smaller than nearby values in the 0.90 proportion tabloid news row. We do not classify this point as a saddle point because it lies on the edge of the table. In order to identify a saddle point visually in a table or on a contour graph, we must be able to identify a point that is a maximum in one direction and a minimum in another direction. We cannot visually identify relative extrema of cross sections on the edges of tables or contour graphs, because we cannot observe the edges lying within concentric closed contours. Similarly, we cannot visually identify saddle points on edges.

> Relative extreme points and saddle points cannot be visually identified on the edges of tables or contour graphs.

Sketching contour curves on a table is very helpful when identifying critical points.

Estimating Absolute Extrema Using Tables and Contour Graphs

Recall from Chapter 4 that in order to find absolute extrema of a continuous function over a specified interval, we first find all relative extrema and then compare the outputs of the relative extrema with the function outputs at the endpoints. If we are not given an interval over which to find the absolute extrema, then we must also consider the end behavior of the function. This process can be extended to find absolute extrema of a continuous function with two input variables (a three-dimensional function). We first locate all relative extrema (which lie within concentric closed contour curves), and we then compare the output values of the relative extrema with any output values on the edges of the function. Some functions are restricted on the basis of the context or the nature of the function. Some functions have no edges—that is, they extend infinitely in all directions. In this case, we must also consider the end behavior of the function.

When using tables and contour graphs to estimate absolute extrema for continuous, three-dimensional functions, we must keep in mind the following steps:

- Consider any restrictions on output suggested by the context.
- Sketch several contour curves on the table.
- Visually locate all relative extrema. In a table, relative extrema will be values that are smaller or larger than all eight values around them. Relative extrema cannot be identified on the edges of a table or contour graph, because to be visually identified, they must lie within concentric closed contour curves.
- Determine whether the edges of the table or contour graph can extend beyond what is shown. We call any edges beyond which the table or graph cannot extend terminal edges. Terminal edges are determined by the context of the situation that the function describes.

- Determine absolute extrema by comparing relative extrema and values on terminal edges of the table or graph and by considering the behavior of the function beyond the nonterminal edges. As with functions of one input variable, all absolute extrema will either be relative extreme points or lie on terminal edges of the graph.

We illustrate these steps in Example 3.

EXAMPLE 3 *Locating Absolute Extrema in a Table of Data*

Cheese Spread Table 10.3 shows a measure of the consistency of cheese spread as a function of the percent of salt and the percent of glycerol used in processing. All of the critical points lie within the region represented by the table.

TABLE 10.3 A measure of the consistency of cheese spread

	Percent glycerol										
	0	1	2	3	4	5	6	7	8	9	10
0	8028	6412	5078	4026	3256	2768	2562	2638	2996	3636	4558
0.3	9153	7593	6315	5319	4604	4172	4022	4154	4568	5263	6241
0.6	9953	8448	7226	6286	5627	5251	5156	5344	5814	6565	7599
1	10513	9083	7935	7069	6485	6183	6163	6425	6969	7795	8903
1.3	10553	9179	8087	7276	6748	6502	6538	6856	7455	8337	9501
1.6	10268	8950	7913	7159	6686	6496	6588	6961	7617	8554	9774
2	9382	8138	7176	6496	6098	5982	6148	6596	7326	8338	9632
2.3	8338	7150	6243	5619	5277	5217	5439	5942	6728	7796	9146
2.6	6968	5836	4985	4417	4131	4126	4404	4963	5805	6929	8334
3	4636	3578	2802	2308	2096	2166	2518	3152	4068	5266	6746
3.3	2507	1505	785	347	191	316	724	1414	2386	3640	5175

(Percent salt shown at left.)

(Source: E. Kombila-Moundounga and C. Lacroix, "Effet des Combinaisons de Chloure de Sodium, de Lactose et de Glycerol sur les Caractéristiques Rhéologiques et la Couleur des Fromages Fondus à Tartiner," *Canadian Institute of Food Science and Technology Journal,* vol. 24, no. 5 (1991), pp. 239–251.)

a. Sketch contour curves on Table 10.3 for consistency values of 4000, 5000, 6000, 7000, 8000, and 9000. Mark the approximate saddle point and the largest and smallest table values.

b. Use the table and contour graph to estimate relative and absolute maximum and minimum consistency measures.

Solution

a. In Figure 10.12, the requested contour curves are sketched, and boxes are drawn around the largest and smallest table values. The approximate saddle point is circled.

Percent glycerol

Percent salt	0	1	2	3	4	5	6	7	8	9	10
0	8028	6412	5078	4026	3256	2768	2562	2638	2996	3636	4558
0.3	9153	7593	6315	5319	4604	4172	4022	4154	4568	5263	6241
0.6	9953	8448	7226	6286	5627	5251	5156	5344	5814	6565	7599
1	10513	9083	7935	7069	6485	6183	6163	6425	6969	7795	8903
1.3	10553	9179	8087	7276	6748	6502	6538	6856	7455	8337	9501
1.6	10268	8950	7913	7159	6686	6496	6588	6961	7617	8554	9774
2	9382	8138	7176	6496	6098	5982	6148	6596	7326	8338	9632
2.3	8338	7150	6243	5619	5277	5217	5439	5942	6728	7796	9146
2.6	6968	5836	4985	4417	4131	4126	4404	4963	5805	6929	8334
3	4636	3578	2802	2308	2096	2166	2518	3152	4068	5266	6746
3.3	2507	1505	785	347	191	316	724	1414	2386	3640	5175

FIGURE 10.12

Note that the 6502 entry corresponding to 5% glycerol and 1.3% salt is an approximate saddle point because it is a maximum in the 5% glycerol column and a minimum in the 1.3% salt row.

We cannot consider the values 4558 (upper right corner) and 2507 (lower left corner) as candidates for absolute extrema, even though they lie in the terminal edges along the top row and left column of Figure 10.12, because these terminal edges can extend down and to the right. In order for a corner entry in a table to be considered in the search for absolute extrema, both the row and the column in which the entry lies must be terminal edges.

b. Because there are no closed contour curves indicated by Figure 10.12, we conclude that the function has no relative extrema. Thus any absolute extrema must occur on terminal edges of the function. Note that the table cannot extend beyond the top and left edges because negative percentages do not make sense in this context. Thus these edges are terminal edges, and we can look in these two edges for approximate absolute extrema. We must also consider the behavior of the function beyond the lower and right edges.

The greatest value in the table is approximately 10,553, and it occurs when the percentages of glycerol and salt are approximately 0 and 1.3, respectively. This value is on a terminal edge; however, the contour curves suggest that the output values will continue to increase for glycerol percentages greater than 10%. If the table were extended far enough to the right, we would probably see an output value greater than 10,553. We conclude that we do not have enough information to identify an absolute maximum.

The smallest value in the table is 191, found in the bottom row. However, if the table were extended downward for percentages of salt greater than 3.3%, we would probably observe an absolute minimum of zero. The places where this minimum occurs are difficult to estimate from the information presented in the table. ●

Example 1 in this section discussed the volume of packages sent at the "bound printed matter" postal rate. Neither the inputs nor the output can be negative in this context, so 0 cubic inches is the absolute minimum volume. Note that in this example, we were given the information that all critical points lie within the region represented by Table

10.1. We can therefore conclude that the relative maximum volume of approximately 11,664 cubic inches is the absolute maximum volume.

Three-dimensional graphs, contour graphs, and tables are helpful in estimating critical points and absolute extrema. However, we are limited to approximations of these points when using graphs and tables and sometimes do not have enough information to identify absolute extrema. In the next section, we will explore a more accurate method of finding critical points and absolute extrema for three-dimensional functions.

10.1 Concept Inventory

- Critical points: relative maxima, relative minima, and saddle points
- Absolute maxima, absolute minima
- Locating critical points and absolute extrema in tables and on contour and 3-D graphs
- Terminal edges of a table or graph
- Interpreting critical points and absolute extrema

10.1 Activities

Discussing Concepts

1. Explain how to determine whether a table of data has each of the following:
   a. Relative maximum
   b. Relative minimum
   c. Saddle point
   d. Absolute maximum
   e. Absolute minimum

2. Explain, illustrating with graphs, how to determine whether a contour graph has each of the following:
   a. Relative maximum
   b. Relative minimum
   c. Saddle point
   d. Absolute maximum
   e. Absolute minimum

Practicing Concepts

3. Is the point at $x = 4.885$ and $y = 1.382$ on the contour graph a relative maximum point, a relative minimum point, or a saddle point? Explain.

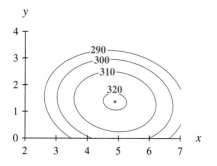

4. Is the point at $x = 4.885$ and $y = 1.382$ on the contour graph a relative maximum point, a relative minimum point, or a saddle point? Explain.

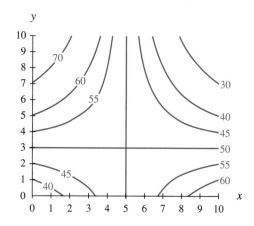

5. Consider the contour graph and a three-dimensional graph for a function R with inputs g and h.

  a. Mark on the contour plot and on the three-dimensional graph the approximate locations of all critical points. Label each point as a relative maximum point, a relative minimum point, or a saddle point.

  b. On the basis of the graphs, approximate the inputs and output of each critical point.

3-D of R (g, h)

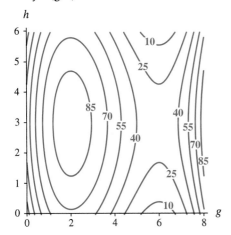

Contours of R (g, h)

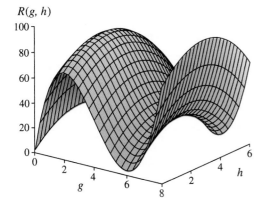

6. Consider the following contour graph and three-dimensional graph for a function T with inputs p and f

3-D of T (p, f)

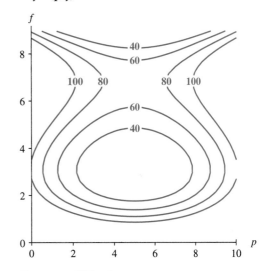

Contours of T (p, f)

  a. Mark on the contour plot and on the three-dimensional graph the approximate locations of all critical points. Label each point as a relative maximum point, a relative minimum point, or a saddle point.

  b. On the basis of the graphs, approximate the inputs and output of each critical point.

Applying Concepts

7. Consider the contour graph and associated three-dimensional graph of $z(x, y)$. Is the point at which $x = 1.8$ and $y = 1.5$ a relative maximum point, a relative minimum point, or a saddle point? Explain.

Contours of $z(x, y)$

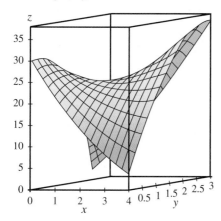

3-D of $z(x, y)$

8. Farmland The contour graph and the three-dimensional graph represent the elevation of a tract of farmland where elevation is measured in feet above sea level. Identify each of the following input values as corresponding to a relative maximum, a relative minimum, a saddle point, or none of these.

a. $e = 0.9$ and $n = 0.5$

b. $e = 0.5$ and $n = 0.5$

c. $e = 1.5$ and $n = 1.5$

Contours of elevation

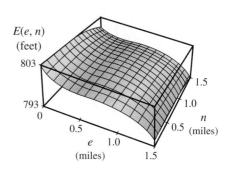

3-D of elevation

9. Lettuce The table shows the average price of iceberg lettuce, in cents per pound, in U.S. cities for selected months and years.

Price of iceberg lettuce (cents per pound)

	February	March	April	May	June
1994	54	61	53	54	52
1995	60	61	134	145	80
1996	59	65	65	61	67
1997	59	61	67	60	59
1998	64	70	84	88	71
1999	66	77	75	69	65

(Source: Bureau of Labor Statistics.)

Locate all critical points in the table. Identify each point as a relative maximum point, a relative minimum point, or a saddle point.

10. Bananas   The table shows the average price of bananas, in cents per pound, in U.S. cities for selected months and years. Locate all critical points in the table. Identify each point as a relative maximum point, a relative minimum point, or a saddle point.

Price of bananas (cents per pound)

	May	June	July	August	Sept.
1994	47	45	45	48	45
1995	48	49	52	51	49
1996	51	50	50	48	46
1997	48	49	49	48	46
1998	51	51	53	49	48
1999	49	50	49	49	48

(Source: Bureau of Labor Statistics.)

11. Radiation   The monthly average global radiation (measured in kilowatt-hours per square meter per day) is shown in the table as a function of the month and the number of degrees of latitude.

a. Is it possible for the table to extend in any direction? Explain.

b. Sketch contour curves on the table for 5.2, 6.2, 7.2, 8.2, and 9.2 kW-h/m^2/day.

c. Use the contours to locate all critical points in the table.

d. Locate the largest and smallest values in the table. Write a sentence interpreting these values.

e. Use the table to estimate the absolute maximum and minimum monthly average global radiation levels. Are these answers the same as those you found in part *d*?

f. Under what conditions will the largest and smallest values in a table also be the absolute extrema of the function represented by the table?

TABLE FOR ACTIVITY 11   **Monthly and yearly means of the diurnal sums of the global radiation, in kW-h/m^2 per day**

	Jan	Feb	Mar	Apr	May	Jun	Jul	Aug	Sep	Oct	Nov	Dec
North Pole	—	—	—	3.1	6.9	8.9	7.9	4.9	0.80	—	—	—
80°	—	—	0.77	3.4	6.9	8.8	7.8	4.8	1.55	0.13	—	—
70°	—	0.51	2.0	4.5	7.1	8.5	7.8	5.5	2.9	0.95	0.06	—
60°	0.55	1.53	3.4	5.7	7.7	8.8	8.2	6.5	4.3	2.2	0.81	0.34
50°	1.66	2.8	4.7	6.7	8.4	9.1	8.8	7.4	5.5	3.4	1.97	1.35
40°	3.0	4.2	5.9	7.5	8.8	9.3	9.0	8.1	6.5	4.8	3.4	2.6
30°	4.4	5.6	6.9	8.1	9.0	9.2	9.1	8.4	7.4	6.1	4.7	4.1
20°	5.8	6.7	7.8	8.5	8.8	8.9	8.8	8.6	8.0	7.1	6.0	5.5
10°	7.1	7.7	8.3	8.5	8.4	8.3	8.3	8.4	8.3	7.9	7.2	6.8
Equator	8.1	8.5	8.6	8.3	7.8	7.5	7.6	8.0	8.4	8.4	8.2	7.9
10°	8.9	8.8	8.4	7.7	6.9	6.4	6.5	7.2	8.1	8.6	8.8	8.8
20°	9.4	9.0	8.1	6.9	5.7	5.1	5.4	6.3	7.5	8.6	9.2	9.5
30°	9.6	8.8	7.4	5.8	4.4	3.8	4.1	5.2	6.7	8.2	9.3	9.8
40°	9.6	8.3	6.5	4.6	3.1	2.5	2.7	3.9	5.6	7.5	9.1	9.9
50°	9.3	7.6	5.4	3.3	1.84	1.25	1.49	2.6	4.5	6.6	8.7	9.7
60°	8.7	6.6	4.1	2.0	0.72	0.31	0.47	1.36	3.1	5.6	8.0	9.3
70°	8.2	5.5	2.8	0.84	—	—	—	0.38	1.78	4.3	7.2	9.1
80°	8.2	4.7	1.42	0.099	—	—	—	—	0.62	3.2	7.0	9.3
South Pole	8.1	4.6	0.60	—	—	—	—	—	—	2.9	7.0	9.4

(Source: W. Rudolff, *World-Climates,* Stuttgart, Germany: Wissenschaftliche Verlagsgesellschaft, 1981.)

12. **Rainfall** The table shows the probability of precipitation in the U.S. corn belt being $\Delta P\%$ above or below normal and the temperature being $\Delta T°C$ above or below normal. Assume that if the table were extended in any direction, all the additional entries would be zero.

Probability (expressed as a percentage) of precipitation and temperature variations

ΔT	$\Delta P(\%)$								
(°C)	**−40**	**−30**	**−20**	**−10**	**0**	**10**	**20**	**30**	**40**
4	0	0	0	0	0	0	0	0	0
3.5	0	0	1	1	0	0	0	0	0
3	0	1	2	3	2	0	0	0	0
2.5	0	1	5	7	5	1	0	0	0
2	0	2	9	15	12	4	1	0	0
1.5	0	3	12	26	24	10	2	0	0
1	0	3	15	37	40	19	4	0	0
0.5	0	2	14	42	54	30	7	1	0
0	0	1	11	39	59	39	11	1	0
−0.5	0	1	7	30	54	42	14	2	0
−1	0	0	4	19	40	37	15	3	0
−1.5	0	0	2	10	24	26	12	3	0
−2	0	0	1	4	12	15	9	2	0
−2.5	0	0	0	1	5	7	5	1	0
−3	0	0	0	0	2	3	2	1	0
−3.5	0	0	0	0	0	1	1	0	0
−4	0	0	0	0	0	0	0	0	0

(Source: *Crop Yields and Climate Change to the Year 2000*, U.S. Department of Agriculture, 1980.)

a. Sketch contour curves on the table at 10%, 20%, 30%, 40%, and 50%.

b. Use the contours to locate and estimate the absolute maximum percentage. Interpret your answer.

13. **Production** Expected annual yield of U.S. corn production as a percentage of the average annual yield is shown on page 629 as a function of the percentage change in precipitation (above or below the average precipitation) and the change in temperature (in °C above or below the average temperature). Assume that no critical points lie outside of the table.

a. If a cold, wet year produces average temperatures 3°C below normal and 50% more precipitation than normal, what is the expected corn yield?

b. If a hot, dry year results in 50% less precipitation than normal and an average temperature 3°C above normal, what is the expected corn yield?

c. Sketch contour curves on the table at 105%, 100%, 95%, and 90%.

d. Locate the absolute maximum in the table, and write a sentence interpreting the corresponding point(s).

14. **Radiation** The amount of extraterrestrial radiation measured in millimeters per day equivalent evaporation in the Northern Hemisphere is given in the table as a function of the month and the number of degrees of latitude.

a. According to the table, approximately how much extraterrestrial radiation does your campus receive in September?

b. Locate any relative extreme points in the table. Give the month, degrees of latitude, and amount of radiation for the relative extreme points.

c. In which directions can the table extend?

d. Estimate the least and greatest amounts of extraterrestrial radiation in the Northern Hemisphere. Give the corresponding months and degrees of latitude.

TABLE FOR ACTIVITY 13   Expected annual corn yield as a percentage of average annual yield

ΔT (°C)	ΔP(%)																		
	−100	−90	−80	−70	−60	−50	−40	−30	−20	−10	0	10	20	30	40	50	60	70	80
6	0	7	14	18	23	27	32	40	48	56	64	67	69	72	74	75	75	75	76
5.5	0	7	15	20	25	29	34	43	51	59	67	70	73	75	78	78	78	78	78
5	0	8	16	21	26	32	37	45	54	62	71	73	76	79	81	81	81	81	81
4.5	0	8	17	22	28	34	39	48	57	65	74	77	79	82	85	85	84	84	84
4	0	9	18	24	30	36	42	51	60	68	77	80	83	86	88	88	88	87	87
3.5	0	9	19	25	32	38	45	54	62	71	80	83	86	89	92	91	91	90	89
3	0	10	20	27	33	40	47	56	65	75	84	87	90	93	96	95	94	93	92
2.5	0	10	21	28	35	42	49	59	69	78	87	91	94	96	98	97	95	94	93
2	0	11	21	29	37	44	52	63	74	82	90	95	99	99	100	98	97	96	94
1.5	0	11	22	30	38	46	54	65	76	85	93	99	101	101	102	100	99	97	95
1	0	12	23	31	40	48	56	67	78	87	95	102	103	104	104	102	100	98	96
0.5	0	12	24	33	41	50	58	69	80	90	98	104	105	106	106	104	102	100	97
0	0	12	25	34	43	51	60	71	83	92	100	107	107	108	109	106	103	101	98
−0.5	0	13	26	35	43	52	61	72	84	93	101	107	108	108	107	105	102	100	97
−1	0	13	27	35	44	53	61	73	85	94	103	108	109	108	106	104	101	99	96
−1.5	0	14	28	36	45	53	62	73	84	93	102	107	108	107	105	103	100	98	95
−2	0	14	29	37	46	54	63	73	84	93	101	105	107	106	104	102	99	97	94
−2.5	0	15	29	38	46	55	63	72	82	90	98	101	103	103	103	101	98	95	93
−3	0	15	30	39	47	55	64	72	80	88	96	97	99	101	102	100	97	94	92
−3.5	0	15	30	38	46	54	62	70	77	85	92	94	95	97	98	96	94	91	89
−4	0	15	31	38	46	53	61	68	74	81	88	90	91	93	95	92	90	88	85
−4.5	0	15	31	38	45	52	59	65	72	78	85	86	88	89	91	89	87	85	82
−5	0	15	31	38	44	51	58	63	69	75	81	82	84	85	87	85	83	81	79
−5.5	0	16	31	37	44	50	56	61	67	72	77	79	80	82	83	81	80	78	76
−6	0	16	31	37	43	49	55	59	64	69	74	75	76	78	79	78	76	75	73

(Source: *Crop Yields and Climate Change to the Year 2000*, U.S. Department of Agriculture, 1980.)

15. **Weight**   The average daily weight gain of a pig (in kilograms per day) is shown in the table as a function of the air temperature and the pig's weight.

   a. Use the table to estimate relative and absolute extrema for temperatures between 4.4°C and 37.8°C and weights between 45 kilograms and 156 kilograms.

   b. Convert the temperatures to degrees Fahrenheit using the equation $°F = \frac{9}{5}(°C) + 32$.

   c. Write a sentence interpreting the absolute extrema found in part a.

TABLE FOR ACTIVITY 14 Extraterrestrial radiation expressed in equivalent evaporation (mm/day)

Latitude (degrees)	Northern Hemisphere											
	Jan	Feb	Mar	Apr	May	Jun	Jul	Aug	Sep	Oct	Nov	Dec
50	3.8	6.1	9.4	12.7	15.8	17.1	16.4	14.1	10.9	7.4	4.5	3.2
48	4.3	6.6	9.8	13.0	15.9	17.2	16.5	14.3	11.2	7.8	5.0	3.7
46	4.9	7.1	10.2	13.3	16.0	17.2	16.6	14.5	11.5	8.3	5.5	4.3
44	5.3	7.6	10.6	13.7	16.1	17.2	16.6	14.7	11.9	8.7	6.0	4.7
42	5.9	8.1	11.0	14.0	16.2	17.3	16.7	15.0	12.2	9.1	6.5	5.2
40	6.4	8.6	11.4	14.3	16.4	17.3	16.7	15.2	12.5	9.6	7.0	5.7
38	6.9	9.0	11.8	14.5	16.4	17.2	16.7	15.3	12.8	10.0	7.5	6.1
36	7.4	9.4	12.1	14.7	16.4	17.2	16.7	15.4	13.1	10.6	8.0	6.6
34	7.9	9.8	12.4	14.8	16.5	17.1	16.8	15.5	13.4	10.8	8.5	7.2
32	8.3	10.2	12.8	15.0	16.5	17.0	16.8	15.6	13.6	11.2	9.0	7.8
30	8.8	10.7	13.1	15.2	16.5	17.0	16.8	15.7	13.9	11.6	9.5	8.3
28	9.3	11.1	13.4	15.3	16.5	16.8	16.7	15.7	14.1	12.0	9.9	8.8
26	9.8	11.5	13.7	15.3	16.4	16.7	16.6	15.7	14.3	12.3	10.3	9.3
24	10.2	11.9	13.9	15.4	16.4	16.6	16.5	15.8	14.5	12.6	10.7	9.7
22	10.7	12.3	14.2	15.5	16.3	16.4	16.4	15.8	14.6	13.0	11.1	10.2
20	11.2	12.7	14.4	15.6	16.3	16.4	16.3	15.9	14.8	13.3	11.6	10.7
18	11.6	13.0	14.6	15.6	16.1	16.1	16.1	15.8	14.9	13.6	12.0	11.1
16	12.0	13.3	14.7	15.6	16.0	15.9	15.9	15.7	15.0	13.9	12.4	11.6
14	12.4	13.6	14.9	15.7	15.8	15.7	15.7	15.7	15.1	14.1	12.8	12.0
12	12.8	13.9	15.1	15.7	15.7	15.5	15.5	15.6	15.2	14.4	13.3	12.5
10	13.2	14.2	15.3	15.7	15.5	15.3	15.3	15.5	15.3	14.7	13.6	12.9
8	13.6	14.5	15.3	15.6	15.3	15.0	15.1	15.4	15.3	14.8	13.9	13.3
6	13.9	14.8	15.4	15.4	15.1	14.7	14.9	15.2	15.3	15.0	14.2	13.7
4	14.3	15.0	15.5	15.5	14.9	14.4	14.6	15.1	15.3	15.1	14.5	14.1
2	14.7	15.3	15.6	15.3	14.6	14.2	14.3	14.9	15.3	15.3	14.8	14.4
0	15.0	15.5	15.7	15.3	14.4	13.9	14.1	14.8	15.3	15.4	15.1	14.8

(Source: A. A. Hanson, ed., *Practical Handbook of Agricultural Science,* Boca Raton, FL: CRC Press, 1990.)

TABLE FOR ACTIVITY 15 Average daily weight gain of a pig (kg/day)

Mean live weight (kg)	Air temperature (°C)						
	4.4	10	15.6	21.1	26.7	32.2	37.8
45		0.62	0.72	0.91	0.89	0.64	0.18
68	0.58	0.67	0.79	0.98	0.83	0.52	−0.09
91	0.54	0.71	0.87	1.01	0.76	0.4	−0.35
113	0.5	0.76	0.94	0.97	0.68	0.28	−0.62
136	0.46	0.8	1.02	0.93	0.62	0.16	−0.88
156	0.43	0.85	1.09	0.9	0.55	0.05	−1.15

(Source: A. A. Hanson, ed., *Practical Handbook of Agricultural Science,* Boca Raton, FL: CRC Press, 1990.)

16. Applesauce   The Food and Drug Administration (FDA) defines Grade A applesauce as having a consistometer value of 6.5 cm or less. It is common for applesauce manufacturers to add to thick applesauce enough water to thin it to a 6.5-cm consistometer value. The table shows the percentage of water that can be added to applesauce while maintaining an FDA Grade A. This percentage of water is a function of the number of months the apples are stored and the blanching temperature.

Percentage of water that can be added to applesauce

Storage time (months)	Blanching temperature (°C)				
	35°	47°	59°	71°	83°
0	43	48	54	53	45
0.5	38	44	48	47	40
1	35	41	45	45	38
1.5	34	40	44	44	35
2	33	39	44	44	34
2.5	33	38	43	43	33
3	34	40	45	45	35
3.5	35	43	47	47	38
4	39	45	50	50	42

a. Sketch contour curves on the table for water percentages of 35, 40, 45, and 50.

b. Locate all critical points in the table.

c. Estimate the absolute maximum and absolute minimum percentage for storage times between 0 and 4 months and temperatures between 35°C and 83°C.

d. Why would a maximum value be of interest to an applesauce manufacturer?

e. If not all harvested apples can be used right away, how long (on the basis of the table) do you think a manufacturer should store apples before processing them?

17. Applesauce   The consistometer table gives the consistency of applesauce as a function of the number of months the raw apples were stored and the temperature at which they were blanched. The consistometer value is a measure of how far (in centimeters) an amount of applesauce flows down a vertical surface in 30 seconds.

Consistometer values for Rome applesauce (cm)

Storage time (months)	Temperature (°C)				
	35°	47°	59°	71°	83°
0	3.0	2.8	2.6	2.6	2.8
1	3.3	3.1	2.8	2.8	3.0
2	3.5	3.2	3.0	2.9	3.2
3	3.4	3.2	3.0	2.9	3.2
4	3.2	2.9	2.7	2.7	3.0

(Source: Based on information in A. M. Godfrey Usiak, M. C. Bourne, and M. A. Rao, "Blanch Temperature/Time Effects on Rheological Properties of Applesauce," *Journal of Food Science,* vol. 60, no. 6 (1995), pp. 1289–1291.)

a. Sketch contour curves on the table for consistometer values of 2.7, 3.0, and 3.3.

b. Locate all critical points in the table.

c. Estimate the absolute maximum and absolute minimum consistometer values for storage times between 0 and 4 months and temperatures between 35°C and 83°C.

d. If you were an applesauce manufacturer, which of the points found in parts *b* and *c* would be of the most interest to you? Explain.

18. Farmland   The elevation table gives elevation $E(e, n)$, in feet above sea level, of a tract of Missouri farmland measured *e* miles east of the western fence and *n* miles north of the southern fence.

a. Find any relative extreme points in the table.

b. Find the saddle point in the table.

c. Explain how you located the saddle point.

TABLE FOR ACTIVITY 18   Elevation (feet above sea level) e miles east of western fence and n miles north of southern fence

$e\rightarrow$	0	0.1	0.2	0.3	0.4	0.5	0.6	0.7	0.8	0.9	1.0	1.1	1.2	1.3	1.4	1.5
1.5	800.3	799.1	798.3	797.8	797.5	797.4	797.5	797.6	797.6	797.7	797.6	797.3	796.8	796.0	794.8	793.2
1.4	800.8	799.6	798.8	798.3	798.0	797.9	797.9	798.0	798.1	798.1	798.1	797.8	797.3	796.5	795.3	793.7
1.3	801.2	800.0	799.2	798.7	798.4	798.3	798.4	798.5	798.5	798.6	798.5	798.2	797.7	796.9	795.7	794.1
1.2	801.6	800.4	799.6	799.1	798.8	798.7	798.7	798.8	798.9	798.9	798.9	798.6	798.1	797.3	796.1	794.5
1.1	801.9	800.7	799.9	799.4	799.1	799.0	799.1	799.2	799.2	799.3	799.2	798.9	798.4	797.6	796.4	794.8
1.0	802.2	801.0	800.2	799.7	799.4	799.3	799.3	799.4	799.5	799.5	799.5	799.2	798.7	797.9	796.7	795.1
0.9	802.4	801.2	800.4	799.9	799.6	799.5	799.6	799.7	799.7	799.8	799.7	799.4	798.9	798.1	796.9	795.3
0.8	802.6	801.4	800.6	800.1	799.8	799.7	799.7	799.8	799.9	799.9	799.9	799.6	799.1	798.3	797.1	795.5
0.7	802.7	801.5	800.7	800.2	799.9	799.8	799.9	800.0	800.0	800.1	800.0	799.7	799.2	798.4	797.2	795.6
0.6	802.8	801.6	800.8	800.3	800.0	799.9	799.9	800.0	800.1	800.1	800.1	799.8	799.3	798.5	797.3	795.7
0.5	802.8	801.6	800.8	800.3	800.0	799.9	800.0	800.1	800.1	800.2	800.1	799.8	799.3	798.5	797.3	795.7
0.4	802.8	801.6	800.8	800.3	800.0	799.9	799.9	800.0	800.1	800.1	800.1	799.8	799.3	798.5	797.3	795.7
0.3	802.7	801.5	800.7	800.2	799.9	799.8	799.9	800.0	800.0	800.1	800.0	799.7	799.2	798.4	797.2	795.6
0.2	802.6	801.4	800.6	800.1	799.8	799.7	799.7	799.8	799.9	799.9	799.9	799.6	799.1	798.3	797.1	795.5
0.1	802.4	801.2	800.4	799.9	799.6	799.5	799.6	799.7	799.7	799.8	799.7	799.4	798.9	798.1	796.9	795.3
0	802.2	801.0	800.2	799.7	799.4	799.3	799.3	799.4	799.5	799.5	799.5	799.2	798.7	797.9	796.7	795.1

$n\uparrow$

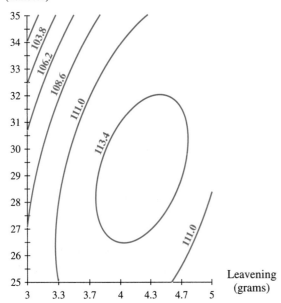

Baking time (minutes)

(Source: A. Li and C. E. Walker, "Cake Baking in Conventional, Impingement and Hybrid Ovens," *Journal of Food Science*, vol. 61, no. 1 (1996), pp. 188–192.)

Figure for Activity 20

Land subsidence in feet, 1934–1960
Santa Clara Valley, California

(Source: Figure from R. A. Freeze and J. A. Cherry, *Groundwater*, Englewood Cliffs, NJ: Prentice-Hall, 1979. Reprinted by permission of Prentice-Hall, Inc. Upper Saddle River, NJ.)

Figure for Activity 22

19. Therapy   A technique commonly used by physical therapists is the application of heat to muscles and tissues. A contour graph showing the change in the temperature of a thigh model after exposure to microwave radiation is given.

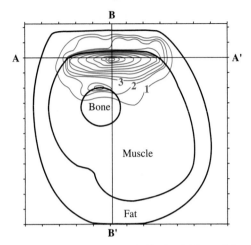

Increase in temperature (°C) of a thigh model
(Source: F. J. Kottke and J. F. Lehman, *Krusen's Handbook of Physical Medicine and Rehabilitation*, Philadelphia: Saunders, 1990.)

a. Mark the approximate location of any relative and absolute extrema, and estimate the output value at each point.

b. Are the points you marked maxima or minima?

20. Baking   The contour graph shows the volume index of a cake baked at 350°F, given the baking time (in minutes) and the amount of leavening used (in grams). An index of 100 corresponds to the volume of the batter. No critical points lie outside the contour graph shown.

a. Would a food scientist be more interested in finding a maximum or a minimum volume index?

b. Approximately where on the contour graph does the optimal point occur?

c. Estimate and interpret the optimal value.

21. Flooding   In the summer of 1993, the midwestern United States experienced catastrophic flooding that resulted in damages estimated at over $10 billion. A particularly heavy rainfall occurred in Missouri on June 6 of that year. A contour map of the number of millimeters of rain that fell on June 6, 1993, is given.

(Source: Missouri Precipitation Contour Map from S. M. Rochette and J. T. Moore, "Initiation of an Elevated Mesoscale Convective System Associated with Heavy Rainfall," *Weather and Forecasting*, vol. 11 (1996), p. 444. Used by permission of the American Meteorological Society.)

a. Identify the Missouri and Mississippi Rivers on the map.

b. Mark the area of greatest rainfall. Estimate the amount of rain that fell on June 6 in the area you marked.

c. Identify any other critical points on the contour map, and classify them as relative maxima, relative minima, or saddle points.

22. Land Subsidence   Even in desert climates, the ground contains water that in some cases can be pumped and used. When major pumping occurs, it is possible for the land to sink. This sinking is referred to as *land subsidence*. The figure shows the land subsidence, in feet, in the Santa Clara Valley between 1934 and 1960.

a. Mark with an X on the contour graph in the figure the approximate location of any relative extreme points.

b. Write a sentence interpreting the points in part *a* and characterizing them as maxima or minima.

10.2 Multivariable Optimization

In Section 4.2 we saw how to locate relative extreme points (maxima or minima) on the graph of a two-dimensional function by analyzing the function's derivative. Because relative extreme points on a smooth, continuous graph can occur only where the tangent line is horizontal (that is, with slope equal to zero), we search for points where the derivative is zero. If we find such a point, we determine whether the graph has a local maximum, a local minimum, or neither by determining whether the graph is concave down, is concave up, or has an inflection point at that location.

Finding Critical Points Algebraically

We now direct our attention to looking for critical points of smooth, continuous multivariable functions. As an example, we again consider the problem of maximizing the volume of a package sent at the "bound printed matter" postal rate. The volume of a rectangular package that contains the maximum amount of printed material according to postal regulations size requirement* for this rate is given by the equation

$$V(h, w) = 108hw - 2h^2w - 2hw^2 \text{ cubic inches}$$

where h inches is the height and w inches is the width of the package. We seek the values of h and w that cause $V(h, w)$ to be as large as possible. The three-dimensional graph in Figure 10.13 helps us visualize what is happening.

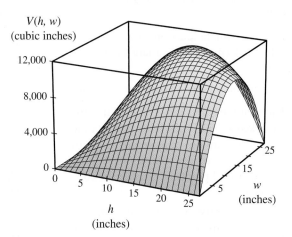

FIGURE 10.13

Concept Development: Relative Extrema   Let us look at the maximum from two different perspectives. First, ignore the effect of height on the volume, and think only about the impact due to the width. In other words, look at a cross-sectional function of V with output $V(h_0, w)$, where h is held constant at some value h_0. Figure 10.14a shows graphs of cross-sectional models for $h = 9$ inches and $h = 17$ inches. Figure 10.14b shows the same cross sections depicted in three dimensions.

---

* Based on information at **www.usps.com** (accessed 1/4/2003).

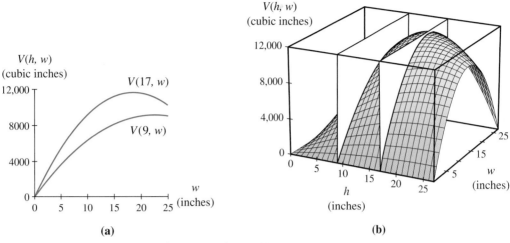

FIGURE 10.14   *Cross sections for h = 9 inches and h = 17 inches*

Next, ignore the effect of weight on the volume, and think only about the impact due to the height. In other words, look at a cross-sectional function of V with output $v(h, w_0)$, where w is held constant at some value w_0. Figure 10.15a shows graphs of cross-sectional functions for $w = 12$ inches and $w = 19$ inches Figure 10.15b shows the same cross sections depicted in three dimensions.

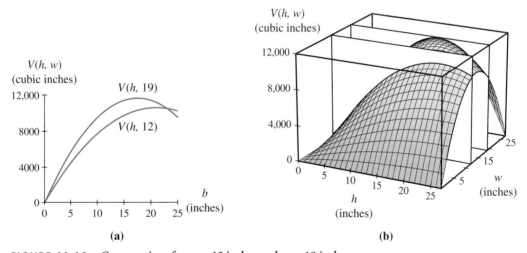

FIGURE 10.15   *Cross sections for w = 12 inches and w = 19 inches*

In order for the volume function to have a maximum, it must have a maximum with respect to height and a maximum with respect to width. That is, there must be a point at which the derivative of the cross-sectional function of V with output $V(h_0, w)$

is zero and the derivative of the cross-sectional function of V with output $V(h, w_0)$ is zero. In order for a maximum of V to occur, both partial derivatives must be zero:

$$\frac{\partial V}{\partial w} = 108h - 2h^2 - 4hw = 0 \tag{1}$$

$$\frac{\partial V}{\partial h} = 108w - 4hw - 2w^2 = 0 \tag{2}$$

We must simultaneously solve this system of equations to find a point (h_0, w_0) that satisfies the condition that both partial derivatives are equal to zero. Without using the partial derivative symbols, we rewrite one of the equations so that one of the variables is expressed in terms of the other variable. Solving equation 1 for w in terms of h yields

10.2.1

$$w = \frac{108h - 2h^2}{4h} \tag{3}$$

Next, we substitute this expression for w into equation 2:

$$108\left(\frac{108h - 2h^2}{4h}\right) - 4h\left(\frac{108h - 2h^2}{4h}\right) - 2\left(\frac{108h - 2h^2}{4h}\right)^2 = 0 \tag{4}$$

Solving equation 4 for h yields

$h = 18$ inches

We use this value of h to determine the value of w. Substituting the unrounded value of h in equation 3 yields

$w = 18$ inches

The point (h_0, w_0) where $h_0 = 18$ inches and $w_0 = 18$ inches satisfies the condition that the partial derivatives are zero. The output corresponding to these input values is 11,664 cubic inches. (Note that this is the same result obtained from a contour graph sketched on the table of data in Figure 10.10 on page 619 because the point $(h_0, w_0) = (18, 18)$ appeared in that table.) Are we certain that $h = 18$, $w = 18$, and $V = 11,664$ is a point of maximum volume rather than a different type of critical point? Figure 10.10 shows that a maximum is the only possibility.

This algebraic method for finding the relative maximum of the volume of a rectangular package mailed at the "bound printed matter" postal rate can be used to find any critical points of smooth, continuous three-dimensional functions because a critical point of such a function has the characteristic that both partial derivatives are zero. We locate critical points of any three-dimensional function as follows:

Critical Points of Three-Dimensional Functions

Let f be a three-dimensional function with input (x, y). A critical point of f occurs at (a, b) if

1. $f_x(a, b) = 0$ and $f_y(a, b) = 0$

or

2. $f_x(a, b)$ does not exist or $f_y(a, b)$ does not exist.

The first case yields critical points that are relative extrema or saddle points. Because the second case does not occur often in nonscientific applications, we will restrict the remainder of our discussion of critical points to the case where both partial derivatives are zero.

How do we determine which type of critical point occurs? As seen in the package volume illustration, if we can produce either a three-dimensional graph or a contour graph of a function, then we can visually verify whether a point at which all of the first partial derivatives are zero is a maximum, a minimum, or a saddle point. However, if we cannot easily produce such a graph, then we can use the second partial derivatives to determine what type of point we have found. To do so, we begin by defining the determinant of a second partials matrix.

The Determinant Test

If a function f has two input variables x and y, then we can calculate the **determinant** D of the second partials matrix evaluated at a point for which $f_x = f_y = 0$ as

$$D = \begin{vmatrix} f_{xx} & f_{xy} \\ f_{yx} & f_{yy} \end{vmatrix} = f_{xx}f_{yy} - f_{xy}f_{yx}$$

If the determinant D is 0, it tells us nothing about the nature of the point. If $D > 0$, then the point is either a relative maximum or a relative minimum. We can determine which it is by looking at f_{xx} at the point. If $f_{xx} < 0$, then the cross section with respect to x is concave down, so the point is a relative maximum in the x direction. Also, when $f_{xx} < 0$ and $D > 0$, then f_{yy} must also be less than zero. Thus there is also a relative maximum in the y direction. Because $D > 0$ guarantees a maximum or minimum, this critical point must be a relative maximum. Similarly, if $f_{xx} > 0$, then the point is a relative minimum. If $D < 0$, then the point is a saddle point regardless of whether f_{xx} and f_{yy} are positive or negative.

Determinant Test

Let f be a continuous multivariable function with two input variables x and y. Let (a, b) be a point at which the first partial derivatives of f are both 0. The determinant of the second partials matrix evaluated at the point (a, b) is

$$D(a, b) = \begin{vmatrix} f_{xx} & f_{xy} \\ f_{yx} & f_{yy} \end{vmatrix} = f_{xx}f_{yy} - f_{xy}f_{yx}$$

If $D(a, b) > 0$ and $f_{xx} < 0$ at (a, b), then f has a relative maximum at (a, b).
If $D(a, b) > 0$ and $f_{xx} > 0$ at (a, b), then f has a relative minimum at (a, b).
If $D(a, b) < 0$, then f has a saddle point at (a, b).
If $D(a, b) = 0$, then the test does not give any information about (a, b).

In the previous package volume example, we found the point representing $h = 18$ inches and $w = 18$ inches to be an extreme point. To use the Determinant Test to verify that the point is a maximum, we first form the second partials matrix:

$$\begin{bmatrix} V_{hh} & V_{hw} \\ V_{wh} & V_{ww} \end{bmatrix} = \begin{bmatrix} -4w & 108 - 4h - 4w \\ 108 - 4h - 4w & -4h \end{bmatrix}$$

Next, because the second partials matrix contains variables, we substitute $h = 18$ and $w = 18$ in the matrix to obtain

$$\begin{bmatrix} -72 & -36 \\ -36 & -72 \end{bmatrix}$$

Then we find the determinant.

$$D = (-72)(-72) - (-36)^2 = 3888$$

Because D is positive, we know the critical point is either a maximum or a minimum. Because $V_{hh} = -72$ is less than zero (and $V_{ww} = -72$ is less than zero), we have a function that is concave down in both the w and h directions. Thus we know the point is a maximum.

Finding Critical Points Using Matrices

A **linear system of equations** is one in which all the variables occur to the first power and there are no terms in which two variables are multiplied or divided. It is possible to solve a linear system of equations by forming a matrix of coefficients and using matrix algebra (detailed mathematics not covered in this text) to obtain a solution. Example 1 illustrates this process.

EXAMPLE 1   *Algebraically Locating and Verifying a Maximum Point*

10.2.2

Baking   Consider the volume index that provides a measure of how much a cake rises. An index of 100 corresponds to the volume of the batter. The index can be modeled by

$$V(l, t) = -3.1l^2 + 22.4l - 0.1t^2 + 5.3t$$

when l grams of leavening are used and the cake is baked at 177°C for t minutes.

a. Find the maximum volume possible and the conditions needed to achieve that volume.

b. Verify that the point you found in part *a* is a maximum.

Solution

a. We begin by finding the partial derivatives of V and setting them equal to zero:

$$V_l = -6.2l + 22.4 = 0$$
$$V_t = -0.2t + 5.3 = 0$$

To solve this linear system using matrices, we form a matrix of coefficients by writing the equations with the variables in the same order in both equations and moving the constants to the other side:

$$-6.2l + 0 \cdot t = -22.4$$
$$0 \cdot l - 0.2t = -5.3$$

A matrix corresponding to these equations is

$$\begin{bmatrix} -6.2 & 0 & -22.4 \\ 0 & -0.2 & -5.3 \end{bmatrix}$$

A calculator or computer software with matrix operations can be used to rewrite this matrix as

$$\begin{bmatrix} 1 & 0 & 3.6129 \\ 0 & 1 & 26.5 \end{bmatrix}$$

which corresponds to the equations

$$l \approx 3.6$$

$$t = 26.5$$

Thus "$l \approx 3.6$ grams of leavening and $t = 26.5$ minutes baking time" is the solution to the system of equations. These values result in a volume index of $V(3.6, 26.5) \approx 110.7$.

b. At $(3.6, 26.5, 110.7)$, $V_{ll} = -6.2$ and $V_{tt} = -0.2$. These second partials are both negative, so V is concave down in both the l and t directions. Figures 10.16a and 10.16b depict the cross sections of V at $l \approx 3.6$ and $t = 26.5$, respectively.

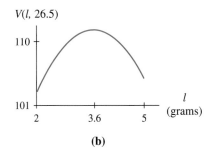

(a)   (b)

FIGURE 10.16

The graphs in Figures 10.16a and 10.16b and negative V_{ll} and V_{tt} suggest that the critical point $(3.6, 26.5, 110.7)$ is a relative maximum. We confirm this by evaluating the determinant of the second partials matrix.

$$D = \begin{vmatrix} -6.2 & 0 \\ 0 & -0.2 \end{vmatrix} = (-6.2)(-0.2) - (0)(0) = 1.24$$

Because D is positive and V_{ll} is negative, the critical point is indeed a relative maximum. ●

Note that it is not possible to use matrices to solve the system of equations that results when finding the point that maximizes the volume of a package sent at the "bound printed matter" postal rate, because that system of partial derivative equations is not linear.

In Example 1 the determinant of the second partials matrix is positive. Example 2 illustrates the occurrence of a critical point for which the determinant of the second partials matrix is negative.

EXAMPLE 2   *Algebraically Locating and Verifying a Saddle Point*

Grazing Cattle   The total daily intake of organic matter required by a beef cow grazing the Northern Great Plains rangeland can be modeled* by

$$I(s, m) = 8.61967 - 1.244s + 0.0897s^2 - 0.20988m + 0.035947m^2 + 0.214915sm$$

kg per day

when the cow produces m kilograms of milk per day. The variable s is a number between -4 and 4 indicating the size of the cow. Find the critical point for I, and determine whether it is a maximum, a minimum, or a saddle point.

Solution

A matrix corresponding to this linear system is

$$\begin{bmatrix} 0.1794 & 0.214915 & -1.244 \\ 0.214915 & 0.071894 & -0.20988 \end{bmatrix}$$

which can be rewritten as

$$\begin{bmatrix} 1 & 0 & -1.3316 \\ 0 & 1 & -6.8999 \end{bmatrix}$$

We find the critical point by finding where the two partial derivatives of I are zero.

$$\frac{\partial I}{\partial s} = -1.244 + 0.1794s + 0.214915m = 0$$

$$\frac{\partial I}{\partial m} = -0.20988 + 0.071894m + 0.214915s = 0$$

Solving the linear system of equations yields $m \approx 6.90$ kg of milk per day and $s \approx -1.33$. When we substitute the unrounded values of m and s in I, we obtain a value of approximately 8.72 kg of organic matter eaten each day. At the point $(-1.33, 6.90, 8.72)$, $I_{ss} = 0.1794$ and $I_{mm} = 0.071894$ are both positive, indicating that the cross sections of I with outputs $I(-1.33, m)$ and $I(s, 6.90)$ are both concave up. We can verify this graphically. See Figure 10.17, which shows these cross sections.

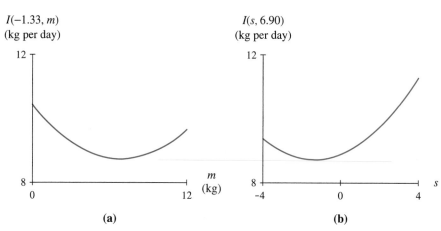

FIGURE 10.17

---

* E. E. Grings et al., "Efficiency of Production in Cattle of Two Growth Potentials on Northern Great Plains Rangelands During Spring-Summer Grazing," *Journal of Food Science,* vol. 74, no. 10 (1996), pp. 2317–2326.

However, to determine whether the critical point $(-1.33, 6.90, 8.72)$ is a minimum or a saddle point, we apply the Determinant Test. The determinant of the second partials matrix is

$$D = \begin{vmatrix} I_{ss} & I_{sm} \\ I_{ms} & I_{mm} \end{vmatrix} = \begin{vmatrix} 0.1794 & 0.214915 \\ 0.214915 & 0.071894 \end{vmatrix} = (0.1794)(0.071894) - (0.214915)^2 \approx -0.033$$

Because this value is negative, we know that I has a saddle point rather than a minimum at $s \approx -1.33$ and $m \approx 6.90$ kg of milk per day. Figure 10.18a shows the planes $s = -1.33$ and $m = 6.90$ depicted on the graph of I. Figure 10.18b shows a contour graph of I.

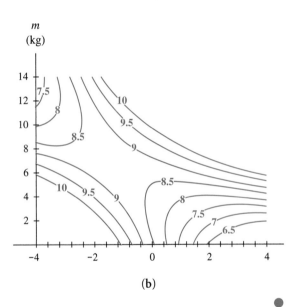

(a)

(b)

FIGURE 10.18

In general, when looking for the critical points of a three-dimensional function, we solve for the point at which the partial derivatives are zero and then determine what type of point we have found either by visually inspecting a three-dimensional graph or a contour graph or by using the Determinant Test.

10.2 Concept Inventory

- Extreme points: maxima and minima
- Saddle points
- Critical points
- Solving systems of equations to find critical points
- Determinant Test

10.2 Activities

Getting Started

For each of the multivariable functions in Activities 1 through 8, find and classify any critical points.

1. $R(k, m) = 3k^2 - 2km - 20k + 3m^2 - 4m + 60$

2. $H(r, s) = rs + 2s^2 + r^2$

3. $G(t, p) = pe^t - 3p$

4. $f(a, b) = a^2 - 4a + b^2 - 2b - 12$

5. $h(w, z) = 0.6w^2 + 1.3z^3 - 4.7wz$

6. $R(s, t) = 1.1s^3 - 2.6s^2 + 0.9s + 6 - 3.1t^2 + 5.3t$

7. $f(x, y) = 3x^2 - x^3 + 12y^2 - 8y^3 + 60$

8. $g(x, y) = 4xy - x^4 - y^4$

Applying Concepts

9. **Revenue**   A restaurant mixes ground beef that costs \$$b$ per pound with pork sausage that costs \$$p$ per pound to make a meat mixture that is used on the restaurant's signature pizza. The quarterly revenue, in thousands of dollars, from the sale of this pizza is given by the equation

$$R(b, p) = 14b - 3b^2 - bp - 2p^2 + 12p$$

   a. Find the prices at which the restaurant should try to purchase ground beef and pork sausage in order to maximize the quarterly revenue from the sale of the pizza.

   b. Explain how the Determinant Test verifies that your result gives the maximum revenue.

   c. What is the maximum quarterly revenue from the sale of the restaurant's signature pizza?

10. **Profit**   A nursery sells mulch by the truckload. Bark mulch sells for \$$b$ per load, and pine straw sells for \$$p$ per load. The nursery's average weekly profit from the sale of these two types of mulch can be modeled by the equation

$$P(p, b) = 144p - 3p^2 - pb - 2b^2 + 120b + 35 \text{ dollars}$$

   a. Find how much the nursery should charge for each type of mulch in order to maximize the weekly profit from the sale of mulch.

   b. Explain in detail how the Determinant Test verifies that your result in part a gives the maximum profit.

   c. What is the maximum weekly profit from the sales of these two types of mulch?

11. **Parasite**   Boll weevils have long presented a threat to cotton crops in the southern United States. Research has been done to determine the optimal conditions for reproduction of *Catolaccus grandis,* a parasitoid that attaches to boll weevils and kills

them. The number of eggs produced in 30 days by one female *C. grandis* under conditions of 16 hours of light each day, a constant temperature of $T°C$, and a relative humidity of $H\%$ can be modeled by

$$E(T, H) = -4191.6877 + 299.7038T + 23.1412H$$
$$- 5.2210T^2 - 0.0937H^2 - 0.4023TH \text{ eggs}$$

(Source: J. A. Morales-Ramos, S. M. Greenberg, and E. G. King, "Selection of Optimal Physical Conditions for Mass Propagation of Catolaccus grandis," *Environmental Entomology,* vol. 25, no. 1 (1996), pp. 165–173.)

   a. Determine the point where the partial derivatives of E are both equal to zero.

   b. Write a sentence interpreting the point in part a and characterizing it as a maximum, a minimum, or a saddle point.

12. **Parasite**   The average time for a *C. grandis* egg to develop into an adult can be modeled by

$$D(H, L) = 25.6691 - 0.838H + 2.4297L + 0.0084H^2$$
$$- 0.0726L^2 - 0.0181HL \text{ days}$$

where the relative humidity is held constant at $H\%$, the eggs are exposed to L hours of light each day, and the temperature is held constant at 30°C.

(Source: J. A. Morales-Ramos, S. M. Greenberg, and E. G. King, "Selection of Optimal Physical Conditions for Mass Propagation of *Catolaccus grandis,*" *Environmental Entomology,* vol. 25, no. 1 (1996), pp. 165–173.)

   a. Determine the point where the partial derivatives of D are both equal to zero.

   b. Write a sentence interpreting the point in part a and characterizing it as a maximum, a minimum, or a saddle point.

13. **Milk Fat**   The increased consumption of low-fat foods in this country has led to a surplus of milk fat. Research is being done to find new uses for milk fat, such as extracting flavor from the milk fat to utilize it in other products. The process of flavor extraction entails hydrolysis—a chemical reaction in which fatty acids are liberated from the milk fat. It is desirable to maximize the rate at which the fatty acids are liberated. The initial liberation rate can be modeled by

$$R(P, T) = 32.614 - 1.544P - 1.625T$$
$$- 4.905P^2 - 7.053T^2 - 3PT \text{ micromoles}$$

of free fatty acids per minute, where $5.5 + 1.5P$ is the pH of the milk fat mixture and the temperature is $(60 + 8T)°C$.

a. Find the pH and temperature that maximize the initial rate.

b. Verify that the optimal point is a maximum.

(Source: M. T. Patel, R. Nagarajan, and A. Kilara, "Hydrolysis of Milk Fat by Lipase in Solvent-Free Phospholipid Reverse Micellar Media," *Journal of Food Science*, vol. 61, no. 1 (1996), pp. 33–38.)

14. **Fatty Acids** In the chemical process described in Activity 13, it is also desirable to maximize the amount of fatty acids liberated in the hydrolysis process. The number of grams of fatty acids per 100 grams of water can be modeled by

$$F(p, t) = 25.224 - 0.129p - 3.052t$$
$$- 0.446p^2 - 3.761t^2 - 1.249pt \text{ grams}$$

where the pH of the milk fat is $5.5 + 1.5p$ and the temperature is $(60 + 8t)°C$. Find the pH and temperature that maximize the amount of fatty acid. Verify that the optimal point is a maximum.

15. **Peptides** The Louisiana crayfish industry produces over 38,600 tons of crayfish-processing byproducts every year. One potential use of the byproducts is in the production of flavor extracts. In order to extract flavoring from the crayfish-processing byproducts, peptides from the byproducts must be drawn out. This process is a complicated one with many variables. Two of these variables are the pH and temperature maintained

during the process. A model for the amount of peptides released is

$$P(x, y) = 2.14 - 0.26x - 0.34y - 0.23x^2$$
$$- 0.16y^2 - 0.25xy \text{ milligrams}$$

where the pH is $9 + x$ and the temperature is $(70 + 5y)°C$. The contour plot shows some of the amounts of peptides released.

a. Use the contour plot to estimate the maximum amount of peptides and the pH and temperature needed to achieve the maximum.

b. Use the model to determine the pH and temperature that will maximize the amount of peptides produced.

16. **Peptides** The amount of peptides in Activity 15 can also be modeled as a function of pH and processing time:

$$P(x, t) = 2.14 - 0.26x + 0.04t - 0.23x^2$$
$$- 0.04t^2 - 0.07xt \text{ milligrams}$$

where the pH is $9 + x$ and the processing time is $(2.5 + t)$ hours. The contour plot shows the amount of peptides.

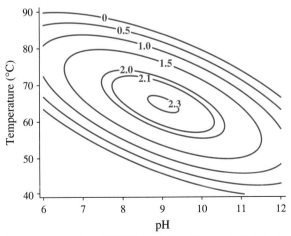

(Source: H. H. Baek and K. R. Cadwallader, "Enzymatic Hydrolysis of Crayfish Processing By-products," *Journal of Food Science*, vol. 60, no. 5 (1995), pp. 929–934.)

a. Use the contour plot to estimate the maximum amount of peptides as well as the pH and time needed to achieve the maximum.

b. Use the model to find the pH and time that will maximize the amount of peptides.

17. **Cooking Loss** Milk proteins are sometimes added to sausage to reduce shrinking due to cooking loss and to improve the texture of the sausage. Research has shown that when sausage is prepared with three milk proteins—sodium caseinate, whey protein, and skim milk powder—the cooking loss (expressed as a percentage of initial weight) can be modeled by

$$L(w, s) = 10.65 + 1.13w + 1.04s - 5.83ws \text{ percent}$$

where w is the proportion of whey protein, s is the proportion of skim milk powder, and the proportion c of sodium caseinate can be calculated as $c = 1 - w - s$. Determine whether the function L has a relative maximum, a relative minimum, or a saddle point, and find the corresponding proportions of sodium caseinate, whey protein, and skim milk powder at that point.

(Source: M. R. Ellekjaer, T. Naes, and P. Baardseth, "Milk Proteins Affect Yield and Sensory Quality of Cooked Sausages," *Journal of Food Science*, vol. 61, no. 3 (1996), pp. 660–666.)

18. **Sunflowers** A process to extract pectin and pigment from sunflower heads involves washing the sunflower heads in heated water. A model for the percentage of pigment that can be removed from a sunflower head by washing for 20 minutes in r milliliters of water per gram of sunflower when the water temperature is $T°C$ is

$$P(T, r) = 306.761 - 9.6544T + 1.9836r$$
$$+ 0.07368T^2 - 0.02958r^2 \text{ percent}$$

(Source: X. Q. Shi et al., "Optimizing Water Washing Process for Sunflower Heads Before Pectin Extraction," *Journal of Food Science*, vol. 61, no. 3 (1996), pp. 608–612.)

a. Find the critical point of the pigment removal function.

b. Identify it as a maximum, a minimum, or a saddle point.

19. **Farmland** A model for the elevation above sea level of a tract of farmland previously discussed is

$$E(e, n) = -10.124e^3 + 21.347e^2 - 13.972e - 2.5n^2$$
$$+ 2.497n + 802.2 \text{ feet above sea level}$$

where e is the distance in miles east of the western fence and n is the distance in miles north of the southern fence.

a. Find the two critical points of E.

b. Use the contour graph for E in the figure to identify each critical point as a maximum, a minimum, or a saddle point.

c. Use the Determinant Test to verify that the critical points are as you identified them in part *b*.

20. **Revenue** A model for the revenue generated by the sale of cheeses in the Netherlands is

$$R(c, r) = -52.196r^2 + 5935.497r - 59.128cr$$
$$+ 10,299.325c - 384.386c^2 \text{ thousand guilders}$$

where c thousand tons of 40% fat cheese and r thousand tons of regular cheese are sold. Find the combination of cheeses whose sales result in maximum revenue.

(Source: S. Louwes, J. Boot, and S. Wage, "A Quadratic-Programming Approach to the Problem of the Optimal Use of Milk in the Netherlands," *Journal of Farm Economics*, vol. 45, no. 2 (May 1963), pp. 309–317.)

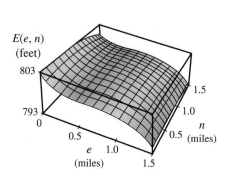

Figures for Activity 19

21. Honey   A measure of the adhesiveness of honey after processing can be modeled by

$$A(g, m, s, h) = -151.78 + 4.26g + 5.69m + 0.67s$$
$$+ 2.48h - 0.05g^2 - 0.14m^2 - 0.03s^2$$
$$- 0.05h^2 - 0.07mh$$

where g is the percentage of glucose and maltose, m is the percentage of moisture, s is the percentage of crystal used to seed the honey, and h is the holding time of the honey in days.

(Source: J. M. Shinn and S. L. Wang, "Textural Analysis of Crystallized Honey Using Response Surface Methodology," *Canadian Institute of Food Science and Technology Journal*, vol. 23, nos. 4–5 (1990), pp. 178–182.)

a. Find the point at which all four partial derivatives are zero. Find the corresponding adhesiveness measure at that point.

b. The Determinant Test applies only to functions of two variables. Use some other method to make a conjecture about the nature of the critical point you found. (That is, is it a maximum or a minimum or something else?)

22. Cheese Spread   A measure of the thickness of processed cheese spread can be modeled by

$$V(g, s, l) = 1000(5.647 - 3.436s + 1.577s^2$$
$$+ 0.375l - 1.757g + 0.141g^2$$
$$+ 1.217sl - 0.533s^2l + 0.186sg)$$

where g is the percentage of glycerol, s is the percentage of salt, and l is the percentage of lactose.

(Source: E. Kombila-Moundounga and C. Lacroix, "Effet des Combinaisons de Chloure de Sodium, de Lactose et de Glycerol sur les Caractéristiques Rhéologiques et la Couleur des Fromages Fondus à Tartiner," *Canadian Institute of Food Science and Technology Journal*, vol. 24, no. 5 (1991), pp. 239–251.)

a. Find the point at which all three partial derivatives are zero. Find the corresponding thickness measure at that point.

b. The Determinant Test applies only to functions of two variables. Use some other method to make a conjecture about the nature of the critical point you found. (That is, is it a maximum or a minimum or something else?)

Discussing Concepts

23. Describe in your own words how to determine algebraically whether a three-dimensional function has each of the following: (a) Relative maximum; (b) Relative minimum; and (c) Saddle point.

24. Using a graphical viewpoint, explain each of the conditional statements in the Determinant Test given in this section.

10.3   Optimization Under Constraints

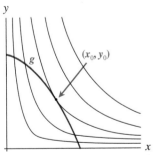

Nonlinear constraint curve g

FIGURE 10.19

Often it is not enough to be able to find the input that leads to a maximum (or minimum) output. In many applications there are constraints on what input values can be used. For example, when trying to optimize revenue made from the sale of cheese, the producer is constrained by the amount of cheese the company is able to produce. In the case where a manufacturer is trying to maximize production, budget constraints must be considered. Often constraints are implied by a particular context. These constraints can be written as functions with the same input variables as the function that is being constrained.

The simplest constraint functions are linear. For other multivariable functions f, the constraint function g may not be linear. The constraint curve drawn on a contour graph may look like the one shown in Figure 10.19.

The Lagrange Multiplier

The point of minimum (or maximum) output of f subject to $g(x, y) = c$ can be determined by first finding the smallest (or largest) value M for which the constraint curve $g(x, y) = c$ and the contour curve $f(x, y) = M$ touch and then determining the point (x_0, y_0) where these two curves meet. Figure 10.19 illustrates that a nonlinear

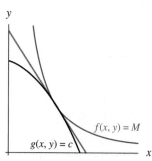

Line tangent to the constraint curve at the optimal point

FIGURE 10.20

constraint curve touches this lowest or highest possible contour curve at only one point on that contour curve and does not pass through the contour curve but remains completely on one side of it. What does this say about the lines tangent to the contour curve and the constraint curve at this point (x_0, y_0)? Compare the tangent lines shown in Figures 10.20 and 10.21. The tangent line in Figure 10.20 is the tangent line at (x_0, y_0) on the constraint curve $g(x, y) = c$, whereas the tangent line in Figure 10.21 is the tangent line at the same point but on the contour curve $f(x, y) = M$. They appear to be the same. In fact, they are the same.*

Concept Development: Setting Up Constrained Systems   We now use the fact that the tangent line at (x_0, y_0) on $g(x, y) = c$ is the same line as the tangent line at the same point on $f(x, y) = M$ to develop a method for solving constrained optimization problems. The tangent line in Figure 10.20 is tangent to the curve $g(x, y) = c$, so from Chapter 9 we know that its slope is

$$\frac{dy}{dx} = \frac{-\left(\frac{\partial g}{\partial x}\right)}{\left(\frac{\partial g}{\partial y}\right)} = \frac{-g_x}{g_y}$$

The tangent line in Figure 10.21 is a tangent to the contour curve $f(x, y) = M$, so its slope is

$$\frac{dy}{dx} = \frac{-\left(\frac{\partial f}{\partial x}\right)}{\left(\frac{\partial f}{\partial y}\right)} = \frac{-f_x}{f_y}$$

Because these two rates of change are equal, we have

$$\frac{-g_x}{g_y} = \frac{-f_x}{f_y}$$

and some algebra shows that

$$\frac{f_x}{g_x} = \frac{f_y}{g_y}$$

For convenience, we denote this common ratio as λ (the Greek letter *lambda*).

We now use λ to set up a system of equations that we solve in the process of finding any extreme points. First, we know that any extreme point on the constraint curve satisfies the condition

$$\frac{f_x}{g_x} = \lambda \qquad \text{so} \qquad \frac{\partial f}{\partial x} = \lambda \frac{\partial g}{\partial x}$$

The point also satisfies the condition

$$\frac{f_y}{g_y} = \lambda \qquad \text{so} \qquad \frac{\partial f}{\partial y} = \lambda \frac{\partial g}{\partial y}$$

*Although we use this result to develop the optimization technique further, you should realize that we have only graphically illustrated it in a special case. We do not give an analytic proof.

Line tangent to the contour curve at the optimal point

FIGURE 10.21

When estimating critical points from contour graphs in constrained optimization problems, remember that you may need to adjust your initial estimate to be certain that the estimated point is actually on the constraint.

Finally, the point we are trying to find must satisfy the constraint $g(x, y) = c$. Thus we have a system of three equations with three unknown variables, x, y, and λ:

$$\frac{\partial f}{\partial x} = \lambda \frac{\partial g}{\partial x}$$

$$\frac{\partial f}{\partial y} = \lambda \frac{\partial g}{\partial y}$$

$$g(x, y) = c$$

Solving this system of equations for x and y gives a point on the constraint curve at which an extreme value may occur. In fact, Joseph Lagrange (1736–1813), an Italian-born French mathematician, showed that any extreme point for the function f subject to the constraint $g(x, y) = c$ occurs among the solutions to the system of equations. For this reason, λ is called the **Lagrange multiplier.**

Once a solution to the system of equations is found, a contour graph of the multivariable function f and the constraint $g(x, y) = c$ may be helpful in identifying the nature of the corresponding extreme point. If a contour graph is not available, testing values of $f(x, y)$ for values of x and y that satisfy the constraint and are near the extreme point may also help identify that point as a maximum or minimum of the function f.

EXAMPLE 1   *Locating a Critical Output Subject to a Constraint*

Find the optimal point of the function $f(x, y) = xy + x + 2y$ subject to the constraint $g(x, y) = x + 1.5y = 8.5$.

a. Write the four partial derivatives and set up the system of equations.

b. Solve the system of equations.

c. Test the solution using the close-point method to classify the solution as a maximum or a minimum.

Solution

a. $f_x = y + 1$, $f_y = x + 2$, $g_x = 1$, $g_y = 1.5$ are the four partial derivatives.

b. $\dfrac{f_x}{g_x} = \lambda$ so $f_x = \lambda g_x$ and $y + 1 = 1\lambda$ (1)

$\dfrac{f_y}{g_y} = \lambda$ so $f_y = \lambda g_y$ and $x + 2 = 1.5\lambda$ (2)

$x + 1.5y = 8.5$ (3)

We can solve the equations using algebra, or we can use matrices and technology because the three equations are all linear.

We begin the solution algebraically by solving equation 3 for x.

$$x = 8.5 - 1.5y$$

Next, we substitute for x in equation 2 and simplify.

$$(8.5 - 1.5y) + 2 = 1.5\lambda$$

$$10.5 - 1.5y = 1.5\lambda \qquad\qquad (4)$$

We solve for y in equation 1 and substitute into equation 4.

$$y = \lambda - 1 \quad \text{so} \quad 10.5 - 1.5(\lambda - 1) = 1.5\lambda$$
$$10.5 - 1.5\lambda + 1.5 = 1.5\lambda$$

$$12 = 3\lambda \quad \text{so} \quad \lambda = 4$$

Substituting $\lambda = 4$ into equation 1, we have $y + 1 = 4$ so $y = 3$.

Substituting $\lambda = 4$ into equation 2, we have $x + 2 = 1.5 \cdot 4$ so $x = 4$.

c. To determine the nature of our critical point $f(x, y) = f(4, 3) = 22$, we will choose close points on the constraint equation. We choose to examine the close points where $y = 2$ and $y = 4$.

If $y = 2$, we solve the constraint equation for x and evaluate $f(x, y)$.

$$x + 1.5 \cdot 2 = 8.5 \quad \text{so} \quad x = 8.5 - 3 = 5.5 \quad \text{and} \quad f(5.5, 2) = 20.5.$$

If $y = 4$, we solve the constraint equation for x and evaluate $f(x, y)$.

$$x + 1.5 \cdot 4 = 8.5 \quad \text{so} \quad x = 8.5 - 6 = 2.5 \quad \text{and} \quad f(2.5, 4) = 20.5.$$

Each of our test points had output less than that of our critical point. We conclude that $f(4, 3) = 22$ is a maximum value for the constrained function. ●

EXAMPLE 2   *Locating a Maximum Output Subject to a Constraint*

10.3.1

Production   Consider a mattress-manufacturing process for which the Cobb-Douglas production function is

$$f(L, K) = 48.1L^{0.6}K^{0.4} \text{ mattresses}$$

where L represents the number of worker hours (in thousands) and K represents the amount invested in capital (in thousands of dollars). Suppose that the plant manager has a budget of \$98,000 to be invested in capital or spent on labor and that the average wage of an employee at the mattress plant is \$8 per hour.

a. Write the budget constraint equation.

b. Use Lagrange multipliers to find the expenditures on labor and capital investment that will result in the greatest number of mattresses being produced subject to the budget constraint. Also find the maximum production level.

c. Verify that the answer to part *b* is a relative maximum.

Solution

a. The manager's budget constraint equation is

$$g(L, K) = 8L + K = 98 \text{ thousand dollars}$$

where L and K are as described in the production function.

b. The point at which the maximum production occurs must satisfy the following
    system of equations:

$$\frac{\partial f}{\partial L} = \lambda \frac{\partial g}{\partial L} \qquad 28.86\, L^{-0.4}K^{0.4} = \lambda(8) \tag{5}$$

$$\frac{\partial f}{\partial K} = \lambda \frac{\partial g}{\partial K} \qquad 19.24\, L^{0.6}K^{-0.6} = \lambda(1) \tag{6}$$

$$g(L, K) = c \qquad 8L + K = 98 \tag{7}$$

To solve this system, we begin by solving equation 5 for one of the variables L, K,
or λ. In this example, we solve for λ.

$$\lambda = \frac{28.86 L^{-0.4}K^{0.4}}{8} = 3.6075\, L^{-0.4}K^{0.4}$$

Substituting this expression for λ into equation 6, we have

$$19.24\, L^{0.6}K^{-0.6} = 3.6075\, L^{-0.4}K^{0.4}$$

Next, we multiply both sides of the equation by $L^{0.4}K^{0.6}$ to remove the negative
exponents, and solve for L:

$$(19.24\, L^{0.6}K^{-0.6})L^{0.4}K^{0.6} = (3.6075\, L^{-0.4}K^{0.4})L^{0.4}K^{0.6}$$
$$19.24\, L^{0.6+0.4}K^{-0.6+0.6} = 3.6075\, L^{-0.4+0.4}K^{0.4+0.6}$$
$$19.24\, L = 3.6075\, K$$
$$L = 0.1875\, K$$

Finally, substituting $L = 0.1875\, K$ into equation 7 enables us to solve for K:

$$8(0.1875\, K) + K = 98$$
$$2.5\, K = 98$$
$$K = 39.2 \text{ thousand dollars}$$

Next we use $K = 39.2$ to find that $L = 0.1875(39.2) = 7.35$ thousand worker
hours. Thus the labor costs are (7.35 thousand worker hours)($8 per hour) =
\$58,800, and the capital investment is \$39,200. With those investments of time
and money, the production level is $f(7.35, 39.2) = 690.608 \approx 690$ mattresses.
Note that we discount the fraction of a mattress and round down the production
level. A production level of 691 mattresses would (technically) result in labor
exceeding the budget constraint.

c. To verify that the values of K and L found in part b give a maximum production
    level subject to the constraint, we consider nearby points on the constraint curve.
    We choose values for L that are close to 7.35. In this case, we choose 7.3 and 7.4.
    Substituting these values into the constraint equation $g(L, K) = 8L + K = 98$,
    we obtain the corresponding values of K, so the points we check are (7.3, 39.6)
    and (7.4, 38.8). We find that the values $f(7.3, 39.6) \approx 690.585$ and $f(7.4, 38.8) \approx$
    690.584 are both less than the extreme value $f(7.35, 39.2) \approx 690.608$, and we
    therefore have good evidence that 690 mattresses is a maximum production level.
    The manager will be able to maximize the production of mattresses by investing
    \$39,200 in capital and having his employees put in a total of 7350 worker hours.
    Note that we could also verify that our solution is a maximum by examining the

graph in Figure 10.22. The budget constraint $g(L, K) = 98$ intersects the $f(L, K) = 290, 490,$ and 690 contours. Because the contour to which the constraint is tangent is the largest of these values, the answer to part b is the location of a relative maximum.

FIGURE 10.22

Interpreting λ

If the level of the constraint function g changes from c to $c + \Delta c$, it will determine a different extreme point because adding Δc to the constraint equation shifts the constraint curve (see Figure 10.23).

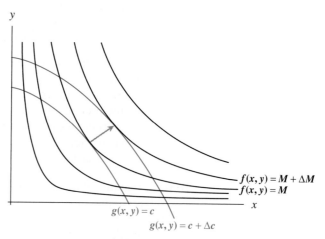

FIGURE 10.23   *A shifted constraint curve*

Note that $g(x, y) = c + \Delta c$ is tangent to the contour curve $f(x, y) = M + \Delta M$, whereas $g(x, y) = c$ is tangent to the curve $f(x, y) = M$. Therefore, we can consider the extreme value M to be a function of the level c of the constraint. In order to analyze the effect that a change in the constraint level c has on the extreme value M, we look at the rate of change of M with respect to c—that is, $\frac{dM}{dc}$. It can be shown using more rigorous mathematics that the Lagrange multiplier λ is this rate of change.

When the level of the constraint changes by a small amount Δc, the extreme value M of $f(x, y)$ changes by

$$\Delta M \approx \Delta c \left(\frac{dM}{dc} \right) = \Delta c(\lambda)$$

When $f(x, y)$ represents the output of a production function, the Lagrange multiplier λ can be used to determine the approximate increase in the optimal production level effected by an additional allocation of resources. Economists often refer to the value of λ as the *marginal productivity of money*.

In the mattress production example, Example 2, we can use Equation 6 to find the value of λ when $L = 7.35$ and $K = 39.2$:

$$\lambda = 19.24 \, (7.35)^{0.6} \, (39.2)^{-0.6} \approx 7.047$$

Because λ can be interpreted as $\frac{dM}{dc}$, its units are mattresses per thousand budget dollars.

This value of λ can be used to approximate the maximum production level that would occur if the budget were increased. For example, if the manager's budget were $99 thousand instead of $98 thousand, the production level would increase by

$$\Delta M = \frac{dM}{dc} \, \Delta c = (\lambda)\Delta c$$

$$= \left(7.047 \, \frac{\text{mattresses}}{\text{thousand budget dollars}} \right) (1 \text{ thousand budget dollars})$$

$$\approx 7 \text{ mattresses}$$

That is, the company could produce approximately 697 mattresses, instead of 690 mattresses, if the manager's budget were $99 thousand instead of $98 thousand.   ●

Interpretation of λ

If the constraint level c is increased by 1 unit, then the extreme value M of the function changes by approximately λ units.

EXAMPLE 3   *Locating a Minimum Output Subject to a Constraint*

10.3.2

Production   Consider the production of sausage, in which the amount of shrinkage due to cooking is reduced by the addition of three milk proteins. The percentage of volume lost in cooking sausage can be modeled* by the equation

$$P(c, w, s) = 10.65c + 11.78w + 11.69s - 5.83ws \text{ percent}$$

where c, w, and s are the proportions of the milk proteins sodium caseinate, whey protein, and skim milk powder, respectively.

a.   Rewrite the function P in terms of w and s, using the fact that $c + w + s = 1$.

b.   Using the constraint $w + s = k$ for $k = 1$, find the minimum value of the function in part *a* and the values of s and w at which the minimum occurs. Use the contour graph in Figure 10.24 to verify that the point is the location of a relative minimum.

FIGURE 10.24

*M. R. Ellekjaer, T. Naes, and P. Baardseth, "Milk Proteins Affect Yield and Sensory Quality of Cooked Sausages," *Journal of Food Science*, vol. 61, no. 3 (1996), pp. 660–672.

c. To determine the effect that changing k in the constraint $w + s = k$ has on the optimal cooking loss P, find the value of $\frac{dP}{dk}$ for $k = 1$.

d. Use the answer to part b to estimate the effect on the minimum cooking loss if sodium caseinate makes up 10% of the total milk proteins.

e. On the basis of your answer to part c, do you believe that a sausage producer would be wise to use sodium caseinate in addition to whey and skim milk powder? Explain.

Solution

a. Substituting $1 - w - s$ for c in the equation, we obtain

$$P(w, s) = 10.65 + 1.13w + 1.04s - 5.83ws \text{ percent}$$

b. The point at which the minimum percentage of volume lost occurs must satisfy the system of equations $P_w = \lambda g_w$, $P_s = \lambda g_s$, and $g\,(w, s) = 1$:

$$1.13 - 5.83s = \lambda$$
$$1.04 - 5.83w = \lambda$$
$$w + s = 1$$

This system of equations can be solved algebraically or using matrices. A matrix for this linear system of equations is

$$\begin{bmatrix} -5.83 & 0 & -1 & -1.13 \\ 0 & -5.83 & -1 & -1.04 \\ 1 & 1 & 0 & 1 \end{bmatrix}$$

Using technology, we find that the solution to this system is $s \approx 0.508$ and $w \approx 0.492$ with $\lambda = -1.83$. With these proportions of whey protein and skim milk powder, the shrinkage is $P(0.492, 0.508) \approx 10.28\%$. To verify that this value is a minimum, we graph the constraint $w + s = 1$ on the given contour graph. (See Figure 10.25.) The contour curve to which the constraint curve is tangent has the smallest value of all contour curves that intersect or touch the constraint curve. This confirms that we have found the minimum of P subject to the constraint $w + s = 1$.

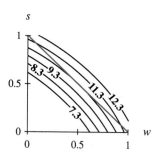

FIGURE 10.25

c. From the solution to the system of equations in part b, we have $\lambda = -1.83$. Therefore, $\frac{dP}{dk} = -1.83$ percentage points per unit of k.

d. We can approximate the effect on optimal cooking loss by using the formula

$$\Delta P \approx \frac{dP}{dk}\Delta k$$

In this case, k is decreased by 0.1 (from 1 to 0.9), so the change in minimum cooking loss is approximately $(-1.83)(-0.1) = 0.183$ percentage point. In other words, if sodium caseinate is added so that the proportions of whey and skim milk proteins sum to 0.9, minimum cooking loss will increase to approximately $10.28 + 0.183 \approx 10.46\%$.

e. Because $\frac{dP}{dk}$ is negative, any decrease in k (the combined proportion of whey and skim milk proteins) will increase P (the percentage cooking loss). Thus the addition of sodium caseinate will increase the percentage loss in cooking. Because a sausage producer desires minimum cooking loss, it probably is not beneficial for producers to use sodium caseinate. We do not know, however, what other benefits sodium caseinate may confer, such as improved texture, improved taste, or decreased processing expenses. A sausage producer would need to evaluate all contributing factors when making a decision. ●

Because the system of equations solved in Example 3 is linear, it can be solved using matrices. However, the system of equations solved in Example 2 is not linear and therefore cannot be solved using the same technique.

10.3 Concept Inventory

- Constrained optimization
- Graphing a constraint on a contour graph
- Classifying optimal points under a constraint
- Lagrange multiplier
- Interpretation of λ

10.3 Activities

Getting Started

1. Consider the multivariable function $f(a, b) = ab$ with constraint $g(a, b) = a + b = 90$.

    a. Use the graph of several of the contour curves of f and the constraint $g(a, b) = 90$ to estimate the optimal point and optimal value of $f(a, b)$ subject to the constraint.

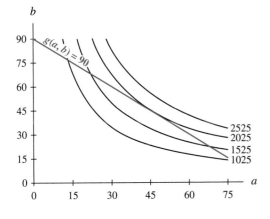

b. Classify the constrained optimal point as a maximum or a minimum of $f(a, b)$.

c. Use the methods of this section to find the optimal point and the optimal value.

2. Consider the multivariable function $f(k, h) = 2k^2h$ with constraint $g(k, h) = k^2 + h = 2$.

    a. Use the graph of several of the contour curves of f and the constraint $g(k, h) = 2$ to estimate each optimal point and optimal value of $f(k, h)$ subject to the constraint.

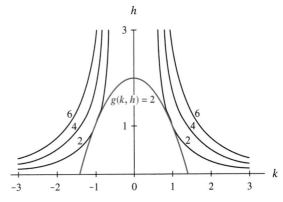

b. Classify each constrained optimal point as a maximum or a minimum of $f(k, h)$.

c. Use the methods of this section to find the optimal points and the optimal values.

3. **Honey**   The contour graph shows a measure of the cohesiveness of honey as a function of the percentage of glucose and maltose and the percentage of moisture.

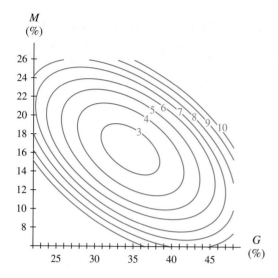

a. Estimate the critical point indicated by the contour graph. Interpret your answer.

b. Graph the constraint $g(G, M) = G + M = 40\%$ on the contour graph. Estimate the optimal point of cohesiveness subject to the constraint. Is the point the location of a maximum or a minimum?

4. Honey   The contour graph shows a measure of the adhesiveness of honey as a function of G, the percentage of glucose and maltose, and M, the percentage of moisture.

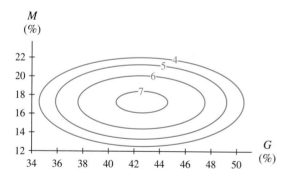

a. Estimate the critical point indicated by the contour graph. Interpret your answer.

b. Graph the constraint $g(G, M) = G + M = 55\%$ on the contour graph. Estimate the optimal point of adhesiveness subject to the constraint. Is the point the location of a maximum or a minimum?

5. Find the optimal point of

$$f(r, p) = 2r^2 + rp - p^2 + p$$

under the constraint

$$g(r, p) = 2r + 3p = 1$$

Identify the output at the point as a maximum or a minimum using:

a. A contour graph

b. Close points

6. Find the optimal point of

$$f(x, y) = 80x + 5y^2$$

under the constraint

$$g(x, y) = 2x + 2y = 1.4$$

Identify the output of the point as a maximum or a minimum using:

a. A contour graph   b. Close points

Applying Concepts

7. Cooking Loss   Use the model given in the solution to part *a* of Example 3 and the constraint $w + s = 0.9$ to find the minimum percentage cooking loss if 10% sodium caseinate is used. Compare your answer to the approximation given in part *d* of Example 3.

8. Production   Use the Cobb-Douglas model for mattress production given in Example 2 to find maximum production if the manager's budget were increased to $99 thousand. Compare your answer to the estimate given above the box on page 651.

9. Advertising   A health club is trying to determine how to allocate funds for advertising. The manager decides to advertise on the radio and in the newspaper. Previous experience with such advertising leads the club to expect $A(r, n) = 0.1r^2n$ responses when r ads are run on the radio and n ads appear in the newspaper. Each ad on the radio costs $12, and each newspaper ad costs $6.

a. Find the optimal allocation for advertising to produce the maximum number of responses if the club has budgeted $504 for advertising.

b. What is the maximum number of responses expected with the given advertising costs?

c. Suppose the manager budgeted an additional $26 for advertising. What is the approximate change in the optimal value as a result of this change in the constraint level?

10. **Honey** A measure of the adhesiveness of honey can be modeled by

$$A(G, M) = -125.48 + 4.26G + 4.85M$$
$$- 0.05G^2 - 0.14M^2$$

where G is the percentage of glucose and maltose and M is the percentage of moisture. A contour graph of A is shown in Activity 4.

(Source: J. M. Shinn and S. L. Wang, "Textural Analysis of Crystallized Honey Using Response Surface Methodology," *Canadian Institute of Food Science and Technology Journal,* vol. 23, nos. 4–5 (1990), pp. 178–182.)

a. Find the absolute maximum of the adhesiveness of honey. Compare your answer with the estimate in the answer to part *a* of Activity 4.

b. If FDA restrictions for Grade A honey require that the combined percentages of glucose, maltose, and moisture not exceed 55%, what is the maximum measure of adhesiveness possible?

c. Verify that the point in part *b* corresponds to a maximum.

d. Compare your answer in part *b* to the estimate in the answer to part *b* of Activity 4.

11. **Honey** A measure of the cohesiveness of honey can be modeled by

$$C(G, M) = 106.35 - 3.76G - 4.71M + 0.04G^2$$
$$+ 0.08M^2 + 0.06GM$$

where G is the percentage of glucose and maltose and M is the percentage of moisture. A contour graph of C is shown in Activity 3.

(Source: J. M. Shinn and S. L. Wang, "Textural Analysis of Crystallized Honey Using Response Surface Methodology," *Canadian Institute of Food Science and Technology Journal,* vol. 23, nos. 4–5 (1990), pp. 178–182.)

a. Find the absolute minimum cohesiveness of honey. Compare your answer with the estimate in the answer to part *a* of Activity 3.

b. If FDA restrictions for Grade A honey require that the combined percentages of glucose, maltose, and moisture not exceed 40%, what is the minimum measure of cohesiveness possible?

c. Verify that the point in part *b* corresponds to a minimum.

d. Compare your answer in part *b* to the estimate in the answer to part *b* of Activity 3.

12. **Cost** A manufacturer is designing a packaging carton for shipping. The carton will be a box with fixed volume of 8 cubic feet. The cost to construct each box is

$$C(l, w) = lw + \frac{4.8}{w} + \frac{3.2}{l} \text{ dollars}$$

where the box is l feet long and w feet wide. If shipping requirements are such that the length and width of the box are constrained by $l + 2w = 5$ feet, what size box will cost the least to produce? What is the minimum cost?

13. **Production** The daily output at a plant manufacturing transistor radios is approximated by the function

$$f(L, K) = 10.5463L^{0.3} K^{0.5} \text{ radios}$$

where L is the size of the labor force measured in hundreds of worker hours and K is the capital investment in thousands of dollars.

a. Suppose that the plant manager has a daily budget of $15,000 to be invested in capital or spent on labor and that the average wage of an employee at the radio plant is $7.50 per hour. What combination of worker hours and capital expenditures will yield maximum daily production?

b. Verify that the output value in part *a* is a maximum.

c. Find and interpret the marginal productivity of money for this manufacturing process.

14. **Honey** Refer to the model and constraint in Activity 10 and its contour graph in Activity 4.

a. If $f(G, M) = k$ is the constraint equation and A is the maximum adhesiveness measure, find $\frac{dA}{dk}$ for $k = 55\%$.

b. Use the answer to part *a* to estimate the change in the maximum adhesiveness measure if the FDA approves the percentage of glucose, maltose, and moisture to be 56%.

c. Find the maximum measure of adhesiveness if there are no restrictions on the percentage of glucose, maltose, and moisture.

15. **Honey** Refer to the model and constraint in Activity 11 and its contour graph in Activity 3.

a. If $f(G, M) = k$ is the constraint equation and C is the minimum cohesiveness measure, find $\frac{dC}{dk}$ for $k = 40\%$.

b. Use the answer to part *a* to estimate the change in the minimum cohesiveness measure if the FDA approves the percentage of glucose, maltose, and moisture to be 42%.

c. Find the minimum measure of cohesiveness if there are no restrictions on the percentage of glucose, maltose, and moisture.

16. Cost Refer to Activity 12 to answer the following questions.

a. If M is the minimum cost and $f(l, w) = k$ is the constraint equation, find $\frac{dM}{dk}$ for $k = 5$.

b. Use the answer to part *a* to estimate the minimum cost if the constraint curve equation is $l + 2w = 5.5$

17. Production Refer to Activity 13 to answer the following questions.

a. If P is the maximum daily production and the budget constraint equation is $g(L, K) = c$, find $\frac{dP}{dc}$ for $c = \$15,000$.

b. Use the answer to part *a* to estimate the change in maximum production if the budget amount is increased by $1500.

c. Estimate the maximum production if the budget amount is decreased to $14,000.

18. Corral A rancher removed 200 feet of wire fencing from a field on his ranch. He wants to reuse the fencing to create a rectangular corral into which he will build a 6-foot-wide wooden gate. The dimensions of the corral with the greatest possible area are found using the multivariable functions for the amount of fencing and for the resulting area of the corral:

$F(l, w) = 2w + 2l - 6 = 200$ feet is the amount of fencing needed for the specified rectangular corral of width, w feet, and length, l feet. The area of the specified corral is

$A(l, w) = lw$ feet squared where w feet is the width and l feet is the length.

a. What is the multivariable function to be maximized?

b. What is the constraint function?

c. Maximize the equation in part *a* subject to the constraint in part *b*, using the method of Lagrange multipliers.

19. Popcorn Tin In an effort to be environmentally responsible, a confectionery company is rethinking the dimensions of the tins in which it packages popcorn. Each cylindrical tin is to hold 3.5 gallons. The bottom and the lid are both circular, but the lid must have an additional $1\frac{1}{8}$ inch around it in order to form a lip. (Consider the amount of metal needed to create a seam on the side and to join the side to the bottom to be negligible.) The multivariable functions for the volume of the tin and the surface area are:

$V(r, h) = \pi r^2 h = 3.5$ gallons (808.5 cubic inches), where r inches is the radius of the circular base of the tin, and h inches is the height of the tin.

$S(r, h) = 2\pi rh + \pi r^2 + \pi\left(r + \frac{9}{8}\right)^2$ square inches is the surface area of the tin, where r inches is the radius of the circular base of the tin, and h inches is the height of the tin.

What are the dimensions of a tin that meets these specifications but uses the least amount of metal possible?

a. What is the multivariable function to be minimized?

b. What is the constraint function?

c. Minimize the equation in part *a* subject to the constraint in part *b*, using the method of Lagrange multipliers.

20. Revenue A travel agency offers spring-break cruise packages. The agency advertises a cruise to Cancun, Mexico, for $1200 per person. In order to promote the cruise among student organizations on campus, the agency offers a discount for student groups selling the cruise to over 50 of their members. The price per student will be discounted by $10 for each student in excess of 50. For example, if an organization had 55 members go on the cruise, each of those 55 students would pay $1200 - 5(\$10)$ = \$1150.

a. Write revenue as a multivariable function of the number of students in excess of 50 and the price per student.

b. Write a constraint function in terms of the number of students in excess of 50 and the price.

c. Maximize the equation in part *a* subject to the constraint in part *b*, using the method of Lagrange multipliers.

Discussing Concepts

21. Explain why any constrained extreme point of a function *f* on the constraint curve *g*, each with inputs *x* and *y*, satisfies the conditions $\lambda = \frac{f_x}{g_x} = \frac{f_y}{g_y}$.

22. When estimating a critical point from a contour graph in a constrained optimization problem, why is it important to check the input values of the estimated point?

10.4   Least-Squares Optimization

We have used different models in this text to represent real-world situations. We are now in a position to understand a procedure that is used to fit functions to data. This section is devoted to the **least-squares method** of determining the linear model that best fits a set of data points.

In Chapter 1, we learned how to model data using a "best-fitting" equation. Let us review how we decide when a particular line best fits the data in the context of an application dealing with retirement plans.

The average number of investment choices for people who invested in 401(k) plans at their place of employment during certain years is given in Table 10.4.

TABLE 10.4

Year	1990	1991	1992	1993
Average number of 401(k) plans	3.5	4.0	4.2	4.8

(Sources: *USA Today*, November 5, 1993; Foster Higgins.)

Let *x* represent the number of years since 1990, and let *y* be the average number of 401(k) plans. A scatter plot of the data and a linear model are shown in Figure 10.26.

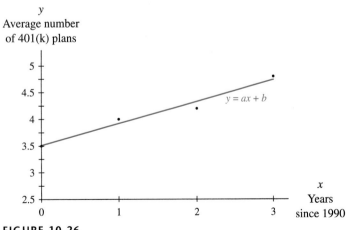

FIGURE 10.26

A visual indication of how well the line fits the data is given by the extent to which the data points deviate from the line. We determine a numerical measure of this visual observation by calculating the vertical distance (the deviation) from each data point to the line. (See Figure 10.27.)

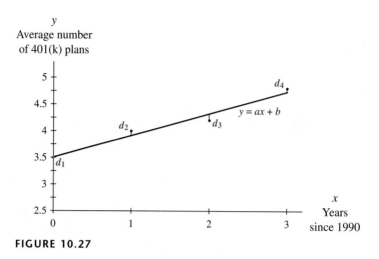

FIGURE 10.27

Each **deviation** measures the **error** between the associated data point and the line.

$$\text{Deviation} = \text{error} = y_{\text{data}} - y_{\text{line}}$$

To obtain a single numerical measure, we square the errors and sum. When there are n data points, we have

SSE = the sum of squared errors

$$= (\text{first error})^2 + (\text{second error})^2 + \cdots + (\text{last error})^2$$

$$= d_1{}^2 + d_2{}^2 + d_n{}^2 = \sum_{i=1}^{n} d_i^2$$

This number, denoted by SSE (sum of squared errors), is our overall measure of how well the line fits the data. The key to its correct use is to remember that smaller values of SSE arise from lines where the errors are small, and larger values of SSE arise from lines where the errors are large. The strategy for choosing the best-fitting line is to choose the line for which the sum of squared errors (SSE) is as small as possible. Such a line is designated the *line of best fit* (also called the *regression line*), and this procedure for choosing it is called the **method of least squares.**

The Line of Best Fit

The method of least squares is the procedure that is used to find the best-fitting line based on the criterion that the sum of squared errors is as small as possible—that is, at a minimum value. The linear model obtained by this method is called the **least-squares line.**

Note $n = 4$ because we have 4 parts.

Thus our task is to find the values of a and b in the model $y = ax + b$ such that $\text{SSE} = \sum_{i=1}^{n} d_i^2$ is a minimum. Because each deviation is the y-value of the data minus the y-value on the line, we proceed as follows using the data:

$$\sum_{i=1}^{4} d_i^2 = [3.5 - (a \cdot 0 + b)]^2 + [4 - (a \cdot 1 + b)]^2$$
$$+ [4.2 - (a \cdot 2 + b)]^2 + [4.8 - (a \cdot 3 + b)]^2$$
$$= (3.5 - b)^2 + (4 - a - b)^2 + (4.2 - 2a - b)^2 + (4.8 - 3a - b)^2$$

This sum of squares of errors is a function of the slope, a, and the y-intercept, b, of the least-squares line. Thus it is a multivariable function with two input variables:

$$f(a, b) = (3.5 - b)^2 + (4 - a - b)^2$$
$$+ (4.2 - 2a - b)^2 + (4.8 - 3a - b)^2$$

Recall that to find the minimum value of $f(a, b)$, we first find $\frac{\partial f}{\partial a}$ and $\frac{\partial f}{\partial b}$:

$$\frac{\partial f}{\partial a} = 0 + 2(4 - a - b)(-1) + 2(4.2 - 2a - b)(-2)$$
$$+ 2(4.8 - 3a - b)(-3)$$

$$\frac{\partial f}{\partial b} = 2(3.5 - b)(-1) + 2(4 - a - b)(-1) + 2(4.2 - 2a - b)(-1)$$
$$+ 2(4.8 - 3a - b)(-1)$$

Next, we set $\frac{\partial f}{\partial a} = 0$ and $\frac{\partial f}{\partial b} = 0$. Some algebraic simplification results in the equations

$$28a + 12b = 53.6$$
$$12a + 8b = 33$$

An algebraic or matrix solution to this system of equations is $(0.41, 3.51)$.

Finally, we must verify that the point $(0.41, 3.51)$ is a minimum for the function f by considering the determinant of the second partials matrix:

$$D = \begin{vmatrix} 28 & 12 \\ 12 & 8 \end{vmatrix} = 224 - 144 = 80$$

Because $D(0.41, 3.51) > 0$ and $f_{aa} > 0$, we conclude that the sum of squared errors, SSE, is at a minimum for the linear model with slope $a = 0.41$ and y-intercept $b = 3.51$. The minimum value of SSE is $f(0.41, 3.51) = 0.027$.

The best-fitting line determined by the least-squares method for the investment data is $y = 0.41x + 3.51$ investment choices of 401(k) plans x years after 1990. You should verify that this is the equation found by using the linear regression routine in your calculator or computer.

The least-squares method is illustrated in this section with small data sets to simplify calculations. In real-world situations, you should be cautious when using only a few data points, because a small error in one of the points may lead to a large error in the least-squares line.

10.4 Concept Inventory

- Least-squares method
- Sum of squared errors
- Line of best fit

10.4 Activities

Getting Started

For the data given in Activities 1 and 2:

a. Express SSE as a multivariable function of a and b for the best-fitting line $y = ax + b$.

b. Find $\frac{\partial f}{\partial a}$, $\frac{\partial f}{\partial b}$, and the determinant of the second partials matrix.

c. Find the minimum value of $f(a, b)$, and verify that the value you obtain is a minimum.

d. Use the results of part c to give the linear function that best fits the data.

1.

x	1	6	12
y	7	11	19

2.

x	2	3	6	8
y	5	7	11	15

Applying Concepts

3. **Kitchens**   The U.S. Census questionnaire defines kitchens with complete facilities as those having a sink with piped water, a range, and a refrigerator. Homes that lack complete kitchen facilities have been rare in the United States for many years. The first census for which data were tabulated on this subject was in 1970. The table shows the percentage of housing units lacking complete kitchen facilities in the western United States.

Year	1970	1980	1990
Percent lacking	3	2	1

(Source: Census Questionnaire Content, 1990 CQC-25, U.S. Bureau of the Census, December 1993.)

a. Use the method of least squares to find the multivariable function f with inputs a and b for the best-fitting line $y = ax + b$, where x is years since 1970.

b. Find the minimum value of $f(a, b)$, and verify that it is a minimum value. Interpret the meaning of this minimum value in terms of the data and the best-fitting line.

c. Give the linear model that best fits these data.

d. Use the best-fitting line to predict the percentage of housing units lacking complete kitchen facilities in the western United States this year. Is this a reasonable prediction? Why or why not?

4. **Singles**   Are young adults staying single longer? The percentage of adults 20–24 years of age who have not yet been married is given in the table.

Year	1970	1980	1990
Percent never married	46	60	72

(Sources: Census Questionnaire Content, 1990 CQC-6, U.S. Bureau of the Census, April 1993; *Statistical Abstract*, 2001.)

a. Use the method of least squares to find the multivariable function f with inputs a and b for the best-fitting line $y = ax + b$, where x is the number of years since 1970.

b. Find the minimum value of $f(a, b)$, and verify that it is a minimum value.

c. Give the linear model that best fits these data.

d. Use your model to estimate the percentage of adults 20–24 years old who had never been married in 2000.

e. The percentage of adults 20–24 years old who had never been married in 1960 was 41. Add this data point, and use technology to find a linear model. Use this model to estimate the percentage of adults 20–24 years old who had never been married in 2000.

f. The percentage of adults 20–24 years old who had never been married was 78% in 2000. How close are your estimates from parts d and e?

g. Use the results of parts d, e, and f, to discuss what effect additional data may have when one is predicting by using models.

5. **Cost**   A factory makes 7-mm aluminum ball bearings. Company planners have determined how

much it costs them to make certain numbers of cases of ball bearings in a single run. These costs are shown in the accompanying table.

Cases of ball bearings	Cost (dollars)
1	3.10
2	4.25
6	8.95
9	12.29
14	18.45

a. Construct a scatter plot of these data.

b. Use your calculator or computer to find the best-fitting linear model, and sketch the model on the scatter plot. Interpret the slope and vertical-axis intercept in the context of this situation.

c. Find the deviation of each data point from the line, and find the sum of the squares of the deviations.

d. Without performing any computations, discuss the process you would use to find the multivariable function f with inputs a and b for the best-fitting line $y = ax + b$. How is this line related to the results of parts b and c?

6. **Rainfall**   The table gives the number of inches of precipitation that fell in New York City in early 1855.

Month	Jan	Feb	March
Precipitation (inches)	5.50	3.25	1.35

(Source: H. Helm Clayton, ed., *World Weather Records*, Washington, DC: The Smithsonian Institution, 1927.)

a. Use the method of least squares to find the multivariable function f with inputs a and b for the best-fitting line $y = ax + b$, where x is 1 in January, 2 in February, and 3 in March.

b. Find the minimum value of $f(a, b)$, and verify that it is a minimum value. Interpret the meaning of this minimum value in terms of the data and the best-fitting line.

c. Give the linear model that best fits these data.

7. **Animal Experiments**   The number of animal experiments in England declined between 1970 and

1980. The numbers for selected years are shown in the table. Use the method of least squares to find the best-fitting linear model for the data.

Year	1970	1975	1978	1980
Experiments (millions)	5.5	5	4.8	4.6

(Source: A. Rowan, *Of Mice, Models, and Men*, Albany: State University of New York Press, 1984.)

8. **Milk Storage**   The table shows the number of days that milk will keep as a function of the temperature. Use the method of least squares to find the best-fitting linear model for the data.

Temperature (°F)	30	38	45	50
Days	24	10	5	0.5

(Source: Data taken from a milk carton produced by Model Dairy.)

9. **Population**   Before the technology was available to fit many kinds of models to data, researchers and others were restricted to using linear models. Because exponential data are common in many fields of study, it has always been important to be able to fit an exponential model to data. Consider the table showing past and predicted world population.

Year	Population (billions)
1850	1.1
1930	2.0
1975	4.0
2013	8.0

(Source: *Information Please Almanac*, 1994.)

a. Construct a scatter plot of the data. Comment on the curvature.

b. Change the data so that they represent the year and the natural log of the population. Construct a scatter plot of the new data, and comment on the curvature.

c. Use the technique discussed in this section to find the best-fitting linear model for the changed data in part b. You should keep the data in the form ln y and should not round the values until the final calculation. Label input and output units on your model.

d. If a and b are the parameters of the linear function $y = ax + b$ found in part c, graph the function $y = e^b(e^a)^x$ on the scatter plot of the original data. Label the input and output units on the exponential model.

e. Use technology and an exponential regression routine to find the best exponential model for the population data. Compare it with the model in part d, and reconcile any differences.

10. Infants   Repeat Activity 9 for the data shown in the table, which gives the numbers of infants born to each of five generations in a certain family.

Generation	1	2	3	4	5
Infants	11	7	5	3	2

Discussing Concepts

11. Another possible measure of goodness of fit could involve the sum of absolute values of the errors instead of the sum of squared errors. Explain how this might change the fit of a line to data. How would the use of such a measure affect the algebraic difficulty of finding a "best-fitting" line?

SUMMARY

Multivariable Optimization

In this chapter, we consider optimization techniques for multivariable functions. On a three-dimensional function, points where the partial derivatives with respect to both input variables are both zero are called critical points and can be relative extremum points or saddle points. Critical points can be estimated visually on a table or contour graph or can be located algebraically on a smooth, continuous function f with inputs x and y by solving the system of equations $\frac{\partial f}{\partial x} = 0$ and $\frac{\partial f}{\partial y} = 0$. We then classify any point found as a solution as a relative maximum, a relative minimum, or a saddle point by looking at a three-dimensional graph or contour plot or by using the Determinant Test.

Optimization Under Constraints

Many practical problems involve constraints on the optimization process. At the point where a multivariable function f has an extreme point subject to the constraint $g(x, y) = c$, the constant contour curve $f(x, y) = M$ and the constraint $g(x, y) = c$ have the same tangent line with slope

$$\frac{dy}{dx} = \frac{-\left(\frac{\partial f}{\partial x}\right)}{\left(\frac{\partial f}{\partial y}\right)} = \frac{-f_x}{f_y}$$

To find the constrained extreme points, or to determine whether they exist, we solve the system of equations

$$\frac{\partial f}{\partial x} = \lambda\frac{\partial g}{\partial x}$$
$$\frac{\partial f}{\partial y} = \lambda\frac{\partial g}{\partial y}$$
$$g(x, y) = c$$

We classify the solution to this system of equations as the location of a relative maximum or relative minimum by viewing a contour graph or three-dimensional graph or by checking the value of the function at nearby points on the constraint curve.

The number λ is called a Lagrange multiplier. When M is the extreme value and c is the constraint level, λ equals $\frac{dM}{dc}$, the rate of change of the extreme value with respect to a change in the constraint.

Least-Squares Optimization

We end the chapter with a calculus explanation for the intuitive idea of the line of best fit that was presented in Chapter 1. We define the line of best fit to be the one for which the sum of squared errors, SSE, attains a minimum. The optimization technique that finds the minimum SSE is called the method of least squares and is an application of the method of unconstrained optimization.

CONCEPT CHECK

Can you	To practice, try	
• Identify critical points and absolute extrema on three-dimensional and contour graphs?	Section 10.1	Activities 5, 21
• Estimate critical points and absolute extrema in tables?	Section 10.1	Activities 7, 17
• Find critical points using equations?	Section 10.2	Activities 1, 5
• Use the Determinant Test?	Section 10.2	Activity 19
• Use the method of Lagrange multipliers?	Section 10.3	Activities 1, 11
• Interpret the Lagrange multiplier l?	Section 10.3	Activities 13, 17
• Use multivariable optimization to find a line of best fit for a set of data?	Section 10.4	Activities 1, 3

CONCEPT REVIEW

1. **Ozone Levels**   The contour graph shows ozone levels (in thousandths of a centimeter) as a function of the month (beginning and ending in June) and the degrees of latitude from the equator.

   (Source: From H. W. Nurenberg, ed., *Pollutants and Their Eco-toxicological Significance*, New York: Wiley, 1985. Reproduced with permission.)

   a. On the graph, label relative maxima with an *H*, relative minima with an *L*, and saddle points with an *S*.

   b. Approximate the highest and lowest ozone concentrations. Tell when and where they occur.

2. **Bananas**   Banana chips, a deep-fried snack food, are popular in many countries. Research has shown that blanching the bananas before peeling increases the crispness of the chips. The accompanying table shows observed measures of crispness for selected blanching times and temperatures. (The larger the measure, the crisper the banana chip.)

Month

The measure of crispness can be modeled by

$$C(x, y) = -5.2x^2 + 299.7x - 0.1y^2 + 23.1y$$
$$-0.4xy - 4671$$

where x is the blanching time in minutes and y is the blanching temperature in degrees Celsius.

Measures of crispness of banana chips

Blanching temperature (°C)	Blanching time (minutes)		
	2	15	30
50	4.2	6.8	4.2
60	4.5	4.7	7.1
70	8.2	11.4	8.6
80	7.3	6.9	3.9

(Source: J. C. Jackson et al., "Optimization of Blanching for Crispness of Banana Chips Using Response Surface Methodology," *Journal of Food Science,* vol. 61, no. 1 (1996), pp. 165–166.)

a. Sketch contour curves on the table for crispness measures of 6, 8, and 10.

b. Using only the table values, estimate the point of maximum crispness.

c. Use the equation to find the time and temperature that produce the maximum crispness. What is the crispness measure at that point?

d. Verify that the point found in part *c* is a relative maximum. Is it an absolute maximum?

3. **Profit** A company sells Superbowl T-shirts and hats each year. The company has modeled data from previous years and has obtained a model for profit as a function of s, the number of Superbowl T-shirts sold, and h, the number of Superbowl hats sold. Both s and h are measured in thousands. The graph shows contour curves for values of profit (in dollars).

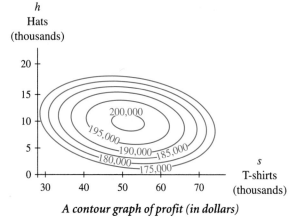

A contour graph of profit (in dollars)

a. If there are no restrictions on sales, estimate the maximum profit possible and the corresponding numbers of shirts and hats sold.

b. T-shirts cost the company $4 each, and hats cost $1.25 each. The budget for the cost of producing next year's Superbowl shirts and hats is $150 thousand. Write this constraint as a mathematical equation.

c. Graph the constraint function on the contour graph. Estimate the maximum profit subject to the constraint, and give the corresponding shirt and hat sales.

4. **Profit** The model for the profit function in Activity 3 is

$$P(s, h) = -52.2s^2 + 5935.5s - 59.1sh$$
$$+ 10,299.3h - 384.3h^2 \text{ dollars}$$

when s thousand T-shirts and h thousand hats are sold.

a. Set up the system of equations used to find the optimal profit if the constraint in part *b* of Activity 3 applies.

b. Solve the system of equations in part *a*. Find the profit corresponding to the solution.

c. Find and interpret the value of λ.

d. Approximate the change in the maximum profit if the cost budget in part *b* of Activity 3 is increased to $152 thousand.

5. **Weight** The data give the average body weight of an 8-week-old pig that is kept in an environment with a fixed temperature.

Temperature (°C)	10	15	20
Body weight (kg)	29.9	33.4	37.5

(Source: A. A. Hanson, ed., *Practical Handbook of Agricultural Science,* Boca Raton, FL: CRC Press, 1990.)

a. Use the method of least squares to find the multivariable function f with inputs a and b for the best-fitting line $y = ax + b$, where x is the temperature.

b. Find and interpret the minimum value of $f(a, b)$, and verify that it is a minimum value.

c. Give the linear model that best fits these data.

Project 10.1 Snow Cover

Setting

Often contour maps of a geographical region are not topographical maps showing land elevation. Contour maps could indicate other features, such as depth of the water table, richness of mineral deposits, population density, precipitation levels, or atmospheric conditions. You are probably most familiar with weather maps where contours called *isotherms* indicate temperature or contours called *isobars* indicate air pressure. The contour graph in the figure shows the probability of snow cover in January in the Northern Hemisphere.

Tasks

1. Carefully examine the contour graph in the figure. You may wish to make several copies of the graph for use in this project. An enlarged copy may also be helpful. Begin by marking on a copy of the graph all the relative high and low percentages indicated in the graph. Use Hs and Ls to distinguish between high and low percentages.

2. Find a map or atlas of the world that indicates special topographical features. Choose at least five of the relative extreme points in the figure, and determine the precise topographical characteristic of the planet at each location that results in the corresponding relative extreme point.

3. What would you expect the snow cover probability on Mt. Everest to be in January? Locate Mt. Everest on the contour map. Does the graph indicate the probability you expected? If not, why not?

Reporting

Prepare a poster to present the contour map in such a way as to highlight the relative extrema and the corresponding topography at each point. Give some information about each point (such as latitude, longitude, elevation, and topography). Include on the poster the location of and information about Mt. Everest. Make the poster attractive and readable from a distance of 3 feet.

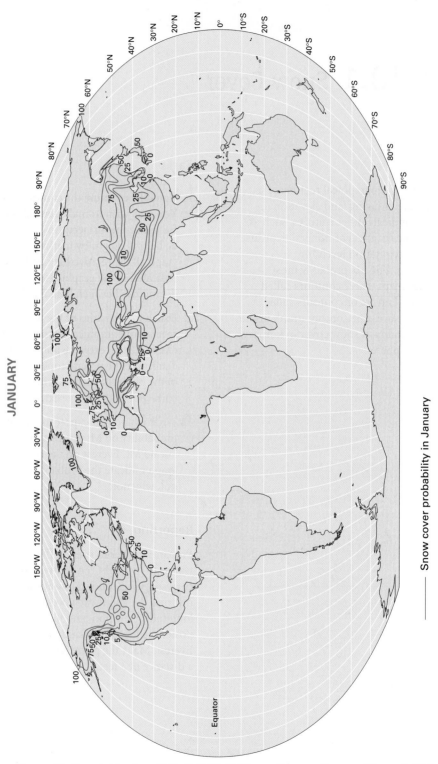

JANUARY

Snow cover probability in January

Equator

(Source: The figure is taken from W. Rudloff, *World Climates,* Stuttgart, Germany: Wissenschaftliche Verlagsgesellschaft, 1981, p. 100. Reproduced by permission of the publisher.)

Project 10.2 Carbonated Beverage Packaging

Setting

A new firm that wants to compete with Pepsi and Coca-Cola has enlisted your services to design the optimal can shape for its product. The can is to hold 12 fluid ounces of a carbonated beverage.

Tasks

1. Find equations giving the volume and the surface area of a cylindrical can in terms of its height and radius. Use these equations to determine the height and diameter of a can that will hold 12 fluid ounces but will require the least amount of aluminum to construct.

2. Carefully measure the diameter and height of a 12-ounce can made by Pepsi and of a 12-ounce can made by Coca-Cola. Compare these dimensions to the optimal dimensions you found in Task 1. Are there any beverage cans on the market that conform to the optimal dimensions?

3. Repeat Tasks 1 and 2, considering that it will cost twice as much to form the ends of the can as it does to form the cylindrical surface.

Reporting

1. Write a letter to the company directors explaining what dimensions you recommend that they use for their cans. Include your findings on the optimal dimensions as well as the dimensions of cans produced by competitors. Attach your mathematical work as an appendix to support your conclusions.

2. Prepare an oral presentation to be given in front of the company directors. You should prepare visual aids in order to enhance your presentation. Your goal is to persuade the directors to construct cans according to the dimensions you suggest. Keep in mind that the company directors are probably not as concerned with all of the mathematical details as they are with your analysis of your findings. However, be prepared to answer mathematical questions in case any of the directors asks you to elaborate.

Answers to Odd-Numbered Activities

CHAPTER 1

Section 1.1

1. **a.** Input: weight of a letter
    Input variable: w
    Input units: ounces
    Output: first-class domestic postage
    Output variable: $R(w)$
    Output units: cents
  b. R is a function of w
  c.

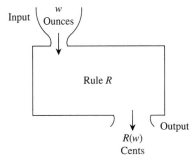

3. **a.** Input: day of the week
    Input variable: m
    Input units: none
    Output: amount spent on lunch
    Output variable: $A(m)$
    Output units: dollars
  b. A is not a function of m unless you always spend the same amount on lunch every Monday, Tuesday, and so on, or unless the input is the days in only 1 week.
  c.

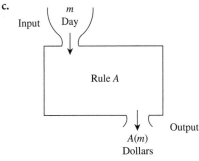

5. This is a function.
7. This is a function.
9. Graphs b and c represent functions.
11. **a.** $P(\text{Honolulu, HI}) = 295$
   b. $P(\text{Providence, RI}) = 137.8$
   c. $P(\text{Portland, OR}) = 170.1$
13. **a.** In 1988 cotton exports had a value of $1,975,000,000.
   b. In 1992 cotton exports had a value of $1,999,000,000.

15. **a.**

   b. $90
   c. 2 CDs
   d. 6 CDs

17.

Weight
(pounds)

19. **a.** Approximately $9000
   b. Approximately $340
   c. Approximately $105
   d. The graph for 12.5% would pass through $(0, 0)$ but would lie below the graph for 10%.
21. **a.** Approximately 2.6%
   b. 2001; Approximately 3.5%.
   c. 2004
   d. Benefits increased, but they increased by a lower percentage in 2002 than 2001.
23. $s = 5, t = 21$
    $s = 10, t = 36$
25. $w = 3, R = 54.8208$
    $w = 0, R = 9.4$
27. $t(s) = 18$ when $s = 4$
    $t(s) = 0$ when $s = -2$
29. $R(w) = 9.4$ when $w = 0$
    $R(w) = 30$ when $w \approx 1.974$
31. Input is given.
    $A(15) \approx 57,857.357$
33. Output is given.
    $f(x) = 3.65$ when $x \approx 5.000$

35. a. $1.1 million

b. $P(x) = R(x) - T(x)$ million dollars gives the profit from the production and sale of x units.

37. a. $16 million

b. $T(x) = R(x) - P(x)$ million dollars gives the total cost for the company during the xth quarter.

39. a. $0.13 per bottle

b. $A(x) = \dfrac{C(x)}{x}$ dollars per unit gives the average cost for producing x units.

41. a. $r(y) = 100 \cdot \dfrac{P(y)}{D(y)}$

b. percent

43. a. $Y(t) = S(t) + 1000 \cdot C(t) + 650{,}000$
$= -31{,}670t^2 + 206{,}525t + 1{,}263{,}708$ dollars
gives the VP's total yearly salary package t years after 1996, $0 \le t \le 2$.

b. $T(1) = \$1{,}438{,}563$

45. a. $A(y) = \dfrac{D(y)}{H(y)} = \dfrac{42.4y + 219.5}{1.7y + 140.3}$ thousand dollars gives the average credit card debt per cardholder y years after 1990, $8 \le y \le 15$.

b. $A(15) \approx 5.16$ thousand dollars per cardholder

47. $c(x) = n(x)p(x)$
$= (-0.034x^3 + 1.331x^2 + 9.913x + 164.447) \cdot$
$(-0.183x^2 + 2.891x + 20.215)$
cesarean-section deliveries
performed x years after 1980 on women who were 35 years of age or older.

49. The functions cannot be combined using function composition.

51. $(D \circ R)(x) = D(R(x))$ is the revenue in dollars from the sale of x soccer uniforms.

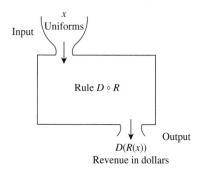

53. $h(p(t)) = h(1 + 3e^{-0.5t}) = \dfrac{4}{1 + 3e^{-0.5t}}$

55. $c(x(t)) = c(4 - 6t)$
$= 3(4 - 6t)^2 - 2(4 - 6t) + 5$
$= 108t^2 - 132t + 45$

57. To combine functions using addition or subtraction, the input units must be the same, and the output units must be the same or must be able to be converted to the same unit (i.e., dollars and thousand dollars). To combine functions using multiplication or division, the input units must be the same and the output units must be such that when combined, they have a practical interpretation. To combine functions using composition the output units of one function must match the input units of the other function.

Section 1.2

1. a. 3 dollars per year

b. $f(0) = \$5$

3. a. 2 thousand dollars per hundred units, or 20 dollars per unit

b. $r(0) = -\$4.5$ thousand

5. a. negative

b. decreasing

c. -4

7. a. negative

b. decreasing

c. 7

9. $C(x) = 0.30x + 150$ dollars is the total cost for x units.

11. $S(h) = 0.25h + 3$ inches of snow on the ground h hours from noon, $-12 \le h$.

13. a. decreasing; negative

b. $Slope = \dfrac{0 - 2.5}{5 - 0} = -0.5$ million dollars per year. Over the 5-year period, the corporation's profits decreased 0.5 million dollars each year.

c. -0.5 million dollars per year

d. Input is zero at $(0, 2.5)$: At the beginning of the period of interest, the corporation's profits were $2.5 million dollars.
Output is zero at $(5, 0)$: After 5 years, the corporation was not making a profit.

15. a. positive; increasing

b. 382.5 donors per year

c. slope $= 382.5$ donors per year

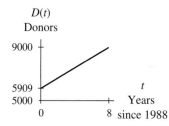

d. $D(0) = 5909$; In 1988 there were 5909 organ donors in the United States.

17. a. $356.6 million per year

b. $89.175 million per quarter

c.

Year	Revenue (millions of dollars)
2003	2128.1
2004	2484.8
2005	2841.5
2006	3198.2

d. $R(y) = 356.7y + 2128.1$ million dollars y years after 2003, $0 \le y \le 3$.

19. a. Rate of change $= \dfrac{\$112{,}000 - \$97{,}500}{2007 - 2000}$

$\approx \$2071$ per year

b. $\$112{,}000 + (3 \text{ years})\left(\dfrac{\$2071}{\text{year}}\right) \approx \$118{,}214$

c. The value was $100,000 in early 2002 and $150,000 in early 2026.

d. $V(t) = 2071.429t + 97{,}500$ dollars gives the value of the house t years after 2000, $0 \le t \le 7$. The model assumes that the rate of increase of the market value remains constant.

21. a. $107 billion per year

b. $2361 billion

c. *One possible answer:* No, the rate at which consumers are willing to borrow money will fluctuate with changes in the state of the national economy.

d. Approximately 2012

23. a. 78 million people per year

b. $P(t) = 0.078t + 6$ billion people gives the world's population t years after the beginning of 2000.

c. Approximately 2076; No

d. The prediction in part c assumes that the world population will grow at a constant rate of 78 million people per year between now and 2076. In making this prediction, the Census Bureau must have assumed that the growth rate will increase so that the 12 billion population will be reached sooner than our prediction based on the linear model.

25. a. Yes

b. The first differences are all equal to $0.23.

c. $P(w) = 0.14 + 0.23w$ dollars is the first-class domestic postage rate for weight not exceeding w ounces, $1 \le w \le 9$.

27. a. $S(x) = 499.3x - 976{,}088.3$ students enrolled in year x, $1965 \le x \le 1969$.

b. Approximately 7533 students

c. The estimate from the models is 505 less than the actual enrollment. Answers may vary. For a school the size of the one in this activity, an error of 500 students could be significant, especially in housing and faculty loads.

d. No; This model should not be used to predict enrollment in the year 2000, because the data are too far removed from 2000 to be of any value in such a prediction.

29. a. 1990: $e(0) = 5.11$ million gigagrams
1997: $e(7) = 5.859$ million gigagrams
2002: $e(12) = 6.394$ million gigagrams

b. 0.107 million gigagrams per year

c. $e(22) = 7.464$ million gigagrams

31. The equation makes it possible for us to use mathematics to answer numerical questions concerning the situation being modeled. The units of measure on the output and the description (including units of measure) on the input make it possible for us to interpret the numerical answers in the context of the situation. The interval of inputs helps us to know when we are extrapolating.

Section 1.3

1. $f(x) = 2(1.3^x)$ is the black graph.
$f(x) = 2(0.7^x)$ is the teal graph.

3. $f(x) = 3(1.2^x)$ is the teal graph.
$f(x) = 2(1.4^x)$ is the black graph.

5. $f(x) = 2 \ln x$ is the teal graph.
$f(x) = -2 \ln x$ is the black graph.

7. $f(x) = 2 \ln x$ is the teal graph.
$f(x) = 4 \ln x$ is the black graph.

9. $f(x)$ is increasing, with a 5% change in output for every unit of input.

11. $y(x)$ is decreasing, with a 13% change in output for every unit of input.

13. The number of bacteria declines by 39% each hour.

15. a. $I(t) = 4.81(1.0547^t)$ quadrillion Btu is the projected amount of petroleum imports t years after 2005, $0 \le t \le 15$.

b. 2019

c. The projected petroleum product imports increase without bound as time increases.

17. a. $W(t) = 3.3(0.9854^t)$ workers per Social Security beneficiary t years after 1996 between 1996 and 2030.

b. $W(34) \approx 2$ workers per beneficiary. Fewer workers per beneficiary will mean that the program will have to find other means of supplementing payments rather than relying solely on withholdings from workers' wages.

19. a. The sales declined approximately 59.6% each month.

  b. $S(t) = 520{,}000(0.404^t)$ videotapes sold per month t months after publicity was discontinued.

  c. 3 months: $S(3) \approx 34{,}288$ videotapes per month
    12 months: $S(12) \approx 10$ videotapes per month

21. a. $T(y) = 0.002(1.397^y)$ million transistors in Intel processor chips y years after 1970, $1 \le y \le 35$.

  b. 39.746% each year

  c. Yes, the data seem to support Moore's Law. If anything the number of transistors has been doubling faster than every 2 years.

23. a. $L(x) = 0.845x + 0.790$ gallons per person per year gives the per capita consumption of bottled water in the United States x years after 1980, $0 \le x \le 23$.
    $E(x) = 2.714(1.099^x)$ gallons per person per year gives the per capita consumption of bottled water in the United States x years after 1980, $0 \le x \le 23$.

Consumption

The exponential model appears to better describe the per capita bottled water consumption on the given interval.

  b. Rate of change: 0.845 gallon per person per year per year
    Percentage change: 9.927% each year

  c. $L(25) \approx 21.9$ gallons per person per year
    $E(25) \approx 28.7$ gallons per person per year

  d. $L(x) = 25$ when $x \approx 28.651$ and $E(x) = 25$ when $x \approx 23.521$.
    According to the linear model, water consumption will exceed 25 gallons per person in 2009. According to the exponential model, water consumption exceeded 25 gallons per person in 2004.

25. a. $t = \dfrac{30 \cdot (\ln 0.5)}{\ln 0.8} \approx 93.2$ hours

  b. The amount of radon gas present after t hours is given by $R(t) = R_0 e^{(\ln 0.8)t/30}$ units.

c. $\lim\limits_{t \to -\infty} (R_0 e^{(\ln 0.8t)/30}) = 0$. Eventually, there won't be any radon present in the building.

27. $t = 35$ hours

29. a. $D(t) = 406.401(0.906^t)$ is the number of days that milk will keep when stored at a temperature of t degrees Fahrenheit, $30 \le t \le 70$.

  b. $D(40) - D(37) \approx -2.7$; The milk will spoil approximately 2.7 days sooner.

  c. $t(D) = 60.547 - 9.913 \ln D$ degrees Fahrenheit is the temperature at which milk should be stored in order for the milk to keep for D days, $0.5 \le D \le 24$.

  d. $t(7) \approx 41.257$; The refrigerator should be set at 41.3 degrees Fahrenheit.

31. a. $R(y) = 8.435 - 0.639 \ln y$ percent gives the New Zealand bond rate for a maturity time of t years, $0.25 \le y \le 10$.

  b. The model estimates 15-year bond rates as $R(15) \approx 6.70$, which is 0.3 percentage point less than the fund manager's estimate.

  c. $T(p) = 461{,}733.212(0.213^p)$ years is the time to maturity for a New Zealand bond with a $p\%$ rate, $7.10 \le p \le 9.40$.

  d. $R(T(9.4)) \approx 9.4; R(T(7.5)) \approx 7.5; R(T(7.1)) \approx 7.1$
    $T(R(2)) \approx 2; T(R(4)) \approx 4; T(R(10)) \approx 10$
    These calculations suggest that R and T are approximate inverse functions because $R(T(p)) \approx p$ and $T(R(y)) \approx y$.

33. a. $C(d) = 1.182 + 2.216 \ln d$ µg/mL is the concentration of a drug in the blood stream after d days, $1 \le d \le 17$.

  b. $\lim\limits_{t \to 0} C(d) = \infty$ $\lim\limits_{t \to 0^+} C(d) = -\infty$

  c. One possible answer: The context tells us that the amount of concentration will continue to increase. The logarithmic model also indicates an increase so fits the end behavior suggested by the context.

  d. $C(2) \approx 2.7$ µg/mL

35. a. $p(x) = -9.792 \cdot 10^{-5} - 0.434 \ln x$ is the pH of a solution, where x is the H_3O^+ concentration in moles per liter, $5.012 \cdot 10^{-9} \le x \le 3.981 \cdot 10^{-7}$.

  b. $p(1.585 \cdot 10^{-3}) \approx 2.8$

  c. Approximately $1.0 \cdot 10^{-5}$ mole per liter

  d. Beer is acidic, with a pH of approximately 4.5.

37. For an exponential model the length of the input interval over which the output values either double or halve will be the same no matter where the interval starts. For a linear model the length of the input interval over which the output values double or halve is directly affected by the starting endpoint of the interval.

39. An exponential model in standard form ($f(x) = ab^x$) increases (or decreases) without bound in one direction and approaches zero in the other direction. By contrast, a logarithmic model either increases without bound as x approaches ∞ and decreases without bound as x approaches 0 from the right, or decreases without bound as x approaches ∞ and increases without bound as x approaches 0 from the right.

Section 1.4

1. Exponential

3. Logarithmic

5. None of these; the scatter plot indicates an inflection point but does not indicate a limiting value.

7. Increasing; upper limiting value is 100

9. Decreasing; upper limiting value is 39.2

11. a. $C(t) = \dfrac{37.195}{1 + 21.374e^{-0.183t}}$ countries in Europe, North America and South America t years after 1840, $0 \le t \le 40$. The model is a good fit.

b.

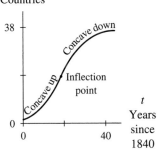

$C(t)$

Countries

13. a., b. $N(t) = \dfrac{3015.991}{1 + 119.250e^{-1.024t}}$ navy deaths t weeks after August 31, 1918, $0 \le t \le 13$.

$N(t)$

Navy deaths

$A(t) = \dfrac{20{,}492.567}{1 + 1744.15e^{-1.212t}}$ army deaths t weeks after August 31, 1918, $1 \le t \le 13$.

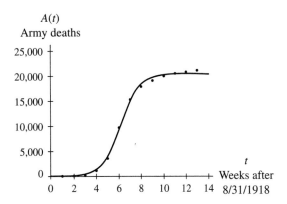

$A(t)$

Army deaths

$C(t) = \dfrac{91{,}317.712}{1 + 1181.203e^{-0.951t}}$ civilian deaths t weeks after August 31, 1918, $2 \le t \le 13$.

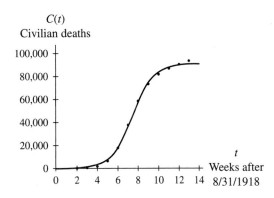

$C(t)$

Civilian deaths

c. No; The models given in part b have limiting values less than the number of deaths in the table for November 30. The models are not good indicators of the eventual number of deaths.

15. a. The limiting value appears to be approximately 2 U/100μL. The inflection point occurs at approximately 9 minutes. (Answers may vary.)

b. $A(m) = \dfrac{1.937}{1 + 29.064e^{-0.421m}}$ U/100μL gives the reaction activity after m minutes, $0 \le m \le 18$. The limiting value is approximately 1.94 U/100μL.

c. Approximately 0.74 U/100μL

17. a. $P(x) = \dfrac{11.742}{1 + 154.546e^{-0.026x}}$ billion people gives the world's population x years after 1800, $4 \le x \le 271$.

The equation appears to be a good fit for the later (1960–2071) data but a poor fit for the early (1800–1960) data.

b. According to the model, the world population will level off at 11.7 billion. This is probably not an accurate prediction of future world population.

c. 1850: $P(50) \approx 0.266$ billion people

1990: $P(190) \approx 5.320$ billion people

The model does a poor job of estimating the 1850 population and a good job of estimating the 1990 population.

19. a. $g(t)$ is concave up.

b. $\lim\limits_{t \to -\infty} g(t) = 0$; $\lim\limits_{t \to \infty} g(t) = \infty$

c. As t decreases without bound, g approaches zero. As t increases without bound, g also increases without bound.

21. a. $y(x)$ is concave down.

b. $\lim\limits_{x \to 0^+} y(x) = -\infty$; $\lim\limits_{x \to \infty} y(x) = \infty$

c. As x approaches zero from the right-hand side, y decreases without bound. As x increases without bound, y also increases without bound.

23. a. $l(t)$ is concave up until $t \approx 0$ is concave down.

b. $\lim\limits_{t \to -\infty} l(t) = 0$; $\lim\limits_{t \to \infty} l(t) = 52$

c. As t decreases without bound, l approaches zero. As t increases without bound, l approaches the limiting value of 52.

25. a. $n(k)$ is concave up

b. $\lim\limits_{k \to \pm\infty} n(k) = \infty$

c. As k increases or decreases without bound, $n(k)$ increases without bound.

27. a. $C(q)$ is concave up from $-\infty$ to approximately $q \approx 0.8$ and then is concave down.

b. $\lim\limits_{q \to -\infty} C(q) = \infty$; $\lim\limits_{q \to \infty} C(q) = -\infty$

c. As q decreases without bound, $C(q)$ increases without bound. As q increases without bound, $C(q)$ decreases without bound.

29. A logistic equation of the form $f(x) = \dfrac{L}{1 + Ae^{-Bx}}$ is unlike either the exponential or logarithmic equations in that it is bounded above and below so that when $B > 0$, $\lim\limits_{x \to -\infty} f(x) = 0$ and $\lim\limits_{x \to \infty} f(x) = L$, or when $B < 0$, $\lim\limits_{x \to -\infty} f(x) = L$ and $\lim\limits_{x \to \infty} f(x) = 0$. An exponential equation is bounded only in one direction and is unbounded in the other. A logarithmic equation must have positive input and increases or decreases unbounded as its input increases without bound.

Section 1.5

1. Concave up, decreasing from $x = 0.75$ to $x = 3$, increasing from $x = 3$ to $x = 4$

3. Concave up, decreasing from $x = 13.5$ to $x = 18$, increasing from $x = 18$ to $x = 22.5$

5. Concave down, always decreasing

7.

9.

11.

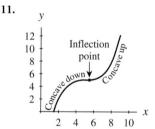

13. a. Second differences are -8, so the data are quadratic.

b. After 3.5 seconds the height is 44 feet. After 4 seconds the height is 0 feet.

c. $H(s) = -16s^2 + 32s + 128$ feet is the height of the missile after s seconds, $0 \leq s \leq 4$.

d. $H(s) = 0$ when $s = 4$

The missile hits the water after 4 seconds.

15. a. Because the data are evenly spaced and the second differences are constant, the data are perfectly quadratic.
   b. 26.5 years of age
   c. $A(x) = 0.0035x^2 - 0.405x + 32$ years is the median age at first marriage of females in the United States x years after 1900, $60 \le x \le 90$.
   d. $A(100) = 26.5$ years of age; yes

17. a. $D(x) = 0.025x^2 - 2.021x + 43.78$ deaths per thousand people gives the 1998 death rate for the United States for people aged x years, $40 \le x \le 65$.
   b.

Age	Model prediction	Actual rate
51	$D(51) \approx 4.6$	4.7
52	$D(52) \approx 5.2$	5.1
53	$D(53) \approx 5.7$	5.6
57	$D(57) \approx 8.4$	8.1
59	$D(59) \approx 10.1$	9.7
63	$D(63) \approx 14.0$	14.1
70	$D(70) \approx 22.7$	25.5
75	$D(75) \approx 30.5$	38.0
80	$D(80) \approx 39.4$	59.2

   c. The model is more accurate when used for interpolation than when used for extrapolation.

19. a. The scatter plot indicates an inflection point and does not indicate a limiting value.
   b. $A(t) = 0.427t^3 - 5.286t^2 + 22.827t + 3.014$ million dollars spent t years after 1990, $0 \le t \le 8$.
   c. 1993: $A(3) \approx \$35$ million
   1999: $A(9) \approx \$92$ million
   The 1993 estimate is more likely to be accurate because it is an interpolation rather than an extrapolation.
   d. The 1993 estimate exceeded the actual amount by $1 million. The 1999 estimate is $7 million short of the actual amount. These figures confirm the statement in part c.

21. a. The scatter plot suggests an inflection point, a relative maximum, and a relative minimum.
   b. $G(x) = 15.051 \cdot 10^{-5}x^3 - 0.007x^2 + 0.085x + 105.027$ males per 100 females is the gender ratio in the United States x years after 1900, $0 \le x \le 100$. The graph of G rises beyond 2000. One possible answer: No; The gender ratio will not continue to increase indefinitely.

23. a. The numbers of females and males are approximately equal for 40-year-olds.

b. Using "under age" as 0 and "100 and over" as 100 for modeling, but not prediction purposes, the model is
$C(a) = -19.590 \cdot 10^{-5}a^3 + 18.421 \cdot 10^{-4}a^2 + 0.037a + 104.601$ males per 100 females gives the gender ratio in the United States for individuals who are a years old, $0 \le a \le 100$.
$$L(a) = \frac{104.3}{1 + 9.817 \cdot 10^{-4}e^{0.082a}}$$ males per 100 females
gives the gender ratio in the United States for individuals who are a years old, $0 \le a \le 100$.
The logistic equation fits the data better than the cubic equation, especially for ages above 60.
   c. Among 86-year-olds there are approximately twice as many women as men. This implies that men die younger than women.

25. A graph of $y = ax^2 + bx + c$ will be concave up when a is positive. It will be decreasing to a minimum, after which it will be increasing. When a is negative, a graph of $y = ax^2 + bx + c$ will be concave down—increasing to a maximum and then decreasing.
   A graph of $y = ax^3 + bx^2 + cx + d$ could take on one of four forms. If a is positive, a graph could be concave down, increasing to an inflection point and then concave up, increasing; or it could be concave down and increasing to a maximum and then decreasing to an inflection point after which it would be concave up and decreasing to a minimum and then increasing. On the other hand, if a is negative, a graph could be concave up, decreasing to an inflection point and then concave down, decreasing; or it could be concave up and decreasing to a minimum and then increasing to an inflection point after which it would be concave down and increasing to a maximum and then decreasing.

Chapter 1 Concept Review

1. a. The scatter plot is concave up. It is decreasing over $(0, 2)$ and increasing over $(2, 6)$.
   b. The scatter plot appears to be increasing without bound as x approaches $\pm\infty$.
   c. Quadratic
   d. $\lim\limits_{x \to \pm\infty} f(x) = \infty$

2. a. The scatter plot is increasing, concave up.
   b. End behavior to the left is not apparent from the scatter plot. As x increases, the scatter plot appears to be increasing without bound.
   c. Either quadratic or exponential (shifted up 8)
   d. Quadratic: $\lim\limits_{x \to \pm\infty} f(x) = \infty$
   Exponential: $\lim\limits_{x \to -\infty} f(x) = 8$, and $\lim\limits_{x \to \infty} f(x) = \infty$

3. a. The scatter plot is decreasing and does not indicate any curvature.
  b. The scatter plot appears to be increasing without bound as x approaches $-\infty$ and decreasing without bound as x approaches ∞.
  c. Linear
  d. $\lim\limits_{x \to -\infty} f(x) = \infty$ and $\lim\limits_{x \to \infty} f(x) = -\infty$

4. a. The scatter plot is increasing from $x = 0$ to $x = 2$ and from $x = 4$ to $x = 6$. It in concave down over $x = 0$ to $x = 3$ and concave up from $x = 3$ to $x = 6$. It appears to have an inflection point near $x = 3$.
  b. The scatter plot appears to be decreasing without bound as x approaches $-\infty$ and increasing without bound as x approaches ∞.
  c. Cubic
  d. $\lim\limits_{x \to -\infty} f(x) = -\infty$, and $\lim\limits_{x \to \infty} f(x) = \infty$

5. a. The scatter plot is increasing and concave up from $x = 0$ to $x = 3$ and concave down from $x = 3$ to $x = 6$.
  b. The scatter plot appears to be increasing toward 40 as x approaches ∞ and decreasing toward zero as x approaches $-\infty$.
  c. Logistic
  d. $\lim\limits_{x \to -\infty} f(x) = 0$, and $\lim\limits_{x \to \infty} f(x) = 40$

6. a. The scatter plot is increasing, concave down.
  b. The scatter plot appears to be decreasing without bound as x approaches 0 from the right and increasing without bound but more and more slowly as x approaches ∞.
  c. Logarithmic
  d. $\lim\limits_{t \to 0^-} f(x) = -\infty$, and $\lim\limits_{x \to \infty} f(x) = \infty$

7. a.

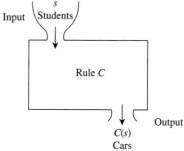

  b. Composition
  c. $T(x) = (C \circ S)(x) = C(S(x))$
  d. Input: hours; Output: cars

8. a.

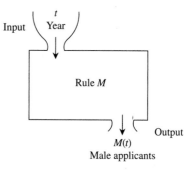

  b. Subtraction
  c. $F(t) = S(t) - M(t)$
  d. Input: none; Output: applicants

9. a.

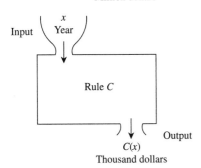

b. The profit function can be constructed from the revenue and cost functions.

c. $P(x) = 1,000,000R(x) - 1000C(x)$ (Answers may vary.)

d. $P(x) = 1,000,000R(x) - 1000C(x)$ dollars is the company's profit after it has been in business x years.

10. a. Multiplication

b. $P(p) = \dfrac{40p}{1 + 0.03e^{0.4p}}$

c. $P(p) = \dfrac{40p}{1 + 0.03e^{0.4p}}$ million dollars when p dollars is the price of a pound of beef.

11. a. $C(x) = 2.2(1.021^x)$ million children living with their grandparents x years after 1970, $0 \le x \le 27$.

b. Approximately 2.1% each year

c. $C(x) = 5$ when $x \approx 38.717$. According to the model, the number of children living with their grandparents will reach 5 million in 2009.

d. $C(x) = 4.4$ when $x \approx 32.689$ years; The number of children living with their grandparents in 1970 will have doubled by 2003.

12. a. decreasing; The number 0.88 is less than 1 so indicates a decreasing exponential function.

b. $7: D(7) \approx 2.55$ trillion pounds
$14: D(14) \approx 1.04$ trillion pounds
$21: D(21) \approx 0.43$ trillion pounds

c. Logarithmic

d. $P(d) = 14.336 - 7.823\ln d$ dollars per pound when d trillion pounds of fish is demanded.

13. a. The scatter plot indicates a single concavity, which indicates that a quadratic or exponential model could be used. In this instance, an exponential model will not fit the original data set well because the output data are not approaching zero.
$J(m) = 0.546m^2 - 141.763m + 21,382.5$ dollars is the 2002 private-party resale value of a 2000 Jeep Grand Cherokee Laredo with m thousand miles on it, $20 \le m \le 120$.

b. $J(52) \approx \$15,487$

c. $M(x) = 4x + 68$ thousand miles on the 2002 Jeep by the end of the xth month of 2002, $0 \le x \le 12$.
Slope: 4 thousand miles per month
Rate of change: 4 thousand miles per month

d. $J(M(x)) = 0.546(4x + 68)^2 - 141.763(4x + 68) + 21,382.5$ dollars is the 2002 private-party resale value of a 2000 Jeep Grand Cherokee Laredo at the end of the xth month of 2002, $0 \le x \le 12$.

14. a. The scatter plot is concave up to the left of $m = 8$ and concave down to the right of $m = 8$. There is an inflection point near $(8, 21,200)$.
Logistic

b. As m decreases the data approach 0. As m increases the data approach a limiting value.

c. Logistic

d. $P(m) = \dfrac{42,183.911}{1 + 21,484.252e^{-1.249m}}$ polio cases by the mth month of 1949.

CHAPTER 2

Section 2.1

1. For five days, the stock price increased an average of 46 cents per day.

3. For the past three months, the company has lost an average of $8333 each month.

5. *Change*: Between 2004 and 2005, the number of passengers flown by Northwest Airlines increased by 1.1 million. *Percentage change*: Between 2004 and 2005, the number of passengers flown by Northwest Airlines increased by approximately 2%. *Average rate of change*: Between 2004 and 2005, the number of passengers flown by Northwest Airlines increased by 1.1 million passengers per year.

7. *Change*: Between 1930 and 2000, the American Indian, Eskimo, and Aleut population in the United States increased by 2,072,000. *Percentage change*: Between 1930 and 2000, the American Indian, Eskimo, and Aleut

population in the United States increased by 572.4%.
Average rate of change: Between 1930 and 2000, the American Indian, Eskimo, and Aleut population in the United States increased, on average, by 29.6 thousand people per year.

9. a. Percent change: 57.039%

   Average rate of change: 3.8 million shares per day

b.

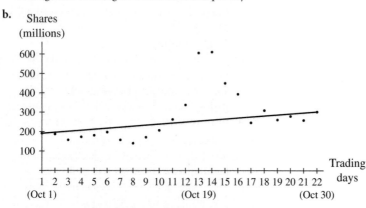

The volume of shares traded on a given day in October 1987 stayed near (or below) 200 million shares until mid-October when it spiked near 600 million shares. It then declined to near 300 million shares for the remainder of the month. Average rate of change ignores the spike during "October Madness."

11. a. Approximately $\dfrac{4.25 - 3.25}{2001 - 1996} = \$0.2$ billion per year:

   Between 1996 and 2001 sales at Kelly Services, Inc. increased by an average of $0.2 billion each year.

b. Approximately $\dfrac{4.25 - 3.25}{3.25} \cdot 100\% = 30.7\%$:

   Between 1996 and 2001, sales at Kelly Services, Inc. increased by 30.7%.

13. a. $P(x) = -0.037x^2 + 25.529x - 527.143$ thousand dollars monthly profit for an airline from a roundtrip flight from Denver to Chicago, where x dollars is the average cost of a roundtrip ticket and average ticket prices range from $200 to $450.

b. Approximately $4.943 thousand per dollar (thousand dollars profit per dollar of ticket price)

c. Approximately $-\$4.414$ thousand per dollar (thousand dollars profit per dollar of ticket price)

15. a. Approximately -0.81 year per year (year of life expectancy per year of age)

b. 10 to 20: approximately -0.96 year per year (year of life expectancy per year of age)

   20 to 30: approximately -0.89 year per year (year of life expectancy per year of age)

   Life expectancy decreases with increasing age, but the magnitude of the rate of decrease gets smaller as a black male gets older.

17. a. Change ≈ 9.965 million people

   Percentage change $\approx 47\%$

b. Average rate of change ≈ 1.69 million people per year

19. Approximately 488.5%

21. a. i. 3;   **ii.** 3;   **iii.** 3

b. i. Approximately 85.7%

   ii. Approximately 69.2%

   iii. Approximately 54.5%

c. The average rate of change of any linear function over any interval will be constant because the slope of a linear function is constant. The percentage change for a linear function is not constant.

23. a. Change: $419.25

   Percentage change: $\approx 28.15\%$

b. $104.81 per year; The balance in the account increased, on average, by $104.81 per year from the end of the first year until the end of the fifth year.

c. No; There are no data available for the balance in the account at the middle of the fourth year. There is no way to find the average rate of change in the balance from the middle to the end of the fourth year.

d. The balance in the account can be modeled as $B(x) = 1400(1.064^x)$ dollars, where x is the number of years since the initial investment, $1 \le x \le 5$. Average rate of change: $109.52 per year.

25. a. 18%

b. Approximately 19.562%

27. a. 11.03 years

b. 8.66 years

c. 10.21 years

29. a. $A(n) = 1\left(1 + \dfrac{1.00}{n}\right)^n$ dollars, when $1 is invested at 100% interest compounded n times each year

b., c.

Compounding	n	Amount
Yearly	1	2
Semiannually	2	2.25
Quarterly	4	≈2.44
Monthly	12	≈2.61
Weekly	52	≈2.69
Daily	365	≈2.71
Every hour	24·365 = 8760	≈2.72
Every minute	60·8760 = 525,600	≈2.72
Every second	60·525,600 = 31,536,000	≈2.72

d. $2.72

e. $\lim\limits_{n\to\infty}\left(1 + \dfrac{1}{n}\right)^n \approx 2.72$

31. Change is simply a report of the difference in two output values. Percentage change is a report of the difference in two output values so that the relative magnitude of the change may be considered. Average rate of change is a report of the difference in two output values in a way that considers the associated spread of the input values.

Section 2.2

1. a. A continuous function is defined for all possible input values on an interval. A discrete function is defined for specific input values. A continuous graph can be drawn without lifting the pencil from the paper. A discrete graph is a scatter plot. A continuous model or graph can be used to find either average or instantaneous rates of change. Discrete data or a scatter plot can be used to find only average rates of change.

b. An average rate of change is the change in the output values for two points evenly spread over the change in the input values at the two points. An instantaneous rate of change is the slope at a single point on a graph.

c. A secant line connects two points on a graph. A tangent line is drawn at a single point on a graph.

3. Average rates of change are slopes of secant lines. Instantaneous rates of change are slopes of tangent lines.

5. $\dfrac{19 - 0 \text{ miles}}{17 \text{ minutes}} \cdot \dfrac{60 \text{ minutes}}{\text{hour}} \approx 67.1$ mph

7. a. The slope is positive at A, negative at B and E, and zero at C and D.

b. The graph is steeper at point B than at point A.

9.

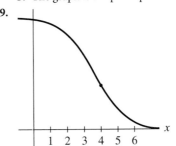

11. The graph shows a decreasing linear function. The slope is a constant, negative number.

13. The graph shows an increasing, logistic function. The slope is positive. The magnitude of the slope increases, then decreases, but is always positive.

15. The lines drawn at points A and C are not tangent lines.

17.

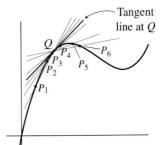

19. a. The graph is concave down at point A; the graph is concave up at points C and D; and because the graph has an inflection point at point B, the graph is neither concave up nor concave down at point B.

b. The tangent line at point A should lie above the curve; the tangent line at point B should lie below the curve to the left of point B and above the curve to the right of point B; the tangent lines at points C and D should lie below the curve.

c.

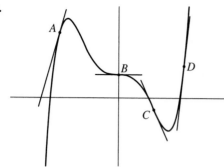

d. The slope of the tangent line is positive at points A and D; the slope of the tangent line is negative at point C.

21. Slope at point $B \approx \dfrac{4 - 2.25}{70 - 40} \approx 0.058$ (Answers may vary.)

23. Slope at point $C \approx \dfrac{50 - 0}{25 - 10} \approx 3.3$

Slope at point $D \approx \dfrac{580 - 550}{100 - 80} = 1.5$ (Answers may vary.)

25. a. Million subscribers per year
  b. In 2000, the number of subscribers was increasing by 23.1 million subscribers per year.
  c. The slope of the tangent line at point A is 23.1 million subscribers per year.
  d. The instantaneous rate of change at point A is 23.1 million subscribers per year.

27. a. The slope at point A is 1.3; the slope at point B is 5.9; the slope at point C is −4.2.
  b. mm per day per degree Celsius
  c. At a temperature of 23 °C, the growth rate is increasing by 5.9 mm per day per degree Celsius.
  d. −4.2 mm per day per degree Celsius
  e. 1.3 mm per day per degree Celsius

29. a. The slope at the solstices is zero.
  b. The steepest points on the graph occur at the equinoxes. The estimated slope for the spring equinox is 0.4 degree per day; the estimated slope at the fall equinox is −0.4 degree per day. A negative slope indicates that the sun is moving away from the north, or toward the south.

31. a.

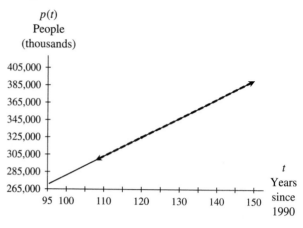

b. Because the function is linear, any line tangent to $p(t)$ coincides with the graph itself.

c., d., e. 2.37 million people per year

33.

a. $\dfrac{2050 - 1825}{4 - 3} = 225$: In 1994, the number of employees was increasing by approximately 225 employees per year.

b. The slope of the graph cannot be found at $x = 5$ because a tangent cannot be drawn at a sharp point on a graph.

c. $\dfrac{3250 - 2875}{9 - 8} = 375$: In 1998, the number of employees was increasing by approximately 375 employees per year.

35. The line tangent to a graph at a point P is the limiting position of secant lines through P and nearby points on the graph.

Section 2.3

1. a. Miles per hour
  b. Speed or velocity

3. a. The number of words per minute cannot be negative.
  b. Words per minute per week
  c. Yes; If the student's typing speed were decreasing, then $W'(t)$ would be negative.

5. a. When the price of a ticket from Washington to Boston is $65, the airline's weekly profit is $15,000.

b. When the price of a ticket from Washington to Boston is $65, the airline's weekly profit is increasing by $1500 per dollar of ticket price. Raising the ticket price by $1 (to $66) will increase profit by approximately $1500.

c. When the price of a ticket from Washington to Boston is $90, the profit is decreasing by $2000 per dollar of ticket price. Raising the ticket price by $1 (to $91) will result in a decrease in profit of approximately $2000.

7.

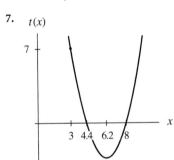

9. a. At the start of the diet, you weighed 167 pounds.

b. After 12 weeks of dieting, your weight was 142 pounds.

c. After 1 week of dieting, your weight was decreasing by 2 pounds per week.

d. After 9 weeks of dieting, your weight was decreasing by 1 pound per week.

e. After 12 weeks of dieting, your weight was neither increasing nor decreasing.

f. After 15 weeks of dieting, your weight was increasing by one fourth of a pound per week.

g.

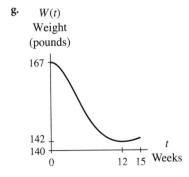

11. We know that the graph has the following points: (1940, 4), (1970, 12), (2000, 33), and (1980, 18); we know that the graph has no horizontal tangents; and we know that

the graph is concave up on (1940, 1990) and concave down on (1990, 2000).

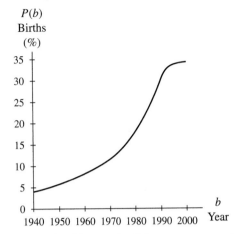

13. a. Yes, $P(x)$ will be negative if the costs are more than the revenue.

b. Yes, $P'(x)$ will be negative if the profit declines as more shirts are sold. This might happen if the price of a shirt is lowered in order to sell more shirts.

c. All that is certain if $P'(200) = -1.5$ is that the fraternity's profit is declining as the number of shirts that are sold exceeds 200. Profit may still be positive (which means that the fraternity is making money), but the negative rate of change indicates that it is not making the most profit possible.

15. a. Years per percentage point

b. As the rate of return increases, the doubling time for the investment decreases.

c. **i.** When the interest rate is 9%, it takes approximately 7.7 years for the investment to double.

ii. When the interest rate is 5%, the doubling time is decreasing by approximately 2.8 years per percentage point.

iii. When the interest rate is 12%, the doubling time is decreasing by approximately one half year per percentage point.

17.

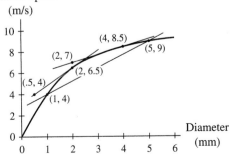

a. Slope $\approx \dfrac{9-4}{5-1} = 1.25$ m/s per mm of diameter. The slope of the secant line gives the average rate of change of the terminal speed of a raindrop between two diameters.

b. The slope of the tangent line drawn at a diameter of 4 mm gives the instantaneous rate of change of the terminal speed of a 4-mm raindrop.

c. Slope $\approx \dfrac{8.5-7}{4-2} = 0.75$ m/s per mm: The terminal speed of a 4-mm raindrop is increasing by approximately 0.75 m/s per mm of diameter.

d. Slope (at 2 mm) $\approx \dfrac{6.5-4}{2-0.5} = 1.7$ m/s per mm: The terminal speed of a raindrop 2.5 mm in diameter would be approximately 7.35 m/s.

e. Approximately 26.2% per mm: The terminal speed of a 2-mm raindrop is increasing by approximately 28% per mm (of increased diameter).

19.

$G(t)$

a. 4 hours ≈ 5.5 points per hour

11 hours ≈ 2.7 points per hour

b. Approximately $\dfrac{(86-50) \text{ points}}{(10-4) \text{ hours}} = 6$ points per hour: As the number of hours that you study increases from 4 to 10 hours, your expected grade on the calculus test increases by an average of 6 points per hour.

c. $\dfrac{6 \text{ points/hour}}{50 \text{ points}} \cdot 100\% = 12\%$ per hour: After studying for 4 hours, your expected grade is increasing by 12% per hour.

d. $G(4.6) \approx G(4) + 0.6 \cdot G'(4) = 50 + 0.6 \cdot 5.5 = 53.3$ points

21. a. Slope $\approx \dfrac{7-4}{3-2} = 3$

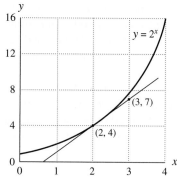

b. The slope is approximately 4.

Close point	Slope of the secant line between point and $x = 2$
1.9	3.732132
1.99	3.972370
1.999	3.997228
1.9999	3.999723
2.1	4.287094
2.01	4.027822
2.001	4.002774
2.0001	4.000277

23. a. Approximately 3 million passengers per year

b. In 2004, the number of passengers going through the Atlanta International Airport each year was increasing by 3.34 million passengers per year.

Close point	Slope of the secant line between point and $t = 4$
3.9	3.3931
3.99	3.3456
3.999	3.3406
3.9999	3.3401
4.1	3.2811
4.01	3.3344
4.001	3.3394
4.0001	3.3400

c. Approximately 4% per year: In 2004, the number of passengers going through the Atlanta International Airport each year was increasing by 4% per year.

d. Using numbers based on an equation is more accurate, but there are many situations when the equation of a graph is not provided. (Answers will vary.)

25. a. Approximately -3.757 seconds per year

Close point	Slope of the secant line between point and $x = 13$
12.9	-3.7751
12.99	-3.7588
12.999	-3.7572
12.9999	-3.7570
13.1	-3.7389
13.01	-3.7552
13.001	-3.7568
13.0001	-3.7570

b. Approximately -5.529 percent per year

c. The 13-year-old swimmer is improving his time because the rate of change is negative.

27. a. $A(x) = \frac{1.02^x}{1.5786}$ is the profit in American dollars from the sale of x mountain bikes.

b. Canadian: $C(400) \approx \$2754.66$
American: $A(400) \approx \$1745.00$

c. $A'(400) \approx \$34.56$ per mountain bike sold

29. The *percentage change* gives the relative amount of change in the output from an initial input value to a second input value. The *percentage rate of change* is a relative measure of the rate of change at a particular input value in comparison to the output value at that point.

31. Finding the rate of change *numerically* using numbers found with an equation is both more accurate and more time-consuming than drawing a *tangent line* to a graph and estimating the slope of that tangent line. However, there are many situations when the equation of a graph is not provided and the rate of change must be estimated graphically.

Section 2.4

1.

$x \to 2^-$	$\dfrac{x^3}{x-2}$	$x \to 2^+$	$\dfrac{x^3}{x-2}$
1.9	-68.59	2.1	92.61
1.99	-788.0599	2.01	812.0601
1.999	-7988.00599	2.001	8012.006001
1.9999	-79988.0006	2.0001	80012.0006

$$\lim_{x \to 2^-} \frac{x^3}{x-2} \to -\infty; \ \lim_{x \to 2^+} \frac{x^3}{x-2} \to \infty;$$

$$\lim_{x \to 2} \frac{x^3}{x-2} \text{ does not exist}$$

3.

$x \to 0^-$	$\dfrac{-2x^3 + 7x}{x}$	$x \to 0^+$	$\dfrac{-2x^3 + 7x}{x}$
-0.1	6.98	0.1	6.98
-0.01	6.9998	0.01	6.9998
-0.001	6.999998	0.001	6.999998
-0.0001	6.99999998	0.0001	6.99999998

$$\lim_{x \to 0^-} \frac{-2x^3 + 7x}{x} = 7; \ \lim_{x \to 0^+} \frac{-2x^3 + 7x}{x} = 7;$$

$$\lim_{x \to 0} \frac{-2x^3 + 7x}{x} = 7$$

5.

$x \to 2^-$	$\dfrac{4x^2 - 16}{x-2}$	$x \to 2^+$	$\dfrac{4x^2 - 16}{x-2}$
1.9	15.6	2.1	16.4
1.99	15.96	2.01	16.04
1.999	15.996	2.001	16.004
1.9999	15.9996	2.0001	16.0004

$$f'(2) = \lim_{x \to 2} \frac{f(x) - f(2)}{x - 2} = \lim_{x \to 2} \frac{4x^2 - 16}{x - 2} = 16$$

7.

$t \to 4^-$	$\dfrac{(-6t^2 + 7) - (-89)}{t - 4}$	$t \to 4^+$	$\dfrac{(-6t^2 + 7) - (-89)}{t - 4}$
3.9	-47.4	4.1	-48.6
3.99	-47.94	4.01	-48.06
3.999	-47.994	4.001	-48.006
3.9999	-47.9994	4.0001	-48.0006

$$g'(4) = \lim_{t \to 4} \frac{g(t) - g(4)}{t - 4} = \lim_{t \to 4} \frac{(-6t^2 + 7) - (-89)}{t - 4} = -48$$

9. Point: $(x, 3x - 2)$

Close Point: $(x + h, 3(x + h) - 2)$

Slope of the Secant: $\dfrac{3x + 3h - 2 - (3x - 2)}{x + h - x} = 3$

Limit of the Slope of the Secant: $\dfrac{dy}{dx} = \lim_{h \to 0} 3 = 3$

11. Point: $(x, 3x^2)$

Close Point: $(x + h, 3(x + h)^2)$

Slope of the Secant: $\dfrac{3(x + h)^2 - 3x^2}{x + h - x}$

$= \dfrac{(3x^2 + 6xh + 3h^2) - 3x^2}{h} = 6x + 3h$

Limit of the Slope of the Secant: $\dfrac{dy}{dx} = \lim_{h \to 0} (6x + 3h) = 6x$

13. Point: (x, x^3)

Close Point: $(x + h, (x + h)^3)$

Slope of the Secant: $\dfrac{(x + h)^3 - x^3}{x + h - x}$

$= \dfrac{(x^3 + 3x^2h + 3xh^2 + 3h^2) - x^3}{h} = 3x^2 + 3xh + h^2$

Limit of the Slope of the Secant:

$\dfrac{dy}{dx} = \lim_{h \to 0} (3x^2 + 3xh + h^2) = 3x^2$

15. a. $T(13) = 67.946$ seconds

b. $T(13 + h) = 0.181(13 + h)^2 - 8.463(13 + h)$

$\qquad + 147.376$

$\qquad = 0.181h^2 - 3.757h + 67.946$

c. $\dfrac{T(13 + h) - T(13)}{13 + h - 13} = \dfrac{0.181h^2 - 3.757h}{h}$

d. $\lim_{h \to 0} \dfrac{0.181h^2 - 3.757h}{h} = \lim_{h \to 0} (0.181h - 3.757)$

$\qquad = -3.757$ seconds per year of age

The time required for an average 13-year-old athlete to swim 100 meters freestyle is decreasing by 3.757 seconds per year of age.

17. a. $f(3) = 2.052$ billion gallons

b. $f(3 + h) = -0.042(3 + h)^2 + 0.18(3 + h) + 1.89$

$\qquad = 2.052 - 0.072h - 0.042h^2$ billion gallons

c. $\dfrac{-0.072h - 0.042h^2}{h}$ billion gallons per year

d. -0.072 billion gallons per year; In 2001, the amount of fuel Northwest Airlines consumed each year was decreasing by 72 million gallons per year.

19. a. Point: $(t, -16t^2 + 100)$

Close Point: $(t + h, -16h^2 - 32th - 16t^2 + 100)$

Slope of the Secant: $\dfrac{-16h^2 - 32th}{h} = (-16h - 32t)$

Limit of the Slope of the Secant:

$\dfrac{dH}{dt} = \lim_{h \to 0} (-16h - 32t) = -32t$ feet per second is

the speed of a falling object t seconds after the object begins falling (given that the object has not reached the ground).

b. After 1 second, the object is falling at a speed of 32 feet per second.

21. a. The number of drivers of age a years in 1997 can be modeled as $D(a) = -0.045a^2 + 1.774a - 16.064$ million drivers.

b. $D'(a) = -0.089a + 1.774$ million drivers per year (of age)

c. $D'(20) \approx -0.012$ million drivers per year (of age); In 1997, the number of drivers of a certain age is decreasing by approximately 12 thousand drivers per year (of age) when the specific age under consideration is 20 years.

d. Approximately -0.79% per year (of age); In 1997, the number of drivers of a certain age is decreasing by approximately 0.79 percent per year (of age) when the specific age under consideration is 20 years.

23. Finding a slope graphically is the only approach if all that is available is a graph of the function without an accompanying equation. Finding a slope graphically may be appropriate if all that is needed is a quick approximation of the rate of change at a point. If a more precise determination of the rate of change at one single point is needed and an equation is available, it may be appropriate to find the slope at that one point numerically, using a table of limiting values of the slopes of increasingly close secant lines. If an equation is available and the rate of change at several different points is needed, it might be appropriate to use an algebraic method to find a formula for the slope. A final consideration when choosing between the algebraic method and the numerical method to find slope is the difficulty involved in using the algebraic method. We are generally limited to using the *algebraic* method for linear, quadratic, or cubic functions.

Chapter 2 Concept Review

1. **a.   i.** A, B, C **ii.** E **iii.** D
    b. The graph is steeper at B than it is at A, C, or D.
    c. Below: C, D, E; above: A; At B: above to the left of B, below to the right of B
    d.

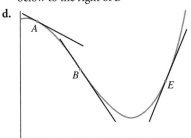

2. **a.** Feet per second squared (feet per second per second); acceleration
    b. The speed of the roller coaster increased after point D.
    c. The roller coaster's speed was slowest at point D.
    d. The roller coaster's speed was falling the fastest at point B.

3. **a.** The number of states associated with the national P.T.A. association grew by an average of 1.125 states per year between 1915 and 1931. Estimates may vary.
    b. The number of states associated with the national P.T.A. association grew by 60% between 1915 and 1931. Estimates may vary.
    c. The number of states associated with the national P.T.A. association grew by an average of 1 state per year between 1923 and 1927. Estimates may vary.

4. **a.** $8144.78
    b. $65,761.77
    c. $A(t) = 25,000\left(1 + \frac{0.065}{4}\right)^{4t}$ dollars in an account after t years when interest is compounded quarterly at 6.5%
    d. Approximately $2625.69 per year
    e. Approximately 38.04%

5.

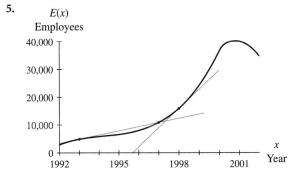

a. The slope of the secant line drawn between $x = 1993$ and $x = 1997$ gives the average rate of change in the number of employees between 1993 and 1997.
b. The slope of the tangent line at $x = 1998$ gives the instantaneous rate of change in the number of employees in 1998.
c. Between 1993 and 1997, the number of employees at Dell Computer Corp. was increasing by an average of approximately 1250 employees each year.
d. $E'(1998) \approx \dfrac{15000 - 8000}{1998 - 1996} = 3500$ employees per year; In 1998 the number of employees at Dell Computer Corp. was increasing by approximately 3500 employees per year.

$\dfrac{3500 \text{ employees/year}}{15000 \text{ employees}} \cdot 100\% \approx 23.3\%$ per year; In 1998 the number of employees at Dell Computer Corp. was increasing by approximately 23.3% per year.

6. **a.** An average 22-year-old athlete can swim 100 meters free style in 49 seconds. The time required for an average 22-year-old athlete to swim 100 meters free style is decreasing by approximately one half second per year of age.
    b. A negative derivative indicates that the swimmer's time to swim 100 meters free style is decreasing as he gets older.

7. **a.** $R(x) = -0.051x^2 + 0.884x + 4.793$ billion dollars passenger revenue for Northwest Airlines between 1991 and 2003, where x is the number of years since 1990.
    b. Approximately -0.14 billion dollars per year

Close point	Slope of the secant line between point and $x = 10$
9.9	−0.13357
9.99	−0.13817
9.999	−0.13863
9.9999	−0.13867
10.1	−0.14879
10.01	−0.13919
10.001	−0.13873
10.0001	−0.13868

c. In 2001, passenger revenue for Northwest Airlines was decreasing by approximately $140 million per year.
d. $R'(x) = -0.102x + 0.884$ billion dollars passenger revenue per year for Northwest Airlines between 1991 and 2003, where x is the number of years since 1990; −$0.241 billion

8. Find a point: $(x, 7x + 3)$; find a close point: $(x + h, 7(x + h) + 3)$; find a formula for the slope of the secant line between the two points and simplify completely:

Slope of the secant $= \dfrac{7x + 7h + 3 - (7x + 3)}{x + h - x} = 7$; find the limit of the slope of the secant as the point and the close point become closer together: $\lim\limits_{h \to 0} 7 = 7$.

CHAPTER 3

Section 3.1

1. The slopes are negative to the left of $x = A$ and positive to the right of $x = A$. The slope is zero at $x = A$.

3. The slopes are positive for all x, near zero to the left of $x = 0$, and increasingly positive to the right of $x = 0$.

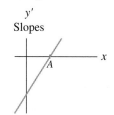

5. The slope is zero everywhere.

$y' = \text{slope} = 0$

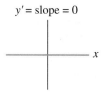

7. The slopes are negative for all x. The magnitude is large close to $x = 0$ and is near zero as x increases without bound.

Slopes

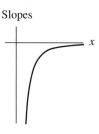

9. The slopes are negative to the left and right of $x = A$. The slope appears to be zero at $x = A$.

11. a.

Graph   Slope graph

b.

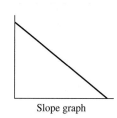

Graph   Slope graph

13. a. Table values may vary.

Year	1991	1993	1997	1999	2001
Slope	−6.6	−6.2	−2.5	1.0	5.4

b.

Rate of change
of average bill
(dollars per year)

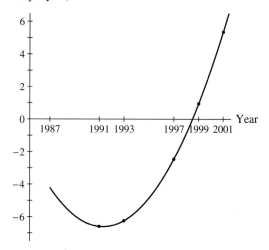

15. a. Table values may vary.

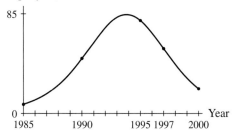

Year	≈1985	1990	1995	1997	≈2000
Slope	7.8	46.8	79.2	55.2	21.4

b.

Rate of change
(cases per year)

17. a. The average rate of change during the year (found by estimating the slope of the secant line drawn from September to May) is approximately 14 members per month. (Answers may vary.)

b. By estimating the slopes of tangent lines, we obtain the following. (Answers may vary.)

Month	Slope (members per month)
Sept	98
Nov	−9
Feb	30
Apr	11

c.

Members
per month

d. Mid-February. This point on the membership graph is an inflection point.

e. The average of change is not useful in sketching an instantaneous rate-of-change graph.

19.

$j'(t)$
(inmates
per year)

21. a. Profit is increasing on average by approximately $600 per car.

b. Table values may vary.

Number of cars	Slope (dollars per car)
20	0
40	160
60	750
80	10
100	−1200

c.

Average
monthly profit
(dollars per car)

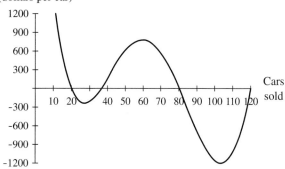

d. The average monthly profit is increasing most rapidly for approximately 60 cars sold and is decreasing most rapidly when approximately 100 cars are sold. The corresponding points on the graph are inflection points.

e. Average rates of change are not useful in graphing instantaneous rates of change.

23. The derivative does not exist at $x = 0$, $x = 3$, and $x = 4$ because the graph is not continuous at those inputs.

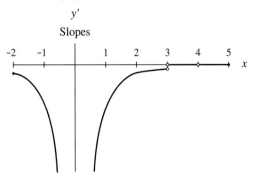

25. The derivative does not exist at $x = 2$ and $x = 3$ because the slopes from the right and left are different at those inputs.

27. Answers may vary.

29. Answers may vary.

31. a. $p'(m)$

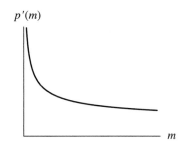

b. $\dfrac{dp}{dm} = \dfrac{2\sqrt{m} + 1}{2\sqrt{m}} = 1 + \dfrac{1}{2\sqrt{m}}$

So $\dfrac{dp}{dm} = 1 + \dfrac{1}{2\sqrt{m}}$. The graph of $\dfrac{dp}{dm}$ is the same as the one in part *a*.

33. When sketching a rate-of-change graph, it is important to identify the following features on the graph of the original function: 1) input values for which the derivative does not exist, 2) input intervals over which the function is increasing, 3) input intervals over which the function is decreasing, 4) input values that correspond to a relative maximum or minimum of the function, 5) input values for which the function appears to be increasing or decreasing most rapidly, 6) input values that correspond to inflection points where the function has zero slope.

Section 3.2

1. The graph of the function $y = 2 - 7x$ is a line with slope -7. $\dfrac{dy}{dx} = -7$.

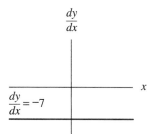

3. The slope formula is $\dfrac{dy}{dx} = 4x^{4-1} = 4x^3$.

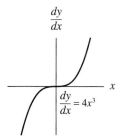

5. The slope of any horizontal line is 0.

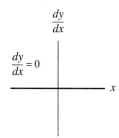

7. The power rule applies: $f'(x) = 5x^4$

9. The power rule and the constant multiplier rule apply: $f'(x) = 9x^2$

11. The linear function rule (or the power rule and the constant multiplier rule) apply: $f'(x) = -5$

13. The constant rule applies: $f'(x) = 0$

15. The linear function rule (or the power rule and the constant multiplier rule) apply: $\dfrac{dy}{dx} = 12$

17. The sum rule, the constant multiplier rule, the power rule, and the constant rule apply: $\dfrac{dy}{dx} = 15x^2 + 6x - 2$

19. $f(x) = \dfrac{1}{x^3} = x^{-3} \rightarrow f'(x) = -3x^{-4} = \dfrac{-3}{x^4}$

21. $f(x) = \dfrac{-9}{x^2} = -9x^{-2} \rightarrow f'(x) = 18x^{-3} = \dfrac{18}{x^3}$

23. $f(x) = \dfrac{3x^2 + 1}{x} = \dfrac{3x^2}{x} + \dfrac{1}{x} = 3x + x^{-1} \rightarrow$

$f'(x) = 3 - \dfrac{1}{x^2}$

25. $f(x) = \sqrt{x} = x^{\frac{1}{2}} \rightarrow f'(x) = \dfrac{1}{2}x^{-\frac{1}{2}} = \dfrac{1}{2\sqrt{x}}$

27. a. $A'(t) = 0.1333$ dollars per year t years after 1990

   b. $A(10) \approx \$1.50$

   c. $A'(9) = \$0.1333$ per year

   In 1999, the ATM transaction fee was increasing by approximately \$0.13 per year.

29. a. $\left| T'(-5) \right| > \left| T'(1.5) \right|$

   b. $-1.6\,(-5) + 2 = 10°$F per hour

   c. $-1.6\,(0) + 2 = 2°$F per hour

   d. $-1.6\,(4) + 2 = -4.4°$F per hour

   A negative derivative indicates that the output (temperature) is decreasing for the related input value.

31. a. 1970: falling

   1995: rising

   b. 1970: ≈ -207 births per year

   1995: ≈ 322 births per year

33. a. $m(w) = 6.930w + 682.188$ kilocalories per day is the metabolic rate for a typical 18- to 30-year-old male who weighs w pounds, $88 \leq w \leq 200$.

b. $m'(w) = 6.930$ kilocalories per day per pound is the rate of change in the metabolic rate for a typical 18- to 30-year-old male who weighs w pounds, $88 \leq w \leq 200$.

c. The metabolic rate for any male in the 18–30-year-old group will increase by approximately 7 kilocalories per day per pound of additional weight gained or will decrease by approximately 7 kilocalories per day per pound of weight lost.

35. a. $R(x) = -3.68x^3 + 47.958x^2 - 80.759x + 166.98$ billion dollars is the revenue when \$$x$ billion is spent on advertising, $1.2 \leq x \leq 6.4$.

b. $R'(x) = -3.68(3x^2) + 47.958(2x) - 80.759(1) + 0$
$= -11.039x^2 + 95.916x - 80.759$ billion dollars per billion dollars (billion dollars of revenue per billion dollars of advertising) is the rate of change of revenue when \$$x$ billion is spent on advertising, $1.2 \leq x \leq 6.4$.

c. $R'(5) \approx \$122.8$ billion per billion dollars (billion dollars of revenue per billion dollars of advertising)
$R(5) \approx \$502.1$ billion

d. Percentage rate of change $\approx 24.5\%$ per billion dollars (advertising)

37. a. $P(x) = 175 - \left(0.015x^2 - 0.78x + 46 + \dfrac{49.6}{x}\right)$
dollars is the profit from the sale of a storm window when x windows are produced each hour.

b. $P'(x) = -0.030x + 0.78 + \dfrac{49.6}{x^2}$ dollars per window is the rate of change of profit when x windows are produced each hour.

c. \$94.78 profit

d. Approximately $-\$1.61$ per window produced
When 80 storm windows are produced each hour, the profit from the sale of one window is decreasing by approximately \$1.61 per additional window produced.

39. If $a > 0$, the graph of $ax^3 + bx^2 + cx + d$ increases, then decreases (or level off if the cubic function does not decreases at all), and finally increase again. The derivative graph for this cubic function will be a concave up parabola. If $a < 0$ in the cubic formula, then the slope graph is a concave down parabola.

Section 3.3

1.

$\dfrac{dy}{dx} = e^x$

3.

$\dfrac{dy}{dx} = \dfrac{1}{x}$

5.

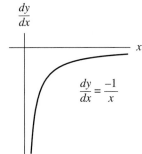

$\dfrac{dy}{dx} = \dfrac{-1}{x}$

7. $h'(x) = -7e^x$

9. $g'(x) = (\ln 2.1)2.1^x$

11. $\dfrac{dh}{dx} = 12\,(\ln 1.6)(1.6^x)$

13. $f'(x) \approx 0.49690(1.05095^x)$

15. $f'(x) = 4.2(\ln 0.8)(0.8^x)$

17. $f'(x) = \dfrac{4}{x}$

19. $\dfrac{dy}{dx} = \dfrac{-7}{x}$

21. a. $A'(t) \approx (\ln 1.0439)(1.0439^t)$ thousand dollars per year, t years after the initial investment is made.

b. $A(5) = 1.23986$ thousand dollars (\$1239.86)

c. $A'(5) \approx 0.0533$ thousand dollars per year

d. Approximately 4.3% per year

23. a. $\dfrac{dA}{dr} = 1000 \ln(e^{10})e^{10r} = 10{,}000e^{10r}$ dollars per 100%

b. $A'(0.07) = 10{,}000e^{10(0.07)} \approx \$20{,}137.53$ per 100%. Working with interest can get interesting when taking derivatives. The increase of $20,137.53 represents the rate of change when the interest rate (currently $r = 0.07$) increased by 1 to 1.07. This means the interest rate is increased from 7% to 107%.

c. $\dfrac{dA}{dr} = 1000 \ln(e^{0.1})e^{0.1r} = 100e^{0.1r}$ dollars per percentage point

d. $A'(7) = 100e^{0.1(7)} \approx \$201.38$ per percentage point. This answer is $\dfrac{1}{100}$ of the answer to part b.

25. a. Approximately 2.041 years

b. $s'(x) = 0.14(\ln 4.106)(4.106^x)$ million iPods per year is the rate of change of iPod sales, where x is the number of years after the fiscal year that ended in September, 2002, $0 \le x \le 3$.

c. Approximately 3.531 million iPods per year

27. a. $w(7) \approx 25.64$ grams
$w'(7) \approx 1.05$ grams per week

b. $\dfrac{w(9) - w(4) \text{ grams}}{9 - 4 \text{ weeks}} \approx \dfrac{5.977 \text{ grams}}{5 \text{ weeks}}$
≈ 1.195 grams/week

c. The formula for the rate of change of the mouse's weight is $w'(x) = \dfrac{7.37}{x}$ grams/week. As the age of the mouse increases, the denominator will increase and the growth rate will slow.

29. a. $T'(d) = \dfrac{-9.9}{d}$ °F per day is the rate of change of the temperature at which milk must be stored in order to remain fresh, where d is the number of days that the milk must be stored

b. As the number of days that the milk must be stored increases, the temperature at which the milk must be stored decreases more slowly. Consequently, the rate of change of the temperature becomes closer to zero.

31. a. $CPI(x) = -351.521 + 227.777 \ln x$ points is the consumer price index for college tuition between 1990 and 2000, where x is the number of years since 1980

b. $CPI'(18) = \dfrac{227.777}{18} \approx 12.7$ points per year

33. a. $R(x) = 3.960(3.584^x)$ million dollars is the revenue realized by Apple from the sales of iPods for fiscal years ending between September 30, 2002, and September 30, 2006, where x is the number of fiscal years since September 30, 2000.

b. $R'(x) = 3.960(\ln 3.584)3.584^x$ million dollars per year is the rate of change of the revenue realized by Apple from the sales of iPods for fiscal years ending between September 30, 2002, and September 30, 2006, where x is the number of fiscal years since September 30, 2000.

c. The revenue realized by Apple for the fiscal year ending in September 30, 2003, from the sale of iPods was approximately $2340.44 million dollars. At that time, the revenue realized by Apple from the sale of iPods was increasing by approximately $2987.53 million dollars per year. This rate of increase in the revenue realized by Apple from the sale of iPods was approximately 127.6% per year.

35. a. $y = e^x = e^{1x} = (e^1)^x \rightarrow \dfrac{dy}{dx} = (\ln e^1)(e^1) = 1e^x = e^x$

b. $y = e^{kx} = (e^k)^x \rightarrow y' = (\ln e^k)(e^k)^x = k(e^k)^x = ke^{kx}$

Section 3.4

1. a. $f(x(2)) = f(6) = 140$

b. $\dfrac{df}{dx} = -27$

c. $\dfrac{dx}{dt} = 1.3$

d. $\dfrac{df}{dt} = (-27)(1.3) = -35.1$

3. The value of the investor's gold is increasing at a rate of $64.62 per day.

5. a. $R(476) = \$10{,}000$ Canadian
On November 25, 2002, 476 units of the commodity were sold, producing revenue of $10,000 Canadian.

b. $C(10{,}000) = \$6334.70$ U.S.
On November 25, 2002, 10,000 Canadian dollars were worth 6334.70 U.S. dollars.

c. $\dfrac{dR}{dx} = \$2.6$ Canadian per unit
On November 25, 2000, revenue was increasing by 2.6 Canadian dollars per unit sold.

d. $\dfrac{dC}{dR} = \$0.6335$ U.S. per Canadian dollar
On November 25, 2002, the exchange rate was $0.6335 U.S. per Canadian dollar

e. $\dfrac{dC}{dx} \approx \$1.65$ U.S. per unit
On November 25, 2002, revenue was increasing at a rate of $1.65 U.S. per unit sold.

7. a. $p(10) \approx 8.303$ thousand people
In 2010, the population of the city was approximately 8300 people.

b. $g(p(10)) \approx g(8.303) \approx 16$ garbage trucks
In 2010, the city owned 16 garbage trucks.

c. $\dfrac{dp}{dt} = \dfrac{-31.2e^{0.02t}}{(1 + 12e^{0.02t})^2}$ thousand people per year

$p'(10) \approx -0.155$ thousand people per year

In 2010, the population was increasing at a rate of approximately 220 people per year.

d. $g'(p) = 2 - 0.003p^2$ trucks per thousand people

$g'(8.303) \approx 1.8$ trucks per thousand people

In 2010, when the population was approximately 8300, the number of garbage trucks needed by the city was increasing by 1.8 trucks per thousand people.

e. When $t = 10$, $\dfrac{dg}{dt} = \dfrac{dg}{dp} \cdot \dfrac{dp}{dt} \approx 1.24$ truck per year

In 2010, the number of trucks needed by the city was decreasing at a rate of 1.24 truck per year, or approximately 5 truck every 4 years.

9. $c(x(t)) = 3(4 - 6t)^2 - 2$

$\dfrac{dc}{dt} = 6(4 - 6t)(-6) = -144 + 216t$

11. $h(p(t)) = \dfrac{4}{1 + 3e^{-0.5t}}$

$\dfrac{dh}{dt} = \dfrac{-4(3)(-0.5)e^{-0.5t}}{(1 + 3e^{-0.5t})^2} = \dfrac{6e^{-0.5t}}{(1 + 3e^{-0.5t})^2}$

13. $k(t(x)) = 4.3(\ln x)^3 - 2(\ln x)^2 + 4\ln x - 12$

$\dfrac{dk}{dx} = \dfrac{12.9(\ln x)^2}{x} - \dfrac{4\ln x}{x} + \dfrac{4}{x}$

15. $p(t(k)) = 7.9(1.046^{14k^3 - 12k^2})$

$\dfrac{dp}{dk} = 7.9(\ln 1.046)(1.046^{14k^3 - 12k^2})(42k^2 - 24k)$

17. Inside function: $u = 3.2x + 5.7$

Outside function: $f = u^5$

$\dfrac{df}{dx} = 5(3.2x + 5.7)^4(3.2) = 16(3.2x + 5.7)^4$

19. Inside function: $u = x - 1$

Outside function: $f = \dfrac{8}{u^3}$

$\dfrac{df}{dx} = 8(-3)(x - 1)^{-4} = -24(x - 1)^{-4}$

21. Inside function: $u = x^2 - 3x$

Outside function: $f = \sqrt{u}$

$\dfrac{df}{dx} = \dfrac{1}{2}(x^2 - 3x)^{\frac{-1}{2}}(2x - 3)$

23. Inside function: $u = 35x$

Outside function: $f = \ln u$

$\dfrac{df}{dx} = \dfrac{1}{35x}(35) = \dfrac{1}{x}$

25. Inside function: $u = 16x^2 + 37x$

Outside function: $f = \ln u$

$\dfrac{df}{dx} = \dfrac{1}{16x^2 + 37x}(32x + 37)$

27. Inside function: $u = 0.6x$

Outside function: $f = 72e^u$

$\dfrac{df}{dx} = 72e^{0.6x}(0.6) = 43.2e^{0.6x}$

29. Inside function: $u = 0.08x$

Outside function: $f = 1 + 58e^u$

$\dfrac{df}{dx} = 58e^{0.08x}(0.08) = 4.64e^{0.08x}$

31. Inside function:

$u = 1 + 18e^{0.6x} \begin{cases} \text{inside:} & w = 0.6x \\ \text{outside:} & u = 1 + 18e^w \end{cases}$

Outside function: $f = 12u^{-1} + 7.3$

$\dfrac{df}{dx} = -12(1 + 18e^{0.6x})^{-2}(18e^{0.6x})(0.6) = \dfrac{-129.6e^{0.6x}}{(1 + 18e^{0.6x})^2}$

33. Inside function: $u = \sqrt{x} - 3x$

Outside function: $f = u^3$

$\dfrac{df}{dx} = 3(\sqrt{x} - 3x)^2\left(\dfrac{1}{2\sqrt{x}} - 3\right)$

35. Inside function: $u = \ln x$

Outside function: $f = 2^u$

$\dfrac{df}{dx} = (\ln 2)(2^{\ln x})\dfrac{1}{x}$

37. Inside function: $u = -Bx$

Outside function: $f = Ae^u$

$\dfrac{df}{dx} = Ae^{-Bx}(-B)$

39. a. $S(x) = 0.75\sqrt{-2.3x^2 + 53.2x + 249.8} + 1.8$ million dollars is the predicted sales for a large firm, where x is the number of years in the future.

b. $S'(x) = \dfrac{0.75}{2}(-2.3x^2 + 53.2x + 249.8)^{\frac{-1}{2}} \cdot (-4.6x + 53.2)$ million dollars per year is the rate of change in predicted sales for a large firm, where x is the number of years in the future.

c. $1.26 million per year

41. a. $R'(q) = 0.0314(0.62285)e^{0.62285q}$ million dollars per quarter q quarters after the beginning of 1998.

b.

Quarter ending June of. . .	1998	1999	2000
Revenue (million dollars)	3.0	4.2	18.8
Rate of change (million dollars per quarter)	0.07	0.82	9.92
Percentage rate of change (percent per quarter)	2.3	19.5	52.7

43. a. $m'(x) = \dfrac{(49)(36.0660)(0.206743)e^{-0.206743x}}{(1 + 36.0660e^{-0.206743x})^2}$

$\approx \dfrac{365.363e^{-0.206743x}}{(1 + 36.0660e^{-0.206743x})^2}$

states per year is the rate of change of states with national P.T.A. membership, where x is the number of years since 1895, $0 \le x \le 36$.

b. Approximately 5 states

c. 1915: $m'(20) \approx 2.4$ states per year
1927: $m'(32) \approx 0.4$ state per year

45. a. $f(x) = 13865.113(1.035^x)$ dollars is the projected tuition at a private 4-year college for the years between 2000 and 2010, where x is the number of years after 2000.

b. $f(x) \approx 13{,}865.113(e^{0.0344x})$

c. $f'(x) = 13{,}865.113(\ln 1.035)(1.035^x)$;
$f'(x) \approx 13{,}865.113(0.0344)(e^{0.0344x})$

d. Because $\ln 1.035 \approx 0.0344$, the answers will be the same: $f'(8) \approx \$632$ per year.

47. a. The data are essentially concave up, suggesting a quadratic or exponential function. We choose a quadratic model: $t(x) = 7.763x^2 + 47.447x + 1945.893$ units is the average weekly production at a manufacturing company during the xth quarter after January 1, 2000, for the period from January 2000 through December 2003.

b. $C(t(x)) = 196.25 + 44.45 \ln (7.763x^2 + 47.447x + 1945.893)$ dollars is the weekly production cost at a manufacturing company during the xth quarter after January 1, 2000, for the period from January 2000 through December 2003.

c. Extrapolating yields
Jan—Mar 2004: $C(t(17)) \approx \$574.81$ per week
Apr—June 2004: $C(t(18)) \approx \$577.56$ per week
July—Sept 2004: $C(t(19)) \approx \$580.27$ per week
Oct—Dec 2004: $C(t(20)) \approx \$582.94$ per week

d. The graph does not predict a decrease between January of 2000 and January of 2005.

e. $\dfrac{d}{dx} C(t(x)) = \dfrac{dC}{dt} \cdot \dfrac{dt}{dx}$

$= 44.25\left(\dfrac{1}{t}\right)(15.525x + 47.447 + 0)$

$= \dfrac{44.25(15.525x + 47.447)}{7.763x^2 + 47.447x + 1945.893}$

dollars per quarter is the rate of change of weekly manufacturing cost at a manufacturing company during the xth quarter after January 1, 2000, for the period from January 2000 through December 2003.

A graph of $\dfrac{d}{dx} C(t(x))$ never crosses the horizontal axis indicating that cost will never decrease.

49. Composite functions are formed by using the output of one function (the inside function) as the input of a second function (the outside function). The output of the inside and the input of the outside must agree both in the quantity measured and in the units of measurement.

Section 3.5

1. $h'(2) = f'(2)g(2) + f(2)g'(2) = -1.5(4) + 6(3) = 12$

3. a.   i. In 2007, there were 75,000 households in the city.

   ii. In 2007, the number of households in the city was decreasing by 1200 per year.

   iii. In 2007, 52% of households in that city owned a computer.

   iv. In 2007, the percentage of households in that city with a computer was increasing by 5 percentage points per year.

b. Input: the number of years since 2005
Output: the number of households with computers

c. $N(2) = 39{,}000$ households with computers.
$N'(2) = 3126$ households with computers per year
In 2007, there were 39,000 households in the city with computers, and the number of households with computers was increasing at a rate of 3126 households per year.

5. a.   i. $S(10) \approx \$15.24$

$S'(x) = \dfrac{-2.6}{(x + 1)^2}$ dollars per week

$S'(10) \approx -\$0.02$ per week

After 10 weeks, one share was worth \$15.24, and the value of one share was declining by \$0.02 per week.

   ii. $N(10) = 125$ shares
$N'(x) = 0.5x$ shares per week
$N'(10) = 5$ shares per week
After 10 weeks, the investor owned 125 shares, and the number of shares was growing by 5 shares per week.

   iii. $V(10) \approx \$1904.55$
$V'(10) \approx \$73.50$ per week
After 10 weeks, the investor's stock is worth approximately \$1905, and the value is increasing at a rate of \$73.50 per week.

b. $V'(x) = \left(\dfrac{-2.6}{(x + 1)^2}\right)(100 + 0.25x^2)$

$+ \left(15 + \dfrac{2.6}{x + 1}\right)(0.5x)$

$= -\dfrac{0.65x^2 + 260}{(x + 1)^2} + \dfrac{1.3x}{x + 1} + 7.5x$

dollars per week is the rate of change of the value of the investor's stock in the company after x weeks.

7. 9000 bushels per year

9. a. 8160 voters

   b. Approximately 4651 votes

   c. Approximately 434 votes per week

11. $f'(x) = \left(\dfrac{1}{x}\right)e^x + (\ln x)(e^x)$

13. $f'(x) = (6x + 15)(32x^3 + 49)$
          $+ (3x^2 + 15x + 7)(96x^2)$

15. $f'(x) = (25.6x + 3.7) \cdot [29(1.7^x)]$
          $+ (12.8x^2 + 3.7x + 1.2) \cdot [29(\ln 1.7)(1.7^x)]$

17. $f'(x) = [3(5.7x^2 + 3.5x + 2.9)^2(11.4x + 3.5)] \cdot$
          $(3.8x^2 + 5.2x + 7)^{-2} + (5.7x^2 + 3.5x + 2.9)^3 \cdot$
          $[-2(3.8x^2 + 5.2x + 7)^{-3}(7.6x + 5.2)]$

19. $f'(x) = [12.6(\ln 4.8)(4.8^x)](x^{-2}) + 12.6(4.8^x)(-2x^{-3})$

21. $f'(x) = 79\left(\dfrac{198}{1 + 7.68e^{-0.85x}} + 15\right) +$
          $(79x)\left(\dfrac{198(7.68)(-0.85)e^{-0.85x}}{(1 + 7.68e^{-0.85x})^2}\right)$

23. $f'(x) = (-430)(\ln 0.62)(0.62^x)[6.42 + 3.3(1.46^x)]^{-1} +$
          $(-430)(0.62^x)[6.42 + 3.3(1.46^x)]^{-2} \cdot$
          $[3.3(\ln 1.46)(1.46^x)]$

25. $f'(x) = 4\sqrt{3x + 2} + (6x)(3x + 2)^{-\frac{1}{2}}$

27. $f'(x) = 14[1 + 12.6e^{-0.73x}]^{-1} +$
          $14x[-(1 + 12.6e^{-0.73x})^{-2}(12.6e^{-0.73x})(-0.73)]$

29. a. $E(x) = \dfrac{0.73(1.2912^x) + 8}{100} \cdot$
          $(-0.026x^2 - 3.842x + 538.868)$

    women received epidural pain relief during childbirth at an Arizona hospital between 1981 and 1997, where x is the number of years after 1980

    $E'(x) = \dfrac{0.73(\ln 1.2912)(1.2912^x)}{100} \cdot$
          $(-0.026x^2 - 3.842x + 538.868)$
          $+ \dfrac{0.73(1.2912^x) + 8}{100}(-0.052x - 3.842)$

    women per year is the rate of change in the number of women who received epidural pain relief during childbirth at an Arizona hospital between 1981 and 1997, where x is the number of years after 1980

   b. Increasing by $p'(17) \approx 14.4$ percentage points per year

   c. Decreasing by approximately 5 births per year

   d. Increasing by $E'(17) \approx 64$ women per year.

   e. Profit = $57 \cdot E(17) \approx \$17,000$

31. a. $R(x) \approx 6250x(0.9286^x)$ dollars is the monthly revenue from CD sales when the price of a CD is x dollars.

   b. $P(x) \approx 6250[x(0.9286^x) - 7.50(0.9286^x)]$ dollars is the monthly profit from CD sales when the price of a CD is x dollars.

   c. $R'(x) = 6250[(1)(0.9286^x) + x(\ln 0.9286)(0.9286^x)]$ dollars of revenue per dollar of price is the rate of change in the monthly revenue from CD sales when the price of a CD is x dollars.
     $P'(x) = 6250[(1)(0.9286^x) + x(\ln 0.9286)(0.9286^x)$
     $- 7.50(\ln 0.9286)(0.9286^x)]$ dollars of profit per dollar of price is the rate of change in the monthly profit from CD sales when the price of a CD is x dollars.

   d. Table entries are rounded.

Price	Rate of change of revenue (dollars of revenue per dollar of price)	Rate of change of profit (dollars of profit per dollar of price)
$13	88.27	1413.83
$14	−82.15	1148.76
$20	−684.05	105.17
$21	−732.93	−0.06
$22	−771.34	−90.79

   e. Because $R'(13) > 0$ and $R'(14) < 0$, the highest revenue will be achieved with a price between $13 and $14.

   f. Because $P'(x) > 0$ for $13 \le x \le 20$, $P'(21) \approx 0$, and $P'(21) < 0$, the price corresponding to the maximum profit is approximately $21.

33. a. $C(x) = 71.459(1.050^x)$ dollars is the cost to produce x units in an hour, $10 \le x \le 90$.

   b. $C'(x) = 71.459(\ln 1.050)(1.050^x)$ dollars per unit produced is the rate of change of the cost to produce x units in an hour, $10 \le x \le 90$.

   c. $A(x) = \dfrac{C(x)}{x} = 71.459(1.050^x)(x^{-1})$ dollars per unit is the average cost to produce one unit when x units are produced each hour, $10 \le x \le 90$.

   d. $A'(x) = 71.459[(\ln 1.050)(1.050^x)(x^{-1}) + (1.050^x)(-x^{-2})]$ dollars per unit per hourly unit produced is the rate of change in the average cost to produce one unit when x units are produced, $10 \le x \le 90$.

   e. 15 units: $A'(15) \approx -\$0.18$ per unit per hourly unit produced
     35 units: $A'(35) \approx \$0.23$ per unit per hourly unit produced

85 units: $A'(85) \approx \$1.97$ per unit per hourly unit produced

f. Average cost is decreasing over the set of inputs from 10 to 21 units.

g. The graph of A' crosses the x-axis near $x = 20.5$. Practically speaking, the average cost is decreasing at 20 units and increasing at 21 units, so a production level of 21 units is the one at which average cost first increases.

35. a. $t(x) = -0.015x^2 + 1.865x + 59.430$ million households owned TVs x years after 1970, $0 \le x \le 32$.

b. $v(x) = \dfrac{0.868}{1 + 4557.412e^{-0.485x}}$ (percent expressed as a decimal) of households with TVs also had VCRs, x years after 1970, $0 \le x \le 32$.

c. $n(x) = (-0.015x^2 + 1.865x + 59.430) \cdot$ $\dfrac{0.868}{1 + 4557.412e^{-0.485x}}$ million households owned TVs and VCRs x years after 1970.

d. $n'(x) = (-0.03x + 1.865) \cdot \dfrac{0.868}{1 + 4557.412e^{-0.485x}}$ $+ (-0.015x^2 + 1.865x + 59.430) \cdot$ $\left(\dfrac{-(0.868)(4557.412)(-0.485)e^{-0.485x}}{(1 + 4557.412e^{-0.485x})^2} \right)$ million households per year is the rate of change in the number of households with TVs and VCRs, x years after 1970, $0 \le x \le 32$.

e. 1990: ≈ 7.4 million households per year
1995: ≈ 1.9 million households per year
2000: ≈ 0.9 million households per year

37. a. $E(x) = -151.516x^3 + 2060.988x^2 - 8819.062x$ $+ 195,291.201$ students is the enrollment in ninth through twelfth grades in South Carolina between 1980–81 and 1989–90, where x is the number of years since the 1980–81 school year.
$D(x) = -14.271x^3 + 213.882x^2 - 1393.655x$ $+ 11,697.292$ students is the number of students dropping out from ninth through twelfth grades in South Carolina between 1980–81 and 1989–90, where x is the number of years since the 1980–81 school year.

b. $P(x) = \dfrac{D(x)}{E(x)} \cdot 100 \%$ is the percent of students dropping out from ninth through twelfth grades in South Carolina between 1980–81 and 1989–90, where x is the number of years since the 1980–81 school year.

c. $P'(x) = D'(x)[E(x)]^{-1} + D(x)[-(E(x))^2 \cdot E'(x)]$ percentage points per year is the rate of change in the percent of students dropping out from ninth through twelfth grades in South Carolina between 1980–81 and

1989–90, where x is the number of years since the 1980–81 school year.

d. The rate of change of the percentage of students dropping out was smallest in the 1980–81 school year, when it was -0.44 percentage points per year. The rate of change of the percentage of students dropping out was greatest in the 1985–86 and 1986–87 school years, when it was -0.19 percentage points per year.

e. Negative rates of change indicate that the number of dropouts in South Carolina was falling during the 1980s. This means that more students were staying in school.

39. The inputs must correspond in order for the result of the multiplication to be meaningful.

Section 3.6

1. 7

3. 1

5. 0

7. $\dfrac{0}{0}$; 1

9. $\dfrac{0}{0}$; $\dfrac{4}{3}$

11. 0

13. 0

15. 0

17. $\dfrac{0}{0}$; $\dfrac{1}{40}$

19. $\dfrac{0}{0}$; $\dfrac{3}{13}$

21. 0

23. $0 \cdot \infty$; 0

25. $\dfrac{\infty}{\infty}$; $\dfrac{3}{5}$

27. $\dfrac{\infty}{\infty}$; ∞

29. Consider the case $\dfrac{0}{0}$. We know that 1) $\lim\limits_{h \to 0} \dfrac{h}{c} = 0$ for any non-zero real number and 2) $\lim\limits_{h \to 0} \dfrac{c}{h}$ is increasing (or decreasing) without bound for any non-zero real number. If we apply these two statements repeatedly with c approaching 0, we end with an apparent contradiction. Similar arguments can be applied for $\dfrac{\infty}{\infty}$ and $0 \cdot \infty$.

Chapter 3 Concept Review

1. a. $x \approx 0.8$
b. positive slope: $0.8 < x < 2$
negative slope: $-3 < x < 0, 0 < x < 0.8$

c. $x = 0$

d. $f'(-2) \approx -4; f'(1) \approx 1.1$

e.

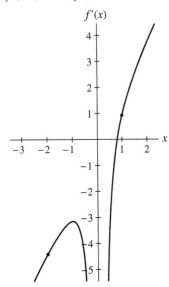

2. a. $D'(t) = \dfrac{8.101(214.8)(0.797)e^{-0.797t}}{(1 + 214.8e^{-0.797t})^2}$ pounds per person per year is the rate of change in the annual per capita consumption of turkey in the United States between 1980 and 2002, t years after 1980.

b. $D'(10) \approx 0.5$ pound per person per year; In 1990 the average annual per capita consumption of turkey in the United States was increasing by 0.5 pound per person per year.

c. $D'(21) \approx 0.0$ pound per person per year; In 2001, per capita consumption of turkey in the United States was not changing.

3. a. 506.3 billion per year

b.

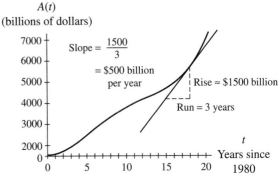

c. $A'(18) \approx \$496.4$ billion per year. In 1998, the total outstanding mortgage debt in the United States was increasing by $496.4 billion per year.

4. a. Rewrite $P(t)$ as $P(t) = 100N(t)[A(t)]^{-1}$. So that using the Product and Chain Rules

$$P'(t) = \frac{100N'(t)}{A(t)} - \frac{100N(t)A'(t)}{[A(t)]^2} \text{ percentage points}$$

per year is the rate of change in the percentage of outstanding mortgage debt that represents new mortgages, t years after 1980.

b. Input units: years

Output units: percentage points per year

CHAPTER 4

Section 4.1

1. Approximately 30.7%

3. Approximately 19.3

5. a. Increasing production from 500 to 501 units will increase cost by approximately $17.

b. If sales increase from 150 to 151 units, then profit will increase by approximately $4.75.

7. A marginal profit of −$4 per shirt means that the fraternity is currently losing $4 for each additional shirt sold. The fraternity should consider selling fewer shirts or increasing the sales price.

9.

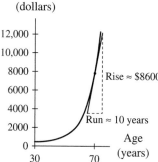

Slope of tangent line: approximately \$860 per year of age
Annual premium for 70-year-old: approximately \$7850
Premium for 72-year-old: approximately \$9570
(Answers may vary slightly.)

11. a.

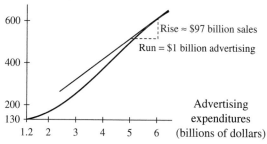

Slope of tangent line: approximately 97 billion dollars
per billion dollars (sales dollars per advertising dollars)
Revenue when \$6 billion is spent on advertising: ap-
proximately \$615 billion
Revenue when \$6.5 billion is spent on advertising: ap-
proximately \$662.5 billion
(Answers may vary slightly.)

b. \$658 billion

c. One possible answer: The answer from part *b* is more
accurate than in part *a* because it is calculated rather
than estimated.

13. a. In 2000 the population of South Carolina was increasing by 53.6 thousand people per year.

b. Between 2000 and 2003, the population increased by
approximately 160.8 thousand people.

c. By finding the slope of the tangent line at 2000 and
multiplying by 3, we determine the change in the tangent line from 2000 through 2003 and use that change
to estimate the change in the population function.

15. a. Approximately 2.5 million people per year

b. Approximately 2.5 million people

17. a. Approximately 1.15 million pieces per year

b. Approximately 1.15 million pieces

c. Approximately 1.13 million pieces

d. 1.5 million pieces

e. The answers in parts *b* and *c* differ by less than 25
thousand pieces. They both differ from the answer in
part *d* by more than 300 thousand pieces. *One possible
answer:* the answer in part *e* (computed directly from
the data) is the most accurate because the only
rounding introduced is in the data themselves.

19. a. $A(t) = 300\left(1 + \dfrac{0.065}{12}\right)^{12t}$ dollars in the account after
t years

b. $A(t) = 300(1.066972^t)$ dollars in the account after t
years

c. \$341.52

d. Approximately \$22.14 per year

e. Approximately \$5.53

21. a. $R(x) = (-7.032 \cdot 10^{-4})x^2 + 1.666x + 47.130$ dollars
when x hot dogs are sold

b. Cost: $c(x) = 0.5x$ dollars when x hot dogs are sold
Profit: $p(x) = (-7.032 \cdot 10^{-4})x^2 + 1.166x + 47.130$
dollars when x hot dogs are sold

c.

x (dollars)	R'(x) (dollars per hot dog)	c'(x) (dollars per hot dog)	p'(x) (dollars per hot dog)
200	1.38	0.50	0.88
800	0.54	0.50	0.04
1100	0.12	0.50	−0.38
1400	−0.30	0.50	−0.80

If the number of hot dogs sold increases from 200 to 201, the revenue increases by approximately $1.38 and the profit increases by approximately $0.88. If the number increases from 800 to 801, the revenue increases by $0.54, but the profit sees almost no increase ($0.04). If the number increases from 1100 to 1101, the increase in revenue is only approximately $0.12. Because this marginal revenue is less than the marginal cost at a sales level of 1100, the result of the sales increase from 1100 to 1101 is a decrease of $0.38 in profit. If the number of hot dogs increases from 1400 to 1401, revenue declines by approximately $0.30 and profit declines by approximately $0.80.

d.

Dollars

The marginal values in part c are the slopes of the graphs shown in the figure above. For example, at $x = 800$, the slope of the revenue graph is $0.54 per hot dog, the slope of the cost graph is $0.50 per hot dog, and the slope of the profit graph is $0.04 per hot dog. We see from the graph that maximum profit is realized when approximately 800 hot dogs are sold. Revenue is greatest near $x = 1100$, so the marginal revenue there is small. However, once costs are factored in, the profit is actually declining at this sales level. This is illustrated by the graph.

23. a. United States: $A(t) = 0.109t^3 - 1.555t^2 + 10.927t + 100.320$;

Canada: $C(t) = 0.150t^3 - 2.171t^2 + 15.814t + 99.650$;

Peru: $P(t) = 85.112(2.01325^t)$;

Brazil: $B(t) = 73.430(2.61594^t)$

For all models t is the number of years since 1980.

b., c.

	United States	Canada	Peru	Brazil
Rate of change in 1987 (CPI points per year)	5.2	7.5	7984	59,193
1988 CPI estimate	143	163	19,134*	136,451*

* Based on 1987 data rather than P(7) and B(7) because the models differ significantly from the data.

25. a. $P(A) = -0.158A^3 + 5.235A^2 - 23.056A + 154.884$ thousand dollars of profit when A thousand dollars is spent on advertising.

b. When $10,000 is spent on advertising, profit is increasing by $34.3 thousand per thousand advertising dollars. If advertising is increased from $10,000 to $11,000, the car dealership can expect an approximate monthly increase in profit of $34,300.

c. When $18,000 is spent on advertising, revenue is increasing by $12.0 thousand per thousand advertising dollars. If advertising is increased from $18,000 to $19,000, the sporting goods company can expect an approximate monthly increase in profit of $12,000.

27. Essay answers will vary but should include a discussion of how the rate of change approximation is following the path of a tangent line instead of following the curve of the function.

29. $f'(x) = \lim_{h \to 0} \dfrac{f(x + h) - f(x)}{h}$

$f'(x) \approx \dfrac{f(x + h) - f(x)}{h}$ for relatively small h

$h \cdot f'(x) \approx h \cdot \left(\dfrac{f(x + h) - f(x)}{h} \right)$

$h \cdot f'(x) \approx f(x + h) - f(x)$

Section 4.2

1. Quadratic or cubic functions could have a relative maximum and/or minimum.

3.

y

The derivative is zero at the absolute maximum point.

5.

The derivative is zero at the absolute maximum point marked with an X.

7.

The derivative is zero at both absolute maximum points. The derivative does not exist at the relative minimum point.

9. One such graph is $y = x^3$.

11. a. All statements are true.

  b. $f'(2)$ does not exist because f is not continuous at $x = 2$.

  c. $f'(x)$ is less than zero for $x < 2$ because the graph to the left of $x = 2$ is decreasing.

  d. $f'(2)$ does not exist because f is not smooth at $x = 2$.

13. One possibility is

15. One possibility is

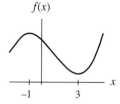

17. a. $f'(x) = 2x + 2.5$

  b. A relative minimum of -7.5625 occurs at $x \approx -1.250$.

19. a. $h'(x) = 3x^2 - 16x - 6$

  b. A relative maximum of approximately 1.077 occurs at $x \approx -0.352$. A relative minimum of -108.929 occurs at $x \approx 5.685$.

21. a. $f'(t) = 12 \ln(1.5)(1.5^t) + 12 \ln(0.5)(0.5^t)$

  b. A relative minimum of approximately 23.182 occurs at $t \approx 0.488$.

23. a. Using technology, the relative maximum value is approximately 19.888, which occurs at $x \approx 3.633$. The relative minimum value is approximately 11.779, which occurs at $x \approx 11.034$.

  b. The absolute maximum and minimum are the relative maximum and minimum found in part *a*.

  c.

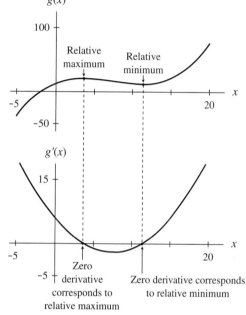

25. a. The greatest percentage of eggs hatching (95.6%) occurs at $9.4°C$.

  b. $9.4°C \approx 49°F$

27. a. $C(0) \approx 123$ cfs and $C(11) \approx 331$ cfs

  b. The highest flow rate is approximately 388.0 cfs; it occurs when $h \approx 8.9$ hours. The lowest flow rate is approximately 121.3 cfs; it occurs when $h \approx 0.4$ hour.

29. a. $S(x) = 0.181x^2 - 8.463x + 147.376$ seconds is the time it takes an x-year-old average athlete to swim 100 meters free style, $8 \le x \le 32$.

  b. The model gives a minimum time of 48.5 seconds occurring at 23.4 years.

  c. The model reaches a minimum slightly earlier and lower than that reported in the data.

31. a. $Q(p) = 316.765(0.949^p)$ dozen roses sold per week when the price per dozen is p dollars, $10 \le p \le 35$

  b. $E(p) = 316.765p(0.949^p)$ dollars spent on roses each week when the price per dozen is p dollars, $10 \le p \le 35$

  c. A price of $\$19.16$ maximizes consumer expenditure.

  d. A price of $\$25.16$ maximizes profit.

  e. Marginal values are with respect to the number of units sold or produced. In this activity, the input is price, so derivatives are with respect to price and are not marginals.

33. **a.** $G(t) = 0.008t^3 - 0.347t^2 + 6.108t + 79.690$ million tons is the yearly amount of garbage taken to a landfill t years after 1975, $0 \le t \le 30$.

b. $G'(t) = 0.025t^2 - 0.693t + 6.108$ million tons per year is the rate of change in the yearly amount of garbage taken to a landfill t years after 1975, $0 \le t \le 30$.

c. Approximately 7.8 million tons per year.

d.

$G(t)$ has no relative extrema because the derivative graph exists for all inputs and never crosses the horizontal axis.

35. The graph indicates there is an absolute maximum to the right of -3 and an absolute minimum to the left of 1. A view of the graph showing more of the horizontal axis indicates that $y = 2$ is a horizontal asymptote for the graph.

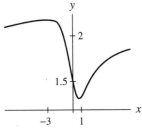

Use technology to find the absolute extrema, or solve the equation

$$y' = \frac{-2x(2x^2 - x + 3)}{(x^2 + 2)^2} + \frac{4x - 1}{x^2 + 2} = 0$$

In either case, you should find the absolute minimum point of approximately $(0.732, 1.317)$ and the absolute

maximum point of approximately $(-2.732, 2.183)$. Thus the absolute maximum is approximately 2.18, and the absolute minimum is approximately 1.32.

Section 4.3

1. **a.** (1982, 25) and (2018, 25); Estimates may vary.

b. The input values of the inflection points are the years in which the rate of crude oil production is estimated to be increasing and decreasing most rapidly. We estimate that the rate of production was increasing most rapidly in 1982, when production was approximately 25 billion barrels per year, and that it will be decreasing most rapidly in 2018, when production is estimated to be approximately 25 billion barrels per year.

3. **a.** Derivative
   b. Function
   c. Second derivative

5. **a.** Second derivative
   b. Derivative
   c. Function

7. $f'(x) = -3; f''(x) = 0$

9. $c'(u) = 6u - 7; c''(u) = 6$

11. $p'(u) = -6.3u^2 + 7u; p''(u) = -12.6u + 7$

13. $g'(t) = 37 \ln(1.05)(1.05^t); g''(t) = 37(\ln 1.05)^2(1.05^t)$

15. $f'(x) = \dfrac{3.2}{x} = 3.2x^{-1}; f''(x) = -3.2x^{-2}$

17. $L'(t) = -16(1 + 2.1e^{3.9t})^{-2}(0 + 2.1e^{3.9t}(3.9))$
    $= -131.04e^{3.9t}(1 + 2.1e^{3.9t})^{-2};$
    $L''(t) = -131.04[e^{3.9t}(-2(1 + 2.1e^{3.9t})^{-3} \cdot$
    $(2.1e^{3.9t}(3.9))) + (1 + 2.1e^{3.9t})^{-2}(3.9e^{3.9t})]$

19. **a.** $f'(x) = 3x^2 - 12x + 12; f''(x) = 6x - 12$
    b. An inflection point may occur when $x = 2$.

21. **a.** $f'(x) = -37(1 + 20.5e^{-0.9x})^{-2}(20.5e^{-0.9x}(-0.9))$
    $= 682.65e^{-0.9x}(1 + 20.5e^{-0.9x})^{-2};$
    $f''(x) = 682.65[e^{-0.9x}(-2(1 + 20.5e^{-0.9x})^{-3} \cdot$
    $(20.5e^{-0.9x}(-0.9))) + (1 + 20.5e^{-0.9x})^{-2}(-0.9e^{-0.9x})]$
    b. An inflection point may occur at $x \approx 3.356$.

23. **a.** $f'(t) = 98(\ln 1.2)(1.2^t) + 120(\ln 0.2)(0.2^t);$
    $f''(t) = 98(\ln 1.2)^2(1.2^t) + 120(\ln 0.2)^2(0.2^t)$
    b. $f(t)$ does not have an inflection point.

25. a.

29. a.

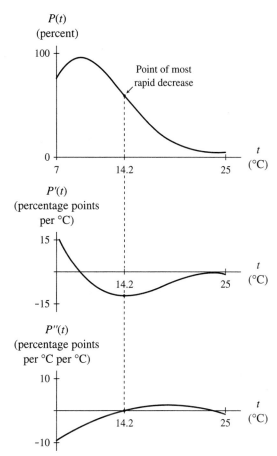

b. The inflection point on the graph of g is approximately (7.333, 15.834). This is a point of most rapid decline.

27. a. The inflection point is approximately (1.838, 22.5). After approximately 1.8 hours of study (1 hour and 50 minutes), the percentage of new material being retained is increasing most rapidly. At that time, approximately 22.5% of the material has been retained.

b. The answer agrees with the one given in the discussion at the end of the section.

b. Because the graph of P'' crosses the t-axis twice, there are two inflection points. These are approximately (14.2, 59.4) and (23.6, 5.8). The point of most rapid decrease is (14.2, 59.4). (The other inflection point is a point of least rapid decrease.) The most rapid decrease occurs at 14.2°C, when 59.4% of eggs hatch. At this temperature, the percentage of eggs hatching is declining by 11.1 percentage points per °C. A small increase in temperature will result in a relatively large decrease in the percentage of eggs hatching.

31. a.

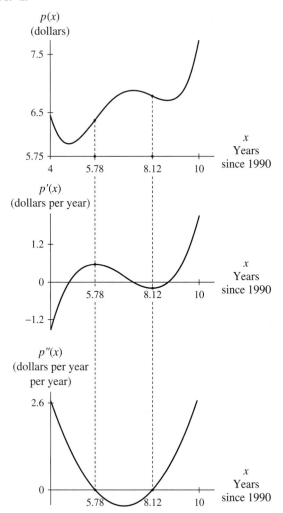

The maximum and minimum points of the graph of p' and the x-intercepts of the graph of p" correspond to the inflection points of the graph of p.

b. The x-intercepts of p" are x ≈ 5.78 and x ≈ 8.12. The price was declining most rapidly in January of 1999 (x ≈ 8.12) at a rate of −$0.19 per year and increasing most rapidly in September of 1996 (x ≈ 5.78) at a rate of $0.57 per year.

c. The price was declining most rapidly at the end of 1994 at a rate of −$1.45 per year and increasing most rapidly at the end of 2000 at a rate of $2.10 per year.

d. The price was declining most rapidly in 1998 at a rate of −$0.19 per year and increasing most rapidly in 1996 at a rate of $0.55 per year.

33. a. (0.418, 9740.089) is a relative minimum point, and (13.121, 20,242.033) is a relative maximum point on the cubic model.

b. The inflection point is approximately (6.8, 14,991.1).

c. i. The inflection point occurs between 1981 and 1982, shortly after the team won the National Championship. This is when the number of donors was increasing most rapidly.

ii. The relative maximum occurred around the same time that a new coach was hired. After this time, the number of donors declined.

35. a. The greatest rate occurs at h ≈ 3.733, or approximately 3 hours and 44 minutes after she began working.

b. Her employer may wish to give her a break after 4 hours to prevent a decline in her productivity.

37. a. $H(w) = \dfrac{10{,}111.102}{1 + 1153.222e^{-0.728w}}$ is the total labor hours spent on a construction job after w weeks, $1 \leq w \leq 19$.

b. $H'(w) = \dfrac{-10{,}111.102(1153.222)(0.728)e^{-0.728w}}{(1 + 1153.222e^{-0.728w})^2}$ labor hours per week is the rate of change in the total number of labor hours spent on a construction job after w weeks, $1 \leq w \leq 19$.

c.

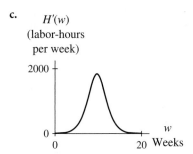

The derivative gives the manager information about the number of labor hours spent each week.

d. The maximum point is approximately (9.685, 1840.134). In the tenth week the most labor hours are needed. That number is $H'(10) \approx 1816$ labor hours.

e. The point of most rapid increase on the graph of H' is (7.876, 1226.756). This occurs approximately 8 weeks into the job, and the number of labor hours per week is increasing by approximately $H''(8) \approx 513$ labor hours per week per week.

f. The point of most rapid decrease on the graph of H' is (11.494, 1226.756). This occurs approximately 12 weeks into the job, and the number of labor hours per week is changing by approximately $H''(12) = -486$ labor hours per week per week.

g. By solving the equation $H'''(w) = 0$, we can find the input values that correspond to a maximum or minimum point on the graph of H'', which corresponds to inflection points on the graph of H', the weekly labor hour curve.

h. The second job should begin approximately 4 weeks into the first job.

39. a. Between 1980 and 1985, the average rate of change was smallest at 1 million tons per year.

b. $g(t) = 0.008t^3 - 0.347t^2 + 6.108t + 79.690$ million tons of garbage taken to a landfill t years after 1970, $0 \le t \le 30$

c. $g''(t) = 0.051t - 0.693$

d. Solving $g''(t) = 0$ gives $t \approx 13.684$ and $g(13.684) \approx 120$ million tons of garbage.

e.

$g'(t)$
(millions of tons per year)

$g''(t)$
(millions of tons per year per year)

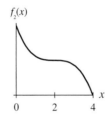

f. The year with the smallest rate of change is 1984, with $g(14) \approx 120$ million tons of garbage, increasing at a rate of $g'(14) \approx 1.4$ million tons per year.

41. a. The first differences are greatest between 6 and 10 minutes, indicating the most rapid increase in activity.

b. $A(m) = \dfrac{1.930}{1 + 31.720e^{-0.439118m}}$ U/100μL m minutes after the mixture reaches 95°C; The inflection point is (7.872, 0.965). After approximately 7.9 minutes, the activity was approximately 0.97 U/100μL and was increasing most rapidly at a rate of approximately 0.212 U/100μL/min.

Because the graph of g'' crosses the t-axis at 13.68, we know that input corresponds to an inflection point of the graph of g. Because $g'(t)$ is a minimum at that same value, we know that it corresponds to a point of slowest increase on the graph of g.

43. The graph of f is always concave up. A concave-up parabola fits this description.

45. a. The graph is concave up to the left of $x = 2$ and concave down to the right of $x = 2$.

b. $f_1(x)$

$f_2(x)$

47. Cubic and logistic models have inflection points.

Section 4.4

1. $\dfrac{df}{dt} = 3\dfrac{dx}{dt}$

3. $\dfrac{dk}{dy} = 12x\dfrac{dx}{dy}$

5. $\dfrac{dg}{dt} = 3e^{3x}\dfrac{dx}{dt}$

7. $\dfrac{df}{dt} = 62(\ln 1.02)(1.02^x)\dfrac{dx}{dt}$

9. $\dfrac{dh}{dy} = \dfrac{6}{a}\dfrac{da}{dy} + 6\ln a\dfrac{da}{dy} = 6\left(\dfrac{1}{a} + \ln a\right)\dfrac{da}{dy}$

11. $\dfrac{ds}{dt} = \dfrac{\pi r h}{\sqrt{r^2 + h^2}} \dfrac{dh}{dt}$

13. $0 = \dfrac{\pi r}{\sqrt{r^2 + h^2}}\left(r\dfrac{dr}{dt} + h\dfrac{dh}{dt}\right) + \pi\sqrt{r^2 + h^2}\,\dfrac{dr}{dt}$

15. **a.** Approximately 52.4 gallons per day

　　b. $\dfrac{dw}{dt} \approx 0.4323$; The amount of water transpired is increasing by approximately 0.4323 gallon per day per year. In other words, in 1 year, the tree will be transpiring approximately 0.4 gallon more each day than it currently is transpiring.

17. **a.** $B = \dfrac{45}{0.00064516h^2}$ points

　　b. $\dfrac{dB}{dt} = \dfrac{-90}{0.00064516h^3} \dfrac{dh}{dt}$

　　c. $\dfrac{dB}{dt} \approx -0.2789$ point per year

19. **a.** Approximately 0.0014 cubic foot per year

　　b. Approximately 0.0347 cubic foot per year

21. **a.** $L = \left(\dfrac{M}{48.10352\,K^{0.4}}\right)^{5/3} = \left(\dfrac{M}{48.10352}\right)^{5/3} K^{-2/3}$

　　b. $\dfrac{dL}{dt} = \left(\dfrac{M}{48.10352}\right)^{5/3}\left(\dfrac{-2}{3} K^{-5/3}\right)\dfrac{dK}{dt}$

　　c. The number of worker hours should be decreasing by approximately 57 worker hours per year.

23. The balloon is approximately 1529.7 feet from the observer, and that distance is increasing by approximately 1.96 feet per second.

25. The runner is approximately 67.08 feet from home plate, and that distance is decreasing by approximately 9.84 feet per second.

27. **a.** Approximately 4188.79 cubic centimeters

　　b. By approximately -167.6 cubic centimeters per minute

29. Approximately 5.305 centimeters per second

31. Begin by solving for h: $h = \dfrac{V}{\pi r^2} = \dfrac{V}{\pi} r^{-2}$

Differentiate with respect to t (V is constant):

$\dfrac{dh}{dt} = \dfrac{V}{\pi}(-2r^{-3})\dfrac{dr}{dt}$

Substitute $\pi r^2 h$ for V: $\dfrac{dh}{dt} = \dfrac{\pi r^2 h}{\pi}(-2r^{-3})\dfrac{dr}{dt}$

Simplify: $\dfrac{dh}{dt} = \dfrac{-2h}{r}\dfrac{dr}{dt}$

Rewrite: $\dfrac{dr}{dt} = \dfrac{r}{-2h}\dfrac{dh}{dt}$

33. *One possible answer:* The most important step in the method of related rates is correctly identifying the independent and dependent variables.

Chapter 4 Concept Review

1. **a.** T has a relative maximum point at $(0.682, 143.098)$ and a relative minimum point at $(3.160, 120.687)$. These points can be determined by finding the values of x between 0 and 6 at which the graph of T' crosses the x-axis.

　　b. T has two inflection points: $(1.762, 132.939)$ and $(5.143, 149.067)$. These points can be determined by finding the values of x between 0 and 6 at which the graph of T'' crosses the x-axis. These are also the points at which T' has a relative maximum and a relative minimum.

　　c.

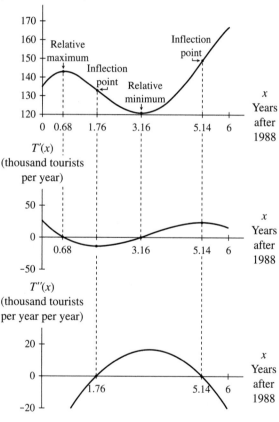

d. The number of tourists was greatest in 1994 at 166.8 thousand tourists. The number was least in 1991 at 120.9 thousand.

e. The number of tourists was increasing most rapidly in 1993 at a rate of 23.1 thousand tourists per year. The number of tourists was decreasing most rapidly in 1990 at a rate of 13.3 thousand tourists per year.

2. **a.** (4.5 thousand people per year)$\left(\frac{1}{4}\text{ year}\right)$ = 1.125 thousand people

   b. $202 + \frac{1}{2}(4.5) = 204.25$ thousand people

3. **a.** $G(x) = (5.051 \cdot 10^{-5})x^3 - 0.007x^2 + 0.085x + 105.027$ is the number of males per 100 females in the United States x years after 1900, $0 \le x \le 100$.

   b. $G''(x) = (30.303 \cdot 10^{-5})x - 0.014$

   c. The output of the model exhibits most rapid decline when $x \approx 44.598$. The gender ratio was decreasing most rapidly in 1945 when the gender ratio was approximately 99.8 males per 100 females. The gender ratio was decreasing by approximately -0.216 males per 100 females per year.

4.

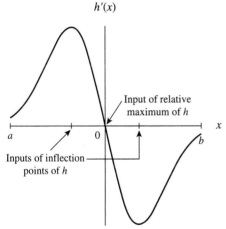

$h'(x)$

Input of relative maximum of h

Inputs of inflection points of h

5. $\dfrac{ds}{dt} = 0.000013(2wv)\dfrac{dv}{dt}$

   $= -31.2$ feet per second

   The length of the skid marks is decreasing by 31.2 feet per second.

CHAPTER 5

Section 5.1

1. **a.** Thousand bacteria per hour

   b. Hours

   c. Thousand bacteria

   d. Thousand bacteria

   e. Thousand bacteria

3. **a.** The area would represent how much farther a car going 60 mph would require to stop than a car going 40 mph.

b. i. The heights are in feet per mile per hour, and the widths are in miles per hour.

   ii. The area is in feet.

5. **a.** Thousand people

   b. Thousand people

   c. Thousand people

7. **a.** This is the change in the number of organisms when the temperature increases from 25°C to 35°C.

   b. This is the magnitude of the change in the number of organisms when the temperature increases from 30°C to 40°C.

9. **a., b.** Between 0 and 300 boxes and between 400 and 600 boxes

   c. NA

   d 300

   e. 400

   f. Approximately 350

   g. dollars

   h. less

11. **a.** On the horizontal axis, mark integer values of x between 0 and 8. Construct a rectangle with width from $x = 0$ to $x = 1$ and height $f(1)$. Because the width of the rectangle is 1, the area will be the same as the height. Repeat the rectangle constructions between each pair of consecutive integer input values. Note that for the rectangles that lie below the horizontal axis, the heights are the absolute values of the function values. Also note that the fourth rectangle has height 0. Sum the areas (heights) of the rectangles to obtain the area estimate.

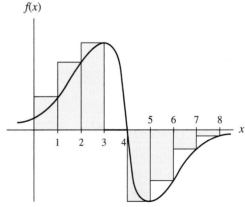

$f(x)$

   b. Repeat part a, except that the height of each rectangle is determined by the function value corresponding to the left side of the interval. In the case of the first rectangle, the height is $f(0)$. When we use left rectangles, the fifth rectangle has height 0.

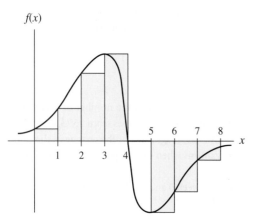

f(x)

13. Divide the interval from a to b into four equal subintervals. Determine the midpoint of each subinterval, and substitute into the function to find the heights of the rectangles. Multiply each height by the width of the subintervals, and add the four resulting areas.

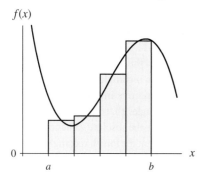

f(x)

15. Possible solution:

a. Each rectangle has a width of 25 years.

Interval	Midpoint height (billion barrels per year)	Rectangle area (billions of barrels)
1900–1925	0	0
1925–1950	3	75
1950–1975	9	225
1975–2000	33	825
2000–2025	33	825
2025–2050	9	225
2050–2075	3	75
2075–2100	1	25

Total area of rectangles ≈ 2275 billion barrels
Total oil production ≈ 2275 billion barrels

b. Each rectangle has a width of 25 years.

Interval	Midpoint height (billion barrels per year)	Rectangle area (billions of barrels)
1900–1925	0	0
1925–1950	3	75
1950–1975	9	225
1975–2000	24	825
2000–2025	13	825
2025–2050	4	225
2050–2075	1	75
2075–2100	0	25

Total area of rectangles ≈ 1625 billion barrels
Total oil production ≈ 1625 billion barrels

c. The graph A estimate is 175 billion barrels above the journal's estimate. The graph B estimate is 275 billion barrels above the journal's estimate.

17. a.

Velocity (feet per minute)

b. 2420 feet

c. The robot traveled 2420 feet during the $3\frac{1}{2}$-minute experiment.

19. a.

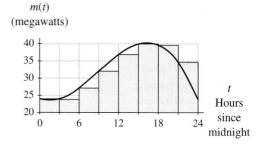

m(t) (megawatts)

Interval	Height (megawatts)	Area (megawatt hours)
0 to 3	24	72.0
3 to 6	23.5	70.5
6 to 9	27.5	82.5
9 to 12	32	96.0
12 to 15	37	111.0
15 to 18	40	120.0
18 to 21	39.5	118.5
21 to 24	34.5	103.5
Total area ≈ 774 megawatt hours		

b.

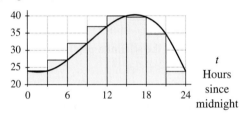

Interval	Height (megawatts)	Area (megawatt hours)
0 to 3	23.5	70.5
3 to 6	27.5	82.5
6 to 9	32	96.0
9 to 12	37	111.0
12 to 15	40	120.0
15 to 18	39.5	118.5
18 to 21	34.5	103.5
21 to 24	23	69.0
Total area ≈ 771 megawatt hours		

c. Answers will vary. The exact area to three decimal places is 774.426, so both estimates are very close.

21. a.

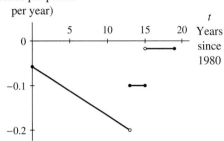

b. 9.504

c. Per capita consumption of cottage cheese decreased by about 9.5 pounds per person between 1980 and 1996.

d. No; We cannot determine the per capita consumption of cottage cheese in 1996 unless we know the value in 1980 (or in some other year between 1980 and 1996). If we knew the 1980 value, we would subtract 9.5 to obtain the 1996 value.

23. a.

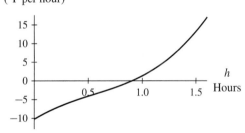

The graph crosses the horizontal axis at $h \approx 0.907$ hour.

b. The area below the axis represents the amount the temperature declined from the time the storm began.

c. The area above the axis represents the amount by which the temperature rose from the time it stopped declining until 1.5 hours after the storm began.

d. Each rectangle has width $\dfrac{0.907 - 0}{3} \approx 0.302$ hour. The area of the region is about 2.775°F.

e. Each rectangle has width $\dfrac{1.5 - 0.907}{3} \approx 0.198$ hour. The area of the region is about 4.624°F.

f. Using a limit of sums, $\displaystyle\int_0^{0.907} T(h)\,dh \approx -4.27\ °F$

g. Using a limit of sums, $\displaystyle\int_{0.907}^{1.5} T(h)\,dh \approx 3.25\ °F$

h. $\int_{0.907}^{1.5} T(h)dh \approx -4.27 + 3.25 = -1.02.$ To determine the temperature when $h = 1.5$, we would have to know the temperature at $h = 0$. One and one half hours after the storm began, the temperature was approximately 1°F lower than it was at the beginning of the storm.

25. a.

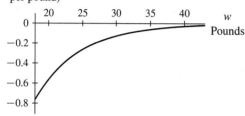

$P(w)$
(percentage points per pound)

b. The percentage of low-birthweight babies was declining as the mother's weight gain increased from 18 to 43 pounds.

c. The signed area is approximately -4.8. When the amount of weight gained during a woman's pregnancy increased from 18 to 43 pounds, the percentage of low-birthweight babies decreased by approximately 4.8 percentage points.

27. a.

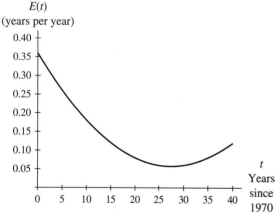

$E(t)$
(years per year)

b. $E(t)$ has a minimum value when $t \approx 27.5$.

c. $Area = 10 \cdot E(5) + 10 \cdot E(15) + 10 \cdot E(25) + 10 \cdot E(35) = 5.2$ years.

d. Life expectancy for women increased approximately 5.2 years from 1970 through 2010. The life expectancy in 1970 is needed to determine the life expectancy in 2010.

29. a.

Number of midpoint rectangles	Approximate accumulated change
5	54.908
10	55.307
20	55.407
40	55.432
80	55.438

From 1990 through 2001, factory sales increased by approximately $55.4 billion.

b. $\int_{0}^{11} s(x)dx \approx 55.4$

c. Approximately $98.4 billion

31. a. $S(t) = \dfrac{695.606}{1 + 0.081e^{0.495438t}}$ thousand cassettes per month gives the sales of a popular movie t months after release, $2 \leq t \leq 18$.

b.

Number of rectangles	Approximation of area
5	3617.9
10	3623.6
15	3625.4

The estimates are about 3,618,000 cassettes, 3,624,000 cassettes, and 3,625,000 cassettes.

c. The sum of the sales figures (iii) will be most accurate because it will give the exact total. (Note that the text does not give all of the data needed to perform this calculation.)

33. a. $n = 5$: 9859 labor hours
$n = 10$: 10,097 labor hours
$n = 20$: 10,100 labor hours

b. *iii*

35. The accumulated change of a function f with input x over an interval from a to b is the sum of the signed areas of regions bounded by the graph of f, the horizontal axis, the vertical lines at a and b, and any points where the graph of f intersects the horizontal axis. This accumulated change is also defined as the definite integral $\int_{a}^{b} f(x)dx$.

Section 5.2

1. a.

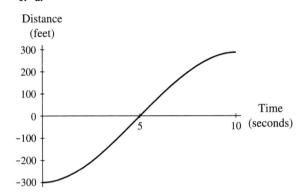

Distance (feet) vs. Time (seconds)

b. $D(x) = \int_5^x f(t)\, dt$

c. The accumulation function gives the distance traveled between 5 seconds and x seconds. For times before 5 seconds, the accumulation function is the negative of the distance traveled, because we are looking back in time.

3. a. The area between days 0 and 18 represents how much the price of the technology stock declined ($15.40 per share) during the first 18 trading days of 2003.

b. The area between days 18 and 47 represents how much the price of the technology stock rose ($55.80 per share) between days 18 and 47.

c. $40.40 more

d. $11.10 less

e.

x	$\int_0^x r(t)\, dt$	x	$\int_0^x r(t)\, dt$
0	0	35	15.0
8	−7.1	47	40.4
18	−15.4	55	29.3

f.

$\int_0^x r(t)\, dt$

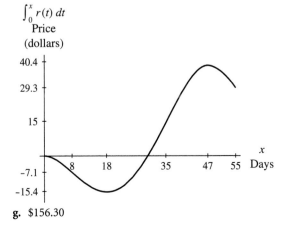

Price (dollars) vs. Days

g. $156.30

5. a. No

b. The peak corresponds to the time when the number of subscribers was increasing most rapidly.

c. The number of new subscribers t days after the end of the twentieth week

d. 280 subscribers

e.

Week	t (days)	Area	Week	t (days)	Area
4	28	350	28	196	8820
8	56	924	36	252	10,430
12	84	1960	44	308	10,920
16	112	3500	52	364	11,060
20	140	5390			

f.

$\int_{140}^t n(x)\, dx$

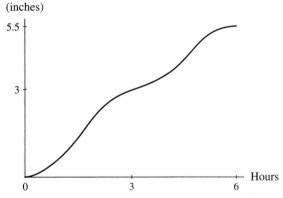

Subscribers vs. Days

7. One possible answer:

Rainfall (inches) vs. Hours

9. a.

$\int_A^x f(t)\, dt$

b.

$\int_B^x f(t)\, dt$

11. a.

$$\int_0^x f(t)\,dt$$

b.

$$\int_A^x f(t)\,dt$$

b.

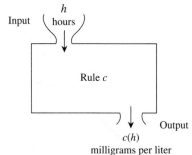

Output
$c(h)$
milligrams per liter

c. The concentration of a drug in the bloodstream is $c(h)$ milligrams per liter h hours after the drug is given.

25. A negative rate of change indicates a loss in the additional accumulated amount. This loss is evidenced in a decrease of the accumulation graph.

c.

$$\int_B^x f(t)\,dt$$

Section 5.3

1. a. ii **b.** i **c.** iii **3. a.** iii **b.** i **c.** ii

5. $\dfrac{d}{dx}\left(\displaystyle\int_2^x 3t\,dt\right) = \dfrac{d}{dx}\left(\dfrac{3t^2}{2}\Big|_2^x\right)$

$$= \dfrac{d}{dx}\left(\dfrac{3x^2}{2} - 6\right) = 3x$$

7. The antiderivative of a derivative formula for a given function returns the original function plus a constant.

9. $\displaystyle\int 19.4(1.07^x)\,dx = \dfrac{19.4(1.07^x)}{\ln 1.07} + C$

11. $\displaystyle\int [6e^x + 4(2^x)]\,dx = 6e^x + \dfrac{4(2^x)}{\ln 2} + C$

13. $\displaystyle\int (10^x + 4x^{\frac{1}{2}} + 8)\,dx = \dfrac{10^x}{\ln 10} + 4\left(\dfrac{2}{3}\right)x^{\frac{3}{2}} + 8x + C$

15. $S(m) = \dfrac{600(0.93^m)}{\ln 0.93} + C$ CDs m months after the beginning of the year

17. $C(x) = 0.8 \ln x + \dfrac{0.38(0.01^x)}{\ln 0.01} + K$ dollars per unit when x units are produced

19. $F(t) = \dfrac{1}{3}t^3 + t^2 - 20$

21. $F(z) = \dfrac{-1}{z} + e^z + \left(\dfrac{3}{2} - e^2\right)$

23. $w(t) = 7.37 \ln t + (26 - 7.37 \ln 7) \approx 7.37 \ln t + 11.66$ grams is the weight of the mouse at age $(t + 2)$ weeks. The specific antiderivative is the formula for the accumulation function of W passing through the point $(7, 26)$.

25. a. $G(t) = \dfrac{(1.67 \cdot 10^{-4})}{3}t^3 - 0.01t^2 - 0.10t + 131.71$ males per 100 females gives the gender ratio for the United States t years after 1900.

b. This specific antiderivative is the formula for the accumulation function of g passing through the point $(70, 94.8)$.

13.

$$\int_0^x f(t)\,dt$$

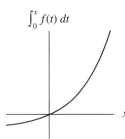

15. Derivative graph: b; accumulation graph: f

17. Derivative graph: f; accumulation graph: e

19. Derivative: left table; accumulation function: right table

21. a. $\dfrac{\text{Million dollars of revenue}}{\text{Thousand advertising dollars}}$

b.

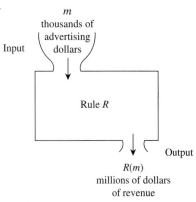

Output
$R(m)$
millions of dollars
of revenue

c. When m thousand dollars are being spent on advertising, the annual revenue is $R(m)$ million dollars.

23. a. $\dfrac{\text{Milligrams per liter}}{\text{Hour}}$

27. a., b. Velocity: $v(t) = -32t$ feet/second

Distance: $s(t) = -16t^2 + 540$ feet

where t is the number of seconds after the penny was dropped

c. Solving for t in $s(t) = 0$, we obtain $t \approx \pm 5.8$ seconds. The penny will hit the ground approximately 5.8 seconds after it was dropped.

29. a. The impact velocity is approximately -64.99 feet/second, or -44.31 mph.

b. Air resistance probably accounts for the difference.

31. a. $N(x) = 593 \ln x + 138x - 748.397$ new employees at an Internet company x years after 1996, $1 \le x \le 6$

b. The function in part a applies from 1997 ($x = 1$) through 2002 ($x = 6$).

c. Approximately 1753; not necessarily; *One possible answer*: The number of employees hired does not take into account the number of people who left the company.

Section 5.4

1. c. Find a specific antiderivative and evaluate in year t

3. b. Find a general antiderivative and evaluate from a to x

5. b. Find a general antiderivative and evaluate from a to x

7. a. Find a derivative and evaluate at a.

9. a.

$f(x)$

(graph showing curve through points near -1, 1, 2 with values from 3 to -7)

b. No; Because $f(x)$ is negative between $x \approx 1.054$ and $x = 2$, the area from a to b is approximately

$$\int_{-1}^{1.054} f(x)dx + \left| \int_{1.054}^{2} f(x)dx \right| \approx 1.603 + 2.218 = 3.821$$

c. $\int_{-1}^{2} (-1.3x^3 + 0.93x^2 + 0.49)dx$

$$= \frac{-1.3x^4}{4} + \frac{0.93x^3}{3} + 0.49x \Big|_{-1}^{2}$$

$$= -1.74 - (-1.125)$$

$$= -0.615$$

11. a.

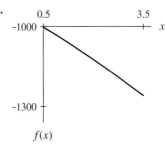

b. No; Because $f(x)$ is negative between $x = 0.5$ and $x = 3.5$, the area from a to b equals

$$\left| \int_{0.5}^{3.5} -965.27(1.079^x)dx \right| \approx 3378.735$$

c. $\int_{0.5}^{3.5} -965.27(1.079^x)dx \approx -3378.735$

13. $\int_{5}^{15} P(x)dx \approx 2305.357$ million calls; Between 1985 and 1995, the number of international calls billed in the United States increased by about 2.3 billion.

15. $\int_{0}^{5} (9.907x^2 - 40.769x + 58.492)dx \approx 195.639$ million dollars; Between 1987 and 1992, the corporation's revenue increased by \$195.639 million.

17. a. $\int_{0}^{70} (0.00241t + 0.02905)dt = 7.938$ cm; In the first 70 days after April 1, the snow pack in the Northwest Territories in Canada increased by about 7.938 cm.

b. Between the 72nd and 76th days after April 1, the snow pack in the Northwest Territories in Canada decreased by about 22.368 cm.

c. It is not possible to find the value of $\int_{0}^{76} N(t)dt$ because we have no information about the rate of change in the snow pack in the Northwest Territories in Canada between the 70th and 72nd days after April 1.

19. a. $\int_{0}^{0.8955} T(h)dh \approx 1.48°F$; The temperature in the museum rose about 1.48° F in the 54 minutes following 8:30 A.M.

b. $\int_{0.8955}^{1.75} T(h)dh \approx -1.61°F$; The temperature in the museum decreased by about 1.65° F between 9:24 A.M. and 10:15 A.M.

c. No, the highest temperature reached was $71 + 1.48 = 72.48°F$.

21. a. $f(x) = 0.161(1.076^x)$ trillion cubic feet per year is the rate of change in natural gas in the United States (excluding Alaska) between 1900 and 1960, where x is the number of years after 1900.

b. From 1940 through 1960, the amount of natural gas produced increased by 138.3 trillion cubic feet.

c. $\int_{40}^{60} f(x)dx$

23. a. $C'(x) = (7.714 \cdot 10^{-5})x^2 - 0.047x + 8.940$ dollars per CD is the marginal cost of production of an addition CD, when x CDs are produced each hour, $100 \leq x \leq 300$

b. $C(x) = \dfrac{7.714 \cdot 10^{-5}}{3}x^3 - \dfrac{0.047}{2}x^2 + 8.940x - 143.893$ dollars is the production cost of CDs, when x CDs are produced each hour, $100 \leq x \leq 300$

c. $\int_{200}^{300} C'(x)dx \approx 196.14$ dollars; When the number of CDs produced each hour increases from 200 to 300, the hourly production cost is increased by about $196.

25. a., b.

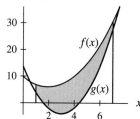

c. 21.33

27. a., c.

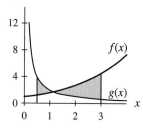

b. $f(x) = g(x) \longrightarrow x \approx 1.134$.

d. Difference $= \int_{0.5}^{3} [f(x) - g(x)]dx \approx 2.812$

e. Area ≈ 4.172

29. a. When the amount invested in capital increases from $1500 to $5500, profit increases by approximately $1.33 thousand.

b. Area $= \int_{1.5}^{5.5} [r'(x) - c'(x)]dx = 13.29$

31. a. The population of the country grew by 3690 people in January.

b. The population declined by 9720 people between the beginning of February and the beginning of May.

c. -6030 people

d. Because the graphs intersect, the area of R_1 represents an increase in population, and the area of R_2 represents a decrease. The net change is the difference Area of R_1 − area of R_2.
The total area is the sum:
Area of R_1 + area of R_2.

33. a. Before fitting models to the data, add the point (0,0), and convert the data from miles per hour to feet per second by multiplying each speed by $\left(\dfrac{5280 \text{ feet}}{1 \text{ mile}}\right)\left(\dfrac{1 \text{ hour}}{3600 \text{ seconds}}\right)$. The speed of the Supra after t seconds can be modeled as
$s(t) = -0.702t^2 + 20.278t + 2.440$ feet per second
The speed of the Carrera after t seconds can be modeled as
$c(t) = -0.643t^2 + 18.963t + 5.252$ feet per second

b. Approximately 17.96 feet

c. Approximately 18.04 feet

35. a.

Rate of change of revenue
(billions of dollars per year)

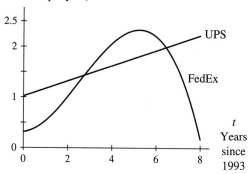

FedEx: $F(t) = -0.026t^3 + 0.198t^2 + 0.06t + 0.317$ billion dollars per year t years after 1993

UPS: $U(t) = 0.15t + 1.022$ billion dollars per year t years after 1993

b. Area of region on left ≈ $1.28 billion
Area of region on middle ≈ $1.20 billion
Area of region on right ≈ $1.59 billion
Between the beginning of 1993 and late 1996 ($t \approx 2.8$), UPS's accumulated revenue exceeded that of FedEx by approximately $1.28 billion. Between late 1996 and the spring of 2000 ($t \approx 6.3$), FedEx's accumulated revenue exceeded that of UPS by approximately $1.2 billion. From the spring of 2000 until the end of 2001, UPS's accumulated revenue exceeded that of FedEx by about $1.59 billion.

c. $\int_{0}^{8} [F(t) - U(t)]dt \approx$ $1.68 billion. This value is the net amount by which UPS's accumulated revenue exceeded that of FedEx between 1993 and 2001.

37. a. $f(x) = \begin{cases} 0 \text{ tons per year} & \text{when } 0 \leq x < 5 \\ \dfrac{557.960}{1 + 91.202e^{-0.318025x}} \\ \text{tons per year} & \text{when } x \geq 5 \end{cases}$

x years after 1990

b., c.

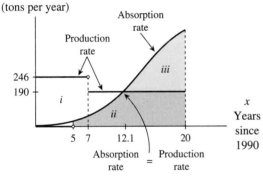

Carbon production and absorption (tons per year)

d.   i. 2054.9 tons
ii. 2137.1 tons
iii. 1269.0 tons
e. No, The factory produces 4192 tons, and the trees absorb 3406 tons. This does not comply with the federal regulation.

39. The height of a rectangle is found by subtracting the height of the bottom line from the height of the top line. For example, the height of the left rectangle is $3 - (-4) = 7$ and the height of the right rectangle is $-1 - (-3) = 2$.

Section 5.5

1. a. $V(t) = -1.664t^3 + 5.867t^2 + 1.640t + 60.164$ mph is the average speed of motorists during rush hour between 4:00 P.M. and 7:00 P.M., where t is the number of hours after 4 P.M.
b. 68.99 mph
c. 72.23 mph

3. a. $f(x) = 1.822(0.899^x)$ dollars per minute is the rate of change in the most expensive charge for a 2-minute long-distance phone call using a carrier between 1982 and 2000, where x is the number of years since 1980.
b. $0.99 per minute
c. $0.65 per minute

5. a. 87.8 million people
b. population ≈ 87.8 ⟶ $t \approx 94.1$. This corresponds to early 1995.
c. ≈ 2.287 million people per year

7. a. −100.6 yearly accidents per year
b. 2810.5 yearly accidents
c.

Accidents

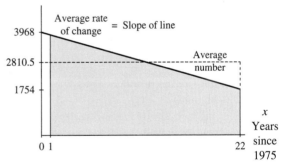

9. a. 2.28 feet per second squared
b. 129.7 feet per second
c. 4540.7 feet
d. 4540.7 feet

e.

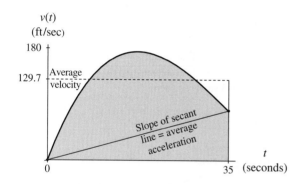

The area of shaded region = the distance traveled = the area of a rectangle with height 129.7 ft/sec and width 35 seconds.

11. a. $V(t) = 1.033t + 138.413$ meters per second is the rate of change of the growth of a crack, t microseconds after the experiment began, $0 \le t \le 60$.

b. 174.58 meters per second

13. a. $B(t) = 0.030t^2 - 0.718t + 3.067$ mm Hg per hour is the rate of change of diastolic blood pressure for a patient with untreated hypertension during one day, where t is the number of hours after 8 A.M.

b. 0.21 mm Hg per hour

c. 93.4 mm Hg

15. −0.32 seconds per year

17. a. The average of the CO concentration is highest between 10 A.M. and 6 P.M.

b. $C(x) = -0.248x^2 + 4.291x + 3.86$ ppm is the concentration of carbon monoxide in the air in a certain metropolitan area between 10 A.M. and 6 P.M., where x is the number of hours since 6 A.M.
Average concentration between 10 A.M. and 6 P.M. is 16.8 ppm.

c. Severe pollution warning

19. Consider the two graphs of a function f shown below, where A is the average value of f from a to b, and k is an arbitrary constant.

We know that the areas of the two shaded regions are equal. If we remove from each graph the rectangular region with height k and width $b - a$, the areas of the resulting regions are still equal, because we have removed the same area from each. See the following graphs.

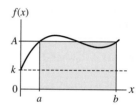

It is true for the graphs in this section with vertical axis shown from k rather than from zero that the area of the region between the function and $y = k$ from a to b is the same as the area of the rectangle with height equal to the average value minus k and width equal to $b - a$.

Section 5.6

1. $\int 2e^{2x}dx = e^{2x} + C$

3. $\int 2xe^{x^2}dx = e^{x^2} + C$

5. $\int (1 + e^x)^2 dx = \dfrac{(1 + e^x)^3}{3} + C$

7. $\int \dfrac{2^x}{2^x + 2} dx = \dfrac{1}{\ln 2}\int \dfrac{2^x \cdot \ln 2}{2^x + 2} dx = \dfrac{1}{\ln 2} \cdot \ln(2^x + 2) + C$

9. $\int_1^4 \ln x\, dx \approx 2.55$

11. Exactly $\dfrac{(\ln 5)^2}{2} - \dfrac{(\ln 2)^2}{2}$

13. $\int_1^2 2x\ln(x^2 + 1)dx \approx 3.66$

15. Exactly $\ln 17 - \ln 10$

17. $\int_1^6 \dfrac{2x^2}{x^2 + 1} dx \approx 8.76$

19. Exactly $\dfrac{13}{12}$

Chapter 5 Concept Review

1. a.

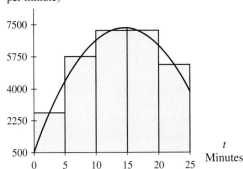

r(t)
(cubic feet
per minute)

b. 139,237.5 cubic feet

c. In the first 25 minutes that oil flowed into the tank, the amount of oil in the tank increased by approximately 139,238 cubic feet.

2. a. $S(t) = -1.643t^2 + 16.157t + 0.2$ miles per hour is the speed at which a hurricane is moving toward the east coast of Florida, where t is the number of hours since 12 midnight, $1 \leq t \leq 5$

b.

n	Sum
5	127.131
10	126.869
20	126.803
40	126.786
Limit ≈ 126.8 miles	

3. a. The area beneath the horizontal axis represents the decrease in weight during the diet.

b. The area above the axis represents the increase in weight between weeks 20 and 30.

c. The person's weight was 11.3 pounds less at 30 weeks than it was at 0 weeks.

d.

Weight
(pounds)

e. The graph in part *d* is the overall change in the person's weight as a function of the number of weeks after the beginning of dieting.

4. a. $R(t) = 10\left(\dfrac{-3.2}{3}t^3 + \dfrac{93.3}{2}t^2 + 50.7t\right) + 5000$ cubic feet is the amount of oil in the tank after t minutes.

b. $R(10) - R(0) \approx 41{,}053.3 \; ft^3$

c. $R(t) = 150{,}000 \longrightarrow t \approx 28$ minutes

5. a. \$2598.60

b. At the end of the third quarter of the third year, the \$10,000 investment had increased by \$2598.60 to a total value of \$12,598.60.

c. \$944.94 per year

6. $\displaystyle\int_{79}^{88} [m(t) - w(t)] \, dt \approx \$123$ thousand

Between the beginning of 1980 and the end of 1988, the wages of a man earning the average full-time wage would have increased by about \$123,000 more than the wages of a woman earning the average full-time wage.

CHAPTER 6

Section 6.1

1. 15

3. 0.3

5. −0.02

7. Diverges

9. Diverges

11. Diverges

13. a. Approximately 0.0002 milligram
Approximately 0.0015 milligram

b. $\displaystyle\int_0^\infty r(t)dt = \lim_{N\to\infty} \dfrac{-1.55(0.9999999845^t) \cdot 10^{-6}}{\ln(0.9999999845)}\Big|_0^N =$

$-99.99999923 \approx -100$ milligrams

15. a. $p \approx \$28.04$

b. $C = qp_0 + \displaystyle\int_{p^0}^\infty D(p)dp$

$\approx 150(28.04) + \displaystyle\int_{28.04}^\infty 499.589(0.958^p)dp$

$\approx \$7702$ million

Consumers are willing and able to spend about \$7.7 million for 150,000 books.

17. $\displaystyle\int_0^\infty 0.1e^{-0.1x}dx = \lim_{N\to\infty}\int_0^N 0.1e^{-0.1x}dx$

$= \lim_{N\to\infty}\left(-e^{-01x}\Big|_0^N\right) = \lim_{N\to\infty}[-e^{-0.1N} - (-e^0)]$

$= \lim_{N\to\infty}(-e^{-0.1N}) + \lim_{N\to\infty}(e^0) = 0 + 1 = 1$

Section 6.2

1. **a.** **i.** $R(m) = 0.2\left(\dfrac{\$47{,}000}{12}\right) = \$783.33$ per month

   ii. $R(m) = 0.2\left(\dfrac{47{,}000}{12} + 100m\right) = 783.33 + 20m$
   dollars a month after m months

   iii. $R(m) = 0.2\left(\dfrac{47{,}000}{12}(1.005^m)\right) = 783.33(1.005^m)$
   dollars a month after m months

   b. **i.** $53{,}493.40

   ii. $92{,}082.72

   iii. $61{,}818.49

   The first option is the only one that will not result in the amount needed for the down payment.

3. $11.2 billion

5. **a.** $51.5 billion

   b. $27.8 billion

7. **a.** $\displaystyle\int_0^6 6000e^{0.0634(6-x)}dx \approx \$43{,}804.70$

   b. $\displaystyle\sum_{m=0}^{71} 500\left(1 + \dfrac{0.0634}{12}\right)^{(72-m)} \approx \$43{,}896.84$

   c. Part b; *One possible answer:* Individuals do not generally have access to continuous compounding.

9. **a.** $r(q) = 82.1(1.05^q)(0.15)$ million dollars per quarter q quarters after the third quarter of 2002

   b. $R(q) = 82.1(1.05^q)(0.15)(1.09)^{16-q}$ million dollars per quarter for money invested q quarters after the third quarter of 2002

   c. If the investment begins with the fourth-quarter 2002 profits, then the initial investment is based on a profit of $(82.1)(1.05) = \$86.205$ million. Thus we calculate
   $$\sum_{q=0}^{15} 86.205(0.15)(1.05^q)(1.09)^{16-q} \approx \$629.8 \text{ million.}$$

11. **a.** $79.87 thousand

    b. $58.29 thousand

13. **a.** $28,324.60

    b. $28,445.37

    c. Part b; *One possible answer:* Individuals do not generally have access to continuous compounding.

15. **a.** $5.4 billion

    b. $6.1 billion

    c. $11.2 billion

17. **a.** $7.3 billion

    b. $5.6 billion

    c. CSX was optimistic about its influence on Conrail, while Conrail assumed that it would decline.

19. $5.2 million

21. Answers given are based on the end of 2007.

    a. 0.14 million terns

b. $T(t) = 2.04(0.83)^{30-t}$ million terns born t years after 1979.

c. 10.91 million terns

23. **a.** None

    b. $S(t) = (60 - 0.5t)(0.67)^{50-t}$ thousand seals born t years from now.

    c. 90.5 thousand seals

Section 6.3

1. **a.** The demand function

   b. The supply function

   c. The producers' surplus

   d. The consumers' surplus

3. **a.** To find the price P above which consumers will purchase none of the goods or services, either find the smallest positive value for which the demand function is zero, $D(p) = 0$, or, if $D(p)$ is never exactly zero but approaches zero as p increases without bound, then let $P \to \infty$.

   b. The supply function, S, is often a piecewise continuous function with the first piece being the 0 function. The value p at which $S(p)$ is no longer 0 is the shutdown price. The shutdown point is $(p_1, S(p_1))$. When S is a continuous function, the shutdown point is $(0, S(0))$.

   c. The market equilibrium price, p_0, can be found as the solution to $S(p) = D(p)$. That is, it is the price at which demand is equal to supply. The equilibrium point is the point $(p_0, D(p_0)) = (p_0, S(p_0))$.

5. **a.** $q_0 \approx 27.5$ thousand units

   b., c.

(a) Mathematician's viewpoint

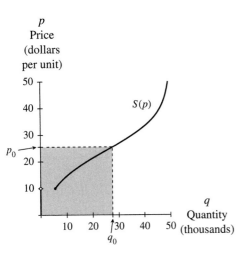

(b) Economist's viewpoint

7. a.

Mathematician's viewpoint

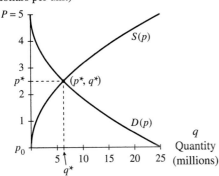

Economist's viewpoint

$p^* \approx 2.5$ dollars per unit, $q^* \approx 6.25$ million units,
$p_1 = 0$ dollars per unit, $P \approx 5$ dollars per unit

b., c.

Mathematician's viewpoint

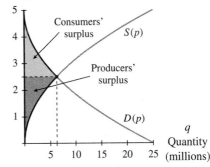

Economist's viewpoint

   d. $TSG = \int_0^{2.5} S(p)\,dp + \int_{2.5}^5 D(p)\,dp$ million dollars

9. a. D is an exponential demand function and so does not have a finite value p at which $D(p) = 0$. Thus the equation does not indicate a price above which consumers will purchase none of the goods or services.
   b. $6128.6 thousand
   c. 17.4 thousand fans
   d. $4331.5 thousand

11. a. $D(p) = 0.025p^2 - 1.421p + 19.983$ lanterns   when the market price is $p per lantern.
   b. $109.18
   c. $31.89

13. a. unit elasticity: $249.50
   b. inelastic: $p < \$249.50$
        elastic: $p \geq \$249.50$

15. a. unit elasticity: $9.34
   b. inelastic: $p < \$9.34$
        elastic: $p \geq \$9.34$

17. a. $40: 18.4 thousand answering machines; $50: 300 thousand answering machines
   b. $9981 thousand; $3131 thousand

19. a. $S(p) = \begin{cases} 0 \text{ hundred prints} & \text{when } p < 5 \\ 0.300p^2 - 3.126p + \\ \quad 10.143 \text{ hundred prints} & \text{when } p \geq 5 \end{cases}$

   where p hundred dollars is the price of a print
   b. $837.12
   c. Producer's revenue $\approx$ $148.5 thousand

   Producer's surplus $\approx$ $27.3 thousand

21. a. $408.3 hundred
   b. 297 sculptures; No
   c. $4542.2 hundred

23. a. $D(p) = 499.589(0.958086^p)$ thousand books when the market price is p per book

   b. $S(p) = \begin{cases} 0 \text{ thousand books} & \text{when } p < 18.97 \\ 0.532p^2 - 20.060p + \\ \quad 309.025 \text{ thousand books} & \text{when } p \geq 18.97 \end{cases}$

   where p is the price of a book
   c. Approximately $27.15; 156.2 thousand books
   d. $4728.6 thousand

Section 6.4

1. a. There is a 46% chance that any telephone call made on a computer software technical support line will last 5 minutes or more.
   b. The likelihood that any two cars on a certain two-lane road are less than 7 feet apart is approximately 25%.
   c. New Orleans will receive between 2 and 4 inches of rain during March 15% of the time.

3. a. Yes, $f(x) \geq 0$ for all x and $\int_{-\infty}^{\infty} f(x)dx = \int_{0}^{1} f(x)dx = 1$.

   b. Yes, $h(x) \geq 0$ for all x and $\int_{-\infty}^{\infty} h(x)dx = \int_{0}^{1} h(x)dx = 1$.

   c. No, the area between the graph of r and the horizontal axis is $0.3 + 0.6 \neq 1$.
   d. No, some values of $s(c)$ are negative.

5. a. $P(x < 1) = \int_{0}^{1} y(x)dx = 0.16$

   b. $\mu \approx 167$ gallons

c.

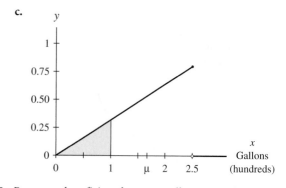

7. Because the $f(x)$ values are all non-negative and $\int_{-\infty}^{\infty} f(x)dx = 1$, the probability (which is the area between the graph of f and the input axis) must always be between 0 and 1. Another view of this explanation is that the probability of some occurrence is the proportion of time it is expected to happen, and all proportions are fractions between 0 and 1.

9. a. $P(20 < t < 30) = \int_{20}^{30} 0.2e^{-0.2t}dt \approx 0.016$
   b. $P(t \leq 10) \approx 0.865$
   c. $P(t > 15) = 1 - P(t \leq 15) = 0.050$

11. a. Mean = 2 minutes
   b. Standard deviation = $\sqrt{0.8} \approx 0.89$ minute
   c. 0.316; The likelihood that any child between the ages of 8 and 10 learns the rules of the board game in 1.5 minutes or less is about 31.6%.
   d. 0.156; There is about a 15.6% chance that any child between the ages of 8 and 10 takes between 3 and 4 minutes to learn the rules of the new board game.

13. a. 137 customers
   b. *One possible answer:* Banks can better schedule servicing, balancing, and restocking of their ATMs.
   c. i. $P(150 \leq x \leq 200) \approx 0.58$

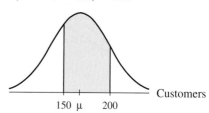

   ii. $P(x < 220) \approx 0.50 + 0.46 = 0.96$

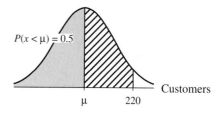

iii. $P(x > 235) = P(x > \mu) - P(\mu < x < 235)$
$$\approx 0.50 - 0.49$$
$$= 0.01$$

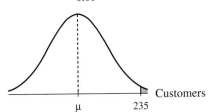
Customers
μ 235

15. a. $6\sigma = 800 - 200$, so $\sigma = 100$

b. The realigned mean score is more for each distribution, because the recentering puts the mean of each at 500.

c. 50% because 475 was the mean math score before recentering.

d. No, the standard deviation is not given.

e. The statement ". . . and realigns the verbal and math scores so that a student with a score of 450 on each test can conclude that his or her math and verbal scores are equal" indicates a change in the shape of the distribution.

f. The scale was recentered for interpretation purposes. The recentering does not reflect any change in student performance. Entrance requirements and other comparisons will now be made on the new scale.

17. a. $P(60 \le x \le 80) \approx 0.272$, so 27.2%

b. $P(x \ge 90) \approx 0.50 - 0.232$, so 26.8%

c.

$P(x > \mu + \sigma$ or $x < \mu - \sigma) = 1 - P(\mu - \sigma \le x \le \mu + \sigma)$
$$= 1 - P(43.65 < x < 100.95)$$
$$\approx 1 - 0.683 = 0.317$$

Approximately 31.7% of the students are likely to make a score more than one standard deviation away from the mean.

d. At $\mu - \sigma = 43.65$

19. a. $\mu = \displaystyle\int_a^b \frac{1}{b-a} x\,dx$

$$= \frac{1}{b-a} \cdot \frac{x^2}{2}\Big|_a^b = \frac{b^2 - a^2}{2(b-a)} = \frac{b+a}{2}$$

b.

$$\sigma^2 = \frac{1}{b-a}\int_a^b (x-\mu)^2 dx = \frac{1}{b-a}\left[\frac{(x-\mu)^3}{3}\right]_a^b$$

$$= \frac{1}{3(b-a)}\left[(b-\mu)^3 - (a-\mu)^3\right]$$

$$= \frac{1}{3(b-a)}\left[\left(b - \frac{b+a}{2}\right)^3 - \left(a - \frac{b+a}{2}\right)^3\right]$$

$$= \frac{1}{3(b-a)}\left[\left(\frac{b-a}{2}\right)^3 - \left(\frac{a-b}{2}\right)^3\right]$$

$$= \frac{1}{24(b-a)}\left[(b-a)^3 - (a-b)^3\right]$$

$$= \frac{1}{24(b-a)}\left[(b-a)^3 + (b-a)^3\right]$$

$$= \frac{2(b-a)^3}{24(b-a)} = \frac{(b-a)^2}{12}$$

Thus $\sigma = \dfrac{b-a}{\sqrt{12}}$

c. The height of the density function is 0 to the left of a, so $F(x) = 0$ when $x < a$. When $a \le x \le b$,

$$F(x) = \int_a^x \frac{1}{b-a}\,dt = \frac{1}{b-a} \cdot t\Big|_a^x = \frac{x-a}{b-a}.$$ When x

so the right of b, the area between the graph of u and the horizontal axis to the left of x is the area of a rectangle with width $b-a$ and height $\dfrac{1}{b-a}$. No more area is accumulated to the right of b because the height of the density function is 0 at all such points. Thus $F(x) = 1$ when $x > b$.

21. a.

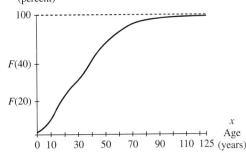
F
U.S. population (percent)

If F equals the cumulative density function, then $F(40) - F(20)$ is $P(20 \le \text{age} \le 40)$.

b.

U.S. population per year of age (percent)

$P(20 \le \text{age} \le 40)$

1.5
1.0
0.5
0.0
0   10   30   50   70   90   110 125   Age (years)

23. a. $F(x) = \begin{cases} 0 & \text{when } x < 0 \\ x^2 & \text{when } 0 \le x < 1 \\ 1 & \text{when } x \ge 1 \end{cases}$

b. $P(x < 0.67) = 0.4489$

c. $P(x > 0.25) = 0.9375$

d.

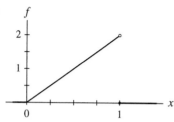

25. a.

x	0	5	10	15	25	35	50	75	100
F(x)	0	8.2	17.8	27.6	46.4	62.2	78.8	92.1	96.4

b. $F(100)$ is not 100 because the incomes of $100,000 or more are not counted in the table.

c. Yes, there appears to be an inflection point near $x = 40$, and the limiting value as x increases appears to be 0.

d. The overall fit is very good.

e. $\int_0^{100} f(x)dx \approx 96.41\% \approx F(100)$

f. $\mu = \int_0^{100} \dfrac{xf(x)}{100}\, dx \approx \$31,000$

27. a. The distribution in graph a, the bell-shaped curve, is characteristic of a normal breeding population. Malcolm argues that the one in graph b, with three peaks, is what would be expected from three separate (controlled) populations.

b. The dinosaurs were supposed to be all female and therefore not reproduce, so Ian first saw the normal curve in graph a.

c. Neither graph is that of a probability density function. Even though all the outputs are non-negative, the area under each curve is more than 1.

Chapter 6 Concept Review

1. a. $R(t) = (0.1)(3000 \cdot 12 + 500t) = 3600 + 50t$ dollars per year after t years

b. $29,064

c. $17,664

2. a. $35,143.80

b. $18,277.65

3. a. Approximately 1 fox

b. $f(t) = 500(0.63)^{20-t}$ foxes born t years after 1990 that will still be alive in 2010

c. Approximately 1083 foxes

4. a. Approximately $635.4 hundred

b. 411 fountains. No, because $D(10) = 594$, supply is smaller than demand at this point.

c. Approximately $6236.0 hundred

5. a. $P(x < 3.8) = 0.9025$. The value of x will be smaller than 3.8 about 90% of the time. This event is likely to occur.

b. $P(1.3 \le x \le 5) \approx 0.8944$

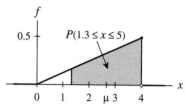

c. $\mu \approx 2.6667$

d. $F(x) = \begin{cases} 0 & \text{when } x < 0 \\ 0.0625x^2 & \text{when } 0 \le x \le 4 \\ 1 & \text{when } x > 4 \end{cases}$

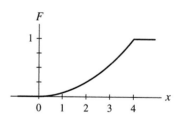

e. $P(1.3 \le t \le 5) \approx 0.8944$

CHAPTER 7

Section 7.1

1.

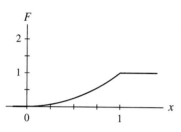

3. a. The maximum is 1 and occurs at $x = \dfrac{\pi}{2}$.

b. The absolute maximum is 1 and occurs at the values $x = \dfrac{\pi}{2} + 2k\pi$, where k is an integer.

c. The minimum is -1 and occurs at $x = \dfrac{3\pi}{2}$.

d. The absolute minimum is -1 and occurs at the values $x = \dfrac{3\pi}{2} + 2k\pi$, where k is an integer.

5. a.

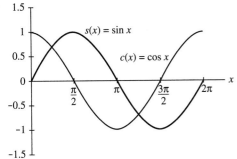

b. $c(x) = s(x) \approx 0.707$ when $x \approx 0.785$, and $c(x) = s(x) \approx -0.707$ when $x \approx 3.927$.

c. $x \approx 0.785 + 2k\pi$, where k is an integer, and $x \approx 3.927 + 2k\pi$, where k is an integer.

7. Amplitude: 1
Period: 2π
Vertical shift: none
Horizontal shift: π
The function is reflected across the horizontal axis, so the cycle starting at $x = \pi$ begins by decreasing.

9. Amplitude: 235
Period: $\dfrac{\pi}{150}$
Vertical shift: 65 down
Horizontal shift: $\dfrac{1}{3}$
The function is reflected across the horizontal axis, so the cycle starting at $x = \dfrac{1}{3}$ begins by decreasing.

11. i. c **ii.** e **iii.** a
iv. f **v.** d **vi.** b

13.

15.

17.

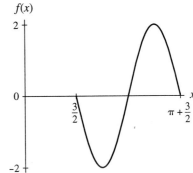

19. The members of each pair of graphs are identical. Generalization: Begin with a sine graph that is not vertically shifted, and reflect it across the horizontal axis. Begin with the same sine graph, and shift it right or left by an integer multiple of half of the period of the original graph. This new graph will be identical to the reflected graph.

21. a. Horizontal axis

b. Vertical axis

c.

(i)

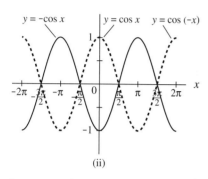

(ii)

It appears from the graphs that the functions $y = \cos(-x)$ and $y = \cos x$ are the same. The graph of $y = -\cos x$ is the reflection, across the x-axis, of the graph of $y = \cos x$; that is, the outputs of $y = -\cos x$ are the negatives of the outputs of $y = \cos x$.

23. In order to estimate amplitude and vertical shift, locate the maximum and minimum output values. Subtract the minimum value from the maximum value and divide by 2 to calculate amplitude. Add the maximum and minimum values and divide by 2 to calculate vertical shift.

Section 7.2

1. a.

Gas usage
(therms per day)

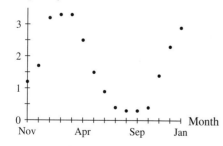

The data are cyclic because the residential gas usage is determined by the daily temperature, which usually repeats itself over a year's time.

b. Amplitude: approximately 1.5 therms per day. Vertical shift: ≈ 1.8 therms per day

c. Period: approximately 12 months
Horizontal shift : approximately 1.5 months to the left

d. $G(x) = 1.5 \sin\left(\dfrac{\pi}{6} + \dfrac{1.5\,\pi}{6}\right) + 1.8$ therms per day of gas used daily in month x

3. a. The data are cyclic because the average daily temperature repeats itself over one year.

Daily mean
temperature
(°F)

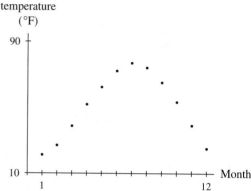

b. Amplitude: approximately 27.9°F
Vertical shift: approximately 49°F

c. Period: approximately 12 months
Horizontal shift: approximately 4 months to the right

d. $m(x) = 27.9 \sin\left(\dfrac{\pi}{6}x - \dfrac{2\pi}{3}\right) + 49$°F during the xth month of the year

e.

$m(x)$
(°F)

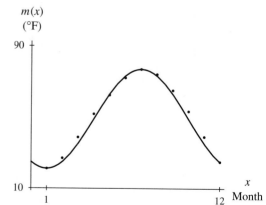

f. The model gives an estimate of 76.9°F as the average July temperature. (Note that this value agrees with the data.) Although the function is an excellent description of the normal mean daily temperature for the years 1961–1990, it cannot predict with any certainty the mean daily temperatures in Omaha this July.

5. a. The low temperatures should have the same period and approximately the same amplitude and horizontal shift as the average temperatures, but they should have a smaller vertical shift.

b. Amplitude: approximately 27.5°F
Vertical shift: approximately 38.4°F
Period: approximately 12 months
Horizontal shift: approximately 4 months to the right
As expected, the period and horizontal shift are the same. The amplitude is slightly lower than for the mean temperature data, and the vertical shift is less.

c. We calculate b using the equation $12 = \dfrac{2\pi}{b}$, so $b = \dfrac{\pi}{6}$.
We calculate h using the equation $\dfrac{|h|}{b} = 4$ and the information that the horizontal shift is to the right, so h is negative: $h = -4b = \dfrac{-2\pi}{3}$. Using $a = 27.5$ and $k = 38.4$, we have $f(x) = 27.5 \sin\left(\dfrac{\pi}{6}x - \dfrac{2\pi}{3}\right) + 38.4°F$ during the xth month of the year.

7. a. $g(x) = 1.610 \sin(0.534x + 0.322) + 1.591$ therms per day x months after November 2000
Amplitude: 1.610 therms per day
Period: approximately 11.8 months
Horizontal shift: approximately 0.603 month to the left
Vertical shift: up 1.591 therms per day

b. Approximately 1.6 therms per day

c. Approximately $26.88

9. $g(x) = 28.533 \sin(0.479x - 1.801) + 47.985°F$ during the xth month of the year; Essay answers will vary.

11. $g(x) = 27.357 \sin(0.489x - 1.878) + 37.641°F$ during the xth month of the year.

$f(x)$
(°F)

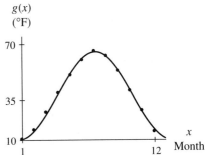

$g(x)$
(°F)

Both models appear to fit the data well.

13. a. $M(x) = 0.932 \sin(0.467x - 2.940) + 8.737$ billion trips x years after 1992

b. $T(x) = -0.0052x^3 + 0.127x^2 - 0.573x + 8.56$ billion trips x years after 1992

c. The cubic function fits the data fairly well, but the sine function better follows the curvature of the data and provides a very good fit.

d. $M(14) \approx 8.32$ billion trips and $T(14) \approx 11.24$ billion trips. Reasons will vary.

15. a. Maximum is 62°F; minimum is $-12°F$.

b. The average is 25°F, which equals k, the vertical shift.

17. a. The data appear concave up between 1949 and 1955, concave down between 1956 and 1960, and concave up between 1961 and 1963.

b. A cubic model is not a good fit and is not appropriate because more than one inflection point are indicated by the data. Possibly a piecewise continuous model that is quadratic between 1949 and 1955 and cubic between 1956 and 1963 would fit the data. However, the sine model seems most appropriate.

c. $f(x) = 41.547 \sin(0.528x - 2.913) + 194.493$ aircraft x years since 1949

d. Approximately 155 aircraft

e. Answers will vary.

19. a.

Hours	°F	Hours	°F
5	37	65	60
11	44.5	71	47
17	52	77	34
23	47	83	45
29	42	89	56
35	49	95	46.5
41	56	101	37
47	49	107	45.5
53	42	113	54
59	51		

b. $y = 8.709 \sin(0.261x - 2.840) + 47.090°F$ x hours after midnight on Wednesday: The period is approximately 24 hours.

c. High: approximately 56°F
   Low: approximately 38°F

21. Essay answers will vary.

23. Without technology: $D(t) = 7 \sin\left(\dfrac{2\pi}{365}t - \dfrac{542\pi}{365}\right) + 11.5$ hours of daylight, where t is the number of days since December 31 of the previous year.
   With technology: $d(t) = 6.677 \sin(0.016t + 1.908) + 11.730$ hours of daylight, where t is the number of days since December 31 of the previous year.

Section 7.3

1. $f'(x) = 3 \cos 3x$

3. $t'(r) = -2.34 \sin(0.45r + \pi) + 80$

5. $h'(x) = -0.3328 \cos(-0.16x + 12.3)$
   $-9.666 \sin[1.35(2x + 6)]$
   $h''(x) = -0.053248 \sin(-0.16x + 12.3)$
   $-26.0982 \cos[1.35(2x + 6)]$

7. a. 2 hours
   b. 3050 km at 48 minutes after launching
   c.

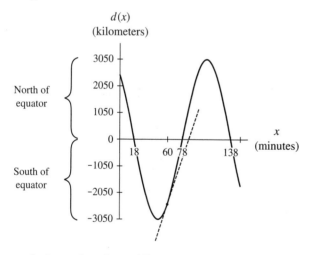

$d(x)$
(kilometers)

North of equator

South of equator

x (minutes)

   d. Approximately 93.9 kilometers per minute
   e. No; speed is the rate of change of the total distance traveled with respect to the traveling time.

9. a. 1992: approximately –0.4 billion trips per year
      1996: approximately 0.2 billion trips per year
      2000: approximately 0.3 billion trips per year
   b. Approximately 9.7 billion trips

11. a. Approximately −8 mm per day
    b. 47.1% decline; −1.6 mm per day per month

c. Approximately 2.4 mm per day per month; Extraterrestrial radiation in Amarillo is increasing by 2.4 millimeters of equivalent water evaporation per day per month in March.

d. 18.4% per month

13. a. $R(x) = 1.32727 \sin(0.0186x + 1.1801) + 1.46052 \cos(0.0197x - 3.7526) + 7.90076$ million dollars where x is the day of the year

    b. $R'(x) \approx 0.0247 \cos(0.0186x + 1.1801) - 0.0288 \sin(0.0197x - 3.7526)$ million dollars per day where x is the day of the year

    c. $R'(46) \approx -0.003$ million dollars per day. Combined daily sales were decreasing by approximately $3000 per day on February 15, 1992.

    d. Approximately 220 days and 293 days after the beginning of 1992. (These values correspond to August 7 and October 19. Note that 1992 was a leap year.)

    e. $x \approx 90$ days (March 30) or 166 days (June 14) or 339 days (December 4).

15. $B'(11) \approx -11.1°F$ per month
    $B'(4.5) \approx 11.6°F$ per month

17. a., b.

Wind speed interval (m/sec)	6–10	10–14	14–18
Change (kilowatts)	−17.4	−17.3	−0.3
Percentage change	−38.4	−61.7	−2.7
Average rate of change (kilowatts/m/sec)	−4.4	−4.3	−0.07

c. $P'(s) \approx 5.2126 \cos(0.258s + 0.570)$ kilowatts per meter per second when the wind speed is s meters per second

d., e.

Wind speed (m/sec)	6	10	14	18
$P'(s)$ (kilowatts/m/sec)	−2.7	−5.2	−2.6	2.5
Percentage rate of change (%/m/sec)	−6.0	−18.6	−24.7	24.1

The power output of the engine is decreasing at the rate of 2.7 kilowatts per meter per second at a wind speed of 6 meters per second. When the wind speed is 10 meters per second and increases to 11 meters per second, the power output of the engine decreases by approximately 5.2 kilowatts. When the wind speed is 14 meters per second and increases to 15 meters per second, the power output of the engine decreases by approximately 2.6 kilowatts. At a wind speed of 18 meters per second, the power output of the engine is increasing at the rate of 2.5 kilowatts per meter per second.

19. a. $d(t) = 60.7407 \sin (0.1206t + 0.3134) + 99.9194$ deaths per 100,000 people per week, where t is the number of weeks since January 1, 1923. Answers will vary.

b.

Date	t	$d'(t)$
Middle of 1924	78	$-7.0111*$
End of 1924	104	$-7.0252*$

*deaths per one hundred thousand people per week per week

21. a. $D(d) = 23.677 \sin (0.017d - 1.312) - 0.292$ degrees on the dth day of the year; the amplitude of the model is 23.7 degrees. This is the greatest angle of declination that the Sun reaches. The period is approximately 374 days (calculated with the unrounded b-value). We expect the Sun's declination to complete a cycle every year. The period in the model is slightly long.

b. The equinoxes occur at $d \approx 78.7$ days and $d \approx 264.4$ days. $D'(78.7) \approx 0.4$ degree per day, and $D'(264.4) \approx -0.4$ degree per day. At the equinoxes, the declination of the Sun is changing by approximately 0.4 degree per day.

c. The summer and winter solstices occur when the declination is greatest in both north and south directions. On the graph, the summer solstice corresponds to the maximum, and the winter solstice corresponds to the minimum. At these points, the rate of change is zero.

23. Inside: $u(x) = 2.4^x$
Outside: $y(u) = \sin u$
$y' = (\ln 2.4)(2.4^x)[\cos (2.4^x)]$

25. Inside: $u(x) = \sin x - 7$
Outside: $y(u) = 4u^2 + 8u + 13$
$y' = 8 \cos x(\sin x - 6)$

27. Inside: $u(x) = \sin x$
Outside: $y(u) = \ln u$
$y' = \dfrac{\cos x}{\sin x}$

Section 7.4

1. a. Between $x = 0$ and $x \approx 13.45$, the maximum value of 9.67 occurs at $x \approx 9.66$. The minimum value of 7.81 occurs at $x \approx 2.93$.

b. The greatest number of yearly mass transit trips between 1992 and 2002 was approximately 9.66 billion (in 2000). The least number of yearly mass transit trips

between 1992 and 2002 was approximately 7.81 billion (in 1995).

3. a. The maximum daily mean temperature is approximately 76.9°F (in July). The minimum daily mean temperature is approximately 21.1°F (in January).

b. $t(x) = 28.533 \sin (0.479x - 1.801) + 47.985°F$ in the xth month of the year. The highest point on the model is (7.041, 76.517), and the lowest point is (0.481, 19.452). The maximum normal daily mean temperature in Omaha between 1961 and 1990 was 76.5°F and occurred at the beginning of August. The normal daily minimum temperature was at a minimum of 19.5°F near the middle of January.

c. The maximum and minimum temperatures obtained with the model are slightly lower than those found using the data. Because the data are based on a monthly average over a 30-year period, actual high and low temperatures in any given year are likely to vary from those found in parts a and b.

5. a. Ten maxima of the sine function i are near a relative maximum of the actual index w. Note that the maxima appear as minima because of the inverted scale. (Answers may vary.)

b. Ten minima of the sine function i are near a relative minimum of the actual index w. (Answers may vary.)

c. A relative maximum of approximately 104.6 occurs at $t \approx 120.25$ years after 1761, and a relative minimum of 95.8 occurs at $t \approx 116.25$ years after 1761. Thus the next maximum and minimum of $i(t)$ after 1874 are predicted to have occurred in 1878 and in 1882, respectively.

d. Answers will vary.

7. a. The teal graph represents daylight hours. The black graph represents nighttime hours.

b. Period: approximately 12 months
Amplitude: approximately 7.5 hours
Vertical shift: approximately 12 hours up

c. Values in table may vary.

Month	Hours	Month	Hours
Jan	5	July	19
Feb	8	Aug	17
Mar	10.5	Sept	14.5
Apr	13.5	Oct	11.5
May	16.5	Nov	8.5
June	19	Dec	6

d. $H(m) = 7.021 \sin(0.480m - 1.619) + 11.786$ hours at the beginning of the mth month.
Period: approximately 13 months
Amplitude: approximately 7 hours
Vertical shift: approximately 11.8 hours

9. a., b. Answers will vary depending on the latitude of the student's hometown.

11. a. $a'(m) = 27.1(0.485) \cos(0.485x - 1.707)$ watts per centimeter squared per month when $m = 1$ in January, $m = 2$ in February, and so on

b. Radiation is at its highest level in July ($m \approx 6.7853$) and at its lowest level in January ($m \approx 0.2808$).

c. The highest level of radiation is 60 watts per centimeter squared. The lowest level of radiation is 5.8 watts per centimeter squared.

13. a. $T'(x) = 0.565 \cos(0.469x - 2.293)$ percent per year x years after 1988

b. For one period of T, between $x = 0$ and $x \approx 13.4$, solve the equation $T'(x) = 0$ to find that $x \approx 1.54$ (input for relative minimum) and $x \approx 8.24$ (input for relative maximum). Compare the outputs at these inputs to $T(0)$ and $T(13.4)$ to find the absolute extrema. The smallest after-tax profit rate on investment, approximately 5.18%, occurred in 1990, and the largest rate, approximately 7.5%, occurred in 1996.
Solve $T''(x) = 0$ to find that the inputs at the inflection points are $x \approx 4.89$ and $x \approx 11.59$. The most rapid increase in the after-tax profit rate was 0.56% per year (in 1993), and the most rapid decrease in the rate was 0.55% per year (in 2000).

c. Explanations will vary.

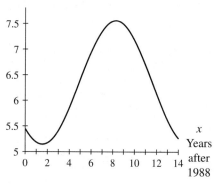

$T(x)$
(percent)

15. a. Approximately 467.2 milliseconds

b. Two possible answers are: The pulse speed was at its highest value, 227 counts per second, after approximately 233.6 milliseconds and 700.7 milliseconds. The pulse speed was at its lowest value of 146 counts per second after approximately 4.2 milliseconds and 467.2 milliseconds.

c. One possible answer is: The speed of the pulses emitted from the star was increasing the fastest after approximately 116.8 milliseconds. The speed at that time was approximately 186.5 counts per second. The speed of the pulses emitted from the star was decreasing the fastest after approximately 350.4 milliseconds when the speed was also 186.5 counts per second.

17. a. $d(t) = 60.741 \sin(0.121t + 0.313) + 99.919$ deaths per 100,000 people per week, where t is the number of weeks since January 1, 1923

b. The period is approximately 52 weeks, so the death rate should peak again at $t \approx 166.8$ weeks since January 1, 1923.

c. $t \approx 153.7$; $d(t) \approx 100$; The first time after 150 weeks since January 1, 1923, that the weekly pneumonia death rate was increasing the fastest was near 154 weeks. The weekly death rate at that time was approximately 100 deaths per 100,000 people per week.

19. a. $a''(m) = -6.3745975 \sin(0.485m - 1.707)$ watts per cm^2 per month, where $m = 1$ in January, $m = 2$ in February, and so on

b. The point of most rapid increase occurs in mid-April ($m \approx 3.5$), and the point of most rapid decrease occurs at the beginning of October ($m \approx 10$).

c. 32.9 watts per cm^2

21. a. $R(x) = 1.327 \sin(0.019x + 1.180) + 1.461 \cos(0.020x - 3.753) + 7.901$ million dollars where x is the day of the year

b. $R'(x) \approx 0.025 \cos(0.019x + 1.180) - 0.029 \sin(0.020x - 3.753)$ million dollars per day where x is the day of the year

c. $8.03 million, $x \approx 193$ (July 12)

d. The absolute minimum value is $7.66 million, occurring at $x \approx 66$ (March 7). A local minimum value of $7.68 million occurs at $x \approx 318$ (November 14).

Section 7.5

1.

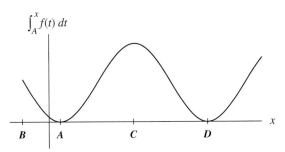

$$\int_A^x f(t)\, dt$$

3. 1

5. $2 + 2a$

7. $-7.3 \cos x + 12x + C$

9. $\dfrac{-1}{7.3} \cos(7.3x + 12) + C$

11. $F(x) \approx -194.583 \cos(0.024x + 3.211) + 14.63x + C$

13. a. Height units are dollars per year, and width units are years. Area units are dollars.

  b. The t-intercepts of w between $t = 7$ and $t = 50$ are $t \approx 21.74$ and $t \approx 43.41$. The area between $t = 7$ and $t \approx 21.74$ is \$1.71, the area between $t \approx 21.74$ and $t \approx 43.41$ is \$2.23, and the area between $t \approx 43.41$ and $t = 50$ is \$0.47. The total area is approximately \$4.41.

  c. $\int_7^{50} w(t)\, dt \approx -\$0.04$, which is not the same as the result of part b because w crosses the t-axis. The federal minimum wage, expressed in constant 2000 dollars, decreased by approximately 4 cents between 1957 and 2000.

  d.

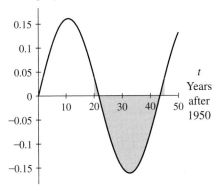

$w(t)$
(dollars per year)

  e. The federal minimum wage, expressed in constant 2000 dollars, decreased by approximately \$2.16 between 1970 and 1995.

15. a. $T(x) = -1.205 \cos(0.469x - 0.722) + 6.404$ percent x years after 1988

  b. The after-tax profit rate was lowest in 1990 ($x \approx 1.54$) at approximately 5.2% and was highest in 1996 ($x \approx 8.24$) near 7.6%.

  c. Approximately 6.4%

  d. The values are close, but not identical, because a model (and not the actual data) was used to determine the average value in part c.

17. a. $\int_1^{16} L(x)\, dx \approx 259$ thousand lizards

  b. 261 thousand lizards. This value is 2 thousand more than the answer to part a.

  c. Answers will vary.

19. $\int_0^{40} r(t)\, dt \approx -4.2$ males per 100 females,

  $\int_{50}^{100} r(t)\, dt \approx -2.33$ males per 100 females, and

  $\int_0^{100} r(t)\, dt \approx -8.8$ males per 100 females. From 1900 to 1940, the number of males per 100 females decreased by approximately 4.2 males per 100 females. From 1950 to 2000, the number of males per 100 females decreased by approximately 2.3 males per 100 females. Between 1900 and 2000, the number of males per 100 females decreased by approximately 8.8 males per 100 females.

21. a. Height in counts per second, width in milliseconds, area in (counts per second)(milliseconds)

  b. $p(s) = 0.0405 \sin(0.0135s - 1.571) + 0.187$ counts per millisecond after s milliseconds

  c. $\int_0^{467.151324} p(s)\, ds \approx 87$ counts

  Approximately 87 pulses are emitted by the star over one period (approximately 0.5 second).

Chapter 7 Content Review

1. a. Amplitude: 712.5
  Vertical shift: 787.5
  Period: 12 months
  Horizontal shift: 3 months

  b. $l(x) = 713.251 \sin(0.525x - 1.557) + 777.883$ lawn mowers ordered x months since December of the previous year. The amplitude is very close, whereas the vertical shift of the model is approximately 10 lawn mowers less than that found using the data. The period of the model is approximately 12 months. The horizontal shift of the model is approximately 3. Both the period and the horizontal shift are very close to those found using the data.

c. $l(16) \approx 1157$ lawn mowers; For this estimate to be valid, the cyclic pattern shown by the data should continue for the following year.

d. Lawn mower orders were highest in June ($x = 6$).

e. Solving $l''(x) = 0$, finding where $l'(x)$ is greatest, or using $\dfrac{-c}{b}$ in the sine model, we find that orders were increasing most rapidly in March ($x = 3$).

2. a. Approximately -1.6 units per year
   b. Approximately 0 unit per year

3. a. Approximately -1.32 units per year
   b. $S'(42) \approx 0.37$ unit per year. According to the model, the Sauerbeck index of general wholesale prices was increasing at the rate of 0.37 unit per year in 1860.
   c. $\dfrac{1}{72 - 42} \displaystyle\int_{42}^{72} S(t)dt \approx 90.8$

4. a. The rate of change was greatest when $t \approx 111$ days, which corresponds to March 20 (1992 was a leap year).
   b. $R(t) \approx 7.305 \cos(0.0197t - 3.753) + 20.383$ million pints t days after January 1, 1992.
   c. The answer to part a is the input corresponding to the inflection point for the model in part b.

5. Approximately 1.24 million pints. At the end of February 1992, the Campbell Soup Company was selling approximately 1.24 million more pints than it was selling at the beginning of February.

CHAPTER 8

Section 8.1

1. $c = kg$

3. $\dfrac{dp}{da} = ka$

5. a. The displayed particular solutions go through the points $(0, 0.5)$, $(2, 2)$, and $(4, 5)$. Answers will vary.

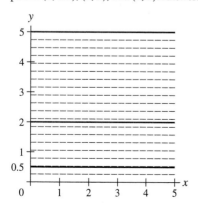

b. All particular solutions are horizontal lines, each passing through the chosen initial condition.

c. $y(x) = C$, where C is a constant

7. a. The displayed particular solutions go through the points $(0, 0.5)$, $(2, 2)$, and $(4, 5)$. Answers will vary.

b. All particular solutions are parallel lines with negative slopes.

c. $y(x) = -x + C$, where C is a constant

9. a. The displayed particular solutions go through the points $(0, 1)$, $(1, 3)$, and $(2, 6.5)$. Answers will vary.

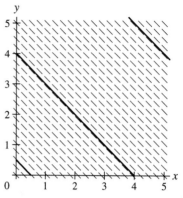

b. All particular solutions are concave-up parabolas with minimum points on the vertical axis.

c. $y(x) = 0.25x^2 + C$, where C is a constant

11. a. The displayed particular solutions go through the points $(0, 1)$, $(2, 3)$, and $(2, 6.5)$. Answers will vary.

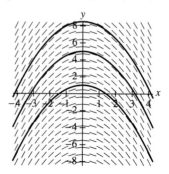

b. All particular solutions are concave-down parabolas with maximum points on the vertical axis.

c. $y(x) = -0.5x^2 + C$, where C is a constant

13. The particular solutions with initial condition $(0, 0)$ all pass through the point $(0, 0)$. Each particular solution has a constant term of zero, but the nonconstant terms all differ.

15. a. $\dfrac{dp}{dt} = 0.98$ quadrillion BTU per year t years after 1975

b. $p(t) = 0.98t + C$ quadrillion BTU t years after 1975

c. $p(t) = 0.98t + 59.9$ quadrillion BTU t years after 1975

d. In 1975, production was 59.9 quadrillion BTU and was increasing by 0.98 quadrillion BTU per year.

e.

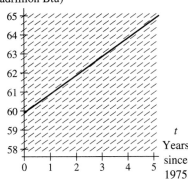

$p(t)$
(quadrillion Btu)

$p(0) \approx 59.9$ quadrillion BTU; They are the same.

17. a. $\dfrac{dc}{dt} = 0.0342$ million square kilometers per year t years after 1970

b. $c(t) = 0.0342t + C$ million square kilometers t years after 1970

c. $c(t) = 0.0342t + 13.828$ million square kilometers t years after 1970

d. Cropland was increasing by 0.0342 million square kilometers per year in both 1970 and 1990. In 1970 there were 13.828 million square kilometers of cropland, and in 1990 there were 14.512 million square kilometers.

19. a. $v(t) = -32t$ feet per second t seconds after the object is dropped

b. $\dfrac{ds}{dt} = -32t$ feet per second t seconds after the object is dropped

c. $s(t) = -16t^2 + C$ feet t seconds after the object is dropped

d. Approximately 1.5 seconds after the object is dropped, it will hit the ground at a velocity of about -47.3 feet per second. (The negative sign on the velocity indicates downward motion.)

21. a. $\dfrac{df}{dx} = kx$

b. $f(x) = \dfrac{k}{2}x^2 + C$

c. $\dfrac{d}{dx}\left(\dfrac{k}{2}x^2 + C\right) = kx$ leads to the identity $kx = kx$.

23. a. $\dfrac{dh}{dt} = \dfrac{k}{t}$ feet per year after t years

b. $h(t) = 20.75 \ln t - 10.39$ feet after t years

c. $h(15) \approx 45.8$ feet. Over time, the tree will continue to grow, but the rate of increase will be smaller and smaller.

25. a.

$h(t)$
(feet)

b. $h(15) \approx 46$ feet

27. a. i. The particular solutions that are sketched go through $(1, 1.5)$, $(2, 1)$, and $(1, 0)$. Answers will vary.

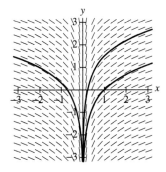

ii. When $x > 0$, the graph of the particular solution rises as x gets larger. When $x < 0$, the particular-solution graph rises as x gets smaller. The particular-solution graphs are concave down.

iii. The family of solutions appears to increase rapidly as x moves away from the origin (in both directions), and then the increase slows down. The line $x = 0$ (lying along the y-axis) appears to be a vertical asymptote for the family.

b. i. The particular solutions that are sketched go through $(10, 0)$, $(10, 0)$, and $(5, 5)$. Answers will vary.

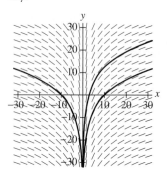

ii. When $x > 0$, the graph of the particular solution rises as x gets larger. When $x < 0$, the particular-solution graph rises as x gets smaller. The particular-solution graphs are concave down.

iii. The family of solutions appears to behave the same as that in part a, but the slope at each point on a particular-solution graph is 10 times the slope at the corresponding point on a particular-solution graph in part a. Again, the line $x = 0$ appears to be a vertical asymptote for the family.

c. i. The particular solutions that are sketched go through $(1, 1.5)$, $(2, 1)$, and $(1, 0)$. Answers will vary.

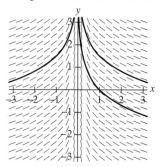

ii. When $x > 0$, the graph of the particular solution falls as x gets larger. When $x < 0$, the particular-solution graph falls as x gets smaller. The particular-solution graphs are concave up.

iii. The slope at each point on a particular-solution graph is the negative of the slope at a corresponding point on a particular-solution graph in part a. The family of solutions appears to decrease rapidly

as x moves away from the origin (in both directions), and then the decrease levels off. Again, the line $x = 0$ appears to be a vertical asymptote for the family.

d. i. The particular solutions that are sketched go through $(0.1, 0)$, $(0.1, 0)$, and $(0.05, 0.05)$. Answers will vary.

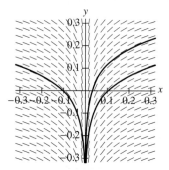

ii. When $x > 0$, the graph of the particular solution rises as x gets larger. When $x < 0$, the particular-solution graph rises as x gets smaller. The particular-solution graphs are concave down.

iii. The family of solutions appears to behave the same as that in part a, but the slope at each point on a particular-solution graph is $\frac{1}{10}$ times the slope at the corresponding point on a particular-solution graph in part a. Again, the line $x = 0$ appears to be a vertical asymptote for the family.

29.

31.

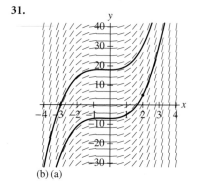

Section 8.2

1. $\dfrac{dT}{dt} = \dfrac{k}{T}$, so $T = \sqrt{2kt + C}$

(We use the positive square root because thickness can't be negative.)

3. $\dfrac{dA}{dt} = kA$, so $A(t) = ae^{kt}$

5. $\dfrac{dx}{dt} = kx(N - x)$, so $x(t) = \dfrac{N}{1 + Ae^{-Nkt}}$

7. $\dfrac{dD}{dt} = \dfrac{k}{\sqrt{D}} - hD$, where k and h are both constants

9. The particular solutions that are sketched go through $(-2, 2)$, $(-2, -1)$, and $(1, 1)$. Answers will vary.

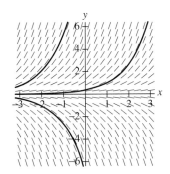

11. The particular solutions that are sketched go through $(0, -2)$, $(-2, -4)$, and $(-1, 6)$. Answers will vary.

13. The particular solutions that are sketched go through $(-2, 1)$, $(2, 1)$, and $(1, -1)$. Answers will vary.

15. The particular solutions that are sketched go through $(0, 0)$, $(-1, -4)$, and $(1, 3)$. Answers will vary.

17. The particular solutions that are sketched go through $(0, 3)$, $(1, 0)$, and $(2, 1)$. Answers will vary.

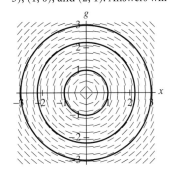

19. Solve by separation of variables; $y(x) = \pm\, ae^{kx}$

21. Solve by antidifferentiation; $y(x) = k\ln|x| + C$

23. Solve by separation of variables; $y(x) = \pm\, ax^k$

25. a. $\dfrac{dq}{dt} = kq$ milligrams per hour

b. $q(t) \approx 200e^{-0.346574t}$ milligrams after t hours

c. Approximately 50 milligrams after 4 hours and 12.5 milligrams after 8 hours.

27. a. $\dfrac{da}{dt} \approx ka$ units per day

b. $a(t) \approx ce^{-0.181262t}$ units after t days

c. Approximately 0.9 gram after 12 hours, 0.5 gram after 4 days, 0.2 gram after 9 days, and 0.004 gram after 30 days

29. a. $\dfrac{dN}{dt} = 0.0049N(37 - N)$ countries per year

b. $N(t) = \dfrac{37}{1 + Ae^{-0.1813t}}$ countries t years after 1800

c. $N(t) = \dfrac{37}{1 + 28{,}097.439e^{-0.1813t}}$ countries t years after 1800

d. 2 countries in 1840 and 24 countries in 1860

e. The upper asymptote is $N(t) = 37$, and the lower asymptote is $N(t) = 0$.

f.

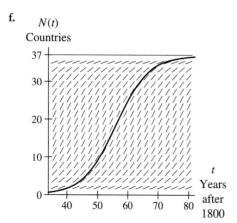

$N(t)$
Countries

31. a. $\dfrac{df}{dx} = kf(L - f)$

b. $f(x) = \dfrac{L}{1 + Ae^{-Lkx}}$

c. $\dfrac{d}{dx}\left(\dfrac{L}{1 + Ae^{-Lkx}}\right) = k\left(\dfrac{L}{1 + Ae^{-Lkx}}\right)\left(L - \dfrac{L}{1 + Ae^{-Lkx}}\right)$

Each side of this equation can be simplified to

$\dfrac{L^2Ake^{-Lkx}}{(1 + Ae^{-Lkx})^2}$

Section 8.3

1. a. $y(4) \approx 2$

x	Estimate of y(x)	Slope at x
0	0	0.5
2	1	0.5
4	2	

b. $y(7) \approx 34$

x	Estimate of y(x)	Slope at x
1	4	2
4	10	8
7	34	

3. a. $y(5) \approx 11.91$

x	Estimate of y(x)	Slope at x
1	1	5
3	11	0.45
5	11.91	

b. $y(8) \approx 12.5$

x	Estimate of y(x)	Slope at x
2	2	2.5
5	9.5	1
8	12.5	

5. a. $\dfrac{dw}{dt} = \dfrac{33.67885}{t}$ pounds per month after t months

b. $w(3) \approx 46.0$ pounds; $w(6) \approx 70.0$ pounds

t (months)	Estimate of w(t) (pounds)	Slope at t (pounds per month)
1	6	33.679
1.25	14.420	26.943
1.50	21.155	22.453
1.75	26.769	19.245
2	31.580	16.839
2.25	35.790	14.968
2.5	39.532	13.472
2.75	42.900	12.247
3	45.961	11.226
3.25	48.768	10.363
3.5	51.359	9.623
3.75	53.764	8.981
4	56.010	8.420
4.25	58.115	7.924
4.5	60.100	7.484
4.75	61.967	7.090
5	63.739	6.736
5.5	67.027	6.123
5.75	68.558	5.857
6	70.022	

c. $w(3) \approx 56.5$ pounds; $w(6) \approx 82.9$ pounds

t (months)	Estimate of w(t) (pounds)	Slope at t (pounds per month)
1	6	33.679
2	39.679	16.839
3	56.518	11.226
4	67.745	8.420
5	76.164	6.736
6	82.90	

d. The answer to part *b* should give a more accurate approximation of the true weight at each input because it uses a smaller step size.

7. a. $\dfrac{dp}{dt} = 3.935t^{3.55}e^{-1.35135t}$ thousand barrels per year t years after production begins, where $p(t)$ is the total amount of oil produced after t years

b. See table for this activity. During the first 5 years, the oil well will produce approximately 10.3 thousand barrels.

t	Estimate of $p(t)$	$p'(t)$
0	0	0
0.5	0	0.17094
1	0.0855	1.0187
1.5	0.5948	2.1865
2	1.6881	3.0891
2.5	3.2326	3.4707
3	4.9680	3.3734
3.5	6.6547	2.9668
4	8.1381	2.4251
4.5	9.3507	1.8744
5	10.2879	

c.

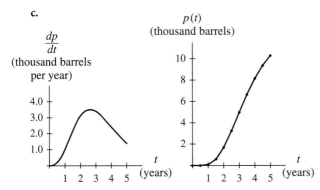

The graph of the differential equation is the slope graph for the graph of the Euler estimates. Similarly, the graph of the Euler estimates is an approximation to the accumulation graph of the differential equation graph.

9. a. $\dfrac{dT}{dt} = k(T - A)°F$ per minute after t minutes

b. $k \approx -0.064$

c.

T	Estimate of $T(t)$	$T'(t)$
0	98	−1.8
1	96.2	−1.684
2	94.516	−1.576
3	92.940	−1.475
4	91.465	−1.380
5	90.085	−1.291
6	88.794	−1.208
7	87.586	−1.131
8	86.455	−1.058
9	85.397	−0.990
10	84.408	−0.926
11	83.481	−0.867
12	82.615	−0.811
13	81.804	−0.759
14	81.044	−0.710
15	80.355	

The temperature of the object is approximately 80.3°F after 15 minutes.

11. Essay answers will vary but should include a discussion of the accuracy of tangent line approximations for function values.

Section 8.4

1. $\dfrac{d^2S}{dt^2} = \dfrac{k}{S^2}$

3. $\dfrac{d^2P}{dy^2} = k$, so $P(y) = \dfrac{k}{2}y^2 + Cy + D$

5. a. $\dfrac{d^2R}{dt^2} = 6.14$

b. $R(t) = 3.07t^2 - 7.01t + 15.94$ jobs in the tth month of the year

c. 156 jobs in August and 310 jobs in November

7. a. $\dfrac{d^2A}{dt^2} = -2099$ cases per year per year

b. $A(t) = -1049.5t^2 + 5988.7t + 33{,}590$ cases t years after 1988

c. -308.3 cases per year and 42,111 cases

9. a. $\dfrac{d^2f}{dx^2} = k$

b. $f(x) = \dfrac{k}{2}x^2 + Cx + D$

c. $\dfrac{d^2}{dx^2}\left(\dfrac{k}{2}x^2 + Cx + D\right) = k$ leads to the identity $k = k$.

11. a. $\dfrac{d^2E}{dt^2} = -0.212531E$

b. $E(t) = -4.713 \sin(0.461011t + 2.248008)$ mm   per day, where t is the month of the year.

c. $E(t) = -4.713 \sin(0.461011t + 2.248008) + 12.5$ mm per day, where t is the month of the year.

d. The model overestimates by 2.2 mm per day in March and 12.0 mm per day in September.

Chapter 8 Concept Review

1. a. The relative risk of having a car accident is changing with respect to the blood alcohol level at a rate that is proportional to the risk of having a car accident at a certain blood alcohol level.

b. $R(b) = ae^{kb}$ percent, where b is the proportion of alcohol in the blood stream.

c. $R(b) = e^{21.398b}$ percent, where b is the proportion of alcohol in the blood stream.

d. A crash is certain to occur (that is, it has a 100% probability of occurring) when the blood alcohol level is 21.5%.

e.

$R(b)$
(percent)

2. a. $\dfrac{dP}{dx} = 0.001175P(16.396 - P)$ million people per year, where x is the number of years since 1800.

b. $P(x) = \dfrac{16.396}{1 + Ae^{-0.019265x}}$ million people, where x is the number of years since 1800.

c. $P(x) = \dfrac{16.396}{1 + 2.108e^{-0.019265x}}$ million people, where x is the number of years since 1800.

d. 8.3 million people in 1840 and 9.1 million people in 1850

3. a. $1840 \approx 8.18$ million people; $1850 \approx 8.97$ million people

b. $1840 \approx 8.24$ million people; $1850 \approx 9.03$ million people

c. These estimates are slightly smaller than those found in part d of Activity 2.

4. a. $\dfrac{dQ}{dx} = -0.008307Q(7.154 - Q)$ million people per year, where the population is $P(x) = Q(x) + 4.4$ million people and x represents the number of years since 1800

b. $Q(x) = \dfrac{7.154}{1 + 0.185e^{0.059428x}}$ million people, where x is the number of years since 1800.

c. $P(x) = \begin{cases} \dfrac{16.396}{1 + 2.108e^{-0.019265x}} \text{ million people when } x \le 40 \\ \dfrac{7.154}{1 + 0.185e^{0.059428x}} + 4.4 \text{ million people when } x \ge 50 \end{cases}$

where x is the number of years since 1800.

d. 6.0 million people in 1850. This answer is significantly smaller than the one found in part *d* of Activity 2.

CHAPTER 9

Section 9.1

1. a. $P(1.2, s)$ is the profit in dollars from the sale of a yard of fabric as a function of s, the selling price per yard, when production cost is $1.20 per yard.

b. $P(c, 4.5)$ is the profit in dollars from the sale of a yard of fabric as a function of c, the production cost per yard, when the selling price is $4.50 per yard.

c. When the production cost is $1.20 per yard and the selling price is $4.50 per yard, the profit is $3.00 for each yard sold.

d.

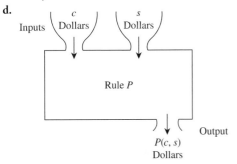

3. a. $P(100,000, m)$ is the probability of the senator voting in favor of the bill as a function of the amount m million dollars invested by the tobacco industry lobbying against the bill when the senator receives 100,000 letters supporting the bill.

b. $P(l, 53)$ is the probability of the senator voting in favor of the bill as a function of the number l of letters in fa-

vor of the bill received by the senator when the tobacco industry spends $53 million lobbying against the bill.

c.

5.

7.

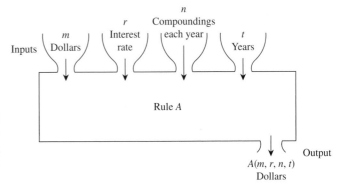

9.　a., b.

Relative humidity (%)													
Air temperature (°F)	40	45	50	55	60	65	70	75	80	85	90	95	100
110	135												
108	130	137											
106	124	130	137										
104	119	124	130	137									
102	114	119	124	130	137								
100	109	113	118	123	129	136							
98	105	108	113	117	122	128	134						
96	101	104	107	111	116	121	126	132					
94	97	100	103	106	110	114	119	124	129	135			
92	94	96	98	101	104	108	112	116	121	126	131		
90	91	92	94	97	99	102	106	109	113	117	122	126	131
88	88	89	91	93	95	97	100	103	106	109	113	117	121
86	85	86	88	89	91	93	95	97	99	102	105	108	111
84	83	84	85	86	87	89	90	92	94	96	98	100	102
82	81	82	83	83	84	85	86	87	88	90	91	93	94
80	80	80	81	81	82	82	83	83	84	85	85	86	87

(curve labels at right: 130, 105, 90)

11.　a. 11.97 hours

　　b. 11.97 hours

　　c. Answers will vary. For example, if your college is at the 45th parallel north, it will receive 9.19 hours of daylight each day during January.

　　d.

Latitude North / South	Month											
	Jan / Jul	Feb / Aug	Mar / Sep	Apr / Oct	May / Nov	Jun / Dec	Jul / Jan	Aug / Feb	Sep / Mar	Oct / Apr	Nov / May	Dec / Jun
0　12	12.12	12.12	12.12	12.12	12.12	12.12	12.12	12.10	12.11	12.12	12.12	12.12
5	11.87	11.96	12.08	12.22	12.35	12.41	12.38	12.28	12.16	12.02	11.90	11.83
10	11.61	11.81	12.06	12.35	12.57	12.70	12.64	12.45	12.17	11.91	11.67	11.55
15	11.34	11.66	12.04	12.47	12.82	13.00	12.92	12.62	12.22	11.81	11.44	11.25
20　11	11.07	11.50	12.01	12.60	13.07	13.32	13.22	12.81	12.26	11.70	11.20	10.94
25	10.78	11.33	11.97	12.74	13.34	13.66	13.53	13.02	12.31	11.58	10.94	10.62
30	10.45	11.14	11.97	12.88	13.65	14.05	13.88	13.23	12.35	11.47	10.67	10.26
35　10	10.09	10.95	11.95	13.06	13.98	14.47	14.27	13.47	12.42	11.33	10.36	9.86
40	9.68	10.71	11.91	13.25	14.36	14.96	14.71	13.76	12.48	11.18	10.00	9.39
45　9	9.19	10.45	11.87	13.48	14.82	15.55	15.25	14.09	12.55	11.01	9.60	8.85
50	8.61	10.13	11.84	13.78	15.38	16.29	15.91	14.48	12.66	10.80	9.07	8.17
55	7.83	9.73	11.79	14.10	16.14	17.28	16.78	14.99	12.76	10.55	8.45	7.28
60	6.79	9.21	11.74	14.62	17.10	18.70	18.01	15.67	12.92	10.22	7.60	6.04

18　17　16　15　14　13

13.

15.

17.

19. a. $P(c, s) = 108.958 - 0.730s + 0.027s^2 + 0.175c$ for a supermarket with s thousand square feet of sales space and a customer base with a per capita income of $\$c$ thousand

b.

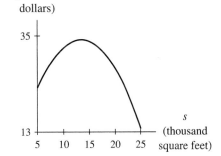

21. a. Answers will vary. For example, the BMI for a person who is 5 feet 8 inches tall and weighs 150 pounds is 22.8 points.

b.

Weight (pounds)	Height (inches)						
	60	62	64	66	68	70	72
90	17.6	16.5	15.4	14.5	13.7	12.9	12.2
100	19.5	18.3	17.2	16.1	15.2	14.3	13.6
110	21.5	20.1	18.9	17.8	16.7	15.8	14.9
120	23.4	21.9	20.6	19.4	18.2	17.2	16.3
130	25.4	23.8	22.3	21.0	19.8	18.7	17.6
140	27.3	25.6	24.0	22.6	21.3	20.1	19.0
150	29.3	27.4	25.7	24.2	22.8	21.5	20.3
160	31.2	29.3	27.5	25.8	24.3	23.0	21.7
170	33.2	31.1	29.2	27.4	25.8	24.4	23.1
180	35.2	32.9	30.9	29.1	27.4	25.8	24.4
190	37.1	34.8	32.6	30.7	28.9	27.3	25.8
200	39.1	36.6	34.3	32.3	30.4	28.7	27.1

c. $w = \dfrac{K(0.00064516)h^2}{0.4536}$ pounds, where h is the height in inches and K is the BMI.

d.

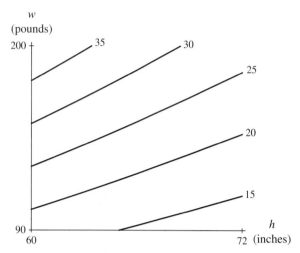

This graph is the upside-down mirror reflection of the graph in part b. It is also more accurately drawn.

23. a. $s = \dfrac{K - 10.65 - 1.13w}{1.04 - 5.83w}$ or $w = \dfrac{K - 10.65 - 1.04s}{1.13 - 5.83s}$

b.

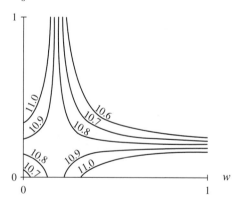

25. a. The center of the 184 thousand contour curve corresponds to approximately 10 thousand tons of lower-fat cheese and 55 thousand tons of regular cheese.

b. From the contour graph, we see that the maximum revenue is greater than 184 million guilders but less than 214 million guilders (or else we would see the 214 contour curve). From the three-dimensional graph, it appears that the maximum revenue is near 200 million guilders. One possible approximation is 190 million guilders.

27. a. Input: $P \approx 10$ hours, $H \approx 70\%$; Output: approximately 12.5 days

When *C. grandis* is exposed to 70% relative humidity and 10 hours of light each day, it will take approximately 12.5 days to develop.

b. Input: $P \approx 10$ hours, $H \approx 60\%$; Output: approximately 11.5 days

When *C. grandis* is exposed to 60% relative humidity and 10 hours of light each day, it will take approximately 11.5 days to develop.

29. a. When y increases, the contour curves have smaller numbers, so $f(x, y)$ decreases. Therefore, the function must increase when y decreases.

b. Because the contour curves are more closely spaced to the left of $(2.5, 2.5)$ than they are directly below that point, the function decreases more quickly as x decreases than it does as y decreases.

c. The change is greater when $(2, 2)$ shifts to $(1, 2.5)$, causing the contour values to change from about 21 to about 14, than it is when $(1, 0)$ shifts to $(4, 1)$, causing virtually no change in contour values.

31. a. The three-dimensional graph has two peaks approximately the same height—one around $(0.7, 0, 0.25)$ and the other near $(-0.7, 0, 0.25)$.

b. The descent is greater from $(0.7, 0.1)$ to $(0, 0.3)$.

c. The output increases as x increases.

d. There are many correct answers. One possible answer is $(-0.4, -0.2)$.

33. a.

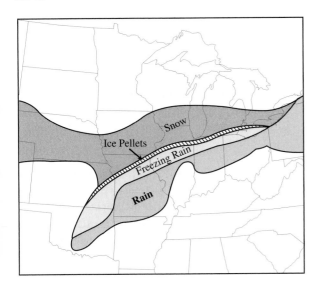

b. The temperature dropped 36°F.

35. To locate a relative maximum on a contour graph, look for contour curves that form a simple, closed curve (or, if completed, appear to form a closed curve). Estimate the point in the center of this closed curve. Moving away from the "center," check that contour levels are decreasing. If the levels are decreasing by a constant amount d, the maximum value at the point can be estimated between the largest indicated contour value k and $k + d$.

On a table of data, locate a number whose eight surrounding numbers are all less than the number itself. It may help to spot this number if you first quickly sketch a couple of contour curves. Once you have located a number that appears to be a maximum value, you describe its location by following its column and row to the edges of the table to determine the input values that produce that maximum.

Keep in mind that for a contour graph as well as a table, there may exist more than one relative maximum.

Section 9.2

1. a. Air temperature
   b. Row
   c. $A(p, 95) = 0.0238p^2 - 2.3455p + 151.31°F$ when the dew point is $p°F$.

3. a. 60% of the time
   b. Constant: hour of the day, Input: fraction of sky covered
   c. column
   d. $C(9, f) = -1.651f^3 + 2.686f^2 - 1.597f + 1.019$, where f is the fraction (expressed as a decimal) of the sky covered by clouds.

5. a. No
   b. Yes, row
   c. $p(m, 9) = 0.017m^2 - 2.091m + 85.977$ dollars when m months is the length of the loan (m between 24 and 60); $p(52, 9) \approx 22.65$ dollars

7. a. $P(x) = -0.857x + 7.781$ pounds/person/year, where $\$(1.50 + x)$ per pound is the price of peaches
   b. $P(0.05) \approx 7.7$ pounds/person/year

9. a. Cost of Coke products
   b. Column
   c. Approximately 201 cans

11. a. 3.88 million people

b.

	Year						
Age	1990	1995	2000	2005	2010	2015	2020
15	3.34	3.65	3.87	4.24	4.31	4.22	4.26
20	4.04	3.51	3.88	4.10	4.48	4.55	4.45
25	4.06	3.79	3.39	3.73	3.94	4.30	4.36
30	4.50	4.38	3.92	3.52	3.86	4.08	4.44
35	4.27	4.59	4.47	4.00	3.61	3.95	4.17
40	3.80	4.28	4.65	4.54	4.07	3.68	4.02
45	2.90	3.70	4.21	4.57	4.46	4.01	3.62
50	2.43	2.93	3.69	4.19	4.55	4.44	4.00

c. Approximately 100 thousand people per year

d. Approximately -16 thousand people per year

13. a. -0.35 kg/day

b. $W(68, t) = -0.00009t^3 + 0.003t^2 - 0.013t + 0.572$ kg/day, where $t°C$ is the temperature. A pig weighing 68 g will (on average) gain/lose $W(68, t)$ kilograms during a day when the temperature is $t°C$.

c. The graph of $W(68, t)$ is concave up, increasing until approximately $t = 10$. After $t = 10$ the graph is concave down. It reaches a maximum just after $t = 21.1$. A pig weighing 68 kilograms will gain the most weight when the temperature is near $21.1°C$. For temperatures in excess of $21.1°C$, the weight gain diminishes more and more rapidly until weight is actually lost at temperatures in excess of approximately $37.5°C$.

15. a. Approximately $0.52°F$ per $°F$

b. First, determine a cross-sectional model: $A(p, 85) = 0.0194p^2 - 2.0052p + 135.832°F$ when the dew point is $p°F$. Second, determine the derivative of this model: $\frac{d(p, 85)}{dp} = 0.0388p - 2.0052$ Third, evaluate the derivative for $p = 65°F$.

17. a. $A(14,000, r) = 1.4r^2 + 280r + 14,000$ dollars, where r is the interest rate expressed as a percentage.

b. When $r = 0.127$, $\frac{dA(14,000, r)}{dr} = \$315.56$ per percentage point.

c. $A(14,000, r) = 14,000r^2 + 28,000r + 14,000$ dollars, where r is the interest rate expressed as a decimal.

d. When $r = 12.7\%$, $\frac{dA(14,000, r)}{dr} = \$31,556$ per 100 percentage points. The derivative tells us approximately how much the output will change when the input increases by one unit. If the input is a percentage expressed as a decimal, then an increase of one unit corresponds to 100 percentage points. For example, if $r = 0.127$ and is increased by 1 to $r = 1.127$, the corresponding percentages are 12.7% and 112.7%.

19. Derivatives of cross-sectional models of a three-dimensional function can be used to pinpoint optimal points on those cross sections. These optimal points in turn may be used to estimate the point at which a critical point may appear on the three-dimensional function.

Section 9.3

1. $\frac{\partial W}{\partial h}$ pounds per inch

3. $\frac{\partial T}{\partial t}\big|_{g=23}°F$ per degree of latitude

5. $\frac{\partial R}{\partial c}\big|_{b=2}$ dollars per cow for $c = 100$

7. a. $\frac{\partial P}{\partial m}\big|_{l=100,000}$ is the rate of change of the probability that the senator will vote for the bill with respect to the amount spent by the tobacco industry on lobbying when the senator receives 100,000 letters in opposition to the bill. We expect this rate of change to be negative, because if the number of letters is constant but lobbying funding against the bill increases, the probability that the senator votes for the bill is likely to decline.

b. $\frac{\partial P}{\partial l}\big|_{m=53}$ is the rate of change of the probability that the senator votes for the bill with respect to the number of letters received when \$53 million is spent on lobbying efforts. We expect this rate of change to be positive, because if the number of letters increases (while lobbying funding remains constant), the probability of the senator voting in favor of the bill is likely to increase.

9. a. $\frac{\partial f}{\partial x} = 6x + 5y$

b. $\frac{\partial f}{\partial y} = 5x + 6y$

c. $\frac{\partial f}{\partial x}\big|_{y=7} = 6x + 35$

11. a. $\frac{\partial f}{\partial x} = 15x^2 + 6xy^3 + 9y + 14$

b. $\frac{\partial f}{\partial y} = 9x^2y^2 + 9x$

c. $\frac{\partial f}{\partial x}\big|_{y=2} = 15x^2 + 48x + 32$

13. a. $M_t = s\left(\frac{1}{t}\right) = \frac{s}{t}$

b. $M_s = \ln t + 3.75$

c. $M_s\big|_{t=3} = \ln 3 + 3.75$

15. a. $\frac{\partial h}{\partial s} = \frac{1}{t} - 2t(st - tr)$

b. $\frac{\partial h}{\partial t} = \frac{-s}{t^2} + \frac{1}{r} - 2(st - tr)(s - r)$

c. $\frac{\partial h}{\partial r} = \frac{-t}{r^2} + 2t(st - tr)$

d. $\frac{\partial h}{\partial r}\big|_{(s, t, r) = (1, 2, -1)} = 14$

17. a. $f_x = 2y + 16xy^3$

b. $f_y = 2x + 24x^2y^2 + 10e^{2y}$

$f_{xx} = 16y^3$

c. $f_{xy} = 2 + 48xy^2$

$f_{yx} = 2 + 48xy^2$

$f_{yy} = 48x^2y + 20e^{2y}$

d. $\begin{bmatrix} 16y^3 & 2 + 48xy^2 \\ 2 + 48xy^2 & 48x^2 + 20e^{2y} \end{bmatrix}$

19.

$$\begin{array}{c} & x & y \\ x & \dfrac{-2y}{x^3} & \dfrac{-1}{y^2}+\dfrac{1}{x^2} \\ y & \dfrac{-1}{y^2}+\dfrac{1}{x^2} & \dfrac{2x}{y^3} \end{array}$$

21.

$$\begin{array}{c} & x & y \\ x & 4e^{2x-3y} & -6e^{2x-3y} \\ y & -6e^{2x-3y} & 9e^{2x-3y} \end{array}$$

23. a. $A(14{,}000, r) = 14{,}000(1 + r)^2$ dollars. This function gives the value of an investment after 2 years when the earned interest is $100r\%$.

b. $\dfrac{\partial A}{\partial r}\Big|_{(P,\, r)=(14{,}000,\, 0.127)} = \$31{,}556$ per 100 percentage points

c. The slope of the line tangent to $A(14{,}000, r)$ at $r = 0.127$ is \$31,566 per 100 percentage points.

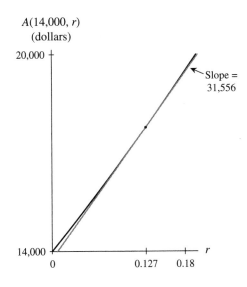

$A(14{,}000, r)$
(dollars)

20,000

Slope = 31,556

14,000

0   0.127   0.18 r

25. a. $R(\text{March}, l) = -0.007l^2 - 0.035l + 49.749$ watts per square meter per month, where l is the number of degrees north of the equator (negative values of l correspond to locations south of the equator). An alternative model is

$R(\text{March}, l) = 35.943 \sin(0.023l + 1.633) + 15.513$
watts per square meter per month

$R(m, -50°) = 27.105 \sin(0.485m + 1.707) + 32.911$
watts per square meter per month, where $m = 1$ corresponds to January, $m = 2$ corresponds to February, and so on. An alternative model is

$$R(m, -50°) = \begin{cases} 0.389m^3 - 3.321m^2 & \text{when} \\ \quad -3.425m + 61.857 & 0 \le m < 7 \\ \quad \text{watts per square} \\ \quad \text{meter per month} \\ -0.565m^3 + 16.008m^2 & \text{when} \\ \quad -137.689m + 381.183 & 7 \le m \le 12 \\ \quad \text{watts per square} \\ \quad \text{meter per month} \end{cases}$$

b. Quadratic model: For $l = -50°$, $R_l\big|_{m=\text{March}} \approx 0.70$ watt per square meter per month per degree of latitude.

Sine model: For $l = 50°$, $R_l\big|_{m=\text{March}} \approx 0.75$ watt per square meter per month per degree of latitude.

c. Sine model: For $m = 3$, $R_m\big|_{l=-50°} \approx -13.13$ watts per square meter per month per month.

Piecewise model: For $m = 3$, $R_m\big|_{l=-50°} \approx -12.85$ watts per square meter per month per month.

d.

$R(\text{March}, l)$
(watts/m²/month)

60

Slope ≈ 0.7

−90   −50   90 $l°$

$R(m, -50)$
(watts/m²/month)

60

Slope ≈ −13

0
1   3   12 m
(months)

27. a. Approximately 0.67 pound/person/year per ten thousand dollars of income

b. Approximately −0.77 pound/person/year per dollar per pound

c. $\left.\dfrac{\partial c}{\partial i}\right|_3 \approx 0.67$ pound/person/year per ten thousand

$\left.\dfrac{\partial C}{\partial p}\right|_{0.2} \approx -0.82$ pound/person/year per dollar per pound

d. The estimates for rate of change with respect to income are close. The estimates for rate of change with respect to price differ by approximately 0.044. *One possible answer:* The method in part c is easier, but the estimate from part b is more reliable.

29. a. $H_t = -10.45 - 10\sqrt{v} + v$ kilogram-calories per square meter per hour per degree Celsius

$H_v = (33 - t)\left(\dfrac{5}{\sqrt{v}} - 1\right)$ kilogram-calories per square meter per hour per meter per second

b. $\dfrac{\partial H}{\partial v}$ should be positive because an increase in wind speed (when temperature is constant) should increase heat loss.

c. When $v = 20$ and $t = 12$, $\dfrac{\partial H}{\partial v} \approx 2.48$ kilogram-calories per square meter per hour per meter per second.

d. $\dfrac{\partial H}{\partial t}$ should be negative because an increase in temperature (when wind speed is constant) should decrease heat loss.

e. When $v = 20$ and $t = 12$, $\dfrac{\partial H}{\partial t} \approx -35.17$ kilogram-calories per square meter per hour per degree Celsius.

31. a. We expect food intake to increase as either milk production or size increases. Therefore, we expect both partial derivatives to be positive.

b. $\dfrac{\partial I}{\partial s} = -1.24 + 0.18s + 0.21m$ kilograms per day per unit of size index. This equation is the rate of change of the amount of organic matter eaten with respect to the size of the cow (when the amount of milk produced is constant).

$\dfrac{\partial I}{\partial m} = -0.21 + 0.072m + 0.21s$ kilograms per day per kilogram of milk per day. This equation is the rate of change of the amount of organic matter eaten with respect to the amount of milk produced (when the size of the cow is constant).

c. $\dfrac{\partial I}{\partial m} \approx 0.64$ kilogram per day per kilogram of milk per day

d. $\dfrac{\partial I}{\partial s} \approx 0.38$ kilogram per day per unit of size index

e.
$$\begin{array}{c} \\ s \\ m \end{array}\begin{array}{cc} s & m \\ \begin{bmatrix} 0.18 & 0.21 \\ 0.21 & 0.072 \end{bmatrix} \end{array}$$
Because all second partials are positive, we know that the rates of change in the s and m directions increase as both s and m increase. This indicates that the surface is concave up in the s and m directions.

33. a. $\dfrac{\partial A}{\partial t} = 1000re^{rt}$ dollars per year, $\dfrac{\partial A}{\partial r} = 1000te^{rt}$ dollars per 100 percentage points

b.
$$\begin{array}{c} \\ t \\ r \end{array}\begin{array}{cc} t & r \\ \begin{bmatrix} 1000r^2e^{rt} & 1000e^{rt} + 1000rte^{rt} \\ 1000tre^{rt} + 1000e^{rt} & 1000t^2e^{rt} \end{bmatrix} \end{array}$$

For $t = 30$ and $r = 0.047$, the second partials matrix is
$$\begin{bmatrix} 9.05 & 9871.25 \\ 9871.25 & 3{,}686{,}359.86 \end{bmatrix}.$$
At the time a $1000 investment has been earning 4.7% compounded continuously for 30 years.

(1) The rate at which the amount is growing with respect to time is increasing with respect to time by $9.05 per year per year.

(2) The rate at which the amount is growing with respect to time is increasing with respect to the interest rate by $9871.25 per year per 100 percentage points.

(3) The rate at which the amount is growing with respect to the interest rate is increasing with respect to time by $9871.25 per 100 percentage points per year.

(4) The rate at which the amount is growing with respect to the interest rate is increasing with respect to the rate by $3,686,359.86 per 100 percentage points per 100 percentage points.

35. a. $\dfrac{\partial A}{\partial t} = (1 + r)^t \ln(1 + r)$ million dollars per year

b. $\dfrac{\partial A}{\partial r} = t(1 + r)^{t-1}$ million dollars per 100 percentage points

c. When $t = 5$ and $r = 0.15$, $\dfrac{\partial A}{\partial t} \approx 0.28$ million dollars per year

d.

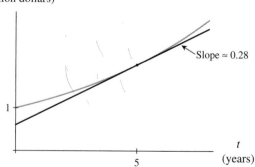

$A(0.15, t)$
(million dollars)

Slope ≈ 0.28

t
(years)

5

37. No, since the y is being treated as a constant during differentiation, it does not matter if the substitution of the specific constant is made before or after the derivative is determined.

Section 9.4

1. $\dfrac{dx}{dy} = \dfrac{-f_y}{f_x} = \dfrac{-45x^2y^2}{30xy^3} = \dfrac{-3x}{2y}$

3. $\dfrac{dm}{dn} = \dfrac{-g_n}{g_m} = \dfrac{-49m}{59.3\left(\dfrac{1}{m}\right) + 49n}$

5.

$\dfrac{dx}{dy} \approx -3.82$

$\dfrac{dy}{dx} \approx -0.26$

7.

$\dfrac{db}{da} \approx -0.016$

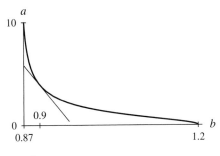

$\dfrac{da}{db} \approx -64.85$

9. $21; \approx -0.2$

The value of n should decrease by approximately 0.2 in order to compensate for an increase of 0.2 in m.

11. Approximately $3.703; \approx 377.57$

13. a. $A(6, 250) \approx \$7.16$

b. $\dfrac{\partial A}{\partial n} = (-0.02c^2 + 0.35c + 0.99)(\ln 0.99897)(0.99897^n)$

$= -\$0.002$ per shirt

c. $\dfrac{dn}{dc} = \dfrac{-A_c}{A_n}$

$= \dfrac{-[(-0.04c + 0.35)(0.99897^n) + 0.46]}{(-0.02c^2 + 0.35c + 0.99)(\ln 0.99897)(0.99897^n)}$

shirts per color

We expect $\dfrac{dn}{dc}$ to be positive because if the number of colors increases, the order size would also need to increase to keep average cost constant.

d. $\dfrac{dn}{dc} \approx 450$ shirts per color. For each additional color, the order size would need to increase by approximately 450 shirts. Similarly, if the number of colors decreases by 1, the order size could decrease by approximately 450 shirts and the average cost would remain constant.

15. a., b.

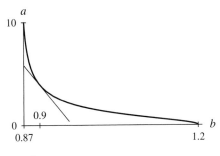

c. $\dfrac{dt}{dr} = \dfrac{-pr}{pt} = \dfrac{-(1.9836 - 0.05916r)}{-9.6544 + 0.14736t}$ °C per milliliter

d. At $t = 86.5°C$ and $r \approx 23.125$ ml, $\dfrac{dt}{dr} \approx -0.199°C$ per milliliter.

At $t = 86.5°C$ and $r \approx 43.9$ ml, $\dfrac{dt}{dr} \approx 0.199°C$ per milliliter.

(Answers for the alternative view with t on the horizontal axis are given in the *Student Solutions Guide*.)

17. a. $w = \dfrac{0.00064516Kh^2}{0.4536}$ pounds, where $K \approx 20.204$

b. $\dfrac{dw}{dh} = \dfrac{2(0.00064516)Kh}{0.4536}$ pounds per inch. When $h = 67$,
$\dfrac{dw}{dh} \approx 3.85$ pounds per inch.

c. The answer to part b agrees with the answer given in Example 1.

19. a. Approximately $193.32

b. Approximately $8232

21. a. From the table, we estimate that Coke would need to lower its prices by more than $0.50 per can.

b. Using the equations $S(1.00, P) = 196P + 25$ cans of Coke products and $S(C, 1.25) = -50.286C^2 + 7.771C + 312.6$ cans of Coke products, where $P is the price of Pepsi products and $C is the price of Coke products, we estimate the change in Coke prices as

$$\Delta C \approx \frac{-S_p}{S_c}\Delta P = \left(\frac{-196}{-92.8}\right)(-0.25) \approx -\$0.53. \quad \text{Coke}$$

would need to lower its price from $1.00 a can to about $0.47 a can.

c. Rather than lower its prices so drastically, Coke should probably consider such alternatives as more advertising on campus.

23. For a function f with inputs x and y, the ratio $\dfrac{f_x}{f_y}$ represents how much more tilted a tangent plane at point (x, y, f) is in the x direction than in the y direction. If $\left|\dfrac{f_x}{f_y}\right| > 1$, then the tangent plane is tilted more in the x direction. If $\left|\dfrac{f_x}{f_y}\right| < 1$, then the tangent plane is tilted more in the y direction. When $\left|\dfrac{f_x}{f_x}\right| = 1$, the tilt in the x direction is the same as that in the y direction.

Chapter 9 Content Review

1. a.

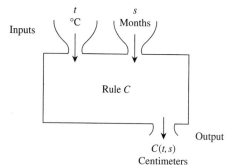

Inputs: t °C, s Months

Rule C

Output

$C(t, s)$ Centimeters

b. 2.9 cm. When apples are stored for 3 months and blanched at 71°C, the applesauce flows 2.9 cm down a vertical surface in 30 seconds.

c. $\begin{cases} -0.05s^2 + 0.35s + 3 \text{ cm} & \text{when } 0 \le s < 2 \\ -0.05s^2 + 0.15s + 3.4 \text{ cm} & \text{when } 2 \le s \le 4 \end{cases}$
where s is the storage time in months.

Assuming that 1 month ≈ 4.3 weeks, 2 weeks corresponds to $s = \dfrac{2}{4.3} \approx 0.465$ month. Thus we have $C(35, 0.465) \approx 3.2$ cm.

d. $\dfrac{\partial C}{\partial t}\Big|_{s=4}$ is the rate of change of the consistometer value with respect to the blanching temperature when the storage time is 4 months.

e. Using $C(t, 4) = (6.944 \cdot 10^{-4})t^2 - 0.087t + 5.412$ cm, when the apples are blanched at t°C, we have
$\dfrac{\partial C}{\partial t}\Big|_{s=4} = (1.389 \cdot 10^{-3})t - 0.087$ cm per °C. When $t = 45$°C, $\dfrac{\partial C}{\partial t}\Big|_{s=4} \approx -0.0244$ cm per°C. When the storage time is a constant 4 months and the blanching temperature is 45°C, the consistometer value is decreasing by approximately 0.024 cm per°C. That is, if the blanching temperature is increased to 46°C, the consistometer value should decrease by approximately 0.024 cm.

f.

Storage time (months)	Temperature (Celsius)				
	35°	47°	59°	71°	83°
0	3.0 3.0 3.2	2.8	2.6	2.6	2.8 2.8
1	3.3	3.1	2.8	2.8	3.0 3.0
2	3.5	3.2	3.0	2.9	3.2 3.2
3	3.4	3.2	3.0	2.9	3.2
4	3.2	2.9	2.7	2.7	3.0

2.8

2. a. $E(24, 60) \approx 466$ eggs. A female insect kept at 24°C and 60% relative humidity will lay approximately 466 eggs in 30 days.

b. For $t = 27$°C and $h = 77\%$, $\dfrac{\partial E}{\partial h} \approx -2.2$ eggs per percentage point. When the temperature is held constant at 27°C and the relative humidity is 77%, the number of eggs is decreasing by 2.2 eggs per percentage point of relative humidity. That is, if the relative humidity were increased to 78%, the number of eggs would decrease by approximately 2.

c. $\dfrac{dh}{dt} = \dfrac{-E_t}{E_h} = \dfrac{-(299.7038 - 10.442t - 0.4023h)}{23.1412 - 0.1874h - 0.4023t}$ percentage points per°C

d. When $t = 25$°C and $h = 63\%$, $\dfrac{dh}{dt} \approx -10.4$ percentage points per°C. Thus $\Delta h \approx \dfrac{dh}{dt}\Delta t \approx (-10.4)(-0.5) = 5.2$ percentage points.

e. On the contour curve corresponding to the egg production for $t = 25°C$ and $h = 63\%$ (the 490.1601 egg contour curve), the slope of the tangent line at $t = 25°C$ and $h = 63\%$ is $\frac{dh}{dt} \approx -10.4$ percentage points per°C. The h-value on the tangent line when $t = 24.5°C$ is $h \approx 63 + 5.2 = 68.2\%$. This is an approximation to the value of h that corresponds to $t = 24.5°C$ on the 490.1601 egg contour curve.

3. a. Inputs: $t \approx 26°C$, $h \approx 56\%$; Output: approximately 485 eggs; When temperatures remain near 26°C and humidity levels remain near 56% over a 30-day period, an average female *Catolaccus grandi* will lay 485 eggs.

b. An increase in temperature of 3°C

c. The number of eggs laid will decrease more rapidly when the temperature decreases than when the humidity decreases.

d. By sketching a tangent line on the figure and calculating its slope, you should obtain an estimate of approximately 13 percentage points per °C.

e. $\frac{dh}{dt} = \frac{-E_t}{E_h} = \frac{-24.1532}{1.8672} \approx -12.9$ percentage points per °C

When the temperature is 24°C and the humidity is 62%, the change in humidity needed to compensate for a small change in temperature (so that the number of eggs remains constant) can be estimated as $\Delta h \approx (-12.9)\Delta t$ percentage points.

4.
$$\begin{array}{c c} & \begin{array}{c c} t & h \end{array} \\ \begin{array}{c} t \\ h \end{array} & \begin{bmatrix} -10.442 & -0.4023 \\ -0.4023 & -0.1874 \end{bmatrix} \end{array}$$

CHAPTER 10

Section 10.1

1. a. A relative maximum occurs when a table value is greater than all the values surrounding it.

b. A relative minimum occurs when a table value is less than all the values surrounding it.

c. If a value appears to be a maximum in one direction but a minimum in another direction, then the value corresponds to a saddle point.

d., e. If all the edges of a table are terminal edges, then the absolute maximum and minimum are simply the largest and smallest values in the table. If all the edges are not terminal edges, then you must know whether any critical points exist outside the table in order to determine whether absolute extrema exist. If no critical points exist outside the table, then in determining absolute extrema, you must consider relative extrema, output values on terminal edges, and the behavior of the function beyond the edges of the table.

It is often helpful to sketch several contour curves on a table when determining critical points and absolute extrema.

3. The point is a relative maximum point because the values of the contour curves decrease in all directions away from the point.

5. a.

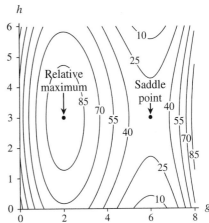

b. Relative maximum point: $g \approx 2$, $h \approx 3$, $R \approx 95$
Saddle point: $g \approx 6$, $h \approx 3$, $R \approx 30$

7. The point is a saddle point because it is a maximum contour level along a cross section extending from the $x = 4$, $y = 0$ corner diagonally back through the point and is a minimum contour level along a cross section extending from the $x = 0$, $y = 0$ corner diagonally through the point.

9. Relative maximum point: (May, 1995, $1.45 per pound); Relative maximum point: (May, 1998, 88 cents per pound)

11. a. Yes; The table gives yearly averages, so it doesn't make sense to extend the columns. However, the choice of January as the first column is not mandatory. The best way to visualize this table is to wrap it around a cylinder so that the January and December columns are adjacent columns and there are no left and right edges of the table. The top and bottom rows are terminal edges.

b.

	Jan	Feb	Mar	Apr	May	Jun	Jul	Aug	Sep	Oct	Nov	Dec
North Pole	—	—	—	3.1	6.9	8.9	7.9	4.9	0.80	—	—	—
80°	—	—	0.77	3.4	6.9	8.8	7.8	4.8	1.55	0.13	—	—
70°	—	0.51	2.0	4.5	7.1	8.5	7.8	5.5	2.9	0.95	0.06	—
60°	0.55	1.53	3.4	5.7	7.7	8.8	8.2	6.5	4.3	2.2	0.81	0.34
50°	1.66	2.8	4.7	6.7	8.4	9.1	8.8	7.4	5.5	3.4	1.97	1.35
40°	3.0	4.2	5.9	7.5	8.8	9.3	9.0	8.1	6.5	4.8	3.4	2.6
30°	4.4	5.6	6.9	8.1	9.0	9.2	9.1	8.4	7.4	6.1	4.7	4.1
20°	5.8	6.7	7.8	8.5	8.8	8.9	8.8	8.6	8.0	7.1	6.0	5.5
10°	7.1	7.7	8.3	8.5	8.4	8.3	8.3	8.4	8.3	7.9	7.2	6.8
Equator	8.1	8.5	8.6	8.3	7.8	7.5	7.6	8.0	8.4	8.4	8.2	7.9
10°	8.9	8.8	8.4	7.7	6.9	6.4	6.5	7.2	8.1	8.6	8.8	8.8
20°	9.4	9.0	8.1	6.9	5.7	5.1	5.4	6.3	7.5	8.6	9.2	9.5
30°	9.6	8.8	7.4	5.8	4.4	3.8	4.1	5.2	6.7	8.2	9.3	9.8
40°	9.6	8.3	6.5	4.6	3.1	2.5	2.7	3.9	5.6	7.5	9.1	9.9
50°	9.3	7.6	5.4	3.3	1.84	1.25	1.49	2.6	4.5	6.6	8.7	9.7
60°	8.7	6.8	4.1	2.0	0.72	0.31	0.47	1.36	3.1	5.6	8.0	9.3
70°	8.2	5.5	2.8	0.84	—	—	—	0.38	1.78	4.3	7.2	9.1
80°	8.2	4.7	1.42	0.099	—	—	—	—	0.62	3.2	7.0	9.3
South Pole	8.1	4.6	0.60	—	—	—	—	—	—	2.9	7.0	9.4

Contour labels (right margin): 5.2, 6.2, 7.2, 8.2, 9.2

c. Relative maximum points: (June, 40° N, 9.3 kW-h/m²), (June, North Pole, 8.9 kW-h/m²), (December, 40° S, 9.9 kW-h/m²)

Relative minima: It is difficult to estimate these accurately because of the dashes in the table, which we can interpret to mean radiation levels of essentially zero. Thus we conclude that the regions of the underlying function represented by the dashes in the table are those in which the minimum radiation level occurs. There are two such regions: one near the North Pole between October and March and one near the South Pole between April and September. If there are two specific relative minima of the underlying function, then we estimate that they occur at the end of December at the North Pole and in the middle of June at the South Pole.

Saddle points: (April, 10°N, 8.5 kW-h/m²), (June, 70°N, 8.5 kW-h/m²), (August, 10°N, 8.4 kW-h/m²), (December, 70°S, 9.1 kW-h/m²)

d. The greatest radiation level shown in the table is 9.9 kW-h/m², which occurs in December at 40°S. The smallest radiation level shown is 0.06 kW-h/m², which occurs in November at 70°N. If we consider the dashes to be zeros, then the smallest radiation level is zero and occurs many times in the table.

e. The absolute maximum value is 9.9 kW-h/m², and the absolute minimum is approximately zero. Because the table cannot be extended in any direction, these answers do correspond to those in part d.

f. The largest and smallest values in a table will be the absolute maximum and minimum, respectively, if the table cannot be extended in any direction. That is, either the edges are terminal edges or the table "wraps around," as in this case.

13. a. The expected corn yield is 100% of the annual average yield. That is, there is no expected increase or decrease in yield from the average.

   b. 40%

c. See table below.

$$\Delta P$$
$$(\%)$$

ΔT (°C)	-100	-90	-80	-70	-60	-50	-40	-30	-20	-10	0	10	20	30	40	50	60	70	80
6	0	7	14	18	23	27	32	40	48	56	64	67	69	72	74	75	75	75	76
	0	7	15	20	25	29	34	43	51	59	67	70	73	75	78	78	78	78	78
5	0	8	16	21	26	32	37	45	54	62	71	73	76	79	81	81	81	81	81
	0	8	17	22	28	34	39	48	57	65	74	77	79	82	85	85	84	84	84
4	0	9	18	24	30	36	42	51	60	68	77	80	83	86	88	88	88	87	87
	0	9	19	25	32	38	45	54	62	71	80	83	86	89	92	91	91	90	89
3	0	10	20	27	33	40	47	56	65	75	84	87	90	93	96	95	94	93	92
	0	10	21	28	35	42	49	59	69	78	87	91	94	96	98	97	95	94	93
2	0	11	21	29	37	44	52	63	74	82	90	95	99	99	100	98	97	96	94
	0	11	22	30	38	46	54	65	76	85	93	99	101	101	102	100	99	97	95
1	0	12	23	31	40	48	56	67	78	87	95	102	103	104	104	102	100	98	96
	0	12	24	33	41	50	58	69	80	90	98	104	105	106	106	104	102	100	97
0	0	12	25	34	43	51	60	71	83	92	100	107	107	108	109	106	103	101	98
	0	13	26	35	43	52	61	72	84	93	101	107	108	108	107	105	102	100	97
-1	0	13	27	35	44	53	61	73	85	94	103	108	109	108	106	104	101	99	96
	0	14	28	36	45	53	62	73	84	93	102	107	108	107	105	103	100	98	95
-2	0	14	29	37	46	54	63	73	84	93	101	105	107	106	104	102	99	97	94
	0	15	29	38	46	55	63	72	82	90	98	101	103	103	103	101	98	95	93
-3	0	15	30	39	47	55	64	72	80	88	96	97	99	101	102	100	97	94	92
	0	15	30	38	46	54	62	70	77	85	92	94	95	98	98	96	94	91	89
-4	0	15	31	38	46	53	61	68	74	81	88	90	91	93	95	92	90	88	85
	0	15	31	38	45	52	59	65	72	78	85	86	88	89	91	89	87	85	82
-5	0	15	31	38	44	51	58	63	69	75	81	82	84	85	87	85	83	81	79
	0	16	31	37	44	50	56	61	67	72	77	79	80	82	83	81	80	78	76
-6	0	16	31	37	43	49	55	59	64	69	74	75	76	78	79	78	76	75	73

d. The maximum percentage yield is 109%. This maximum occurs twice, at the points (40%, 0°C, 109%) and (20%, −1°C, 109%). A yield of 109% above normal can be expected when temperatures are average and there is 40% more precipitation than normal or when temperatures are 1°C below normal and precipitation is 20% above normal.

15. a. absolute minimum: 156 kg, 37.8°C, −1.15 kg/day)
relative minimum: none
absolute maximum: (156 kg, 15.6° C, 1.09 kg/day)
relative maximum: (91 kg, 21.1° C, 1.01 kg/day)

b.

°C	4.4	10	15.6	21.1	26.7	32.2	37.8
°F	40	50	60	70	80	90	100

c. On average, the daily weight gain will be least for a pig weighing 156 kg when the temperature is 100° F, and it will be greatest for a pig weighing 156 kg when the temperature is 60° F.

17. a.

Storage time (months)	Temperature (°C)				
	35°	47°	59°	71°	83°
0	3.0	2.8	2.6	2.6	2.8
1	3.3	3.1	2.8	2.8	3.0
2	3.5	3.2	3.0	2.9	3.2
3	3.4	3.2	3.0	2.9	3.2
4	3.3	3.2	2.9	2.7	3.0

3.0   2.7

b. Saddle point: ≈ (63°C, 2.25 months, 2.9 cm)

c. Absolute maximum: 3.5 cm
Absolute minimum: 2.6 cm

d. One possible answer: The saddle point is important because it shows the optimal storage time and temperature to keep applesauce from getting too thick or too thin.

19. a.

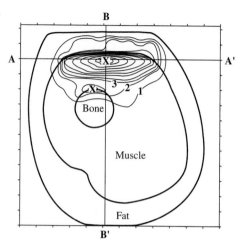

The absolute maximum nearest the fat layer has a value between 12 and 13, and the relative maximum at the bone has a value between 3 and 4.

b. Both points are maxima.

21. a., b.

Section 10.2

1. A relative minimum of 16 is located at $k = 4$ and $m = 2$.

3. A saddle point is located at $(\ln 3, 0, 0)$.

5. A relative minimum of approximately -68.35 is located at $z \approx 4.72$ and $w \approx 18.49$. $(0, 0, 0)$ is the location of a saddle point.

7. Relative minimum point: $(0, 0, 60)$
Relative maximum point: $(2, 1, 68)$
Saddle point: $(0, 1, 64)$
Saddle point: $(2, 0, 64)$

9. a. The manager should try to buy ground beef at $1.91 a pound and sausage at $2.52 a pound.
b. Because the determinant is positive and R_{bb} is negative, the critical point corresponds to a relative maximum.
c. $28.5 thousand

11. a. The critical point is $\approx$ $(26.1°C, 67.4\%, 500 \text{ eggs})$.
b. When exposed to 26.1°C and 67.4% relative humidity, a *C. grandis* female will lay approximately 500 eggs in 30 days. This is the maximum number of eggs possible.

c. There is a relative maximum in the simple, closed, 50-mm contour curve near the eastern side of Missouri.

13. a. A pH of approximately 5.3 and a temperature of approximately 59.3°C will maximize the initial rate.

   b. We verify that this is a maximum by calculating the determinant of the second partials matrix:

$$D = \begin{vmatrix} -9.81 & -3 \\ -3 & -14.106 \end{vmatrix} \approx 129.38$$

   Because D is greater than zero and R_{pp} is less than zero, the critical point must be a maximum.

15. a. The maximum appears to be approximately 2.35 mg when pH $\approx$ 9 and temperature $\approx$ 65°C.

   b. A pH of approximately 9.02 and a temperature of approximately 64.6°C will maximize the amount of peptides produced.

17. The model has a saddle point for $s \approx 0.19$, $w \approx 0.18$, and $c \approx 0.63$.

19. a. The critical points are $A = (0.5185, 0.4994, 799.91)$ and $B = (0.8872, 0.4994, 800.16)$.

   b. Point A is a saddle point, and point B corresponds to a relative maximum.

   c. The determinant at A is $D \approx -55.98$, which indicates that A is a saddle point. Because the determinant at B is $D \approx 55.98$ and E_{nn} is negative, point B must correspond to a relative maximum.

21. a. The critical point is $g = 42.6\%$, $m \approx 17.1\%$, $s \approx 11.2\%$, $h \approx 12.8$ days, and $A \approx 7.29$.

   b. By evaluating the function at many points close to the critical point, it is possible to conjecture that the point is a relative maximum. There are also other methods of arriving at this conjecture.

23. In order to locate a critical point of a three-dimensional function, determine both first partial derivatives, set each of them equal to zero, and solve. Any input (a, b) for which both first partial derivatives are zero will yield a critical point.

To determine the type of critical point found, write the four second partial derivatives of the function. Next evaluate the product of the non-mixed second partials minus the product of the mixed partials at (a, b)—this is known as $D(a, b)$, the determinant of the second partials matrix. If $D(a, b)$ is negative, then (a, b) yields a saddle point. If $D(a, b)$ is positive, then evaluate one of the non-mixed second partials at (a, b). If that second partial is negative, then (a, b) yields a maximum. If it is positive, then (a, b) yields a minimum. Finally, if $D(a, b)$ is exactly zero, then the determinant test fails and estimation graphically or numerically may help.

Section 10.3

1. a. One possible estimate is (45, 45, 2025).

   b. The point is a constrained maximum.

   c. Solving the system of equations

$$b = \lambda$$
$$a = \lambda$$
$$a + b = 90$$

   gives $a = 45$ and $b = 45$, corresponding to $f(45, 45) = 2025$.

3. a. Approximate relative minimum point: (35%, 17%, 2.5). The minimum measure of cohesiveness is about 2.5, which occurs when the percent of glucose and maltose is 35 and the percent of moisture is 17.

   b.

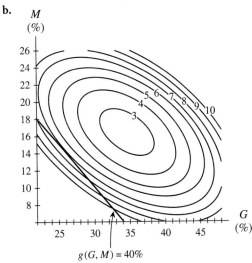

$$g(G, M) = 40\%$$

The constrained minimum is approximately 7, which occurs when $G \approx 26\%$ and $M \approx 15\%$.

5. a. The constrained optimal point is $\left(\frac{-1}{16}, \frac{3}{8}, \frac{7}{32}\right)$.

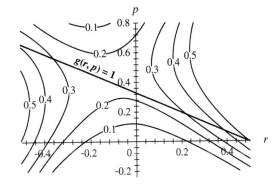

b. i. The contour graph confirms that the point is a constrained minimum, because the contour to which the constraint line is tangent is the smallest-valued contour that the constraint line touches.

ii. Evaluating $f(r, p)$ for values of r near $\frac{-1}{16}$ and p near $\frac{3}{8}$ gives values greater than $\frac{7}{32}$, which suggests that the point is a constrained minimum.

7. 10.45%; The approximation is 0.01% less than that in Example 2 for the constraint $w + s = 1$ was 10.46%.

9. a. The health club should allocate \$336 for 28 radio ads and \$168 for 28 newspaper ads.

b. $A(28, 28) \approx 2195$ responses

c. The Lagrange multiplier is $\lambda = 13.07$ responses per dollar. The change in the number of responses can be approximated as
$$\Delta A \approx (13.07 \text{ responses per dollar}) (\$26)$$
$$\approx 340 \text{ additional responses}$$

11. a. The point of absolute minimum cohesiveness is (34.7%, 16.4%, 2.5). This value is close to the estimate in Activity 3.

b. The minimum cohesiveness is approximately 7.2, which corresponds to approximately 25.4% glucose and maltose and 14.6% moisture.

c. To verify that the value in part b is a minimum, evaluate the cohesiveness function at close points on the constraint curve, or examine the constraint curve graphed on a contour graph of the cohesiveness function.

d. The answers are comparable.

13. a. 750 worker hours and \$9375 in capital expenditures will yield maximum daily production.

b. To verify that the value in part a is a maximum, evaluate the production function at close points on the constraint curve, or examine the constraint curve graphed on a contour graph of the production function.

c. The marginal productivity of money is $\lambda = 3.15$ radios per thousand dollars. An increase in the budget of \$1000 will result in an increase in output of approximately 3 radios.

15. a. $\lambda = \dfrac{dC}{dk} \approx -0.85$ unit per percentage point

b. $\Delta C \approx (-0.85$ unit per percentage point$)$ $(2$ percentage points$) = -1.7$ units. The minimum cohesiveness measure should decline by approximately 1.7.

c. The relative minimum when there are no constraints is approximately 2.5, which is obtained when the percentage of glucose and maltose is approximately 34.7 and the percentage of moisture is approximately 16.4.

17. a. $\dfrac{dP}{dc} \approx 3.15$ radios per thousand dollars

b. $\Delta P \approx (3.15)(1.5) \approx 4.7 \approx 5$ radios

c. Approximately 56 radios

19. a. $S(r, h) = 2\pi rh + \pi r^2 + \pi \left(r + \dfrac{9}{8}\right)^2$ square inches when the radius is r inches and the height is h inches.

b. $V(r, h) = \pi r^2 h = 808.5$ cubic inches

c. Solving the equations
$$2\pi h + 2\pi r + 2\pi \left(r + \frac{9}{8}\right) = \lambda 2\pi rh$$
$$2\pi r = \lambda \pi r^2$$
$$\pi r^2 h = 808.5$$
gives $r \approx 4.87$ inches, $h \approx 10.86$ inches, and $S(r. h) \approx 519.5$ square inches.

21. The condition $\dfrac{f_x}{g_x} = \dfrac{f_y}{g_y}$ is equivalent to guaranteeing that the slope of the extreme-contour curve is the same as the slope of the constraint curve at their point of intersection.

Section 10.4

1. a. $f(a, b) = (7 - a - b)^2 + (11 - 6a - b)^2$
$$+ (19 - 12a - b)^2$$

b. $\dfrac{\partial f}{\partial a} = -2(7 - a - b) - 12(11 - 6a - b)$
$$-24(19 - 12a - b)$$

$\dfrac{\partial f}{\partial b} = -2(7 - a - b) - 2(11 - 6a - b)$
$$-2(19 - 12a - b)$$
$$D = \begin{vmatrix} 362 & 38 \\ 38 & 6 \end{vmatrix} = 728$$

c. The minimum value of $f(a, b)$ is approximately 1.407. We verify that this is a minimum by noting that $D > 0$ and $f_{aa} > 0$.

d. $y = 1.099x + 5.374$

3. a. $f(a, b) = (3 - b)^2 + (2 - 10a - b)^2$
$$+ (1 - 20a - b)^2$$

b. The minimum value of $f(a, b)$ is zero. We verify that this is a minimum by calculating $D = 2400$ and $f_{aa} = 1000$ and noting that both are greater than zero.

Because the minimum SSE is zero, we know that the line of best fit is a perfect fit—that is, all of the data points lie on the line.

c. $y = -0.1x + 3$ percent, where x is the number of years since 1970, $0 \le x \le 20$.

d. No, the extrapolation is too far from the data used to find a trend.

5. a., b.

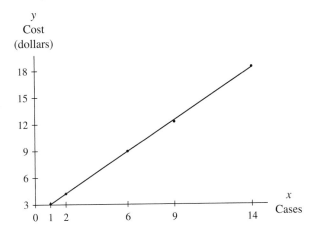

$y = 1.176x + 1.880$ dollars to make x cases of ball bearings. The variable costs to make a case of ball bearings is \$1.176. The fixed cost for making ball bearings is \$1.880.

c. The deviations are approximately 0.044, 0.018, 0.013, -0.176, and 0.102; SSE ≈ 0.044.

d. To find the best-fitting line, first construct the function f with inputs a and b, which represents the sum of the squared errors of the data points from the line $y = ax + b$. Find the partial derivatives of f with respect to a and b. Simplify the partials, and find the point (a, b) where the partials are simultaneously zero. These are the coefficients of the model given in part b. The function f evaluated at (a, b) gives the value of SSE shown in part c.

7. $y = -0.089x + 5.484$ million experiments x years after 1970, $0 \le x \le 10$.

9. a.

The data points appear to be concave up.

b.

The data are also concave up, but less so than in part a.

c. $y = 0.012x - 0.037$, gives the natural log of the population in billions x years after 1850, $0 \le x \le 163$.

d.

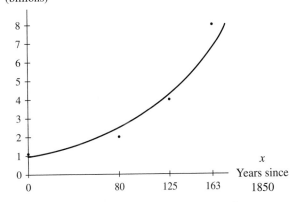

$y = e^{-0.037}(e^{0.012})^x$ billion people x years after 1850

e. $y = 0.964(1.012^x)$ billion people x years after 1850. The model in part d simplifies to this model.

11. A single large outlier will not have as profound an influence on the overall fit of the line if absolute errors are used as it would if squared errors are used. However, algebraically simplifying (and solving) the sum of absolute error expressions is much more complicated than simplifying the sum of squared algebraic expressions.

Chapter 10 Concept Review

1. a.

Month

b. Highest ozone level ≈450 thousandths of a centimeter at 90° N (the North Pole) in mid-March. Lowest ozone level ≈250 thousandths of a centimeter at or just north of the equator between October and March.

2. a. See table below.

Blanching temperature (°C)	Blanching time (minutes)		
	2	15	30
50	4.2	6.8	4.2
60	4.5	4.7	7.1
70	8.2	11.4	8.6
80	7.3	6.9	3.9

b. The maximum crispness appears to be about 11.4, when the blanching temperature is 70°C and the blanching time is 15 minutes.

c. A crispness index of approximately 10 occurs at $x \approx 26.4$ minutes and $y = 62.7°C$.

d. Because the determinant of the second partials matrix is greater than zero ($D = 1.92$) and C_{xx} is negative ($C_{xx} = -10.4$), the point found in part a is a maximum. Yes, There is only one critical point, and the table of values indicates that the function decreases in all directions away from that critical point. These two observations lead to the conclusion that the relative maximum is also an absolute maximum.

3. a. The maximum profit is approximately $202,500 for about 52,000 shirts and 9000 hats. (Answers may vary.)

b. $4s + 1.25h = 150$

c.

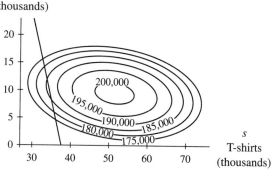

The constrained maximum profit is slightly more than $185,000 for about 34,000 shirts and 10,000 hats.

4. a. $-104.4s + 5935.5 - 59.1h = 4\lambda$
$-59.1s + 10,299.3 - 768.6h = 1.25\lambda$
$4s + 1.25h = 150$

b. $h \approx 10.04$ thousand hats, $s \approx 34.36$ thousand shirts, $P \approx \$186,599$

c. $\lambda \approx 439$ dollars of profit per thousand dollars spent; For each additional thousand dollars budgeted, profit will increase by approximately $439.

d. Profit would increase by approximately $877.

5. a. $f(a, b) = (29.9 - 10a - b)^2 + (33.4 - 15a - b)^2 + (37.5 - 20a - b)^2$

b. The minimum value of f is 0.06. We verify that this is a minimum by calculating the determinant of the second partials matrix ($D = 600$) and noting that it is positive and that $f_{aa} = 1450$ is also positive. The minimum value is the sum of the squares of the deviations of the data from the best-fitting line.

c. $y = 0.76x + 22.2$ kg, where the temperature is $x°C$

Subject Index

A

Absolute extrema
  definition of, 249, 278, 616
  end behavior and, 250, 621
  finding of, 251, 621
  graphs of, 616–617, 621–623
  of linear functions, 249
  in multivariable functions, 616–617,
    621–623
  in normal distribution, 434
  of quadratic functions, 250
  from tabular data, 621–623
  on terminal edges, 621–623
Acceleration
  definition of, 539
  due to gravity, 335
  input/output diagrams for, 320
  units of measure of, 319–320
  velocity and, 334–335
Accumulated change. *See also* Definite
    integrals
  area and, 285–298, 370
  in cubic functions, 288–290, 296–300
  definition of, 287
  difference of, 346–351
  from equations, 290–294, 296–300,
    309
  in exponential functions, 290–292,
    303
  from graphs, 285, 287, 289, 291,
    293–298
  graphs of, 292
  integrals and, 299–300, 339–340
  limits of, 294–299
  in linear functions, 284–287
  in logarithmic functions, 290–292
  in piecewise functions, 290–292
  in quadratic functions, 309
  in sine functions, 495–496
  from tabular data, 287–290
  units of measure of, 286, 289–290
  from words, 284–290
Accumulated density-dependent
    mortality, 357
Accumulated value of investments, 550
Accumulation function. *See also*
    Antiderivatives
  algebraic method for, 339–340
  area of, 326–327
  definition of, 310, 336, 374
  derivative of, 325–328, 374
  of exponential functions, 341
  extrema of, 316–318
  graphs of, 310–318, 325–327
  input/output diagrams for, 319
  notation for, 336

of probability density functions,
    437–439
  starting value for, 310
  units of measure of, 319
Addition, function
  for accumulated change, 295,
    298–299
  definition of, 10–11
  derivatives and, 180–184, 194, 222
  input/output diagrams for, 10, 11
  input variables in, 10, 85
  notation for, 391–392
  output variable in, 10–11, 14, 85
  rules for (*see* Sum Rules)
  Sum Rules for (*see* Sum Rules)
  units of measure of, 14, 85
Aligning data, 32–33
Amplitude of trig functions, 454, 457,
    462
Annual percentage rate (APR)
  average change from, 103–106
  continuous income stream and,
    388–389
  differential equations for, 521–522
  discrete income stream and,
    392–393
  instantaneous change from, 138–140
  multivariable formula for, 550
Annual percentage yield (APY)
  average change from, 103–106
  instantaneous change from,
    138–140
Antiderivatives. *See also* Accumulation
    function; Integrals
  of composite functions, 371–372
  of constant functions, 328, 329, 332
  Constant Multiplier Rule for, 330, 332
  constant term in, 328, 342
  of cosine functions, 494–495, 501
  of cubic functions, 330
  definition of, 328, 374
  Difference Rules for, 330, 332
  of differential equations, 508–512
  from equations, 330–331
  of exponential functions, 331–334,
    370–372
  Exponential Rule for, 332
  e^x Rule for, 331, 332
  general (*see* General antiderivatives)
  from integrals, 329, 340–341
  of linear functions, 329, 330–331
  logarithmic functions from,
    331–334, 341–342, 371
  Natural Logarithm Rule for, 331, 332
  notation for, 328, 336, 341
  of power functions, 329–331, 370,
    372–373

  Power Rule for, 329, 332
  of products of functions, 370–373
  of quotients of functions, 370–373
  of sine functions, 494–495, 501
  specific (*see* Specific antiderivatives)
  Sum Rule for, 330, 332
  from tabular data, 333–334
Approximating change
  concavity and, 240
  in cubic functions, 232–233
  formula for, 230
  from graphs, 373
  in multivariable functions, 598–602,
    609
  in quadratic functions, 229
  in quartic functions, 231–232
  with tangent lines, 228–232,
    598–599
APR. *See* Annual percentage rate (APR)
APY, 103–106, 138–140
Area
  in accumulated change, 285–298, 370
  of accumulation functions, 326–327
  of circles, 293
  between curves, 348–351, 374
  definite integrals and, 336, 340–351
  of demand functions, 400–407
  in histograms, 423–425
  as limit of sums, 295, 374
  median, 430
  of normal density functions, 434
  of probability density functions,
    426, 428
  signed, 287
  of supply functions, 410–414
  surface, of cans, 656
  of total social gain, 415–417
  of trapezoids, 286, 327
  of uniform density functions, 429–430
Avection, 272
Average. *See also* Mean
  costs, 9, 13
  definition of, 430
  rate of change (*see* Average rate of
    change)
  value (*see* Average value)
Average costs, 9, 13
Average rate of change
  average value and, 364
  from continuously compounded
    interest, 105–106
  definition of, 96, 364
  from equations, 102–106, 363–365
  of exponential functions, 365
  formula for, 96, 362, 364, 374
  from graphs, 98–102
  graphs of, 365